1252

EDWIN S. GOULD

Stanford Research Institute

Mechanism and Structure in Organic Chemistry

HOLT, RINEHART AND WINSTON

NEW YORK

23217-0219

Printed in the United States of America

Preface

As a result of the very striking growth of physical organic chemistry during the last thirty years, nearly all colleges and universities that grant advanced degrees in chemistry offer at least one course in this field to graduates, and some offer such a course to promising undergraduates as well. Moreover, many chemists who obtained their degrees during the 1930's or 1940's have felt the need to familiarize themselves with this subject, for much of the most interesting research being carried out today in organic chemistry is strongly influenced by mechanistic thinking.

The bulk of this text is devoted to the consideration of the mechanisms of homogeneous organic reactions, but the first three chapters are structural in outlook. These deal with the structures of atoms and organic molecules and with some of the physicochemical methods used to determine the positions of atoms and to study the distribution of electronic charge. The treatments here, although in accord with modern structural thought, tend to be brief; and, in some cases, the approach is descriptive rather than rigorous. These chapters are included because it is now clear that a satisfactory understanding of many organic chemical phenomena cannot be obtained if molecules are visualized merely as "ball-and-stick" models and atoms as miniature "solar systems." Much of the material in these chapters could be presented equally appropriately in texts in inorganic and physical chemistry; and those who, in previous training, have become familiar with the fundamentals of structural chemistry may wish to start directly with Chapter 4.

A major difference between this text and others in the same field is the incorporation of a rather large number of exercises at the end of each of the sixteen chapters. It is intended that these develop the reader's ability to suggest mechanisms from experimental data, to relate structure to reactivity in many different situations, to predict the course of reactions which are new to him, to explain features about reactions which might otherwise puzzle him, and, if possible, to propose experiments which serve to distinguish between a number of possible mechanisms. Some of the exercises are relatively straightforward, but many require considerable thought. Some, I hope, will challenge the efforts of even the most capable readers.

The level of difficulty in the text and in the exercises rises markedly as the reader passes from the earlier to the later chapters. Such a trend is desirable, for a student should become more proficient in the subject at hand as the term progresses. Nevertheless, a class for whom the material in the first six chapters is new will not, except in rare instances, be able to master the entire remainder of the text within a single term. It is suggested that in an introductory course in theoretical organic chemistry for beginning graduates or undergraduates, the first ten or eleven chapters be covered; for these allow consideration of many of the more usual reactions upon which contemporary mechanistic thought is based. A more sophisticated group of graduates, or one whose major interest is organic chemistry, may, on the other hand, find it more profitable to begin at Chapter 7 or 8, and cover as many of the subsequent chapters as time allows.

The author of a textbook in physical organic chemistry must face the problem of selection. No attempt has been made to consider, even briefly, two broad classes of reactions, polymerization and heterogeneous reactions. Beyond this limitation, I have chosen those of the more familiar organic reactions which, mechanistically speaking, have been investigated most intensively. Less usual reactions are included when they present points of fundamental interest that enable us to put the more usual reactions into better perspective. Inevitably, a number of reactions of some synthetic importance (including the Bucherer, Leuckart, Refortmatsky, Wolff-Kishner, Jacobsen, and Mannich reactions, and the periodic acid and selenium dioxide oxidations) have been left out, largely because they, at present, appear to contribute less to the overall mechanistic picture than many others.

For a text of this sort, complete documentation is not necessary, nor is it desirable. Individual references to early work which has since been reviewed many times are kept at a minimum, but references to papers published since 1945, especially to those appearing in journals most readily available to readers in western countries, are extensive. Altogether, about two thousand separate references have been included.

It is a pleasure to thank Professors Ronald Breslow and Murray Goodman, who read and commented on major portions of the text; Professor George Wheland, who made a number of valuable suggestions on the early chapters; and Professor Harlan Goering, who read the final chapter. I am grateful also for the help of Miss Elizabeth Brown, who prepared the entire manuscript; and for the aid of my wife Marjorie, who made the preliminary sketches for the many figures in the text and exercises and handled innumerable additional details. Finally, my thanks goes to the National Science Foundation for a Science Faculty Fellowship, during the tenure of which this book was completed.

E.S.G.

April, 1959
Brooklyn, New York

Contents

CHAPTER 1

Atomic and Molecular Structure.
The Use of Resonance

IN SPITE OF THE TREMENDOUS ADVANCES made in organic chemistry between 1860 and 1910, many workers in the inorganic and physical chemical fields forty years ago regarded organic chemists not as scientists, but rather as very clever artisans (although such opinions were rarely expressed in face-to-face encounters). Perhaps the chief reason for this was the reluctance of the large majority of organic chemists of that period to push their structural considerations beyond anything more fundamental than the carbon skeleton and the functional groups bonded to it. Then, too, although the course of a new reaction could presumably be predicted by consideration of the carbon skeletons and the functional groups of the reagents, it often seemed to the observer that if the inexplicably "correct" catalyst were omitted or if the correct reaction conditions were not rigorously maintained, the desired reaction would not occur. (In the latter event, the operator might obtain a product formed in a completely unexpected molecular rearrangement or, more likely, a dark, intractable tar.)

Today, although such intractable tars still arise in the laboratory, the outlook toward organic chemistry has largely changed. During the last twenty-five years there has arisen an ever-increasing number of organic chemists who, rather than search for new reactions, have devoted their attention to a close examination of the older reactions in an attempt to obtain a more intimate view of what happens between the time that the reagents are mixed and the product (desired or undesired) is isolated.

Such studies are said to have as their objective the determination of the *mechanisms* of reactions—ideally, step-by-step descriptions of the paths of each of the atoms from start to finish. At present, all but a very small number of

1

important organic type-reactions have been the subject of mechanistic investigations. Very often such investigations involve equilibrium or kinetic studies, formerly considered to be in the province of the physical chemist. Hence, this phase of chemistry is today known as *physical organic chemistry*.

Since organic reactions are essentially a series of formations and breakings of bonds between atoms, the development of the scientists' picture of atoms and chemical bonds during the last forty years has unavoidably affected the outlook of the physical organic chemist; for any mechanistic pictures he proposes must be in harmony with more general structural concepts.

A simplified discussion of the modern view of atoms and of the bonds they form comprises this first chapter.

The Wave-mechanical Picture of the Electron[1]

The schematic sketch of the "solar-system" atom, with a nucleus at its center and electrons revolving about it in circular or elliptical paths, has become increasingly familiar during the last decade. Such sketches appear as insignia for scientific organizations, as commercial trade-marks, and on the pages of popular periodicals.

This type of picture, which shows vividly the division of the atom into the nucleus and orbital electrons, arose from studies of the spectra of atoms. Such spectral studies indicated that electrons bound to an atom could have only a *discrete set* of energies (that is, that atomic energy levels are **quantized**) and it was at the time natural to suppose that the change of an electron's energy corresponded to a shift from an outer "orbit" to an inner "orbit," nearer the positively charged nucleus, or perhaps in the opposite direction. (Why an electron would be allowed in one orbit or another and yet be prohibited from taking an intermediate position between the orbits was an open question.) It was even possible to take such a picture and, with classical physical laws, to draw up equations that described the supposed motion of the electrons in their circular orbits. Using such simple assumptions, Bohr successfully explained the structure of the spectrum of atomic hydrogen.

Bohr's treatment, however, could not be applied successfully to most other atoms without drastic and somewhat unsatisfactory modifications. More important, we are aware today that the laws of classical physics (which Bohr used

[1] For more detailed, but still largely qualitative, descriptions of the wave-mechanical picture of bound electrons see: (*a*) Coulson, *Valence*, Oxford University Press, Oxford, 1952, pp. 1–42; (*b*) Cartmell and Fowles, *Valency and Molecular Structure*, Butterworth's Scientific Publications, London, 1956, pp. 1–63; (*c*) Syrkin and Dyatkina, *Structure of Molecules and the Chemical Bond*, Interscience Publishers, New York, 1950, pp. 1–41. More quantitative treatments are given in a number of textbooks on quantum mechanics; see, for example, (*d*) Pitzer, *Quantum Chemistry*, Prentice-Hall, Inc., New York, 1953, pp. 127–188.

to set up his equations) cannot be used to describe the behavior of very small objects. The ordinary laws of mechanics and electrostatics are adequate for phenomena in our everyday world, but they break down if they are applied without substantial changes to nuclei and to electrons. This does not mean that there are actually two sets of physical laws, one for the macro world and the other for the ultramicro world. Rather this apparent "duality" arises because the laws of classical physics turn out to be only approximations. For large objects, however, they are excellent approximations; the inaccuracies in such approximations become noticeable only when very small objects are being investigated.

For instance, the **Heisenberg uncertainty principle** gives us no trouble in everyday physics. This principle says (among other things) that it is impossible to determine accurately both the position and the momentum (hence, the kinetic energy) of a given object. It maintains further that the more accurately we know the energy, the less accurately we may know the position (and vice versa). We do not concern ourselves with the principle when describing an automobile, for we may specify both the position of the car at a particular instant and its velocity (which allows us to calculate its kinetic energy). Nature, however, opposes our making similarly specific statements about an electron; for to determine the position of an electron, the electron must be observed. This means that it must be seen through a very powerful supermicroscope or it must cause some variation in a test signal which we send out. Essentially all that we see becomes visible by causing variation in a pattern of light rays emerging from a source of illumination. Now, we cannot see an object that is smaller than the wavelength of the light used for illumination, and to determine accurately the position of an electron, we would have to use light having a very short wavelength indeed. If radiation of too long a wavelength were used, the image of the electron would become fuzzy; and the longer the wavelength, the fuzzier would be the image.

Very short wavelength radiation, however, consists of high-energy photons. Although it is generally assumed that we cannot move objects simply by illuminating them, an electron can be moved by collision with a photon. Such a photon may give up a little or much of its energy in such a collision; and the higher the energy of the photon, the greater would be the uncertainty in the energy of the electron after the impact. We see then that in trying to fix the electron's position very exactly by using photons of very short wavelength, we become very uncertain as to the energy of the electron since it would be knocked in an unknown direction with a very energetic photon. Philosophically, the Heisenberg principle arises because of the scientific necessity for the observation of particles, using as a means of observation radiation which itself displays the character of particles.

From what has been said, it follows that the classical picture of the electron as a compact mass in circular or elliptical motion about a heavy nucleus has little significance since the exact fixing of the position of the electron would give it a tremendous energy uncertainty. Because of the uncertainty principle, the description of the size and motion of electrons in terms of everyday physics only cannot be given. Rather, a new system of mechanics, **quantum mechanics,** yields a more satisfactory picture of the behavior of very small objects.

In quantum-mechanical descriptions, the ordinary laws of motion are replaced by equations representing probabilities. As a very crude example, suppose we were to know that if a particular electron had a certain energy— a certain momentum—and was spinning in a certain direction, the probability that it would be in a region a given distance from the nucleus would be "1 in 2" or 0.5. The probability that the same electron would be in a region a little further from the nucleus might be "1 in 5" or 0.2. Suppose, however, that a second electron has a different energy or momentum; the probability that the second electron might be in a region a given distance from the nucleus might be "1 in 3," or 0.333. The quantum-mechanical treatment of the electron seeks to relate mathematically the energy, spin, momentum, and other characteristics of the electron to the probability of finding the electron at any distance from the nucleus (or from any other point of reference). However, these characteristics will never determine with certainty just where the electron lies; all that may be stated is the probability of finding the electron in a particular region as compared to the probability for a different region. The equations thus describe the way that the probability of finding an electron in a given region varies as we look for it farther and farther from the nucleus. The electron is more likely to be found in a "high-probability region" than in a "low-probability region." Indeed, it is possible to imagine the electron as a very small body in rapid motion, darting back and forth over a large area, spending most of its time in the high-probability regions. A more easily visualized picture of the electron is that of a smear or cloud of negative charge, thickest in the regions of high probability, more diffuse in the regions of low probability.

We shall not try to describe rigorously the manner in which equations dealing with such probabilities are set up but will indicate some of the results of greatest interest to chemists. First, we may note that the most fundamental equation used in describing bound electrons was set up because its originator, E. Schroedinger, felt that the equation treating the "position probabilities" of a bound electron was similar in nature to the type that describes the motion of a point on a vibrating string. In order to get useful information from this very general **Schroedinger wave equation,** it first becomes necessary to express the energy of the electron in terms of its charge, its mass, and its other quantities. This general equation must then be simplified using whatever mathematical devices are appropriate. Ultimately, one hopes to obtain a more specific equation pertaining to the atom at hand, relating the "position probability" of an electron at a given point with the position of that point, and allowing us to estimate the energy of the electron.

Now the Schroedinger equation is a *differential equation* and, like other differential equations, it has a very large number of possible solutions. A number of such solutions do *not* correspond to electrons as we know them. Some solutions picture infinite electron densities at some positions, others allow two or more position probabilities at a given position, still others allow sudden "blotches" of electron density to appear in regions where the cloud is otherwise very thin. All such solutions must be described as being inconsistent with our experimental picture of the electron. To obtain meaningful solutions of the Schroedinger equation for a simple atom and, at the same time, a solution consistent with observed atomic spectra, it is necessary to introduce two additional quantities which, because of the wavelike nature of the electron, must be *integers*. (These are the first two of the four quantum numbers described in the next section.) In one of the more useful solutions of the wave equation, a simpler equation is obtained, expressing the energy of the electron in terms of these two "new" quantities, along with the charge and mass of the electron, the charge on the nucleus, and fundamental constants.

The Four Quantum Numbers. The Pauli Exclusion Principle

The two quantities thus arising are termed **quantum numbers**. Although their values may vary, they must follow definite rules in such variation. The energy of the electron is related to the values assumed by these quantum numbers, and if we change the value of one or both of these quantum numbers, the energy of the electron would be expected to change. Furthermore, the character of the spectra of atoms tells us that a bound electron may have only certain energies; it then must follow that the numbers determining the energies may have only *limited combinations* of possible values.

A more complete description of an electron cloud involves two additional quantum numbers which do not however generally affect the energy of an electron (in the absence of applied magnetic fields). The four quantum numbers are called:

> n—the principal quantum number
> l—the subsidiary (or azimuthal) quantum number
> m_l—the magnetic quantum number (sometimes abbreviated m)
> m_s—the spin quantum number (sometimes abbreviated s)

From the way in which these numbers arise in the handling of wave equations and by analysis of atomic spectra, physicists are able to associate each of these numbers with the characteristics of the electrons they describe.

> n, the principal quantum number is a rough measure of the *size* of the electron cloud. The larger the value of n, the greater is the volume of the bulk of charge density.
>
> l, the azimuthal quantum number, is related to the *shape* of the electron cloud. The value of l indicates whether the cloud is spherical, dumbbell-shaped, or perhaps more complicated.
>
> The magnetic quantum number, m is related to the *orientation* of the electron cloud in space.
>
> Finally, the spin quantum number, s, indicates the *direction* of spin of the electron. Experiments using an inhomogeneous magnetic field show that electrons have a property that is roughly analogous to our everyday concept of spin. (Although this language is inexact, it is quite suitable for our present purposes.) Furthermore, this spinlike property is also quantized; that is, a bound electron may "spin" only in two ways.

Now the Schroedinger equation has not been solved for all 102 elements. Solving the equation for atoms or ions having more than one electron is at present thought to be an impossible task, and even approximate treatments are very difficult. Such approximate solutions as have been worked out, however, indicate that we may describe the electrons in the heavier atoms in the same language as that used to describe the energy levels in single-electron systems. In fact, descriptions of the spectra of the elements are often given in the same quantum terms that are used for the hydrogen atom.

In the most common treatment of the wave equation, the restrictions on the values of the four quantum numbers are as follows:

> n—positive integers only; 1, 2, 3 . . . (but not 0)
> l—positive integers less than n; 0, 1, 2 . . . . . $(n - 1)$
> m—0, +1, −1, +2, −2, etc.; up to $+l$ and $-l$
> s—two values only; $+\frac{1}{2}$ and $-\frac{1}{2}$.

Note that n may assume any integral value. For electrons of atoms in unexcited states, n takes values from 1 to 7, corresponding roughly to the seven horizontal rows of the periodic table. For the atoms in which the organic chemist is most interested, n is 1, 2, or 3.

The values assumed by the azimuthal quantum number, l, depend on the values of n. For elements up to calcium, l assumes only the values 0 (corresponding to a *spherical* electron cloud) and 1 (corresponding to a dumbbell-shaped electron cloud). Certain electrons of the atoms of the heavier elements have

$l = 2$; such electrons may be imagined as a quartet of sausages with ends fastened to a point in space (Fig. 1-1).

The third quantum number, m, describes the orientation of the electron cloud in space. For a spherical cloud, however, there is only one possible orientation, for no matter how a sphere is twisted, it still looks the same to an outsider. A dumbbell, on the other hand, may be lined up with one end toward the observer or with its "handle" parallel to the height of the observer or with its "handle" parallel to the line connecting the ears of the observer. There are, in addition to these three orientations of a dumbbell, an infinite number of intermediate positions with the "handle" at various inclinations. For an electron, however, only three of these orientations are possible, meaning that in all such experiments which attempt to investigate electron orientation, the orientation of the electron cloud becomes quantized. Such experiments generally

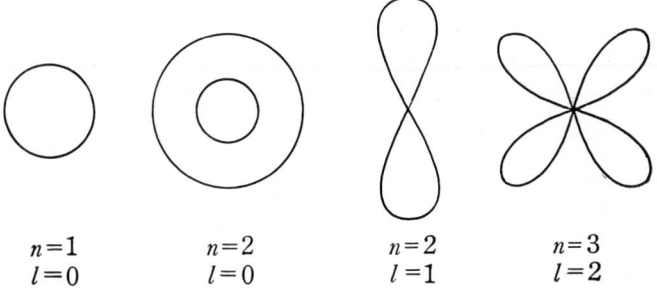

$$n=1 \qquad n=2 \qquad n=2 \qquad n=3$$
$$l=0 \qquad l=0 \qquad l=1 \qquad l=2$$

Fig. 1-1. Electron Clouds and Quantum Numbers

make use of an externally applied magnetic field, and each of the possible values of m relate to a given position of the electron cloud in space with respect to such a magnetic field.

The final quantum number, s, representing the "spin" direction, assumes only two values. When this "spin" exhibits itself in the presence of an external inhomogeneous magnetic field, it is found that electrons may "spin" either in one direction or in the direction roughly opposite. The spin quantum number may assume only two values, $+\frac{1}{2}$ or $-\frac{1}{2}$, but to avoid concerning ourselves with the reason for these fractional values, we shall refer to electrons as having either a + or − spin.

An electron going into an atom takes the quantum numbers that allow it to have the lowest energy. For cases in which we shall be interested, the energy is determined by n and l; and, generally speaking, the lower quantum numbers describe electrons of lower energy than do the higher quantum numbers. (An electron with $n = 1$ and $l = 0$ would have less energy than an electron with $n = 3$ and $l = 1$.) However, this does not mean that all electrons in each of the 102 elements in their unexcited states have $n = 1$ and $l = 0$ (the lowest values for these quantum numbers). Another factor, the **Pauli exclusion principle,** must be considered when electrons are gathered around a nucleus. This principle applies to many problems, but for the purpose at hand we may state the principle as, "No two electrons bound to the same atom may have identical sets of four quantum numbers"; this statement is very roughly analogous to the classical law, "Two bodies cannot be in the same place at the same time." Thus, two electrons of a given atom may have the same values for three of their quantum numbers, but the values of the fourth quantum number must be different.

The one electron of the hydrogen atom in the unexcited state (or *ground state*) will have the lowest possible values for the quantum numbers n and l—that is, $n = 1$ and $l = 0$. Since m may not exceed l, m must also be 0. In helium (atomic number 2) there are two electrons, one with the same set of quantum numbers as the single electron of the hydrogen atom; the second helium electron will have the same values for n, l, and m, but s will be different. If we arbitrarily call s for the first electron $-$, then s for the second electron would be $+$. Thus in helium there are two electrons situated around the nucleus, appearing from the outside as a spherically symmetric electric cloud. The two electrons are identical in all respects except that they are spinning in opposite directions. Removal of an electron from the helium atom is much more difficult than removal of an electron from the hydrogen atom, due chiefly to the added positive nuclear charge (an extra proton). In helium there are thus two spherically symmetric electrons with spins in opposite directions (that is, with spins *paired*).

With lithium, atomic number 3, there are two electrons in a spherical cloud (as with helium) plus a third electron. Generally, in considering the electronic configurations of an element, the "last" electron is the only one that need be considered since each of the remaining electrons is present in the atom preceding it in the periodic table. (The exceptions to this statement are not of importance to the organic chemist.) For the third lithium electron there are no more combinations of quantum numbers where $n = 1$, since neither l nor m can exceed zero if n is unity. The last (outermost) electron in lithium therefore has the quantum numbers:

$$n \quad l \quad m \quad s$$
$$2 \quad 0 \quad 0 \quad -$$

Here, again, the value of s is arbitrary since the two spin states are energetically the same. Note that the additional electron has assumed a value of 2 for n. This last electron has the bulk of its charge density much farther from the nucleus than the first two and thus is held much more loosely than the other two. This electron is easily removed chemically, enabling lithium to assume a valence of $+1$.

"Build-up" of the Periodic Tables; s and p Electrons

The last electrons in beryllium and in boron (atomic numbers 4 and 5, respectively) have quantum numbers:

	n	l	m	s
last electron in Be ($Z = 4$)	2	0	0	+
B ($Z = 5$)	2	1	−1	−

Note that the fourth electron in beryllium "pairs up" with the third, just as the second electron in helium "pairs up" with the first. However, the outer electron in boron is the first unexcited electron in our "build-up" of the elements for which l is unity. This final electron cloud is thus dumbbell-shaped, not spherical as was the case for the preceding electrons. It is emphasized that the assignment of the value of −1 to m for this outer electron is completely arbitrary, just as was the choice of − values of s before + values. The three orientations of the dumbbell-shaped electron cloud are, in the absence of external magnetic fields, energetically equivalent.

Bearing in mind that the order of assignment of the values for m and s is arbitrary, let us now summarize the four quantum numbers for the last electron in each of the elements up to sodium (atomic number 11):

	n	l	m	s
last electron in B ($Z = 5$)	2	1	−1	−
C ($Z = 6$)	2	1	0	−
N ($Z = 7$)	2	1	+1	−
O ($Z = 8$)	2	1	−1	+
F ($Z = 9$)	2	1	0	+
Ne ($Z = 10$)	2	1	+1	+
Na ($Z = 11$)	3	0	0	−

Note that the incoming electrons have taken all possible values for m before "pairing up." Two electrons having the same values for n, l, and m occupy the same region in space and therefore repel each other more strongly than do electrons of different m; therefore the "pairing up" process is to be postponed as long as possible. The last three electrons in the nitrogen atom may be regarded as dumbbell-shaped clouds with their "handles" pointing in different directions; the final electron in oxygen enters one of the clouds occupied by an electron, whereupon the two electrons occupying the same cloud adopt different spin directions. This "doubling up" or coupling must obviously occur since there are no further values that m may assume if n and l remain the same.

A group of bound electrons with the same value of n is generally referred to as a **shell.** Bound electrons having the same value of both n and l belong to the same **subshell.** A pair of electrons having the same values for n, l, and m

are said to occupy the same **orbital**. Thus in the neon atom, there are two filled shells, the first with only two electrons ($n = 1$), the second with eight electrons ($n = 2$). In the second shell of neon there are two subshells, the first having two, the second having six electrons.

After the tenth electron goes into neon ($Z = 10$), there are no more possible combinations of quantum numbers having $n = 2$. The outermost electron of the next element, sodium, must go into a higher energy state with $n = 3$, much farther from the nucleus than the other ten. Thus, the outermost electron of sodium, like that of lithium, is easily lost. More generally, since the properties of elements are determined in a large measure by their outermost (valence) electrons, the periodicity of properties arises naturally from the quantum restrictions. The final electrons for the elements in the second eight-membered period (sodium to argon) have quantum numbers corresponding to those listed for the preceding period with, however, the exception that n is 3 rather than 2.

In describing the ten electrons of the neon atom, chemists often refer to the two inner electrons (for which $n = 1$ and $l = 0$) as $1s$ electrons. The next subshell (for which $n = 2$ and $l = 0$) is called the $2s$ subshell; and the next six electrons (for which $n = 2$ and $l = 1$) comprise the $2p$ subshell. In this shorthand system, the initial number refers to the value of n and the small letter refers to the value of l.

Value of l	Symbol
0	s
1	p
2	d
3	f

(These letters are relics from the old designations that referred to certain spectral lines as "sharp," "principal," "diffuse," and "fundamental.") The organic chemist is interested chiefly in s- and p-type electrons. The d and f electrons become very important when the transition metals and the rare earths are being considered.

Ionic and Other Electrostatic Bonds versus Covalency

In attempting to answer the complex question, "What makes atoms come together to form molecules?" the concept of ionic attraction is exceedingly useful. One has little hesitation in saying that positive and negative ions are held together in pairs or groups because "unlike charges attract." Thus, although the LiCl molecule may not be dissociated into ions in the vapor state, it is still reasonable to say that its stability results from interaction of the positive Li$^+$ ion and the negative Cl$^-$ ion. Electrostatic interpretations are often extended to account for other interactions, even if one or another of the reacting species is not actually charged. We regard many molecules as having "positive ends" and "negative ends" and refer to such molecules as **dipoles.** It is sometimes convenient to designate positive or negative parts of molecules with the symbols $\delta+$ or $\delta-$, thus indicating positions of partial positive or negative charge; for example:

$$\overset{\delta+\ \ \delta-}{\text{Li}-\text{Cl}} \qquad \text{and} \qquad \delta+\ \ \begin{array}{c}\text{H}_3\text{C} \\ \diagdown \\ \diagup \\ \text{H}_3\text{C}\end{array}\text{O}\,\delta-$$

Dipoles may interact, sometimes with ions, sometimes with other dipoles. The methylamine complex of silver ion is conveniently regarded as being held together by attraction between positive Ag^+ and the negative end of the amine molecule:

$$\text{Ag}^+\ldots\ \delta-\overset{\overset{\displaystyle H}{\diagup}}{\underset{\underset{\displaystyle H}{\diagdown}}{\text{N}}}-\text{CH}_3\ \delta+\quad\text{forms}\quad \left[\text{Ag}-\overset{\overset{\displaystyle H}{\diagup}}{\underset{\underset{\displaystyle H}{\diagdown}}{\text{N}}}-\text{CH}_3\right]^+$$

Similarly, interaction of acetic acid with ammonia may be regarded as attraction between the positive end of the water molecule and the negative end of the ammonia molecule. Presumably

$$\underset{\text{CH}_3}{\overset{\text{O}}{\underset{\diagdown}{\overset{\diagup}{\text{O}=\text{C}}}}}\overset{\delta-\ \ \delta+}{-\text{H}}\ldots\ldots\overset{\delta-\diagup^{\text{H}}}{\text{N}}-\text{H}\,\delta+\qquad\text{gives}\qquad \underset{\text{CH}_3}{\overset{\text{O}}{\underset{\diagdown}{\overset{\diagup}{\text{O}=\text{C}}}}}-\text{H}---\overset{\diagup^{\text{H}}}{\text{N}}\underset{\diagdown_{\text{H}}}{-\text{H}}$$

(The above attraction, as we shall see, is an example of the familiar *hydrogen bond.*)

Even though the simplicity of the electrostatic picture makes it attractive, it is obvious that the picture cannot be extended to account for bonds between two atoms of the same element (for example, between the atoms in H_2, N_2, S_8, or between the carbon atoms in C_2H_6). More generally it becomes difficult to assume important coulombic attraction between atoms of elements close to each other in the periodic table.

When G. N. Lewis introduced the **electron-pair bond** or **covalent bond** in 1916,[2] it had been clear for years that simple electrostatics could yield only a portion of the "valence" picture. Lewis's proposal was that *one or more electron pairs "shared" by two atoms could bond them together.* Since stability of simple ions

[2] Lewis, *J. Am. Chem. Soc.,* **38,** 762 (1916). See also Lewis, *Valence and the Structure of Atoms and Molecules,* Chemical Catalog Co., New York, 1923.

having eight valence electrons had already been recognized, it was reasonable that the bond between atoms would be most stable if each atom was associated with *eight* electrons, either by sole "ownership" or by sharing. Interpretations using the electron-pair bond and the so-called *rule of eight* yielded a surprisingly good correlation of the chemical properties of a great number of compounds. The majority of compounds of nonmetals in the first two (eight-membered) periods can be formulated using the Lewis rules (although not without some serious objections). The arrangements of atoms in some polyatomic ions (such as NH_4^+, $SO_4^=$, AlH_4^-, and BF_4^-) can also be pictured.

In considering compounds containing carbon, oxygen, nitrogen, and (perhaps) sulfur, chemists had long been aware that more than one type of bond could link two given atoms. The bond between the two carbons in ethane is different from the bond between two carbons in ethylene; similarly, the bond between carbon and nitrogen in methylamine is different from the bond between carbon and nitrogen in acetonitrile. Such differences were readily apparent from the chemistries of the compounds and were later to be confirmed by measurements of bond lengths and bond energies. Lewis represented multiple (*double* and *triple* bonds) as quartets and sextets of electrons, arranged (perhaps for typographical convenience) in adjacent groups of two.

H   H   H

.C::C.   H:C:C:::N:

H   H   H

ethylene   acetonitrile

Such pictures tend to suggest that the two bonds comprising a double bond are equivalent and that the three bonds comprising a triple bond are also equivalent. Although the question cannot be regarded as settled, there is at present considerable evidence indicating that this is not so.

In spite of the successes of the Lewis picture, it was obvious (even before the development of the more recent pictures of covalent bonding) that important exceptions existed. Stable compounds having odd numbers of electrons (for example, NO, NO_2, and ClO_2) had long been familiar. Certain compounds of boron and aluminum had too few electrons to form the necessary number of covalent bonds (for example, B_4H_{10} and $Al_2(CH_3)_6$). Other compounds are known which have more electrons than can be accommodated by octets around each of the atoms (for example, SF_6 and PCl_5).

Finally, there are an uncomfortably large number of cases where more than one permissible Lewis structure can be drawn for a compound but where only one compound exists (for example, N_2O, CH_3N_3, and *o*-xylene); in cases of this sort, the *resonance* concept (to be described shortly) becomes important.

Formal Charge

This term is used less frequently but occasionally becomes important in discussions of the structures of a number of molecules having multiple bonds. To find the formal charge of a given atom in a structure: (a) Start with the group number of the atom in the periodic table, (b) subtract the number of unshared electrons about the atom, and (c) subtract one half the number of shared electrons. In the structures for diazomethane (CH_2N_2) below, the formal charges have been indicated:

$$H\overset{..}{\underset{..}{C}}::\overset{+}{N}::\overset{..}{\underset{..}{N}}:\,^{-}$$

(A)

$$H:\overset{..}{\underset{..}{C}}:N:::N:\,^{-}_{+}$$

(B)

"Formal charge" may be loosely defined as the measure of excess charge about a bound atom. A bond such as the N—O bond is trimethylamine oxide, $(CH_3)_3\overset{+}{N}:\overset{..}{\underset{..}{O}}:\,^{-}$, having *unlike* formal charges on adjacent atoms is called by some workers a **coordinate link** or **semipolar double bond.** The latter term was introduced at a time when it was generally felt that the distinction between ionic and covalent bonding was a sharp one. (Thus, it was believed that if charges could be assigned to two atoms bound together by an electron pair, then two bonds were present, one ionic and one covalent.) However, we now recognize that almost all covalent linkages between different elements have some ionic character (whether or not formal-charged structures can be drawn) and that therefore the "coordinate link" is not different in kind from many other covalent bonds between unlike elements.

Recent Interpretations of Covalent Bonding[3]

It is often asked, "If the covalent bond is not due to ordinary electrostatic attraction, just what keeps the bound atoms together?" Such a question is sometimes answered by describing the covalent bond as electrostatic in nature but with the charges situated in a "new" manner. One could argue, for instance, that the hydrogen molecule consists of two positively charged protons held on either side of a "smear" of negative electronic charge, which is situated largely near the middle of the molecule. Yet, it is difficult to see offhand why such an arrangement should be more stable than a system of two isolated hydrogen atoms, each with its own electron. The situation is certainly more complicated

[3] For more detailed descriptions see: Coulsen (Ref. 1a), pp. 71–257; Syrkin and Dyatkina (Ref. 1c), pp. 43–141; Pitzer (Ref. 1d), pp. 127–188; Ferguson, *Electronic Structures of Organic Molecules*, Prentice-Hall, Inc., New York, 1952, pp. 1–79.

than that in which a single electron is attracted to a singly charged nucleus. In spite of the fact that the H_2 molecule is one of the simplest molecules used in the chemist's laboratory, it nevertheless contains four bodies—two electrons (diffuse and light), and two protons (tiny and massive). There are attractions between each proton and each of the two electrons, a repulsion between the two protons, and repulsion between the two electrons. Without knowing the answer beforehand, it would be a very wise man who could guess the stable layout of this four-bodied system and also predict how the probability densities of each of the two electrons would depend on the geometry of the system.

These are problems in quantum mechanics. As with single atoms, the approach is made through the very general Schroedinger wave equation, which, it will be remembered, treats the probability density functions of electrons in a manner mathematically analogous to the motion of a point on a vibrating string. The energy of the system may be expressed algebraically in terms of the distances between bodies, and if the initial equation can be handled competently, three desired items of information may be obtained. These items are:

(a) The relationship between electron density at a point and the position of that point;

(b) The distance between the nuclei in the most stable layout of the system;

(c) An estimate of just how much more stable the bonded system is than the isolated atoms (that is, an estimate of the **bond energy**).

For the isolated hydrogen atom, the energy depends on one coulombic interaction between two bodies. For the hydrogen *molecule*, the energy depends on *six* interactions among four bodies, a much more formidable system. In the wave-mechanical treatment of molecules, more is involved than the ability to select and use mathematical tricks. The problem is so complicated that it must first be broken down into simpler problems, so that each of these may be handled individually. Then the parts must be brought together in a rational way, and, most important, the dimensions and energy of the molecule which have been calculated must be checked against the dimensions and energy determined by experiment. Such a "breakdown" of the problem requires both chemical and quantum-mechanical experience, and care must be taken that, in the breakdown and subsequent recombination, an error does not slip in due to some subtle limitation of the working method. There are indeed a number of chemical physicists who have spent years devising methods of attack on molecular-wave equations. For many simple molecules, the quantum-mechanical picture is not greatly different from the Lewis picture. For H_2, theoretical treatment predicts a cloud of two electrons (spins paired), relatively thick between the two nuclei; the F_2 molecule, a much more complicated system, can also be treated (making use of a number of simplifying approximations), arriving ultimately at a picture qualitatively similar to that of H_2. For F_2, although there are fourteen valence electrons, only two have appreciable probability densities on the line joining the two nuclei. Such a description conforms to the Lewis single bond in elemental fluorine.

The single bonds in H_2 and in F_2 are referred to as σ bonds—that is, electron clouds shaped much like elongated eggs with both nuclei inside, one near each end (Fig. 1-2). The Greek designation σ is chosen in analogy with the Roman s, for, as may be visualized from the sketch, if the bound atoms were to approach each other until the nuclei coalesced, the electron cloud would assume the spherical symmetry typical of s electrons. Also shown in the sketch is the so-called π bond, occurring in compounds whose Lewis structures include double or triple bonds. If the nuclei bonded by a π bond are considered to come together, the electron cloud shrinks into the typical dumbbell-shaped p electron.

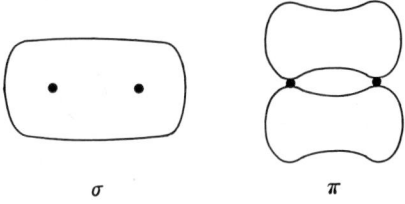

σ $\qquad$ π

Fig. 1-2. σ and π Bonds

However, whether we are considering σ bonds or π bonds, it can be said that the wave nature of the electron is such that when two bound electron clouds approach to form a bond, there will occur a thickening of the cloud in the regions where overlap is greatest. What is not easy to visualize without some physical insight is that wave interaction may allow a greater thickening than can be accounted for by mere addition of the thicknesses of the separate clouds. Valence electrons that formerly were associated with just one of the atoms become associated with the entire system.

Such a change in the configuration of an electron cloud may be called "delocalization." Extensive delocalization is not favored for an electron bound to a single atom because of the considerable coulombic energy required to move the negative charge appreciable distances from the nucleus. Delocalization becomes possible for polynuclear systems because there is more than one center of positive charge. Indeed it is delocalization that largely accounts for the stability of the covalent bond.

A covalent bond may be formed between two atoms only if the valence electron clouds of the two atoms overlap. In particular, an atom having unpaired valence electrons would be expected to form covalent linkages if overlap with the orbital of an unpaired electron of another atom is possible. Such a process would occur with the pairing of spins. Knowing the layout of the electron clouds, it is sometimes possible to predict the type of bonds that will form and the layout of the resulting molecule. In the simplest case, we have seen that two hydrogen atoms will combine by overlap of their single s electrons if the electrons are spinning in opposite directions. Similarly, hydrogen can form a single bond with chlorine by pairing its s electron with the one unpaired p electron of the chlorine atom.

The oxygen atom, as we have pointed out, contains two unpaired p electrons; the nitrogen atom has three unpaired p electrons. Since the p electrons are dumbell-shaped and oriented at right angles, one might expect the bonds in H_2O and NH_3 to be oriented at right angles as shown in Figure 1-3. Spectral studies show that the actual H—O—H bond angle in water is 104°, whereas

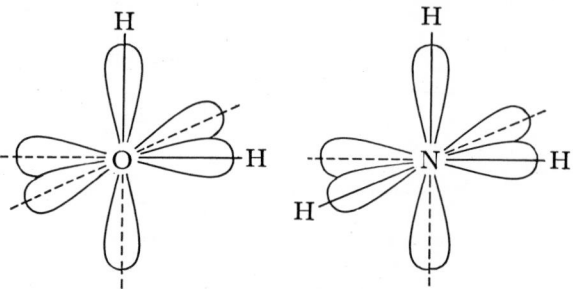

Fig. 1-3. Simplified Valence-bond Pictures of Water and Ammonia

the H—N—H bond angles in ammonia are 106°.[4] Although these values are not far from the predicted 90°, they are also suspiciously close to 109°. The latter figure is the bond angle in methane, CH_4, for which the bonding must be described differently. It is sometimes suggested that electrostatic repulsions between the positive hydrogen nuclei distort the bond angles in water and ammonia from the "expected" 90°.[5] (However it appears at present that the attractively simple pictures of these two compounds with bonds lying along the p orbitals may not be applicable without substantial modification.)

Promotion, Hybridization, and the Tetrahedral Carbon Atom

In almost all of its covalent compounds, the element carbon forms four bonds. However, the carbon atom in its normal state (p. 9) has only *two* unpaired

[4] Dennison, *Revs. Mod. Phys.*, **12**, 175 (1940).
[5] For example, Heath and Linnett, *Trans. Faraday Soc.*, **44**, 556 (1948), have calculated that repulsion between the two hydrogens in water should open up the bond angle to about 95°.

electrons. By a process of reasoning similar to that in the preceding paragraph, carbon would be expected to form only two covalent bonds. Confronted with this inconsistency, one looks for ways in which the electrons around the carbon atoms can be shuffled to yield four unpaired electrons. Suppose, for instance, that the outside "*s*" subshell were broken up and one of the electrons were "promoted" to the *p* level. The resulting atom, would have four outer electrons with quantum numbers as tabulated below. However, this is an excited state, and the energy required for the "promotion" of "electron 4" must be compen-

Table 1-1. Quantum Numbers of the Valence Electrons in Carbon

Electron Number	"normal"				"excited"			
	n	*l*	*m*	*s*	*n*	*l*	*m*	*s*
3	2	0	0	−	2	0	0	−
4 (to be "promoted")	2	0	0	+	2	1	+1	−
5	2	1	−1	−	2	1	0	−
6	2	1	0	−	2	1	−1	−

sated for by the energy released when two extra bonds are formed. Often the energy released in forming strong covalent bonds is sufficient to allow promotion, providing electrons are not promoted to levels beyond those characteristic of the next rare gas.

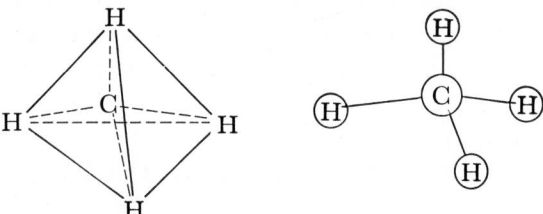

Fig. 1-4. The Tetrahedral Carbon Atom

Since the three *p*-electron clouds of an unbound atom are dumbbell-shaped and oriented at right angles and since the *s*-electron cloud is spherically shaped, it might be expected that three of the four bonds to tetravalent carbon would be oriented at right angles and that the fourth would be oriented at random. It is well known, however, that the four bonds formed by carbon point to the corners of a regular tetrahedron (that is, a pyramid having four faces, each of which is an equilateral triangle, Fig. 1-4). Thus, the contours of the electron clouds of the carbon atom have been substantially changed by the approach of four additional groups to form bonds. This change is not unexpected, for there is no good reason to suppose that the electron clouds whose shapes are the result of wave interaction in the field of a single nucleus should retain their shapes when brought into the vicinity of additional positive centers. Wave mechanics must again decide what new shapes the electron clouds may assume to allow formation of the most stable bonds (that is, those for which overlap with electron clouds from neighboring atoms is greatest). A rigorous treatment of the problem is quite difficult, but several approximate treatments[6] confirm that the most stable "electronic layout" for four-bonded carbon is that of four *similar* bonds pointing to the corners of a regular tetrahedron. The carbon atom is at the center of gravity of the tetrahedron (three-fourths the distance from a corner to the midpoint of the opposite triangular face). This corresponds (Ex. 7) to a H—C—H bond angle of 109.5°.

By "reshuffling" the valence electrons in the lone carbon atom, we have permitted the formation of four bonds, but the directions of the four bonds do *not* correspond to the directions of the four original orbitals. The quantum-mechanical treatment is said to **hybridize** these electrons (that is, reorient the shape of the electron-cloud picture without increasing the number of bonds). The bonds formed by carbon are said to be sp^3 *hybrid bonds*, the bonding presumably made possible by vacancies in the *s*- and *p*-type subshells. Such hybridization is possible using other sets of orbitals; in particular, for compounds of the transition metals, hybridization involving *d* orbitals becomes important.

It has been suggested that the departures of the bond angles in water and ammonia from the "expected" 90° are greater than can be accounted for by mere electrostatic repulsion of the hydrogen atoms,[5] and that the observed bond angles in H_2O and NH_3 are better explained by the presence of hybridized bonds than by simple *p* bonds that have been distorted. Ultimately, however, hybridization, like any wave-mechanical treatment of electron systems, must be based on an energy expression, itself electrostatic in nature, and this difference in interpretation need not worry the organic chemist.

Double and Triple Bonds

Single covalent bonds (σ bonds) consist of electrons whose densities lie mainly between one pair of atoms. Double bonds present a much different picture. In addition to the σ bond (as is present in single-bonded compounds), there is bonding interaction between the "dumbbell" electrons on adjacent atoms, forming a π bond, or, in the case of triple-bonded atoms, two π bonds. The bond-

---

[6] See, for example, (a) Pauling, *Proc. Nat. Acad.*, **14,** 359 (1928) and (b) Slater, *Phys. Rev.*, **37,** 481 (1931). For a summary of such a treatment, see (c) Pauling, *Nature of the Chemical Bond*, Cornell University Press, Ithaca, 1948, pp. 84–85.

ing in ethylene and in acetylene is often represented as in Figure 1-5. To simplify the picture, the σ bonds are represented only as straight lines so that the π bonds are more easily seen. Two drawings of ethylene appear in Figure 1-5. The first attempts to show overlap between neighboring "dumbbell" electrons. The second picture is simply "stretched out" so that the portions of the molecule may be more clearly labeled (although the interaction between the π electrons then becomes less clearly pictured). In acetylene, two pairs of π-electron

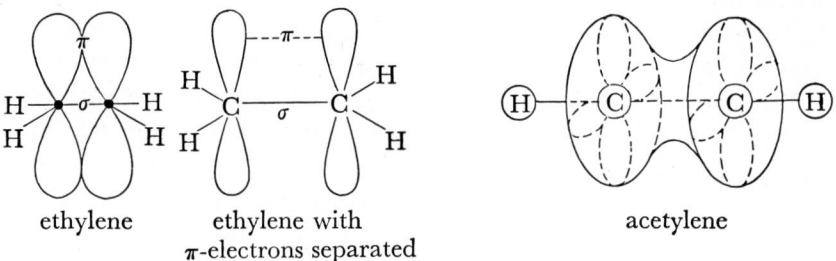

ethylene   ethylene with   acetylene
                π-electrons separated

Fig. 1-5 Bonding in Ethylene and Acetylene

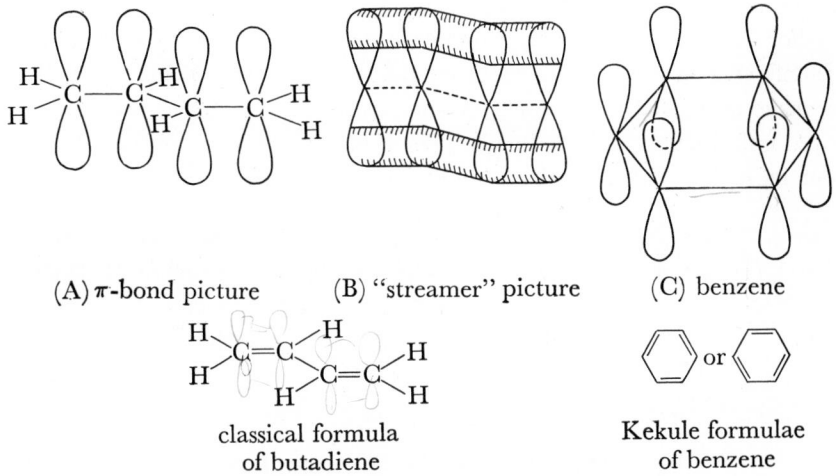

(A) π-bond picture   (B) "streamer" picture   (C) benzene

classical formula   Kekule formulae
of butadiene   of benzene

Fig. 1-6. Bonds in Butadiene and Benzene

lobes are shown at right angles by use of dotted lines. However, wave mechanics tells us that the superposition of two perpendicular π bonds in this way leads to *cylindrical symmetry;* hence, the π-electron cloud in acetylene may be represented as a sort of "cylinder of revolution" which would be formed by rotating a pair of π-bonded atoms about the axis connecting them.

In many molecules that contain more than one conjugated double or triple bond the π electrons are not strongly localized and will spread themselves as a group over a large section of the molecule. Figure 1-6 shows the π-electron structures for 1,3-butadiene and benzene. Again, the single (σ) bonds are represented merely by lines.

In this figure, the π-bond picture of butadiene (A) fails to show the delocalization of the π electrons. Picture B, the "streamer" picture of butadiene, shows the delocalization more clearly but is more difficult to draw (all C—H bonds have been deliberately omitted). The "streamers" indicate that none of the four electrons belongs to any particular carbon but that a composite cloud is spread over the four-carbon chain. Benzene is shown as a π-bond picture only, but a similar streamer picture may be drawn for it also, showing hexagonal "streamers" of electric charge above and below the plane of the ring.

The classical formulas of the two hydrocarbons are pictured below the more "modern" formulas. In contrast to the Lewis picture, which puts a single bond between the two center carbons in butadiene, the more recent pictures show that the middle bond actually has "double-bond character," as do the end bonds. Moreover, it is to be emphasized that the π-bond picture of benzene can correspond to either of the two "Kekule" forms but is "better" than either alone because it does not convey the erroneous impression that three of the six carbon-to-carbon bonds are single bonds.

For delocalization of π-electron density along the length of a chain or the circumference of a ring, it is necessary that *each atom* comprising the chain or ring have associated with it at least one p-type electron that is not being employed in formation of single bonds. (The classical chemist would say that each atom in such a chain or ring should have some "unsaturated character.")

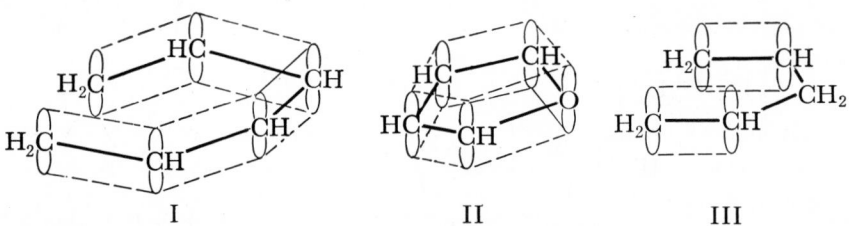

Fig. 1-7. Delocalized and Localized π-electron Systems

Thus, the π-electron cloud is delocalized over the entire chain in 1,3,5-hexatriene (I) and over the ring of the cyclic ether, furan (II), but the central methylene group in 1,4-pentadiene prevents interaction between the π-electron clouds on the ends of the chain. As will be seen later, important differences in chemical and physical properties stem from such differences in π-electron configurations.

It also should be noted that centers of atoms comprising a chain or ring over which π-electron density is extensively delocalized must lie in the same plane. In the solid state, and possibly in the liquid state as well, all twelve carbon atoms in biphenyl lie in the same plane, and we may visualize single clouds of π-electron density spread above and below the double-ring system. In contrast, the two rings in hydrocarbon IV lie in different planes. Although one might not believe it from the structural formula of this compound, it may be calculated from the van der Waals' radius of the methyl group (Chap. 2) that the methyl groups on the two rings would collide with each other if the rings were

H_3C CH_3

H_3C CH_3

IV

to lie in the same plane. In IV, therefore, there is essentially no interaction between the π-electron systems of the two rings. The interaction or lack of interaction may often be deduced from spectral studies. A number of examples in which planarity (or departures from planarity) affects the properties of molecules will be described in later chapters.

The Use of Resonance[7]

For most simple compounds having no more than one double bond, the "modern picture" may be quite adequately represented by the Lewis structures. However, in cases where there is extensive delocalization of electron density, the classical structures are not as suitable as either the π-electron structures or the "streamer" pictures. Both of the latter type structures, however, are more difficult to draw and are far less convenient for the large number of chemists who were trained in the days before the concepts of σ and π electrons were extensively used.

Because of the convenience of thinking in terms of classical structures, there is in extensive use today a concept by which molecules that cannot be represented adequately by single classical structures are represented instead by a "combination" of two or more Lewis structures. This concept is called **resonance;** we shall presently see why. When two or more legitimate Lewis structures can be drawn for a compound, we say that the "true" structure

[7] (a) For detailed discussions of a number of areas in which the resonance concept has proved most useful to organic chemists, see Wheland, *Resonance in Organic Chemistry*, John Wiley and Sons, Inc., New York, 1955; the final chapter of this work is devoted to quantitative treatments of some aspects of the resonance picture. (b) For a number of objections to certain *uses* of the resonance concept (but not to its theoretical basis), together with pertinent references, see Huckel, *Structural Chemistry of Inorganic Compounds* (translated by L. Long), Elsevier Publishing Co., Inc., New York, 1950, pp. 434–437.

(often called a **resonance hybrid**) is similar to each of the structures but identical to neither. In short, it is intermediate in character. In the most familiar case, the π-bond picture of benzene (Fig. 1-5) may be regarded as being a "combination" of the two Kekule structures, both of which are wrong if considered alone.

Similarly, resonance pictures may be used to show that there is double-bond character in certain of the bonds in 1,3,5-hexatriene (V), furan (VI), and biphenyl (VII) which would be represented as single bonds in the classical

| V | VI | VII |

pictures. Thus, classical pictures represent the bonds labeled a and b in 1,3,5-hexatriene, bond d in furan, and bond e in biphenyl as single bonds; but the resonance forms above represent each of these as double bonds. (Other resonance pictures, in addition to those shown, may be drawn.)

In recent years the dimensions of a large number of molecules have been measured, and in many cases the resonance concept has been useful in rationalizing observed dimensions that are significantly different from those predicted from classical structures. The distance between the nuclei of two bonded atoms is called a **bond length.** We shall see in the next chapter that a triple bond between two atoms is shorter than a double bond between the same two atoms, and that a single bond is longer than a double bond. Thus, the carbon-to-carbon bond in ethane is longer than the carbon-to-carbon bond in ethylene, which is, in turn, longer than the carbon-to-carbon bond in acetylene. In benzene, each of the carbon-to-carbon bond lengths is the same, being greater than that corresponding to a double bond but less than that corresponding to a single bond. The length of the bonds in benzene then confirms what the resonance picture tries to show, that the carbon-carbon bonds in benzene are actually intermediate in character between double and single. Likewise, bonds a and b in 1,3,5-hexatriene, bond d in furan, and bond e in biphenyl are each intermediate in length between a "normal" double and a "normal" single bond.

Often resonance is indicated by a double-headed arrow, $\leftrightarrow$, and the two or more contributing structures are called **primary** or **canonical forms**; for example, for diazomethane:

| (A) | (B) |

We have already seen that delocalization of electron clouds (that is, spreading of electronic charge over the region of several nuclei) often leads to structural stability. Since resonance is one way of picturing delocalization, one might expect that if two or more permissible primary structures can be drawn for a molecule, it should be more stable than a hypothetical molecule of the same type with no delocalization. Stability of compounds is often determined experimentally by measuring heats of chemical reactions; speaking very roughly, a stable molecule will give off less heat in a given reaction than would a less stable molecule of the same type. Now classical thermochemistry has been developed to the point where heats of reactions can be broken down into a series of makings and breakings of chemical bonds; and the heats of reactions of the large majority of classical-structure compounds can be accurately predicted by considering *bond energies* (Chap. 2). However, such predictions often fail when applied to compounds for which two or more canonical forms may be drawn. In such cases, measured stabilities are almost always greater than the predicted stabilities of *any* of the canonical forms.

Consider, for example, the combustion of benzene. The heat liberated in burning a mole of benzene to carbon dioxide and water is sometimes estimated by considering benzene as six C—H bonds, three C—C single bonds, and three C=C double bonds. However the experimental heat of combustion of benzene is *36 kilocalories per mole lower* than the value predicted by using bond energies. Thus, it is often said that benzene is "stabilized by resonance" and has a *resonance energy* of 36 kcal per mole. It would seem that this choice of terms leaves something to be desired. Actually the experimental energy of benzene is the "correct" quantity. The resonance energy in a sense arises from the surprise of the chemist when he realizes that the energy he incorrectly predicted using an oversimplified picture was not what he found. The greater his surprise, the greater would be the resonance energy. It should be noted, however, that resonance energies are somewhat more fundamental than mere "fudge-factors," used to adjust incorrect values to obtain better second guesses, for it is possible to estimate relative resonance energies of a number of molecules by using one of several quantum-mechanical treatments.[8]

Granted that the concept of resonance is useful in correlating the dimensions, stability, and other properties of many compounds inadequately represented by classical structures, one might well ask whether there is any fundamental basis for the idea that a "true" structure can be represented at all by a combination of pictures. We may indicate briefly the theoretical justification for the resonance concept by introducing a quantity called a **wave function, eigen function,** or (since it is generally abbreviated by the Greek letter psi,

[8] See, for example: (*a*) Lennard-Jones, *Proc. Roy. Soc.* (London), **A158,** 297 (1937); (*b*) Wheland, *J. Am. Chem. Soc.*, **63,** 2025 (1941).

ψ), simply the ψ function. It will be recalled that quantum mechanics handles electron probabilities in space by using a mathematical analogy to the motion of a point on a vibrating string. In the treatment of the string, ψ refers to the *displacement* of a given point from its position of rest; on the other hand, in the treatment of electron probabilities, the square of the wave function, ψ^2, determines the probability density at the position being considered. (Generally, in a series of calculations, it is most convenient to work with ψ itself, waiting until near the end of the calculations to square ψ to obtain a picture of probability density relationships.) This correspondence (although it probably would not be predicted beforehand) is rational since probability density (or cloud thickness) can never be less than zero, whereas the displacement of a point can be $+$ or $-$, depending upon whether the point is above or below the position of rest.

Now, for each Lewis picture, there exists, in principle at least, a particular ψ function. For simple structures such wave functions can be and have been developed, whereas for more complicated structures they presumably could be developed if workers wished to expend the time and effort. These Lewis pictures, and the ψ functions that correspond to them, represent "limiting" structures. For molecules in which the resonance treatment is important, electron density in these "limiting" structures is more localized than in the true structure; and for a closer approximation to the truth, the mathematician must express delocalization of electronic charge over a greater area than indicated by the limiting structures. Such delocalization may be handled in wave mechanics by a *linear combination* of the wave functions of the individual limiting structures. (A linear combination of two quantities is obtained by multiplying each by a constant and then adding.) More particularly, if we call the wave functions associated with the two Lewis structures of diazomethane on page 22 ψ_A and ψ_B, it is possible to obtain a third function ψ_{AB} where

$$\psi_{AB} = c_1\psi_A + c_2\psi_B$$

and c_1 and c_2 are the constants. From the wave-mechanical treatment of the problem, it can be shown that ψ_{AB}, corresponding to a structure over which electron density is considerably delocalized, represents a "better" structure (that is, a structure of lower energy) than is represented either by ψ_A or ψ_B. Thus, the mental combination of structures A and B of diazomethane corresponds, in a sense, to the mathematical combination of the wave functions ψ_A and ψ_B to obtain ψ_{AB}, the wave function of a structure of lower energy. In carrying out the calculations expressing this delocalization, the treatment becomes mathematically similar to the handling of certain vibrating systems— such as strings, tuning forks, or pendulums, in particular—to the mutual modification in vibrations when two independently vibrating bodies are suddenly attached to each other. We can see how the vibrations of one of such bodies affects the other and often call this a "resonance" effect. However, the vibrations of the bodies are observable, whereas the contributing wave functions are hypothetical. To say that an electron cloud "resonates" like a string or tuning fork is clearly carrying the mathematical analogy too far.

The Transition Between Ionic and Covalent Character

Although we have devoted much space to discussion of the covalent bond, it will be remembered that many bonds between metals and nonmetals are conveniently considered as being formed from ions. In an extreme case such as potassium chloride, the bond between a potassium ion and a neighboring chloride ion in the KCl lattice results almost exclusively from classical electrostatic attraction. Although the positive and negative ions in the lattice are kept from too close an approach to each other by repulsions of the electron clouds, there is essentially no distortion of the clouds themselves as the ions approach each other. Between two adjacent ions there is very little electron density that can be thought of as belonging to the pair as a unit.

Suppose we regard the hydrogen molecule as being formed from the coming together of a hydrogen ion, H^+, and a hydride ion, $H:^-$. As these two ions approach each other, the spherical electron cloud of the hydride ion becomes very much distorted by the tiny positively charged proton. The electron cloud spreads itself over the region of both nuclei with much of the cloud lying in the space between the nuclei. The bond, of course, is the familiar covalent bond in H_2; in this interpretation, the covalent bond has resulted from extensive distortion of the negative ion by the positive ion.

Logically, between these two extremes in bond character there are cases where there is an intermediate degree of distortion or deformation of the electron clouds. Generally one regards the anions as being distorted by the cations (although the cations are also appreciably distorted in some cases). Such a distortion is often called a **polarization;** a portion of the negative cloud of the anion becomes "pulled" over toward the region of the positive cation. As the distortion is increased, the bond between anion and cation takes on more and more covalent character. Figure 1-8 crudely illustrates this trend. Such a picture is not easily translated into quantitative language, for one does not generally speak of an ion as being "35-percent distorted" and "65-percent nondistorted." By means of the resonance concept, however, the character of a bond between two different atoms can be described in more quantitative form (although it might well be argued that in this case the mathematics do not help to give the picture much additional physical significance).

A bond between two different atoms A and B is, we have said, neither completely ionic nor completely covalent but intermediate in character. Such a description is analogous to that used to describe compounds represented as resonance hybrids. Accordingly, let us consider a completely ionic structure as one extreme (having associated with it a wave function, $\psi_{A^+B^-}$) and a completely covalent structure as the second extreme (having associated with it a wave function, $\psi_{A:B}$). A better wave function, more nearly representing the "actual" structure, is then obtained by a linear combination:

$$\psi_{better} = c_1\psi_{A^+B^-} + c_2\psi_{A:B}$$

In such a linear combination, the relative importance of the ionic and covalent structures is related to the ratio of the coefficients c_1 and c_2. For predominantly covalent bonds $c_2 \gg c_1$.

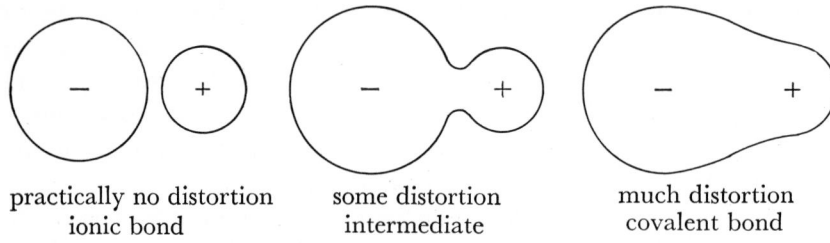

practically no distortion   some distortion   much distortion
ionic bond   intermediate   covalent bond

Fig. 1-8. Covalent Character and Distortion

Now the energy of the form A^+B^- may be estimated from electrostatics, whereas the energies of both the actual molecule, AB, and its hypothetical completely covalent structure, $A:B$, may be estimated from thermochemistry (as described in Chap. 2). When comparisons are made between the experimental stability of AB and the hypothetical stabilities of the two extreme structures, the molecule itself proves more stable than either extreme form. This must be so if the resonance treatment has been used correctly.

Limitations of the Use of Resonance

By shrewd and practised use of the resonance idea, one may make qualitative and sometimes quantitative predictions about the structure and reactivity of organic compounds. To the chemist, probably the greatest appeal of this treatment is its ability to correlate behavior previously regarded as anomalous in terms of pictures that he already understands. However, it is obviously (and perhaps fortunately) possible to draw and to manipulate resonance pictures without understanding the nature of the physical wave picture that makes the resonance concept a legitimate one. Given this human situation, it is not surprising that the language of resonance has sometimes been taken over uncritically, that meanings have been attached to pictures and operations that were never meant to apply, and that the ideas are sometimes modified to apply to situations for which they were not originally intended. Chemists who presumably should know better are sometimes caught saying that a molecule "stays in this resonance form only a small portion of the time," that "one resonance form is more reactive than the other," or that "resonance is decreased since two types of resonance are going in opposite directions in the molecule."

Aside from such misuses, however, there are aspects of the resonance treatment that are open to criticism. The selection of the admittedly arbitrary primary (canonical) structures is the point at which the resonance treatment is often attacked. There are three rules governing the selection of such canonical structures; two of these are easy to apply, whereas the third sometimes causes trouble. The three rules are these:

(1) Structures may contribute only if the relative positions of the atoms are not changed. Thus

$$H:\ddot{C}::N::\ddot{N}: \quad \text{and} \quad H:\ddot{N}::C::\ddot{N}:H$$

with H above the first structure's C.

cannot contribute to the same hybrid. Similarly,

$$H:C::\ddot{C}:\ddot{O}:H \quad \text{and} \quad H:\ddot{C}:C::\ddot{O}:$$

(with H atoms above and below),

are different compounds (tautomers), even though they are readily interconvertible.

(2) Only structures with the same number of unpaired electrons may contribute to a given resonance hybrid. (This restriction is important in the consideration of organic biradicals, Chap. 16.)

(3) Only those structures having similar energies (stabilities) can contribute appreciably to a given hybrid. For example, there are three Lewis structures of methyl azide, CH_3N_3:

$$CH_3:\overset{..}{N}::\overset{+}{N}:\overset{-}{\overset{xx}{N}}: \qquad CH_3:\overset{-}{\overset{..}{N}}:\overset{+}{N}:::N: \qquad CH_3:\overset{+}{N}:::\overset{+}{N}:\overset{=}{N}:$$

$$(A) \qquad\qquad (B) \qquad\qquad (C)$$

Of these, structures (A) and (B) are considered to contribute to the hybrid form of methyl azide, but the contribution of form (C) is considered negligible. Form (C) is sometimes termed a "high-energy form," meaning that considerable electrostatic energy would be needed to arrange the charges so that a double-negative charged atom is at one end of the structure and two single-positive charges are on adjacent atoms near the middle.

In many cases, it seems obvious that the primary structures chosen have the same energies since they are equivalent. The two Kekule structures for benzene are, except for rotation, identical. The case of carbon dioxide, however, is more troublesome. In CO_2, generally represented as O=C=O, the carbon-to-oxygen bond lengths are significantly less than the C-to-O bond lengths in aldehydes and ketones. At an early point in the development of the resonance treatment, it was suggested that this bond shortening indicated contribution of triple-bonded structures, and CO_2 was accordingly represented as the hybrid:

$$O=C=O \quad \longleftrightarrow \quad {}^-O-C\equiv O^+ \quad \longleftrightarrow \quad {}^+O\equiv C-O^-$$
$$\text{(A)} \qquad\qquad\qquad \text{(B)} \qquad\qquad\qquad \text{(C)}$$

To explain the bond shortening, Pauling estimated that the two triple-bonded structures are about as important as the double-bonded one. Now it is not easy to estimate the energy of a hypothetical structure such as (B) or (C), but such estimates that have been made[7b] indicate that (B)—and hence (C)—is far less stable (about 100 kcal per mole) than (A), chiefly because of the reluctance of the oxygen atom to assume a positive charge. Even if it is assumed that the estimated value of the energy difference between (A) and (B) is considerably in error, the energy difference is almost certainly not small. Although it is indisputable that there is a difference between the C=O bonds in CO_2 and those in aldehydes and ketones, it is doubtful that the difference is best expressed by heavy contributions of high-energy triple-bonded structures.

This is just a single example. At present a more satisfactory (and more sophisticated) picture of the electron structure of CO_2 is available,[9] and the treatment indicated above may be said to be largely of historical importance. Nevertheless, it serves to show that application of the concept of resonance to such species as carbon dioxide, ketene, the azide ion, or the cyanate ion is not always as straightforward as we would like. On the other hand, the resonance theory itself, for the most part, stands on firm ground. Moreover, the considerable success of resonance in correlating the physical and chemical properties of a host of multiple-bonded organic compounds makes the concept not only legitimate, but, as will be seen, exceedingly useful.

The Hydrogen Bond[10]

No discussion of chemical bonding should omit mention of the **hydrogen bond.** The organic chemist finds evidence of this type of bond in a large number of compounds having O—H linkages and in a considerable number containing

[9] See, for example, Coulsen (Ref. 1a), p. 211.
[10] For more complete discussions of the hydrogen bond, see Pauling (Ref. 6c), pp. 284–334; and Syrkin and Dyatkina (Ref. 1c), pp. 273–286.

N—H linkages. Perhaps the most familiar evidences of the hydrogen bond are the "abnormally high" boiling points of carboxylic acids, alcohols, and many amines. For example, the two compounds, dimethyl ether, $(CH_3)_2O$, and ethanol, C_2H_5OH, have the same formula weight, but the latter (with an O—H bond) boils over 100° higher than the former. Similarly, acetic acid (bp 118°) and methyl formate (bp 31°) have the same formula weight, but display a marked difference in volatility. The hydrogen bond is best considered as a special example of dipole-dipole interaction in which the "negative" oxygen atoms of one molecule are attracted electrostatically to the "positive" hydrogen atoms of a second molecule.

Such attraction must be stronger than the weak *van der Waal's forces* that hold uncharged molecules together in the liquid and solid states. However, hydrogen bonding cannot be as strong as ordinary ionic or covalent bonding, otherwise the boiling points of alcohols and carboxylic acids would become comparable to those of substances having multiple-bonded continuous networks such as NaCl or diamond. Thus, the hydrogen bond is a moderately weak one, generally about 5 to 10 percent as strong as ordinary covalent single bonds. The vast majority of organic compounds that dissolve in water do so with attendant formation of hydrogen bonds with the solvent.

In cases where hydrogen bonding occurs, the two heavier atoms approach each other quite closely; in the solid state, this closeness of approach is detectable by x-ray methods and is an important indication of hydrogen bonding (even though the hydrogen atoms themselves often cannot be located). Occasionally hydrogen bonding persists in the vapor state. Thus, gaseous HF is associated at low temperatures, and formic acid exists as a dimer in both the vapor phase at low temperatures and in solutions in inert solvents. The structure of this dimer is shown.[11]

As indicated, the hydrogen bond between the two oxygen atoms is *not* symmetric; that is, the hydrogen is closer to one oxygen than to the other.

[11] Karle and Brockway, *J. Am. Chem. Soc.*, **66**, 574 (1944).

Important effects may be traced to the presence of hydrogen bonding *within* a single molecule (*intramolecular*). In an extreme case, the hydrogen-bonded molecule, 2,6-dihydroxybenzoic acid (VIII), has an ionization constant approximately 10 thousand times as great as that of its isomer, 3,5-dihydroxy-benzoic acid (IX), in which intramolecular hydrogen bonding cannot occur. Another curious difference due to hydrogen-bonding effects is illustrated by comparing *o*-nitrophenol (X) with its *para* isomer. Hydrogen bonding is

VIII	IX	X	XI

present in both isomers, but an intramolecular hydrogen-bonded structure corresponding to XI is not possible for the *para* compound. Therefore, hydrogen bonding in the latter must be between the hydroxyl group of one molecule and the nitro group of another; that is, the *para* compound is associated whereas the *ortho* compound is not. This structural difference is reflected in the much greater volatility and solubility in nonpolar solvents exhibited by the *ortho* compound.

When the hydrogen atom of an —OH group attached to an aromatic ring participates in intramolecular hydrogen-bond formation, the vibration between the oxygen and hydrogen atom of the O—H bond (which may generally be observed in the infrared spectrum of the molecule) decreases in frequency. In effect, hydrogen bonding has "loosened" the O—H bond. In such cases, the sharp infrared absorption peaks in the region of 7050 and 3525 cm^{-1}, present in "normal" phenols, are either absent or very much "smeared out" (Chap. 3).[12]

In the majority of instances where intramolecular hydrogen bonding is important, the hydrogen atom finds itself a member of a *six-membered planar ring*. In such cases, each of the remaining five atoms constituting the ring has a π electron associated with it (essentially equivalent to the classical statement that such rings can be drawn with two double bonds). Thus, the intramolecular hydrogen bonding present in salicylaldehyde (XII) is absent in its alicyclic analog (XIII) since the H—O—C—C—C=O system in the latter cannot be twisted

---

[12] Wulf, *et al.*, *J. Am. Chem. Soc.*, **58**; 548, 1991, 2287 (1936): Errera, *et al.*, *Jour. de Physique et le Radium*, **6**; 154, 281 (1935).

into a planar configuration. Likewise, intramolecular hydrogen bonding present in the enol form of acetylacetone (XIV) would not be expected in the enol form of its homolog, acetonylacetone (XV), since there are too many carbon atoms

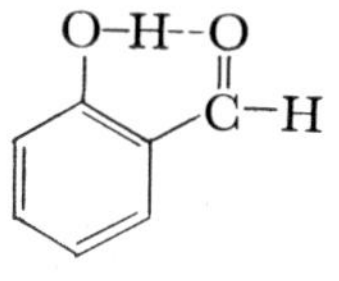

XII

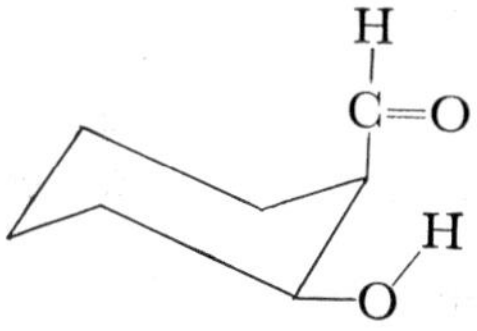

XIII

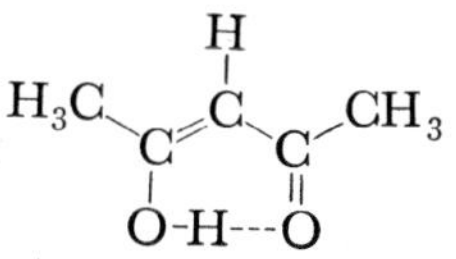

XIV

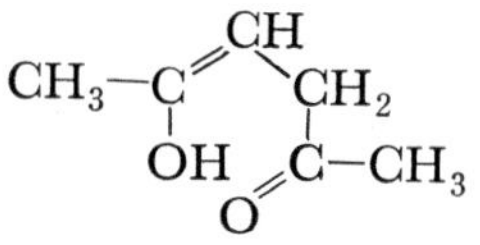

XV

between the two oxygen atoms. When a compound containing an N—H or an O—H linkage cannot undergo intramolecular hydrogen bonding, some degree of association by intermolecular hydrogen bonding (for which steric requirements are much less stringent) will almost always occur.

EXERCISES FOR CHAPTER 1

1. List all four quantum numbers for each of the 11 electrons in the sodium atom.

2. How many different electrons are possible with $n = 4$ and $l = 3$? How many (total) with $n = 4$?

3. Calculate the number of unpaired electrons in the atoms of Na, Al, and P.

4. (a) Write Lewis formulas for HN_3, $(CH_3)_3SBr$, BH_3CO, and CH_3OCl.
   (b) Show that Lewis formulas cannot be written for B_2H_6, PF_5, and NO_2.

5. Arrange the following bonds in order of increasing ionic character:

$$Be—O, \ C—O, \ N—O, \ O—O, \ Si—O, \ Se—O$$

6. Draw three Lewis structures for nitrogen(I) oxide, N_2O. Label the formal charges, and decide which structure would be most likely to be discarded.

7. The height of a regular tetrahedron is $\sqrt{2/3}$ times as long as its side. The carbon atom in methane is $3/4$ times the distance between the apex of the tetrahedron and the opposite side. Using trigonometry, verify the bond angle for methane (109.5°).

8. (a) Sketch a picture of allene, $CH_2\!=\!C\!=\!CH_2$, representing the "double bonds" as π electrons. Which of the carbons is most like the carbon atoms in acetylene?

(b) Draw π-bond pictures of naphthalene and azulene (shown below). Show that the Kekule forms of naphthalene are identical when represented in this way and that the two forms of azulene are also identical.

napthalene   azulene

9. (a) Draw the possible Lewis structures for: CO_3^{-2} (3 forms); C_3O_2 (3 forms); $C_6H_5O^-$ (5 forms).

(b) Sketch the canonical forms for each of the following, and label the formal charges. Ignore structures in which more than one carbon bears a formal charge.

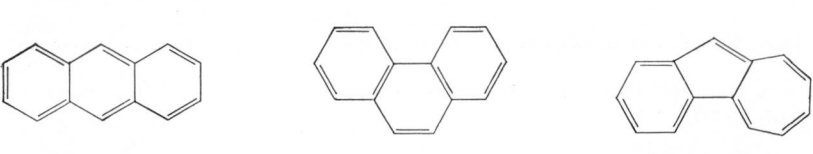

2 Lewis structures
5 "non-Lewis" structures

6 Lewis structures
5 "non-Lewis" structures

10. The resonance theory stipulates that if two compounds have the same set of atoms and bonds, then that compound for which the more canonical structures may be drawn will be the more stable. On this basis, which would be the most stable, anthracene, phenanthrene, or benzazulene?

anthracene   phenanthrene   benzazulene

11. Explain why water has a higher boiling point than either hydrogen fluoride or ethanol.

12. Certain of the compounds below participate in hydrogen bonding that may affect their boiling points through association. Arrange them in the order of extent of intermolecular hydrogen bonding (as would be evidenced by boiling-point abnormalities):

acetic acid, acetaldehyde, ammonia, ethane, ethanol, fluoroform, hydrocyanic acid, oxalic acid, salicylaldehyde, p-hydroxybenzaldehyde.

13. Of the eight compounds shown below, four participate in intramolecular hydrogen bonding (either in the indicated form or the enol form) and the remaining four do not. Predict which four exhibit effects of intramolecular hydrogen bonding and give the reasons for your choices.

✳ (a) 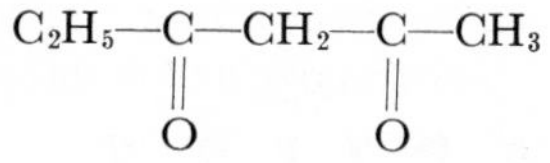 $C_2H_5-\underset{\underset{O}{\|}}{C}-CH_2-\underset{\underset{O}{\|}}{C}-CH_3$

(b) $CH_3-\underset{\underset{O}{\|}}{C}-C(CH_3)_2-\underset{\underset{O}{\|}}{C}-CH_3$

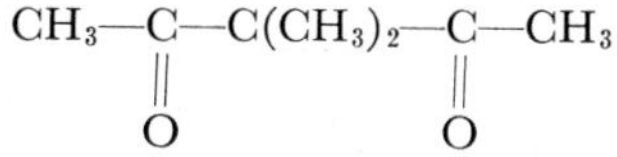

✳ (c) $CH_3-\underset{\underset{O}{\|}}{C}-\underset{\underset{OH}{|}}{CH}-CH_3$

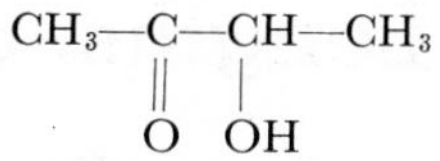

(d)

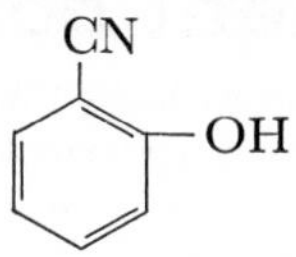

(e) 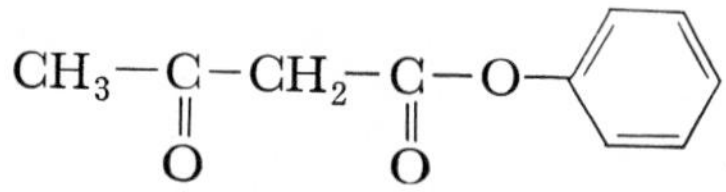 $CH_3-\underset{\underset{O}{\|}}{C}-CH_2-\underset{\underset{O}{\|}}{C}-O-$

✳ (f)

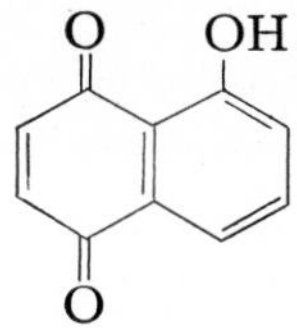

(g)

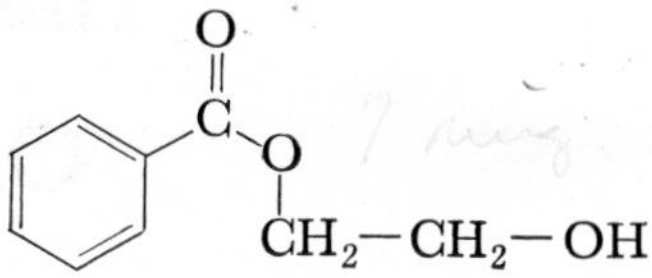

✗ (h) 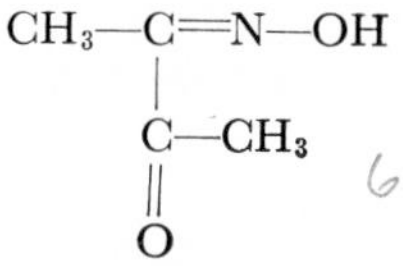 $CH_3-C{=}N-OH$

$\underset{\underset{O}{\|}}{C}-CH_3$ 6 ring.

The Energies, Lengths, and Orders of Covalent Bonds

ALTHOUGH THE MAJORITY of organic chemists today picture the configurations of molecules in much the same way as did the chemists of 1910, our ideas concerning molecules have been brought into somewhat sharper focus by the ability to assign energies to such molecules and to the bonds within them, and further by the increased knowledge of atomic and molecular dimensions.

Bond Energies

For a diatomic molecule, the bond energy is defined as the energy needed to split the molecule into atoms (both the molecule and component atoms being in their ground states). Such a bond energy or "energy of dissociation" may often be determined from the band spectrum of the molecule[1] or may be closely approximated by measurements of the equilibrium constants for dissociation of the molecule at high temperatures. The important *van't Hoff equation* states that a plot of the logarithms of such dissociation constants (values of ln K) at different temperatures against the reciprocals of the temperatures themselves should yield a straight or nearly straight line whose slope is simply related to the desired heat of dissociation,

$$\frac{d(\ln K)}{d(1/T)} = -\frac{H}{R}$$

where H is the heat of dissociation and R is the gas constant (1.99 calories per mole). Such thermodynamically determined heats of dissociation (which are, in actuality, *enthalpy* values) lie close to the energies of dissociation determined

---

[1] See, for example, G. Herzberg, *Spectra of Diatomic Molecules*, Van Nostrand, Inc., Toronto, 1950, pp. 437–450.

spectrally, but more detailed considerations indicate that the two types of values should and do differ by small amounts. This distinction will be ignored in the following discussions, and we shall conveniently (although somewhat incorrectly) refer merely to bond "energies" whatever their source.

For diatomic molecules, single-bond energies range from 135 kcal per mole for HF to 36 kcal per mole for I_2. By convention, bond energies are generally given positive signs.

For a molecule with three or more atoms (hence, two or more bonds), the heat of formation from the isolated atoms may be regarded as the sum of all the bond energies. The heat of formation of the S_8 ring from eight sulfur atoms should be eight times the average energy of formation of a single S—S bond; similarly, the O—H bond energy may be considered as being just half of the heat of formation of a water molecule from individual hydrogen and oxygen atoms. Now the energy of the reaction $2H + O \rightarrow H_2O$ is not easily measured, but the energy of the reaction $2H_2 + O_2 \rightarrow 2H_2O$ has been measured calorimetrically many times. The latter value (116 kcal for 2 moles of steam) may be combined with the known heats of dissociation of the O_2 and H_2 molecules to find the O—H bond energy. For such combinations, we use the familiar *law of Hess* that allows thermochemical equations to be handled as algebraic equations:

$$2H_2 + O_2 \rightarrow 2H_2O \text{ (gas)} \qquad + 116 \text{ kcal}$$
$$4H \qquad \rightarrow 2H_2 \qquad\qquad + 207 \text{ kcal}$$
$$2O \qquad \rightarrow O_2 \qquad\qquad\; + 118 \text{ kcal}$$

adding, $\qquad 4H + 2O \rightarrow 2H_2O$ (4 O—H bonds) $+ 441$ kcal

The O—H bond energy thus calculated (110 kcal) is an *average* value, for it should not be assumed that the formation of OH· from an oxygen and hydrogen atom will release the same energy as the formation of H_2O from OH· and H·.

The values of the C—H, C—C, C=C, and C≡C bond energies may be determined by combining the readily measured *heats of combustion* of hydrocarbons with the known heats of combustion of carbon and hydrogen; thus, for methane:

$$CH_4 \qquad + 2O_2 \longrightarrow 2H_2O \text{ (gas)} \quad + CO_2 + 192 \text{ kcal}$$
$$C \text{ (graphite)} \quad \xrightarrow{\text{sublime}} C \text{ (gas)} \qquad\qquad\qquad - 170 \text{ kcal}$$
$$2H_2 \qquad\qquad \longrightarrow 4H· \qquad\qquad\qquad\quad - 207 \text{ kcal}$$
$$2H_2O \qquad\quad \longrightarrow 2H_2 \qquad\quad + O_2 \quad - 116 \text{ kcal}$$
$$CO_2 \qquad\qquad \longrightarrow C \text{ (graphite)} \quad + O_2 \quad - \quad 94 \text{ kcal}$$

adding, $\quad CH_4 \qquad\qquad\qquad \longrightarrow 4H· + C \text{ (gas)} \qquad\qquad - 395 \text{ kcal}$
$$\text{(breakup of 4 C—H bonds)}$$

The *average* value for the C—H bond energy, 99 kcal, is thus one fourth of the energy released in the reaction C + 4H· → CH_4—that is, the formation of methane from the free atoms in the gaseous state.

It is important to emphasize the distinction between the ordinarily used bond energies and *bond-dissociation energies*—the energies needed to rupture specific bonds in specific gaseous molecules (for example, the C—H bond in chloroform). The latter values are somewhat more useful and although they are more difficult to obtain than "average bond energies," a large number are now available.[2] However, we shall be mainly interested in carbon-hydrogen and carbon-carbon bonds, and bond-dissociation energies have been determined for only a few of these. Subsequent discussions will therefore be based on "average" bond energies.

Of the values necessary in calculating bond energies, the heat of atomization of graphite to gaseous carbon atoms is subject to greatest doubt. The recent value of 170 kcal per gram atom[3(a)] has been selected here, but a smaller value, about 133 kcal,[3(b)] is used by a number of workers. As will be shown in Exercise 4, the value chosen will affect the apparent values of bond energies involving carbon, but many conclusions based upon comparisons of such bond energies should not change. A similar uncertainty exists as to the true value of the N≡N triple-bond energy.

Single-bond energies for the more familiar bonds appear in Table 2-1. A number of these have been compiled by Huggins.[4] The energies of double and triple bonds, often evaluated from heats of combustion or heats of hydrogenation (Ex. 3), are found to be higher than the corresponding single-bond energies.

C—C	80 kcal		C—N	62 kcal
C=C	142 kcal		C=N	121 kcal
C≡C	186 kcal		C≡N	191 kcal

Bond-energy values such as those given in Table 2-1 would be most useful if we could assume that the energy of a bond between two given atoms in a polyatomic molecule is independent of other atoms in the molecule, and that therefore, for example, the heat of formation of ethanol, CH_3CH_2OH, from the free atoms would be exactly equal to the bond energies for one C—C bond, one C—O bond, one O—H bond, and five C—H bonds. There are indeed

[2] For summaries of the methods by which bond-dissociation energies are evaluated, see: Cottrell, *The Strengths of Chemical Bonds*, Butterworth's Scientific Publications, London, 1954, pp. 47–102; Szwarc, *Quart. Revs.*, **V**, 22, (1951). A large number of recently determined bond-dissociation energies have been tabulated by Walling in *Free Radicals in Solution*, John Wiley and Sons, Inc., New York, 1957, pp. 48–50.

[3] (a) Chupka and Ingraham, *J. Chem. Phys.*, **22**, 1472 (1954). (b) Langer, Hipple, and Stevenson, *ibid.*, **22**, 1836 (1954).

[4] Huggins, *J. Am. Chem. Soc.*, **75**, 4125 (1953).

many cases where bond energies determined by investigation of one molecule may be used to calculate the heats of formation and heats of reaction of other molecules having similar bonds. If this were not the case Table 2-1 would be of very little use. On the other hand, there are a considerable number of organic compounds to which simple bond-energy calculations may not be applied without substantial modification of treatment.

The most important class of compounds for which bond energies alone will not predict correct heats of formation or reaction are those compounds having conjugated double bonds and which are commonly represented as "resonance hybrids" of classical structures. The very familiar case of benzene

Table 2-1. Energy Values for Some Single Bonds
(kcal per gram-bond)

H–	C–	N–	O–	F–	Si–	S–	Cl–	Br–	I–	
104	99	84	110	135	81	81	103	87	71	–H
	80	62	81	102	68	65	77	64	56	–C
		32		66			37			–N
			33	44	89		49			–O
				37	128	71	61	61		–F
					43	61	66	73	51	–Si
						49	61	53		–S
							58	52	51	–Cl
								46	43	–Br
									36	–I

has been noted on page 23. As with benzene, the heats of formation of a number of benzene derivatives (toluene, the xylenes, phenol, anisole, aniline, benzaldehyde, etc.) are each roughly 36 kcal per mole greater than would be predicted by considering these compounds as constructions of ordinary single and double bonds. Likewise, the heats of combustion and hydrogenation of each of these derivatives are roughly 36 kcal per mole *less* than would be predicted from single classical structures. The word "roughly" is not used here because of the experimental errors that arise in measuring heats of combustion and hydrogenation; actually such measurements can be carried out to accuracies of better than 0.02 kcal per mole. On the other hand, as will soon be evident, the variation in bond energies of "normal" C—C and C=C bonds is large enough to allow a considerable latitude in guessing what the heat of combustion or hydrogenation would be if a compound could be represented adequately by a single classical structure.

The heats of hydrogenation and combustion of compounds having two or more benzene rings fall even further below the values that would be predicted from bond energies alone (naphthalene—61 kcal per mole less; anthracene—84 kcal per mole less, etc.), whereas nonbenzenoid compounds containing conjugated double bonds tend to show smaller departures (pyrrole—21 kcal per mole less; 1,3-butadiene—roughly 3 kcal per mole less). Similarly, if the heats of formation of esters or amides are estimated by considering the $C\!\!=\!\!O$ linkages in these compounds similar to those in ketones, the values obtained are about 20 kcal per mole less than the true heats of formation.

In each of the instances cited, the true heat of formation is *more* than the value calculated from bond-energy values alone. The differences, the so-called *resonance energies*, arise because classical structures ignore the stability associated with the spread of π-electron density over the conjugated systems. It is interesting that certain contemporary workers have carried out theoretical evaluations of resonance energies for a number of conjugated systems, using structural considerations alone. For descriptions of such calculations (an understanding of which requires some familiarity with the fundamentals of wave mechanics) the reader should consult more advanced works.[5]

Aside from conjugation effects, there are other cases in which strict additivity of bond energies is not observed. Consider, for example, the heats of combustion of isomeric paraffin hydrocarbons—for example, *n*-pentane, isopentane, and neopentane. Since each of these pentanes has the same number of C—C bonds and C—H bonds, one might expect them to have the same heats of combustion. However, very accurate measurements by Rossini and co-workers[6] show that the heats of combustion of the three isomers are, respectively, 845.16, 843.24, and 840.49 kcal per mole. Similarly, the isomeric octanes have different heats of combustion, ranging from 1317.45 kcal for the straight-chain isomer, *n*-octane, to 1313.27 kcal for the highly branched isomer, 2,2,3,3-tetramethylbutane. If bond energies were constant, we should also expect that the heats of hydrogenation of all olefins having just one double bond would be the same since the hydrogenation process in each case involves the breakage of an H—H bond, the creation of two new C—H bonds, and the conversion of a $C\!\!=\!\!C$ double bond to a single bond. However the heats of hydrogenation of monoölefins have been found to vary from 32.8 kcal per mole for ethylene to 23.5 kcal per mole for cyclooctene.[7]

Such differences in heats of combustion and hydrogenation, as well as a

[5] See, for example, G. W. Wheland, *Resonance in Organic Chemistry*, John Wiley and Sons, Inc., New York, 1955, pp. 629–641, 665–672; H. Eyring, J. Walter, and G. E. Kimball, *Quantum Chemistry*, John Wiley and Sons, Inc., New York, 1944, pp. 249–257.

[6] Rossini, *et al.*, "*Selected Values of the Properties of Hydrocarbons*," U.S. Government Printing Office, Washington, D.C., 1952.

[7] Kistiakowski, *et al.*, *J. Am. Chem. Soc.*, **57**, 65, 876 (1935); **58**, 137 (1936).

number of additional discrepancies of similar magnitude, cannot easily be ignored although, admittedly, they are small compared to the values of the bond energies themselves. It is possible to refine work with bond energies, using, in effect, a number of slightly different C—H, C—C, and C=C bond energies, the choice of which depends upon groups adjacent to the bond being considered.[8] However, for many purposes it is acceptable (and certainly more convenient) to use the value of 99 kcal per gram bond for C—H and to adopt those single values for the C—C and C=C bonds that give the best approach to additivity in the greatest number of cases. The values on pages 36 and 37 have been chosen on this basis.

Electronegativity

A variety of physical and chemical evidence indicates that the atoms of oxygen, nitrogen, and the lighter halogens attract electrons more strongly than do the atoms of carbon, hydrogen, or the metals. Consider, for example, the formation of a C—Cl bond from the free atoms. As the atoms approach each other, there occurs a redistribution of electron density with a marked thickening of the valence electron cloud in the space between the two nuclei. After the bond is formed, the bonding electrons are attracted simultaneously by both nuclei. These electrons, however, do not feel the pull of the *entire* nuclear charge. Situated between the valence electrons and the nuclei are the inner (non-valence) electrons, almost spherically symmetrical clouds of negative charge which behave toward the outsider as if their charge were concentrated at their centers—that is, in the nuclei. The effective positive charges on the nuclei are thereby *decreased by the nonvalence electrons*, this being the so-called **screening effect.** On this basis, the electrons constituting the C—Cl bond should be attracted to the carbon nucleus by the action of four $(6 - 2)$ protonic charges and to the somewhat more distant chlorine nucleus by the action of seven $(17 - 10)$ protonic charges. Although a more complete picture also requires that we consider additional screening of each valence electron by those portions of the remaining valence electrons lying close to the nuclei, the following qualitative generalization is a safe one: The electron-attracting power of an atom (which is due to the portion of its nuclear charge that survives screening) depends upon (a) the difference between its atomic number and the number of its nonvalence electrons and (b) the proximity of the bulk of the valence-electron density to the nucleus. In more familiar terms, an atom will be a good electron attractor if it has a large number of outer valence electrons (that is, lies to the right of the periodic table) and if it is small. Somewhat paradoxically, we say that an element which attracts electrons strongly is highly **electronegative,** meaning that

[8] Klages, *Ber.*, **82**, 358 (1949).

it will acquire the greater share of electron density when it competes with a poorer electron attractor. Since the chlorine atom in the C—Cl bond is a better electron attractor (that is, is more electronegative) than carbon, we frequently regard this bond as *polar* with the chlorine at the negative end and the carbon at the positive end. Fluorine is still more electronegative and a C—F bond is even more polar.

The concept of electronegativity is both important and useful. Differences in electronegativity have been called upon to account for variations in molecular dimensions, in dipole moments, and in molecular spectra as one atom is substituted for another. Similarly, there are countless variations in reaction rates and in positions of equilibria which are conveniently attributed to the electron-attracting (or electron-repelling) abilities of atoms at or near the sites of reaction. However, the electronegativities of atoms *cannot* be measured directly and there is some question as to which of a number of indirect methods[9] of evaluation is open to the least objection. Familiar electronegativity scales have been based upon ionization potentials and electron affinities,[10] on bond-stretching force constants,[11] and on atomic radii.[12] A particularly convenient scale based on bond energies, has been developed by Pauling.[13]

If we select any bond between unlike atoms from Table 2-1, designating such a bond $A—B$, it appears that the energy of bond $A—B$ is always greater than the geometric mean of the energies of bonds $A—A$ and $B—B$. Three examples are listed as follows:

$\sqrt{E_{A-A} \times E_{B-B}}$	E_{A-B}	Differences, Δ	$\Delta^{\frac{1}{2}}$
$\sqrt{E_{Si-Si} \times E_{O-O}} = 38$ kcal	$E_{Si-O} = 89$ kcal	51 kcal	7.2
$\sqrt{E_{O-O} \times E_{F-F}} = 35$ kcal	$E_{F-O} = 44$ kcal	9 kcal	3.0
$\sqrt{E_{Si-Si} \times E_{F-F}} = 40$ kcal	$E_{Si-F} = 128$ kcal	88 kcal	9.4

Note that the greater values of Δ are associated with bonds between atoms lying far apart in the periodic table, that is, the value of Δ increases as the "electronegativities" of the bound atoms diverge. Now Pauling suggests that the geometric mean of the energies of the bonds $A—A$ and $B—B$ is the energy that the bond $A—B$ would have if it were completely covalent (as are the bonds $A—A$ and $B—B$). The "extra" bond energy, Δ, is considered to be related to

[9] The construction of electronegativity scales has been recently reviewed by Pritchard and Skinner, *Chem. Revs.*, **55**, 745 (1955). This paper also makes clear some of the limitations of the electronegativity concept.

[10] Mulliken, *J. Chem. Phys.*, **2**, 782 (1935): **3**, 573 (1935).

[11] Gordy, *J. Chem. Phys.*, **14**, 304 (1946).

[12] Sanderson, *J. Am. Chem. Soc.*, **74**, 4792 (1952).

[13] Pauling, *The Nature of the Chemical Bond*, 2d ed., Cornell University Press, Ithaca, 1940, pp. 58–69.

the ionic resonance picture of the pair of bonded atoms (page 26) and is thus called the "extra ionic resonance energy" of the bond. If the bond energies of A—A and B—B are not greatly different (Ex. 6), their arithmetic mean rather than their geometric mean may be used.

From the figures on silicon, oxygen, and fluorine, we see that the values of Δ are not additive (that is, $\Delta_{\text{Si-O}} + \Delta_{\text{O-F}} \neq \Delta_{\text{Si-F}}$); however, the *square roots* of these "ionic resonance energy" terms are much more nearly so. Thus, square roots of the Δ values may be taken as electronegativity differences on which a linear scale of electronegativities may be based. If the "extra ionic resonance energies" are expressed in electron volts (1 ev per bond = 23 kcal per gram-bond), electronegativity differences lie in the convenient range between 3.3 units and zero. Electronegativity differences for the triad silicon-oxygen-fluorine are then: 1.4 $(\text{ev})^{\frac{1}{2}}$ for Si—O, 0.6 $(\text{ev})^{\frac{1}{2}}$ for F—O, and 1.9 $(\text{ev})^{\frac{1}{2}}$ for Si—F.

Having thus obtained *differences* in electronegativity, Pauling fixes the electronegativity of the most negative element, fluorine, as 4.0 and assigns values to the other elements on the bases of experimental $(\Delta)^{\frac{1}{2}}$ values. A typical set of electronegativities appears in Table 2-2.

Table 2-2. Electronegativities (Pauling)

	H				
	2.1				
	B	C	N	O	F
	2.0	2.5	3.0	3.5	4.0
Si	P	S	Cl		
1.8	2.1	2.5	3.0		
	As	Se	Br		
	2.0	2.4	2.8		
Sb	Te	I			
1.8	2.1	2.5			
	2.0	2.5	3.0	3.5	4.0

On this scale, nitrogen and chlorine have equal electronegativities, as do carbon, sulfur, and iodine. Thus, N—Cl, C—S, and C—I bonds should be almost completely covalent. Conveniently, the electronegativities of the first-row elements progress in units of 0.5 $(\text{ev})^{\frac{1}{2}}$. Oxygen and fluorine are far more electronegative than the other elements.

This treatment is only approximate; note that $(\Delta_{\text{Si-O}})^{\frac{1}{2}} + (\Delta_{\text{O-F}})^{\frac{1}{2}}$ approaches the value $(\Delta_{\text{Si-F}})^{\frac{1}{2}}$ but is not exactly equal to it. Similar comparisons for other groups of three elements for which Δ values have been determined generally give even poorer agreement. The values in Table 2-2 have been adjusted to give the best approach to additivity in the largest number of cases.

Bond Lengths and Covalent Radii

The mean distance between the nuclei of two bonded atoms is called a **bond length.** Interatomic distances and bond lengths have been generally determined either by *electron diffraction, x-ray diffraction*, spectral studies, or by a combination of these methods.[14] A newer method, *neutron diffraction*, has been of use only for a small number of substances.[15]

For uniformity within this chapter, interatomic distances are expressed to the "nearest" 0.01 Å unit; however, the values obtained by electron diffraction are often far less reliable, whereas some of the values obtained by x-ray diffraction and by spectral studies are known to greater precision (a few, indeed, to the nearest 0.001 Å).

It has been found that the length of a covalent bond between two given atoms is often (but not always) essentially independent of the nature of the molecule or crystal network in which such a bond occurs. In most aliphatic hydrocarbons, for example, the C—C single-bond length is very close to 1.54 Å, the same length as the C—C bond in diamond. Where shorter C—C bonds occur, we shall see that the compounds concerned are often best represented by combinations of structures.

The single-bond **covalent radius** of carbon is then 0.77 Å—just one half of the C—C bond length. Similarly, the covalent radii of chlorine and iodine may be set at 0.99 Å and 1.33 Å, respectively—one half of the internuclear distances in the Cl_2 and I_2 molecules.

For a small number of compounds (which probably should be regarded as exceptional) such radii are nearly additive. The C—Cl bond length in methyl chloride is 1.76 Å, almost exactly the sum of the covalent radii of carbon and chlorine as determined from the elements. Similarly, the C—I bond in methyl iodide has been found to be 2.10 Å; this again is the sum of the covalent radii. Far more often, however, the length of a bond between two unlike atoms is appreciably shorter than the sum of the covalent bond lengths as determined from the elements.

Covalent radii for the nonmetals are listed in Table 2-3. Note that for a given

---

[14] For discussions of electron diffraction, see, for example, Livingston, *Ann. Rev. Phys. Chem.*, **5**, 395 (1954); and Karle and Karle, in Braude and Nachod's *Determination of Organic Structures by Physical Methods*, Academic Press, Inc., New York, 1955, pp. 427–459. The application of x-ray diffraction to organic compounds is described by Robertson in *Organic Crystals and Molecules*, Cornell University Press, Ithaca, 1953. Extensive discussions of spectral methods appear in Herzberg's books, *Spectra of Diatomic Molecules*, Van Nostrand, Inc., Toronto, 1950; and *Infra-red and Raman Spectra of Polyatomic Molecules*, Van Nostrand, Inc., New York, 1945. A compilation of the interatomic distances determined for a very large number of organic compounds before July, 1954, is given by Wheland, *Resonance in Organic Chemistry*, John Wiley and Sons, Inc., New York, 1955, pp. 695–799.

[15] Thewlis, *Ann. Reports*, **47**, 420 (1950).

group in the periodic table, covalent radii generally decrease as one moves from left to right. Students sometimes find this trend surprising, reasoning that the addition of an electron could scarcely make an atom smaller. It should be recalled, however, that the valence electrons of elements in the same period generally have the same principal quantum number. Adding electrons tends more to "thicken" the electron cloud about the outside of an atom than to expand it. An element in a period also differs from the element preceding it in its number of protons, and the addition of a proton to the nucleus tends to draw the electron clouds inward. The largest element in each period thus has the smallest atomic number.

Contraction in Bond Lengths with Increasing Polarity

As the difference in the electronegativity of two bound atoms increases, departures from additivity of bond lengths become more and more marked. For example, the covalent radii of carbon and nitrogen (half the C—C bond length in diamond and half the N—N bond length in hydrazine, respectively) add up to 1.51 Å, whereas the "normal" C—N bond length is observed to be about 1.47 Å. Normal C—O bonds tend to be even shorter (about 1.42 Å), even though the covalent radii of nitrogen and oxygen are almost the same. Much greater "shrinkages" are observed for bonds such as Si—Cl, Si—F, Si—O, As—Cl, and P—F for which the more positive member is beyond the first eight-membered period in the periodic table.

The *Schomaker-Stevenson relationship* proposes that such bond shrinkage is directly proportional to the electronegativity difference between the bound atoms, and that the interatomic distance, r_{A-B}, for a single bond is thus linearly related to the covalent radii, r_A and r_B:[16]

$$r_{A-B} = r_A + r_B - 0.09|x_A - x_B| \tag{1}$$

where the x's represent electronegativity values. Although the bond distances predicted by this equation are often closer to the true values than are those obtained merely by adding covalent radii, much better agreement with the observed values is obtained by use of the treatment proposed by Huggins.[17] The latter shows that there is a number, r'_{AB}, associated with almost all covalent bonds, having dimensions of length and related to the actual bond length and bond energy such that

$$r'_{AB} = r_{AB} + \frac{1}{a} \ln E_{AB} \tag{2}$$

---

[16] Schomaker and Stevenson, *J. Am. Chem. Soc.*, **63**, 37 (1941).
[17] Huggins, *J. Am. Chem. Soc.*, **75**, 4126 (1953).

Now, a is a constant; when E is expressed in kcal per gram-bond, a is happily close enough to the value 4.6 to permit equation (2) to be rewritten

$$r'_{AB} = r_{AB} + \frac{1}{2} \log_{10} E_{AB} \qquad (3)$$

The r' values are called *constant-energy distances;* these are about 0.8 Å greater than ordinary covalent bond lengths and may be separated into contributions of each of the two member atoms (just as may bond lengths in very nearly covalent bonds). In analogy with atomic radii, the r' value for each atom is called a *constant-energy radius.* Typical constant-energy radii are 1.22 Å for carbon (as compared to the covalent radius 0.77 Å) and 1.73 Å for iodine (covalent radius 1.33 Å). The Huggins relationship then becomes

$$r_{AB} = r'_A + r'_B - \frac{1}{2} \log_{10} E_{AB} \qquad (4)$$

Only in the case of hydrogen, for which it is apparently not possible to assign a good single constant-energy radius, does this treatment meet with appreciable

Table 2-3. Covalent Radii and "Constant-energy Radii"

	Covalent Radius	Constant-energy Radius		Covalent Radius	Constant-energy Radius
H	0.28 Å	0.82–0.88 Å	Ge	1.22 Å	1.61 Å
			As	1.21	1.63
C	0.77	1.22	Se	1.17	1.58
N	0.75	1.12	Br	1.14	1.56
O	0.74	1.12			
F	0.72	1.11	Sn	1.40	1.80
			Sb	1.41	1.83
Si	1.17	1.57	Te	1.37	1.79
P	1.10	1.53	I	1.33	1.73
S	1.04	1.46			
Cl	0.99	1.44			

difficulty. The chief objection to this treatment would seem to be that the r' values are actually parameters whose values are fixed to give the best fit to Equation (4) for the greatest number of bonds; thus they lack the physical significance of covalent radii, which may be obtained by direct measurements. Table 2-3 summarizes both the covalent radii and the "constant-energy radii" for a number of the nonmetallic elements.

In Chapter 1 it was noted that a double bond (often referred to as a bond of **bond order** 2) between two atoms is shorter than a single bond (bond order 1) between the same two atoms; triple bonds are still shorter than double bonds.

C—C	1.54 Å	C=C	1.33 Å	C≡C	1.19 Å
N—O	1.46 Å	N=O	1.14 Å	N≡O	1.11 Å[18]

This shrinkage may be considered due to the attraction of the π-electron "dumbbells" present on each atom forming a multiple bond. Recall that a single bond is quite closely directed along the line of centers of the bonded atoms but that the double bond has, in addition to this cylindrically symmetric bonding cloud, extra attraction between the π electrons, one on each atom. The atoms forming a triple bond have *two* π electrons each, resulting in two π bonds in addition to the σ bond (which, when alone, comprises the ordinary single bond). We might note that the decrease in bond length with bond order parallels an increase in bond energy; extra stability is often accompanied by bond shrinkage (as is, of course, testified by both the Schomaker-Stevenson and Huggins equations for single bonds).

Bond Lengths in Resonance Hybrids

In discussing the resonance concept, we saw that a bond represented as a single bond in one canonical form might well be represented as a double bond in another form. In benzene, one of the simplest cases, the three double bonds in one Kekule structure become single bonds in the other, and the same is true for the carbon-carbon bonds in the heterocyclic compound, pyrazine (I). In

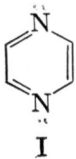

I

this sense, the carbon-carbon bonds in benzene and in pyrazine are "midway" between single and double in character and, with this rough sort of reasoning, may be ascribed an order of 1.50. Similarly, in the planes of six-membered rings comprising the graphite structure (Fig. 2-1) each carbon is bonded to

[18] The N=O "double-bond" length is that in NOCl; the N≡O "triple-bond" length is that reported for nitrosyl perchlorate, $NO^+ClO_4^-$. See Addison and Lewis, *Quart. Revs.*, (London), **9**, 120, (1955).

Note that the difference in bond length between the C—C single bond and the C≡C triple bond is almost the same as the difference between the lengths of the respective nitrogen-to-oxygen bonds. However, the "double-bond" length in nitrosyl chloride is suspiciously close to the "triple-bond" length in nitrosyl perchlorate. On this basis, it may be argued that the nitrosyl chloride molecule has considerable ionic character; that is, the structure $N≡O^+Cl^-$ is an important contributing form.

three surrounding carbons. Since carbon must form the equivalent of four bonds, we may assign to each of the bonds in graphite an order of $\frac{4}{3}$ or 1.33. Although the bond lengths in benzene, pyrazine, and graphite are, as expected,

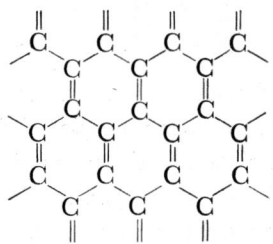

Fig. 2-1. The Structure of Graphite

less than the C—C single-bond length and greater than the double-bond length, the relationship between bond order and bond length is not a linear one (to anticipate this, one would have to expect unusual cooperativeness on Nature's part).

However, Pauling has derived a relatively simple relationship between the bond order y and the bond length r for bonds of order between 1.0 and 2.0.[19] In this relationship,

$$r = r_1 - \frac{(3y - 3)(r_1 - r_2)}{(2y - 1)} \tag{5}$$

r_1 and r_2 are the respective bond lengths for single and double bonds. The observed bond lengths in benzene, pyrazine, and graphite fall very close to the values predicted by equation (5) (1.39 Å for benzene and pyrazine, 1.42 Å for graphite).

It is interesting that the lengths of the carbon-carbon bonds in the organo-iron compound ferrocene[20] (II) may be estimated in a similar manner. This

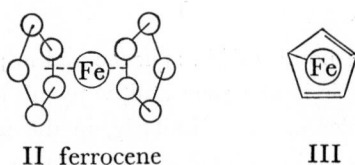

II ferrocene   III

compound consists of an iron atom "sandwiched" between two cyclopenta-dienide pentagons, each of the ten carbons being the same distance from the iron.[21] It is possible to represent the molecule as a combination of structures,

[19] Pauling and Brockway, *J. Am. Chem. Soc.*, **59**, 1223 (1937).
[20] Wilkinson, *et al.*, *J. Am. Chem. Soc.*, **74**, 2125 (1952).
[21] (a) Eiland and Pepinsky, *J. Am. Chem. Soc.*, **74**, 4971 (1952). (b) Dunitz and Orgel, *Nature*, **171**, 121 (1953).

each having one carbon per ring bonded to iron with the remaining carbons forming double bonds. (That this is not the manner in which this molecule is generally regarded need not concern us now.) Considering, for simplicity, just one of the two rings, five structures similar to III may be drawn, each having two double bonds. Each of the carbon-carbon linkages is represented as a double bond in two of the five structures and as a single bond in three of the five. Setting the bond order then as $1\frac{2}{5}$, a bond length of 1.41 Å could be predicted from equation (5); this is in excellent agreement with the observed length. Similar treatment may be applied to a member of the polynuclear benzenoid hydrocarbons (see Ex. 12) and the bond lengths predicted are sometimes in surprisingly good agreement with those observed.

Table 2-4 lists five of the many additional cases where bond shortening is observed. For each of these compounds, the resonance interpretation predicts

Table 2-4. Bond Lengths in Some Resonance Hybrids

Classical Structure	Typical Additional Canonical Form

partial double-bond character in the "shortened" bonds. One typical canonical form, in addition to the classical structure, is shown for each compound.

As shown, the central bonds in diacetylene (A) and cyanogen (B), and the exocyclic bonds in diphenylacetylene (C) are much shorter than the ordinary C—C single bonds (1.54 Å). In the structures on the right each of these bonds is represented as a double bond, indicating that each has some double-bond character. The same applies also to the C—Cl bond in vinyl chloride (D) ("ordinary" C—Cl bond length, 1.76 Å) and to the "single" bonds in furan (E). For these five compounds, consideration of the structures on the right of Table 2-4 might allow the anticipation of these bond shortenings[22] but the *magnitudes* of the shrinkages cannot be calculated. Even though we may draw the important contributing structures for these compounds, the reasoning applied to benzene, graphite, and ferrocene cannot be applied since the various forms used to describe each of the compounds in Table 2-4 are not equivalent. The forms on the right, showing a "charge separation" are generally called *high-energy forms* because electrical work has been presumably expended to separate the charges to the positions shown; such forms are therefore "less important" than the classical forms, although how much less important it is difficult to say. It is, of course, possible to estimate the order of a particular bond *after* its length has been determined, but at present there is no simple and generally applicable way to confirm such an estimate independently. Considerable work has been carried out on theoretical methods for evaluating bond orders from quantum-mechanical principles,[23] and the bond orders so obtained may be related to the observed bond lengths by equations somewhat different from equation (5). These more complex treatments, which have been confined almost exclusively to hydrocarbons, allow calculation of the bond orders in compounds such as styrene and butadiene which cannot be directly treated by inspection of resonance forms. However, for the benzenoid hydrocarbons, bond lengths predicted by the more refined treatments are not, in general, significantly closer to the observed values than those predicted by merely inspecting

---

[22] In considering these structures, it might be noted that the canonical forms on the right of Table 2-4 for diacetylene, cyanogen, and diphenylacetylene represent as double bonds those bonds which the classical structures represent as triple. Since the lengths of these bonds are found to be essentially identical with the lengths of "normal" triple bonds (C≡N, 1.15 Å; C≡C, 1.19 Å), it might well be asked why the contributions of the forms do not result in the *lengthening* of these bonds due to a *decrease* in bond order. This illustrates the danger in attaching too great a physical significance to the individual canonical forms. What the forms on the right indicate is that the carbons joined by the "single" bonds are brought "abnormally" close together by attraction between their π electrons. This "extra" attraction need not take place at the expense of the stability of the adjacent triple bonds, a point that cannot easily be made by representing such compounds as combinations of Lewis structures.

[23] See, for example, Penney, *Proc. Roy. Soc.* (London), **A 158**, 306 (1937); Coulson, *Proc. Roy. Soc.*, (London) **A 169**, 413 (1939).

the bonds in the resonance structures in the manner described above for graphite and illustrated in Exercise 12 for naphthalene.

Hyperconjugation

A carbon-carbon single bond, if adjacent to a carbon-carbon triple bond, is almost invariably shorter than the "normal" length, 1.54 A. The C—C bond lengths in methylacetylene and acetonitrile are, respectively, 1.46 and 1.49 Å —considerably longer than the "single" bonds in diacetylene and cyanogen (for which the resonance treatment would predict shortening) but undeniably shorter than the single bonds in ordinary paraffins and olefins. These "shrink-ages" are sometimes rationalized by assuming appreciable contribution of struc-tures such as IV and V; these are termed *hyperconjugated* structures in which a shift

$$H^+ \quad CH_2=C=\overset{..}{C}H^- \qquad\qquad H^+ \quad CH_2=C=\overset{..}{N}:^-$$
$$\text{IV} \qquad\qquad\qquad\qquad \text{V}$$

of electron density toward the C—C bond has left the C—H bonds with partial no-bond character.[24] If these contractions were the only evidence of hyper-conjugation in molecules, one might justifiably be extremely skeptical about this effect, for the differences are slight and similar contractions are not observed for C—C bonds adjacent to *double* bonds. However, other evidence that this (or a related) effect operates comes from comparing the heats of combustion of isomeric olefins or isomeric acetylenes. As an example, the heat of combustion of isobutylene is 646.1 kcal per mole; this is significantly less than that for 1-butene, 649.8 kcal per mole[6], even though the two isomers have, of course, the same number of C—C, C=C, and C—H bonds. To rationalize this and similar differences using the hyperconjugation concept, we may note that hyperconjugation of the type indicated involves a C—H bond one carbon removed from a double or triple bond, that is, α-hydrogen atoms. It is therefore reasonable that the effects of hyperconjugation become more pronounced as the number of α-hydrogen atoms increases. Thus, hyperconjugation is more

important in isobutylene, $CH_2{=}C{\overset{\displaystyle CH_3}{\underset{\displaystyle CH_3}{\big\langle}}}$, with six α-hydrogens, than in

[24] The theoretical basis for the concept of hyperconjugation is given by Mulliken, Rieke, and Brown, *J. Am. Chem. Soc.*, **63**, 41 (1941), and by Lofthus, *ibid.*, **79**, 24 (1957). For a differ-ent view, see Kreevoy and Eyring, *ibid.*, **79**, 5121 (1957). The role of hyperconjugation in organic chemistry is discussed in detail by Baker in *Hyperconjugation*, Oxford University Press, Oxford, 1952.

1-butene, $CH_2\!=\!CH\!-\!CH_2\!-\!CH_3$, with only two α-hydrogens; in the absence of any more important effects, isobutylene should be slightly more stable (hence should have a lower heat of combustion). Likewise, tetramethylethylene, with twelve α-hydrogens, should (and does) have a slightly lower heat of combustion than 2-methyl-2-pentene, $CH_3CH_2CH\!=\!C(CH_3)_2$, with eight α-hydrogens.

There is evidence also for C—C hyperconjugation (for example, VI ↔ VI′) which is, however, generally less important than C—H hyperconjugation (see, for example, p. 87).

Many differences in the *heats of hydrogenation* of olefins can be explained, at least in part, by hyperconjugative effects. As we have already noted, if bond energies did not vary with environment, all monöolefins would have the same heat of hydrogenation. However, the heat of hydrogenation on ethylene (with no α-hydrogens) is 32.8 kcal per mole, that for 1-butene (with two α-hydrogens) is 30.3 kcal per mole, and that for tetramethylethylene is 26.6 kcal per mole.[7] Again, these small but real differences and others like them give support to the concept of hyperconjugation. In later chapters the reader will see how hyperconjugation may be called upon to "explain" a number of trends in reactivity.

Van der Waals' Radii[25]

When two molecules approach each other without forming a chemical bond, there is a slight attraction between them due to a mutual distortion of their electron clouds. Such a force, called a *van der Waals' force* or a *dispersion force*,[26] exerts little effect on the molecules of a gaseous system, for their average separation is too great. However, van der Waals' forces draw together the molecules of a liquid (although a great deal of "rolling over" obviously occurs); and these same forces hold molecules in their places in a crystal at low temperatures where kinetic energies have been cut down. For many polar molecules, van der Waals' forces are considerably augmented by dipole-dipole attractions. In the condensed states, such forces tend to bring the molecules closer together; but

[25] See also Pauling, *Nature of the Chemical Bond*, 2d ed., Cornell University Press, Ithaca, 1940, pp. 187–193.

[26] For an elementary and semiquantitative treatment of van der Waals' forces, see Rice, *Electronic Structure and Chemical Bonding*, McGraw-Hill Book Co., Inc., New York, 1940, pp. 354–358. For a more extended treatment, see Rowlinson, *Quart. Revs.*, **VIII**, 168 (1954).

they must not approach each other too closely, for a repulsion sets in when the respective electron clouds overlap appreciably. For each atom on the outside of a molecule there is an optimum distance from the nucleus beyond which the electron cloud of a nonbonded atom cannot easily advance; this distance is called the **van der Waals' radius.** From early crystallographic studies[27] the van der Waals radii of chlorine and bromine were estimated to be, respectively, 1.80 Å and 2.02 Å, these values being just half the shortest distance between halogen atoms of *adjacent molecules* in solid β-benzene hexachloride (VII) and in solid hexabromobenzene. For organic chemistry, the van der Waals' radii of

VII

the methyl group and methylene group are of considerable importance. These two values, which should be roughly the same (Ex. 11b), represent half of the shortest distance between the carbon atoms of methyl or methylene groups in adjacent molecules; they have been found by a large number of investigations to approach 2.0 Å.[28] The van der Waals' radii of oxygen, nitrogen, or sulfur may be obtained by subtracting this figure from *intermolecular* carbon-to-oxygen, carbon-to-nitrogen, or carbon-to-sulfur distances in crystals where there is contact between the respective "hetero-atom" of one molecule and a methyl or methylene group of another.

Van der Waals' radii of atoms of greatest interest to the organic chemist are listed in Table 2-5.[25] Since there is a far wider variation in intermolecular

Table 2-5. Van der Waals' Radii

H	1.2 Å	F	1.4 Å
N	1.5	Cl	1.8
O	1.4	Br	2.0
S	1.9	I	2.2

nonbonded than in bonded distances between two given atoms among a series of compounds, these values are given only to the nearest 0.1 Å. Pauling has observed that the van der Waals' radii of the nonmetals lie very close to their *ionic* radii and rationalizes this picturesquely by stating that " . . . the bonded atom presents the same face to the outside world in directions away from its

[27] For a summary of this work see Hendricks, *Chem. Revs.*, **7**, 431 (1930).
[28] Two examples should suffice. The shortest intermolecular methyl-to-methyl distance in octamethyl cyclotetrasiloxane, Steinfink, *et al.*, *Acta Cryst.*, **8**, 420 (1955), is 4.04 Å. That in tetramethyl pyrazine, Cromer, *et al.*, *J. Am. Chem. Soc.*, **73**, 5587 (1951) is 3.84 Å.

bond as the ion does in all directions."[29] It should be noted that the van der Waals' radius is the *maximum nonbonded radius* of an atom—the distance between the nucleus and the effective "outside" of the atom at a point directly opposite the site of bonding. It is the radius of the atom as set off by a line forming an angle of 180° with the bond direction. The atomic radius set off by a line through the nucleus at any other angle must be greater than the covalent radius but less than the van der Waals' radius. This may be seen from Figure 2-2,

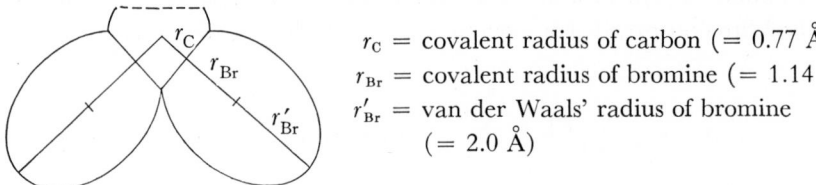

r_C = covalent radius of carbon (= 0.77 Å)

r_{Br} = covalent radius of bromine (= 1.14 Å)

r'_{Br} = van der Waals' radius of bromine (= 2.0 Å)

Fig. 2-2. Covalent and van der Waals' Radii

which shows two of the C—Br bonds in a compound such as CBr_4. Often two atoms bound to a common atom, but not to each other, are separated by a distance significantly less than the sum of their van der Waals' radii. For example, the nuclei of the bromine atoms in CBr_4 (Br—C—Br bond angle 109°) are separated by a distance of 3.1 Å, almost 25 percent less than twice the van der Waals' radius of bromine. From Figure 2-2, we see also what is meant by the phrase "pear-shaped atoms," which is sometimes used to describe hydrogen and halogen atoms in organic molecules.

Along with the radii in Table 2-5, one additional value should be noted.

---

[29] Some care, however, should be exercised in using ionic radii as van der Waals' radii. To cite a single example, the shortest intermolecular selenium-to-oxygen distance in *trans*-ethanediseleninic anhydride (VIII) (Gould and Post, *J. Am. Chem. Soc.*, **78**, 5161 (1956)) is

$$\begin{array}{c}
\text{O} \\
\diagup \\
\text{Se} \\
\diagup \quad \diagdown \\
\text{CH}_2 \quad \quad \text{O} \\
| \quad \quad \quad | \\
\text{CH}_2 \quad \quad \text{O} \\
\diagdown \quad \diagup \\
\text{Se} \\
\diagup \\
\text{O}
\end{array}$$

VIII

only 2.70 Å, much less than 3.40 Å, the sum of the ionic radii of selenium and oxygen. While the radius of the selenide ion may be quite close to the van der Waals' radius of selenium in a compound such as dimethyl selenide, it is apparently not appropriate for the selenium atom in compound VIII. This discrepancy may be rationalized by supposing that the positive formal charge on the selenium atom in VIII draws its electron cloud in more tightly than would be the case for a formally uncharged atom; or, alternatively, one might visualize strong dipole-dipole interaction between molecules pulling them abnormally close together. Whatever the detailed explanation however, a safe (and perhaps not particularly useful) generalization is that the selenium atom in VIII is of a substantially different *character* from that in dimethyl selenide. That the two types of selenium atom have different van der Waals' radii is less surprising than if they were found to have the same radii.

This distance, about 1.85 Å, is the "half thickness" of aromatic molecules—that is, half the distance between parallel benzene rings of adjacent molecules in the crystals of such compounds as naphthalene and anthracene. Note that this value is much larger than the van der Waals' radii of any of the nonmetals of the first eight-membered period, indicating that the π electrons extending above and below the planes of aromatic rings impart substantial thicknesses to such rings. In graphite, however, the layers of rings (Fig. 2-2) are unexpectedly close (3.4 Å), suggesting that the layers are held together, not only by van der Waals' attraction, but by some auxiliary force, the nature of which cannot at present be simply described.

EXERCISES FOR CHAPTER 2

1. The equilibrium constant for the reaction $Cl_2 \rightarrow 2Cl$ is 0.1 at 1800° K but only 10^{-10} at 800° K. Estimate the Cl—Cl bond energy and compare it with the value in Table 2-1.

2. The formation of NH_3 gas from the elements N_2 and H_2 liberates 11 kcal per mole of NH_3. The formation of hydrazine, NH_2—NH_2, from the elements is slightly endothermic, requiring 10 kcal per mole. The H—H bond energy is 104 kcal, whereas the N≡N triple bond energy is 170 kcal.
   (a) Calculate the N—H bond energy.
   (b) Calculate the N—N single-bond energy.
   (c) Using appropriate data from Table 2-1, calculate the heat released in the reaction:

$$H_2N—NH_2 + 2H_2O_2 \rightarrow 4H_2O_{(gas)} + N_2$$

3. The heats of hydrogenation of cyclohexene and benzene are, respectively, 28.6 and 49.8 kcal per mole.
   (a) Calculate the C=C bond energy in cyclohexene.
   (b) Estimate the resonance energy of benzene.

4. There is an uncertainty of about 44 kcal per gram atom in the heat of atomization of graphite. Show that if this heat of atomization is used in the calculation of bond energies, the following uncertainties should arise:
   (a) 11 kcal for the C—H bond energy.
   (b) 22 kcal for the C—C bond energy.
   (c) 66 kcal for the C≡C bond energy.
   (d) 33 kcal for the C≡N bond energy.

5. Show that the uncertainty in the value for the heat of atomization of graphite does not affect the following values:
   (a) The difference between the C—C and C=C bond energies.
   (b) The resonance energy of benzene.

6. (a) Show that the arithmetic mean of two bond energies, E_{A-A} and E_{B-B}, must be greater than, or equal to, the geometric mean of these energies.

(b) What percent difference must there be between the values of two bond energies before their arithmetic mean exceeds their geometric mean by more than 10 percent of the latter?

(c) Show that by using the arithmetic mean, rather than the geometric mean, of bond energies E_{A-A} and E_{B-B} to estimate the energy of the hypothetical "completely covalent bond" between A and B, it becomes possible to calculate the "extra ionic resonance energy" of bond A—B merely by knowing the heat of formation of the A—B molecule from the elements (that is, without knowing the heats of atomization of A—A or B—B).

(d) Why is an estimate such as described in (c) possible for the "extra ionic resonance energy" of the H—Cl bond but not for that of the N—H bond?

7. (a) From the data in Table 2-1, calculate the electronegativity difference between H and Cl. Check with Table 2-2.

(b) Using Table 2-3 and the Schomaker-Stevenson relationship, estimate the interatomic distance in HCl.

8. (a) Calculate the length of the Si—F bond in SiF$_4$ using the Huggins relationship.

(b) Estimate the (nonbonded) fluorine-to-fluorine distance in the SiF$_4$ molecule. (Hint: See Chap. 1, Ex. 7.)

9. Predict which member of each of the following pairs of compounds has the higher resonance energy and justify your choice:

(a) Anthracene or phenanthrene?

(b) Ammonium acetate or acetamide?

(c) Cyclooctatetraene or styrene?

(d)  or

(e) Benzene or hexamethylbenzene?

(f) p-Benzoquinone or benzaldehyde?

(g)  or

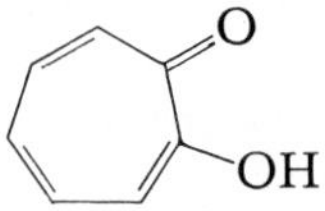

10. Arrange the following compounds in the order of their heats of hydrogenation:

$$CH_2{=}CH{-}CH{=}CH_2 \qquad CH_2{=}CH{-}CH_2{-}CH{=}CH_2 \qquad$$

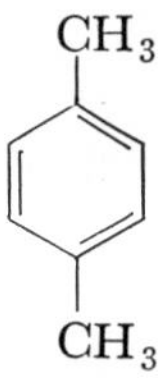

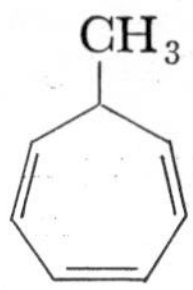

11. (a) Arrange the following in order of decreasing radius of the atom specified: carbon in cyclohexane, carbon in benzene, carbon in CF$_4$, central carbon in

CH_2=C=CH_2, central carbon in CH≡C—CH_2—C≡CH, silicon in SiH_4, silicon in $SiCl_4$, sulfur in SF_6.

(b) Explain why the van der Waals' radius of the methylene group is about equal to that for the methyl group even though the latter has one additional hydrogen atom.

12. Draw pictures of the three Kekule forms of naphthalene. Assuming the three forms are of equal importance, and neglecting high-energy forms, estimate the bond order of the bonds designated as 1, 2, and 3. Estimate the lengths of each of the numbered bonds and compare these lengths with the observed values (bond No. 1—1.43 Å; bond No. 2—1.37 Å; bond No. 3—1.40 Å).

CHAPTER 3

Dipole Moments and Spectral Studies

INORGANIC CHEMISTS SOMETIMES REFER to the "revolution" that has taken place in their field during the last forty years. These years have seen the development of the modern methods of structural investigation; and today the structures of inorganic compounds are the subject for systematic study, whereas before 1910 they were largely matters for speculation. Although the same methods have inevitably affected organic chemistry, they have not revolutionized it in quite the same way. Excellent structure determinations for thousands of organic compounds have been based solely on the study of their chemistry, and physical methods of investigation have often served to show that the older concepts of molecular geometry of organic compounds were, in the large part, correct. However, two types of study, formerly carried out almost exclusively in physical chemistry laboratories, have been particularly valuable to organic chemists.

The first of these, the study of electric dipole moments, is occasionally used for settling difficult questions concerning molecular geometry, but is more generally used to provide hints as to the distribution of electron density in molecules. Dipole moments have influenced organic thinking, but the measurement of such moments is still generally regarded as being in the province of certain physical chemists who are especially interested in the subject.

With molecular spectra, it is a different story. One of the most striking differences between the organic publications of 1920 and those of 1955 is the very prominent role that spectral data have come to assume. While it is still possible for an organic research chemist to do good work without access to spectral facilities, it is becoming increasingly rare. In many laboratories the infrared spectrum of a new compound has come to be a routine item in its characterization, just as are its melting point and chemical analysis.

A large area of information arising from spectral studies is of only passing interest in the present text. We shall not be concerned here with the detection of functional groups by infrared analysis, with the identification of compounds, nor with the analysis of mixtures by infrared or ultraviolet spectroscopy. It is also beyond the scope of this text to treat quantitatively the relatonships between the electronically excited states of molecules and their ultraviolet spectra. There are, however, a number of points of structural interest arising from spectral studies with which we shall deal briefly after a somewhat more detailed treatment of electric dipole moments. The reader, however, is cautioned against evaluating the relative importance of these two types of investigations from the lengths of the sections devoted to each.

Part I—DIPOLE MOMENTS[1,2]

Definitions

We have already (p. 11) referred to molecules with "positive ends" and "negative ends" as **dipoles**. One of the simplest of these dipoles is the HCl molecule, in which the hydrogen atom is the positive end and the chlorine atom obviously the negative. Similarly, the region between the two hydrogen atoms of the water molecule and the region between the three hydrogen atoms in the ammonia molecule may be considered as the positive ends of these molecules, whereas the respective heavier atoms are at the negative ends. It is sometimes convenient to regard the positive or negative charges of a polyatomic molecule as concentrated at single points in space. These points are then, in effect, "centers of gravity" of positive (or negative) charge; such *centers of charge* are indicated below for the H_2O and CH_2Cl_2 molecules.

centers of positive charge

H · H
O

Cl═══C═══H
H
Cl

centers of negative charge

[1] For more detailed discussions, see, for example, Partington, *An Advanced Treatise on Physical Chemistry*, Vol. 5, Longmans, Green, and Co., London, 1954, pp. 287–541; and Le-Fevre, *Dipole Moments*, 3d. ed., Metheun and Co., London, 1953.

[2] (a) A recent, readable, and quite detailed treatment of dipole moments is given by Smyth, *Dielectric Behavior and Structure*, McGraw-Hill Book Co., Inc., New York, 1955, in which pp. 202–392 are of particular interest to organic chemists. Dipole moments for which references are not given are taken from this work. (b) Applications of dipole moments to

The electric **dipole moment** is abbreviated μ. For a molecule (in which the positive and negative charges must be equal in magnitude), μ is defined

$$\mu = zd \tag{1}$$

where z is the value of the charge at either center and d is the distance between centers.

Suppose, for example, that the hydrogen chloride molecule were completely ionic. It would then consist of a hydrogen ion (whose charge would be the same magnitude as that of the electron, 4.8×10^{-10} esu) at one end of the molecule and a chloride ion (with equal and opposite charge) at the other end, 1.27 Å away. The dipole moment would then be 6.1×10^{-10} Å-esu units, more conveniently represented 6.1 *Debye units*. Experimentally, the dipole moment of HCl has been found to be only 1.03 Debye, showing that the hydrogen electron has not been transferred cleanly to the chlorine but has been smeared between the atoms, perhaps a little thicker near the chlorine.[3] Often, the presence of a dipole is represented on the structural formula of a molecule by an arrow, pointing from what is believed to be the positive end to the negative end—for example,

Compounds such as CO_2, CH_4, BF_3, benzene, and $HgCl_2$, in which the centers of positive and negative charge coincide, have no dipole moment; that is, they are *nonpolar*.

Polarization

In determining a dipole moment, the sample is dissolved in a nonpolar solvent or vaporized, then placed between two oppositely charged plates, becoming, in effect, the *dielectric material* of a large electric condenser. As expected, the dipoles

structural organic chemistry are also discussed by Sutton in Braude and Nachod's *Determination of Organic Structures by Physical Methods*, Academic Press, Inc., New York, 1955, pp. 373–420.

[3] One is perhaps tempted to divide the observed dipole moment by that calculated for a completely ionic structure and to use the resulting quotient, in this case 0.17, as a measure of the "fraction ionic character" of the H—Cl bond. (This has indeed been done in the past—see for example, Pauling, *The Nature of the Chemical Bond*, 2d ed., Cornell University Press, Ithaca, 1940, p. 46.) Implicit in such an interpretation is the assumption that a completely covalent bond between two different atoms should result in a completely symmetric distribution of charge and, hence, no net dipole. This assumption can be neither verified nor disproved experimentally since it is an open question as to whether such a bond occurs; however, there is substantial theoretical basis for the belief (see, for example, Coulson, *Valence*, Oxford University Press, Oxford, 1952, p. 145) that two different atoms, even if linked by a completely covalent bond, may have associated with them a substantial dipole moment.

tend to orient themselves so that the negative ends point toward the positive plate and the positive ends toward the negative plate. (This orientation is opposed by the random motion of the molecules, the "randomness" increasing with temperature.) The substance, which is said to be thus *polarized*, increases the *capacitance* of the condenser; that is, there is a slight increase of positive and negative charge at the respective plates although the potential is kept the same. Although the circuits and techniques used in measuring the capacitances of condensers will not be described here, we might note that in practically all such measurements, alternating currents are used. The polarity of the condenser plates reverses itself from 10^6 to 10^7 times each second, and any polar molecules present between the plates rotate back and forth in an attempt to keep up with the alternating polarity.

In addition, distortions within the molecules themselves occur in the presence of an electric field. Electron clouds, being negatively charged, are pulled slightly toward the positive plate (*electron polarization*). If the polarity of the plates is alternated, the electron clouds will shift, first in one direction, then in the opposite direction. This polarization occurs both for polar and nonpolar molecules. Less important, but sometimes appreciable, is *atom polarization*, involving slight twists or stretchings of bonds between unlike atoms such that the more electronegative atoms suffer slight displacements in one direction, the more electropositive atoms slight relative displacements in the other.

Both electron and atom polarization effects may be grouped together as *induced polarizations*—that is, separations of charge that occur only under the influence of electric fields. Unlike the orientation of permanent dipoles in an electric field (often called *orientation polarization*), induced polarization is generally not affected by thermal agitation.

Dielectric Constants and Dipole Moments

A perfect vacuum between condenser plates yields the lowest possible capacitance. The *dielectric constant* of a material is defined simply as the capacitance of a condenser having the given material between charged plates, as compared to the capacitance of the same condenser in vacuo. Dielectric constants of gases at ordinary pressures are slightly greater than unity (for example, at 25° C and 1 atm: CH_4, 1.0008; $(C_2H_5)_2O$, 1.0060; CH_3Cl, 1.0104; CH_3CN, 1.0392).[4] Note that methane, which has no permanent dipole moment, has a dielectric constant appreciably less than those of the other compounds listed. The departures from unity exhibited by the dielectric constants of nonpolar gases must be attributed to induced polarization.

[4] Watson, *et. al., Proc. Roy. Soc.* (London), **132**, 569 (1931); **143**, 558 (1934); **156**, 130 (1936).

The relationship between the dipole moment of a dilute material and its dielectric constant (the Clausius-Mosotti-Debye relationship) is[5]

$$\frac{(D-1)3M}{(D+2)4\pi d} = N\alpha + N\frac{\mu^2}{3kT} \qquad (2)$$

where

D = the dielectric constant α = the polarizability

M = molecular weight μ = the dipole moment

d = density k = Boltzmann's constant

N = Avogadro's number T = the absolute temperature

Note that one of the two terms on the right side of Equation (2) is temperature-dependent whereas the other is not. The *polarizability* per molecule, α, which includes effects of both electron polarization and atom polarization, is a constant for a given substance; this may sometimes be obtained from its refractive index toward infrared radiation, or, more often, is estimated from its refractive index toward visible radiation. In cases where the substance is stable in the vapor state over a large range in temperature, both α and μ^2 can be estimated from measurements of the dielectric constant at two (or more) temperatures. The value of μ is obviously zero if the quotient $\dfrac{(D-1)M}{(D+2)d}$ (called the *molar polarization*) is independent of temperature.

When the material to be tested cannot conveniently be vaporized, it may be dissolved in a *nonpolar* solvent, and the dielectric constants of the solutions may be measured. Under these conditions, handling of the data is somewhat more complicated, for there is often interaction between solvent and solute.[6] Generally the dipole moment of a substance in the vapor state will differ slightly from its dipole moment in solution. The dipole moments of simple organic compounds lie in the range 0 to 6 D. The following values, which are taken from Smythe[2] and which refer to the vapor state, are representative:

Toluene	0.37 D
Monomethylamine	1.28
Methyl chloride	1.87
Acetone	2.85
Nitrobenzene	4.21

[5] For the derivation of this equation, together with a number of relationships for concentrated systems and their critical evaluation see, Ref. 2(a), pp. 3–51.

[6] Recently, the dipole moments of a number of volatile organic compounds have been obtained by the study of the variation in their rotation spectra (in the microwave region) caused by application of an external electric field. For a description of this method, which may give values far more precise than those obtained by dielectric measurements, see Gordy, Smith and Trambarulo, *Microwave Spectroscopy*, John Wiley and Sons, Inc., New York, 1953, pp. 287–294. There are also listed (pp. 361–362) the dipole moments of organic compounds that had been obtained in this way before 1953.

Bond Moments and Group Moments

Dipole moments are generally handled as vectors, and the dipole moment of a molecule may be regarded as being the resultant of individual vectors associated with each of the bonds within the molecule (and therefore called **bond moments**). For a diatomic molecule such as HCl, the dipole moment is the same as the bond moment, whereas molecules with three or more atoms must be treated by vector addition, in which case it is necessary to know or to estimate interbond angles in the molecule. Evaluations of the O—H and C—O bond moments from the measured dipole moments of water and methanol (1.84 and 1.69 D, respectively) are illustrated in Figure 3-1. Note that in (A) the

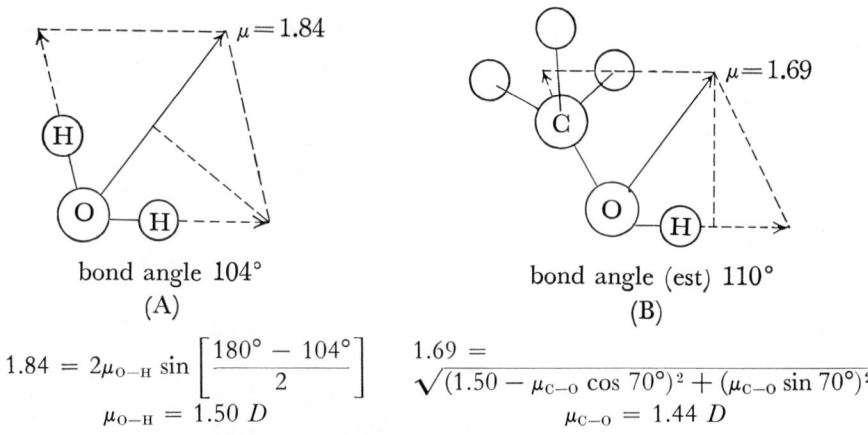

$$1.84 = 2\mu_{O-H} \sin \left[\frac{180° - 104°}{2} \right]$$
$$\mu_{O-H} = 1.50 \ D$$

$$1.69 = \sqrt{(1.50 - \mu_{C-O} \cos 70°)^2 + (\mu_{C-O} \sin 70°)^2}$$
$$\mu_{C-O} = 1.44 \ D$$

Fig. 3-1. Calculation of O—H and C—O Bond Moments

observed dipole moment of the water molecule has been "resolved" into two vectors, equal in magnitude and making an angle with each other correspond-ing to the observed bond angle. Each of these component vectors is thus an O—H bond moment (designated μ_{O-H}). After the value of μ_{O-H} has been deter-mined, we may use this and the observed dipole moment of methanol (B) to estimate the C—O bond moment. The simplified treatment of methanol illus-trated in Figure 3-1 assumes that in both the O—H and O—C bonds the oxygen atom is the more negative and that, therefore, the bond moments are to be added in the same manner as those in water. Furthermore, in (B) we have ignored the C—H bonds and moments associated with them. The C—H bond moment is known to be relatively small (about 0.3 to 0.4 D) and there is con-siderable contention among workers in the field as to its *direction* (that is, whether the carbon or the hydrogen atom is the more negative).[7] Conveniently,

[7] For a short summary of this question, see Wheland, *Resonance in Organic Chemistry*, John Wiley and Sons, New York, 1955, pp. 207—208. For a more detailed treatment, see Gent, *Quart. Revs.* (London), **2**, 383 (1948).

conclusions based upon the discussions to follow will not be changed by assuming blandly that this moment is vanishingly small. A representative set of bond moments, obtained much in the same manner as μ_{C-O} and μ_{O-H}, is

bond	H—N	H—O	H—S	C—N	C—O	C—Cl	C—Br	C=O
moment (D)	1.3	1.5	0.7	1.0	1.2	1.9	1.8	2.7

As was the case with bond energies (Chap. 2), bond moments obtained from one compound may often be applied to other compounds, but, again, the exceptional cases are sometimes the most interesting.

Since the organic chemist tends to regard compounds as carbon chains or aromatic rings to which one or more functional groups are attached, it is often convenient to assign moments to groups as a whole. These **group moments** are then the sum of the individual bond moments, possibly modified by any

Table 3-1. Group Moments[8]

Group	Moment (D)		Group	Moment (D)	
	Alkyl	Aryl		Alkyl	Aryl
—OCH$_3$	1.22	1.35	—COOH	1.68	1.73
—NH$_2$	1.2	1.48	—CHO	2.73	2.76
—Br	2.01	1.73	—COCH$_3$	2.78	3.00
—Cl	2.05	1.70	—NO$_2$	3.68	4.21
—OH	1.69	1.4	—C≡N	4.00	4.39

[8] These values are taken from Smyth (Ref. 2, p. 253). The aryl moments stem from measurements of benzene derivatives, the alkyl moments from ethane derivatives. The moments for the —COOH and —CHO groups refer to solutions (in benzene), whereas the remainder are taken from studies in the vapor phase.

Group moments for substituents on the higher aliphatic hydrocarbons lie very close to the "alkyl" values in the table, whereas group moments obtained from methyl derivatives tend to be about 0.1 D lower than those given.

special interaction which is typical of the group. In general (for reasons that will soon be evident) the moment of a group bound to an aliphatic carbon is different from that of the same group bound to an aromatic ring. Thus, in Table 3-1, two moments are given for each group. Group moments have been particularly helpful in considering aromatic compounds; here, the vector treatment is especially easy if the direction of the group moment is the same as that of the bond joining the group to the ring (for example, —C≡N or —NO$_2$). Figure 3-2 illustrates the use of group moments to estimate the dipole moment of *m*-bromonitrobenzene.

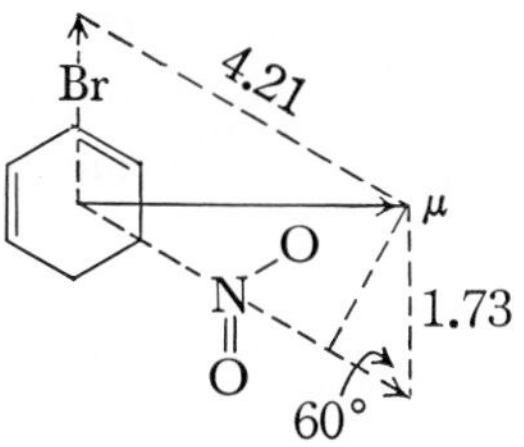

$$\mu = \sqrt{(4.21 - 1.73 \cos 60°)^2 + (1.73 \sin 60°)^2}$$
$$= 3.66 \ D$$

Fig. 3-2. Addition of Group Moments in m-BrC₆H₄NO₂

The calculated moment, 3.66 D, is considerably greater than the observed moment 3.4 D (for benzene solution). However, it must be remembered that the bond moments used are those taken from gas-phase measurements. The dipole moment of nitrobenzene in benzene solution is about 5 percent less than the value for the vapor, whereas the moment for bromobenzene in benzene is about 10 percent less than for the vapor. If we use instead the bond moments calculated for solutions in benzene (1.54 and 3.98 D), the calculated dipole moment becomes 3.48 D, in rather good agreement with the observed value.

Hydrocarbons

The zero (or almost zero) dipole moment of each of the paraffin hydrocarbons suggests that, in the absence of complicating effects, the dipole moment of a compound should not change if a methyl group is substituted for an aliphatic hydrogen; that is, that the C—H and C—CH₃ moments are equivalent.

The small but definite dipole moment (0.4 D) of toluene then leads to two questions: (a) which end of the toluene molecule is the "negative" end? and (b) what is the nature of the "complicating effect" in this molecule? The first question must be answered by comparing the dipole moments of *two or more compounds* (since the study of a single compound may yield only the *magnitude* of its moment, never the direction). The reasoning is as follows: If two negative (or two positive) groups are placed, say, at the *para* positions of a benzene ring, the two group moments will tend to oppose each other, just as will two men pulling at opposite ends of a rope or pushing at opposite ends of a box. If the directions of the group moments are the same as those of the bonds joining the groups to the ring, the resultant moment may be obtained simply by subtraction. On the other hand, if one of the groups is negative and the other positive, the "electronic push" at one end will reinforce the "electronic pull" at the other, and the resultant moment may be obtained by addition. Now, it is found that the dipole moments of *p*-nitrotoluene, *p*-chlorotoluene, and *p*-fluorotoluene are *greater* than those for the corresponding benzene derivatives. Since the nitro, chloro, and fluoro substituents are undoubtedly negative with respect to the benzene ring, we may conclude that the methyl group is positive.

The positive character of the side chain in toluene may be cited as evidence for the contribution of *hyperconjugated* structures (Chap. 2) of the type I' (eight others may be drawn). A similar structure, II', may be drawn for propylene to rationalize its small but appreciable dipole moment (also 0.4 *D*). Since the

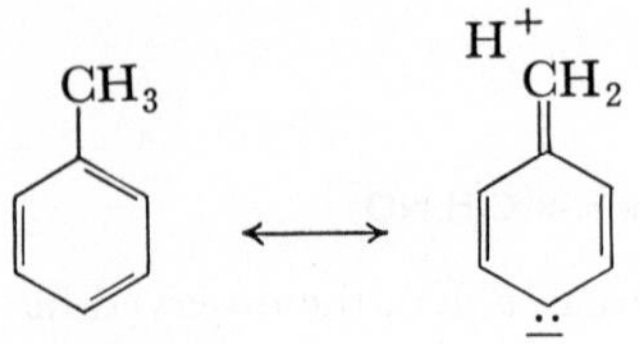

$$\mu = 0.4\,D$$

I

I'

$$CH_3-CH=CH_2 \longleftrightarrow {}^+H\ CH_2=CH-\ddot{C}H_2^-$$

$$\mu = 0.4\,D$$

II

II'

effect of the benzene ring is the same as that of the vinyl group, one would expect the dipole moment of styrene to be zero or very close to zero (which is the case). The dipole moment of methylacetylene is 0.74 *D*, suggesting that in this molecule, hyperconjugation plays an even more important role—a conclusion consistent with the marked shortening of the C—C single bond in this compound (p. 49). Here, however, another factor probably should be considered, for it is now thought (Chap. 7) that, quite apart from hyperconjugation effects, triple-bonded carbon atoms are more electronegative than single- or double-bonded carbons.

Two of the most interesting of the "polar hydrocarbons" which have been the subject of recent theoretical treatments[9] are 6,6-diphenylfulvene (III) and azulene (IV). Substitution of chlorine atoms at the *para* positions of the benzene

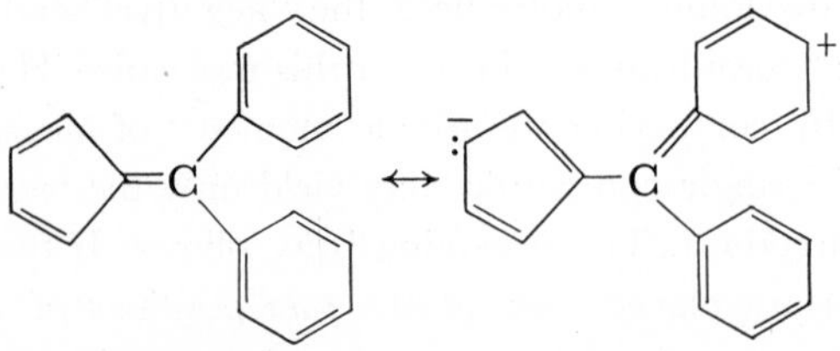

$$\mu = 1.34\,D$$

III

III'

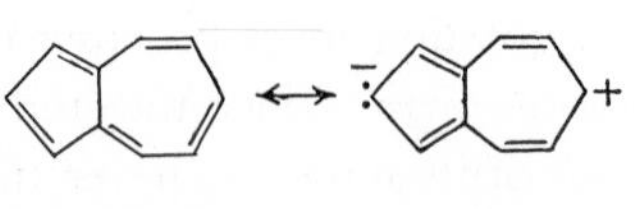

$$\mu = 1.0\,D$$

IV

IV'

rings in diphenylfulvene lowers the dipole moment to 0.7 *D*, showing that the cyclopentadiene "end" of the molecule is negative; and it is thought from chemical evidence[10] that the same is true for azulene. This indicates a substantial drift of electron density into the five-membered rings of these two hydrocarbons from the remainder of the molecules, a charge distribution that may

[9] See, for example, Berthier, *J. Chem. Phys.*, **21**, 953 (1953).

[10] For example, treatment of azulene with $C_6H_5N\equiv N^+$ results in substitution on the *five-membered* ring (Treibs and Ziegenbein, *Ann.* **586**, 149 (1954)), indicating that this end of the molecule is more "electron-rich" than the seven-membered ring.

be indicated by contributions of forms such as III′ and IV′. The cyclopentadiene ring acquires part of an extra electron which brings its π electron total nearer to six. As we shall see in Chapter 11, conjugated cyclic systems containing *six π electrons* have special stability. (In structure IV′, the seven-membered ring in azulene also has six π electrons.)

Halogen Derivatives

Dipole moments (vapor state) for some chloro compounds are listed in Table 3-2. It is interesting that the moments of the corresponding bromo and iodo compounds tend to lie within 0.1 D of the values for the chloro compounds, the differences in electronegativity being offset partially by the increase in molecular dimensions and partially perhaps by more subtle factors.

Table 3-2. Dipole Moments of Some Chloro Compounds

	μ		μ
CH_3Cl	1.87 D	$CH_2{=}CHCl$	1.44 D
C_2H_5Cl	2.05	$HC{\equiv}CCl$	0.44
$n\text{-}C_3H_7Cl$	2.10	C_6H_5Cl	1.70
$n\text{-}C_5H_{11}Cl$	2.12	$o\text{-}ClC_6H_4Cl$	2.53

The substitution of a methyl group for a hydrogen atom in alkyl halides having three or more carbon atoms results (as we should expect) in practically no change in dipole moment. However the ethyl halides have dipole moments 0.1 to 0.3 D greater than those of the respective methyl halides, whereas the n-propyl halides have moments about 0.1 D greater than the respective ethyl halides. (Similar but less pronounced effects are observed for aliphatic nitro and cyano compounds.) One current interpretation of this trend (which has recently been expanded into a satisfactory quantitative treatment)[11] may be summarized in the following argument: (a) At the carbon-halogen linkage, the halogen atom is more negative, the carbon therefore more positive. (b) Electrons from atoms or groups bound to the halogenated carbon will be drawn slightly toward the positive charge, resulting in a greater separation of positive and negative charge (and an increase in dipole moment). (c) The valence electrons associated with a bound methyl group are more easily distorted by the nearby partial positive charge than are the valence electrons of a bound hydrogen atom (that is, the methyl group is more *polarizable* than the hydrogen atom). (d) There-

[11] See Smith and Mortensen, *J. Am. Chem. Soc.*, **78**, 3932 (1956). A number of older treatments (see, for example, Groves and Sugden, *J. Chem. Soc.*, **1937**, 1992) are somewhat less satisfactory.

fore a methyl group attached to a halogenated carbon is more effective in removing the positive charge from the halogenated carbon, and thus in increasing the dipole moment. (e) This effect, like a number of electrostatic effects that we shall encounter (Chap. 7), falls off very rapidly as the distance from the "primary dipole" (that is, $\overset{+}{C}$—$\overset{-}{Cl}$) increases. (f) Therefore, the change in dipole moment in passing from ethyl to propyl halides is small and further changes on increasing the chain length are negligible.

The relatively low dipole moments of vinyl chloride, chloroacetylene, and chlorobenzene (and the correspondingly low moments of the respective bromo and iodo compounds) also indicate that another effect of importance has come into play. In vinyl chloride, one of the p "dumbbells" of unshared electrons on the chlorine atom is parallel to the pair of π-electron clouds of the double bond, allowing delocalization of part of the excess negative charge over the three-atom system and a corresponding decrease in dipole moment. (This would mean also that the C—Cl bond had acquired partial double-bond character—a situation we have already inferred from its short length, p. 47.) In chloroacetylene, *both* p orbitals of the chlorine atom are parallel to the π orbitals associated with the triple bond, and a further spreading of the excess negative charge is possible. This lowering of moment is often termed a "resonance effect" because it may be described by the use of extra structures such as V' for the halides involved. Because of the same effect, we would expect the

$$\text{HC} \equiv \text{C—Cl} \leftrightarrow \text{H}\overset{-}{\underset{..}{\text{C}}} = \text{C} = \overset{+}{\underset{..}{\text{Cl}}} :$$
$$\text{(V)} \qquad\qquad \text{(V')}$$
$$\mu = 0.44 \ D$$

dipole moments of the aryl halides to be lower than those of the corresponding alkyl compounds (indeed, that is why Table 3-1 gives two separate group moments for halo substituents); however, it is somewhat surprising that this effect for aryl compounds is much less marked than for vinyl compounds.

Monosubstituted Benzene Derivatives

The relatively low dipole moment of chlorobenzene (as well as the low values for the other monohalogenated benzenes) may thus be explained by assuming that forms such as VI' contribute to the structure of the molecule. Form VI' is similar to form I'—used to explain the dipole moment of toluene—since in both the benzene ring has assumed a partial negative charge. However, it should be noted from Table 3-1 that the moments of nitrobenzene and benzo-nitrile are considerably *higher* than those of their aliphatic analogs. Since there is no doubt in our mind at present that both the nitro and the cyano groups are negative with respect to carbon, it appears then that the action of the benzene rings in nitrobenzene and benzonitrile has made the substituents *more negative;* that is, that electron density has been drawn out of the benzene ring and has been spread somewhat more thickly over the substituents, leaving the ring with a partial *positive* charge. Such an effect, which is represented by resonance forms such as VII′ and VIII′, serves to emphasize what may be termed the "electronic versatility" of the conjugated system of bonds of the benzene ring.

Electron density may be "pushed into" the ring from halogen atoms, from nitrogen atoms of amino groups, or from oxygen atoms of —OH groups. On the other hand, electron density may be "drawn out" of the ring by a —C=O,

—C≡N, or —N⟨O⟩ group. (In Chap. 11 we shall see why these two classes of substituents correspond, as the reader must surely have noticed, to the "*ortho-para*-directing groups" and the "*meta*-directing groups" of classical organic chemistry.)

The same type of resonance that results in a *lowering* of the dipole moment of chlorobenzene (as compared to alkyl halides) *raises* the moment of aromatic amines to about 1.6 *D* (in comparison to aliphatic amines, whose moments lie in the range 1.0 to 1.4 *D*). Note that in the representation of aniline in Figure 3-3, the resultant *a* of the two N—H bond moments is almost directly opposed to the N—C bond moment *b*. Electron loss from the nitrogen atom to the benzene ring (as represented by structure IX) lowers the N—C bond moment, and the net moment, μ, increases. It then follows that the —NH₂ group in aniline is *positive* with respect to the benzene ring and, therefore, that the dipole

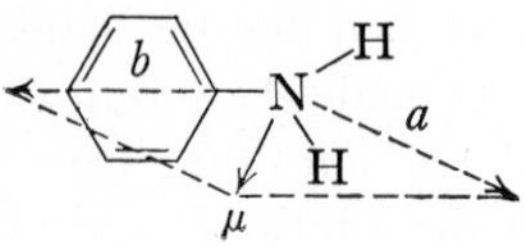

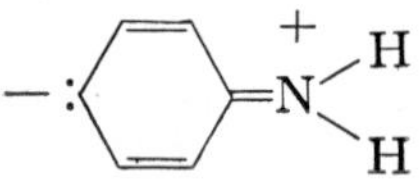

Fig. 3-3. The Dipole Moment of Aniline

moments of nitrobenzene and chlorobenzene should be *increased* by introduction of a —NH₂ group *para* to these negative substituents; Table 3-3 shows this to be the case. Similar arguments apply to dimethylaniline ($\mu = 1.6$ *D*) and its derivatives.

Disubstituted Benzene Derivatives

Further points of interest arise from consideration of the moments of disubstituted benzenes. In Table 3-3, the observed values for a number of such moments (in benzene solution) are compared with those calculated by vector addition, using the moments of the monosubstituted benzenes on the left of the table.[12] Note that in spite of the partial double character of the bond linking the nitrogen atom in aniline to the benzene ring (see structure IX), the —NH₂ group is not quite coplanar with the ring (if it were, the moment of *p*-phenylenediamine would be zero instead of 1.5 *D*). The calculation of moments for benzene derivatives having only halo, nitro, or cyano substituents is more straightforward than for substituted anilines, phenols, and anisoles for which it is necessary to know not only the group moments but also the *moment angles*—that is, the angles between the bond moments and the bonds linking the —NH₂, —OH, or —OCH₃ substituents to the ring. These angles have been evaluated,[13] principally by considering substituted toluenes, and are used in calculating the moments of *p*-nitrophenol and of *p*-nitro- and *p*-chloroaniline in the table. The treatment of *ortho*- and *meta*-substituted phenols and anilines is even more complicated and the results subject to considerable doubt; the moments change as the —OH or —NH₂ groups rotate with respect to the ring, and it is necessary to make somewhat arbitrary assumptions as to the ease of such rotation and the possibility of favored configurations.

Note that the agreement between calculated and observed moments is quite good for the *meta*- and most of the *para*- disubstituted benzenes but much poorer for the *ortho* compounds. In calculating moments for the *ortho* compounds, it is generally assumed that the bonds holding the two substituents to the benzene ring lie in the plane of the ring and make an angle of 60° with each other.

[12] The values for monosubstituted benzenes refer to solutions in benzene and therefore differ slightly from the group moments in Table 3-1, which refer to the gas phase.
[13] Marsden and Sutton, *J. Chem. Soc.*, **1936**, 599.

This, however, is an oversimplification which ignores the possibility that *ortho* substituents, because of their small separation in space, may interfere with each other sterically. We now know, for example, that the halogen atoms in *o*-dichloro and *o*-dibromobenzene are pushed out of the plane of the ring by about 18°, one above the ring, one below.[14] It is probable that similar inter- ference occurs in other *ortho* compounds, increasing the angle between bond moments and accounting, at least in part, for the differences. The situation is further complicated by mutual distortion (polarization) of the electron clouds associated with the two *ortho* substituents; although we cannot discuss the latter

Table 3-3. Dipole Moments of Some Substituted Benzenes

Mono- substituted		Disubstituted						
			o		*m*		*p*	
Sub- stituent	D	Sub- stituents	Ob- served	Calcu- lated	Ob- served	Calcu- lated	Ob- served	Calcu- lated
Cl	1.58	Cl, Cl	2.27	2.74	1.48	1.58	0	0
Br	1.54	Br, Br	2.1	2.67	1.46	1.54	0	0
NO_2	3.98	NO_2, NO_2	6.00	6.90	3.89	3.98	0	0
NH_2	1.53	NH_2, NH_2	1.45		1.79	1.80	1.5	
OH	1.6	NO_2, Cl	4.1	4.97	3.4	3.47	2.50	2.40
		NO_2, NH_2	4.24	3.66	4.94	4.72	6.2	5.17
		Cl, NH_2	1.77	1.71			2.27	2.30
		NO_2, OH					5.04	4.34

effect in detail here,[15] it is clear that it too should reduce the reliability of dipole moments that are calculated from simple vector addition.

The two most interesting discrepancies in Table 3-3 are associated with the moments of *p*-nitrophenol and *p*-nitroaniline, the moments of which are considerably larger than the calculated values. Currently, it is felt that the π-electron density has been spread over the lengths of these molecules, *resulting in an unusually large separation of positive and negative charge*. Such a distribution suggests that the molecules have much of the character represented by the "quinonoid" structures X′ and XI′. Here again we are using the language of resonance, and these two compounds furnish perhaps the most striking examples

---

[14] Allen and Sutton, *Acta Cryst.*, **3**, 46 (1950).
[15] For a theoretical treatment of this effect, see Smallwood and Herzfeld, *J. Am. Chem. Soc.*, **52**, 1919 (1930).

of such resonance effects on dipole moments. Unexpectedly large moments are observed also for *p*-nitrosophenol and *p*-aminobenzonitrile; for these, forms similar to X′ and XI′ may be drawn. The same effect is almost certainly im-

portant for *o*-nitroaniline which, it will be observed, is the only *ortho* derivative in Table 3-3 for which the observed dipole moment is significantly *greater* than that calculated. On the other hand, the observed and calculated moments of *m*-nitroaniline are in much better agreement, and a few attempts with pencil and paper should convince the reader that quinonoid structures cannot be drawn for this compound.[16]

Steric Inhibition of Resonance

Structures such as X′ take on added reality when moments of derivatives of durene are compared with those of the corresponding benzene derivatives. Typically, the moment of nitroaminodurene (XII) is only 4.98 D in benzene, about 1.2 D less than that of *p*-nitroaniline, although we might have expected

that substitution of four methyl groups, symmetrically arranged, would have no effect upon the moment of the latter amine. A closer look at the problem, however, can be taken by constructing scale models of XII. If the two oxygen atoms and the ring methyl groups are made to lie in the same plane (as should presumably be the case if form XII′ is of considerable importance), one finds

[16] For a more extensive discussion of resonance effects on dipole moments, see Wheland, *Resonance in Organic Chemistry*, John Wiley and Sons, Inc., New York, 1955, pp. 216–234.

that the oxygen atoms come uncomfortably close to the hydrogen atoms of the methyl groups that are *ortho* to them. Apparently then, this steric interference forces the oxygen of the nitro groups well out of the plane of the ring, creating a sort of "bottleneck" between the nitro group and the carbon bonded to it, and segregating the π electrons of the benzene ring from those of the nitro group. Nitroaminodurene thus has little, if any, of the character of **XII'**.

The same effect is even more pronounced in nitrodimethylaminodurene (**XIII**), which has a dipole moment of only 4.11 D—almost 3 D less than that of *p*-nitrodimethylaniline (6.87 D). Here it seems, both the nitro oxygens and the N-methyl groups have been pushed well out of the plane of the ring by interference with the *ortho*-methyl groups. The bonds linking the —NO$_2$ and —N(CH$_3$)$_2$ groups to the ring have lost their double-bond character and the π-electron systems of the —NO$_2$ group, of the benzene ring, and of the amino nitrogen have become independent of each other; this is in contrast to the situation in *p*-nitrodimethylaniline, in which composite π-electron clouds are

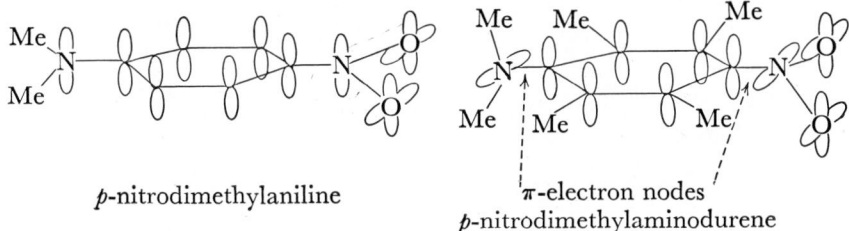

p-nitrodimethylaniline

π-electron nodes
p-nitrodimethylaminodurene

Fig. 3-4. π-Electron Distribution in p-Nitrodimethylaniline and Nitrodimethylaminodurene

delocalized along the entire length of the (almost) planar molecule, both above and below the plane of the ring. The two molecules are compared schematically in Figure 3-4.

Similar but smaller decreases have been observed[17] in the dipole moments of benzaldehyde, acetophenone, and benzoyl chloride when methyl groups are substituted into the 2 and 6 positions of these compounds. The differences are of the order of 0.3 D, obviously far less spectacular than the effects we have noted for nitrated aromatic amines.

Molecular Geometry

Although relationships between dipole moments and electron distribution in molecules have been emphasized, we should note a few of the considerable number of cases where dipole moment studies have given information concerning the arrangement of atoms. A classical example is the assignment of the *cis* and *trans* configurations to the two 1,2-dichloroethylenes having moments,

[17] Kadesch and Weller, *J. Am. Chem. Soc.*, **63**, 1310 (1941).

respectively, of 1.8 D and zero. Similarly, the dipole moments of the two isomers formed in the monochlorination of 1,4-endoxocyclohexane (XIV)[18] support the assignment of structures shown below:

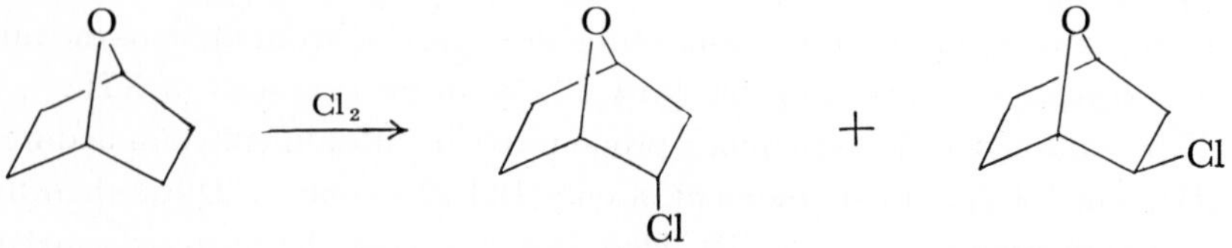

$\mu = 1.70\,D$
XIV

$\mu = 1.08\,D$

$\mu = 3.07\,D$

The zero dipole moment of cyanogen $(CN)_2$ indicates a symmetric linear configuration, $N\equiv C-C\equiv N$ (the configuration $^-:C\equiv\overset{+}{N}-\overset{+}{N}\equiv C:^-$, which would also result in a zero moment, is ruled out by a variety of other considerations). The very small moment of 1,4-dioxane suggests that this molecule exists

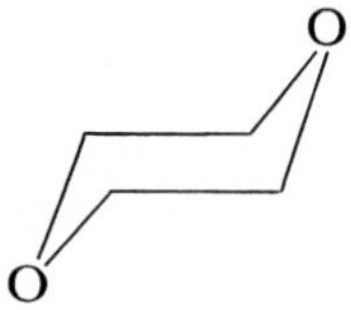

XV

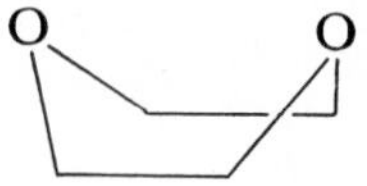

XV′

chiefly in the "chair" (XV) rather than the "boat" (XV′) conformation, whereas the moment of 3.5 D observed for gaseous diketene $(C_4H_4O_2)$ rules out the structure XVI (formerly regarded as possible) although it does not allow a choice between XVII, XVIII, and XIX, the last of which is now accepted as correct.[19] As a final example,

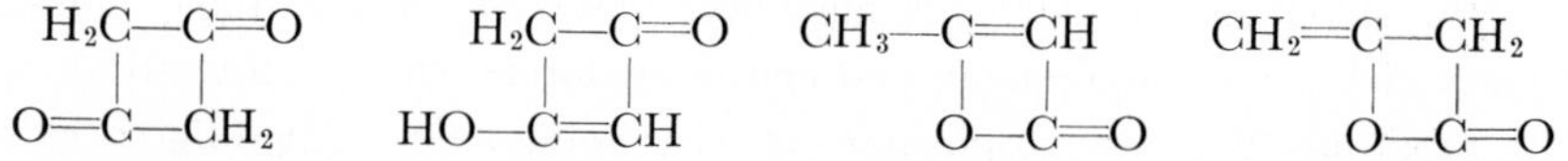

H₂C—C=O	H₂C—C=O	CH₃—C=CH	CH₂=C—CH₂
O=C—CH₂	HO—C=CH	O—C=O	O—C=O
XVI	XVII	XVIII	XIX

Exercise 5 illustrates the use of the dipole moment of *p*-nitrophenyl azide to calculate the angle between the azido group and the bond linking this group to the benzene ring.

Intramolecular Rotation

One of the basic tenets of elementary stereochemistry is that rotation of groups around the axis of a normal double bond does not generally occur. Rotation

---

[18] Martin and Bartlett, *J. Am. Chem. Soc.*, **79**, 2533 (1957).
[19] Katz and Lipscomb, *Acta Cryst.*, **5**, 313 (1952).

about single bonds, however, was assumed in the early days of chemistry to be free. We now realize that even this freedom has important limitations. Let us consider rotation in the molecule of ethylene chloride (1,2-dichloroethane). Three possible **conformations** of this molecule are shown in Figure 3-5, both in perspective and in a useful mode of stereochemical abbreviation[20] that we shall occasionally use in subsequent chapters. (In this abbreviation the bond joining the two carbons is perpendicular to the paper and thus hidden from view, the intersection of the three full bonds is the carbon nearest the eye, and the circle represents the farther carbon.) From a glance, it seems apparent that the two "staggered" conformations on the left should be preferred to that at

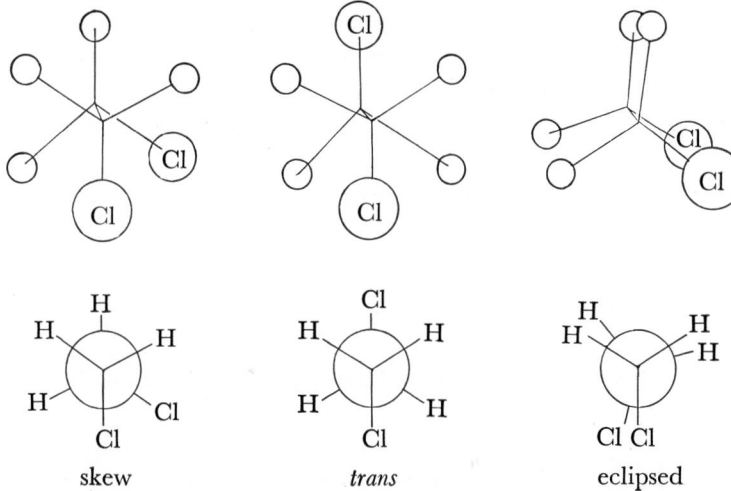

skew   trans   eclipsed

Fig. 3-5. Conformations (Rotational Forms) of 1,2-Dichloroethane

the right, for in the latter the atoms bonded to the two carbons are very much "in each other's way." Moreover, the *trans* conformation should be the most stable form since it is here that the large chlorine atoms interfere the least with each other. Recently, electron-diffraction studies have shown that about three fourths of the molecules of ethylene chloride vapor assume the *trans* conformation at room temperature, the others adopting the *skew* (sometimes called *gauche*) conformation.[21] Now the dipole moment of this vapor is 1.12 D at 32° C but rises with temperature, reaching the value 1.54 D at 271°. This strongly suggests that as the temperature is raised, there is a shift in equilibrium, and more and more of the molecules in the *trans* conformation (which should have practically no dipole moment) pass over into the skew conformation (with μ about 2.5 D). The moment at 271° corresponds quite closely to a *random*

[20] Newman, *J. Chem. Ed.*, **32,** 344 (1955).
[21] Ainsworth and Karle, *J. Chem. Phys.*, **20,** 425 (1952).

mixture having two skew molecules per *trans* molecule (if one chlorine is regarded as fixed, there are two positions skew to it but only a single position *trans* to it). Thus, rotation in the range of temperatures studied is not "free" in the sense that the two halves of the molecule rotate without restriction; they may indeed rotate in passing from one staggered conformation to another, but they may not tarry on the way. This rotation is similar in principle to that occurring in a number of additional aliphatic compounds, but derivatives of the higher hydrocarbons generally have two or more axes about which dipole rotation may occur and there are therefore a larger number of possible conformations.

A different situation prevails for most aliphatic carboxylic acids and their esters. These show no significant variation of dipole moment with temperature. Moreover, the moments of most simple acids and esters lie in the range 1.7–1.9 D. Let us ignore possible rotation about all single bonds except the C—O bond, for the dipole moment should depend almost solely on the configuration

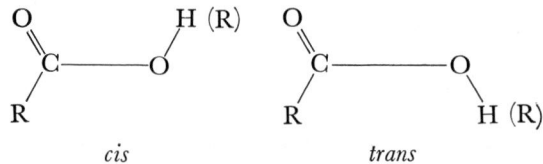

cis   *trans*

Fig. 3-6. Rotational Forms of Carboxylic Acids (and Esters)

about this bond. The two extreme conformations of a carboxylic acid molecule are shown in Figure 3-6. These may be designated as *cis* and *trans* conformations. Assuming the O=C—O bond angle to be about 120° and the C—O—H bond angle to be 110°, and neglecting (for simplicity) the R—C bond moment, the moments of the *cis* and *trans* conformations may be shown (Ex. 7) to be 1.2 and 3.7 D, respectively. The apparent dipole moment of a 1:1 mixture of the two conformations should be 2.8 D (which would also be the value corresponding to completely free rotation around the C—O bond). The low moments for acids therefore suggest that rotation about the C—O bond is definitely restricted and the conformation of most, if not all, of the molecules is *cis* or a close approximation to it.[22] A similar argument applies to esters. For acids, it thus appears that the electrostatic interaction between positive hydrogen and the

[22] The difference between the range of observed moments (1.7 to 1.9 D) and that calculated for the *cis* form (1.2 D) does not necessarily suggest that some of the molecules have adopted the *trans* configuration. It should be remembered that in the calculations, the bond angles, and the bond moments were relatively rough approximations and the neglect of the R—C bond moment may result in an error of as much as 0.4 D. Then, too, a planar configuration was assumed, whereas electron-diffraction studies (Ref. 14) show that deviations from planarity as much as 30° may occur for the simple esters.

partially negative oxygen atom of the carbonyl group favors the *cis* configuration, whereas the same conformation is assumed by esters because it permits
maximum separation of the large alkyl groups. It also seems that one π orbital
of the oxygen atom on the left has been lined up nearly parallel to the π orbital
of the carbonyl carbon. In the language of resonance, participation of structure
XX imparts significant double-bond character to the acyl-oxygen bond, and
rotation about this bond becomes almost completely restricted.

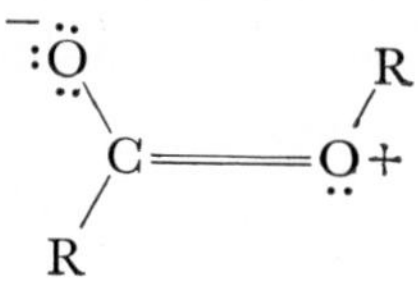

XX

Note that in these arguments concerning rotation, the *variation* (or lack of
variation) of dipole moment *with temperature* has been a key point. When attempts are made to interpret data at only one temperature in terms of rotation,
ambiguities generally arise. For example, the moment of terephthalaldehyde
(XXI) is 2.35 *D*, whereas that of benzaldehyde is 2.76 *D*. We can then be sure

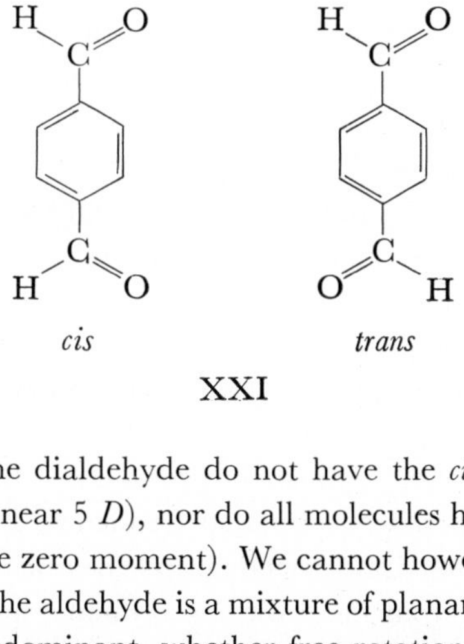

cis   trans

XXI

that *all* molecules of the dialdehyde do not have the *cis* conformation (which
should have a moment near 5 *D*), nor do all molecules have the *trans* conformation (which should have zero moment). We cannot however tell, in the absence
of other data, whether the aldehyde is a mixture of planar *cis* and *trans* conformations with the *trans* predominant, whether free rotation of the —CHO groups
around the C—C bonds is possible (perhaps with some configurations slightly
favored), or whether the aldehyde consists mainly of a nonplanar conformation,
intermediate in structure to the two planar extremes.[23]

---

[23] However, for an exceptional case in which conclusions concerning the restriction of rotation were obtained from dipole moments at a single temperature, see the work of Everard and
Sutton, *J. Chem. Soc.*, **1951**, 16, on the methoxy-substituted naphthalenes and anthracenes.

Part II—MOLECULAR SPECTRA[24]

Ultraviolet, visible, and infrared spectra of molecules are almost always *absorption spectra* rather than *emission spectra*. Polychromatic light from an outside source is passed through (or reflected off of) the sample, the resulting beam is separated into its component wavelengths using a prism or similar device, and the extent of absorption of light at each wavelength is measured photoelectrically. A plot of the relative absorptions at the various wavelengths against the values of the wavelengths themselves constitutes the *spectrum* of the sample. Often, particularly for infrared spectra, the wavelengths are replaced by their reciprocals, the *wave numbers*. Maxima in such plots are *absorption maxima;* light at such wavelengths is selectively absorbed and brings about some type of excitation of the molecule. The energy, E, required for the excitation is related by the Planck equation to the wavelength (λ) of light absorbed by the sample:

$$E = \frac{hc}{\lambda} \tag{3}$$

where h is Planck's constant and c is the velocity of light.

Raman spectra are obtained somewhat differently. Monochromatic light is passed through the sample, and a small portion of the light is scattered, emerging in directions other than that of the incident beam. Most of the scattered light has the same frequency as the incident light; but a small number of additional frequencies appear. The differences between the frequencies of incident and scattered light are the *Raman frequencies*. The Raman spectrum is thus a measure of the *alteration* of the frequencies of photons, whereas absorption spectra are records of photons that are "destroyed." In Raman scattering, only a portion of the energy of each incident photon is required to excite the sample, the remainder of the energy being emitted as a photon of lower frequency. (The frequency of an incident photon may also be *raised* by interaction with an excited molecule.)

In microwave and radio-frequency spectroscopy, the incident radiation is a single wave of very precisely regulated frequency, generated electronically. The types of apparatus used for detecting and measuring the radiation are, of necessity, very different from those used in ordinary spectroscopy. The radiation absorbed is of high wavelength (ranging from 1 mm to several kilometers),

---

[24] A very detailed treatment of the spectra of relatively simple molecules may be found in Herzberg's two books, *Spectra of Diatomic Molecules*, Van Nostrand, Inc., Toronto, 1950, and *Infra-red and Raman Spectra of Polyatomic Molecules*, Van Nostrand, Inc., New York, 1945. The book *Chemical Aspects of Spectroscopy* (Volume IX of Weissberger's *Technique of Organic Chemistry*, Interscience Publishers, Inc., New York, 1956, is of particular interest to organic chemists. Microwave spectroscopy is treated by Gordy, *et al.*, Ref. 6, and Raman spectra by Cleveland in Braude and Nachod (Ref. 2b), pp. 231–259.

corresponding, by the Planck equation, to transitions of very low energy, which often arise from mere reorientations of atomic nuclei.

Absorption of Energy by Molecules

Photons of high energies (about 1.5 to 8.0 ev) can bring about electronic excitation of molecules, just as photons of similar energies can raise the energy levels of the valence electrons of atoms. Such energy changes correspond to wavelengths between 1500 and 8000 Å—that is, the ultraviolet and visible regions of the spectrum. Lower energy photons (0.05 to 1.2 ev) may increase the intensities of vibrations within a molecule without causing electronic excitation; these energies correspond to wavelengths between 10,000 and 250,000 Å (or to wave numbers between 400 and 10,000 cm^{-1})—that is, the "near" and "medium" infrared. The *vibrational energy levels* between which transitions may occur are, like the electronic energy levels of atoms and molecules, *quantized* rather than continuous, although the energy differences between levels are obviously much less. Even smaller energies (0.00025 to 0.0025 ev) bring about transitions between rotational energy levels; the corresponding range of wave numbers (20 to 200 cm^{-1}) lie in the "far" infrared and near the low-wavelength end of the microwave region.

Complications in the study of molecular spectra arise from the fact that the various types of excitation occur in combination rather than alone. Changes in rotational levels generally accompany changes in vibrational levels, and changes both in rotational and vibrational levels often accompany electron transitions. Figure 3-7 (a *Grotrian energy-level diagram*, in which only the vertical coordinate has significance) illustrates these transitions schematically. The two sections of the diagram ($n = 1$ and $n = 2$) represent electronic energy levels. These are divided into vibrational levels which are, in turn, subdivided into rotational levels. The distances between horizontal lines are a very rough indication of the magnitude of the energy differences between the levels. An electron transition between the two n levels is shown, but it is obvious from the figure that a large number of additional transitions are possible from the level $n = 2$ to $n = 1$, the energy gaps associated with such transitions being very nearly equal. There are thus many similar but nonidentical wavelengths for electron transitions, resulting in a large number of closely spaced spectral lines. If the spectrum is poorly resolved or, more particularly, if the energy levels are further "smeared out" by intermolecular interactions in the liquid state, the lines appear to coalesce into a "band"; but with good resolution, the individual lines may appear as "vibrational fine structure" in the electronic spectrum. Similarly, rotational effects are observable as fine structure in vibrational spectra, and the nuclear orientation effects responsible for the fine

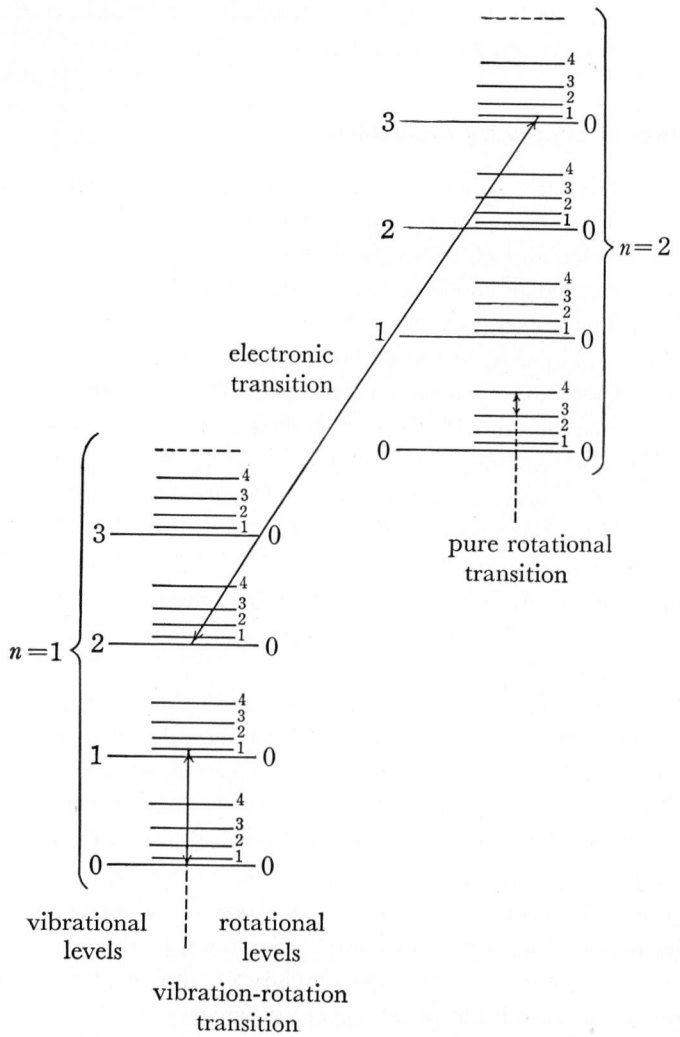

Fig. 3-7. Energy Levels for a Simple Molecule (Schematic)

structure in rotational spectra may in turn be observed directly by measurements in the microwave region.

Rotational Spectra

Consider a molecule rotating in space about an axis passing through its center of gravity. The *moment of inertia* of the molecule about this axis is defined as the sum of a number of terms of the type mr^2 (one term for each atom), where m is the mass of an atom and r is the distance separating it from the axis of rotation.

There are a great many ways in which a molecule can rotate, but rotational spectral lines give us values for the moments of inertia only about certain of a very small number of special axes (sometimes called the *principal axes of rotation*). For linear molecules, for example, we may observe only one set of spectral lines, corresponding to shifts between rotational levels about an axis perpendicular to the molecule. If the molecule has an axis of threefold or higher symmetry (that is, if it is a "symmetric-top molecule"), we may obtain the moment of inertia only about a second axis perpendicular to this symmetry axis. For less symmetric molecules, three moments of inertia about mutually perpendicular axes may sometimes be obtained, whereas if the molecule has no dipole moment, it will exhibit no rotational spectrum at all.

Whether such moments are evaluated from measurements in the far infrared, from microwave spectra, or from the fine structure of vibration spectra, their usefulness depends largely upon how readily they may be converted to interatomic distances and bond angles. For diatomic molecules (in which, however, the organic chemist has only minor interest), such a conversion is very easy. For polyatomic molecules, determination of dimensions from a single moment of inertia amounts to solving two equations in three or more unknowns. In many such cases, the data may be supplemented with the moment of inertia of the same compound *in which one or more isotopic substitutions have been carried out* (see Ex. 14). Such substitutions are assumed not to alter the geometry of the molecule. Although the analysis of rotational spectra has been confined to relatively simple compounds (two of the most complex are $CF_3C\equiv CH$ and trimethylene oxide), the bond lengths and bond angles obtained may generally be applied to more complicated molecules.

Vibration Spectra and Characteristic Frequencies

The problem of vibrations within polyatomic molecules would be appallingly difficult if it were not possible to handle the equations of motion for even the most complicated vibrations by combining the equations of motion of rather simple vibrations. For example, all possible vibrations of the cyanogen chloride molecule are said to be derived from "superposition" of the four modes of vibration indicated in Figure 3-8. These vibrations are the so-called *normal*

Fig. 3-8. Normal Modes of Vibration for ClCN

modes of vibration; during each of them, all atoms pass through their equilibrium positions at the same instant. All absorption in the infrared or Raman spectra is associated with one of the normal modes of vibration, or with overtones or combinations of these. This condition drastically limits the number of vibration bands that may be observed, but it still may be shown that for a nonlinear molecule of N atoms there are $3N - 6$ normal modes of vibration (and one extra if the molecule happens to be linear). There are thus 30 normal modes for the relatively simple molecule, benzene, and 216 for the more complicated molecule, cholesterol. Even though these numbers are sometimes further diminished by "selection rules" (which may be derived theoretically *if* the structure of the compound is known and which are generally not the same for infrared spectra as for Raman spectra), it should be quite clear that a complete analysis of the vibration spectrum for any but the very simplest molecules is no job for the chemist who is in a hurry. This does not mean, however, that vibration spectra are useful only in the hands of a very competent mathematical physicist. On the contrary, infrared examinations have aided in the identification and structure determination of thousands of very complicated organic compounds, largely by workers whose analyses of the spectra amount to little more than hurried scannings. Although the stretching or bending of a bond between two atoms may be affected by other atoms in the same molecule, such influence is often not sufficient to prevent the appearance of a *characteristic frequency* derived from such a stretching or bending. For example, almost all compounds having a carbonyl group (without α-β unsaturation) display a strong "C=O frequency" band between 1700 and 1800 cm^{-1}; a compound having one or more nonconjugated C=C bonds will generally absorb between 1640 and 1680 cm^{-1} (the region of the "C=C stretching frequency"). Likewise, compounds having an aliphatic —OH group generally absorb near 3600 cm^{-1}, and various deformations of methyl and methylene groups (picturesquely called "scissoring," "wagging," "twisting," and "rocking") may give rise to recognizable bands. Thus significant progress toward the structure proof of a new compound may often result from even a superficial examination of its vibration spectrum.

The nature of functional groups themselves may occasionally be clarified in much the same way. A class of compounds thought to be disulfoxides of the type R—S—S—R′ was found to absorb strongly at 1340 and 1150 cm^{-1}, the

 | |

   O O

regions characteristic of sulfones $\left(\begin{array}{c} \text{O} \\ | \\ \text{—S—} \\ | \\ \text{O} \end{array} \text{ derivatives} \right)$, but not near 1040 cm^{-1}, the region characteristic of sulfoxides.[25] On this basis the disulfoxide structure for

$$R-\overset{\displaystyle O}{\underset{\displaystyle O}{\overset{|}{\underset{|}{S}}}}-SR'.$$

this compound does not seems as likely as a thiosulfonate structure, $R-\overset{O}{\underset{O}{S}}-SR'$.

Similarly, N-nitroso compounds (generally represented with an $\diagdown N-N{=}O$ linkage) exhibit bands near 1400 and 1200 cm^{-1}, but none near 1520 cm^{-1}, the wave number to which the N$=$O stretching frequency has been assigned;[26] this would suggest that the N-nitroso linkage might better be represented as

$\diagdown \overset{+}{N}{=}N-O^{-}.$

As with rotational spectra, additional useful data may arise from isotopic substitution in a molecule. Substitution of C^{14} for C^{12} or O^{18} for O^{16} may cause small but noticeable shifts in the positions of spectral bands, and very substantial "isotopic shifts" result when deuterium or tritium is substituted for hydrogen. (It has been shown[27] that such a substitution may lower the C—H stretching frequency by as much as 30 percent.) If it is possible to replace all hydrogen atoms in a given position by deuterium, a band may seem to vanish from the spectrum and reappear at a lower frequency region. As a single example of the use to which this effect may be put,[28] consider the identification of bands associated with individual methyl groups in the spectrum of the steroid, XXII. This compound has four narrowly separated maxima in the region

XXII

[25] Cymerman and Willis, *J. Chem. Soc.*, **1951**, 1332.
[26] Luttke, *J. Phys. Radium*, **15**, 633 (1954).
[27] See, for example, Weissberger, ref. 24, p. 334; also Halverson, *Rev. Mod. Phys.*, **19**, 87 (1947).
[28] Jones, Cole, and Nolin, *J. Am. Chem. Soc.*, **74**, 5662 (1952). For a second example, in which the deuterium isotope effect in spectra has aided in the characterization of cyclopropane rings in triterpenoids, see Barton, Page and Warnhoff, *J. Chem. Soc.*, **1954**, 2715.

1355–1385 cm^{-1}, each presumed to be due to symmetrical bending vibration of one or more of the methyl groups in the structure. The first of these, at 1357 cm^{-1}, disappears if the compound is treated with D_2O and NaOD, suggesting that this maximum is associated with the enolizable hydrogen atoms, alpha to the keto group, attached to the cyclopentane ring. Two additional maxima, at 1365 and 1375 cm^{-1}, disappear if CD_3COOH rather than CH_3-COOH is used to esterify the parent alcohol, showing that both of these maxima are associated in some way with the methyl of the acetate group. The remaining maximum, at 1380 cm^{-1}, is presumed to be associated with one or both of the "angular" methyl groups as indicated.

Additional Structural Information

Sometimes an even more detailed picture may be obtained from the study of vibration spectra. As an important example, it is largely through spectral evidence that we have become sure as to which of the two "strainless" conformations of the cyclohexane ring is the correct one. Both the "chair" (XXIII) and the "boat" (XXIV) forms of cyclohexane have 48 normal modes of vibration, but selection rules stipulate that far fewer of these vibrations should appear in

XXIII   XXIV

the infrared spectrum of the more symmetric chair form. It turns out, for example, that there are 18 "infrared active" C—C stretching and CH_2 rocking and twisting vibrations possible for the boat form but only five of these for the chair form. Examination of the spectrum of cyclohexane in the region where these vibrations should appear (700 to 1350 cm^{-1}) reveals the five bands expected for the chair form.[29]

We have already seen (p. 73) how dipole moment studies of 1,2-dichloroethane indicate that the *trans* conformation predominates at low temperature with the "skew" conformation becoming more important as the temperature is raised. Spectral studies of this compound over a range of temperatures tell much the same story. The band at 1291 cm^{-1}—attributed to the "rocking vibrations" of the *trans* conformation—becomes less intense as the temperature

[29] Rasmussen, *J. Chem. Phys.*, **11**, 249 (1943).
[30] Bernstein, *J. Chem. Phys.*, **17**, 262 (1949).

is raised, whereas the band at 1235 cm^{-1}—attributed to the same type of vibrations in the skew conformation—becomes more intense.[30] Similar temperature variations in the infrared spectra of alkyl nitrites suggest a shift in the equilibrium between the rotational forms

$$\overset{R}{\underset{O-N}{\diagdown}}\diagup\overset{O}{} \quad \text{and} \quad \overset{R}{\underset{O-N}{\diagdown}}\diagdown\underset{O}{}\quad .^{31}$$

Quite commonly, significant structural information may be obtained from relatively small shifts in the position of characteristic frequencies. Some of the best evidence for hydrogen bonding (p. 28) has arisen this way. The "free" O—H vibration band at a frequency of about 3620 cm^{-1} generally appears strongly in the spectra of dilute solutions of alcohols and phenols in inert solvents. As the concentration of solute is increased, this band almost invariably diminishes in intensity, with one or more new bands appearing at slightly lower frequencies (3350–3500 cm^{-1}). As a result of association, a number of linkages of the type —O—H · · · O—H appear; the hydrogen bonded to one oxygen atom is pulled slightly away by its attraction to a second oxygen atom; and the energy involved in the vibration of the somewhat weakened O—H bond becomes less. As the strength of hydrogen bonding increases, the position of the "associated O—H" band becomes farther and farther removed from that of the "free O—H" band.[32]

<table>
<tr><td>cis</td><td>trans (equatorial)</td><td>trans (axial)</td></tr>
<tr><td>XXV</td><td>XXVI</td><td>XXVII</td></tr>
</table>

With compounds for which intramolecular hydrogen bonding is important the associated O—H vibration bands will also occur, but they will persist at very low concentrations. The *cis* and *trans* forms of cyclohexane-1,2-diol display associated O—H vibration bands at concentrations below 0.005 molar, indicating intramolecular hydrogen bending in both compounds and showing that in the *trans* compound the OH groups are in equatorial (XXVI) rather than in

[31] Haszeldine and Jander, *J. Chem. Soc.*, **1954**, 691.

[32] A second effect accompanying the strengthening of hydrogen bonding is a shortening of the O—H · · · O distance. It is interesting that the magnitudes of these two effects are linearly related; that is, a plot of the O—H · · · O bond distances in various compounds against the difference between the two types of O—H frequency for each compound yields a straight line. See Badger, *J. Chem. Phys.*, **8**, 288 (1940); Lord and Merrifield, *J. Chem. Phys.*, **21**, 166 (1953).

axial (**XXVII**) positions.[33] (Note that in the axial diol the hydroxyl groups are much too far apart to allow intramolecular hydrogen bonding.)

Shifts in the C=O stretching frequencies have also proved instructive. The stretching frequency of any bond depends not only on the masses of the bound atoms but also on a *bond-force constant* (actually a sort of Hooke's Law constant for the bond). The C=O bond-stretching constant must be affected when nearby substituents alter the charge distribution around the bond. More particularly, substituents such as —Cl, —F, or —NO₂, which attract electron density away from the carbon atom (leaving it with additional positive charge), are found to tighten the C=O bond—that is, increase its vibration frequency. This effect is very striking in the halogenated acetones.

Compound	C=O Stretching Frequency
CH_3COCH_3	1715 cm⁻¹
CH_3COCH_2Cl	1724
CH_3COCF_3	1769
CF_3COCF_3	1801

As the carbon atom is made more and more positive, the extra polarity augments the already strong carbon-to-oxygen attraction. The C=O stretching frequencies of substituted acetic[34] and benzoic acids[35] show the same trend; those substituents that boost the dissociation constants of these acids are found to tighten the C=O bond, whereas those substituents that lower the dissociation constants loosen the C=O bond.

A C=C double bond in conjugation with the C=O linkage generally *lowers* the stretching frequency of the latter by about 30 cm⁻¹ (for example, cyclohexanone, 1715 cm⁻¹; 2-cyclohexene-1-one, **XXVIII**, 1680 cm⁻¹). Since bond-force constants are known to decrease as bond order decreases, this shift

XXVIII   **XXVIII′**

suggests that the smearing of electron density over the conjugated system has left the carbonyl linkage with a bond order slightly less than 2—a situation that may be represented by contributions from additional resonance forms such as **XXVIII′**. It is interesting that conjugation effects in the infrared are in the same direction as conjugation effects in the visible and ultraviolet (that is, in both cases conjugation shifts absorption to greater wavelengths). We should note,

[33] Kuhn, *J. Am. Chem. Soc.*, **74**, 2492 (1952).
[34] Gillette, *J. Am. Chem. Soc.*, **58**, 1143 (1936).
[35] Flett, *Trans. Faraday Soc.*, **44**, 767 (1948).

however, that the two types of "bathochromic shifts" have wholly different causes. Conjugation effects in infrared and Raman spectra arise because of variations in bond-force constants, whereas conjugation effects in the visible and ultraviolet stem from variations in the energy gaps between the ground states and electronically excited states.

Electronic Spectra

Although in the past, visible and ultraviolet spectra were employed by organic chemists largely for identification and analyses, electronic spectra are physically important because of the information they should yield concerning the excited states of molecules.

At present, however, we cannot translate spectra of organic molecules into quantitative descriptions of their energy levels (as is possible for atomic spectra). The electronic energy levels for molecules are more numerous and the relationships between them more complicated than for atoms. Experimentally, rather large uncertainties in the gaps between levels arise because of the smearing of electronic lines by vibrational fine structure and because of modification of the levels by solvation. Frequently, there is real difficulty in identifying each of the observed absorption peaks with one of the theoretically possible transitions. The following section is only a very brief sampling of types of qualitative correlations that may be made between structural features and electronic bands.

Interest in electronic spectra of organic molecules is largely centered, directly or indirectly, about conjugated systems, for the characteristic spectra of conjugated compounds lie within the range of wavelengths accessible to conventional instruments. Saturated aliphatic hydrocarbons absorb in the range 1250 to 1750 Å—that is, in the far (and relatively inaccessible) ultraviolet; electronic excitation of these compounds involves the boosting of an electron already participating in a C—C or C—H bond to a higher level. Such a process requires considerably more energy than does the excitation of π electrons in olefins, and the presence of a C=C double bond will result in the appearance of one or more additional maxima at wavelengths above 2000 Å.[36] These maxima arise from the excitation of the π electrons to higher energy orbitals, also of pi (dumbbell-like) character, but called (for reasons that need not concern us here) *antibonding* π orbitals. A π electron in such an excited state is not localized on one atom, but may be regarded as "belonging" to the pair of atoms connected by the double bond. Moreover, if the double bond is part of a conjugated system, the excited π electron is spread over the entire length of

---

[36] It is of interest that cyclopropane shows a maximum at about 1900 Å, suggesting that because of the strain associated with a three-membered ring, the bonding electrons are somewhat more easily excited than those in paraffins.

conjugation; such delocalization further lowers the energy of the excited state. Since conjugation is found to shift absorption to longer wavelengths, it is tempting to associate such a spectral shift directly with the drop in energy of the excited state. It should be remembered, however, that conjugation lowers the energy level of the ground state also (p. 38), and the observed bathochromic shifts associated with conjugation must arise because the energy levels of the excited states are somehow affected *more* than the energy levels of the ground states. This situation is too complicated to be treated here, but the effect itself is of extreme importance.[37]

Conjugation shifts in the ultraviolet, in the absence of complicating factors, are roughly "cumulative." Polyenes with 2, 6, and 10 conjugated double bonds display maxima, respectively, near 2200, 3600, and 4500 Å, the last being well within the visible range; similarly, biphenyl shows a maximum near 2500 Å, whereas the polyphenyls **XXIX** and **XXX** absorb, as indicated, at somewhat greater wavelengths.

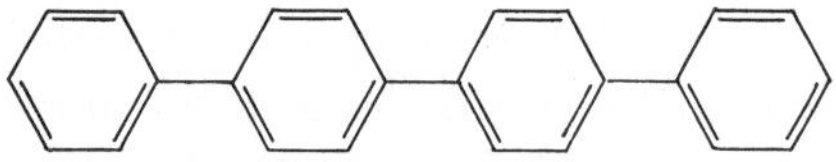

XXIX λ_{max} 3000 Å

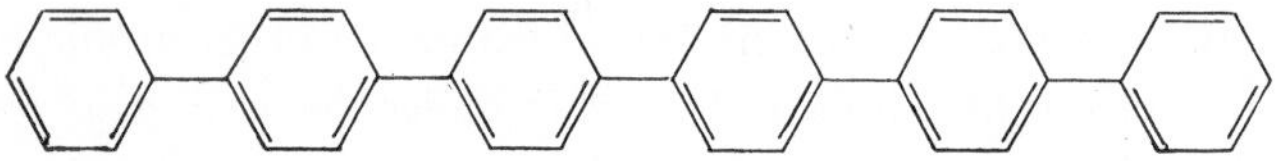

XXX λ_{max} 3175 Å

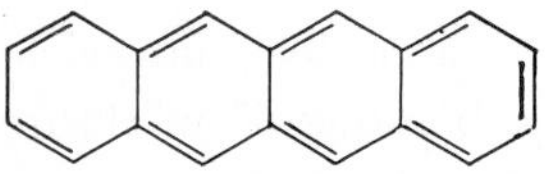

XXXI 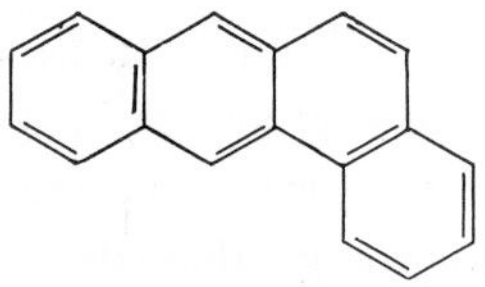   **XXXII** 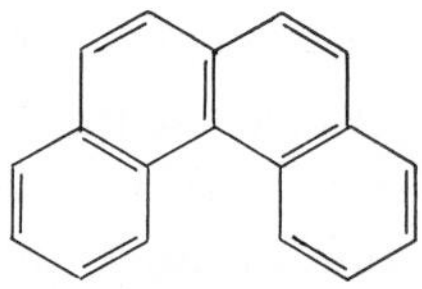   **XXXIII**

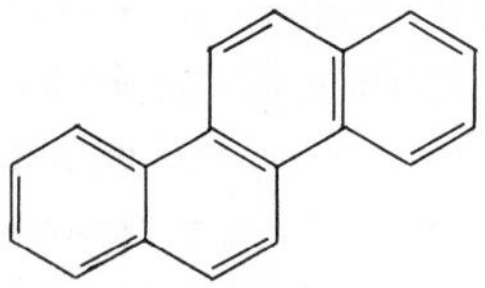

XXXIV

Such conjugation effects tend to be most marked when the molecular geometry allows maximum separation in space between the ends of the con-

---

[37] For two qualitative explanations of conjugation effects in electronic spectra (from rather different points of view), see Wheland, (Ref. 16), pp. 257–278; and Weissberger, (Ref. 24), pp. 654–657.

jugated system. Of the four isomeric polycyclic aromatic hydrocarbons shown below, naphthacene (XXXI) absorbs near 4600 Å, whereas maxima for the remaining three lie near 3500 Å.[38] Likewise, the *trans* form of a polyene (XXXV) will generally absorb at higher wavelengths than will the *cis* form (XXXVI).[39] On the other hand, conjugation effects are diminished when the molecule becomes unable to assume a planar configuration (Ex. 11).

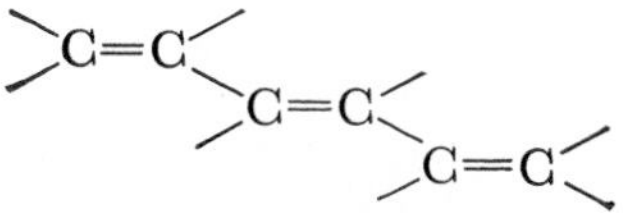

XXXV 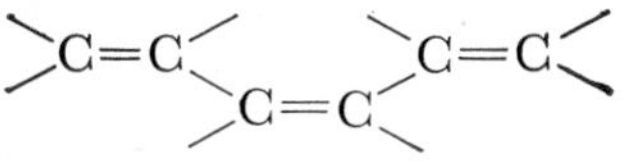   XXXVI

Hyperconjugation, which, as we have seen, affects heats of combustion (p. 49,) and dipole moments (p. 64), also influences electronic spectra. Generally the absorption maximum for an olefinic or aromatic compound is shifted toward greater wavelengths when a methyl group is substituted for an α-hydrogen. Typically, 1,3-butadiene absorbs at 2170 Å, whereas both of the 1,3-pentadienes absorb near 2250 Å; similarly, benzene absorbs at 2625 Å, toluene at 2668, and mesitylene at 2700 Å.[40] Such shifts lend reality to forms such as I' and II' (p. 64) which attempt to show an effective extension of conjugation by the methyl group.

Unshared electrons are more easily excited than electrons involved in ordinary σ bonding. Alkyl halides, alcohols, and amines thus absorb at greater wavelengths than do their parent hydrocarbons. Moreover, if unshared electrons are associated with double-bonded atoms, these electrons are very easily excited to the antibonding π level; most of the classical chromophoric groups (for

example, $\text{C}=\ddot{\text{O}}:$, $\text{C}=\ddot{\text{S}}:$, $-\ddot{\text{N}}=\ddot{\text{N}}-$, $-\ddot{\text{N}}=\ddot{\text{O}}$ and $-\text{N}$) are of

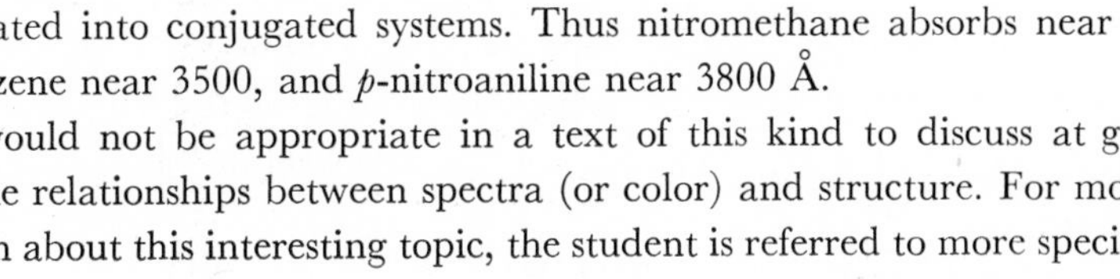

this type. Again, electronic excitation is further facilitated if these groups are incorporated into conjugated systems. Thus nitromethane absorbs near 2700, nitrobenzene near 3500, and *p*-nitroaniline near 3800 Å.

It would not be appropriate in a text of this kind to discuss at greater length the relationships between spectra (or color) and structure. For more information about this interesting topic, the student is referred to more specialized

[38] Klevins and Platt, *J. Chem. Phys.*, **17**, 470 (1949).

[39] See, for example, Zechmeister and Pinckard, *J. Am. Chem. Soc.*, **76**, 4144 (1954), on the stereoisomeric diphenyloctatetraenes.

[40] The absorption maximum for *t*-butylbenzene lies at 2655 Å, considerably greater than λ_{max} for benzene. This may be taken as evidence for C—C hyperconjugation (p. 50, structure VI'). The fact that this value is significantly less than that for toluene suggests that, as was indicated, C—C hyperconjugation is less important than C—H hyperconjugation.

works.[41] It should be clear, however, that behind correlations such as we have presented (which are little more than educated "rules of thumb") lies an extremely complicated picture of the electronically excited states of organic molecules which today is just beginning to come into focus.

EXERCISES FOR CHAPTER 3 —
PART I

1. Indicate which of the following molecules have dipole moments, representing the dipole (if any) by an arrow pointing from the more positive end of the molecule to the more negative end:

   CH_2Cl_2, naphthalene, OCS, HN_3, $(CH_3)_2O$, p-fluoronitrobenzene, $COCl_2$, o-chlorotoluene, iodoacetylene, pyrrole, p-dimethoxybenzene

2. From the Clausius-Mosotti-Debye relationship (Eq. 2) show that a plot of the dielectric constant, D, for a gas vs. the reciprocal of the temperature should approach a straight line (remember that D is quite close to unity), and that the slope, S, of the line is related to the dipole moment by the relationship:

$$\mu^2 = \frac{3MkS}{4\pi N\rho}$$

where ρ is the density and the other symbols are defined on page 60.

3. (a) Use the bond moments on page 62 to calculate the dipole moment for phosgene, $Cl_2C{=}O$. The molecule is planar with a Cl—C—Cl bond angle of 113°.
   (b) The observed moment for phosgene is 1.18 D. Why is this value so much different from the one calculated in (a)?

4. Consider a benzene ring having two substituents with moments μ_1 and μ_2, and assume that both group moments lie in the plane of the ring. Show that a simple vector treatment predicts a resultant moment of $\sqrt{\mu_1^2 + \mu_2^2 - \mu_1\mu_2}$ if the groups are *meta* to each other, and a moment of $\sqrt{\mu_1^2 + \mu_2^2 + \mu_1\mu_2}$ if the groups are *ortho* to each other.

5. Given the moments below, and assuming that the N_3 group is linear, calculate the angle between the N_3 group and the C—N bond in p-nitrophenyl azide.

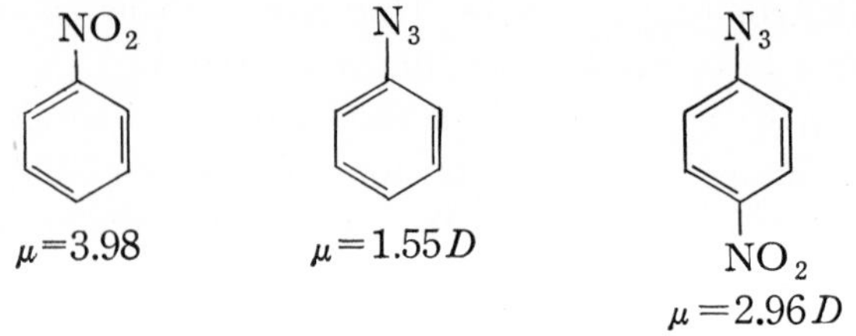

NO_2 $\mu = 3.98$

N_3 $\mu = 1.55 D$

N_3 / NO_2 $\mu = 2.96 D$

[41] See, for example, Mayer and Cook, *The Chemistry of Natural Coloring Matters*, Reinhold Publishing Corp., New York, 1943; Venkataraman, *Chemistry of Synthetic Dyes*, Academic Press, Inc., New York, 1952; Grimmel in Gilman's *Organic Chemistry, an Advanced Treatise*, Vol. 3, John Wiley and Sons, Inc., New York, 1953, p. 243.

6. Predict which compound in each of the following pairs has the higher dipole moment and justify your guess in each case.
   (a) NH_3 or PH_3?
   (b) Carbon tetrachloride or iodoform?
   (c) CH_3NO_2 or $(CH_3)_2CHNO_2$?
   (d) *p*-Chloronitrobenzene or *m*-chloronitrobenzene?

   (e) 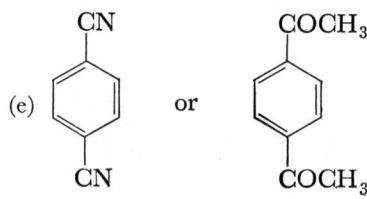 or

   (f) Benzaldehyde or *p*-methylacetophenone?
   (g) *m*-Dinitrobenzene or *p*-nitrotoluene?
   (h) $CH{\equiv}C{-}CH_2Cl$ or $CH_3{-}C{\equiv}C{-}Cl$?
   (i) 1,2-Dibromonaphthalene or 1,8-dibromonaphthalene?

   (j) [structure with NO_2, H_3C, CH_3] or [structure with NO_2, H_3C, CH_3, CH_3] ?

   (k) [naphthalene structure with CN, HO] or [naphthalene structure with CN, HO] ?

   (l) Furan or tetrahydrofuran?
   (m) 1,4-Dimethoxynaphthalene or 1,5-dimethoxynaphthalene?

   (n) [structure with NMe_2] or [structure with NMe_2, $CH{=}CH$] ?

   (o) O_2N-[structure with CH_3, CH_3]$-NH_2$ or O_2N-[structure with CH_3, H_3C]$-NH_2$?

   (p) Ethyl propionate or γ-butyrolactone?

   (q) $NC-$[azulene structure] or [azulene structure]$-CN$?

7. Using the sketches below and the bond moments on page 62, estimate the dipole moments of the *cis*- and *trans*- rotational forms of acetic acid. Neglect the C—H bond moments, assume the forms to be planar, and take the O=C—O and C—O—H bond angles as 120° and 110°, respectively.

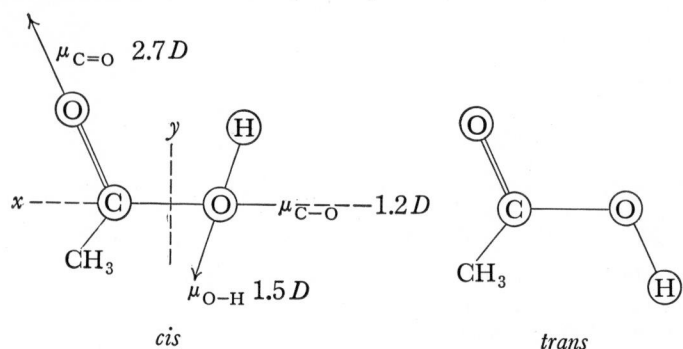

cis   trans

8. (a) Show that the apparent dipole moment of an equimolar mixture of two isomers is the root mean square of the individual moments, that is, $(\mu_1^2 + \mu_2^2)^{1/2}$.

(b) What would the dipole moment of acetic acid be if it consisted of an equimolar mixture of the two forms in Exercise 7? Compare your value with that given on page 74.

PART II

9. (a) The wavelength of visible light lies between 4000 and 7000 Å. Show that a molecule will be colored if the energy needed to excite it lies between 1.75 and 3.0 electron volts (1.0 ev = 1.6 × 10^{-12} erg).

(b) Explain why many compounds with absorption maxima well below 4000 Å and with no maxima above 4000 Å (for example, *m*-nitroaniline λ_{max} 3600 Å) are colored to the eye.

10. (a) The IR spectrum of an 0.01 molar solution of cyclohexanol in CCl_4 displays only one O—H stretching frequency. An 0.03-molar solution shows two such peaks, an 0.1-molar solution shows three such peaks, but a 1.0-molar solution shows only two peaks. Explain.

(b) The IR spectrum of $(CH_3)_3C—\overset{\overset{\displaystyle OH}{|}}{\underset{\underset{\displaystyle CH}{|}}{C}}—C(CH_3)_3$ displays only one O—H stretching

$$\underset{CH_3 \qquad CH_3}{\overset{CH}{\diagup \quad \diagdown}}$$

frequency, irrespective of dilution. Why is this?

(c) Suggest a reason why two O—H stretching frequencies appear in the spectra of very dilute solutions of *o*-chlorophenol, but only one each in the spectra of very dilute solutions of phenol and 2,6-dichlorophenol.

11. Equal weights of toluene and 4,4'-bitolyl are diluted to equal volumes with alcohol. The UV spectra of the two solutions are very much different. If the same experi-

ment is carried out with equal weights of mesitylene (XXXVII) and bimesityl (XXXVIII), the two spectra are almost the same. Explain.

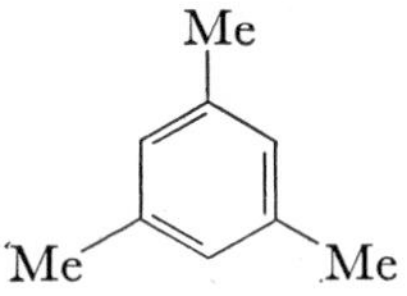

XXXVII 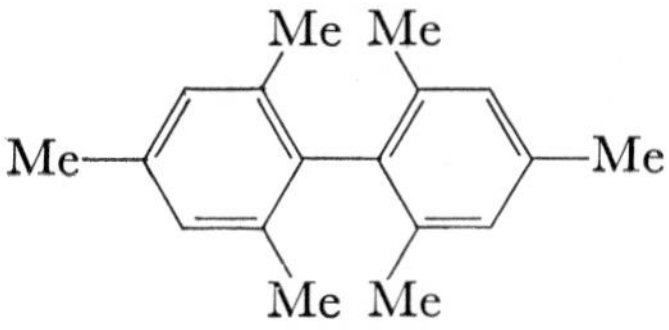   XXXVIII

12. Cyclopropane derivatives of type (A) are known to rearrange under treatment with HCl to yield olefins of type (B).

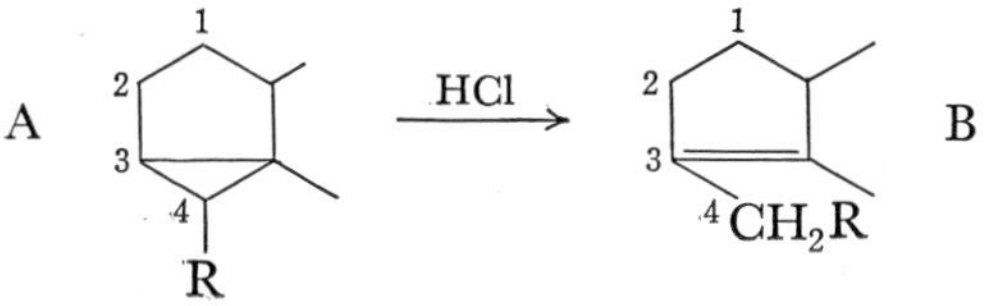

A compound of type (A) has a CH_3 group attached either to position 2 or to position 4 (but not to both). A sample of the compound is treated with HCl, and a second sample with DCl. The IR spectra of the two products show the same intensities for the peaks attributed to CH_3 bending frequencies. Decide whether the CH_3 group in compound (A) is at position 2 or position 4.

13. Predict which compound in each of the following pairs displays an absorption maximum nearer the red (high wavelength) end of the UV or visible spectrum. Justify your choice in each case.

(a) CH_3—CH=CH—$\overset{\overset{\displaystyle O}{\|}}{C}$—$CH_3$ or CH_2=CH—CH_2—$\overset{\overset{\displaystyle O}{\|}}{C}$—$CH_3$?

(b) p-Nitrophenol or m-nitrophenol?

(c) p-Nitroaniline or its hydrochloride?

(d)

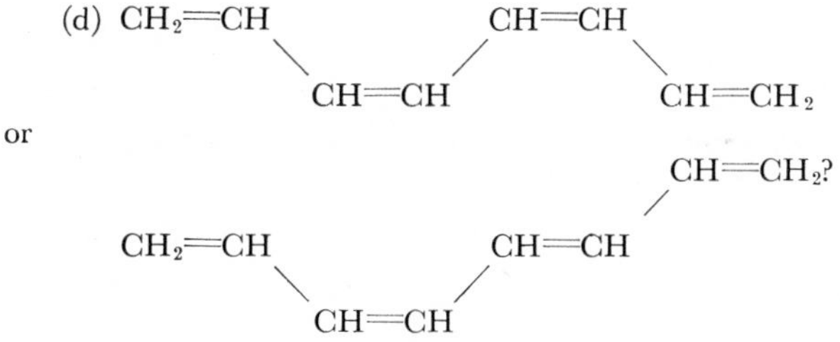

(e) Biacetyl or acetonylacetone?

(f)

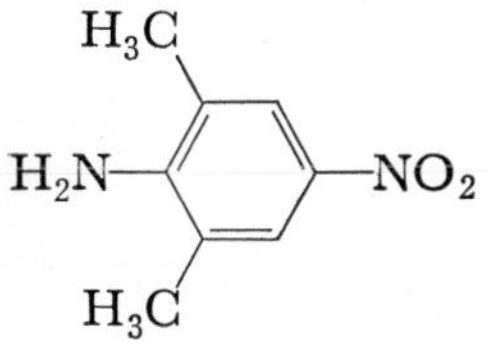

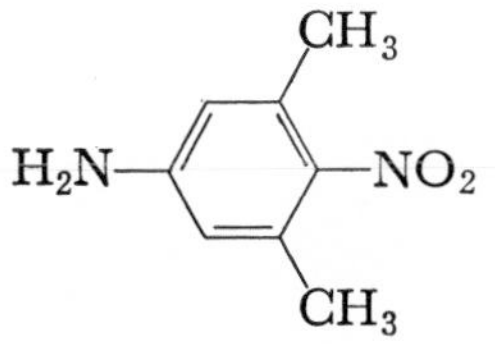

(g) $(C_6H_5)_3C$—OH or $(C_6H_5)_3C$—O—SO_3H?

(h) Phenol or thiophenol?

(i)

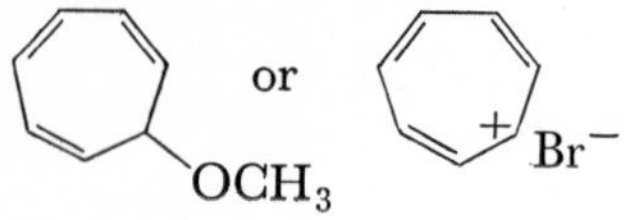

or

?

(j)

or

?

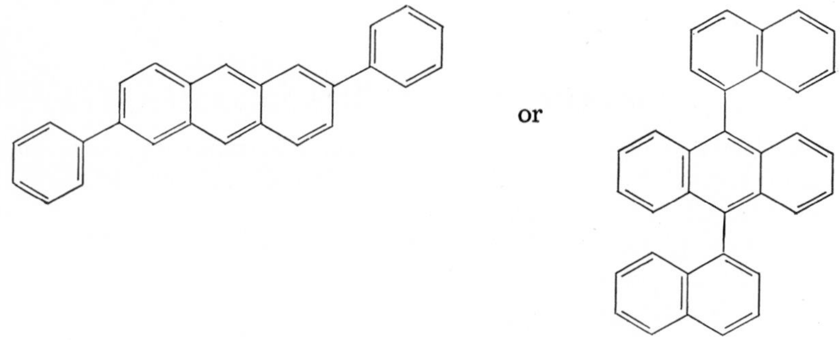

14. Consider the rotation of the linear H—C≡C—Cl³⁵ molecule about the principal axis A which passes through the center of gravity of the molecule at a distance x from

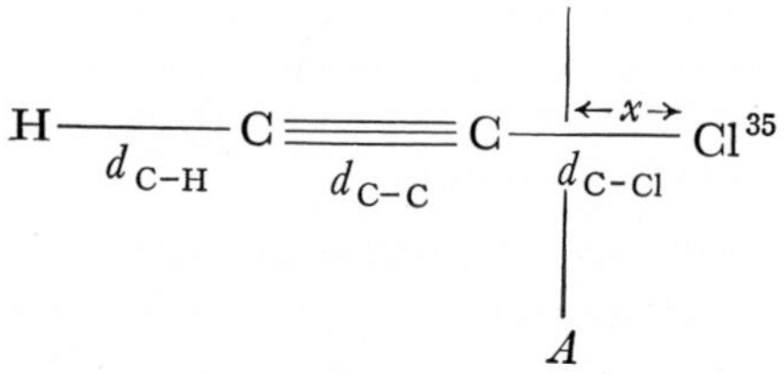

the nucleus of the chlorine atom. Designate the (observed) moment of inertia of this molecule as I.

(a) Set up two independent equations in four unknowns, relating I, x, and the internuclear distances in the molecule.

(b) Assume that the dimensions of the molecule will not change with isotopic substitution. Show that if the moment of inertia, I', of D—C≡C—Cl³⁵ is known, we may obtain four equations in five unknowns, whereas if the moment of inertia, I'', for H—C≡C—Cl³⁷ is also known, we may obtain six equations in six unknowns, thus allowing the calculation of the three bond lengths in the molecule.

Acids and Bases. Nucleophiles
and Electrophiles

BY THE CLASSICAL OR ARRHENIUS DEFINITIONS, bases are compounds that yield hydroxide ions when dissolved in water, whereas acids are compounds that yield hydrogen ions. Such definitions are quite adequate if one considers reactions only in water; in particular, they serve nicely for the student of elementary chemistry whose experiments are confined (for the sake of his own safety and the peace of mind of his instructor) to aqueous solutions. However, the acid-base concept is such a useful one that workers have redefined and generalized the terms "acid" and "base" in a number of ways; today many reactions are described as acid-base reactions, even though neither the H_3O^+ ion nor the OH^- ion participates. In all such cases, however, there is some analogy to the classical "neutralization" reaction. Of the many generalized acid-base systems that have been proposed,[1] the two extensions most useful to organic chemists are the *proton-exchange* approach (Brønsted system) and the *electron-pair transfer* approach (Lewis system).

Hydrogen Ion Transfer. The Brønsted-Lowry System

In the Brønsted system, an acid is defined as a species that can *give up* a proton (an H^+ ion) to another species. A *Brønsted base* is a species that will *accept* a proton. Thus the classical acids are also Brønsted acids.

[1] The more modern acid-base concepts are described by Moeller, *Inorganic Chemistry*, John Wiley and Sons, Inc., New York, 1952, pp. 306–335; and in more detail by Luder and Zuffanti, *The Electronic Theory of Acids and Bases*, John Wiley and Sons, Inc., New York, 1946, pp. 1–106.

$$HNO_3 \quad\;\; \rightarrow H^+ + NO_3^-$$
$$CH_3COOH \rightarrow H^+ + CH_3COO^-$$
$$C_6H_5OH \quad \rightarrow H^+ + C_6H_5O^-$$

} conjugate bases

The ions on the right which remain after protons depart from each of the acids are called the **conjugate bases** of the respective acids.

Although the Brønsted definition of an acid is very similar to the classical definition, it includes a number of molecules or ions that classically might not have been regarded as acids.

$$CH_3NO_2 \rightarrow H^+ + {}^-CH_2\!-\!N \overset{O}{\underset{O}{\diagup}}$$

$$(CH_3)_3NH^+ \rightarrow H^+ + (CH_3)_3N$$
$$Al(H_2O)_6^{+3} \rightarrow H^+ + Al(H_2O)_5OH^{+2}$$

Note that these reactions are not "spontaneous" ionizations. Rather, the H^+ is "pulled off" by an approaching base. Thus, the reactions above are actually half reactions.

Brønsted bases, species that will take on protons, are generally negative ions or neutral molecules, although there are a few of such bases (for example, $Zn(H_2O)_3OH^+$) that are positively charged. Basic half reactions of the hydroxide ion, the carbonate ion, aniline, the methoxide ion, γ-pyrone, and acetic acid are listed below:

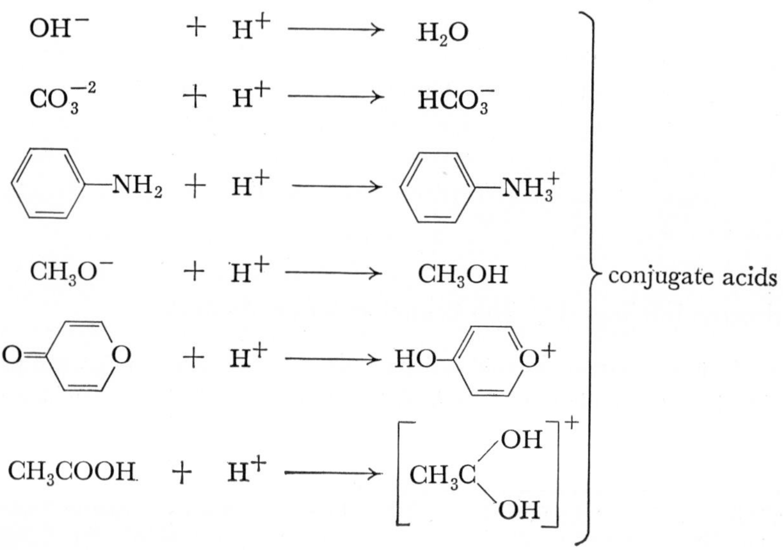

$$OH^- \quad + \; H^+ \longrightarrow H_2O$$

$$CO_3^{-2} \quad + \; H^+ \longrightarrow HCO_3^-$$

} conjugate acids

As indicated, the species formed when a proton is added to a base is called the **conjugate acid** of that base.

A full acid-base reaction is a transfer of a hydrogen ion from an acid to a base, yielding the respective conjugate base and conjugate acid (Table 4-1).

Table 4-1

	Acid	Base		Conjugate Base		Conjugate Acid
1.	H_3O^+	$+ OH^-$	$\rightleftarrows$	H_2O	$+$	H_2O
2.	H_2O	$+ H^-$	$\rightarrow$	OH^-	$+$	H_2
3.	H_2SO_4	$+ H_2O$	$\rightleftarrows$	HSO_4^-	$+$	H_3O^+
4.	CH_3COOH	$+ HCO_3^-$	$\rightleftarrows$	CH_3COO^-	$+$	H_2CO_3
5.	H_2O	$+ H_2O$	$\rightleftarrows$	OH^-	$+$	H_3O^+

We see that water (in common with many hydroxylic solvents) may be either an acid or a base; it may gain or lose a proton, depending upon the presence of other acidic or basic species. Reaction 5 represents the so-called **autoprotolysis** of water; similar "self-ionizations" occur to some extent in other polar solvents, yielding equal quantities of *lyonium* (conjugate acid of the solvent) and *lyate* (conjugate base of the solvent) ions; for example, in methanol[a]

$$2CH_3OH \rightarrow CH_3{-}O{\overset{+H}{\underset{H}{\diagup\diagdown}}} \quad + CH_3O^-. \quad K = (CH_3OH_2^+)(CH_3O^-) = 2 \times 10^{-17}$$

and in formic acid

$$2HCOOH \rightarrow H{-}C{\overset{OH}{\underset{OH}{\diagup\diagdown}}}^+ \quad + HCOO^-.$$

$$K = (HCOOH_2^+)(HCOO^-) = 6 \times 10^{-17}$$

From the manner in which the Brønsted definitions are set up, it follows that very strong acids should have very weak conjugate bases (and vice versa); that is, if the acid HX is stronger than HY, then Y^- will be a stronger base than X^-. (Note, however, that it is possible for HX to be a better acid than HY and also a better base than HY; for example, compare water and acetone.)

[a] The autoprotolysis constants refer to solutions at 25°. These, together with values for other solvents, are given by Hammett in *Physical Organic Chemistry*, McGraw-Hill Book Co., Inc., New York, 1940, p. 256.

The Leveling Effect

When we say that an acid, HA, is "fully ionized" in a solvent S, we mean that its reaction with the solvent is virtually complete, being of the type

$$HA + S \rightarrow HS^+ + A^-$$

We see then that the apparent strength of an acid will depend on the ability of the solvent to accept protons—that is, on the basicity of the solvent. The carboxylic acids, with very few exceptions, are "weak" in water, but they become fully ionized when dissolved in liquid ammonia since their reactions with this very basic solvent are almost complete.

$$RCOOH + NH_3 \rightarrow NH_4^+RCOO^-$$

The extreme basicity of liquid ammonia may be said to exert a **leveling effect** on the apparent strengths of the acids that are dissolved in it. All carboxylic acids have about the same degree of ionization in this solvent, and, moreover, appear to be as strong as the common mineral acids. Experiments in the weaker base, water, show us that the mineral acids are actually the stronger and also allow us to arrange the weaker acids in the order of their strengths. To tell further which of the mineral acids is the strongest, it is necessary to carry out experiments in solvents of even lower basicity, or lower ionizing ability, or both. In methanol, for example, nitric acid is partially ionized,[3] but hydrochloric acid is fully ionized. In anhydrous formic acid, however, HCl becomes partially ionized, whereas the first ionization of sulfuric acid is still virtually complete.[4]

Thus in comparing a number of different acids in the *same* solvent, that acid is strongest which is most ionized. On the other hand, if we compare the acidities of solutions of a single acid in a number of *different* solvents, we should remember that the most strongly acid solution is that in which ionization is *least*. A comparison between the strengths of aqueous HCl and HCl in benzene is often made. In water, the solute is mainly in the form of H_3O^+ and Cl$^-$ ions; that is, the water has, in a sense, "neutralized" the HCl. In benzene, the HCl is practically unionized. If we were to test the two solutions with the same indicator, the indicator would have to compete with the base H_2O for protons in aqueous solutions, but would compete with the much weaker base Cl$^-$ for protons in benzene solution. More of the indicator would then be converted to its conjugate acid in benzene than in water (where the competition is keener), thus showing that the benzene solution is the better proton donor.

[3] Deyrup, *J. Am. Chem. Soc.*, **56**, 60 (1934).
[4] Hammett and Deyrup, *J. Am. Chem. Soc.*, **54**, 4239 (1932).

Very Weak Acids

Among organic compounds there are a number of very weak acids which, even in the basic solvent, ammonia, are not measurably ionized. These may be persuaded to part with H^+ ions only by the stronger negatively charged bases. The most common of such bases is, of course, the OH^- ion, but this is too weak a base to convert many of the very weak organic acids to their own conjugate bases. For such purposes, even stronger bases (that is, conjugate bases of acids weaker than water) are needed. However, the strongest base that can exist in appreciable quantities in aqueous solutions is the OH^- ion; stronger bases will react with water to yield this ion. It then follows that the acidic properties of very weak proton donors may not be observed by experiments in aqueous media. A number of alcohols and amines, however, and some especially acidic hydrocarbons may be converted to their conjugate bases by action of the amide ion, NH_2^-, in liquid ammonia. For acids still weaker than ammonia, proton transfers may be carried out in ethers or hydrocarbons.

The reactions given in Table 4-2 illustrate the conversion of some very weak organic Brønsted acids to their conjugate bases. In (1), acetoacetic ester is converted to its "enolate" ion by ethoxide ion in ethanol. "Deprotonations" of t-butyl alcohol (2), fluorene (3), and diphenylamine (4) may be carried out in liquid ammonia or ether,[5] and the transfer of a proton between the methyl

Table 4-2

Acid	Base	Conjugate Base	Conjugate Acid

^{5} Conant and Wheland, *J. Am. Chem. Soc.*, **54**, 1212 (1932); Kraus and Rosen, *ibid.*, **47**, 2739 (1925); McEwen, *ibid.*, **58**, 1124 (1936).

group of toluene[5] and the sodium salt of the benzene anion may be carried out in hydrocarbon solvents.[6]

Very Weak Bases. Studies in Concentrated Sulfuric Acid

On the other side of the coin, we find a very large number of organic compounds having very weak basicities. Among these are ethers, carboxylic acids, amides, ketones, nitro compounds, and even some aromatic hydrocarbons. Although certain of such compounds are appreciably soluble in water, additions of strong acid to the dilute aqueous solutions result almost exclusively in the formation of H_3O^+, the conjugate acid of water. Since only tiny quantities of the conjugate acids of the weak organic bases are formed under such conditions, it is necessary to observe the basicities in other ways.

The most widely used solvent for studying the basicities of very weak bases is 95 to 100 percent sulfuric acid. Particularly instructive data have arisen from cryoscopic studies in this solvent.[7] The freezing point, 10.36°, of the pure acid lies conveniently between room temperature and "ice-bath" temperature and its cryoscopic constant (over three times that of water) is relatively high. More important, it is the most acidic solvent readily available, and cryoscopic measurements of electrolytes at convenient concentrations turn out to be less subject to large "departures from ideality" than are measurements in aqueous solutions.[8] Somewhat paradoxically, data from such studies are most easily interpreted if the sulfuric acid used is not 100 percent pure but contains about 5 percent or more of water (Ex. 4c).

In such studies, the freezing-point lowering caused by a given solute is compared with that caused by the same concentration of a nondissociated solute; the ratio of the two depressions is the *i factor* or *ν factor* of the solute, representing the average number of separate dissolved particles produced by dissolving one solute "molecule."

Trifluoroacetic acid, sulfuryl chloride (SO_2Cl_2), and perchloric acid, which ionize neither as acids nor bases in sulfuric acid, exhibit *ν* factors very close to unity. On the other hand, substances that behave as simple "monoacid bases" in this solvent show *ν* factors near 2. Their reactions may be represented by

$$B + H_2SO_4 \rightarrow HB^+ + HSO_4^- \qquad (\nu = 2)$$

[6] Schorigin, *Ber.*, **43**, 1938 (1910).

[7] The early work in this field was carried out by Hantzsch and co-workers between 1907 and 1930. This, and further contributions by Hammett and his co-workers, have been summarized (together with pertinent references) by Hammett, Ref. 2, pp. 45–49, 277–283. For a more recent and detailed picture, see Gillespie and Leisten, *Quart. Revs.*, **VIII**, 40 (1954).

[8] The "pseudo-ideal" behavior of convenient concentrations of electrolytes in sulfuric acid is discussed by Brand, James, and Rutherford, *J. Chem. Soc.*, **1953**, 2447.

In this category are: monobasic amines, simple ethers that form cations of the type $\overset{R}{\underset{R'}{>}}\overset{+}{O}-H$, ketones that are converted to acids of the type $\overset{R}{\underset{R'}{>}}\overset{+}{C}-OH$, simple carboxylic acids (but not substituted mesitoic acids) that are converted to cations of the type $R-\overset{+}{C}\overset{OH}{\underset{OH}{<}}$, esters that are protonated to $R-\overset{+}{C}\overset{OH}{\underset{OR'}{<}}$, amides that form cations of the type $R-\overset{+}{C}\overset{OH}{\underset{NR'_2}{<}}$, and many additional compounds with less commonly occurring functional groups. Nitro compounds, cyclic carboxylic anhydrides, and sulfonic acids display ν factors lying between 1 and 2, indicating that these compounds are incompletely converted to their conjugate acids.[9]

Of further interest are a number of compounds that exhibit ν factors greater than 2. In the three cases shown below, the cryoscopic data indicate formation of *carbonium ions* (more will be said about these later).

$$(C_6H_5)_3C-OH + 2H_2SO_4 \longrightarrow (C_6H_5)_3C^+ + H_3O^+ + 2HSO_4^- \quad (\nu=4)^{[10]}$$

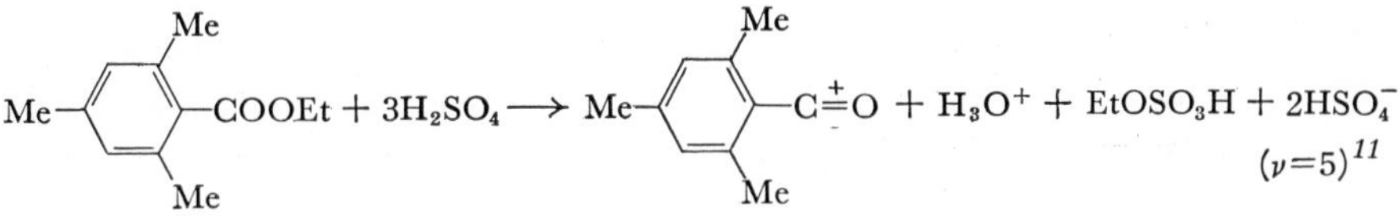

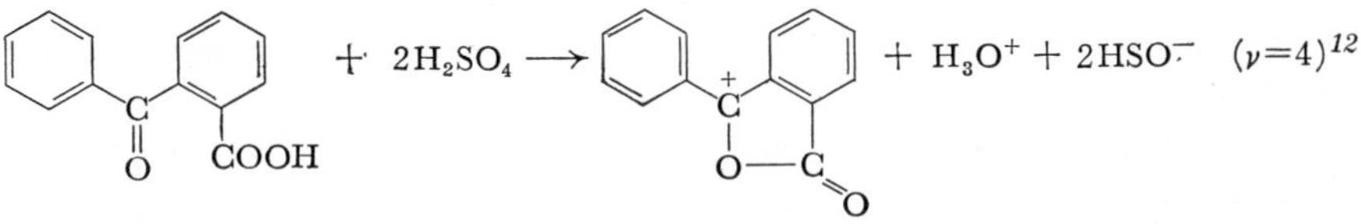

$$Me\text{-}\underset{Me}{\overset{Me}{\bigcirc}}\text{-}COOEt + 3H_2SO_4 \rightarrow Me\text{-}\underset{Me}{\overset{Me}{\bigcirc}}\text{-}C\overset{+}{=}O + H_3O^+ + EtOSO_3H + 2HSO_4^-$$
$$(\nu=5)^{[11]}$$

$+ 2H_2SO_4 \rightarrow$ $+ H_3O^+ + 2HSO^- \quad (\nu=4)^{[12]}$

Although aromatic hydrocarbons having three or more fused rings are soluble in concentrated sulfuric acid, the simpler hydrocarbons are almost insoluble. However, benzene and the methylated benzenes will dissolve in

[9] Gillespie, *J. Chem. Soc.*, **1950**, 2542; Newman and Deno, *J. Am. Chem. Soc.*, **73**, 3561 (1951). See also Gillespie and Leisten, Ref. 4.
[10] Hammett and Deyrup, *J. Am. Chem. Soc.*, **55**, 1900 (1933).
[11] Treffers and Hammett, *ibid.*, **59**, 1758 (1937).
[12] Newman, Kuivila, and Garrett, *ibid.*, **67**, 704 (1945).

absolute hydrofluoric acid, yielding solutions of easily measurable conductivity,[13] indicating that such hydrocarbons are acting as bases in the reaction,

$$ArH + 2HF \rightarrow ArH_2^+ + HF_2^-$$

The hydrocarbons may be recovered by prompt dilution of the hydrofluoric acid solutions with water. The basicity of benzene may be demonstrated in another way; if it is treated with D_2SO_4, deuterium atoms from the deuterosulfuric acid are found to *exchange* with the hydrogen atoms on the ring. This exchange is best interpreted in terms of the equilibria:[14]

$$C_6H_6 + D_2SO_4 \rightleftharpoons \left[+ \left\langle \begin{array}{c} H \\ \\ D \end{array} \right\rangle \right] \rightleftharpoons C_6H_5D + DHSO_4$$

I

Note that the proposed cation intermediate I is the conjugate acid of benzene.

Quantitative Evaluation of Acidity. Concentrations vs. Activities

Comparison of the acidities of a number of solutions in a single solvent system using indicators or potentiometric measurements is generally straightforward, and it is a relatively simple matter for a worker to determine which of two acids is the stronger (provided, of course, both are not weaker acids than the solvent nor so strong that complications due to the leveling effect set in). The results of such comparisons lead to an interesting and important question, "Why are certain acids stronger than others?" Why, for example, should HI be stronger than HF, phenol be stronger than ethanol, formic acid be stronger than acetic acid, and *p*-nitrobenzoic acid be stronger than benzoic acid? Each of these questions concerns the effect of structure on reactivity, a complex subject that will be treated at some length in Chapter 7.

Quite apart from this, however, is the perplexing question of the comparison of acidities in different solvents. In deciding which acid catalyst to use for a given reaction, the chemist frequently faces questions such as, "Which of the three media is more acidic: dilute nitric acid in water, hydrogen chloride in benzene, or anhydrous formic acid?" This type of question poses the double problem of the methods of measurement and the interpretations of such measurements. To those whose early chemical training was based chiefly on the

---

[13] Kilpatrick and Luborski, *J. Am. Chem. Soc.*, **75**, 577 (1953).

[14] Ingold, Raisin, and Wilsin, *J. Chem. Soc.*, **1936**, 1637. It might be argued that the occurrence of exchange does not, in itself, prove the intervention of cation I as an intermediate—that is, that the observed exchange could take place by direct displacement of H^+ by D^+. The latter path is not, however, consistent with our present knowledge of the mechanisms by which similar aromatic substitution reactions occur (Chap. 11).

study of dilute aqueous solutions, for which acidities could be compared merely by comparing H_3O^+ concentrations, it may seem perhaps a little surprising that the quantitative comparison of acidities should become so much more complicated when more than one solvent is considered. However, first let us admit that the evaluation of acidities of aqueous solutions is not ideally simple, for the more convenient methods of estimating hydrogen ions (potentiometric measurements or experiments with indicators) generally yield the *activity*, *a*, of hydrogen ions (a sort of "effective concentration") rather than the true *concentration*, *c*. The ratio of these two quantities, a/c, is the *activity coefficient*, γ. Activities, it will be recalled, are the quantities that must be used in equilibrium constants for reactions in solutions if it is desired that such constants do not vary when extra salts are added. Thus for the ionization of acetic acid in water,

$$HA + H_2O \rightarrow H_3O^+ + A^-$$

$$K_{eq} = \frac{a_{H_3O^+} a_{A^-}}{a_{HA}} = \frac{C_{H_3O^+} C_{A^-}}{C_{HA}} \times \frac{\gamma_{H_3O^+} \gamma_{A^-}}{\gamma_{HA}}$$

(The solvent generally does not appear in equilibrium constants.)

In dilute aqueous solutions, activities lie very close to concentrations; indeed, the activity coefficients of ions may be regarded as measures of departures from the ideal behavior that would prevail at infinitely dilute solutions. In more concentrated solutions, electrostatic attraction between positive and negative ions cuts down the "freedom" of both, causing the activities of ions to fall well *below* their concentrations. For very concentrated solutions, the activities of ions sometimes rise *above* their concentrations; in such cases, a sizable fraction of the water present has been incorporated into the hydration shells surrounding each ion, and there is less water to exert what we may term non-committally (for there is controversy on this point) "normal dilution effects."

Activity coefficients for single ions ordinarily cannot be determined. Instead, *average* activity coefficients for all monovalent ions in a given solution may be calculated by considering all electrolytes present.[15] Activity coefficients for use in a solvent other than water may measure the departure from an ideality represented by infinitely dilute solutions in that solvent or, in favorable instances, a different set of activity coefficients may be derived which represent the departure from an ideality represented by infinitely dilute aqueous solutions.[16] Such a set of coefficients, called *degenerate activity coefficients*, must be evaluated indirectly (p. 107).

[15] The calculation of activity coefficients in dilute aqueous solutions by the Debye-Huckel treatment is described in most physical chemistry textbooks; see, for example, Moore, *Physical Chemistry*, 2d ed., Prentice-Hall, Inc., New York, 1955, p. 461. For treatment of more concentrated solutions, see Harned and Owen, *The Physical Chemistry of Electrolyte Solutions*, Reinhold Publishing Corp., New York, 1950, pp. 40, 341.

[16] Gutbezahl and Grunwald, *J. Am. Chem. Soc.*, **75**, 565 (1953).

Dielectric Constants. Formation of Ion Pairs, Triplets, and other Aggregates

A dilute aqueous solution of a strong electrolyte (which we may arbitrarily designate as A^+B^-) contains solute mainly in the form of ions of the type $A(H_2O)_x^+$ and $B(H_2O)_y^-$. Each ion is thus surrounded by a "hydration shell" of water molecules. Such shells may be several molecules thick; the number of water molecules per ion and the tightness with which they are bound depend upon the cation and anion involved. The ions in such solutions are quite "free" in the classical sense and are often represented simply as A^+ and B^- ions. As we increase the concentration of the electrolyte or, more particularly, if we substitute an electrolyte containing polyvalent ions (such as $A^{+2}B^{-2}$), the percentage of solute existing as free ions falls and more and more of the ions come together, forming relatively small aggregations, the simplest of which is the **ion pair.**[17] Although it is sometimes convenient to represent such pairs as species of the type A^+B^-, it should be remembered that such pairs have associated with them a number of solvent molecules, one or more of which may separate A^+ and B^- within the pair itself. The ion pair will behave as a single particle in its effect on the freezing point and vapor pressure of the solvent; moreover, a solution consisting largely of ion pairs will be a much poorer conductor than would be expected if the solution consisted chiefly of free ions. On the other hand, the spectrum associated with a given ion will be much the same whether the ion is free, is part of a pair, or part of a higher aggregate. In very concentrated aqueous solutions appreciable portions of dissolved electrolytes exist as "ion triplets" (of the type ABA^+ and BAB^-), as "quadruplets," and even as higher polymers. We see then why it is necessary to distinguish between *ionization* and *dissociation*.

Such a distinction is even more important for nonaqueous solutions, for water is almost unique among the solvents commonly used by organic chemists. Table 4-3 lists the *dielectric constants D* (page 59) of a number of solvents.[18] These are rough measures of the relative abilities of the solvents to *facilitate the separation of positive and negative ions in solution*. The dielectric constant of water is about 50 percent greater than that of formic acid, several times as large as those of the lower alcohols and acetone, ten times as large as that of acetic acid, and many times greater than the dielectric constants of ether and benzene. This means that ion association, such as occurs in *concentrated* aqueous solutions,

[17] A detailed picture of ion pairs and higher aggregates is given by Kraus, *J. Phys. Chem.,* **57,** 673 (1954); and by Basolo and Pearson, *Mechanisms of Inorganic Reactions*, John Wiley and Sons, Inc., New York, 1958, pp. 376–385.

[18] These values are taken in large part from Robinson and Stokes, *Electrolytic Solutions*, Butterworth's Scientific Publications, London, 1955, p. 448. Unless otherwise stated, they refer to liquids at 25°.

may occur in *very dilute* solutions of electrolytes in alcohols, ketones, carboxylic acids, or in ethers. Indeed the concentrations of lone ions in such nonaqueous solutions tend to be very small. A strong acid, HA, added to a solvent, S, of low dielectric constant, may well undergo complete ionization to form the conjugate acid of the solvent, but this conjugate acid will be tied up in ion pairs of the type SH^+A^- or in higher aggregates.

Table 4-3. Dielectric Constants of Some Liquids

Liquid	D	Liquid	D
Hydrogen Cyanide	123 (15.6°)	Ethanol	24.2
Formamide	110	Acetone	22
Sulfuric acid	110 (20°)	Acetic acid	7.1
Water	79	Ether	4.5
Formic acid	50	Benzene	2.3
Methanol	31.5	Pentane	1.8

We now appreciate, at least partially, the difficulty encountered in constructing an acidity scale that applies to a number of different solvents and that will measure on a single yardstick the proton-donating abilities of various solutions in various of these solvents. Not only must we compare different acidic species in different media, but we must also consider solutions under conditions where the degree of association of the ions present may vary widely.[19] A single, thermodynamically rigorous acidity scale, applicable to solvents ranging in basicity from sulfuric acid to ammonia (and covering the range of dielectric constants lying between those of liquid hydrogen cyanide and pentane), seems, at present, to be completely out of the question, and even an approximate scale covering a large number of solvent systems is probably too large an order. Nevertheless, more limited success has been achieved in setting up acidity scales covering more modest, but still substantial, ranges in solvent character.

The Use of Indicators in Media of High Acidity. The Hammett h_0 Function.[20]

The most familiar acidity scale for solvent series is that proposed by Hammett, best applicable to acidic media ranging in dielectric constant from about 50 (anhydrous formic acid) to 110 (anhydrous sulfuric acid). This scale makes use of indicators—that is, bases (designated In) that are converted partially by

[19] For a discussion of the problems connected with the construction of acidity scales, see Bates, *Electrometric pH Determinations*, John Wiley and Sons, Inc., New York, 1954, pp. 122–155.

[20] (a) Hammett and Deyrup, *J. Am. Chem. Soc.*, **54**, 2721 (1932). (b) Hammett and Paul, *ibid.*, **56**, 827 (1934). (c) Paul and Long, *Chem. Revs.*, **57**, 1 (1957).

acidic solvents (designated SH) to their conjugate acids (designated InH^+). Success in working with indicators depends upon accurate estimate of the ratio $(InH^+)/(In)$; this is generally done spectrophotometrically or colorometrically. Note that such measurements yield the *ratio* of the *concentrations* of the two forms of the indicator, rather than the ratio of *activities*. For work in very acidic media, very weakly basic indicators (for instance, substituted nitroanilines and azobenzenes) must be used, otherwise the fraction of the indicator present in the basic form, In, becomes too small to measure. For the present discussion, we shall compare indicators by considering the acidity constants of their acid forms (which we shall designate as K_{InH^+} values).

Although we recognize that a given acid ionizing in two different solvents (and perhaps in two different mixtures of the same two solvents) is actually undergoing two different reactions that should have different equilibrium constants, thermodynamics prefers to regard the acidity constant of a given acid at a given temperature as a fixed quantity, independent of solvent. Apparent variations of the acidity constant are then taken as reflections of variations of the activity coefficients of the participating species. Letting a's represent activities, C's represent concentration, and γ's represent activity coefficients, we may write the acidity constant of indicator InH^+ as

$$K_{InH^+} = \frac{a_{H^+} a_{In}}{a_{InH^+}} = \frac{C_{In}}{C_{InH^+}} \times \frac{\gamma_{In}}{\gamma_{InH^+}} \times a_{H^+} \tag{1}$$

or

$$pK_a = \log\left(\frac{C_{InH^+}}{C_{In}}\right) + \log\left(\frac{\gamma_{InH^+}}{\gamma_{In}}\right) - \log a_{H^+} \tag{2}$$

Determination of the pK_a value for an indicator such as p-aminoazobenzene —which is about as basic as the familiar indicator, methyl orange—is straightforward, since the concentrations of both the acidic and basic forms are easily measurable in solutions of dilute acid where the γ values approach 1. Assume that the pK_a value for p-aminoazobenzene has thus been found to be 2.80. Now, consider an HCl solution containing both this indicator (designated In) and the weaker base p-nitroaniline (designated In'). The concentration of acid must be raised in order to convert measurable amounts of the latter amine to the acid form; in which case almost all of the p-aminoazobenzene is converted to its own acid form, leaving only a small (but measurable) amount in the basic form. Expressions such as Equation (2) may be written for both indicators in the solution, then subtracted.

$$pK_a - pK_{a'} = \log\left(\frac{C_{InH^+} C_{In'}}{C_{In} C_{In'H^+}}\right) + \log\left(\frac{\gamma_{InH^+} \gamma_{In'}}{\gamma_{In} \gamma_{In'H^+}}\right) \tag{3}$$

Since the value of pK_a is known and the value of the first term on the right of equation (3) may be estimated colorimetrically, we may calculate $pK_{a'}$ if we know the value of the logarithmic term involving the activity coefficients. It would be particularly convenient if this term were zero; happily it turns out to be negligibly small for the high dielectric-constant media under consideration. In other words, although the ratio $\gamma_{In}/\gamma_{InH^+}$ varies if the medium is changed, the *ratio is nearly the same for all uncharged indicators in a given solution.* Experimentally, this means that the concentration term in equation (3) may be shown to be constant for a number of different acid solutions containing the same two indicators, and from the value of this term we may calculate the value of $pK_{a'}$ (for p-nitroaniline). This turns out to be 1.11; and by carrying out similar measurements with both this base and the still weaker base, 2,4-nitro-chloroaniline, we may show that the apparent difference in the pK_a values for these two very weak bases is 2.02 units in HCl solutions, 2.08 in aqueous HNO$_3$, 1.96 in aqueous H$_2$SO$_4$, and 2.02 in aqueous HClO$_4$. To a rather good approximation, therefore, the difference in the apparent pK_a values of two indicators is independent of the solvent. The procedure may be repeated by comparing, in turn, weaker and weaker bases in solutions that are more and more strongly acid, arriving ultimately at bases so weak that only concentrated sulfuric acid will convert appreciable fractions to the respective conjugate acids. The least basic of Hammett's indicators is picramide (2,4,6-trinitro-aniline) whose pK_a value is -9.29, about 12 units less than pK_a for p-amino-azobenzene. Typical intermediate indicators are p-nitroazobenzene (pK_a, -3.3), benzalacetophenone (pK, -5.6), and anthraquinone (pK, -8.2) (note that the very weak bases have very negative pK_a values).

To understand the acidity scale that is constructed with these indicator constants, let us rewrite equation (1):

$$a_{H^+} = K_{InH^+} \frac{C_{InH^+}}{C_{In}} \frac{\gamma_{InH^+}}{\gamma_{In}} \tag{4}$$

In a solution containing measurable amounts of the two forms of an indicator whose constant is known, we are prevented from calculating the activity of hydrogen ions by our ignorance of the value of $\gamma_{InH^+}/\gamma_{In}$. However, since this ratio, to a very good approximation, is independent of the indicator used but is characteristic of the medium, the quantity $a_{H^+} \frac{\gamma_{In}}{\gamma_{InH^+}}$ (which may be abbreviated h_0) is a property of the solution in much the same sense as in a_{H^+} itself. Moreover h_0 is measurable whereas a_{H^+} is not. We see also from the equation defining h_0,

$$h_0 = a_{H^+} \frac{\gamma_{In}}{\gamma_{InH^+}} = K_{InH^+} \frac{c_{InH^+}}{c_{In}} \tag{5}$$

that it is a measure (in terms of concentrations rather than activities) of the ability of a solution to convert a neutral basic molecule to its conjugate acid, since h_0 is proportional to the ratio of concentrations of the acidic and basic forms of the indicator. Note also that h_0 becomes identical to a_{H^+} in very dilute aqueous solutions where the γ values approach unity. The properties of h_0 thus make it a rather useful quantitative measure of the relative proton-donating abilities of solutions of high dielectric constant and high acidity. The quantity H_0 is defined by Hammett (in analogy to pH for hydrogen-ion activity) as $-\log h_0$. Typical H_0 values are: $+7.0$ for water, -1.5 for 6 molal HNO_3, -2.0 for 6.9 molal HCl, -2.63 for 8 molal $HClO_4$ (and about the same for 8 molal H_2SO_4), -5.54 for 70 percent H_2SO_4, and -10.60 for 100 percent H_2SO_4. (On this basis 100 percent sulfuric acid is over 100,000 times as efficient a proton donor as 70 percent sulfuric acid.)

In order that the same acidity scale measure also the ability of a solution to donate a proton to a *negatively charged* base A^-, it would be necessary that the ratio γ_{HA}/γ_{A^-} for negative bases be equal to the ratio γ_{BH^+}/γ_B for neutral bases in a given solution. Since these two ratios are *practically never the same*, we might then ask, "Is there a different but analogous acidity function that measures the ability of a solution to protonate negative ions?" Such a function, designated by H_- (in analogy to H_0 for acidity toward neutral bases), was proposed by Hammett over twenty-five years ago, but it is still an open question as to whether a useful H_- scale can be constructed. The ratio γ_{HA}/γ_{A^-} varies greatly with the structure of the anion in ethanol-water solutions,[16] and similar variations occur for neutral acids in mixtures of isopropyl alcohol and ethanol[21] and almost certainly for acids in solvents of even lower dielectric constant. An H_- scale then, if it can be constructed at all, must apply (as does the H_0 scale) to solutions of high dielectric constant. Indicators of the charge type In^- would be converted very nearly completely to their conjugate acids by the more acidic of such solvents (for example, H_2SO_4, HF, and HCOOH), but measurable amounts of both forms of the indicators should exist in hydrazine, formamide, dimethyl sulfoxide, and in aqueous solutions of these. An H_- scale has been set up by Deno[22] for mixtures of water and hydrazine, using as indicators such uncharged weak acids as 3-nitrocarbazole (II), 4,4'-dinitrodiphenylmethane (III), and p-nitrobenzeneazoresorcinol (IV), proceeding successively from indicator to indicator and from solution to solution in the same manner as was described for the construction of Hammett's H_0 scale. The H_- value for pure water is 7.0, whereas the values for 30 and 60 percent hydrazine have been found to be 13.15 and 15.93, respectively. Thus, 30 percent hydrazine is almost a thousand times as effective a proton donor (to negatively charged bases) as is 60 percent hydrazine. Deno's scale, however, cannot be said to be general, for it is based on measurements involving only a single pair of solvents.[23]

[21] Hine and Hine, *J. Am. Chem. Soc.*, **74**, 5266 (1952).

II

III

IV

The Grunwald Acidity Scale

The Grunwald scale[24] is one of the more interesting acidity scales proposed during recent years, although it has been applied to organic systems in only a very few cases (see, for example, p. 192) and although its theoretical basis appears somewhat less firm than that of the Hammett scale. This scale correlates acidities in mixtures of ethanol and water, thus covering a range of dielectric constants between 24 and 79. The data on which this scale is based are a collection of acidity constants for a number of carboxylic acids and for a number of substituted ammonium and anilinium ions in ethanol, in water, and in various mixtures of the two solvents.

The carboxylic acids are more fully ionized in water than in ethanol; their ionization involves separation of charge and this is greatly facilitated in the medium of higher dielectric constant. On the other hand, the acidities of the substituted ammonium ions show considerably less variation with solvent. The acid reactions of these ions,

$$BH^+ + S \rightarrow SH^+ + B$$

involves no marked separation of charge and is thus far less sensitive to variation in the ionizing power of the solvent.[25]

---

[22] Deno, J. Am. Chem. Soc., **74**, 2039 (1952).

[23] The same criticism may be directed toward the high-acidity end of Hammett's H_0 scale, for the H_0 values between -4.5 and -9.3 were established by measurements in only one pair of solvents—sulfuric acid and water. Moreover, an attempt by Schwarzenbach and Sulzberger, *Helv. Chim. Acta*, **27**, 348 (1944), to establish an H_- scale solely by measurements in aqueous solutions is subject to the same objection.

[24] See Grunwald, J. Am. Chem. Soc., **73**, 4934 (1951); Grunwald and Berkowitz, *ibid.*, **73**, 4939 (1951); Gutbezahl and Grunwald, *ibid.*, **75**, 559, 565 (1953).

[25] The trends in the acidities of substituted ammonium ions with solvent composition are not simple. Certain of these ions (for example, anilinium and *p*-toluidinium ions) exhibit higher acidity constants in water than in ethanol, whereas the reverse is true for others (for

Each of the acidity constants, designated K_A, is compared with the constant for the same acid in pure water, designated K_A^W, using for such comparisons the *logarithms* of the constants. The constants for the carboxylic acids were found to fit nicely into a relationship

$$\log K_W^A - \log K_A = \log f + m_A Y_-$$

or, using the familiar abbreviation whereby pA is defined as $-\log A$,

$$pK_A - pK_A^W = \log f + m_A Y_- \tag{6}$$

Here, m_A is a constant depending on the acid being considered, and f and Y_- are constants depending upon the solvent being considered. The term, m_A, is a rough measure of the sensitivity of the acid to changes in the ionizing power of the solvent mixture. For benzoic acid, whose pK value changes 2.59 units in going from water to 80 percent ethanol, m_A is 1.57; for formic acid, whose pK value changes only 1.89 units as a result of a similar change in solvent, m_A is 0.77. The quantity, Y_-, called by Grunwald an *activity function*, is in essence a measure of the relative ability of the solvent mixture to repress ionization of —COOH groups; typically, Y_- is 0.35 for 20 percent ethanol but 0.96 for 80 percent ethanol. (The significance of $\log f$ will become clear in a moment.) The acidity constants of the substituted ammonium and anilinium ions obey a similar relationship; that is,

$$pK_{BH} - pK_{BH}^W = \log f + m_{BH} Y_0 \tag{7}$$

Again, m_{BH} is a constant associated with a particular ammonium or anilinium ion, and Y_0 and f depend upon the solvent. The Y terms are different for the two types of Brønsted acids, indicating, as expected, that the relative abilities of the various solvent mixtures to repress ionization of —COOH groups are not linearly related to the relative abilities to repress the ionization of the various substituted ammonium ions (the subscripts indicate simply that the conjugate bases of the carboxylic acids are negatively charged whereas those from the ammonium salts are uncharged). It is important, however, that the f terms, which at first glance might appear to have been included merely "to make the answer come out right," *are the same for both series of acids;* that is, f is a function only of the solvent system. Equations (6) and (7) are *extrathermodynamic relationships;* that is, thermodynamics does not predict them and they are almost certainly approximate.

---

example, N, N-dimethylanilinium and m-toluidinium ions). Maximum values for the constants of a number of such ions are observed in solutions containing from 70 to 80 percent ethanol, but these maxima, so far as the present author knows, have not been simply explained. What should be emphasized is that there is likely to be little more than a 10-fold variation in the acidity constants of substituted ammonium ions in going from ethanol to water, in contrast to the 100,000-fold increases in the constants of carboxylic acids in going from ethanol to water.

The thermodynamic relationship proposed to relate "apparent ionization constants" in these mixtures to the ionization constants in dilute aqueous solutions is

$$K_A^W = \left(\frac{C_{H^+}C_{A^-}}{C_{HA}}\right) \times \left(\frac{\gamma_{H^+}\gamma_{A^-}}{\gamma_{HA}}\right) \times \left(\frac{\gamma'_{H^+}\gamma'_{A^-}}{\gamma'_{HA}}\right) = K_A\gamma'_{H^+} \times \left(\frac{\gamma'_{A^-}}{\gamma'_{HA}}\right) \qquad (8)$$

Note the *two* sets of activity coefficients; the γ terms convert the concentrations of the species (C values) to their activities (referred to very dilute solutions *in the solvent itself*). These coefficients for the ions may be readily calculated by the Debye-Huckel treatment, and the γ value for HA is assumed to be unity; hence, these terms need not concern us further. The γ' terms, which further link the activities of the species in the solvent at hand to the activities of the corresponding species *in very dilute aqueous solutions*, are the designated "degenerate activity coefficients." If we assume that the latter have meaning (an opinion which is by no means unanimous), it becomes interesting to rewrite equation (8) in the logarithmic form,

$$pK_A - pK_A^W = \log \gamma'_{H^+} + \log\left[\frac{\gamma'_{A^-}}{\gamma'_{HA}}\right] \qquad (9)$$

Comparing Equations (9) and (6), we see that $(\log f + m_A Y_-)$ is equal to $\left(\log \gamma'_{H^+} + \log \frac{\gamma'_{A^-}}{\gamma'_{HA}}\right)$. Moreover, the two expressions have the same form; one term of each ($\log f$ and $\log \gamma'_{H^+}$) is independent of the acid under consideration but depends only on the solvent. The other term in each of the expressions depends not only on the *type* of acid but also on the particular acid being treated. A completely analogous argument applied to the substituted ammonium and anilinium salts shows that for these $(\log f + Y_0 m_{HB})$ equals $\left(\log \gamma'_{H^+} + \log \frac{\gamma'_B}{\gamma'_{HB}}\right)$, and again we may note the same correspondence in the nature of the terms in the two expressions. Since the properties of the series of empirical $\log f$ values are the same as those expected from a series of $\log \gamma'_{H^+}$ values (independence of the nature of the acid considered, approach to 0 for 100 percent water, and quantitative correlation of pK values), Grunwald's scale makes use of these f values in the same way that one would make use of activity coefficients.[26] These then are the values by which hydrogen-ion activities in the various solvent mixtures must be multiplied to fit them to the same "proton-donating-ability scale" as is represented by the scale of H_3O^+ activities in water. Typically, hydrogen-ion degenerate activity coefficients for 65 and 80 percent ethanol are

[26] The arguments showing that f and γ'_{H^+} are actually equal (or nearly equal) are somewhat involved and are strongly indicative rather than rigorously conclusive. For these, see Ref. 16.

found to be 3.6 and 14.2, respectively. This means that a solution in 65 percent EtOH, having a total lyonium ion $(H_3O^+ + EtOH_2^+)$ concentration of 0.01 molar, is approximately 3.6 times as efficient a proton donor as is aqueous 0.01 molar HCl, whereas a similar solution in 80 percent ethanol is approximately 14 times as efficient. These high activity coefficients are quantitative reflections of a trend that has already been noted (p. 96); that is, a given acid is strongest in the solvent of least basicity.

Acid-base Catalysis

To the organic chemist, it would be difficult to overemphasize the importance of acid-catalyzed and base-catalyzed reactions. Among the many reactions falling into these two very broad categories are the saponification, hydrolysis, and synthesis of countless esters and amides, the hydrolysis of anhydrides and alkyl and acyl halides, the bulk of carbonyl-addition reactions, and the aldol, Claisen, Perkin, and Michael condensations. Of the 76 chapters describing reactions of general utility in the eight volumes of *Organic Reactions*, almost half are devoted to reactions that are catalyzed by acids, by bases, or by both.[27]

The strongest acid that can exist in large concentrations in a given solvent is the conjugate acid derived from that solvent (the lyonium ion). This is generally the most effective acid catalyst for reactions carried out in the solvent. Often it appears to be the only effective acid catalyst, and weak acids that are present appear to accelerate the reaction only to the extent that they convert the solvent to the lyonium ion. Such reactions are said to be subject to *specific lyonium-ion catalysis* (or, for aqueous solutions, in which the large majority of quantitative studies have been carried out, *specific hydronium-ion catalysis*.) Among these are the acid hydrolyses of a number of esters and acetals. One of the earliest reactions of this type to be examined was the hydrolysis of diethyl acetal, $CH_3CH(OC_2H_5)_2$, in formic acid-sodium formate buffer solutions.[28] The formic acid concentration in a number of such solutions was varied from 0.02 to 0.18 molar, but the *ratio* $(HCOOH/HCOO^-)$ was held at 2.96; enough sodium chloride was added to each solution to bring the total concentration of positive ions to 0.100, keeping activity coefficient effects for all solutions the same. Each solution thus had the same H_3O^+ concentration, and it was further found that the *rate of acetal hydrolysis was, within experimental error, the same in each.* (Note, however, that the concentration of formic acid was relatively low, even in the most concentrated of the solutions.)

[27] For a detailed discussion of this subject, see Bell, *Acid-base Catalysis*, Oxford University Press, Oxford, 1941. For a shorter but somewhat more recent view, see Frost and Pearson, *Kinetics and Mechanism*, John Wiley and Sons, Inc., New York, 1953, pp. 204–220.

[28] Brønsted and Wynne-Jones, *Trans. Faraday Soc.*, **25,** 59 (1929).

Similarly, a number of base-catalyzed reactions appear to be catalyzed specifically by the conjugate base of the solvent in which they are carried out. Among these are the ring closure of β-styrene chlorohydrin, C_6H_5—CH—CH_2Cl,
$$\overset{\displaystyle |}{OH}$$
to the oxide, C_6H_5—CH———CH_2, in water[29] and the formation of benzalaceto-
$$\overset{\diagdown\;\diagup}{\underset{O}{}}$$
phenone, C_6H_5CH=CH—C—C_6H_5, from benzaldehyde and acetophenone in
$$\overset{\parallel}{O}$$
ethanol.[30] These reactions are said to be subject to *specific lyate-ion (hydroxide- or ethoxide-ion) catalysis.*

On the other hand, a large number of reactions suffer either *general acid* or *general base catalysis.* Consider for example the rate of hydrolysis of ethyl orthoacetate, $CH_3C(OC_2H_5)_3$, in a series of buffers derived from *m*-nitrophenol and its sodium salt. This rate increases as the concentration of the phenol is increased—even under conditions where both (H_3O^+) and total ionic strength are kept constant—showing that this hydrolysis, in contrast to the hydrolysis of diethyl acetal described above, is catalyzed by *m*-nitrophenol (and, presumably, by other acids), as well as by H_3O^+.[28] A somewhat analogous experiment in basic catalysis is the bromination of bromoacetylacetone,

$$BrCH_2\text{—}\overset{\parallel}{\underset{O}{C}}\text{—}CH_2\text{—}\overset{\parallel}{\underset{O}{C}}\text{—}CH_3,$$

in buffers of chloroacetic acid and its sodium salt.[31] This reaction is catalyzed not only by OH^-, but also by chloroacetate ion and by water. The halogenations of several additional ketones are also subject to general basic catalysis and some are subject to general acid catalysis as well. Of particular interest is the mutarotation of glucose, which is catalyzed by acids and by bases,[32] but even more effectively when both an acidic and basic center are appropriately located in the same molecule[33] (see p. 139).

Catalysis by more than one acid or base in a given solution complicates the kinetic picture. For a reaction between species X and Y (first order in both) and subject to *specific* hydronium-ion catalysis, the rate expression will generally be of the form:

$$\text{rate} = k(X)(Y)(H_3O^+) \qquad (10)$$

[29] Bergkvist, *Svensk Kem. Tid.,* **59,** 194, 244 (1947).
[30] Coombs and Evans, *J. Chem. Soc.,* **1940,** 1295.
[31] Bell, Gelles, and Moller, *Proc. Roy. Soc.* (London), **A198,** 308 (1949).
[32] Brønsted and Guggenheim, *J. Am. Chem. Soc.,* **49,** 2554 (1927).
[33] Swain and Brown, *J. Am. Chem. Soc.,* **74,** 2538 (1952).

whereas if general acid catalysis prevails, the observed rate will be the sum of terms, each corresponding to one of the acids present in solution.

$$\text{rate} = (X)(Y)[k_{H_3O^+}(H_3O^+) + k_{H_2O}(H_2O) + k_{HA}(HA) + k_{HA'}(HA') \cdots] \tag{11}$$

Here the k values are *catalytic constants* for the reaction at hand, one constant being associated with each of the various acidic species present in solution. (Analogous expressions may be written for the rates of reactions subject to general basic catalysis.) The stronger the acid, the higher is its catalytic constant for a given acid-catalyzed reaction, but, as we shall see, the relationship between ionization constants and catalytic potencies of acids is logarithmic rather than linear. If the reaction is subject to both general acid and general base catalysis, the kinetics may be even more complex.

In attempting to distinguish general acid catalysis from specific hydronium-ion catalysis, it is important that kinetic experiments be extended to solutions in which the total concentration of the weaker acid or acids heavily exceeds the concentration of hydronium ion. The opening of the epoxide ring of epichloro-hydrin by iodide ion in acetic acid-acetate buffers

$$I^- + CH_2\underset{\diagdown O \diagup}{-\!\!-}CH-CH_2Cl \xrightarrow{HA} ICH_2-CH-CH_2Cl + A^- \tag{12}$$
$$\hspace{6cm} | \hspace{2.2cm}$$
$$\hspace{6cm} OH \hspace{2cm}$$

might appear to be catalyzed only by H_3O^+ if fairly rough measurements are carried out on solutions in which the ratio $(HOAc)/(H_3O^+)$ is less than 1000; but if this ratio is boosted to about 100,000 by using higher concentrations of buffer, catalysis by unionized HOAc becomes clearly evident.[34] It is likewise possible that other reactions that appear subject to specific catalysis would, if examined at higher buffer concentrations, show evidence of general catalysis.

The possible reaction mechanisms suggested by the various types of acid and base catalysis will be considered after the fundamentals of kinetics have been briefly reviewed in Chapter 6. At that point there will also be discussed the closely related question as to why the rates of some acid-catalyzed reactions are governed by the concentration of H_3O^+ ions whereas others depend upon the Hammett H_0 function.

[34] Swain, *J. Am. Chem. Soc.*, **74**, 4108 (1952). Since there is a net conversion of the acid HA to its conjugate base A^- during this reaction, it cannot be said actually to be acid catalyzed in the classical sense. However, the reaction is otherwise very similar to true acid-catalyzed reactions such as the hydrolysis of acetals and the formation of semicarbazones and is conveniently considered along with these. Similarly, we often refer to the "base-catalyzed" halogenations of ketones even though the base consumed in one step of the reactions is *not* regenerated in subsequent steps.

The Brønsted Catalysis Law

We have seen that for a reaction subject to general acid (or general base) catalysis, the strongest acids (or strongest bases) generally are the best catalysts. Typically, the dehydration of acetaldehyde hydrate,

$$CH_3CH(OH)_2 \xrightarrow{HA} CH_3CHO + H_2O$$

has been found to be catalyzed by 32 carboxylic acids.[35] Catalytic constants (in liters per mole-minute at 25°) associated with three typical acids are:

Acid	K_a	$k_{cat.}$ (liters per mole-min)
Propionic	1.35×10^{-5}	18.0
Phenoxyacetic	7.6×10^{-4}	92.0
Dichloroacetic	5.0×10^{-2}	773

If the logarithms of the catalytic constants for the 32 acids be plotted against the respective pK_a *values, the points are found to lie very close to a straight line.* Similar plots for other reactions subject to general acid catalysis also yield points lying near straight lines although the slopes of such lines vary from reaction to reaction. For general base catalysis, similar linear relationships exist between the logarithms of the catalytic constants for a given reaction and the pK_b values of the various basic catalysts. Again, the slope of the line representing such a relationship will depend upon the particular reaction under consideration.

Mathematically, this type of relationship may be expressed

$$\log k_{cat.} = a \log K_a + b \tag{13}$$

where the constant a is the slope of the line and the constant b an axial intercept, (actually the value of the catalytic constant, $k_{cat.}$, for a hypothetical acid whose dissociation constant is unity). This, together with a similar expression for base catalysis, constitutes the **Brønsted catalysis law.** It is subject to two limitations. First, and most important, the relationships hold only if the catalytic action of acids or bases of the "same type" are being compared. For example, aliphatic nitro compounds and β-diketones (weak acids with strengths comparable to those of the less acidic phenols) will also catalyze the dehydration of acetaldehyde hydrate, but their catalytic constants are less than one twentieth those for phenols of comparable acidities. On the other hand, the catalytic constants of ketoximes are over twenty times those that would be predicted from the Brønsted catalysis law using a and b parameters derived from the data on carboxylic acids. The same is true for reactions subject to general base catalysis; although equation (13) may apply to catalysis both by carboxylate ions and by

[35] Bell and Higginson, *Proc. Roy. Soc.* (London), **A197**, 141 (1949).

substituted anilines, we should expect different a and b parameters for the two types of bases.

A second stipulation concerns statistical corrections that sometimes must be applied to acidity or basicity constants. For example, even though the acid constant of benzoic acid (6.3×10^{-5}) is about twice that of the hydrogen fumarate anion (V) ($K_a = 3 \times 10^{-5}$), it might be argued that the proton-donating abilities of the two acids are nearly equal. The acidity constant may be regarded as the ratio of rate constants for the forward (proton-leaving) and reverse (proton-returning) reactions. Now the conjugate base of the hydrogen fumarate ion has four oxygens to which a proton may return, whereas the benzoate ion

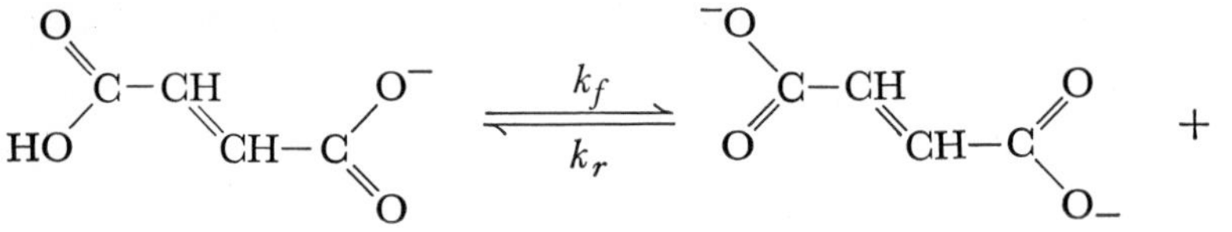

V

has only two such oxygens. This twofold statistical advantage for proton return to the fumarate ion results in a twofold lowering of the acidity constant of its conjugate acid. Since this effect is not, however, connected with the act of proton leaving, a "fair" comparison between the proton-donating ability of the hydrogen fumarate ion and that of any monocarboxylic acid requires that the ionization constant of the former by multiplied by 2. By the same argument, the basicity constant of an ion such as $H_2N-CH_2-CH_2-NH_3^+$ should be doubled if a Brønsted law relationship being set up also involves monofunctional amines.[36]

At first glance, it might be suspected that a log-log relationship such as the Brønsted catalysis law was drawn up by a worker who felt that there must surely be some type of quantitative relationship between the catalytic constants of acids for a given reaction and their ionization constants, but who found that simple linear, quadratic, cubic, and various other algebraic relationships did not hold. If this were so, the Brønsted relationship would be of very limited interest. Let us recall, however, that the logarithm of a dissociation constant is proportional to the *free energy of dissociation*. Furthermore, in Chapter 6 it will be shown that the logarithm of the catalytic constant is proportional to the free energy of the initial proton-transfer step in a reaction subject to general acid or general base catalysis. The Brønsted catalysis law is then a *linear rela-*

---

[36] Using similar reasoning, acid catalysis by phenols may be compared with acid catalysis by monobasic carboxylic acids by doubling the acidity constants of the latter group. For the acid-catalyzed dehydration of acetaldehyde hydrate (Ref. 35), Brønsted law plots for catalyses by the two groups of acids fall surprisingly close to the same straight lines after this statistical correction is made. However, it should be noted that in the limited range for which the pK values of these two classes of acids overlap, the substituted phenols are appreciably more effective catalysts than are the fatty acids.

tionship between free energies—the first of such relationships that we have encountered in this text, and also chronologically the first significant relationship of this type proposed. Linear free-energy relationships will be further discussed in Chapter 7.

Electron-pair Transfer. The Lewis Acid-base System

A more general interpretation of acid-base behavior was proposed by G. N. Lewis in 1923[37] and has become widely adopted since then, most especially for descriptions of reactions in nonhydroxylic solvents. We have seen that a proton is acidic because it may become bound to a basic species through an unshared electron pair on the latter. However, a number of additional ions and molecules (which we may call *electron-pair acceptors*) may likewise attach themselves to the unshared electron pairs of bases. Lewis proposed that all such acceptors be termed acids and that an acid-base reaction be simply *the donation of a pair of electrons from the base to the acid.*

Lewis acids are of several types. First, there are a number of compounds in which one atom has *less than a full octet of electrons*. Typical members of this class are trimethylboron, boron trifluoride, and sulfur trioxide. The reaction of these acids with the *Lewis bases*, ammonia, ether, and pyridine are shown below:

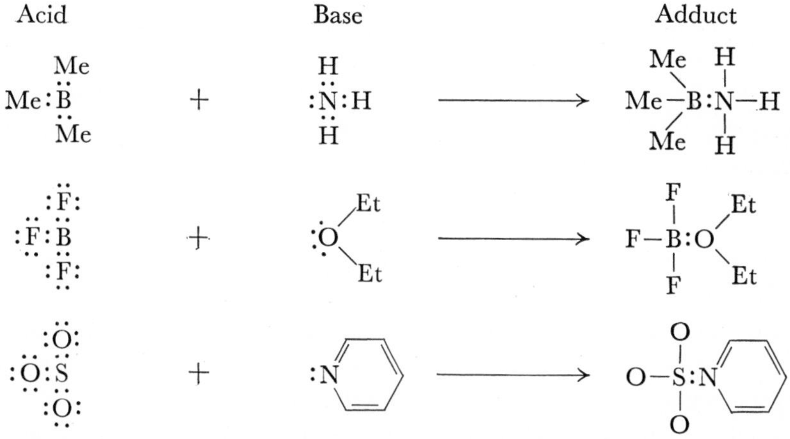

Acid		Base		Adduct

In two of these acids, the boron atoms are "*electron deficient*"; that is, they have six valence electrons instead of the maximum eight. Similarly, the sulfur atom in SO_3 is *electron poor*. Since the acidic species become affixed to electron-rich sites on the basic molecules, Lewis acids are often said to be **electrophilic** (electron-seeking) **reagents** or, simply, **electrophiles**. Similarly, basic species

[37] Lewis, *Valence and the Structure of Atoms and Molecules*, Chemical Catalog Co., New York, 1923, p. 141.

are often called **nucleophilic reagents** or **nucleophiles** since they generally attack another molecule at a site where the atomic nucleus is poorly shielded by the outer electrons.

Positive ions may also be regarded as Lewis acids. Typically, the lithium and silver ions will react with methanol and ammonia, respectively:

Acid	Base	Adduct

$$Li^+ \quad + \quad :\!\overset{\displaystyle Me}{\underset{\displaystyle H}{O}} \quad \longrightarrow \quad \left[Li\!:\!\overset{\displaystyle Me}{\underset{\displaystyle H}{O}} \right]^+$$

$$Ag^+ \quad + \quad \overset{\displaystyle H}{\underset{\displaystyle H}{:\!N\!:\!H}} \quad \longrightarrow \quad \left[Ag\!:\!\overset{\displaystyle H}{\underset{\displaystyle H}{N\!-\!H}} \right]^+$$

(In both of the reactions above, more than one molecule of base may coordinate with the acidic cation.) In aqueous solutions, many positive ions, particularly polyvalent ions, are strongly hydrated and are thus Brønsted acids. The salts of tripositive iron, for example, form the ion $Fe(H_2O)_6^{+3}$, an acid whose dissociation constant in water is close to that for H_3PO_4.

$$Fe(H_2O)_6^{+3} + H_2O \rightarrow Fe(H_2O)_5(OH)^{+2} + H_3O^+ \qquad K = 0.006$$

Of particular importance in organic chemistry is a group of positive ions (not derived from metals), the salts of which, although not unknown, are not generally found in ordinary chemistry laboratories. Among these are the nitronium ion (NO_2^+), the nitrosonium ion (NO^+), the bromonium ion ($:\overset{..}{\underset{..}{Br}}$), and the various acylium ions ($R\!-\!\overset{+}{C}\!=\!O$). All of these are thought to be active intermediates in aromatic substitution reactions (Chap. 11).

Certain halides in which the central atom may hold more than an octet of electrons may show acidic properties. Tin (IV) chloride combines with ethanol to form the addition compound $SnCl_4 \cdot 2EtOH$,[38] whereas titanium (IV) chloride forms adducts with ethers at low temperatures.[39] Although the structural formulas of $SnCl_4$ and $TiCl_4$ might tend to put them in the same class as the tetrahalides of carbon (which are nonacidic), it should be remembered that associated with both tin and titanium there are vacant d orbitals of relatively low energies. These may be used in bond formation with donor molecules. Similarly, the pentahalides of niobium and tantalum form addition compounds

[38] Thiessen and Koerner, *Z. anorg. Chem.*, **195**, 88 (1931).
[39] Stadnikov and Kaschanov, *Ber.*, **61**, 1389 (1928).

with benzene and naphthalene, respectively.[40] Elemental iodine may also be considered with such Lewis acids, for the I_2 molecule coordinates with many basic solvents, as evidenced by the familiar change in color when violet solutions of iodine in CCl_4 or aliphatic hydrocarbons are diluted with alcohols, ethers, or amines.

In a similar sense, compounds having C=O, C=N, or N=O double bonds or C≡N triple bonds are electrophilic. Although the Lewis classification in its original form did not specifically regard compounds such as acetone or benzonitrile as acids, we see from reactions (14) and (15) that they accept electron pairs from basic species in the process of coordination. The rate-determining step in the conversion of acetone to its oxime in basic media is probably the attack by the conjugate base of hydroxylamine, HO—NH⁻, on the C=O double bond, reaction (14),[41] whereas the initial step in the basic hydrolysis of nitriles is almost certainly the attack by OH⁻ on the C≡N triple bond (15).

Base	Acid	Adduct

$$\text{HO}-\overset{\text{H}}{\underset{..}{\text{N}}}\text{:} \quad + \quad \overset{\text{Me}}{\underset{\text{Me}}{}}\text{C}=\text{O:} \quad \longrightarrow \quad \left[\text{HO}-\overset{\text{H}}{\underset{|}{\text{N}}}-\overset{\text{Me}}{\underset{\text{Me}}{\text{C}}}-\ddot{\text{O}}\text{:}\right]^- \quad (14)$$

$$\text{H}\ddot{\text{O}}\text{:}^- \quad + \quad \text{R}-\text{C}\equiv\text{N:} \quad \longrightarrow \quad \left[\overset{\text{OH}}{\underset{|}{\text{R}-\text{C}}}=\ddot{\text{N}}\right]^- \quad (15)$$

Even the simple neutralization of aqueous CO_2 may be regarded in the same way:

$$\text{H:}\ddot{\text{O}}\text{:}^- \quad + \quad \text{O}=\text{C}=\text{O} \quad \longrightarrow \quad \left[\overset{\text{OH}}{\underset{|}{\text{O}=\text{C}}}-\ddot{\text{O}}\text{:}\right]^-$$

Note that in such cases the base attacks the *more positive* member of the double- (or triple-) bonded pair of atoms and pushes a π-electron to the more negative member.

A C=C double bond does not generally act as an acidic site unless electron density has been withdrawn from it by an *electron-attracting group* (Chap. 7) situated nearby. The most important class of acidic C=C double bonds are those conjugated with carbonyl groups. These are attacked by a number of anions; in the familiar Michael reaction, a *carbanion* such as the conjugate base of malonic ester is the basic reagent (16). Fluorinated olefins may also suffer

[40] Funk and Niederlander, *Ber.* **61B**, 1385 (1928).
[41] Olander, *Z. physik Chem.*, **129**, 1 (1927).

attack by anions, such as occurs in the initial step of the base-catalyzed addition of ethanol to tetrafluoroethylene (17).[42]

Base	Acid	Adduct

$$\text{(EtOOC)}_2\overset{\overset{\displaystyle H}{|}}{\text{C}}: \;+\; \text{R}-\text{CH}=\text{CH}-\overset{\overset{}{\underset{\underset{\displaystyle O}{\|}}{}}{\text{C}}-\text{R}' \longrightarrow \text{R}-\overset{\overset{\displaystyle \text{CH(COOEt)}_2}{|}}{\text{CH}}-\text{CH}=\underset{\underset{\displaystyle O-}{|}}{\text{C}}-\text{R}' \quad (16)$$

$$\text{EtO}^- \;+\; \text{CF}_2=\text{CF}_2 \longrightarrow \text{EtO}-\text{CF}_2-\overline{\text{C}}\text{F}_2 \quad (17)$$

Although the Lewis system allows many species besides the hydrogen ion to display acidic behavior, the species acting as bases under this system are largely those that behave also as Brønsted bases. The important nucleophilic reagents fall into three broad classes:

(a) Molecules in which fifth- or sixth-group elements have unshared electron pairs (such as, amines, alcohols, ethers, and mercaptans).
(b) Negative ions (for instance, halide, hydroxide, alkoxide, sulfide ions, and carbanions).
(c) Olefins and aromatic hydrocarbons.

The basic behavior of olefins and aromatic hydrocarbons assumes somewhat more importance in the Lewis system than in the Brønsted system. We have seen (p. 100) that the basicity of aromatic hydrocarbons toward the H^+ ion is indicated by evidence of an indirect sort, and the same might be said for the Brønsted basicity of olefins. On the other hand, a substantial number of addition compounds of olefins or aromatic hydrocarbons with metal salts have been isolated.[43] Typical adducts of this type are: $(CH_3)_2C=CHCH_3 \cdot ZnCl_2$,[44] $(C_2H_4)_2 \cdot PtCl_2$,[45] $C_6H_6 \cdot AgClO_4$,[46] and $C_6H_5-CH=CH-C_6H_5 \cdot 2FeCl_3$.[47] In these, the positive metal ion is presumably linked in some way to the unsaturated site in the hydrocarbon molecule. In the benzene-silver perchlorate addition compound, the silver ion is not bonded to a particular carbon but rather is located equidistant from two carbon atoms, sitting, in effect, on the lobes of two π electrons as shown in Figure 4-1.

[42] Griswold, J. Am. Chem. Soc., **70**, 431 (1948).
[43] Addition compounds of metal salts with aromatic molecules are listed by Andrews, Chem. Revs., **54**, 740 (1954). This article also discusses addition compounds of aromatic hydrocarbons with polynitro compounds that may be considered to be "acid-base adducts" in the very broadest sense of the term.
[44] Kondakov, et al., Chem. Zentr., **1930**, I, 3287.
[45] Chatt and Wilkins, Nature, **165**, 859 (1950).
[46] Rundle and Goring, J. Am. Chem. Soc., **72**, 5337 (1950).
[47] Brass and Tengler, Ber., **64B**, 1650 (1931).

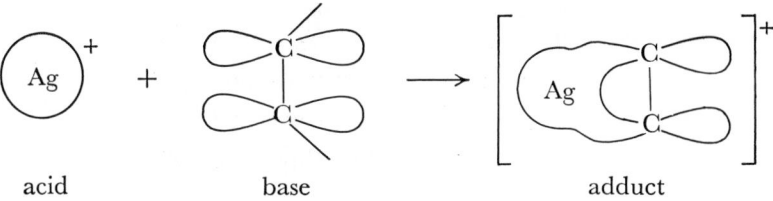

acid   base   adduct

Fig. 4-1. Formation of a π Complex

Thus, this adduct is called a π *complex*.

At present we are not certain as to which of the addition compounds derived from olefins or from aromatic hydrocarbons are π complexes and which have the Lewis acid bound to a particular carbon atom by an ordinary single (σ-type) bond. If the addition compound is isolable in the solid state and if the acceptor species is not a hydrogen ion, it is possible (at least in principle) to locate the position of the acid with respect to the remainder of the adduct, using the methods of x-ray diffraction. However, a number of such adducts of considerable theoretical interest (including the intermediates in certain of the aromatic substitution reactions) are formed only in relatively small concentrations in solution, and for these we may only speculate as to structural details. In this connection, let us compare the addition compounds formed by HCl and aromatic hydrocarbons in the absence of $AlCl_3$ to those formed in the presence of $AlCl_3$.[48] The former are largely dissociated (even at $-79°$ C) and are colorless nonconductors. Furthermore, if the aromatic hydrocarbon is recovered from such a complex, in which DCl is substituted for HCl, it may be shown that none of the deuterium has entered the benzene ring. (Were it not for the fact that HCl is considerably more soluble in aromatic than in aliphatic hydrocarbons, we probably would not suspect that there was any interaction between the components.) In contrast, the complexes formed in the presence of aluminum halides are colored and conduct the electric current. With these, if DCl is substituted for HCl, the deuterium atoms "exchange" with the hydrogen atoms of the benzene ring. Clearly, the two types of complexes are very different in character, and it seems likely that complexes of the first class are π complexes (of the type VI), whereas complexes of the second class are σ complexes (of the

VI   VII

type VII), although, in the absence of further structural information, we cannot be absolutely certain of this.

[48] Brown and Brady, *J. Am. Chem. Soc.*, **74,** 3570 (1952). In this paper, a number of criteria for distinguishing between π and σ complexes are proposed.

Substitution Reactions[49]

The terms "electrophilic" and "nucleophilic" are often applied to *substitution reactions*—that is, reactions in which a new covalent bond is formed and an old one is broken. Typical nucleophilic substitution reactions are, for example:

Attacking reagent	Substrate	Product	Leaving group

$$:NH_3 \ + \ CH_3CH_2I \ \longrightarrow \ CH_3\overset{\overset{\displaystyle NH_3^+}{|}}{C}H_2 \ + \ I^- \quad (18)$$

$$C_2H_5O^- + O_2N{-}\langle\bigcirc\rangle{-}Cl \longrightarrow O_2N{-}\langle\bigcirc\rangle{-}OC_2H_5 + Cl^- \quad (19)$$

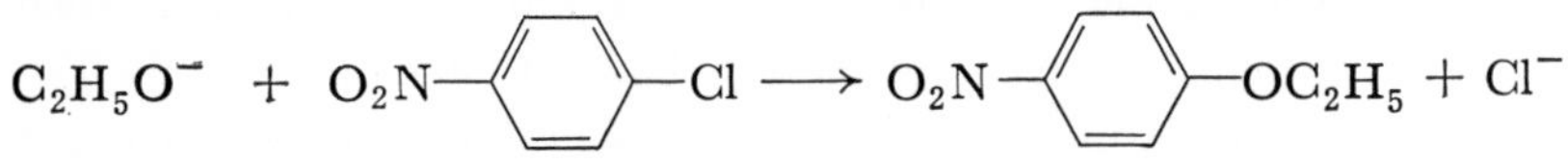

$$HO^- \ + \ (CH_3)_3C{-}Br \ \longrightarrow \ (CH_3)_3C{-}OH \ + \ Br^- \quad (20)$$

In these, the attacking reagents and the leaving groups are Lewis bases or nucleophiles. The electron pair that bonds the attacking reagent to the product is furnished by the former species. More specifically, reaction (18) may be described as a nucleophilic substitution *by* nitrogen *for* iodine *on* carbon, whereas (19) is a nucleophilic substitution by oxygen for chlorine on carbon. Although reactions (18), (19), and (20) are classified together due to the similarity in the net changes, it should not be assumed that the paths by which these three reactions occur are the same or closely analogous. As we shall presently see, there are almost certainly fundamental differences in the mechanisms. Similarly, the conversion of benzhydrol to benzhydryl chloride

$$H^+Cl^- + (C_6H_5)_2CH{-}OH \rightarrow (C_6H_5)_2CH{-}Cl + HOH \quad (21)$$

is a nucleophilic substitution by chlorine for hydroxyl on carbon, even though the hydrogen ion is necessary for the reaction (being, in fact, the species which initially attacks the hydrol).[50]

---

[49] For a detailed discussion of the classification of organic reagents and reactions, see Ingold, *Structure and Mechanism in Organic Chemistry*, Cornell University Press, Ithaca, N.Y., 1953, pp. 198–220.

[50] In considering the mechanism of a reaction, as will be done in subsequent chapters, we may find that certain of the actual steps may be described as substitution reactions. For example, before the carbon-to-chlorine bond is formed in reaction (21), the carbon-to-oxygen bond is broken by the following reaction:

$$H^+ + (C_6H_5)_2CH{-}OH \rightarrow HOH + (C_6H_5)_2CH^+$$

which may be considered as electrophilic substitution *by* hydrogen *for* the benzhydryl group *on* oxygen. Where possible, however, we shall adhere to current usage and base our primary classification of reactions on the *overall change* that occurs. Subclasses will be introduced where there is evidence of mechanistic differences.

In an *electrophilic substitution*, an electron-deficient species attacks the substrate, becoming bonded to it through a pair of electrons furnished by the latter, and a second electron-deficient species departs from the reaction site. Of by far the greatest importance in this category is the large group of aromatic substitution reactions which includes alkylations, acylations, nitrations, sulfonations, halogenations (except for fluorinations), and diazonium coupling reactions. In each of these types, the leaving group is simply the H^+ ion. The attacking species may be the incoming substituent in an electron-deficient form—for example, the NO_2^+ ion in nitration or the $:\overset{..+}{\underset{..}{Br}}$ ion in bromination:

Attacking reagent	Substrate	Product	Leaving group
$[O{=}N{-}O]^+$ + $Cl{-}C_6H_5$	$\rightarrow$ p-$ClC_6H_4{-}NO_2$ +		H^+
$:\overset{..+}{\underset{..}{Br}}$ + C_6H_6	$\rightarrow$ C_6H_5Br		H^+

or a so-called "carrier" of such a species (for example, $ClSO_3H$ in sulfonation or the RCl + $AlCl_3$ reagent in alkylation).

Attacking reagent	Substrate	Products
$ClSO_3H$ + $CH_3\overset{\displaystyle O}{\overset{\|}{C}}{-}NH{-}C_6H_5$	$\rightarrow$ p-$CH_3\overset{\displaystyle O}{\overset{\|}{C}}{-}NH{-}C_6H_4{-}SO_3H$ + H^+ + Cl^-	
$RCl : AlCl_3$ + C_6H_6	$\rightarrow$ $C_6H_5{-}R$ + H^+ + $AlCl_4^-$	

As with nucleophilic substitutions, coclassification of these reactions on the basis of similarity of overall changes does not imply that the attacking species in the various reactions are necessarily analogous.[51]

The reactions that we have been discussing have one feature in common. Electrons are transferred *in pairs* during the processes of bond formation and breakage. When two species come together to form a bond, both bonding electrons come from just one of the species; likewise, when a bond is broken, both bonding electrons depart with *one* of the fragments. Because of the electric dissymmetry of acid-base reactions, electrophilic and nucleophilic substitutions, and electrophilic and nucleophilic additions, all such reactions are sometimes classified together as **polar reactions** or **heterolytic reactions** or (less correctly, since free ions are not always involved) ionic reactions. Normally, all intermediates in such reactions have even numbers of electrons.

[51] It has already been shown that $C{=}O$, $C{=}N$, and $C{\equiv}N$ multiple bonds tend to be susceptible to attack by nucleophiles, whereas $C{=}C$ and $C{\equiv}C$ bonds tend to be more vulnerable to electrophiles. In line with such differences, distinction is occasionally drawn between *electrophilic* and *nucleophilic additions* (see, for example, Ref. 49, pp. 212–215). These descriptions do not seem as useful as the corresponding descriptions of substitution reactions, and their adoption is, at present, far less widespread.

The reader is doubtless aware, however, that a number of important reactions take place through intermediates with odd numbers of electrons. In these reactions, covalent bonds may be broken *homolytically*—that is, with one bonding electron departing with each of the two fragments. Since species having odd numbers of electrons are known as free radicals, such reactions are classified together as **free-radical reactions** or **homolytic reactions.** Among these are the halogenation and nitration of aliphatic hydrocarbons, the addition of HBr to olefins in the presence of peroxides, the arylations of aromatic hydrocarbons using diazonium compounds, and a large number (but not all) of the polymerizations of olefins. Dissociations, substitutions, and additions are observed among free-radical reactions just as with polar reactions.

$$F_2 \xrightarrow{\text{heat}} 2F\cdot \qquad\qquad\qquad (22)$$
$$(C_6H_5)_3C\!-\!C(C_6H_5)_3 \longrightarrow 2(C_6H_5)_3C\cdot \qquad (23) \Bigg\} \text{dissociations}$$
$$Cl\cdot + CH_3CH_2COOH \longrightarrow HCl + \cdot CH_2CH_2COOH \quad (24)\ \ \text{substitution}$$
$$Br\cdot + CH_2\!\!=\!\!CHBr \longrightarrow BrCH_2\!-\!\underset{\cdot}{C}HBr \qquad (25)\ \ \text{addition}$$

However, as we shall see in the chapter devoted to free-radical reactions, the reactions in (22) through (26) are very different in character from their respective counterparts among polar reactions—so much so, in fact, that correspondences between the two broad classes of reactions are little more than formal.

EXERCISES FOR CHAPTER 4

1. (a) Arrange the following in the order of decreasing acidity:

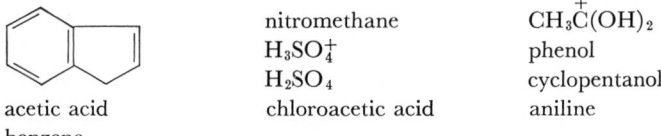

	nitromethane	$CH_3\overset{+}{C}(OH)_2$
	$H_3SO_4^+$	phenol
	H_2SO_4	cyclopentanol
acetic acid	chloroacetic acid	aniline
benzene		

   (b) Arrange the following in the order of decreasing basicity:

   OH⁻   Br⁻ $C_2H_5^-$ $C_6H_5O^-$ $(CH_3)_3C\!-\!O^-$

   H_2O $(C_6H_5)_2CH^-$ $HOOC(CH_2)_2COO^-$ $Cl_2CHC(OH)_2^+$ NH_2^-

2. Given a *p*H meter on which readings reliable to 0.02 *p*H unit may be made, what is the minimum K_a value that a weak acid may have in order that the acidity of its 0.01 *M* solution in water may be detected by this meter?

3. Outline an experiment that would show which acid in each of the following pairs is the stronger:

(a) 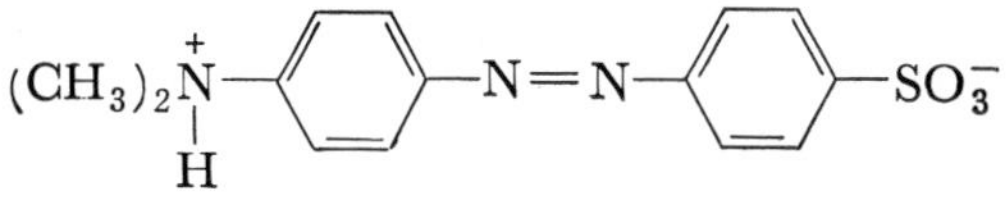 $(CH_3)_2\overset{+}{\underset{H}{N}}$—⟨benzene⟩—N=N—⟨benzene⟩—SO_3^- or

$(CH_3)_2\overset{+}{N}H$

⟨benzene⟩—N=N—⟨benzene⟩—SO_3^- ?

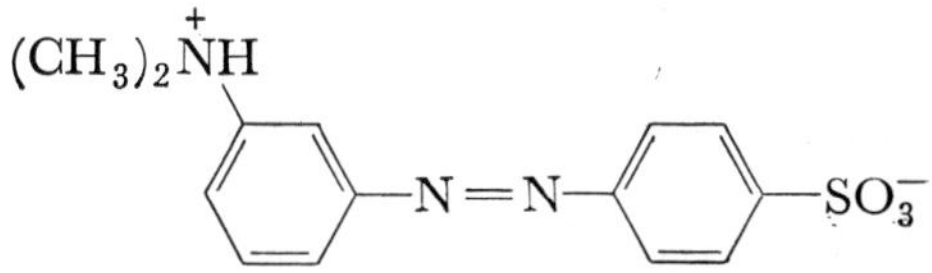

(b) $C_6H_5SO_2H$ (contaminated with a trace of $C_6H_5SO_3H$) or $C_6H_5SeO_2H$ (contaminated with a trace of $C_6H_5SeO_3H$)?

(c) $Cl_2CH—\overset{+}{C}(OH)_2$ or $Br_2CH—\overset{+}{C}(OH)_2$?

(d) Benzene or cyclohexane?

(e)

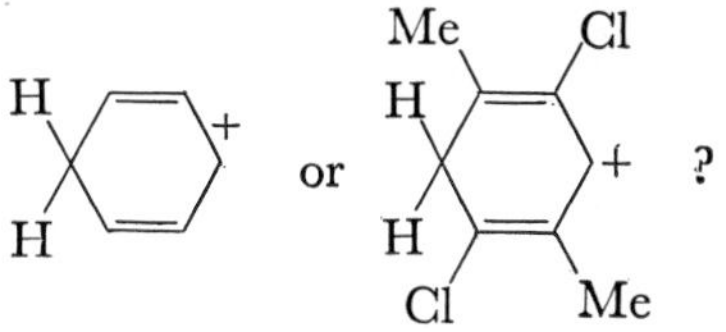

or   ?

4. (a) Predict approximate ν factors for each of the following in concentrated sulfuric acid:

water   ethylenediamine   chloroacetic acid
sodium acetate   sodium carbonate

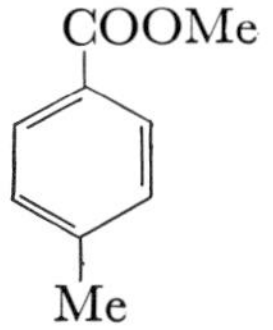

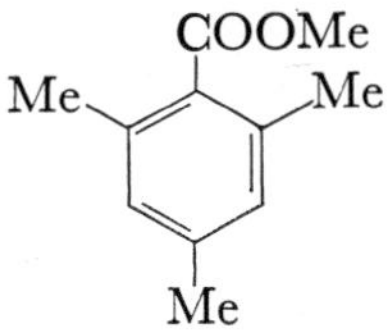

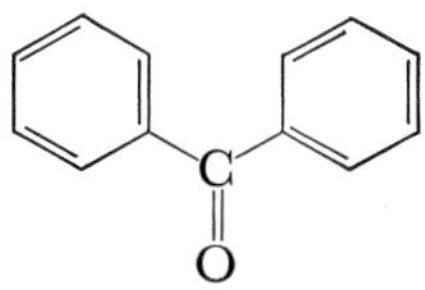

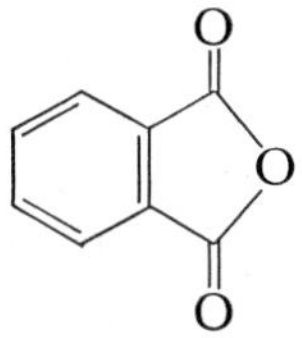

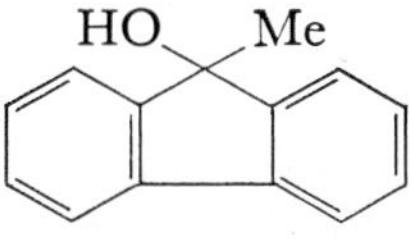

(b) In freshly prepared solutions, the ν factor of anisole ($C_6H_5OCH_3$) in concentrated sulfuric acid is close to 2. As the solutions are allowed to stand, the apparent ν factor increases to a value near 3. Explain.

(c) Pure sulfuric acid is slightly ionized into $H_3SO_4^+$ and HSO_4^-. Explain why the addition of 0.1 mole of water to 1000 grams of pure sulfuric acid lowers its freezing point by about 0.8°, whereas addition of 0.2 moles of water to 1000 grams of pure sulfuric acid lowers its freezing point by about 2.0°. Why is sulfuric acid to which a small amount of water has been added a better solvent for cryoscopic studies than pure sulfuric acid?

5. (a) Why does the ratio K_1/K_2 for long-chain dibasic acids approach 4.00?

(b) The acids O$_2$N—

$$NO_2$$

—OH and Cl$_2$CHCOOH have about

$$NO_2$$

the same strength in water. Which is the stronger acid in ethanol? Explain.

6. The following data, collected by Deno,[22] refer to the ratio of the concentrations of the two forms (In$^-$ and HIn) of three indicators in water-hydrazine mixtures.

Indicator		Percent Hydrazine	log (c_{In}/c_{HIn})
I	($pK_a = 13.4$)	20.2	−1.18
II		20.2	−0.82
II		33.2	+0.42
III		33.2	−1.18
III		50.1	+0.55

Calculate the pK_a values for indicators II and III and the H_- value for 50.1 percent hydrazine.

7. Given the following pK_a values in water, 35 percent ethanol, and absolute ethanol:

Percent EtOH	pK_a values	
	HOAc	HOBz
0	4.76	4.20
35	5.43	5.24
100	10.32	10.25

(a) From these data, show that the ratio γ_{HA}/γ_{A^-} in water-alcohol solutions is *not* independent of the acid HA.
(b) Y_- for absolute ethanol is set at 1.000 on Grunwald's scale. Calculate Y_- for 35 percent ethanol.
(c) Calculate the difference in the m_- values of HOAc and HOBz.

8. (a) From the data on page 113, estimate the value of $k_{cat.}$ associated with phenylacetic acid ($K_a = 4.9 \times 10^{-5}$) for the dehydration of acetaldehyde hydrate. (The observed value is 44.2 liters per mole-min.)

(b) For the same reaction, estimate $k_{cat.}$ associated with the hydrogen citrate ion,

$$^-O—C—CH_2—\overset{\overset{\displaystyle OH}{|}}{C}—CH_2—C—O^-,$$

$K_a = 4 \times 10^{-6}$. For the statistical correction, assume that the proton affinities of the three carboxylate groups of the citrate ion are essentially the same.

9. Two reactions are subject to general acid catalysis. For reaction (1), the Brønsted parameter, a, is 0.1; for reaction (2), a is 1.0. Both reactions are carried out in buffers made from an equimolal solution of a weak acid HA ($K_a = 10^{-5}$) and its salt,

Na^+A^-. Calculate, in each of the cases below, the fraction of the reaction due to H_3O^+, HA, and H_2O. (Assume that the ionic strengths in all cases are the same.)

(a) Reaction (1); for the buffer $(HA) = (A^-) = 0.01$ molar
(b) Reaction (2); for the buffer $(HA) = (A^-) = 0.01$ molar
(c) Reaction (2); for the buffer $(HA) = (A^-) = 1.0$ molar

Show that if reaction (2) were studied only in dilute buffer solutions, it might appear to be subject to specific hydronium-ion catalysis.

10. Decide whether each of the following species may be Lewis acids, Lewis bases, both, or neither:

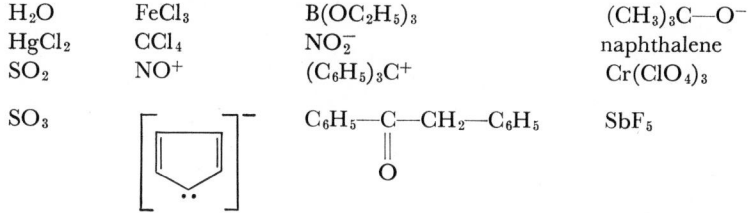

H_2O	$FeCl_3$	$B(OC_2H_5)_3$	$(CH_3)_3C$—O^-
$HgCl_2$	CCl_4	NO_2^-	naphthalene
SO_2	NO^+	$(C_6H_5)_3C^+$	$Cr(ClO_4)_3$

SO_3 C_6H_5—C—CH_2—C_6H_5 SbF_5

11. Classify each of the following substitution reactions using the terms introduced in the final section of this chapter; (for example, the first reaction is a nucleophilic substitution by hydride ion for hydroxide on hydrogen).

Example: $H^- + H_2O \rightarrow H_2 + OH^-$

(a) ⟨⟩—SO_3H + OH^- ⟶ ⟨⟩—OH + SO_3H^-

(b) $Cl\cdot$ + ⟨⟩—CH_3 ⟶ HCl + ⟨⟩—$CH_2\cdot$

(c) C_6H_6 + CH_3C—Cl $\xrightarrow{AlCl_3}$ ⟨⟩—CCH_3 + $H^+AlCl_4^-$

(d) D_2SO_4 + ⟨⟩—O—CH_3 ⟶

                      D—⟨⟩—OCH_3 + $DHSO_4$

(e) Na^+I^- + CH_3—O—S—⟨⟩ ⟶ Na^+ [O—S—⟨⟩]$^-$

                                         + CH_3I

(f)

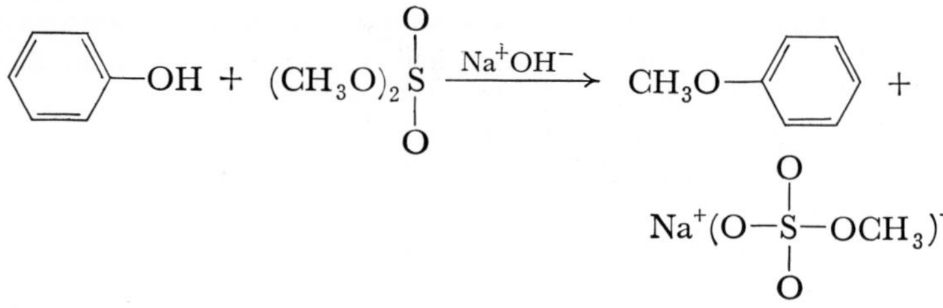

$$\text{C}_6\text{H}_5\text{-OH} + (CH_3O)_2 \overset{O}{\underset{O}{S}} \xrightarrow{\text{Na}^+\text{OH}^-} CH_3O\text{-C}_6\text{H}_5 +$$

$$\text{Na}^+(\text{O}-\overset{O}{\underset{O}{S}}-\text{OCH}_3)^-$$

(g) $AlCl_3 + ICl \rightarrow I^+ + AlCl_4^-$

(h)

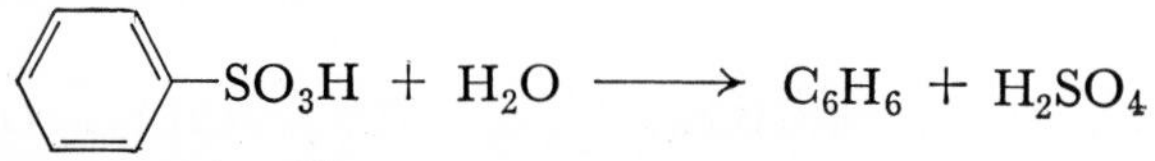

$$\text{C}_6\text{H}_5\text{-SO}_3\text{H} + H_2O \longrightarrow C_6H_6 + H_2SO_4$$

(i) $2CH_3COOEt \xrightarrow{\text{OEt}^-} CH_3CCH_2COOEt + EtOH$
$$\quad\quad\quad\quad\quad\quad\quad\quad \overset{\|}{O}$$

(j) $Fe^{+2} + H_2O_2 \rightarrow Fe(OH)^{2+} + HO\cdot$

Methods for Determining
Reaction Mechanisms
I. Nonkinetic Studies

The Meaning of "Reaction Mechanism"

In the ideal case, we may consider the mechanism of a chemical reaction as a hypothetical motion picture of the behavior of the participating atoms. Such a picture would presumably begin at some time before the reacting species approach each other, then go on to record the continuous paths of the atoms (and their electrons) during the reaction, and come to an end after the products have emerged. Since it is not generally possible to obtain such an intimate picture, the investigation of a mechanism has come to mean obtaining information that can furnish a picture of the participating species at one or more crucial instants during the course of the reaction.

However, even this more modest aim is very seldom achieved; for, as will become evident, the experimental methods that are used to study chemical mechanisms yield results that are indicative rather than conclusive. A group of experiments may, if considered together, exclude certain mechanisms which might otherwise have been considered possible, but a number of mechanisms might well remain; between these a choice may not be possible. For practical purposes, therefore, a mechanism of an organic reaction is open for consideration if it allows us to predict the limitations of the reaction and the structure of the products (especially in cases in which the reaction might "go astray"). The reliability of the proposed mechanism increases if it leads to quantitative predictions as to how the speed of the reaction is affected by concentrations of

127

reactants, temperature, solvent, and the presence of catalysts. It is also desirable that a proposed mechanism allow prediction of the manner in which the rate of the reaction will change as the structures of one or more of the reactants are subjected to a given change. Clearly, all of this constitutes a large order. In actuality, experimental investigation of one or more of the above points leads to a proposed mechanism that may then be confirmed (or excluded) by investigation of the remaining items.

Energy Profile Diagrams. Intermediates vs. Transition States

An *intermediate* in a chemical reaction may be defined as a species which is formed (preferably in detectable amounts) from the reactants and which under the reaction conditions, is eventually converted to the reaction product or products. As an example, consider the conversions of N-bromoamides to isocyanates in basic solution (a part of the well-known Hofmann rearrangement).

$$CH_3CONHBr + OH^- \rightarrow CH_3N{=}C{=}O + Br^- + H_2O$$

In this case, we feel quite certain that the anion CH_3CONBr^- is an intermediate in the reaction, for, with care, salts containing this anion may be isolated[1] and such salts undergo the conversion to isocyanate at a rate no less than that of the brominated amide.

A large number of the known types of organic reactions proceed through one or more intermediates, but there are some that do not. The basic hydrolysis of methyl iodide is thought to be one of these.

$$CH_3I + OH^- \rightarrow CH_3OH + I^-$$

Although this type of reaction will be treated at some length in Chapter 7, let us anticipate the discussion by picturing the course of such a reaction. Temporarily closing our eyes to the fact that both the hydroxide ion and the iodide ion are "solvated" (hydrated, if the solvent is water), we may visualize an energetic hydroxide ion approaching the methyl iodide molecule from a direction opposite to that of the C—I bond. As the OH⁻ ion gets nearer to the carbon atom, the molecule "spreads out," the C—I bond weakens, and a C—O bond begins to form. At some point in the reaction we may consider the C—I bond as "half broken" and the C—O bond as "half formed." At this point (Fig. 5-1), the three nonparticipating hydrogen atoms will lie in or near a common plane, perpendicular to the O‥C‥I line. Further approach of the OH⁻ ion finishes the breaking of the C—I bond and the making of the C—O bond, during which time the three hydrogen atoms again assume tetra-

[1] Mauguin, *Ann. Chim.* (8), **22**, 297 (1911).

hedral positions about the carbon. The situation represented in the center section of Figure 5-1 may be regarded as the "halfway point" in the reaction— that is, the point beyond which the system is more likely to progress to the products than to retreat to the reactants. Such a configuration is generally called the **transition state** or **activated complex.** Considerable energy is neces- sary to drive the reactants into this configuration; that is why the reaction pro- ceeds at only a moderate rate, for only the more energetic OH⁻ ions can push the CH_3I into the necessary transition state configuration. Furthermore, if the reaction were to be carried out in reverse, it would require still more energy to drive the system consisting of I⁻ and CH_3OH into the same transition state.

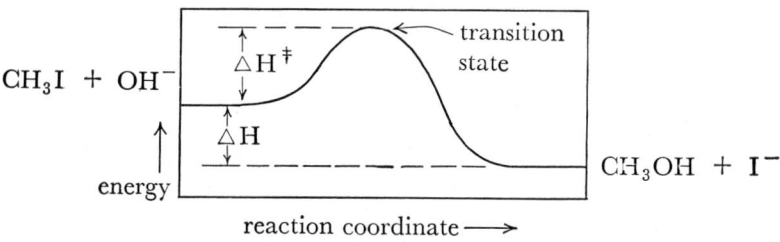

reactants   transition state   products

Fig. 5-1. The Basic Hydrolysis of Methyl Iodide

Either the forward or the reverse reaction may then be imagined as going up, then down, an "energy hill" with the transition state at the top. The transition state is thus, in effect, defined as that point in the reaction where the total energy of the system of atoms under consideration is maximum.

Such a picture is sometimes extended by representing the course of reac- tions in energy profile diagrams. Such representations, of which Figure 5-2

$CH_3I + OH^-$ $\Delta H^\ddagger$ transition state

ΔH

energy $CH_3OH + I^-$

reaction coordinate $\longrightarrow$

Fig. 5-2. Energy Profile (Schematic) for $CH_3I + OH^- \longrightarrow CH_3OH + I^-$

is an example, will be discussed here only very briefly. In such diagrams, ver- tical distances represent energies. The abscissa (often called the *reaction coordi- nate*) represents, in a general way, the progress of a particular molecular unit (in this case an OH⁻ ion and a CH_3I molecule) along the course of the reaction. Horizontal distances have no exact quantitative significance. Note that the energy difference between the initial and final levels represents the heat of reaction, ΔH. The energy difference between the initial level and the top of the "hill" (the transition state) corresponds quite closely, but not exactly, to $H\ddagger$—the **activation energy** of the forward reaction. (The reason for this small discrepancy need not concern us now.) This activation energy is the energy that must be added to an "average" OH^- ion and an "average" CH_3I molecule to drive them into the transition state. Often, activation energies are expressed in kcal, under which circumstances they would refer to moles of "average" particles, rather than individual units.

For a reaction proceeding through true *intermediate*, there is a "dip" or minimum in the energy profile diagram. The deeper the dip, the more stable will be the intermediate and the more sure we may be of its existence. For the anion intermediate in the Hofmann conversion (mentioned at the beginning of the chapter), the dip is deep, perhaps reaching below the energy level of the reactants. In contrast, the presence of the cation I in the nitration of benzene is

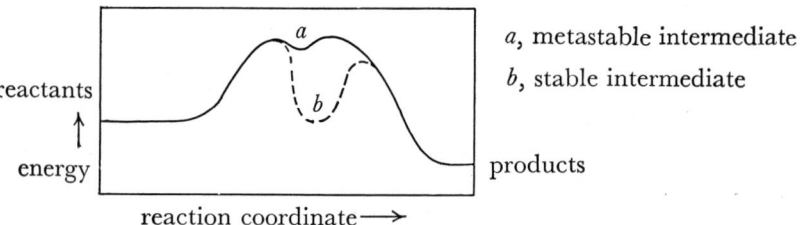

(I)

inferred only by indirect means (Chap. 11) and the energy profile, if it dips at all, must do so very slightly. The two types of intermediate are compared schematically in Figure 5-3. In the extreme case the dip becomes so slight that the intermediate *a* is experimentally indistinguishable from a transition state. If the intermediate is isolable, we are in effect considering two reactions, each with its own transition state. In such cases, a substance becomes designated as an intermediate simply because the "reaction" originally chosen is a composite one.

reactants
↑
energy

a

b

a, metastable intermediate
b, stable intermediate

products

reaction coordinate ⟶

Fig. 5-3. Energy Profiles for Reactions Proceeding through Intermediates

In any event if the configuration and energy of each of the intermediates and transition states through which a reacting system passes are known, it is not too much to say that the mechanism of the reaction is understood.

Since studies on the *rates* of reactions have become so important in giving us information about reaction mechanisms, it is not surprising that in many minds "mechanistic studies" have become synonymous with "kinetic studies." Although an entire chapter is devoted to a discussion of kinetic evidence, let us first examine a number of nonkinetic methods for obtaining mechanistic information.

Identification of Products

The most fundamental basis for mechanistic speculation is the identification of the reaction products (generally carried out whether or not a mechanistic question is at stake), for without such identification we cannot be sure which reaction is actually under consideration. The student of elementary organic chemistry learns that the chlorination of toluene yields benzyl chloride when carried out in the vapor state with illumination, but that if the chlorination is carried out in the liquid phase in the presence of aluminum chloride, o-chlorotoluene and p-chlorotoluene result. On this basis, he becomes aware that a different chlorination mechanism operates in each case.

There might be some temptation to liken the replacement of chloride by cyanide in benzyl chloride (II) to the replacement of chloride by cyanide in furfuryl chloride (III) until the product of the latter reaction is identified as

1,4-cyanomethylfuran (IV), showing that the position occupied by the incoming cyano group is not the same as that occupied by the outgoing chloro group.[2]

As a third example, let us compare two reactions of esters of p-toluenesulfonic acid. The toluenesulfonate anion (abbreviated TosO⁻) may be replaced by iodide from compound V, and the same anion may be replaced by methoxide from compound VI.[3] It is evident, however, that the two replacements must be mechanistically dissimilar when the product from reaction V is shown to have the *same* carbon skeleton as the starting material whereas the product from VI has undergone rearrangement.

[2] Reichstein, Ber., **63,** 749 (1930).
[3] Bordwell, Pitt, and Knell, J. Am. Chem. Soc., **73,** 5004 (1951).

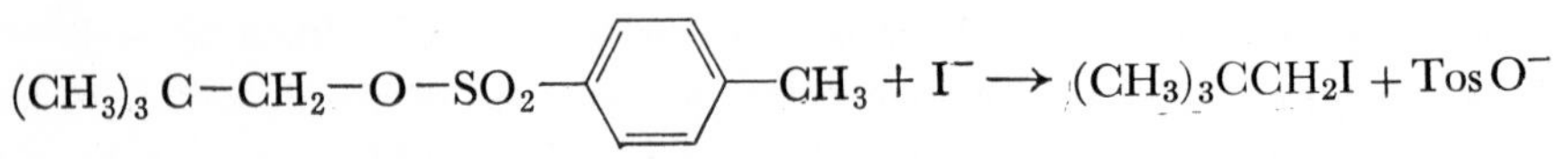

$$(CH_3)_3 C-CH_2-O-SO_2-\langle\bigcirc\rangle-CH_3 + I^- \rightarrow (CH_3)_3CCH_2I + Tos\,O^-$$

neopentyl tosylate, **V**

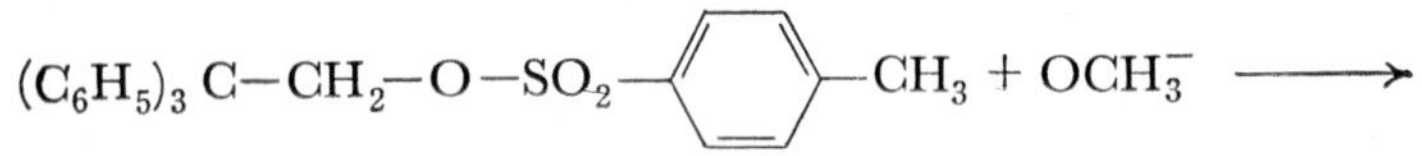

$$(C_6H_5)_3 C-CH_2-O-SO_2-\langle\bigcirc\rangle-CH_3 + OCH_3^- \longrightarrow$$

tritylmethyl tosylate, **VI**

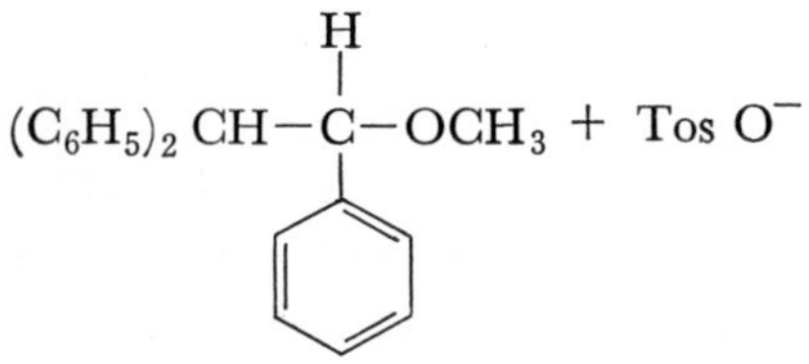

$$(C_6H_5)_2 CH-\overset{\overset{\displaystyle H}{|}}{\underset{\underset{\displaystyle \bigcirc}{|}}{C}}-OCH_3 + Tos\,O^-$$

Note that in the three examples cited, we have suggested no mechanistic details. Nevertheless, the correct identifications of the products strongly suggest *differences* in mechanism.

Occasionally a reaction is used in the laboratory for many years, furnishing satisfactory yields of a desired product and, at the same time, additional products that may be discarded without identification. The present author has converted aryl selenocyanates (VII) to diaryl diselenides many times using methanolic KOH, yet knows essentially nothing of the path through which the conversion occurs, mainly because the water-soluble products

$$2Ar-Se-CN + OH^- \rightarrow Ar-Se-Se-Ar + ???$$
VII

are extracted and discarded. The identification of these products would seem to be the first step in clarifying the mechanism of this reaction.

Sometimes the absence of a particular product can be just as important as the presence of another. The familiar Sommelet reaction converts halides such as benzyl chloride to aldehydes by treatment with hexamethylene tetramine, $(CH_2)_6N_4$. Since the latter compound is, in effect, a sort of "mixed anhydride" of formaldehyde and ammonia, Sommelet[4] proposed that the reaction terminated in the three steps shown below.

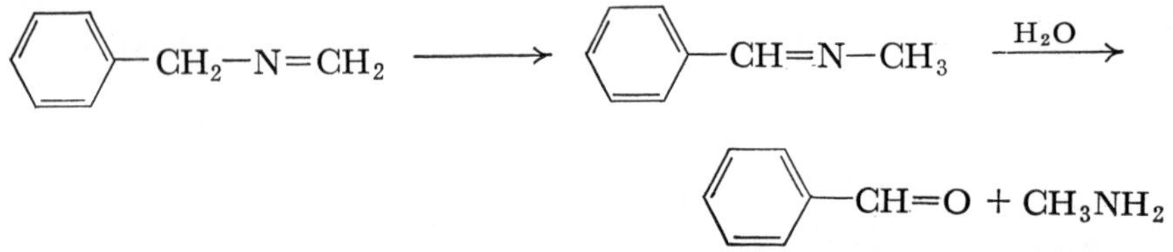

$$\langle\bigcirc\rangle-CH_2-N=CH_2 \longrightarrow \langle\bigcirc\rangle-CH=N-CH_3 \xrightarrow{H_2O}$$

$$\langle\bigcirc\rangle-CH=O + CH_3NH_2$$

[4] Sommelet, *Compt. rend.*, **157**, 852 (1913).

Today, however, although agreement is not complete as to what the mechanism of this reaction *is*, we are quite certain that the mechanism proposed by the discoverer is *not* the correct one since careful examination of the reaction mixture failed to reveal appreciable quantities of methylamine.[5]

Often the most vexing question concerning the mechanism of a reaction is, "Which of the bonds is broken during the reaction, and where is the new bond (or new bonds) formed?" Consider, for example, the reaction between chlorobenzene and KNH_2 to form aniline:

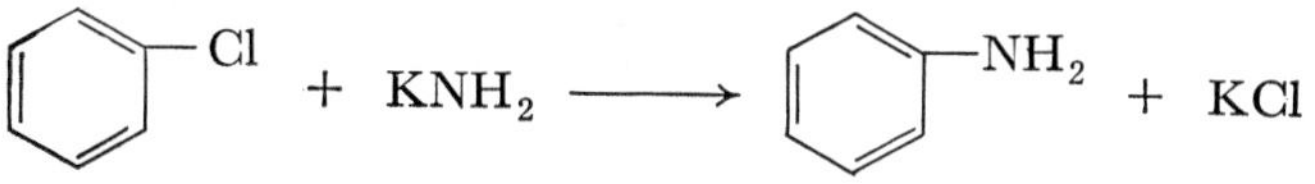

Without knowing better, we might easily put this reaction in the same class as the replacement of I^- by OH^- in methyl iodide (p. 128). It is certainly reasonable that the NH_2^- ion could approach the chlorinated carbon atom, that the C—Cl bond could weaken, and that the new N—C bond could form while the old C—Cl bond breaks (however, the geometry of the collision would have to be slightly different from that in the case of methyl iodide because the geometry of the two halides is not the same). One would have to admit, however, that if the incoming —NH_2 group were to occupy a position *different* from that occupied by the leaving —Cl group (and if protons could move from one carbon to another), such a path would not be detected merely by identification of the reaction products. The fact that the action of $NaNH_2$ on *o*-iodoanisole yields *m*-anisidine[6] suggests, but of course does not prove, that in the "ammonolysis" of chlorobenzene the carbon from which the chlorine departs is not the carbon

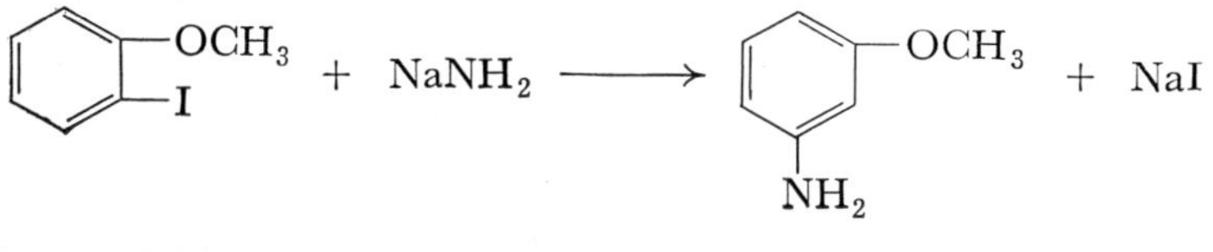

bearing the —NH_2 group in the resulting molecule. As we shall see (page 144), this doubt can be resolved by application of tracer methods.

In the so-called Claisen rearrangement, allylphenyl ethers are converted by heat to *o*-allylphenols:

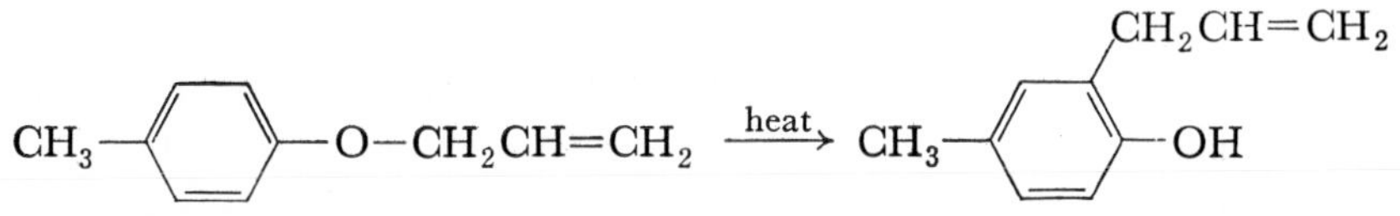

[5] Angyal and Rassack, *J. Chem. Soc.*, **1949**, 2700.
[6] Gilman and Avakian, *J. Am. Chem. Soc.*, **67**, 349 (1945).

Here again, one might ask, "Is the carbon atom that breaks away from the ether linkage the same carbon atom that becomes attached to the benzene ring?" Although in the example shown above, identification of products does not furnish an answer, the same reaction, when carried out with the substituted allyl ether VIII, yields the phenol IX, showing that the γ-carbon, rather than the α-carbon, becomes attached to the ring during the rearrangement.[7]

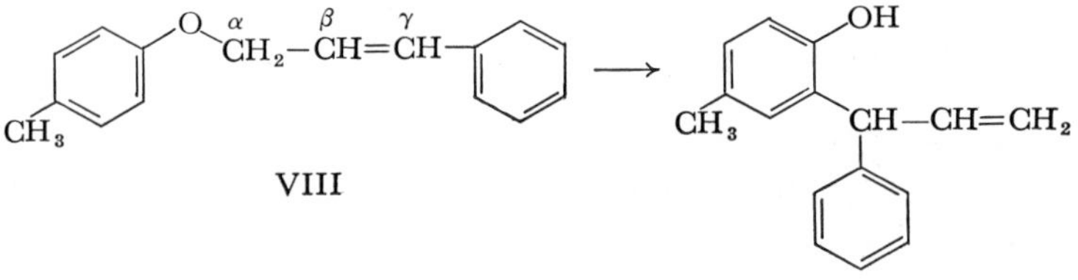

VIII

IX

More will be said about this rearrangement in Chapter 15, but it is emphasized that in this case, as in the five examples previously described, mechanistic information is obtained by the simple process of identifying the reaction products.

Testing Possible Intermediates

A compound suspected of being an intermediate in a reaction may sometimes be isolated, identified, and resubjected to the conditions that prevail during the course of the reaction. If the appropriate products are formed *at a rate no less than that of the "uninterrupted" reaction*, this is strong (although not unequivocal) evidence that the reaction proceeds through the intermediate that has been isolated. For the Hoesch reaction of chloroacetonitrile with resorcinol and HCl to form the hydrochloride X, the imino chloride XI is a likely intermediate

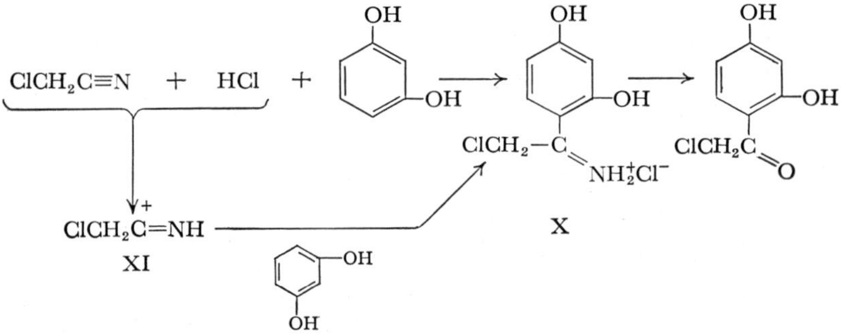

since it has been shown to form from the nitrile and HCl[8] and, upon treatment with resorcinol under Hoesch conditions, readily yields hydrochloride X.[9]

[7] Claisen and Tietze, *Ber.*, **58**, 275 (1925).
[8] Troeger and Luning. *J. prakt. Chem.* (2) **69**, 347 (1904).
[9] Stephen, *J. Chem. Soc.*, **117**, 1529 (1920).

We have already mentioned anions of the type $R-\overset{\underset{\|}{O}}{C}-N-Br^-$ as probable

intermediates in the Hofmann rearrangement (p. 128). This reaction is often regarded simply as a conversion of an amide to an amine having one less carbon atom; that is, the reaction is written

$$RCONH_2 + OBr^- \rightarrow RNH_2 + CO_2 + Br^-$$

Representing the reaction in this way is very much an oversimplification, for it glosses over the fact that it is possible to isolate at least three intermediates, an N-bromoamide, its anion, and an isocyanate.

$$RCONH_2 \xrightarrow{OBr^-} RCONHBr \xrightarrow{OH^-} R\overset{\underset{\|}{O}}{C}NBr^- \xrightarrow{-Br^-} R-N=C=O \xrightarrow{H_2O} \begin{cases} RNH_2 \\ \\ CO_2 \end{cases}$$

In the Reissert reaction, compounds such as XII (N-benzoyl-dihydro-quinaldonitrile) are converted by treatment with acid to quinaldamide (XIII) and aromatic aldehydes. If the original compound is treated with HCl under anhydrous conditions, a reddish-orange product forms; because this compound

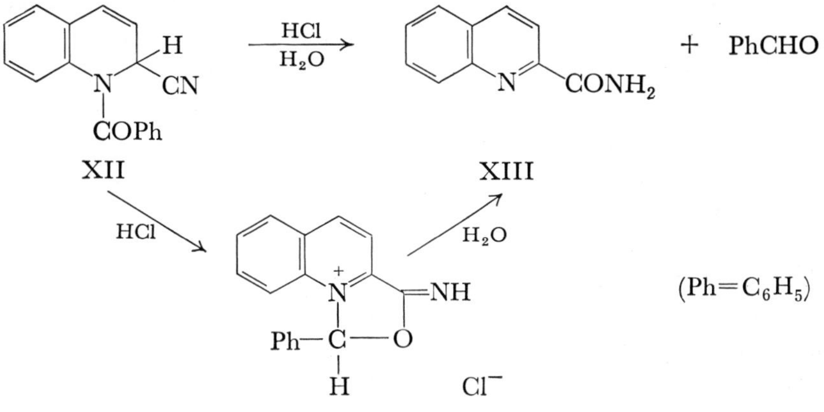

XII   XIII $(Ph = C_6H_5)$

XIV

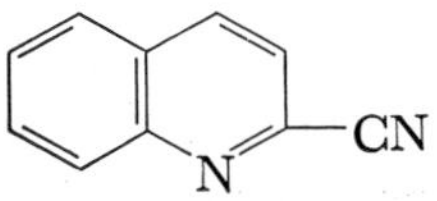

XV 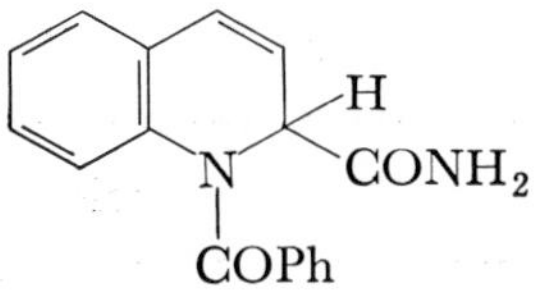   XVI

yields the same amide and aldehyde when treated with water, it deserves serious consideration as an intermediate in the reaction even though its structure is not known with certainty (the structure XIV has been suggested).[10] On the other hand, the substances XV and XVI *cannot* be intermediates in this reaction. The nitrile XV does not give quinaldamide, nor does the amide XVI yield benzaldehyde when subjected to conditions under which the Reissert reaction proceeds smoothly.

Similarly, the reluctance of other presumed intermediates to give the correct products under suitable reaction conditions has caused many a chemist to revise his ideas. The Clemmensen reduction of $C\!=\!O$ groups to CH_2 groups using zinc amalgam and HCl cannot proceed through the corresponding car-

$$\text{binol} \left(\text{that is,} \quad \underset{O}{\overset{\displaystyle \|}{-C-}} \rightarrow \underset{OH}{\overset{\displaystyle H}{-C-}} \rightarrow -CH_2- \right) \text{ since the carbinols are them-}$$

selves not generally reduced with the same combination of reagents.[11] A somewhat different argument may be used against a urethane intermediate in the formation of allophanates (XVII) from alcohols and cyanic acid in ether. Although it is true that urethanes, if treated with cyanic acid, form allophanates, the reaction is much slower than the formation of the allophanates from the alcohols.[12] Since the rate of a composite reaction must be less than or equal to

$$ROH + 2HN\!=\!C\!=\!O \xrightarrow{\text{fast}} RO\!-\!\underset{O}{\overset{\|}{C}}\!-\!NH\!-\!\underset{O}{\overset{\|}{C}}NH_2 \text{ (allophanate)}$$

$$RO\!-\!\underset{O}{\overset{\|}{C}}\!-\!NH_2 \xrightarrow{\text{slow}} \qquad \text{XVII}$$

the rate of any step, the prevailing mode of formation of allophanate cannot be through the urethane (although a minor amount could be formed in this way).

A reaction intermediate that can be formed in more than one way should exhibit a behavior independent of its mode of formation. Possible intermediates may be eliminated from consideration on this basis, even though they cannot be isolated. Until recently, a number of workers felt that the Friedel-Craft type methylation of aromatic hydrocarbons proceeded through a carbonium ion, CH_3^+. However, the relative amounts of the three xylenes produced in the methylation of toluene vary, depending upon whether methyl bromide or methyl iodide is used.[13] In a typical case, the *parà*:*meta* ratio is 1.7 for methyl bromide but climbs to 3.3 when methyl iodide is used under the same conditions.

[10] McEwen and Cobb, *J. Am. Chem. Soc.*, **77**, 5092 (1955).
[11] Martin, in *Organic Reactions*, Vol. 1, John Wiley and Sons, Inc., New York, 1942, p. 156.
[12] Close and Spielman, *J. Am. Chem. Soc.*, **75**, 4055 (1953).
[13] Brown and Jungk, *J. Am. Chem. Soc.*, **77**, 5586 (1955).

$$CH_3X \quad (X=\text{Br or I}) \; + \; \underset{\diagdown \; Al_2Cl_6}{\underbrace{\bigcirc}} \!\!\! - CH_3 \xrightarrow{Al_2Cl_6} o, \; m, \; \text{or} \; p\text{-xylene} + HCl$$

$$Al_2Cl_6 X^- + CH_3^+ \; (??)$$

This means that the CH_3^+ ion is not an intermediate in both methylations and probably not an intermediate in either case.

"Trapping" of Intermediates

Sometimes an intermediate may be detected, although it cannot be isolated, by adding to the reaction a "trapping" reagent. The latter is added so that it will combine with the intermediate to form a product that (the worker supposes) cannot be accounted for otherwise. The addition of bromine to many olefins in polar solvents is thought to proceed through an intermediate, which

we shall represent as $\left(\overset{+}{\underset{Br}{C - C}} \right)$. (The reasons for assignment of a

cyclic structure to this intermediate are discussed in Chap. 13.) In simple additions, this cyclic "bromonium ion" is thought to react with Br^- present in solution to form the observed dibromide. Strong evidence for such an intermediate is that it can be diverted from its ordinary reaction course by the presence of basic reagents other than Br^-. For example, when bromine is added to stilbene (XVIII) in methanol, the bromoether XX may be isolated from the reaction mixture.[14] This is presumably formed when the intermediate XIX

$$Ph-CH=CH-Ph + Br_2 \longrightarrow \left[\underset{H \quad Br \quad H}{\overset{Ph \qquad Ph}{C - C}} \right]^+ \underset{CH_3OH}{\overset{Br^-}{\nearrow}} \begin{array}{l} PhCHBr-CHBrPh \\ \\ PhCHBr-CHPh(OCH_3) \end{array}$$

| XVIII | XIX | XX |

reacts with the added alcohol instead of with Br^-. Isolation of the ether XX, however, is not sufficient to prove that the bromination proceeds through intermediate XIX. It must be shown that the dibromide itself does *not* readily react with methanol to yield the bromoether (otherwise it could be argued that the ether arises from the dibromide). It should also be shown (and this is not so easy) that methanol and bromine alone do not react to give an intermediate

[14] Bartlett and Tarbell, *J. Am. Chem. Soc.*, **58**, 466 (1936).

which itself reacts with the olefin to give the bromoether. We see, then, that the trapping of intermediates by chemical means must be interpreted with caution, for the reaction studied has been altered by addition of an extra reagent. What the worker desires is that the alteration *occurs after* the formation of the intermediate he seeks, rather than before.

For a number of years it was an open question as to whether the reaction of phenylmagnesium bromide with diphenylketene (XXI) involved addition to the C=C bond or to the C=O bond in the ketene. Hydrolysis of the reaction mixture yields a mixture of the ketone XXII and its tautomer, the enol XXIII; the products therefore do not indicate the direction of addition. However, if the reaction mixture is treated with benzoyl chloride prior to addition of water, the benzoate of the enol (XXIV) results.[15] This indicates that the C=O bond, rather than the C=C bond, in the ketene, has been subjected to attack, provided

$$PhMgBr + Ph_2C=C=O \longrightarrow$$
$$XXI$$

$$\begin{array}{c} Br \\ | \\ Mg \\ | \\ Ph_2C-C=O? \\ | \\ Ph \end{array}$$

or

$$Ph_2C=C-O-MgBr? \\ | \\ Ph$$

$\xrightarrow{H_2O}$

$\xrightarrow{C_6H_5COCl}$

$$\begin{array}{c} O \\ \| \\ Ph_2CH-C-Ph \\ XXII \end{array}$$

$$Ph_2C=C-Ph \\ | \\ OH \\ XXIII$$

$$Ph_2C=C-Ph \\ | \\ O \quad XXIV \\ \backslash \\ C-C_6H_5 \\ \| \\ O$$

it is assumed (a) that there is no rearrangement of the addition product during reaction with benzoyl chloride and (b) that the product formed in the reaction with benzoyl chloride was isolated without suffering rearrangement.

Evidence from Reaction Catalysis

Often the manner in which a reaction may be accelerated or inhibited furnishes a hint as to its mechanism. A large number of reactions are catalyzed by acid. In such cases it is reasonable to suppose either that the reaction intermediate is a cation formed by removal of a basic fragment (OH^-, OAc^-, etc.) from a reactant or else that the reaction intermediate is simply the conjugate acid (p. 94) of one of the reactants. It is also possible that the reaction path may involve an intermediate of each type. Conversely, a reaction that is base catalyzed may be thought to proceed through an anion formed by removal of a proton from one of the reactants (that is, through the conjugate base of that reactant), or else through an adduct of the added base with one of the reactants (page 190).

[15] Beel and Vejvoda, *J. Am. Chem. Soc.*, **76**, 905 (1954).

The splitting of the hemiacetal linkage in the sugar derivative, α-D-tetra-methylglucose (XXV) results in formation of the hydroxy aldehyde (XXVI), which is in rapid equilibrium with both the starting material and the second hemiacetal, β-D-tetramethylglucose (XXVII). The conversion of either the pure α or the pure β form in solution to the equilibrium mixture is accompanied

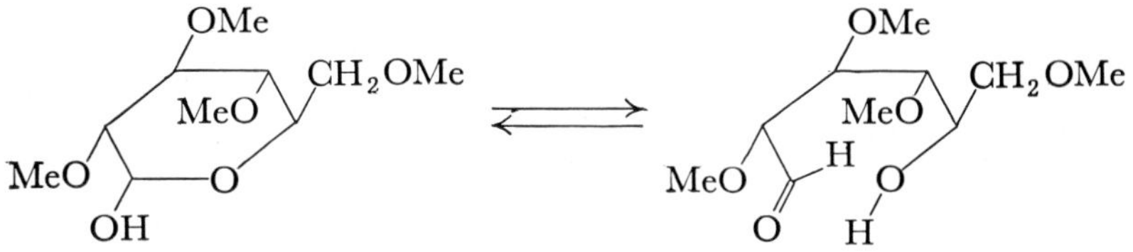

XXV   XXVI

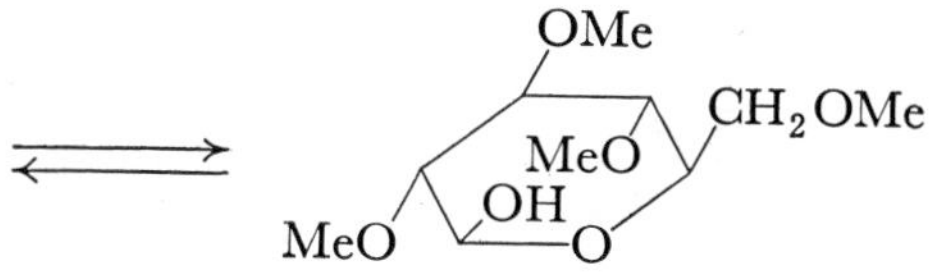

XXVII

by a drift in the value of the optical rotation of the solution until net reaction ceases. This is the familiar phenomenon of *mutarotation* and offers a convenient way for following the progress of the reaction. This reaction requires the presence of both acid *and* base, for it is very slow in pyridine (which is basic but nonacidic) and very slow in cresol (which is acidic but only faintly basic). Mutarotation proceeds far more rapidly in a mixture of pyridine and cresol,[16] and rapidly also in water (which is both acidic and basic). The reaction may be greatly accelerated by using as a catalyst 2-hydroxypyridine, which (although a very weak acid and a very weak base) has its acidic and basic sites held together rigidly in the correct position for attack on the hemiacetal linkage (XXIX).[17]

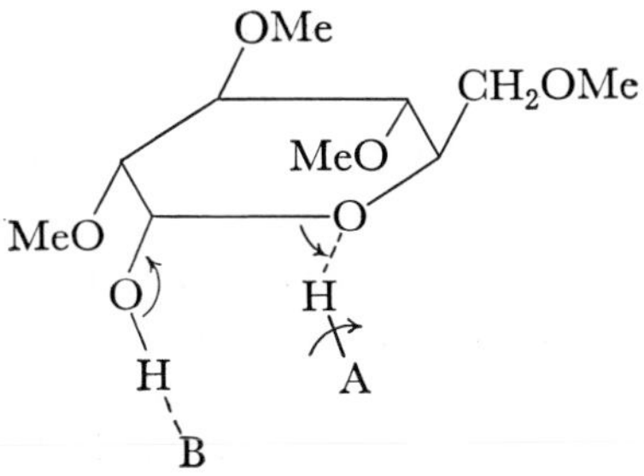

XXVIII 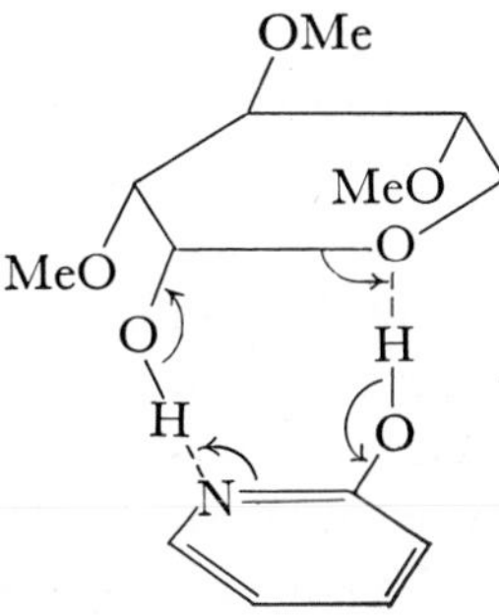   XXIX

[16] Lowry and Faulkner, *J. Chem. Soc.*, **127**, 2883 (1925).
[17] Swain and Brown, *J. Am. Chem. Soc.*, **74**, 2534, 2538 (1952).

The manner in which the ease of hydrolysis of salicyl phosphate (XXX) varies with acidity gives some hint about the hydrolysis intermediate. The rate of hydrolysis is greatest at pH 5.3, diminishes as the pH is either raised or lowered beyond this value, and becomes very small in either very acid or very basic solutions.[18] This trend suggests that the anion XXXI, possibly in its cyclic form XXXII, is an intermediate in the hydrolysis and that the uncharged

XXX XXXI XXXII

molecule XXX (the predominant form in very acid solution) and the conjugate base of XXXI (the predominant form in very basic solution) are relatively inert.

One of the most convincing ways of showing that a reaction proceeds through a path involving free radicals is the demonstration that the reaction is accelerated by substances such as peroxides or azo compounds which readily produce free radicals. If a reaction is photochemically induced, it is almost certainly a free-radical reaction, and if it is inhibited by compounds such as hydrogen iodide or hydroquinone, which are known to lower the concentration of active free radicals, a similar conclusion may be drawn. A very familiar example of a free-radical reaction is the "abnormal" addition of HBr to allyl bromide. If the reagents are carefully purified, then mixed in the dark with care taken to exclude oxidizing agents, the HBr molecule very slowly adds to the double bond to form the 1,2-dibromide,[19] that is, the addition is like that of

HCl. The addition can be accelerated by addition of benzoyl peroxide and, more particularly, by illumination, but under these conditions the product is the 1,3-dibromide. The conditions favoring formation of the 1,3-dibromide thus indicate that it proceeds through a free-radical mechanism, and the inhibition of the "abnormal" addition by hydroquinone or diphenylamine confirms this.

[18] Chanley, Gindler, and Sobotka, *J. Am. Chem. Soc.*, **74**, 5347 (1952).
[19] Kharasch and Mayo, *J. Am. Chem. Soc.*, **55**, 2568 (1933).

Crossover Experiments

A number of molecular rearrangements may be regarded as processes in which a fragment is broken off from its position in the reactant molecule and becomes refastened to a different position in (a) the same or (b) a different molecule. In considering the mechanism of such reactions, it is important to know which of these two possibilities is the correct one—that is, whether the rearrangement is *intramolecular* or *intermolecular*. This question may sometimes be answered by carrying out the reaction with a mixture of two similar but nonidentical reactants and searching the product for compounds having fragments of both reactants, thus seeing whether fragments from one reactant have "crossed over" and have become attached to fragments of the other reactant.

One of the most familiar examples of the use of this mode of investigation is connected with the benzidine rearrangement, a reaction in which hydrazobenzenes are converted by acid to benzidines. If the reaction is carried out on a

mixture of 2,2'-dimethoxyhydrazobenzene (XXXIII) and its diethoxy analog (XXXIV), only two benzidines can be isolated, both of them symmetrically substituted.[20] The nonformation of the unsymmetric benzidine XXXV (which would result if fragments from two different hydrazobenzenes were to combine) is strong evidence that the reaction is intramolecular. For this reaction, it must

[20] Ingold and Kidd, *J. Chem. Soc.*, **1933**, 984.

be inferred either that the "new" bond (the C—C bond between benzene rings) is partially or wholly formed before the "old" bond (the N—N bond) is completely broken, or, if this is not the case, that the two fragments from a given molecule do not become free of each other's influence long enough to allow the fragment from another molecule to intercede. If, however, the reaction turned out to be intermolecular, two types of mechanism could come to mind. The first would involve a transition state in which two molecules collide and the rearranging fragments "exchange partners." The second (and more likely) possibility would be that the dissociating fragments become essentially independent of each other for at least a short time during the course of the rearrangement.

A somewhat different type of crossover experiment is possible if the species thought to be one of the rearranging fragments is isolable. For example, the rearrangements of 9-decalyl peroxybenzoate (XXXVI) and its peroxy-p-nitrobenzoate analog to the ester XXXVII are thought to proceed by migration of a benzoate ion from an oxygen atom to a carbon atom, during which time the remaining fragment of the molecule, the cation XXXVIII, presumably suffers rearrangement (as shown below in the parenthesis). If the reaction does follow such a path, the benzoate ion and the cation never become completely inde-

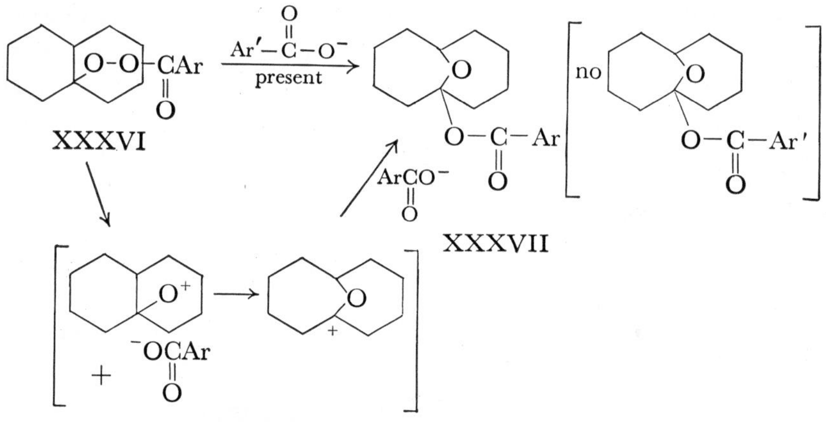

pendent, for if the salt lithium p-nitrobenzoate is added to the reaction mixture, no p-nitrobenzoate ester is found in the product.[21] Likewise, if the experiment is "reversed" and the peroxy-p-nitrobenzoate ester is rearranged in the presence of lithium benzoate (that is, if Ar = p-NO$_2$C$_6$H$_4^-$ and Ar' = C$_6$H$_5^-$), no unsubstituted benzoate ester is found in the product. These experiments, if taken alone, do not rule out the possibility that the rearrangement occurs through collision of two reactant molecules with a change of partners, a point that might

[21] Goering and Olsen, *J. Am. Chem. Soc.*, **75**, 5853 (1953).

best be settled by kinetic studies. It might also be argued that the reaction is intermolecular but the fragments are radicals rather than anions; in this case, added benzoate anions might not intercede in the reaction but added radicals conceivably could. This point might be settled by showing that the rearrangement is not subject to free-radical catalysis.

Isotopic Labeling

We have already seen (p. 131) how, in favorable cases, mere identification of the products of the reaction can indicate to a large degree which bonds are broken and where new bonds are formed. At the same time it was pointed out that more information was needed to answer such a question about the Claisen rearrangement of allyl cresyl ethers or the ammonolysis of chlorobenzene. Both of these reactions have, however, been studied using reactants especially prepared so that certain strategically located carbon atoms are the radioactive isotope, C^{14}. In such cases, only a small percentage of the molecules subjected to the reaction are so labeled, but it is these that trace the reaction.

The Claisen rearrangement has been carried out using allyl p-cresyl ether, labeled with C^{14} at the γ position (XXXIX).[22] When the resulting allyl cresol was subjected to oxidative degradation, the end carbon on the chain was eliminated as formaldehyde. Since none of the radioactive carbon was lost, it follows that the γ-carbon in the original ether does *not* become the end carbon in the rearrangement product. Since it is very difficult to conceive of a reaction

(*) designates labeled atom

path in which the β-carbon becomes attached to the ring during the rearrangement, we may then conclude that the rearrangement of ether **XXXIX** is similar to that of ether **VIII** (p. 134)—that is, that the γ-carbon becomes attached to the benzene ring.

[22] Schmid and Schmid, *Helv. Chim. Acta*, **35,** 1879 (1952).

The ammonolysis of chlorobenzene has been studied, using material in which the chlorine-bearing carbon is isotopically labeled. In this way, it is possible to show that *very nearly half* of the incoming —NH_2 groups become bonded to the carbon from which the chlorine departed. The remaining —NH_2 groups become bonded to carbons *ortho* to the labeled carbon, the other positions in the ring not being attacked.[23] This evidence points to a symmetric intermediate, a "benzyne" (XLIII), which then suffers attack by NH_3 or

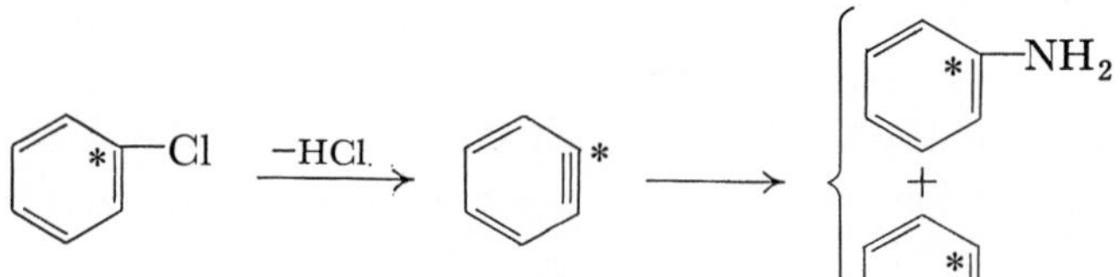

XLIII

NH_2^- at either of the triple-bonded carbons. The formation of a similar intermediate may be used to explain the rearrangement during the ammonolysis of *o*-iodoanisole (p. 133).

[23] Roberts, Simmons, Carlsmith, and Vaughan, *J. Am. Chem. Soc.*, **75**, 3290 (1953). The position(s) of the labeled carbon in the resulting aniline was determined by the following reaction sequence:

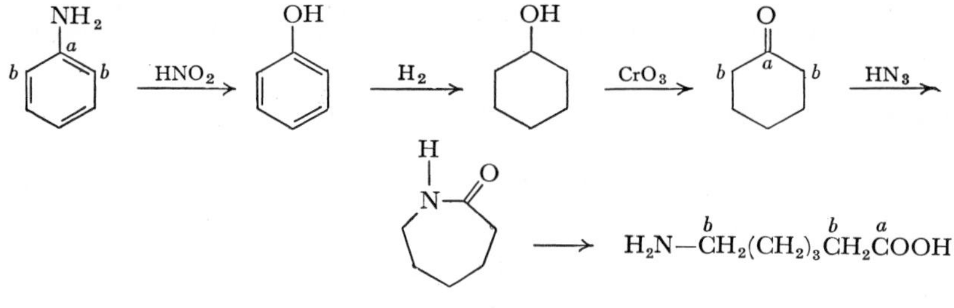

$$H_2N-\overset{b}{C}H_2(CH_2)_3\overset{b}{C}H_2\overset{a}{C}OOH$$

$$H_2N-\overset{b}{C}H_2(CH_2)_3\overset{b}{C}H_2\overset{a}{C}OOH \xrightarrow{HN_3} \overset{a}{C}O_2 + H_2\overset{b}{N}CH_2(CH_2)_3\overset{b}{C}H_2NH_2 \xrightarrow{MnO_4^-}$$

XL

$$\overset{b}{H}OOC(CH_2)_3\overset{b}{C}OOH$$

XLI

$$\overset{b}{H}OOC(CH_2)_3\overset{b}{C}OOH + 2HN_3 \rightarrow 2\overset{b}{C}O_2 + H_2N(CH_2)_3NH_2$$

XLI   XLII

If, in the original ammonolysis, the nitrogen atom had attached itself only to the labeled carbon, all of the labeled carbon should find itself in the keto group of cyclohexanone. If this were the case, *all* of the labeled carbon would be eliminated as CO_2 by two successive treatments of cyclohexanone with hydrazoic acid, HN_3. Actually, very nearly *half* of the radioactivity was eliminated as CO_2 in the formation of diamine (XL). The remainder was eliminated by oxidizing XL to glutaric acid (XLI), then removing two more molecules of CO_2 by additional treatment with HN_3. Thus, half of the labeled carbon is at position *a* in the aniline used, and the remaining half at positions *b*.

When studies are made using C^{14}, the route of the labeled atoms is naturally traced by using a radiation-sensitive device to follow the β^- radiation through a series of operations. Sometimes it is desired to carry out experiments with labeled nitrogen or oxygen, but in these cases the procedure must be substantially different. The greatest half life among the known radioisotopes of oxygen is 126 seconds, and that among the radioisotopes of nitrogen is only 10 minutes. It is thus very difficult to obtain and handle appreciable quantities of these isotopes and essentially impossible to perform a series of syntheses using them. Tracer work with oxygen or nitrogen must be carried out using samples of non-radioactive elements in which the atom percent of the rarer isotopes is substantially greater than that found in nature. Samples of water "enriched" with O^{18} and ammonium chloride "enriched" in N^{15} are available, and these compounds may be used to synthesize oxygen-labeled and nitrogen-labeled organic compounds. In such cases, the path of the "tagged" atoms is often followed by taking samples of the products, converting them to gaseous compounds, and analyzing for the atoms of various masses in the mass spectrograph. Experiments with labeled hydrogen can be carried out in much the same way, using hydrogen enriched with deuterium (H^2); this isotope is much more readily available than is the radioactive isotope tritium (H^3), and its behavior is more nearly the same as that of ordinary hydrogen.

One of the most familiar studies using labeled isotopes is that of the saponification of *n*-amyl acetate,[24] using water enriched with H_2O^{18}. Since the

acetate resulting from the reaction was enriched in O^{18} whereas the amyl alcohol was not, it could be concluded that whatever the mechanism for saponification, the ester had been split at *a* rather than at *b*. In this particular case *acyl-oxygen cleavage*, rather than *alkyl-oxygen cleavage*, had occurred.

A recent example of mechanistic study using deuterium is that of self-oxidation of *p,p′*-dimethoxydiphenyl carbinol (XLIV).[25] This alcohol, when heated in acid solution, is converted to a mixture of the corresponding ketone and the desoxy compound, XLV. If this reaction is carried out using deuterated

[24] Polanyi and Szabo, *Trans. Faraday Soc.*, **30**, 508 (1934). For a more critical treatment of this problem, see Kursanov and Kudryavtsev, *J. Gen. Chem. U.S.S.R.*, **26**, 1040 (1956).
[25] Bartlett and McCullum, *J. Am. Chem. Soc.*, **78**, 1441 (1956).

$$\left[CH_3O-\left\langle\bigcirc\right\rangle \right]_2 \overset{H}{\underset{|}{C}}-OH \xrightarrow{\text{heat}} R_2C=O + R_2\overset{H}{\underset{|}{C}}-H$$

XLIV   XLV

$$(R= CH_3O-\left\langle\bigcirc\right\rangle-)$$

trichloracetic acid, CCl_3COOD, as a solvent, essentially no deuterium enters the desoxy compound. This means that the hydrogen atom forming the new C—H bond in XLV did not come from the solvent and therefore must have come from the starting material. Moreover, it is well known that the hydrogens of the —OH groups in alcohols are *labile;* that is, they easily come off and on and may "exchange" with any acidic hydrogen or deuterium atoms in solution; the hydrogen atoms joined to carbon are generally not labile. Very shortly after the carbinol is mixed with the deuterated solvent, it becomes a mixture of R_2CHOH and R_2CHOD. Since, however, no deuterium entered the desoxy compound, XLV, it follows that none of the hydrogens bound to carbon in this compound arose from O—H linkages. This study thus points to a mechanism in which a hydrogen atom with its pair of electrons (that is, a hydride ion) is transferred from one carbinol molecule to the conjugate acid of another as shown:

$$R_2CH + \overset{H}{\underset{R}{\overset{|}{\underset{R}{C}}}}\overset{+}{OH_2} \longrightarrow R_2C-H \quad \overset{H}{\underset{R}{\overset{|}{\underset{R}{C}}}}\overset{+}{OH_2} \longrightarrow$$

$$\overset{+}{\underset{R_2C}{OH}} + H-\overset{H}{\underset{R}{\overset{|}{C}}}-R + H_2O$$

In carrying out experiments involving isotopic "tagging," it is generally assumed that the tagged atom behaves essentially as would an untagged atom of the same atomic number. Although we recognize today that the rate of a chemical reaction and its position of equilibrium are affected slightly by substitution of one isotope for another, this *isotope effect* for carbon, oxygen, nitrogen, and the heavier elements is almost always so small that it does not effect the interpretation of the results of isotopic mechanistic studies. With deuterium or tritium more caution must be used, for it is not uncommon that substitution of one hydrogen isotope for another in a reaction will change a rate constant or an equilibrium constant by 50 percent or more. It should not, however, be assumed that the "isotope effect" is merely a nuisance phenomenon which the chemist must invariably avoid or correct for. As we shall see (p. 192) mechanistic evidence can sometimes be obtained by shrewdly putting this effect to work.

Stereochemical Studies

Very often, organic reactions are applied to reactants capable of existing in stereoisomeric forms and yield products that are also capable of existing in stereoisomeric forms. In many such cases, an examination of the stereochemistry of the reaction may furnish important clues as to its mechanism. In two such experiments, which are here selected from a vast number performed by Hughes, Ingold, and co-workers,[26] an optically active reactant yielded a product which had practically no optical activity. Here, it must be assumed that both

$$\langle \bigcirc \rangle\!-\!\underset{\underset{CH_3}{|}}{CH}\!-\!Cl \text{ (optically active)} + H_2O \longrightarrow \langle \bigcirc \rangle\!-\!\underset{\underset{CH_3 \text{ (racemic)}}{|}}{CH}\!-\!OH$$
$$+ \ H^+ \ + \ Cl^-$$

$$\langle \bigcirc \rangle\!-\!\underset{\underset{CH_3}{|}}{CH}\!-\!NH_2 \text{ (optically active)} + HNO_2 \longrightarrow \langle \bigcirc \rangle\!-\!\underset{\underset{CH_3}{|}}{CH}\!-\!OH$$
$$\text{(racemic)}$$
$$+ \ N_2 \ + \ H_2O$$

| XLVI | XLVII | XLVIII |

reactions passed through at least one intermediate or transition state that was not optically active—that is, superimposable on its mirror image. This and other

[26] Hughes, Ingold, and co-workers; (a) J. Chem. Soc., **1937**, 1196–1243; (b) Nature, **166**, 178 (1950).

evidence suggests that both of the reactions have the planar *carbonium ion* XLVI as an intermediate. (In such a carbonium ion, the positive charge can be spread over the benzene ring by partial extension of the π-electron density to the carbon atom adjacent to the ring, a situation that is shown schematically by including resonance pictures XLVII and XLVIII for the carbonium ion.) It is this carbonium ion that then reacts with the solvent, water, to form the conjugate acid of the observed product.

Far more commonly, reactions of optically active substances yield products that display at least some optical activity. If this is so, more information must be obtained before mechanistic conclusions can be drawn. Even if there is only one asymmetric center in the reactant and one in the product, it is necessary to know (a) whether the configuration of the product is the same as or different from that of the reactant, and (b) whether the product is as optically pure as the reactant or appreciably less so. (The answer to either of these questions is obtained not by a single experiment but rather by a series of interconversions and comparisons as will be described in Chap. 7.)

If it can be determined that the configuration of the optically active product is *different* from that of the optically active reactant, the reaction is said to proceed with **inversion of configuration.** This occurs if the reaction path is similar to the basic hydrolysis of methyl iodide described on page 129. The basic hydrolysis of 2-*n*-octyl bromide in aqueous alcohol is just such a case.[26a] Here, the OH⁻ ion hits the halide molecule on one side, the Br⁻ group leaves from the opposite side, and the molecule in effect becomes "turned inside out." This

$$OH^- \dashrightarrow \underset{\text{Me}}{\overset{\text{Hx}}{H-C}}-Br \longrightarrow HO \text{---}\underset{\text{Me}}{\overset{H \ \ Hx}{C}}\text{---}Br \longrightarrow HO-\underset{\text{Me}}{\overset{\text{Hx}}{C}}-H + Br^-$$

$$(Hx=C_6H_{13}-)$$

$$\text{XLIX}$$

reaction is an example of the so-called *Walden inversion*; the transition state, XLIX, like the reactant and product, is nonsuperimposible on its mirror image. We may in fact make the generalization that any reaction yielding an optically active product cannot proceed through an intermediate or transition state that has lost its asymmetry. In particular, free carbonium ions, $\left[\begin{array}{c} R' \\ R-C \\ R'' \end{array} \right]^+$,

$$\text{R}'$$
$$|$$

and free radicals of the type $\text{R}-\overset{|}{\underset{|}{\text{C}}}\cdot$ are excluded as intermediates in such

$$\text{R}''$$

reactions, since neither of these types of fragments can ordinarily support asymmetry.

In the Wolff rearrangement of *sec*-butyl diazomethyl ketone (L) to 3-methyl-valeric acid, the *sec*-butyl group migrates from the carbonyl carbon to the adjacent carbon. If the diazoketone used is optically active, the resulting acid

L

also is optically active, with an optical purity essentially the same as that of the starting material,[27] showing that the migrating *sec*-butyl group does not escape from the remainder of the molecule for sufficient time to allow it to racemize. More important, the *configuration* of the resulting acid was shown to be the *same* as that of the diazoketone (L)—that is, the reaction occurred with **retention of configuration**—indicating that the breaking of bond *a* and the formation of bond *b* occurred on the same side of the *sec*-butyl group. Less frequently, a reaction occurs with retention of configuration because two steps are involved, both with an inversion; the first step turns the molecule "inside out" and the second turns it "outside out" again.

We have already seen (p. 137) how the trapping of monobrominated intermediates indicates that the addition of bromine to olefins often takes place in steps. This stepwise mechanism applies to the bromination of maleic and fumaric acids, and stereochemical studies further indicate that the intermediate in the bromination of maleic acid must be different from that in the bromination of fumaric acid. The chief dibromosuccinic acid obtained from maleic acid is the resolvable racemic form LI, whereas the chief dibromosuccinic acid obtained from fumaric acid is the nonresolvable *meso* form, LII.[28] Now suppose that the monobrominated intermediate in these reactions had bromine attached to only *one* carbon atom (that is, could be represented by structure LIII).

[27] Wiberg and Hutton, *J. Am. Chem. Soc.*, **78**, 1640 (1956).
[28] McKenzie, *J. Chem. Soc.*, **101**, 1196 (1912).

Assuming the configuration about the positively charged carbon to be planar and assuming free rotation about the C—C bond, the pair of enantiomorphic intermediate ions from maleic acid would be the same as that from fumaric acid, and the same mixture of dibromo acids should result in each case. Since this is not what is observed, an intermediate other than LIII must be involved

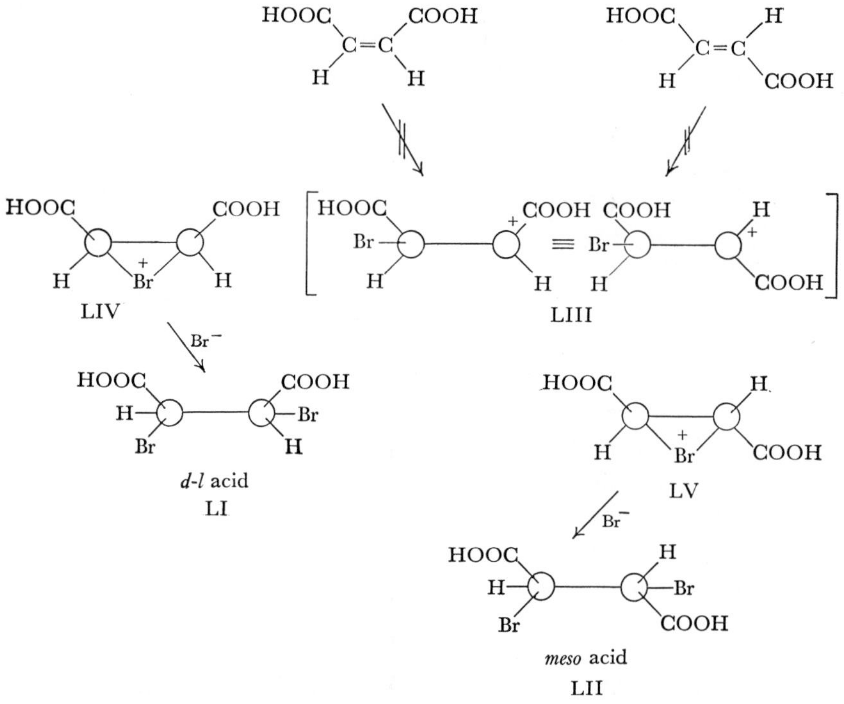

in one or both cases. The cyclic bromonium ions LIV and LV are consistent both with the stereochemistry[29] and the stepwise nature of the addition reaction and are thus possible intermediates, whereas the cation LIII is not. The conversion of the intermediates LIV and LV to the acids LI and LII, respectively, is most easily visualized by imagining the bromide ion attacking the right-hand carbon atoms of the intermediates LIV and LV from the rear of the page.

Limitations of Reactions

Organic chemists are all too familiar with instances in which one compound will undergo a given reaction successfully but another compound, apparently similar to the first, will stubbornly refuse to react under the same conditions.

[29] Roberts and Kimball, *J. Am. Chem. Soc.*, **59**, 947 (1937).

Such differences are sometimes best explained by assuming a transition state or intermediate into which the second compound, for some good reason, cannot be converted. As a very simple example, the conversion of an amide $R\!-\!\overset{\displaystyle O}{\overset{\|}{C}}\!-\!NH_2$ to the amine RNH_2 by the "Hofmann rearrangement" (p. 128) cannot be used to convert the amide $R\!-\!\underset{\displaystyle O}{\underset{\|}{C}}\!-\!NHCH_3$ to $RNH\!-\!CH_3$, simply because species analogous to the necessary intermediates $R\!-\!\overset{\displaystyle O}{\overset{\|}{C}}\!-\!NBr^-$ and $R\!-\!N\!\!=\!\!C\!\!=\!\!O$ cannot form from the N-methyl amide.

Similarly, most α,β-unsaturated acids are readily decarboxylated, but the acid LVI is not.[30] This difference may be explained by assuming that intermediates in the decarboxylations of α,β-unsaturated acids are the isomeric β,γ-unsaturated acids. The latter are known to suffer decarboxylation readily, possibly through a cyclic intermediate or transition state such as LVII. On this

$$(CH_3)_3C\!-\!CH\!\!=\!\!CH\!-\!COOH$$

LVI   LVII

basis, acid LVI would be stable simply because it cannot be converted without skeletal rearrangement to a β,γ-unsaturated acid.

More subtly, dimethylaniline readily undergoes condensation with the benzenediazonium ion to form p-dimethylaminoazobenzene (LVIII), whereas the apparently similar xylidene, LIX, does not.[31] An intermediate or transition state such as LX is consistent with this disparity if it is assumed that in such a

LVIII   LIX   LX

[30] Arnold, Elmer, and Dodson, J. Am. Chem. Soc., 72, 4359 (1950).
[31] Friedlaender, Monatsh., 19, 627 (1898).

structure the substituents on the 2 and 6 positions of the benzene ring must lie in or near the same plane as the two N-methyl groups. If the 2 and 6 substituents are hydrogen atoms (that is, R=H), such coplanarity is possible, but if they are both methyl groups, it may be shown with atomic models that the hydrogen atoms of the ring methyl groups interfere with those of the N-methyls, preventing the necessary coplanarity. Thus, when the PhN$_2^+$ ion attempts to attack the 4 position in LIX, there is no way the p electrons of the amine nitrogen atom can spread themselves over the π orbitals of the ring to help accommodate the added positive charge, and the new bond does not form.

As a final example in which a reaction is rendered unsuccessful by a small structural modification in the reactant, consider the rearrangement of the bromomagnesium derivative of *cis*-2-chloro-1-methyl-1-indanol (LXI) to 2-methyl-1-indanone (LXII). If the *trans* isomer is used in place of the *cis*, the yield of indanone drops from 80 to 5 percent,[32] and large amounts of tars appear in the reaction mixture. This indicates that a successful reaction requires that the C—Cl bond be broken by the magnesium atom on one side of the ring while, at the same time and on the opposite side of the ring, a methyl group migrates from one carbon atom to another. A transition state such as LXIII is thus consistent with the difference in reactivity of the two stereoisomers.

Physical Detection of Intermediates

In a few favorable cases the presence of an intermediate that may be difficult or impossible to isolate from the reaction mixture may be detected by physical

[32] Geissman and Akawie, *J. Am. Chem. Soc.*, **73**, 1993 (1951).

measurements. One of the most familiar examples is the nitronium ion, NO_2^+, the active nitrating agent in those mixtures of nitric and sulfuric acids used to nitrate aromatic hydrocarbons. Examinations of the Raman spectra of such nitrating mixtures revealed the existence of this ion[33] many years before its important role in nitration reactions became appreciated as a result of other studies (Chap. 11).

In another case, cryoscopic (freezing-point) measurements have helped to explain some puzzling differences in behavior. Under ordinary conditions mesitoic acid (LXIV) is esterified only with difficulty. However, if this acid is dissolved in concentrated sulfuric acid and the resulting mixture added to an excess of alcohol, esterification is rapid and essentially complete. On the other hand, this method for esterification is ineffective for benzoic acid. Now cryoscopic measurements show that *two* moles of particles are produced for each mole of benzoic acid dissolved in concentrated H_2SO_4, but *four* moles of particles are produced for each mole of mesitoic acid dissolved.[34] By assuming that benzoic acid exhibits ordinary basic behavior in sulfuric acid, but that mesitoic acid is converted to the carbonium ion, LXV, we may explain the differences both in chemistry and cryoscopy. As is indicated, a carbonium ion of the type

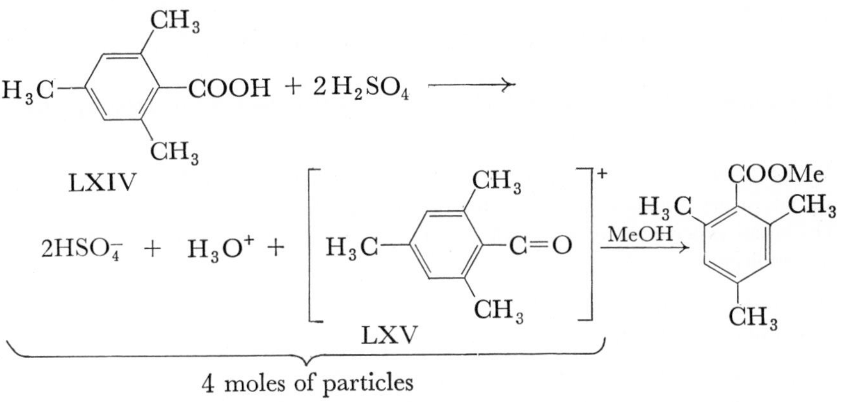

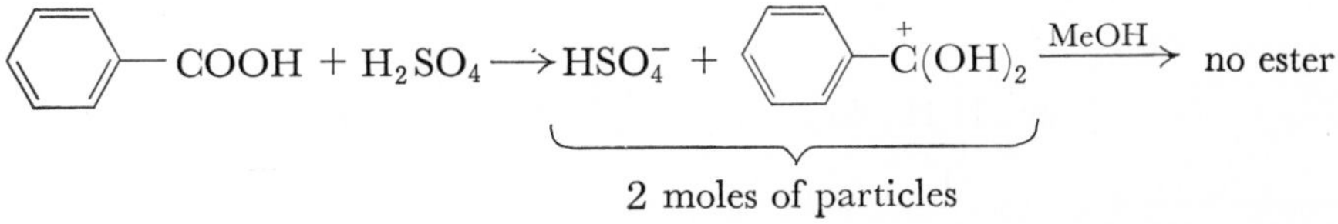

$$\text{LXIV} + 2\,H_2SO_4 \longrightarrow 2\,HSO_4^- + H_3O^+ + [\text{LXV}]^+ \xrightarrow{\text{MeOH}} \text{(ester)}$$

4 moles of particles

$$\text{Ph-COOH} + H_2SO_4 \longrightarrow HSO_4^- + \text{Ph-}\overset{+}{C}(OH)_2 \xrightarrow{\text{MeOH}} \text{no ester}$$

2 moles of particles

$Ar-\overset{+}{C}=O$ is the required intermediate for esterification under these conditions.

In a few cases, free radicals of long life occurring as reaction intermediates can be detected by magnetic measurements. We shall see later (Chap. 16) that

[33] Medard, *Compt. Rend.*, **199**, 1615 (1934)
[34] Treffers and Hammett, *J. Am. Chem. Soc.*, **59**, 1708 (1937).

species with unpaired electrons tend to move *into* an externally applied magnetic field whereas essentially all other compounds and ions tend to move away from such a field. When the anion of phenanthraquinone-3-sulfonic acid (LXVI) is reduced in aqueous alkali with glucose, the solution turns brown

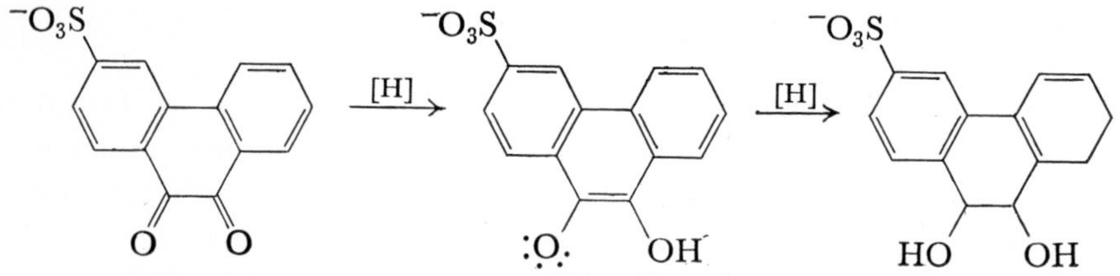

LXVI   LXVII   LXVIII

brown,
paramagnetic

and becomes paramagnetic; then, as the reaction proceeds, the color fades and the paramagnetism disappears,[35] suggesting that the brown intermediate species is a free radical of the semiquinone type (LXVII). The final yellow product is the corresponding hydroquinone, LXVIII.

EXERCISES FOR CHAPTER 5

1. How can it be shown that the Wolff-Kishner reaction does not proceed by a free-radical mechanism?

2. In the so-called Fries rearrangement, aryl esters such as phenyl acetate are converted to acyl phenols such as *o*-hydroxyacetophenone by action of Lewis acids. Devise an experiment to show whether this "rearrangement" is intramolecular or intermolecular.

3. Phenanthrene dibromide (I) is known to lose HBr on standing to yield 9-bromo-phenanthrene (II). How would you show that I is not an intermediate in the

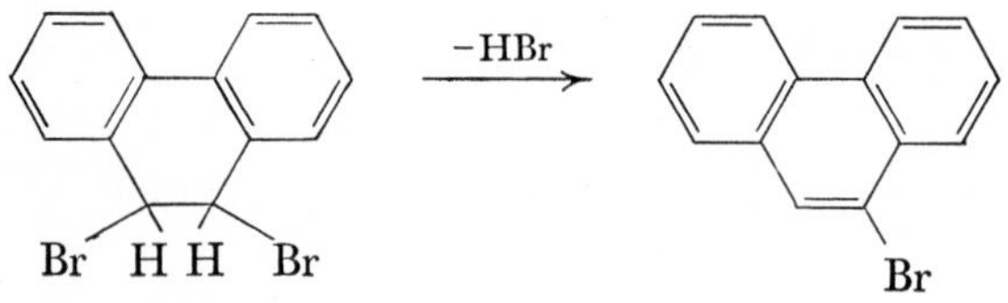

Br H H Br   Br

I   II

bromination of phenanthrene itself to form II?

4. Why would you expect the hydrolysis of α-cyclohexylethyl chloride (III) to be less likely to go through a carbonium ion intermediate than the hydrolysis of α-phenylethyl chloride (IV)? Devise an experiment to show that the first of these halides does not form a free carbonium ion during its hydrolysis.

[35] Michaelis, Boeker, and Reber, *J. Am. Chem. Soc.*, **60**, 202 (1938).

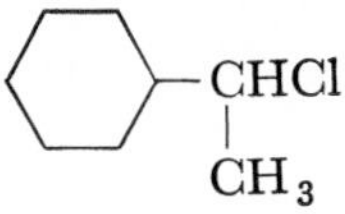

III 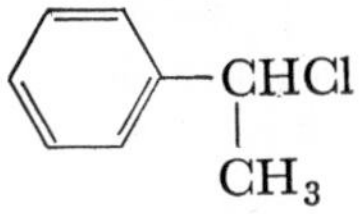   IV

5. The decarboxylation of oxaloacetic has been found to be accelerated by Cu^{2+}.

$$HO-C-C-CH_2COOH \xrightarrow{Cu^{2+}} CO_2 + HO-C-C-CH_3$$

It has been suggested that an intermediate is a chelate involving the anion of the acid. Devise an experiment to show which of the chelate structures shown below is more likely to be the active intermediate in this reaction.

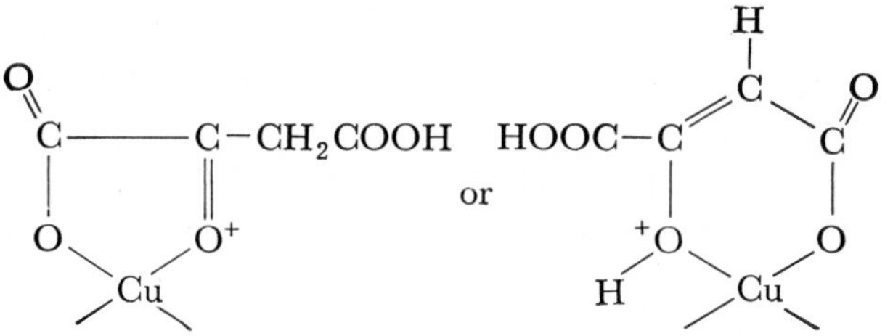

6. In the Curtius rearrangement, benzoyl azide, $C_6H_5-C-N_3$, is converted to N_2 and phenyl isocyanate, $C_6H_5-N=C=O$. How could you show that the four-membered ring-compound V is not an intermediate in this reaction?

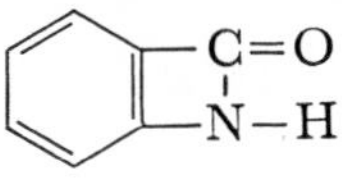

V

7. What evidence indicates that the hydrolyses of the two chlorides below proceed through different mechanisms?

$$(CH_3)_3CCH_2Cl$$

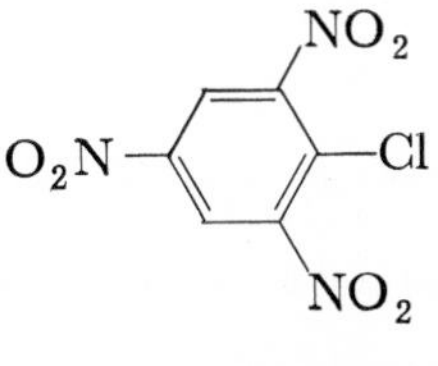

8. Diaryl sulfones are converted to diaryl selenides on heating with selenium.

$$Ar-S-Ar + Se \rightarrow Ar-Se-Ar + SO_2$$

Devise experiments that would show:

(a) Whether the carbon atoms bound to selenium in the product are those bonded to sulfur in the original sulfone.

(b) Whether the two aryl groups in a molecule of the product came from a single molecule or from two different molecules of sulfone.

9. In the Fischer indole synthesis, an example of which is shown below, a phenylhydrazone is converted to an indole by action of acid.

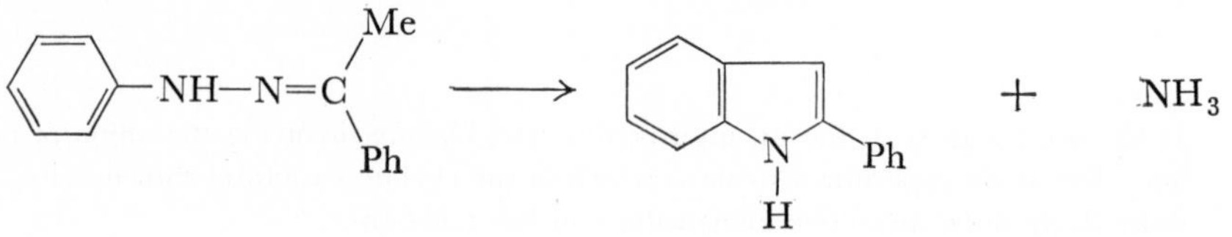

Outline two experiments, one using isotopic labeling, the other without, to determine which of the two nitrogens of the phenylhydrazone is lost during the reaction.

10. If the quaternary ammonium iodide VI is heated with aqueous base, the olefin VII is slowly formed and trimethylamine is eliminated. Two mechanisms are proposed: (a) a two-step process, and (b) a "concerted" process. Devise two separate experiments, one with isotopic labeling, the other without (neither involving kinetics) to choose between (a) and (b).

(a)

$$\underset{\text{VI}}{PhCH_2-\overset{\overset{\displaystyle Me}{|}}{CH}-CH_2NMe_3^+ \ I^-} \underset{\longleftarrow}{\overset{OH^-}{\longrightarrow}} \underset{\text{(fast, equilibrium)}}{PhCH_2-\overset{\overset{\displaystyle Me}{|}}{\overset{-}{C}}-CH_2NMe_3^+}$$

$$PhCH_2\overset{-}{\underset{\underset{\displaystyle Me}{|}}{C}}-CH_2NMe_3^+ \longrightarrow \underset{\text{VII}}{PhCH_2-\overset{\underset{\displaystyle Me}{|}}{C}=CH_2} + NMe_3 \quad \text{(slow)}$$

(b)

$$PhCH_2-\overset{\overset{\displaystyle Me}{|}}{\underset{\underset{\displaystyle H}{|}}{C}}\text{—}CH_2\text{—}\overset{+}{N}Me_3 \longrightarrow \underset{\text{VII}}{PhCH_2-\overset{\underset{\displaystyle Me}{|}}{C}=CH_2} + NMe_3 \,\text{(slow)}$$

$$HO\overset{..}{:}$$

Which method is the less equivocal?

11. Outline an experiment, starting with available materials, to show whether the carbonyl carbon or the carboxyl carbon is eliminated in the decarbonylation of phenylpyruvic acid:

$$PhCH_2\text{—}\overset{\overset{\displaystyle }{\underset{\underset{\displaystyle O}{\|}}{C}}}{}\text{—}COOH \rightarrow PhCH_2COOH + CO$$

12. Benzil, Ph—C—C—Ph, is converted by base to benzilic acid, Ph₂C—COOH (with OH on the carbon).

   $$\text{Ph}-\underset{\underset{O}{\|}}{C}-\underset{\underset{O}{\|}}{C}-\text{Ph}, \qquad \overset{\overset{OH}{|}}{Ph_2C}-COOH$$

   Devise a nonkinetic experiment to choose between the stepwise mechanism (a) and the "concerted" mechanism (b).

(a)

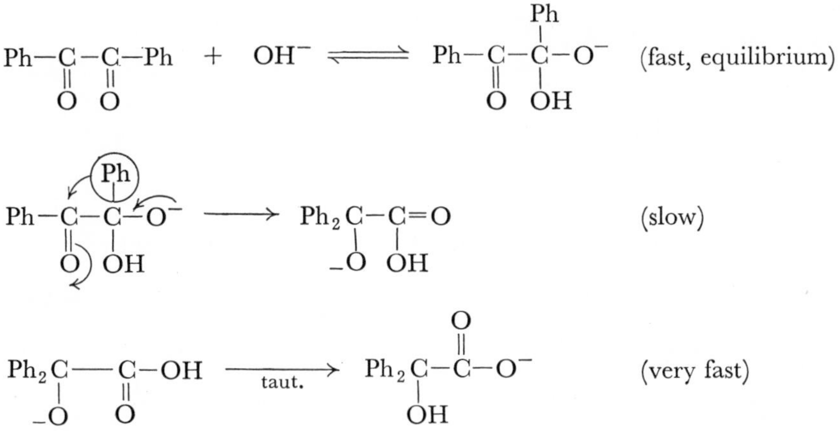

$$\text{Ph}-\underset{O}{\overset{\|}{C}}-\underset{O}{\overset{\|}{C}}-\text{Ph} \;+\; OH^- \;\rightleftharpoons\; \text{Ph}-\underset{O}{\overset{\|}{C}}-\overset{\overset{Ph}{|}}{\underset{OH}{C}}-O^- \quad \text{(fast, equilibrium)}$$

$$\text{Ph}-\underset{O}{\overset{\|}{C}}-\overset{\overset{(Ph)}{}}{\underset{OH}{C}}-O^- \;\longrightarrow\; Ph_2C{\underset{-O\; OH}{-}}C=O \quad \text{(slow)}$$

$$Ph_2C{\underset{-O \quad O}{\overset{\quad\|}{}}}C-OH \;\xrightarrow{\text{taut.}}\; Ph_2\underset{OH}{\overset{\overset{O}{\|}}{C}}-C-O^- \quad \text{(very fast)}$$

(b)

$$HO^- \;\; \overset{(Ph)\;\; Ph}{\underset{O \quad O}{C-C}} \;\xrightarrow{\text{slow}}\; HO-\underset{O\; O^-}{C}-CPh_2 \;\xrightarrow{\text{fast}}\; {}^-O-\underset{OH}{\overset{\overset{O}{\|}}{C}}-C(Ph)_2$$

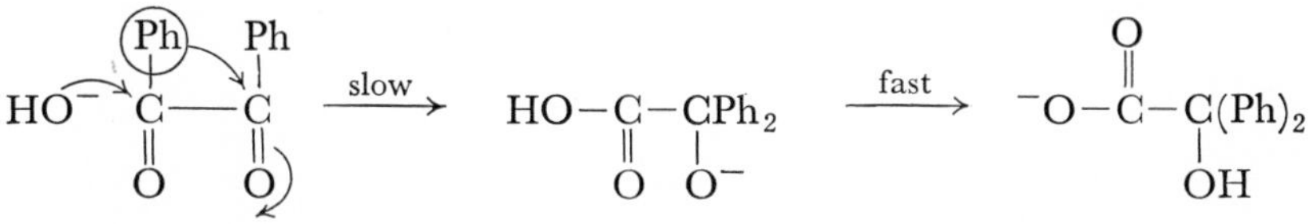

13. In the "Favorskii rearrangement," 2-chlorocyclohexanone is converted with sodium ethoxide to cyclopentanecarboxylic ester. Devise an experiment to choose between proposed mechanisms (a) and (b) below. Note that (b) involves a cyclopropanone intermediate whereas (a) does not.

(a)

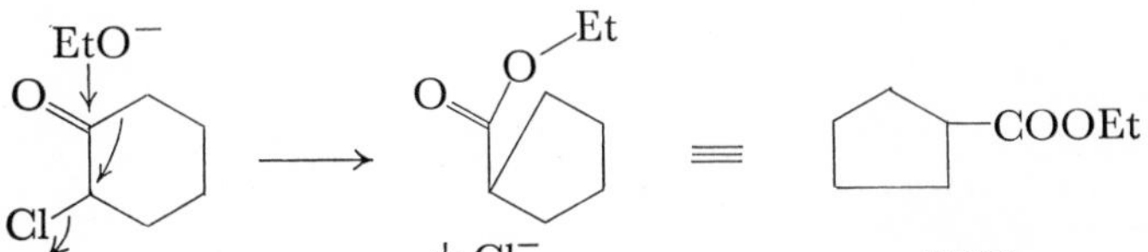

VIII

(b)

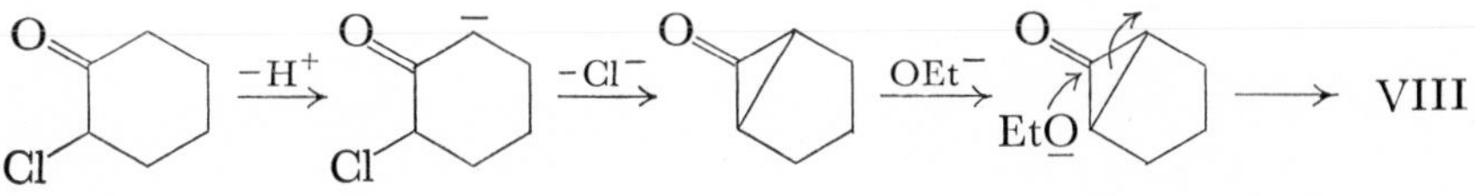

VIII

See how your method compares with that of Loftfield, *J. Am. Chem. Soc.*, **73**, 4707 (1951).

14. When the toluenesulfonic ester IX is dissolved in glacial acetic acid, it is converted to the acetate XI. The cyclic ion X has been proposed as an intermediate. Devise an experiment that would indicate that such an ion is an active intermediate.

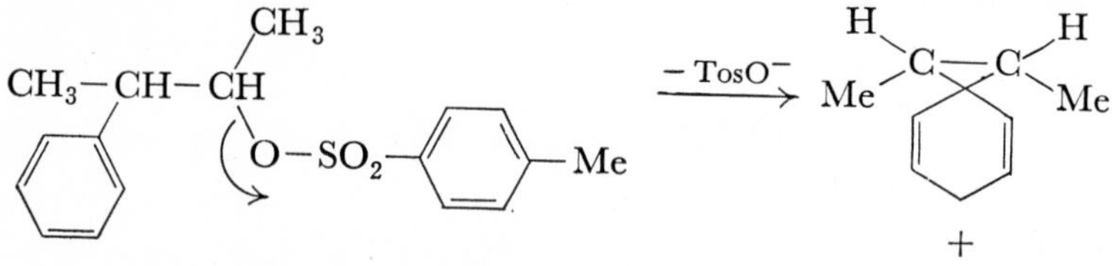

IX

X

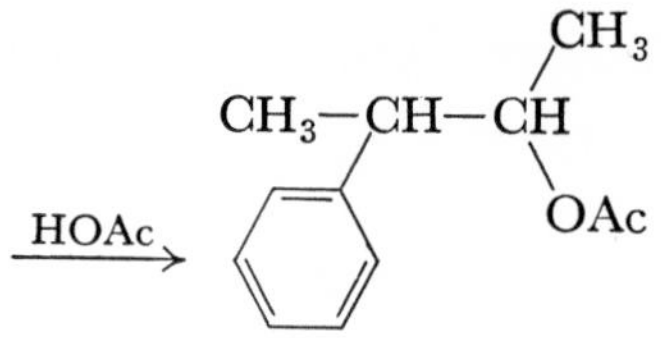

XI

CHAPTER 6

Methods for Determining

Reaction Mechanisms

II. Kinetic Studies[1]

IN DISCUSSING THE TOOLS used for the investigation of reaction mechanisms, we have postponed until last the method of most general applicability. For virtually all reactions there is (at least in principle) a quantitative relationship between the reaction speed at a given temperature and the concentration of the reagents. The chief object of a kinetic study is the determination of this relationship. In addition, mechanistic hints may sometimes arise from measurements of variations in the reaction velocity with temperature, with the ionic strength of the reaction medium, or with the solvent composition. The majority of useful organic reactions are complex, taking place in a series of steps. One of these steps must be slower than the others, and this step often (but unfortunately not always) determines the rate of the overall reaction; in such cases the slow step acts as a sort of "kinetic bottleneck." The kinetic study of a reaction will often allow us to say, with a reasonable degree of confidence, just which species participate in this **rate-determining step,** but for some reactions, as we shall point out, ambiguities may arise in interpretation of the data.

[1] The fundamentals of kinetics are treated in most textbooks in elementary physical chemistry. See, for example, (a) Moore, *Physical Chemistry*, 2d. ed., Prentice-Hall, Inc., New York, 1955, pp. 528–580. For more detailed presentations, see (b) Frost and Pearson, *Kinetics and Mechanism*, John Wiley and Sons, Inc., New York, 1953; and (c) Glasstone, Laidler, and Eyring, *The Theory of Rate Processes*, McGraw-Hill Book Co., Inc., New York, 1941. (d) Of particular interest to organic chemists is Friess and Weissberger, "Investigations of Rates and Mechanisms" (Vol. VIII of Weissberger's *Technique of Organic Chemistry*), Interscience Publishers, Inc., New York, 1953, pp. 169–535.

This text is concerned mainly with reactions *in solution*. Gas-phase reactions are much less common in organic chemistry laboratories, and the treatment of heterogeneous reactions is sufficiently complex so that it is best deferred to more specialized works.[2]

Experimental Methods

Success in a kinetic study depends largely on the selection of a suitable method for following the course of the reaction. Chemical analyses are very frequently used. Aliquots may be taken from a given reaction mixture at accurately determined time intervals and then titrated for one or more of the reactants or products. Alternately, a number of identical reaction mixtures may be made up, the individual mixtures taken one by one at fixed times during the course of the reaction, and the total contents of each mixture titrated. The methods for following the rates of a large number of organic reactions have been recently summarized by Friess.[1(d)]

Unless the titration reaction is very much faster than the reaction being studied, it is necessary to stop or slow down (to "quench") the latter by cooling, by high dilution, or by chemical action before beginning the titration, otherwise the titration results obviously will not reflect the composition of the mixture at the time the sample was removed.

Where possible, it is generally preferable to follow the reaction by measuring some physical property of the solution that changes as the reaction progresses. The need for quenching is eliminated in such cases, the system is not disturbed by the sampling process, and more measurements may be carried out within a given time. Spectrophotometric methods have proven particularly valuable, especially in cases where one of the reactants absorbs strongly at one wavelength with one of the products absorbing strongly at another. Measurements of changes in optical rotation, refractive index, conductivity, and dielectric constant have also been employed. Even the measurement of the small volume changes accompanying a reaction in solution (dilatometry) is frequently used, but in such cases, the temperature of the reaction must be kept constant to within 0.002° or less.[3]

Reactions which are inconveniently slow at room temperatures may be studied at elevated temperatures, whereas those too fast for measurements by conventional methods may often be studied in so-called *flow reactors*—devices ingeniously constructed to allow the composition of the reaction mixture to

---

[2] See, for example, Laidler, *Chemical Kinetics*, McGraw-Hill Book Co., Inc., New York, 1950, pp. 145–179.

[3] See, for example, the study of aromatic nitration reported by Hughes, Ingold, and Reed, *J. Chem. Soc.*, **1950**, 2438.

be determined after the reactants have been in contact with each other for only a fraction of a second.[4]

First-, Second-, and Third-order Reactions

It will be recalled that the rate of a *first-order reaction* is proportional to the concentration of just *one* reactant. Representing the rate of decrease of the concentration of reactant A in the usual manner as $-d(A)/dt$, the defining equation for a first-order reaction is then

$$-\frac{d(A)}{dt} = k_1(A) \tag{1}$$

or, in its integrated form,

$$\ln \frac{(A)_0}{(A)} = k_1 t \tag{2}$$

(here, the concentration of reactant A at the beginning of the reaction is $(A)_0$; after time, t, the concentration drops to (A); and k_1 is the first-order rate constant).

Equation (2) emphasizes an important feature of first-order reactions; the time in which a given fraction of the reactant is consumed does *not* depend upon concentration; that is, A/A_0 depends only on the value of t. This characteristic is exemplified by the most familiar type of first-order reaction, radioactive decay, for which the half-life period (or, if you wish, the third-, fourth, or tenth-life period) of a decaying species is characteristic of the species but wholly independent of the size of sample.

A typical first-order reaction is the hydrolysis of t-butyl chloride in formic acid containing small amounts of water. The rate depends only upon the concentration of the alkyl chloride, being independent of the concentration of water:[5]

$$Me_3CCl + H_2O \rightarrow Me_3COH + HCl. \quad \frac{-d(t\text{-BuCl})}{dt} = k_1(t\text{-BuCl}) \tag{3}$$

Similarly, first-order kinetics have been observed for the loss of halide from a large number of *tertiary* alkyl halides in aqueous alcohol and in other solvents. However, such reactions, sometimes called *solvolyses* (splitting by solvent), are generally complex; several products may often be isolated from a single reaction mixture in spite of the apparent simplicity of the kinetics.

[4] Flow reactors are discussed by Harris, *J. Phys. and Colloid Chem.*, **51**, 505 (1947); and by Denbigh, *Trans. Faraday Soc.*, **40**, 352 (1944). For a discussion of a number of methods of attack on very rapid reactions, see Ref. (1d), pp. 669–738.

[5] Bateman and Hughes, *J. Chem. Soc.*, **1937**, 1187.

A first-order reaction of a very different nature is the decomposition of di-t-butyl peroxide $(CH_3)_3C$—O—O—$C(CH_3)_3$.[6] Carried out in the vapor phase in the presence of a large quantity of glass wool, the reaction is

$$(CH_3)_3C—O—O—C(CH_3)_3 \xrightarrow{150°} (CH_3)_2C{=}O + C_2H_6$$

$$\frac{-d(t\text{-}Bu_2O_2)}{dt} = k_1(t\text{-}Bu_2O_2) \quad (4)$$

As we shall see (Chap. 16), the yields and identities of the products may be changed by removing the glass wool, or more particularly, by carrying out the decomposition in a variety of solvents. The decomposition itself, however, continues to obey first-order kinetics.

For most *second-order reactions*, the rate is proportional to the product of *two* concentrations. Calling these two concentrations (A) and (B), the defining equation is then

$$\frac{-d(A)}{dt} = k_2(A)(B) \quad (5)$$

which, when integrated, gives

$$\frac{1}{(B)_0 - (A)_0} \ln \frac{(A)_0(B)}{(B)_0(A)} = k_2 t \quad (6)$$

where $(A)_0$ and $(B)_0$ are the concentrations of the reagents at the beginning of the reaction. Such a reaction, although "second-order overall," is said to be first-order with respect to (B) and first order with respect to (A).

Typical of second-order reactions are a tremendous number of nucleophilic substitution reactions on *primary* alkyl halides—for example, the basic hydrolysis of methyl bromide in dilute aqueous alcohol.

$$CH_3Br + OH^- \rightarrow CH_3OH + Br^- \quad \frac{-d(MeBr)}{dt} = k_2(MeBr)(OH^-) \quad (7)$$

The bromination and iodination of acetone in dilute aqueous base are, to a good approximation, second-order reactions:

$$CH_3—C—CH_3 + I_2 \xrightarrow{OH^-} CH_3—C—CH_2I$$
$$\quad\; \| \qquad\qquad\qquad\qquad \|$$
$$\quad\; O \qquad\qquad\qquad\qquad O$$

$$\frac{-d(Me_2C{=}O)}{dt} = k_2(OH^-)(Me_2C{=}O) \quad (8)$$

[6] Raley, Rust, and Vaughan, *J. Am. Chem. Soc.*, **70**, 1336 (1948).

Note that the rate here is proportional to the concentrations of acetone *and* *hydroxide* but *independent* of the concentration of iodine.[7]

Less often, the rate of a second-order reaction is proportional to the square of the concentration of a single reagent. The "Diels-Alder type" dimerization of cyclopentadiene is such a case.[8]

$$\frac{-d(C_5H_6)}{dt} = k_2(C_5H_6)^2 \qquad (9)$$

The integrated form of equation (9) is simply $1/A - 1/A_0 = k_2 t$, an expression that may be applied also to a second-order reaction between two different reagents whose initial concentrations are the same.

The rate of a *third-order* reaction may be proportional to the product of three concentrations. The reaction of ethylene oxide, H_2C———CH_2, with HBr in water is of this type.[9]

$$H_2C\text{———}CH_2 + H^+ + Br^- \rightarrow H_2\overset{HO}{C}-\overset{Br}{C}H_2$$

$$\frac{-d(C_2H_4O)}{dt} = k_3(C_2H_4O)(H^+)(Br^-) \qquad (10)$$

The cyanide-catalyzed benzoin condensation is also a third-order reaction, first order in cyanide and second order in benzaldehyde.[10,11]

$$2PhCHO \xrightarrow{CN^-} Ph\text{—}CH\text{—}\overset{O}{\overset{\|}{C}}\text{—}Ph$$
$$\underset{OH}{}$$

$$\frac{-d(PhCHO)}{dt} = k_3(PhCHO)^2(CN^-) \qquad (11)$$

Many reactions, a number of them treated in subsequent chapters, present kinetic pictures that are even more complicated. For example, the formation of

[7] Dawson and Spivey, *J. Chem. Soc.*, **1930**, 2180. This is a case where a reagent not present in a very large excess is nevertheless not included in the kinetic expression. As we shall presently see, the action of this reagent occurs *after* the rate-determining step.

[8] Kaufmann and Wassermann, *J. Chem. Soc.*, **1939**, 870.

[9] Brønsted, Kilpatrick, and Kilpatrick, *J. Am. Chem. Soc.*, **51**, 428 (1929).

[10] Stern, *Z. physik. Chem.*, **50**, 513 (1905).

[11] The integrated rate equations for reactions (10) and (11) are rather complex algebraically. For a tabulation of integrated rate equations and "half-life" equations for a number of kinetic situations, see Livingston, Ref. 1(d), pp. 172–173.

acetone semicarbazone, $(Me_2C{=}N{-}NH{-}\overset{\overset{\textstyle O}{\|}}{C}{-}NH_2)$, from acetone and semi-carbazide[12,13] is subject to general acid catalysis. If the reaction be carried out in the presence of a weak acid, HA, two terms will appear in the rate equation, one involving the catalytic constant of the hydronium ion, k_{H^+}, the other involving the catalytic constant associated with the weak acid, k_{HA}.

$$Me_2C{=}O + NH_2{-}NH{-}\overset{\overset{\textstyle O}{\|}}{C}{-}NH_2 \xrightarrow[H^+]{HA} Me_2C{=}N{-}NH{-}\overset{\overset{\textstyle O}{\|}}{C}{-}NH_2 + H_2O$$

$$\frac{-d(Me_2C{=}O)}{dt} = \frac{(Me_2C{=}O)(\text{``}NH_2{-}NH{-}\overset{\overset{\textstyle O}{\|}}{C}{-}NH_2\text{''})}{1+(H)/K_{s^+}} [k_{HA}(HA) + k_{H^+}(H^+)] \quad (12)$$

where ($\text{``}NH_2{-}NH{-}\overset{\overset{\textstyle O}{\|}}{C}{-}NH_2\text{''}$) refers to the total stoichiometric concentration of added semicarbazide, including that which is converted to its conjugate acid (acidity constant K_{s^+}). The denominator in reaction (12) serves merely to convert this total concentration to the concentration of unionized semicarbazide (Ex. 2(b), p. 195), the reactive nucleophilic species. The rate law is thus less formidable than it might seem at first glance.

An equally complex rate law governs the reaction between H_2S and cyanamide in slightly acid solution to form thiourea:[14]

$$NH_2{-}C{\equiv}N + H_2S \rightarrow NH_2{-}\overset{\overset{\textstyle S}{\|}}{C}{-}NH_2$$

$$\frac{-d(NH_2CN)}{dt} = \frac{k_2(\text{``}H_2S\text{''})(\text{``}NH_2CN\text{''})}{[1 + K_c/(H^+)][1 + (H^+)/K_{H_2S}]} \quad (13)$$

(Again, the quantities in quotation marks refer to "stoichiometric" concentrations, whereas K_c and K_{H_2S} are the acidity constants of cyanamide and H_2S, respectively.)

It is appropriate to emphasize at this point the distinction between the *order* of a reaction and its *molecularity*. We have seen that the order of a simple reaction is merely a description of the algebraic form of its differential-rate equation. On the other hand, we shall define the molecularity of a reaction as the *number of distinct chemical species* (ions, molecules, or free atoms) *that form new bonds or suffer the breakage of old bonds during the rate-determining step*. The molecularity of a reaction thus depends upon an assumed mechanism (which may be

[12] Conant and Bartlett, *J. Am. Chem. Soc.*, **54**, 2881 (1932).
[13] Westheimer, *ibid.*, **56**, 1962 (1934).
[14] Buchanan and Barsky, *J. Am. Chem. Soc.*, **52**, 195 (1930); **53**, 1270 (1931).

right or wrong) and depends further on the borderline one wishes to draw between bond formation and electrostatic attraction. We see then how there may be considerable controversy concerning the molecularity of a reaction, whereas if adequate kinetic data are available there should be substantial agreement as to its order.

Determination of the Order of Reactions

Kinetic data generally consist of reagent concentrations (or quantities that can be converted to concentrations) at various times. For relatively simple reactions of integral orders, such as reactions (7) through (10), the reaction order and rate constant may be obtained from the available data in a number of different ways. Often it is convenient to assume an order, to calculate the values of k corresponding to each experimental point, and then to note whether the calculated "k values" are substantially the same or whether they show a "drift" as the reaction progresses. (Thus, all values of $\dfrac{\ln[(A_0)/(A)]}{t}$ should be the same if the reaction is first order, whereas all values of $\dfrac{1/(A) - 1/(A)_0}{t}$ should be the same if the reaction is second order with the reactants present in equal concentrations.) Alternatively, the values of the appropriate concentration functions $\left[\ln(A), \;\; 1/(A), \;\; \dfrac{\ln(A)_0(B) - \ln(B)_0(A)}{(B)_0 - (A)_0}, \;\; \text{etc.}\right]$ may be plotted against time, noting which of these plots most closely approximates a straight line. The rate constant may then be obtained by measuring the *slope* of the linear plot.

In using such methods, two provisions are important. First, the reaction should be followed until it is considerably more than half complete, for during the early stages of a reaction the observed rate often shows a satisfactory "fit" to two or more of the common integrated rate expressions.

Secondly, a *number* of runs should be made, varying the initial concentrations of *each* of the reactants and any suspected catalysts. Since the concentration of a catalyst presumably remains constant during a reaction, its kinetic effect cannot generally be detected in a single run. The same may be said for a reagent present in very large excess; only a small fraction of such a reagent will be consumed during the reaction, its effect on the rate may pass unnoticed, and a deceptively simple kinetic picture may be formed. For example, if a single experiment on the basic hydrolysis of methyl bromide (reaction 7) were carried out with a large excess of base, the rate would appear to depend only on the concentration of the bromide, thus displaying so-called "pseudo-first-order kinetics". However, if the same reaction is run with two different concentrations of hydroxide, the apparent "first-order rate constant" will be found to be proportional to the concentration of base, showing that this concentration should also be included in the rate law.[15]

Since the concentration of solvent remains very nearly constant as a reaction proceeds, conventional kinetic studies alone cannot detect the participation of the solvent in a reaction. It is, of course, possible to select a reaction that is generally carried out in, say, methanol and carry it out instead in benzene, noting whether the reaction in benzene is accelerated by addition of small amounts of methanol. By varying the concentration of methanol, the order of the reaction with respect to methanol (in benzene) may be determined. The transfer from methanol to benzene, however, involves a drastic change in the reaction environment, and there is no guarantee that the nature of the reaction in the two solvents is even approximately the same.

Reactions having more complex rate laws, such as (12) and (13), cannot truly be said to have a "reaction order." For these, integrated rate expressions, if they can be derived at all, are apt to be extremely unwieldy. Rate laws are obtained most conveniently by estimating the various values of the *rate itself* $(d(A)/dt)$ in a number of reaction mixtures having different concentrations of reagents, catalysts, and possible inhibitors. The rate at a given instant is the slope of a curve made by plotting concentration against time; this slope (except for a zero-order reaction) must vary with the progress of the reaction, but may be estimated at any desired moment by drawing a tangent to the curve and measuring the slope of the tangent. This procedure, although simple in principle, is somewhat unsatisfactory in practice unless carried out with the aid of a prism,[16(a)] a mirror, [16(b)] or other such device. The most significant datum is generally the *initial* rate of the reaction (that is, the slope when $t = 0$), for at this point the concentrations of the various species are presumably known; complications due to reversibility or to the occurrence of side reactions have not yet set in.[17]

Reversible Reactions

Although in theory no reaction goes entirely "to completion," the reader is doubtless aware that a very large number proceed until the concentration of

[15] Similarly, the nitration of toluene in acetic acid or nitromethane appears to have *zero-order* kinetics (rate independent of *all* concentrations) if carried out with a large excess of HNO_3. The toluene does not appear in the rate expression since it is attacked *after* the rate-determining step, whereas there is only a very small decrease in the concentration of the rate-determining reagent, HNO_3, during the course of the reaction. Under these conditions, the nitration proceeds at a constant rate and suddenly stops when all of the toluene is consumed.

[16] (a) Frampton, *Science*, **107**, 323 (1948). (b) Pearlson and Simons, *J. Am. Chem. Soc.*, **67**, 352 (1945).

[17] For discussions of methods for determining rate constants, see: Swain, *J. Am. Chem. Soc.*, **66**, 1696 (1944); French, *ibid.*, **72**, 4806 (1950); Frost and Schwemer, *ibid.*, **73**, 4541 (1951) and **74**, 1268 (1952).

one or more reactants is immeasurably small. However, for cases in which considerable quantities of reactants remain when equilibrium has been reached, kinetics must account for the "slowing down" of the net reaction as the products formed in the forward reaction become involved in the reverse reaction, regenerating the reactants. We shall consider here only the simplest possible example of a reversible reaction,[18] the first-order conversion of reactant A to product B, opposed by the first-order reconversion of B to A:

$$A \underset{k_r}{\overset{k_f}{\rightleftharpoons}} B \tag{14}$$

The rate constants for the forward and reverse reactions are designated as kf and k_r, respectively. For further simplicity, assume that initially no B is present. Reactant A is destroyed in the forward reaction but reformed in the reverse reaction, so the differential rate equation is

$$-\frac{d(A)}{dt} = k_f(A) - k_r(B) \tag{15}$$

or, (since every molecule of B is formed at the expense of a molecule of A)

$$-\frac{d(A)}{dt} = k_f(A) - k_r[(A)_0 - (A)] \tag{16}$$

From this, we may obtain the integrated rate expression (Ex. 2a):

$$\ln \frac{k_f(A)_0}{k_f(A)_0 - [k_f + k_r][(A)_0 - (A)]} = (k_f + k_r)t \tag{17}$$

If we let $(A)_e$ be the concentration of A when equilibrium is reached, equation (17) may be simplified to

$$\ln \frac{(A)_0 - (A)_e}{(A) - (A)_e} = (k_f + k_r)t \tag{18}$$

Note that equation (18) is similar in form to equation (2), suggesting that the approach toward equilibrium is a "first-order process" having a rate constant $(k_f + k_r)$. This sum may thus be obtained from the concentrations of A at the start of the reaction, at time t, and at equilibrium. Furthermore, the quotient k_r/k_f is simply the equilibrium constant for the reaction; this may be calculated from the concentrations of A and B at equilibrium, allowing separation of the forward and reverse rate constants in equation (18). The above treatment may also be applied to pseudo-first-order reactions and is particularly valuable for treating a number of acid- or base-catalyzed isomerizations such as the mutarotation of sugars and the enolization of certain ketones and diketones.

[18] For treatments of more complex reversible reactions, see, for example, Frost and Pearson, Ref. 1(b), pp. 172–176.

Consecutive Reactions; The Steady-state Approximation

The ease in handling **consecutive reactions** (a set of reactions in which the product from one step becomes the reactant in another) depends largely on the relative magnitudes of the individual rate constants. Consider, for example, the reaction sequence,

$$A \xrightarrow{k} B \xrightarrow{k'} C$$

The mathematical treatment of such a sequence is most difficult when the rate constants k and k' are of the same order of magnitude,[19] but, happily, such cases are quite rare. If k is much greater than k' and if the conversion of A to B is essentially irreversible, a large quantity of the product B will be formed in a short time and will then be converted slowly to C. Thus, B will generally be isolable, and if this is so, the "reaction sequence" is most simply studied as two separate reactions.

Often, however, the first step in such a sequence is rapid but reversible. A small equilibrium concentration of B is rapidly formed from A, and as B is slowly consumed to form C, the $A \rightleftharpoons B$ equilibrium shifts, yielding more B. The benzoin condensation may be regarded in this way:[10]

$$\text{PhCHO} + \text{CN}^- \rightleftharpoons \underset{\underset{\text{CN}}{|}}{\overset{\overset{\text{OH}}{|}}{\text{Ph}-\text{C}:^-}} \quad \text{(rapid, reversible)} \qquad K_{eq} = \frac{\left(\text{Ph}\ddot{\text{C}} \diagdown \begin{matrix} ^{\text{OH}} \\ _{\text{CN}} \end{matrix} \right)}{(\text{PhCHO})(\text{CN}^-)}$$

$$(19)$$

$$\underset{\underset{\text{CN}}{|}}{\overset{\overset{\text{OH}}{|}}{\text{Ph}-\text{C}:^-}} + \text{PhCHO} \rightarrow \underset{\underset{\text{O}}{\overset{|}{}}}{\overset{\overset{|}{}}{\text{Ph}-\text{CH}}}\underset{\underset{\text{OH}}{|}}{\overset{\overset{\text{Ph}}{|}}{-\text{C}}}-\text{CN} \quad \text{(slow)}$$

$$\text{rate} = k_2 \left(\underset{\underset{\text{CN}}{|}}{\overset{\overset{\text{OH}}{|}}{\text{Ph}-\text{C}:^-}} \right) (\text{PhCHO}) \quad (20)$$

Eliminating the concentration of the cyanohydrin anion from reactions (19) and (20) yields a third-order rate expression identical to equation (11):

$$\text{rate} = k_2 K_{eq}(\text{PhCHO})^2(\text{CN}^-) = k_3(\text{PhCHO})^2(\text{CN}^-) \qquad (21)$$

---

[19] The treatment for consecutive first-order reactions with similar rate constants is presented by Esson, *Phil. Trans. Roy. Soc.*, **156**, 220 (1866). See also Moore, Ref. 1(a), pp. 539–541. Typical of this class of reactions are the hydrolyses of a number of diesters and diamides in excess acid, and hydrolyses of a number of nitriles (first to amides, then to carboxylate salts), in excess base.

The reaction of ethylene chlorohydrin with base to yield ethylene oxide simi-larly proceeds through the following steps:[20]

$$Cl—CH_2—CH_2—OH + OH^- \rightleftharpoons Cl—CH_2—CH_2—O^- + H_2O$$

(rapid, reversible; K_{eq})

$$Cl—CH_2—CH_2—O^- \rightarrow CH_2\underset{\underset{O}{\diagdown\diagup}}{\quad}CH_2 + Cl^- \text{ (slow, } k_1)$$

Again, the rate of the reaction is the rate of the slow step:

$$\text{rate} = k_1(ClCH_2CH_2O^-) = k_1K_{eq}(ClCH_2CH_2OH)(OH^-) \qquad (22)$$

Suppose, on the other hand, that one or more fast steps of a reaction se-quence *follow* the slow step. Since the rate of the slow step will generally deter-mine the rate of the overall reaction, a simple kinetic study can tell little about subsequent steps (except that they are rapid). The substitution reactions of many tertiary halides, for example, are thought to begin with a slow ionization step.

$$R_3C—Cl \rightarrow R_3C^+ + Cl^- \qquad \text{rate} = k_1(R_3CCl) \qquad (23)$$

The *carbonium ion*, R_3C^+, then combines rapidly with the appropriate nucleo-philic species in solution.

$$R_3C^+ + OH^- \rightarrow R_3C—OH \qquad (24)$$

or $\qquad R_3C^+ + OAc^- \rightarrow R_3C—OAc \qquad (25)$

or $\qquad R_3C^+ + OC_6H_5^- \rightarrow R_3C—O—C_6H_5 \qquad (26)$

If the slow ionization step is essentially irreversible, the rate of the overall sub-stitution reaction is, in each case, the rate of this step. The substitution would be first order in the alkyl chloride but independent of both the identity and the concentration of the substituting reagent. Under such conditions, if three aliquots of a solution of $R_3C—Cl$ are treated respectively with sodium hydroxide, sodium acetate, and sodium phenoxide, the three different substitution reac-tions would proceed at very nearly the same rate.

For a similar reason, the rates of nitration of benzene, toluene, *p*-xylene, and *p*-chloroanisole are equal when the reactions are carried out in nitro-methane, using a given excess of nitric acid.[3] The presently accepted mechanism for such nitrations (to be discussed in Chap. 11) involves the following steps (ArH is the aromatic compound undergoing nitration):

$$2HNO_3 \rightleftharpoons H_2NO_3^+ + NO_3^- \text{ (rapid, reversible autoprotolysis, } K_{eq}) \qquad (27)$$
$$H_2NO_3^+ \rightarrow H_2O \quad + \quad NO_2^+ \text{ (nitronium ion)} \quad \text{(slow, } k) \qquad (28)$$

[20] Winstein and Lucas, *J. Am. Chem. Soc.*, **61**, 1576 (1939).

$$NO_2^+ + ArH \rightarrow \left[Ar \begin{smallmatrix} NO_2 \\ \diagup \\ \diagdown \\ H \end{smallmatrix} \right]^+ \quad \text{(fast, } k')$$

(29)

$$\left[Ar \begin{smallmatrix} NO_2 \\ \diagup \\ \diagdown \\ H \end{smallmatrix} \right]^+ + NO_3^- \rightarrow ArNO_2 + HNO_3 \text{ (fast)}$$

(30)

The rate of the overall reaction should then be equal to the rate of reaction (28), the dissociation of the conjugate acid of nitric into the *nitronium ion* and water:

$$\text{rate} = k(H_2NO_3^+) = kK_{\text{eq}}^{\frac{1}{2}}(HNO_3)$$

(31)

The rate is thus proportional only to (HNO_3), and when this is in large excess, the nitration rate is very nearly constant ("zero order"). The kinetic picture changes, however, for less reactive aromatic compounds such as chlorobenzene and ethyl benzoate. With these, step (29) becomes the slow, hence rate-determining, step. Since this step involves (ArH), the nitration of these compounds now becomes first order in the aromatic compound. Still another kinetic situation arises when one or more fast steps follow a slow step that is, however, reversible. This is the case, for example, in the hydrolysis of benzhydryl chloride ($Ph_2CH—Cl$) in aqueous acetone:[21]

$$Ph_2CH—Cl \underset{k_r}{\overset{k_f}{\rightleftharpoons}} Cl^- + Ph_2CH^+ \xrightarrow[k']{H_2O} Ph_2CH—OH$$

(32)

As shown, benzhydryl chloride ionizes slowly (rate constant k_f) to the benzhydryl ion, which may be converted back to the starting material (rate constant k_r) or, alternatively, may react with water to form benzhydrol (rate constant k'). The reaction is thus a competition between chloride and water for the benzhydryl ion. The rate of the overall reaction depends not only on the rate of the slow step but also upon the efficiency with which water competes against chloride.

The rigorous treatment of rate equations describing such a reaction sequence, although possible, is difficult. The kinetics in this case may be handled conveniently by calling upon the so-called **steady-state approximation**. This is used when all of the intermediates in a reaction are present in relatively small quantities. In particular, considering the hydrolysis of benzhydryl chloride, we may assume that the concentration of the benzhydryl ion does not

[21] Hughes, Ingold, and Taher, *J. Chem. Soc.*, **1940**, 949. Church, Hughes, and Ingold, *ibid.*, 966.

vary appreciably during the course of the reaction.[22] The rate of formation of this ion from benzhydryl chloride must then be equal to its rate of consumption by the combined action of water and chloride.

$$k_f(\text{Ph}_2\text{CHCl}) = k_r(\text{Cl}^-)(\text{Ph}_2\text{CH}^+) + k'(\text{Ph}_2\text{CH}^+) \qquad (33)$$

$$\quad\text{formation} \qquad\qquad \text{consumption by Cl}^- \qquad \text{consumption by water}$$

(Since water is a component of the solvent, its concentration, which remains very nearly constant throughout the reaction, is incorporated into k'.) The rate of the overall reaction is actually the rate of formation of benzhydrol from the benzhydryl ion and water.

$$\text{rate} = k'(\text{Ph}_2\text{CH}^+) \qquad (34)$$

If we solve for the concentration of benzhydryl ion in reaction (33) and substitute this expression in (34) we obtain:

$$\text{rate} = \frac{k' k_f(\text{Ph}_2\text{CHCl})}{k' + k_r(\text{Cl}^-)} = \frac{k_f(\text{Ph}_2\text{CHCl})}{1 + \dfrac{k_r(\text{Cl}^-)}{k'}} \qquad (35)$$

From this, it may be seen that the rate of the reaction will be lowered by addition of chloride ion. If no extra chloride is added, the reaction will appear to follow first-order kinetics during the early stages since the concentration of chloride ion will at first be very small.[23]

Parallel Reactions

Quite often we are confronted with a system in which two or more reactions are proceeding independently. (If this were not the case, the practicing organic chemist would be pleased with quantitative yields of products from a large percentage of his preparations.) Among the simplest systems involving **parallel reactions** are substitution reactions in which more than one isomer may be formed from the same starting material. In the nitration of chlorobenzene, for example, three nitrochlorobenzenes (abbreviated NCB) are formed, each at a different rate. Suppose the reaction is carried out in nitromethane with a large excess of nitric acid; under these conditions, the formation of each of the three isomers is first order in chlorobenzene.

[22] If this ion were formed appreciably faster than it is used up, its concentration should increase steadily as the reaction proceeds until its presence could be eventually detected by physical means. On the other hand, if the ion were consumed appreciably faster than it is formed, the reaction could not get under way.

[23] Treatments based on the steady state approximation have proved extremely useful for complex reaction sequences involving a number of unstable intermediates; for many of these, exact solutions become almost prohibitively difficult. A generalized formulation for treating reaction sequences of many steps has been devised by Christiansen, *Z. physik. Chem.*, **33B**, 145 (1936) and **37B**, 374 (1937). See also Hammett, *Physical Organic Chemistry*, McGraw-Hill Book Co., Inc., New York, 1940, p. 107.

$$\frac{d(o\text{-NCB})}{dt} = k_o(\text{PhCl}); \quad \frac{d(m\text{-NCB})}{dt} = k_m(\text{PhCl}); \quad \frac{d(p\text{-NCB})}{dt} = k_p(\text{PhCl}) \quad (36)$$

$$\quad\quad ortho \quad\quad\quad\quad\quad\quad\quad\quad\quad meta \quad\quad\quad\quad\quad\quad\quad\quad\quad para$$

The disappearance of chlorobenzene, $\dfrac{-d(\text{PhCl})}{dt}$, is also a first-order reaction

having a rate constant $(k_o + k_m + k_p)$. To evaluate the three individual rate constants, we must know not only their sum (calculated by following the date of disappearance of chlorobenzene), but also their ratio. The ratio of any two of the three rate constants may be obtained by dividing two of the three rate equations in (36), then integrating. In this way, it may be shown that if the reaction is stopped at any instant, the concentrations of the three isomers present will stand in the same ratio as the respective rate constants; that is,

$$(o\text{-NCB}):(m\text{-NCB}):(p\text{-NCB}) = k_o:k_m:k_p \quad\quad\quad (37)$$

The reliability of the values of the individual rate constants depends largely upon how accurately the composition of a mixture containing three closely related compounds can be determined. Although "analyses" have been carried out in the past by fractional crystallization or distillation, such separation methods are generally not as well suited for quantitative work as physico-chemical analyses that do not involve losses during separation. If three products are involved, spectrophotometric analyses may often be used; with only two products, measurements of refractive index, freezing point or other physical properties may yield the necessary information. Recently, analysis by isotopic dilution has become an effective analytical tool[24] (Ex. 3).

Similar considerations may be shown to apply to any system of parallel reactions yielding two or more products if the order of each of the individual reactions with respect to the given reactants is the same. Analyses of the products will yield the relative rate constants even though it is not known whether the reaction is first, second, or even zero order. There, is, however, one additional proviso—no significant reversal of the individual reactions may occur before the mixture is analyzed. If the individual reactions are substantially reversible, the composition of the resulting mixture will drift toward that prevailing at equilibrium, and the analysis of the product will reflect equilibrium conditions rather than the relative rates of the forward reactions. (In such a case the composition of the product is said to be *thermodynamically controlled*, rather than *kinetically controlled*.)

Very frequently, two reactants will compete for the same starting material or for the same reaction intermediate. The kinetic treatment in such cases is straightforward if the competing reactions are of the same order. For example,

---

[24] See, for example, the work of Roberts and co-workers on the nitration of the halo-benzenes, *J. Am. Chem. Soc.*, **76**, 4525 (1954).

when methyl iodide is treated with a solution containing both hydroxide and phenoxide ions, both anions may bring about substitution reactions.

$$CH_3I + OH^- \rightarrow CH_3OH \qquad \frac{d(MeOH)}{dt} = k_{OH}(MeI)(OH^-) \qquad (38)$$

$$CH_3I + OPh^- \rightarrow CH_3OPh \qquad \frac{d(MeOPh)}{dt} = k_{OPh}(MeI)(OPh^-) \qquad (39)$$

If both OH^- and OPh^- are in large excess, the disappearance of methyl iodide becomes "pseudo first order" with a rate constant $[k_{OH}(OH^-) + k_{OPh}(OPh^-)]$. Dividing reaction (38) by (39), and integrating, we may obtain:

$$\frac{(MeOH)}{(MeOPh)} = \frac{k_{OH}(OH^-)}{k_{OPh}(OPh^-)} \qquad (40)$$

By following the disappearance of methyl iodide, then analyzing the mixture of products resulting from a solution in which (OH^-) and (OPh^-) are known, we may evaluate the individual rate constants. If smaller amounts of OH^- and OPh^- are present initially so that the concentrations of these species show substantial decrease during the reaction, division of reactions (38) by (39) and integration gives:

$$\frac{k_{OH}}{k_{OPh}} = \frac{\log\left[1 - \dfrac{(MeOH)}{(OH^-)_0}\right]}{\log\left[1 - \dfrac{(MeOPh)}{(OPh^-)_0}\right]} = \frac{\text{log of fraction } OH^- \text{ remaining}}{\text{log of fraction } OPh^- \text{ remaining}} \qquad (41)$$

Similar treatments are appropriate for competitions between two or more species for a reaction intermediate. For example, if a mixture having known quantities of benzene and p-xylene is nitrated and the reaction is quenched before either of the aromatics is entirely consumed, analysis of the reaction mixture will determine the *relative rates* at which the two hydrocarbons react with the NO_2^+ ion. Here, however, the *individual* rates *cannot* be readily evaluated since, as we have seen, the overall nitration rate is simply the rate of formation of the NO_2^+ ion and in this case is independent of the species being nitrated.

Sometimes a single reagent will appear to participate simultaneously in two reactions having different orders. The hydrolyses of a number of secondary alkyl bromides[25] may be regarded as a competition between a first-order reaction (independent of OH^-, as with the hydrolysis of t-butyl bromide) and a second-order reaction (of the same type as the hydrolysis of methyl bromide).

[25] See, for example, the work of Hughes and Shapiro, *J. Chem. Soc.*, **1937**; 1177, 1192, on the basic hydrolysis of isopropyl bromide. Such a kinetic situation may arise because the reagent is actually being consumed in two different ways; or it may be that the process by which the reagent is destroyed is kinetically complicated, but conveniently approximated as the sum of two simple reactions (see Chap. 8, Ex. 12).

$$\text{rate} = \frac{-d(\text{RBr})}{dt} = k_1(\text{RBr}) + k_2(\text{RBr})(\text{OH}^-) \tag{42}$$

There are several ways for treating such "pairs" of reactions. Suppose, for example,[26] that the rate of appearance of bromide ion (disappearance of alkyl bromide) is determined graphically for a number of mixtures containing known concentrations of hydroxide and alkyl bromide. Since reaction (42) may be rewritten,

$$\frac{\text{rate}}{(\text{RBr})} = k_1 + k_2(\text{OH}^-) \tag{43}$$

we see that a new plot of the values of [rate/(RBr)] vs. (OH$^-$) should yield a straight line with k_2 as a slope. The intercept—the specific rate when (OH$^-$) is zero—should be k_1.

Mechanistic Implications from Rate Laws

There is no general way of proceeding from the empirical rate law for a reaction to its mechanism. Commonly, the worker lists the most plausible mechanisms, derives hypothetical rate laws for each, and then decides which of these corresponds most closely to the observed rate law. If the reaction is relatively simple, the experienced kineticist can often make a good guess (but still only a guess) as to its mechanism merely by inspection of the rate law.

The benzidine rearrangement, reaction (44), for example, has been found to show third-order kinetics, being *second order* in (H$^+$):[27]

$$\text{Ph-NH-NH-Ph} \rightarrow \left[\text{Ph-}\underset{\underset{\text{H}}{|}}{\overset{\overset{\text{H}}{|}}{\text{N}}}\text{-}\underset{\underset{\text{H}}{|}}{\overset{\overset{\text{H}}{|}}{\text{N}}}\text{-Ph}\right]^{+2} \rightarrow \text{H}_2\text{N-}\langle\!\langle\ \rangle\!\rangle\text{-NH}_2 \tag{44}$$

I

$$\frac{-d(\text{PhNHNHPh})}{dt} = k_3(\text{PhNHNHPh})(\text{H}^+)^2$$

This indicates that *two* hydrogen ions are involved in this reaction during, or before, the rate determining step—that is, that the dipositive cation, I, is an intermediate. The kinetics of the reaction, together with our knowledge that the rearrangement is intramolecular (p. 141) and is subject to specific hydrogen-ion catalysis, are the basis of much of our present picture of its mechanism (Chap. 15).

Similarly, the diazotization of aniline in moderately concentrated (about

[26] Young and Andrews, *J. Am. Chem. Soc.*, **66**, 421 (1944).
[27] Hammond and Shine, *J. Am. Chem. Soc.*, **72**, 220 (1950); Carlin, *et al.*, *ibid.*, **73**, 1002 (1951); Croce and Gettler, *ibid.*, **75**, 874 (1953).

0.2 M) acid has been found to be second order in HNO_2, suggesting that *two* molecules of nitrous acid somehow participate in the sequence leading to the rate-determining step, even though the stoichiometry of the reaction demands only one.[28]

$$PhNH_3^+ + HNO_2 \rightarrow PhN\equiv N^+ + H_2O \qquad \text{rate} = k_3(HNO_2)^2(PhNH_2) \quad (45)$$

The kinetic data are consistent with a rate-determining step involving the amine and a species containing *two* atoms of tripositive nitrogen, probably N_2O_3:

$$2HNO_2 \rightleftharpoons H_2O + N_2O_3 \qquad \text{(fast, equilibrium)}$$

$$[Ph-NH_2-N=O]^+ \longrightarrow \longrightarrow PhN\equiv N^+ + H_2O \qquad \text{(fast)}$$

As indicated, the third step in the above sequence is composite; but since kinetic data are singularly ineffective in furnishing information about the course of a reaction sequence after the slow step, we can say little about the conversion of the N-nitroso compound to the diazonium cation except that all the steps involved are faster than the nitrosation step. Without the kinetic study, however, we would be unaware of the participation of the second molecule of nitrous acid earlier in the reaction.

On the other hand, if a reagent is known to be consumed but does *not* appear in the rate law, one may assume that its action is delayed until after the rate-determining step. We have seen this to be the case for the nitration of toluene (p. 169), where the rate law does not include toluene. A similar conclusion may be drawn from the kinetics of the base-catalyzed iodination of acetone reaction (8). The rate law, which includes the first powers of the concentrations of acetone and hydroxide (but not iodine), may be explained by assuming that before acetone may be iodinated, it must be converted in a slow step to its conjugate base.

---

[28] Schmid and Muhr, *Ber.*, **70**, 421 (1937). Note that the rate expression involves the concentration of aniline rather than that of anilinium ion. The concentration of the free base in moderately acid solution is small and must be calculated from the concentrations of *added* base and acid, using the known basicity constant of aniline. It should also be emphasized that diazotizations of aromatic amines may exhibit a number of rate laws, depending upon reaction conditions; for a detailed discussion of the kinetics and mechanism of diazotization, see Hughes, Ingold, and Ridd, *J. Chem. Soc.*, **1958**, 58–98.

From this mechanism, we would predict that any reagent that reacts rapidly with the conjugate base of acetone should react with a given basic solution of acetone at the same overall rate as is exhibited by iodine. Thus, the base-catalyzed bromination of acetone has the same specific rate as the base-catalyzed iodination[29] since both reactions are governed by the same rate-determining step.

A species appearing in the denominator of a rate law is generally formed in a reversible reaction *preceding* the rate-determining step. An excess of this species slows down the overall reaction by shifting the equilibrium so that a smaller quantity of a reactive intermediate is available. The rate of base-catalyzed iodination of aniline in the presence of excess iodide is, for example, *inversely* proportional to the square of the iodide concentration[30]

$$\text{Ph—NH}_2 + I_3^- + B^- \longrightarrow I\text{—Ph—NH}_2 + BH + 2I^-$$

$$\frac{-d(\text{PhNH}_2)}{dt} = \frac{k(B^-)(\text{PhNH}_2)(I_3^-)}{(I^-)^2} \tag{46}$$

where B^- represents the base. This suggests that an active intermediate is formed along with *two* iodide ions in a reversible step early in the reaction. One of the three possible mechanisms consistent wi h this rate law (Ex. 5) assumes the attacking agent to be the iodonium ion, $:\overset{..}{I}{}^+$ (or its hydrated form, H_2OI^+).

$$I_3^- \rightleftharpoons \; :\overset{..}{\underset{..}{I}}:^+ \; + \; 2I^- \qquad \text{(rapid equilibrium, } K_1\text{)}$$

$$:\overset{..}{\underset{..}{I}}{}^+ + \text{Ph—NH}_2 \rightleftharpoons \left[\begin{array}{c} I \\ H \end{array} \text{—} =\text{NH}_2\right]^+ \qquad \text{(rapid equilibrium, } K_2\text{)}$$

$$\left[\begin{array}{c} I \\ H \end{array} \text{—}=\text{NH}_2\right]^+ + B^- \longrightarrow BH + I\text{—}=\text{NH}_2 \qquad \text{(slow, } k\text{)}$$

The overall rate (that is, the rate of the final step) is then in agreement with reaction (46).

$$\text{rate} = k\left[\begin{array}{c} I \\ H \end{array}=\text{NH}_2^+\right](B^-) = kK_2(\text{PhNH}_2)(I^+)(B^-) =$$

$$kK_2K_1 \frac{(\text{PhNH}_2)(I_3^+)(B^-)}{(I^-)^2} \tag{47}$$

[29] Bartlett, *J. Am. Chem. Soc.*, **56**, 967 (1934).
[30] Berliner, *J. Am. Chem. Soc.*, **72**, 4003 (1950).

A simple but unusual rate law governs the conversion of camphene hydrochloride (II) to isobornyl chloride (III) in nitrobenzene.[31]

$$\text{rate}_a = k \text{ (camphene hydrochloride)}^{3/2} \qquad (48)$$

In the absence of added electrophilic reagents, the rearrangement a requires the presence of hydrogen chloride. This, however, must be generated in the side reaction b—the reversible dissociation of camphene hydrochloride to *equivalent quantities* of camphene (IV) and HCl.

$$\text{camphene·HCl} \rightleftharpoons \text{camphene} + \text{HCl} \qquad \text{(rapid, reversible)}$$

$$K_b = \frac{(\text{camphene})(\text{HCl})}{(\text{camphene·HCl})} = \frac{(\text{HCl})^2}{(\text{camphene·HCl})} \qquad (49)$$

The rate-determining step involves a molecule of camphene hydrochloride and one of HCl:

$$\text{rate} = k_a(\text{camphene·HCl})(\text{HCl})$$
$$= k_a(\text{camphene·HCl}) \sqrt{K_b(\text{camphene·HCl})} \qquad (50)$$

This is in agreement with equation (48). The novice kineticist might perhaps feel that the three-half order character of the reaction indicates that "three halves of a molecule" of the hydrochloride is involved in the rate-determining step. This conclusion has an element of truth in it, for the slow step does involve one entire molecule of the hydrochloride together with a portion of a second.

An interesting and particularly important class of reactions are nucleophilic substitutions on alkyl halides. We have seen that there are at least *three* different rate laws which may govern such reactions, and the differences between these rate laws presumably reflect differences in reaction mechanisms. The rate of basic hydrolysis of methyl bromide (reaction 7) is first order both in OH^- and CH_3Br; we may then assume that *both* of these species participate

[31] Bartlett and Pockel, *J. Am. Chem. Soc.*, **60**, 1585 (1938).

in the rate-determining step,[32] and that this step is simply a direct displacement of bromide by hydroxide.

$$\text{HO:}^- \quad + \quad \text{H}_3\text{C}-\text{Br} \quad \longrightarrow \quad \text{HO}-\text{CH}_3 \quad + \quad :\overset{..}{\underset{..}{\text{Br}}}:^- \quad (51)$$

However, if the concentration of the entering group does not appear in the rate law (indicating that this group enters the picture *after* the rate-determining step), we may conclude that the slow step is the breakage of the carbon-halogen bond in the alkyl halide (reaction 23). A similar mechanism is indicated by a rate law such as given in reaction (35), but here the slow step is reversible.

Much more will be said about the substitution reactions of alkyl halides in Chapter 8.

The Transition-state Theory. Energy of Activation[33]

One of the most familiar general phenomena of chemistry is the increase in the rate of a reaction as the temperature is raised. This acceleration cannot be due merely to the increased number of molecular collisions, for as a rule the reaction rate increases with temperature far more sharply than does the collision frequency. It will be recalled that reactant molecules having "average" velocities generally do *not* undergo chemical reactions since they have insufficient energy to allow the formation of the necessary *transition state*. The transition state has already been described (p. 129) as the summit of an "energy hill": reactants must have enough energy to "roll up" this hill before they may "roll down" the other side, releasing energy and forming the products. The rate of the reaction is then related to the number of molecules that pass from the "reactant side" to the "product side" in a given time. Raising the temperature increases the concentration of molecules with sufficient energy to make the ascent, and more conversions from reactants to products then occur.

A molecule or group of molecules passing through the transition state is said to be an **activated complex.** Considering a reaction between species A and B, we may designate the activated complex as $AB^{\ddagger}$ and represent the reaction as

$$A + B \rightarrow \quad AB^{\ddagger} \quad \rightarrow \text{products} \qquad (52)$$
$$\text{activated}$$
$$\text{complex}$$

[32] If, however, methyl bromide were known to be appreciably acidic, we would have to consider the possibility that neither OH^- nor CH_3Br participates in the rate-determining step but rather that this step involves the conjugate base $BrCH_2 : ^-$, formed rapidly and reversibly in the reaction, $OH^- + CH_3Br \rightleftharpoons H_2O + BrCH_2 : ^-$. The kinetic analysis of the reaction might then be similar to that for the ring closure of ethylene chlorohydrin (reaction 22).

[33] For detailed discussions of the transition-state theory, see (a) Eyring, *Chem. Revs.*, **17**, 65 (1935); (b) Frost and Pearson (Ref. 1b), pp. 74–99. The alternate method of handling the reaction-rate problem, the *collision theory* will not be discussed here; for a treatment of this topic, see Glasstone, Laidler, and Eyring (Ref. 1c), pp. 298ff.

The **transition-state theory** treats the activated complex as a chemical species whose formation from the reactants is associated with an equilibrium constant, $K^{\ddagger}$, where

$$K^{\ddagger} = \frac{(AB^{\ddagger})}{(A)(B)} \frac{\gamma_{AB}^{\ddagger}}{\gamma_A \gamma_B} \tag{53}$$

We shall, for the time being, consider only dilute solutions in which the activity coefficients approach unity, thus allowing us to ignore the γ terms in (53).

Since the rate of reaction is assumed to be proportional to the number of A-B couples passing through the transition state—that is, proportional to $(AB^{\ddagger})$—the specific rate $[k_r = \text{rate}/(A)(B)]$ for the reaction should be proportional to $K^{\ddagger}$. Furthermore, using the principles of statistical mechanics, it is possible to show[34] that the constant of proportionality is very close to kT/h, where k is Boltzmann's constant, T is the absolute temperature, and h is Planck's constant. The transition-state theory further defines the following quantities, analogous to the corresponding thermodynamic functions used in the description of ordinary chemical changes:

The *free energy of activation*, $\Delta F^{\ddagger}$:

$$\Delta F^{\ddagger} = -RT \ln K^{\ddagger} = -RT \ln \left[\frac{k_r h}{kT} \right] \tag{54}$$

The *heat of activation*, $\Delta H^{\ddagger}$:

$$\Delta H^{\ddagger} = -R \frac{d(\ln K^{\ddagger})}{d(1/T)} = -R \left[\frac{d(\ln k_r)}{d(1/T)} + T \right] \tag{55}$$

The *entropy of activation*, $\Delta S^{\ddagger}$:

$$\Delta S^{\ddagger} = \frac{\Delta H^{\ddagger} - \Delta F^{\ddagger}}{T} = R \left[T \frac{d(\ln k_r)}{dT} + \ln \frac{k_r h}{kT} - 1 \right] \tag{56}$$

(See Ex. 8a.)

In addition to these quantities, workers often refer to the *Arrhenius energy of activation*, E_a, obtained simply by plotting the logarithms of the rate constants for a given reaction at a number of temperatures against the reciprocals of the temperatures themselves, measuring the slope of the "line" resulting,[35] and multiplying by $-R$:

$$\frac{d(\ln k)}{d(1/T)} = -\frac{E_a}{R} \tag{57}$$

Note that E_a differs from $\Delta H^{\ddagger}$ only by about 0.6 kcal (the value of RT at ordi-

[34] Eyring, *J. Chem. Phys.*, **3**, 107 (1935).
[35] Although such plots often appear to be straight lines, suggesting that the activation energy for a reaction is independent of temperature, careful measurements on very sensitive reactions show that such plots are actually curved—that is, that the energy of activation is a function of temperature. See, for example, LaMer and Miller, *J. Am. Chem. Soc.*, **57**, 2674 (1935).

nary temperatures). Since this difference is less than the uncertainty in many measurements of activation energies, either E_a or $\Delta H^{\ddagger}$ may be regarded as the extra energy that must be imparted to an average molecular ensemble consisting of discrete species A and B in order to allow formation of activated complex $AB^{\ddagger}$. The energy of activation is an important item in any mechanistic description of a reaction, just as the free energy of reaction is an important item in its thermodynamic description.

In our earlier picture of the transition state in the reaction $OH^- + CH_3I \rightarrow HOCH_3 + I^-$, we saw that the new bond (C—O) was being formed at the same time the old bond (C—I) was breaking. The activated complex in such a reaction has a higher energy than either the reactants or the products, largely because the energy released in the partial formation of the new bond is considerably less than the energy needed to stretch the old bond well past its most stable configuration. It has indeed been suggested that the activation energy of a reaction is proportional to the strength of the bond that suffers breakage.[36] However, this is only a rough estimate that is approximately true for a number of gas-phase reactions but completely inapplicable to reactions in solution where solvation effects contribute to a much more complex picture.

There appears to be considerable variation among reactions in the degree of completeness with which the new bond is formed in the activated complex. Greater progress toward complete bond formation results in the availability of more energy for the necessary distortion of the old bond, thus lowering the activation energy. For example, the energy of activation for the reaction

$$(C_2H_5)_3N: + R—I \rightarrow [(C_2H_5)_3N—R]^+ + I^- \qquad (58)$$

is only 9.7 kcal per mole when R is CH_3— but is 16.0 kcal when R is $(CH_3)_2CH$—.[37] The attacking nitrogen atom may approach the carbon in methyl iodide and, with little interference, begin the process of bond formation that results ultimately in the displacement of the iodide ion and the "Walden inversion" (p. 148) of the methyl group. The reaction of the amine with isopropyl iodide is subject to what is classically termed "steric hindrance"—meaning that there is a great deal of interference between the bulky ethyl groups of the amine and the α-methyl groups of the iodide when the amine draws near to the iodinated carbon. The amine molecule must therefore show sufficient energy to press on toward the reaction site while intermolecular interference is forcing the α-methyl groups of the iodide out of the way. This initiates both the inversion process and the breakage of the C—I bond well before substantial energy from the newly forming C—N bond has become available.

We can also understand why the saponifications of esters have relatively

[36] Hirschfelder, *J. Chem. Phys.*, **9**, 645 (1941).
[37] Brown and Eldred, *J. Am. Chem. Soc.*, **71**, 445 (1949).

low activation energies (about 11 kcal)[38] even though they involve the breakage of the relatively strong C—O bond. The incoming OH^- group can bind itself completely to the carbonyl carbon before the alkoxide group begins to break off.

$$OH^- + CH_3-C\overset{O}{\underset{OR}{\Big\langle}} \longrightarrow \left[CH_3-\underset{OR}{\overset{OH}{\underset{|}{\overset{|}{C}}}}-O \right]^- \longrightarrow CH_3-C\overset{OH}{\underset{O}{\Big\langle}} + OR^- \quad (59)$$

$$V$$

The energy barrier that hampers the reaction is lowered when the saponification proceeds through anion V; for along such a route the system receives much of its "energy payment" from the formation of the new C—OH bond before having to pay its "energy debt" for the breaking of the C—OR bond.[39]

Entropy of Activation

Entropy is the measurement of the randomness of a system. If a reaction occurs with an *increase* in entropy, *there is more disorder possible among the products than among the reactants*—that is, there are more restrictions to the motion of the reactant molecules than to the motion of the product molecules. Analogously, *the entropy of activation*, which may be calculated from reaction (56), is a measure of the freedom from restraint of motion among the reactants. For reactions in solution, entropy effects also include changes in the randomness of the solvent molecules as new species requiring differing degrees of solvation are formed from the reactants.

Although it is not easy to account for small entropy effects, we may note a few generalities. First, reactions in which the *total number of molecules decreases* are usually attended by a negative entropy of activation. Thus, gaseous dimerizations, Diels-Alder reactions, and additions to double bonds exhibit entropies of activation ranging from about −10 to −25 calories per degree. When two molecules come together to form a single molecule of activated complex, the restrictions on their freedom of motion obviously increase, for they can no longer move independently. Similarly, if a cyclic transition state is formed from noncyclic products, a negative entropy of activation is to be ex-

[38] Smith and Ollson, *Z. physik. Chem.*, **118**, 99 (1925).

[39] The discussion of this reaction is somewhat oversimplified since the ion V is actually a metastable intermediate rather than an activated complex (Chap. 9). There are therefore *two* transition states in the saponification: one preceding the formation of V, the other preceding the breakup of V; the energy levels of both of these transition states must be somewhat higher than that of V. Nevertheless, the essential argument is unchanged; the apparent activation energy of the overall reaction is low because the bond breaking is postponed virtually until the completion of the bond making.

pected since free rotation about the single bonds becomes restricted during the cyclization. Thus, the isomerization of allyl vinyl ether to β-vinylpropionaldehyde (VII), thought to proceed through the cyclic intermediate VI, shows an entropy of activation of -7.7 calories per degree.[40]

$$
\begin{array}{ccc}
\underset{\text{VI}}{\left.\begin{array}{c} \text{CH}_2\!=\!\text{CH} \\ \text{H}_2\text{C} \qquad\qquad \text{O} \\ \text{CH}\!-\!\text{CH}_2 \end{array}\right.} & \longrightarrow & \underset{\text{VII}}{\left.\begin{array}{c} \text{CH}_2\!-\!\text{CH} \\ \text{H}_2\text{C} \qquad\qquad \text{O} \\ \text{CH}\!=\!\text{CH}_2 \end{array}\right.}
\end{array} \qquad (60)
$$

A low entropy of activation may also reflect a crowded transition state in which freedom of motion of the substituents is unduly hindered. The entropy of activation for the reaction,

$$
\text{EtO}^- + \text{RCH}_2\text{I} \rightarrow \left[\begin{array}{c} \text{H} \\ \text{EtO}\text{-----}\overset{\displaystyle|}{\text{C}}\text{-----I} \\ \diagup \quad \diagdown \\ \text{H} \qquad \text{R} \end{array} \right]^- \rightarrow \text{EtO}\text{---CH}_2\text{R} + \text{I}^- \qquad (61)
$$

is -9.5 calory per degree if R is H, but falls to -19.9 calory per degree if R is t-Bu.[41] The three extra methyl groups in the latter compound obviously add to the crowding in the transition state.

Reactions of neutral molecules to yield ions invariably show negative entropies of activation. For such cases, the charge separation begins in the transition state and each end of the dipole becomes solvated with a sheath of solvent molecules, which must however be suitably oriented. The increase in orientation means, of course, a decrease in entropy. When a reaction in which charge is being created is carried out in a number of solvents of varying polarity, the greatest entropy decrease in the formation of the transition state will generally be observed for the *least polar* solvent. For example, the reaction between aniline and phenacyl bromide,

$$
\text{PhNH}_2 + \text{Ph}\text{---}\underset{\underset{\text{O}}{\|}}{\text{C}}\text{---CH}_2\text{Br} \rightarrow \left[\text{Ph}\text{---}\underset{\underset{\text{O}}{\|}}{\text{C}}\text{---CH}_2\text{---NH}_2\text{Ph} \right]^+ + \text{Br}^- \qquad (62)
$$

exhibits an entropy of activation of -56 calories per degree in benzene, -39 calories per degree in acetone, and -28 calories per degree in ethanol.[42] This may seem surprising since it might be argued that the greatest degree of orientation should occur with the most polar solvents. However, it should be remem-

[40] Stein and Murphy, *J. Am. Chem. Soc.*, **74**, 1041 (1952).
[41] Dostrovsky and Hughes, *J. Chem. Soc.*, **1946**, 157.
[42] Cox, *J. Chem. Soc.*, **119**, 142 (1921).

bered that the entropy of activation represents a *change* in randomness and that the molecules of polar solvents have a considerable measure of orientation, even in the absence of solutes. The molecules of the less polar solvents therefore suffer the *greatest increase* of orientation under the influence of a polar transition state since they begin with so little orientation. As one would expect, a reaction involving two ions of the same charge also exhibits a negative entropy of activation (the transition state has a charge greater than either of the reactants), whereas reactions in which two oppositely charged ions react to yield uncharged products exhibit positive entropies of activation.

For a reaction having a negative entropy of activation, we see that it is not enough that the reactant molecules come together with the necessary activation energy; they must also acquire an additional measure of orientation. Now, one of the fundamental characteristics of our physical world is that a mixture in which the molecules are randomly oriented is a more probable system than the same mixture in which there is a high degree of order among the molecules. It follows then that only a fraction of the collisions with the necessary activation energy will actually result in reaction; the more highly negative the entropy of activation, the less this fraction will be.[43] A reaction therefore may be slowed down quite as effectively by a highly negative entropy of activation as by a large positive energy of activation.

Influence of Solvent

Changes in solvent will affect reaction rates much in the same way as they effect equilibria. This is not surprising since the rate of a reaction is closely related to the position of an equilibrium—the equilibrium between reactants and transition state. The most pronounced solvent effects are observed for reactions between ions and for those reactions in which ions are generated from uncharged molecules. Reactions in which charge is *created* proceed most rapidly in polar solvents; typical of this group of reactions are the quaternization of amines by the "Menschutkin reaction" ($R_3N + R'I \rightarrow R'NR_3^+ + I^-$), and the hydrolysis of benzhydryl chloride ($Ph_2CHCl + H_2O \rightarrow Ph_2CHOH + H^+ + Cl^-$). These involve charge separation in the transition state; and, as we have seen, the extremely polar solvents are most capable of dispersing charge by solvation while themselves undergoing the least reorganization.

Conversely, since ions tend to be least "comfortable" in nonpolar solvents,

---

[43] Using the principles of statistical mechanics it is possible to estimate the number of collisions per unit time having the necessary energy of activation (see, for example, Ref. 1(b), pp. 54–73). In most cases this figure is, as expected, far greater than the number of molecules reacting per unit time. If we define p as the probability that molecules having the necessary energy will react upon collision, it may further be shown that $\ln p$ is quite nearly equal to $\Delta S^{\ddagger}/R$.

such solvents will tend to facilitate the destruction of charge. Thus reactions such as the Hofmann elimination (R_3N^+—C_2H_5 + OH^- → R_3N + CH_2=CH_2 + H_2O), in which uncharged molecules are formed from ions, proceed more *rapidly* in less polar solvents.[44] When an ion reacts with an *uncharged* molecule (for example, the reaction CH_3I + OH^- → CH_3OH + I^-), the charge, which is localized to a single ion before reaction, becomes dispersed over a somewhat larger area in the transition state. Since the charge density has been thus (temporarily) diminished, the transition state requires less solvation than the reactants. In this respect such a reaction is similar to that between ions of opposite charge and should therefore be more rapid in poorly ionizing solvents. However, the effect of solvent upon velocity should be much less marked than for reactions in which charge is destroyed. For reactions in which both the reactants and products are uncharged, the effects of solvent on rate are slight and need not be considered here.

It should be noted that a variation in solvent may change not only the speed of a reaction but also its apparent order. The ethanolysis of α-phenylethyl chloride in absolute ethanol is, like the hydrolysis of isopropyl bromide (reaction 42), a competition between a first- and second-order reaction:[45]

$$Ph\text{—}\underset{\underset{\displaystyle CH_3}{|}}{CH}\text{—}Cl + OEt^- \rightarrow Ph\text{—}\underset{\underset{\displaystyle CH_3}{|}}{CH}\text{—}OEt + Cl^-$$

$$\frac{-d\left(\underset{\underset{\displaystyle Me}{|}}{PhCHCl}\right)}{dt} = k_1 \left(\underset{\underset{\displaystyle Me}{|}}{PhCHCl}\right) + k_2 \left(\underset{\underset{\displaystyle Me}{|}}{PhCHCl}\right)(OEt^-) \qquad (63)$$

However, if water is added to the mixture, increasing the polarity, the first-order component of the reaction (which presumably involves an ionization) is accelerated, whereas the second-order component (which presumably involves the direct attack of an ion on a neutral alkyl halide molecule) is retarded. In 80 percent alcohol, the latter component effectively vanishes, and the reaction appears to obey an ordinary first-order rate law.[46]

[44] These arguments may be put on a semiquantitative basis by assuming a suitable charge distribution in the transition state, calculating the electrostatic energies necessary to form such a transition state from the reactants in media of differing dielectric constants, and equating these energy values to the respective values of $\Delta F^\ddagger$. See, for example, Laidler and Eyring, *Ann. N.Y. Acad. Sci.*, **39**, 303 (1940); Scratchard, *Chem. Revs.*, **10**, 229 (1932). See also Ex. 6.

Such treatments, however, are oversimplifications, for they assume, in essence, that a solvent affects a reaction only through its dielectric constant. It would then follow that a reaction should have identical rates in two solvent mixtures having the same dielectric constant, a conclusion which is wholly out of agreement with experience. See, for example, Brown and Hudson, *J. Chem. Soc.*, **1953**, 3352; and Hudson and Saville, *ibid.*, **1955**, 5114.

[45] Hughes, Ingold, and Scott, *J. Chem. Soc.*, **1937**, 1201.

[46] Ward, *J. Chem. Soc.*, **1927**, 445.

Influence of Ionic Strength. Salt Effects

Let us reconsider a reaction between species A and B—first-order in both—proceeding through the activated complex $AB^{\ddagger}$.

$$A + B \rightarrow (AB^{\ddagger}) \rightarrow \text{products}$$

The expression for the rate constant, k_r, for this reaction is given by the transition state theory as

$$k_r = \frac{kT}{h} \frac{(AB)^{\ddagger}}{(A)(B)} = \frac{kT}{h} K^{\ddagger} \frac{\gamma_A \gamma_B}{\gamma_{AB\ddagger}} \tag{64}$$

Since the activity coefficients (the γ terms) of dissolved species vary with the ionic strength[47] of a solution, it follows that the rate constant for a reaction should likewise depend upon the total concentration of ions in solution, whether or not these ions participate in the reaction at hand. This is especially so if both of the reactants are ions; for such cases, the effect of variations in ionic strength may be predicted by the simple Debye-Huckel theory.[48] According to this treatment, the logarithm of the activity coefficient γ for ion A in a solution having an ionic strength less than 0.01 is, to a fair approximation,

$$\log \gamma_A = -1.83 \times 10^6 z_A^2 \sqrt{\frac{\mu}{D^3 T^3 \rho}} \tag{66}$$

where z_A is the charge on the ion, μ the ionic strength, D the dielectric constant, T the absolute temperature, and ρ the density of the solution. Substituting such an expression for each of the activity coefficients in the logarithmic form of equation (64), we obtain

$$\log k_r = \log \frac{kTK^{\ddagger}}{h} - 1.83 \times 10^6 \sqrt{\frac{\mu}{D^3 T^3 \rho}} (z_A^2 + z_B^2 - z_{AB\ddagger}^2) \tag{67}$$

Since the charge on the transition state, $z_{AB\ddagger}$, is the sum $z_A + z_B$, and $kTK^{\ddagger}/h$ is the rate constant for the reaction in infinitely dilute soluton (k_r^0), we may write equation (67) as

$$\log k_r = \log k_r^0 + 1.83 \times 10^6 \sqrt{\frac{\mu}{D^3 T^3 \rho}} (2 z_A z_B) \tag{68}$$

[47] The *ionic strength*, μ, for a solution containing ions A, B, C, etc., is defined:

$$\mu = \frac{1}{2} [(A)z_A^2 + (B)z_B^2 + (C)z_C^2 + \cdots] \tag{65}$$

where the z's represent the charges on the respective ions. If the solution contains only uni-univalent electrolytes, μ is simply the square of the total molal concentration of ionized salts.

[48] Brønsted, *Z. physik. Chem.*, **102**, 169 (1922); **115**, 337 (1925).

Thus, a reaction between two positive or between two negative ions will be accelerated by increases in ionic strength, whereas a reaction between a positive and a negative ion will be slowed down. It is emphasized that equation (68) applies quantitatively only to dilute solutions in which the added salts are fully dissociated and interionic attraction is at a minimum. For more concentrated solutions, particularly in solvents of low dielectric constant, more complex expressions must be used, but equation (68) still predicts the *direction* in which ionic strength influences reaction rates.

If one of the reactants (say A) is an ion, whereas B is a neutral molecule, the activated complex, $AB^{\ddagger}$, should have the same charge as A, and, according to equation (66), the same activity coefficient. If the activity coefficient of B is also independent of ionic strength, equation (64) would predict that the rate constant should not be subject to a salt effect (that is, the final term in equation (68) should vanish). Although such reactions are considerably less sensitive to salt effects than are reactions between ions, their rates are often measurably affected by high concentrations of added salt. Not only is the activity coefficient of a neutral solute generally raised by addition of salts (the "salting-out" effect), but at high ionic strengths where equation (66) is no longer applicable, the activity coefficient of an ion depends on factors other than its charge. There is, at present, no simple way of predicting the magnitude, or even the direction, of the salt effect on such reactions.[49] Equation (68) predicts that the rate of a reaction between neutral molecules to form ions should not be affected by ionic strength. It is known, however, that such reactions (for example, t-BuCl + $H_2O \rightarrow t$-BuOH$^+$ + Cl$^-$) show *positive salt effects*—that is, they go faster at high ionic strengths. Although the activated complex in such a reaction has no net charge, it is a *strong dipole* since the separation of charges has already begun. Its activity coefficient $\gamma_{AB^{\ddagger}}$, which appears in the denominator of equation (64), decreases (and k_r thus increases) with an increase in ionic strength.[50] We can now understand why, in the absence of added electrolytes, the rate constant for a reaction that produces ions will show an upward drift as the reaction progresses. As more and more ions are formed, the magnitude of the positive salt effect increases, and the specific rate rises.

---

[49] See, however, Amis and Jaffe, *J. Chem. Phys.*, **10**, 598 (1942).

[50] A simplified treatment of the effect of ionic strength on a reaction that produces ions, given by Bateman, *et al.* (*J. Chem. Soc.*, **1940**, 979), yields the relationship

$$\ln k_r = \ln k_r^0 + \alpha Z^2 \mu d \qquad (69)$$

where k_r^0 is the rate constant at zero ionic strength, α a constant characteristic of the solvent and the temperature, μ the ionic strength, Z the fractional charge on each "end" of the dipole, and d the distance between the "ends." The application of this equation to the quantitative prediction of salt effects is limited largely by the difficulty in estimating, *a priori*, the fractional charge, Z, and the separation of charge, d, associated with an activated complex whose existence is momentary and which therefore may be studied only by indirect means.

In summary, then, reactions in which ionic charge is created are facilitated by solvents having high dielectric constants and by high ionic strengths. Reactions in which ionic charge is destroyed are facilitated by solvents having low dielectric constants and by low ionic strengths.

The salt effects that we have been discussing are generally grouped together as *primary salt effects*. They arise because of variations in the activity coefficients of the species participating in the rate-determining step and the activity coefficient of the activated complex. There is, however, another important way in which the rate of a reaction may be influenced by ionic strength. In a number of reactions, the rate-determining step occurs *after a rapid, reversible step involving ions*, and the position of equilibrium in the preliminary step must also be subject to salt effects. For example, an acid-catalyzed reaction occurring in the presence of an uncharged weak acid, HA, may show a positive salt effect simply because the degree of ionization of HA,

$$HA \rightleftharpoons A^- + H^+ \text{ (solvated)}$$

rises as the ionic strength is increased—that is, addition of salt results in a greater conversion of HA into a more powerful catalyst, the lyonium ion. This so-called *secondary salt effect* would be far less important, perhaps negligible, if the catalyzing acid were of the type BH^+. The equilibrium is subject only to minor salt

$$BH^+ \rightleftharpoons B + H^+ \text{ (solvated)}$$

effects since here ionic charge is neither created nor destroyed.

In view of the complications that may be engendered by salt effects, control of ionic strength is essential in kinetic studies of reactions involving ions. Often, the ionic strength is kept essentially constant by the addition of a large quantity of a salt which (it is hoped) does not otherwise influence the reaction. If k_r^0 is desired, the reaction rate is measured in a number of solutions of different ionic strengths, and the resulting rate constants extrapolated to zero ionic strength.

Ambiguities in Interpreting Kinetic Data

We have already seen[32] that the rate law for the basic hydrolysis of methyl bromide may be interpreted in terms of a rate-determining step involving CH_3Br and OH^-, or, alternately, involving the ion $BrCH_2{:}^-$ and H_2O. Although the second possibility is consistent with the kinetic picture, it is out of accord with a substantial body of chemical experience and, justifiably, is excluded. Similar ambiguities in interpretation often arise and sometimes are not so easily resolved. Consider, for example, the chlorination of methylamine with hypochlorous acid, momentarily ignoring all salt effects. The reaction is first order in both reagents;[51] the rate law may thus be written

$$RNH_2 + HOCl \rightarrow RNHCl + H_2O \qquad rate = k_2(RNH_2)(HOCl) \quad (70)$$

On the other hand, since the acid and the amine participate in the acid-base equilibrium,

$$RNH_2 + HOCl \rightleftharpoons RNH_3^+ + OCl^- \qquad K = \frac{(RNH_3^+)(OCl^-)}{(RNH_2)(HOCl)} \quad (71)$$

the product $(RNH_2)(HOCl)$ is proportional to the product $(RNH_3^+)(OCl^-)$, and the rate law has an alternate form,

$$rate = k_2'(RNH_3^+)(OCl^-) \tag{72}$$

which suggests that the chlorination reaction instead involves the RNH_3^+ and OCl^- ions. If we now bring the salt effect into the picture, a choice between the two mechanisms might at first appear possible, since a reaction between oppositely charged ions should show a pronounced negative salt effect whereas a reaction between uncharged species should show little or none. However, a closer look shows us that an examination of the salt effect will not give the answer; although reaction (70) would not exhibit a negative *primary* salt effect, it is subject to a negative *secondary* salt effect. An increase in ionic strength shifts the equilibrium (71) so that more of the ions are formed at the expense of the unionized acid and base. In fact, a rigorous analysis of this problem (Ex. 9) shows that the primary salt effect influencing reaction (72) and the secondary salt effect influencing reaction (70) are the same, both in direction and magnitude. In short, both reaction paths would result in identical rate laws even when activity coefficients are included.

This type of dilemma confronts the kineticist, whenever a choice must be made between one set of reactants and another set that is in rapid equilibrium with the first. It is indeed one of the most important limitations on mechanistic conclusions derived from kinetic studies.

Mechanisms of Acid and Base Catalysis

Having examined the rate laws of a number of reactions, we are now in a position to understand why some reactions are subject to general acid or base catalysis, whereas others are subject to specific lyonium- or lyate-ion catalysis. Suppose, for example, that a substance X can undergo a given reaction only when converted to its conjugate acid, HX^+. If the formation of HX^+ is rapid

[51] Weil and Morris, *J. Am. Chem. Soc.*, **71**, 1664 (1949).

and reversible, the reaction sequence is

$$X \underset{K_{eq}}{\overset{H^+}{\rightleftharpoons}} HX^+ \overset{Y}{\underset{k_2}{\rightarrow}} \text{products}$$

and the rate law is

$$\text{rate} = k_2(HX^+)(Y) = k_2 K_{eq}(H^+)(X)(Y) \qquad (73)$$

The reaction is thus subject to *specific lyonium-ion catalysis*. However, if the formation of HX^+ is slower than its reaction with Y, the rate-determining step becomes the transfer of a proton from an acid HA present in the mixture,

$$X \underset{\text{slow}}{\overset{HA}{\longrightarrow}} HX^+ \underset{\text{fast}}{\overset{Y}{\longrightarrow}} \text{products}$$

If there are a number of acids (HA, HA', HA'', etc.) present, each will transfer
protons to X at a different rate, and the rate of the overall reaction will be the
sum of a number of terms, each containing the concentration and rate constant
for one of the acids present.

$$\text{rate} = k(X)(HA) + k'(X)(HA') + k''(X)(HA'') \cdots \qquad (74)$$

This is a rate law for *general acid catalysis*.

General acid catalysis is also observed if the rate-determining step involves
a hydrogen-bonded complex of reagent X and acid HA, reversibly and rapidly
formed.

$$X \underset{K_{eq}}{\overset{HA}{\rightleftharpoons}} X \cdot HA \overset{Y}{\underset{k_2}{\rightarrow}} \text{products}$$

If there are several acids present, several complexes are possible, each one
reacting with reagent Y at its own rate.

$$\begin{aligned}
\text{rate} &= k_2(X \cdot HA)(Y) + k'_2(X \cdot HA')(Y) + k''_2(X \cdot HA'')(Y) \cdots \\
&= (X)(Y)[K_{eq}k_2(HA) + K'_{eq}k'_2(HA') + K''_{eq}k''_2(HA'') \cdots]
\end{aligned} \qquad (75)$$

A third situation which might result in general acid catalysis is the reaction
of the conjugate acid of X with the base B.

$$X \underset{K_{eq}}{\overset{H^+}{\rightleftharpoons}} XH^+ \overset{B}{\underset{k_2}{\rightarrow}} \text{products}$$

If the formation of XH^+ is reversible and rapid, the rate law is

$$\text{rate} = k_2(B)(XH^+) = k_2 K_{eq}(B)(X)(H^+) = k_2 K_{eq} K^a_{BH^+}(BH^+)(X) \qquad (76)$$

The reaction rate is thus proportional to the concentration of the acid BH^+,
a conclusion perhaps not immediately evident on inspection of the reaction
sequence. Remember, however, that an increase in (BH^+) must be attended by
a corresponding increase in the value of the product $(B) \times (H^+)$, and both B

and H^+ are present in the activated complex. Furthermore, if there are a number of bases present, each may react with XH^+ at its own rate; the rate of disappearance of X would be the sum of a number of terms of the same type as given in equation (76), each with the same value of K_{eq} and (X), but with different values of k_2, $K^a_{BH^+}$, and (BH^+). The reaction is therefore subject to general catalysis by acids of the type BH^+.

By similar reasoning, it is easy to show that reactions which may be represented by the following sequences are subject to general base catalysis,

$$HX \xrightarrow[\text{slow}]{B} X^- \xrightarrow{Y} \text{products}$$

and
$$X + B \underset{\text{eq}}{\overset{\text{fast}}{\rightleftharpoons}} X{\cdot}B \xrightarrow[\text{slow}]{Y} \text{products}$$

whereas a reaction sequence of the following type:

$$HX + B \underset{\text{eq}}{\overset{\text{fast}}{\rightleftharpoons}} X^- + BH^+ \xrightarrow[\text{slow}]{Y} \text{products}$$

should be subject to specific lyate-ion catalysis.

Finally, if the reaction sequence is of the type:

$$X + HA \underset{\text{eq}}{\overset{\text{fast}}{\rightleftharpoons}} X{\cdot}HA \xrightarrow[\text{slow}]{B} \text{products}$$

the reaction is subject to *general catalysis, both by acids and bases*. (See, for example, the mutarotation of tetramethyl glucose, p. 139.)

Reaction Rates and Acidity Scales[52]

It is now recognized that the rates of a number of acid-catalyzed reactions in strongly acid media are proportional to Hammett's h_0 function (p. 103), whereas the rates of others are more nearly proportional to the concentration of lyonium ion (in water, to (H_3O^+)). In the present text, we shall assume as is generally done, that reactions in the first class proceed through activated complexes that differ from the reactants *only by addition of a proton*. The justification of such an inference is as follows. Suppose the reaction sequence is

$$X + H^+ \underset{K_{eq}}{\overset{\text{fast, eq}}{\rightleftharpoons}} XH^+ \xrightarrow[k]{\text{slow}} \text{products}$$

The rate of this reaction at finite concentrations is given by the transition-state

[52] For more detailed discussions of this problem, see: (a) Zucker and Hammett, *J. Am. Chem. Soc.*, **61**, 2791 (1939); (b) Paul and Hammett, *ibid.*, **58**, 2182 (1936); (c) Long and Paul, *Chem. Revs.*, **57**, 935 (1957); (d) Satchell, *J. Chem. Soc.*, **1957**, 2878; (e) Hammett (Ref. 23), pp. 273–277.

theory as

$$\text{rate} = k^0(XH^+)\frac{\gamma_{XH^+}}{\gamma^{\ddagger}} \tag{77}$$

where k^0 is the specific rate at infinite dilution and $\gamma^{\ddagger}$ is the activity coefficient of the activated complex. Since the equilibrium constant for the first step is

$$K_{eq} = \frac{(XH^+)}{(X)(H^+)} \times \frac{\gamma_{XH^+}}{\gamma_X\gamma_{H^+}} = \frac{1}{K^a_{XH^+}} \tag{78}$$

the rate may be rewritten:

$$\text{rate} = \frac{k^0}{K^a_{XH^+}}(H^+)(X)\frac{\gamma_{H^+}\gamma_X}{\gamma^{\ddagger}} = \frac{k^0}{K^a_{XH^+}}(X)a_{H^+}\frac{\gamma_X}{\gamma^{\ddagger}} \tag{79}$$

Now if the activated complex differs from reactant X only by addition of a proton, the activity coefficients on the extreme right of equation (79) refer merely to a neutral base and its conjugate acid. This ratio converts a_{H^+} (by definition) to h_0. The rate then becomes equal to $k^0(X)h_0/K^a_{XH^+}$—that is, proportional to h_0.

Suppose, however, that the species XH^+ becomes solvated during the rate-determining step. If the solvent is water, the reaction sequence may be represented as follows:

$$X + H^+ \underset{K_{eq}}{\overset{\text{fast, eq}}{\rightleftharpoons}} XH^+ \xrightarrow[k]{H_2O,\ \text{slow}} \text{products}$$

and the reaction rate will be

$$\text{rate} = k^0(XH^+)(H_2O)\left[\frac{\gamma_{XH^+}\gamma_{H_2O}}{\gamma^{\ddagger}}\right] \tag{80}$$

Since XH^+ and H_2O are in equilibrium with X and H_3O^+,

$$K_{eq} = \left(\frac{(XH^+)(H_2O)}{(X)(H_3O^+)}\right) \times \left(\frac{\gamma_{XH^+}\gamma_{H_2O}}{\gamma_X\gamma_{H_3O^+}}\right) \tag{81}$$

and (80) may be rewritten

$$\text{rate} = k^0 K_{eq}(X)(H_3O^+) \times \left(\frac{\gamma_X\gamma_{H_3O^+}}{\gamma^{\ddagger}}\right)$$

The rates of a number of reactions believed, on the basis of other evidence, to proceed by such a path are very nearly proportional to (H_3O^+). For these, it appears that the activity coefficient term, $\gamma_X\gamma_{H_3O^+}/\gamma^{\ddagger}$, remains very nearly constant in a number of different solutions. Explanations for the supposed invariance of this ratio have been submitted,[52(e)] but none, in the opinion of this author, are fully satisfactory. Thus, although proportionality between rate and (H_3O^+) is generally taken (probably, in most cases, correctly) to indicate participation of one or more molecules of solvent in the rate-determining step, the question must be considered open.[52(c,d)]

It will be remembered that the h_0 function is a useful one in solutions of high dielectric constant because the ratio γ_X/γ_{XH^+} in a given solvent mixture is largely independent of the nature of X. This is not the case for solutions in aqueous ethanol,[52(d)] for which, however, a treatment roughly analogous to that given in equations (77)–(79) may be set up using the Grunwald acidity scale (p. 107). This is most easily done by expressing $K_{XH^+}^a$ in the solvent at hand in terms of the corresponding acidity constant in pure water, using the additional parameters m_0 (specific for reactant X), Y_0 (specific for the solvent mixture), and f_{H^+} (the degenerate activity coefficient for the hydrogen ion in the given mixture). It may thus be shown (Ex. 12) that if the log (k_r/f_{H^+}) for a number of mixtures be plotted against the Y_0 values of these mixtures, the resulting curve should be very nearly a straight line of slope m_0. The second-order rate constants for the acid-catalyzed isomerization VIII $\rightarrow$ IX in water-ethanol mixtures containing from 35 to 100 percent ethanol have been found to fit such a relationship.[53]

$$ \text{VIII} \qquad\qquad\qquad \text{IX} $$

Isotope Effects

In the discussion of isotopic labeling in the previous chapter, it was pointed out that isotopic substitution may cause appreciable variation in the rate of a reaction. This **isotope effect** is greatest when deuterium (H^2) or tritium (H^3) is substituted for ordinary hydrogen, particularly when the reaction involves breaking the bond to the labeled atom. Since the chemistry of a species is generally thought to depend upon its electronic configuration rather than on the mass of its nucleus or nuclei, the existence of this effect may perhaps be puzzling. To understand its cause,[54] let us remember that two atoms bound to each other are vibrating, even in their lowest energy state. The energy associated with this vibration, which persists down to absolute zero, is called *zero-point*

[53] Braude and Stern, *J. Chem. Soc.*, **1948**, 1982; Gutbezahl and Grunwald, *J. Am. Chem. Soc.*, **75**, 572 (1953).

[54] (a) For a rigorous treatment of the isotope effect, see Bigeleisen, *J. Chem. Phys.*, **17**, 675 (1949). (b) A review of chemical aspects of the deuterium isotope effect is given by Wiberg, *Chem. Revs.*, **55**, 713 (1955).

energy; it is greatest for the very light atoms. A C—H bond, for example, has a greater (about 1.2 kcal per mole greater) zero-point energy than a C—D bond of the same type; hence the C—H bond is a "looser bond" and is more easily broken. Furthermore, if the formation of an activated complex requires partial or total rupture of a carbon-hydrogen bond, the activated complex will be formed more easily from a C—H bond than from a C—D bond, and the C—H compound will react more rapidly than the C—D compound. Such an isotope effect may be detected by actual comparison of the reaction rates of the labeled and nonlabeled compounds. A more subtle method is to subject a known isotopic mixture to an incomplete reaction, isolate the unreacted starting material, and determine whether the isotopic composition has changed (that is, whether the percentage of C—D compound in the reactant has increased because the C—H compound is consumed more rapidly).

Since the chemical equilibria depends upon the rates of the forward and reverse reactions, the position of an equilibria may also be slightly affected by isotopic substitution. The direction of shift will depend upon whether the difference between zero-point energies of labeled and unlabeled compound is greater for the reactant or for the product. Specifically, substitution with a *heavier* isotope will favor that bond for which the zero-point energy is *less sensitive* to isotopic substitution.

It follows then that a complex reaction may show an isotope effect for one of two reasons. The bond to the labeled atom may be broken or stretched in the rate-determining step or, alternatively, a rapid and reversible reaction preceding the slow step may involve breakage of this bond, the isotope effect on this equilibrium being reflected in an observable kinetic isotope effect for the overall reaction. If the bond to the labeled atom is broken *after* the rate-determining step, little or no kinetic isotope effect is to be expected.

Consider, for example, the oxidation of benzaldehyde by permanganate. There is much about this reaction that we do not know, for its path is complicated by the plurality of possible oxidation states of manganese. We can, however, say with considerable certainty that the C—H bond in the aldehyde group is broken during the rate-determining step, since ordinary benzaldehyde at pH 7 is oxidized in this reaction 7.5 times as fast as is $C_6H_5—C\!\!=\!\!O$.[55] The

$$\overset{|}{D}$$

very slight possibility of a preliminary equilibrium involving breakage of the C—D bond could be excluded by carrying out an incomplete oxidation of the deuterated aldehyde in ordinary water and determining whether any "light" hydrogen has replaced the deuterium in the unreacted starting material.

On the other hand, there is *no* observable hydrogen isotope effect in the

[55] Wiberg and Steward, *J. Am. Chem. Soc.*, **77**, 1786 (1955).

nitration of benzene and its derivatives. Deuterated nitrobenzene, $C_6D_5NO_2$, for example, is nitrated at the same rate as ordinary nitrobenzene under the same conditions.[56] This means that the C—H (or C—D) bond is not broken in any equilibrium prior to the rate-determining step, and it is often taken to mean that the C—H bond is not broken *during* the rate-determining step either —that is, that the breakage of the C—H bond occurs in a rapid step following the slow formation of intermediate X. While the absence of a hydrogen

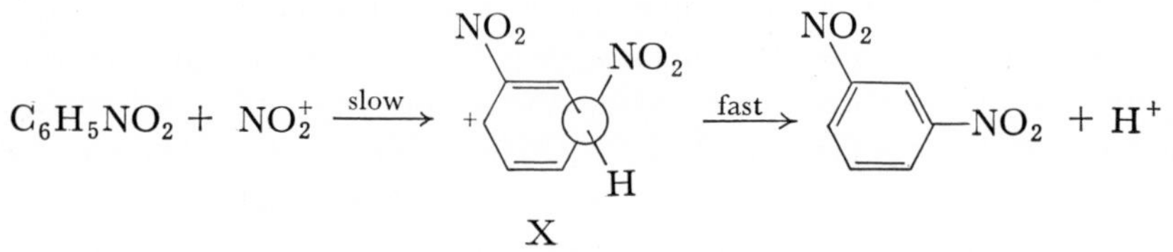

isotope effect is consistent with the existence of intermediate X, it does not demand it. Strictly speaking, we may infer only that the stretching of the carbon-hydrogen bond (which should be more difficult for C—D than for C—H) does not play a significant role in the activation process for the slow step—that is, that the stretching of this bond does not effect the energy of activation for this step. Thus, although the reactants almost certainly pass through a configuration corresponding to X, we cannot say, without further knowledge, whether this represents an actual intermediate (a point of minimum energy in the progress of the reaction) or simply an activated complex (a point of maximum energy).[57]

EXERCISES FOR CHAPTER 6

1. Suggest a method for following the rate of each of the reactions below:

(a) Ph—NH—C(=O)—Ph + C_6H_6 → Ph—Ph + N_2 + Ph—COOH
   (with N=O on the nitrogen)

(b) C_2H_4 (gas) + H_2 → C_2H_6 (gas)

(c) $PhCH_2F$ + H_2O → $PhCH_2OH$ + HF

(d) CH_3—O—SO_3^- + Br^- → CH_3Br + SO_4^{2-}

(e) PhN=O + $PhNH_2$ → Ph—N=N—Ph + H_2O

(f)

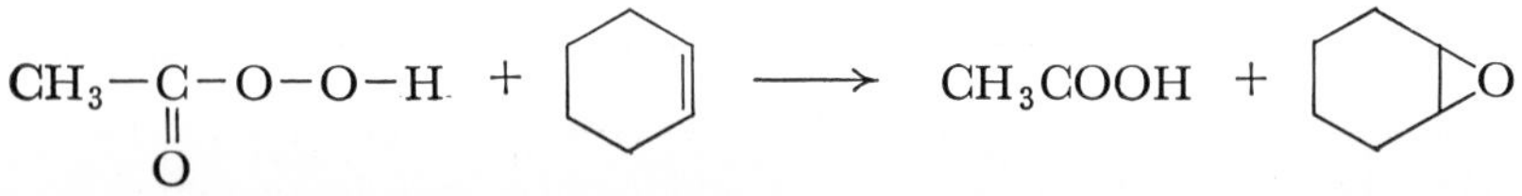

$$CH_3-\overset{\text{O}}{\underset{\|}{C}}-O-O-H \ + \ \bigcirc \longrightarrow CH_3COOH \ + \ \bigcirc\!\!=\!\!O$$

---

[56] Gold and Hawes, *J. Chem. Soc.*, **1951**, 2102.
[57] For further discussion of this question, see Hammond, *J. Am. Chem. Soc.*, **77**, 334 (1955).

(g)

$$O_2N-\langle\bigcirc\rangle-O^- + CH_3-O-SO_3^- \longrightarrow O_2N-\langle\bigcirc\rangle-OCH_3 + SO_4^{2-}$$

(h)

$$\langle\bigcirc\rangle S + CH_3OSO_2Ph \longrightarrow \left[\langle\bigcirc\rangle S-CH_3\right]^+ + PhSO_3^-$$

2. (a) Show how the integrated expressions for the simple reversible reaction

$$A \underset{k_r}{\overset{k_f}{\rightleftharpoons}} B$$

(equations 17 and 18) are obtained from the differential rate equation (16).

(b) The reaction of semicarbazide with acetone

$$Me_2C\!\!=\!\!O + NH_2-NH-\overset{\overset{\displaystyle O}{\|}}{C}-NH_2 \overset{HA}{\longrightarrow} Me_2C\!\!=\!\!N-NH-\overset{\overset{\displaystyle O}{\|}}{C}-NH_2 + H_2O$$

is subject to general acid catalysis and is first order both in acetone and in semi-carbazide. On this basis derive the rate law given for this reaction (equation 12).

3. Chlorobenzene in which some of the chlorine atoms are radioactive Cl^{36} is subjected to nitration in nitromethane. The resulting mixture is neutralized and the organic layer separated into three portions having the weight ratio 1:8:1. To the first portion is added 10.0 grams of pure o-nitrochlorobenzene; the mixture is heated until all of the solid dissolves, then cooled. The o-nitrochlorobenzene which precipitates is recrystallized repeatedly until its activity remains constant (after a small correction for decay) at 1638 counts per minute per gram.

The second and third portions of the neutralized nitration mixture are treated with 10.0-gram samples of pure m-nitrochlorobenzene and p-nitrochlorobenzene, respectively, and the corresponding isomeric nitrochlorobenzenes similarly purified to constant activity. The resulting activities are 426 counts per minute per gram for the m-isomer and 3499 counts per minute per gram for the p-isomer.

Assuming that the formation of each of the three isomers follows the same type of rate law, calculate the ratios, k_p/k_m and k_p/k_o.

4. Show that a reaction following the sequence:

$$HS + X \rightleftharpoons S^- + XH^+ \text{ (fast, reversible)}$$
$$S^- + Y \rightarrow \text{products} \quad \text{(slow)}$$

should be subject to specific lyate-ion catalysis.

5. (a) Suggest two mechanisms (in addition to that shown on p. 176) for the iodination of aniline which are consistent with the rate law (equation 46).

(b) One of these mechanisms is extremely unlikely, being inconsistent with the formation of the observed major isomer, p-iodoaniline. Explain.

(c) Propose an experiment to distinguish between the remaining two mechanisms, using the isotope effect.

6. Two reacting ions, charges z_A and z_B, are brought from a very large separation through a solvent of dielectric constant D to a distance $r^{\ddagger}$ in an activated complex. Equate the electrostatic energy in this process to the free energy of activation of the reaction, $\Delta F^{\ddagger}$. Consider the rates of the reaction in a number of solvents of different dielectric constants, keeping the temperature the same. Show that a plot of log k_r vs. $1/D$ should yield a straight line.

7. For each of the following reactions, predict whether the rate would be increased, decreased, or essentially unchanged if (a) the dielectric constant of the solvent were increased (b) the ionic strength were increased.

$$CH_3\overset{\displaystyle O}{\overset{\displaystyle \|}{C}}Cl + H_2O \rightarrow CH_3COOH + H_3O^+ + Cl^-$$

$$PhN_2^+BF_4^- \rightarrow PhF + N_2 + BF_3$$

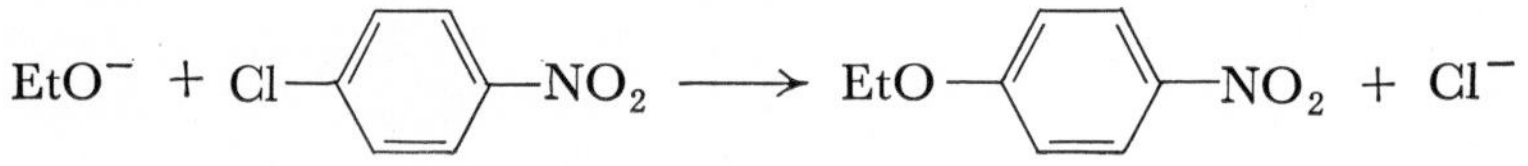

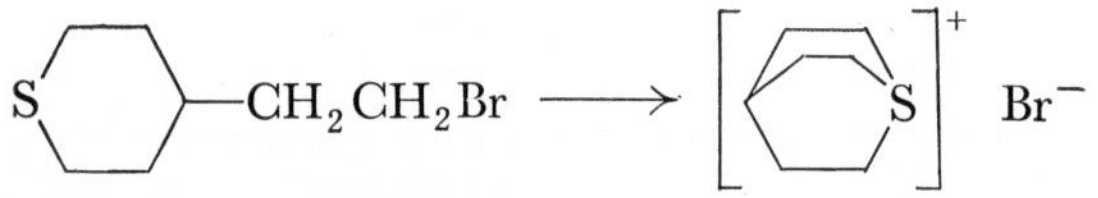

$$EtO^- + Cl-\!\!\!\langle\ \rangle\!\!\!-NO_2 \longrightarrow EtO-\!\!\!\langle\ \rangle\!\!\!-NO_2 + Cl^-$$

$$S\!\!\!\langle\ \rangle\!\!\!-CH_2CH_2Br \longrightarrow \left[\ \overset{\bigcirc}{S}\ \right]^+ Br^-$$

$$CH_2\!\!=\!\!CH-O-CH_2-CH\!\!=\!\!CH_2 \rightarrow CH_2\!\!=\!\!CH-CH_2-CH_2-CH\!\!=\!\!O$$

$$Cl-CH_2-\overset{\displaystyle O}{\overset{\displaystyle \|}{C}}-O^- + S_2O_3^{=} \rightarrow {}^-O_3S-S-CH_2-\overset{\displaystyle O}{\overset{\displaystyle \|}{C}}-O^- + Cl^-$$

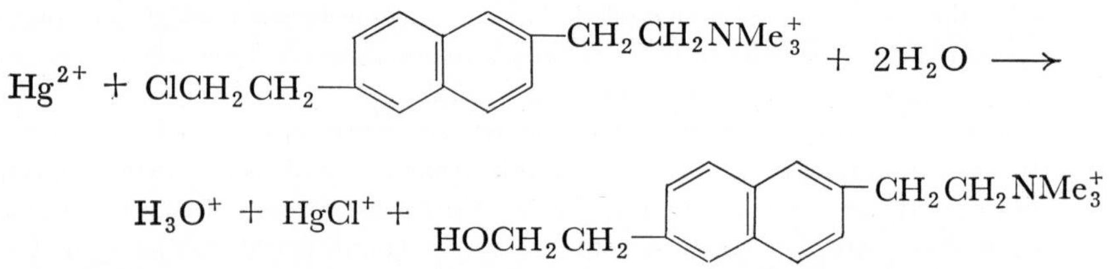

$$Hg^{2+} + ClCH_2CH_2-\!\!\!\langle\text{naphthalene}\rangle\!\!\!-CH_2CH_2NMe_3^+ + 2H_2O \longrightarrow$$

$$H_3O^+ + HgCl^+ + HOCH_2CH_2-\!\!\!\langle\text{naphthalene}\rangle\!\!\!-CH_2CH_2NMe_3^+$$

8. (a) Show how the expression for the entropy of activation (equation 56) is derived.
   (b) Predict which reaction in each of the following pairs has the greater entropy of activation:

   (1) $Me_2S + MeI \rightarrow Me_3S^+ + I^-$; or $SH^- + MeI \rightarrow MeSH + I^-$?

   (2) $Et_3N + EtBr \longrightarrow Et_4N^+Br^-$; or $\langle\text{pyridine}\rangle N + EtBr \longrightarrow \langle\text{pyridine}\rangle N\!-\!Et^+Br^-$?

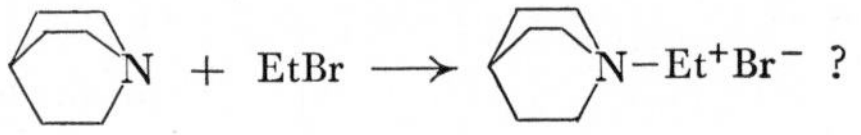

   (3) 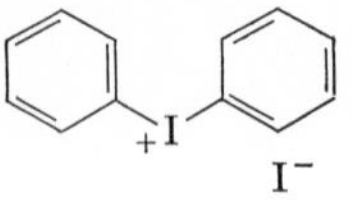 $\langle\ \rangle\overset{+}{\underset{I^-}{I}}\langle\ \rangle \longrightarrow 2C_6H_5I$; or $PhCH\!-\!Br + I^- \longrightarrow PhCH\!-\!I + Br^-$?
   (with CH_3 and CH substituents respectively)

   (4) 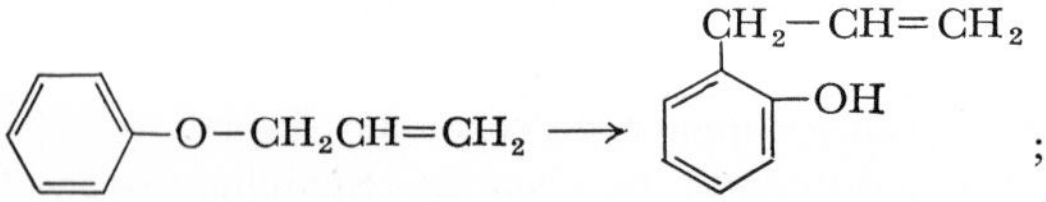 $\langle\ \rangle\!\!\!-O-CH_2CH\!\!=\!\!CH_2 \longrightarrow \langle\text{phenol with }CH_2\!-\!CH\!\!=\!\!CH_2\text{ and }OH\rangle$; or $Ph-\underset{\overset{|}{Ac}}{N}-Cl \xrightarrow{HCl} p\!-\!Cl\!-\!C_6H_4\!-\!NHAc$

(5) 2 ⬡⬡ ⟶ ⬡⬡ ; or $2CH_2$=$C(CH_3)_2 \longrightarrow (CH_3)_3C-CH$=$C(CH_3)_2$?

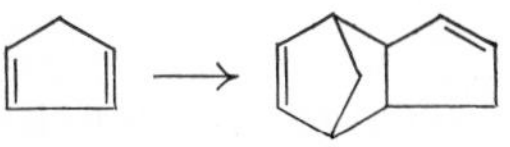

(6) t-BuBr (gas) $\rightarrow CH_2$=$C(CH_3)_2 + HBr$;   or $CH_3CH(OAc)_2$ (gas) $\rightarrow$
$$CH_2$$=$CH-OAc + CH_3COOH$?

9. Consider the two possible rate laws for the chlorination of methylamine with hypo-chlorous acid (equations 70 and 72), this time including the activity coefficients. Rewrite the equilibrium expression (71), again including activity coefficients, and show that the primary salt effect on the reaction between $CH_3NH_3^+$ and OCl^- is identical in magnitude to the secondary salt effect on the reaction between CH_3NH_2 and $HOCl$.

10. Consider the following reactions carried out with "tagged" compounds. Decide in each case whether the reaction would be subject to an appreciable isotope effect (that is, whether the rate would be appreciably different from that of the same reaction carried out with unlabeled compounds). Justify your guesses.

(a) D_2C=$CH_2 + Br_2 \rightarrow CD_2Br-CH_2Br$

(b) $2Ph-C$=$O + CN^- \xrightarrow{H_2O} Ph-CD-C-Ph$
      | | ||
      D   OH O

(c) $DO-CH_2-CH_2-Cl + OH^- \rightarrow CH_2\overbrace{\qquad}CH_2 + Cl^- + DOH$
                                               O

(d) t-BuCl + $D_2O \xrightarrow{\text{liquid, SO}_2} t$-BuOD + DCl

(e) CH_2=$CH_2 + Br_2 + CH_3OD \rightarrow Br-CH_2-CH_2-OCH_3 + DBr$

(f)

F^{20} ring with $-NO_2$ and NO_2 + $OH^- \longrightarrow$ OH ring with $-NO_2$ and NO_2 + $^{20}F^-$ 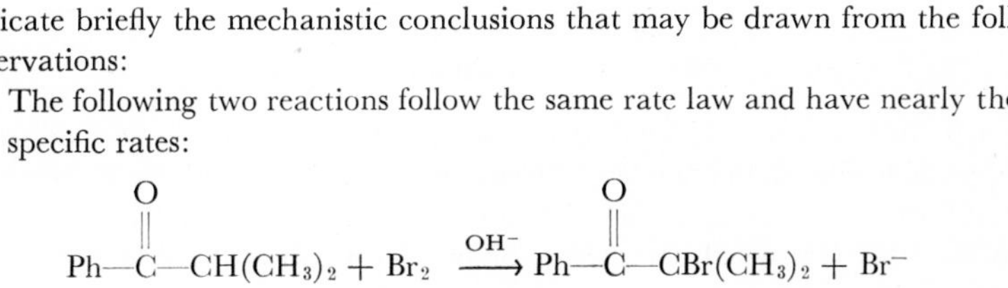 ?

11. Indicate briefly the mechanistic conclusions that may be drawn from the following observations:

(a) The following two reactions follow the same rate law and have nearly the same specific rates:

$$Ph-\overset{\overset{\textstyle O}{||}}{C}-CH(CH_3)_2 + Br_2 \xrightarrow{OH^-} Ph-\overset{\overset{\textstyle O}{||}}{C}-CBr(CH_3)_2 + Br^-$$

and $Ph-\overset{\overset{\textstyle O}{||}}{C}-CH(CH_3)_2 + D_2O \xrightarrow{OH^-} Ph-C-CD(CH_3)_2 + OD^-$
                                                          ||
                                                           O

(b) The hydrolysis of acetyl fluoride is catalyzed by acid whereas that of acetyl chloride is not.

(c) If the reaction: $CH_3-\overset{\overset{\displaystyle O}{\|}}{C}-CH_2-\overset{\overset{\displaystyle O}{\|}}{C}-CH_3 \xrightarrow[\text{EtOH}]{\text{OEt}^-} CH_3COOEt + CH_3-\overset{\overset{\displaystyle O}{\|}}{C}-CH_3$
is carried out in the presence of excess ethoxide, its rate is proportional to the concentration of added acetylacetone. If it is carried out in the presence of excess acetylacetone, the rate is proportional to the concentration of added ethoxide.

(d) The reaction $C_6H_5-\overset{\overset{\displaystyle Cl}{|}}{N}-COCH_3 \rightarrow p\text{-}ClC_6H_4NHAc$ is accelerated by HCl but not by HOAc or H_2SO_4.

(e) The formation of semicarbazones from ketones and semicarbazide is accelerated by small concentrations of acid but retarded by large concentrations of acid.

(f) The bromide $C_5H_{12}-CH_2-\overset{\overset{\displaystyle Br}{|}}{CH}-CH_3$ reacts with water over 30 times as fast as does the corresponding chloride. The products in both cases are the alcohol $C_5H_{12}-CH_2-CHOH-CH_3$ and the olefin $C_5H_{12}-CH=CH-CH_3$; and the ratio olefin to alcohol in the mixture of products is the same for the bromide as for the chloride, despite the difference in rates.

(g) The decomposition of azomethane, $CH_3-N=N-CH_3 \rightarrow C_2H_6 + N_2$ has an entropy of activation of $+17$ calories per degree, whereas the decomposition of acetic anhydride in the vapor phase, $(CH_3CO)_2O \rightarrow CH_3COOH + CH_2=C=O$, has an entropy of activation of -4 calory per degree.

(h) The hydrolysis of benzhydryl chloride, Ph_2CHCl, is more effectively accelerated by addition of Li_2SO_4 than by addition of LiN_3. However, LiN_3 is more effective in diverting the benzhydryl group to benzhydryl azide than is Li_2SO_4 in diverting the benzhydryl group to benzhydryl hydrogen sulfate or benzhydryl sulfate.

(i) The benzidine rearrangement and the acid-catalyzed hydrolyses of esters and acetals proceed more rapidly in D_2O than in H_2O.

(j) The oxidation of $(CH_3)_2CDOH$ by chromate is subject to a much more marked isotope effect than is the oxidation of $(CH_3)_2CHOD$.

(k) The nitration of toluene in nitromethane with excess nitric acid is retarded by addition of $LiNO_3$, but the reaction continues to obey zero-order kinetics.

12. Consider the reaction sequence,

$$X \quad + H^+ \rightleftharpoons XH^+ \quad \text{(fast, eq)}$$
$$XH^+ + Y \quad \rightarrow \text{products (slow, } k_2)$$

carried out in a series of water-ethanol mixtures in which the Grunwald treatment is applicable. Set up the rate law in terms of k_2 and $K^a_{XH^+}$, and express the apparent specific rate ($k_r = \text{rate}/(X)(H^+)(Y)$), in terms of the value of $K^a_{XH^+}$ in pure water and the other Grunwald parameters. Show that a plot of the values of $\log (k_r/f_{H^+})$ for the various solvent mixtures vs. the Y_o values for these mixtures is nearly a straight line of slope m_o. What approximation is necessary?

CHAPTER 7

Inductive, Resonance, and Steric Effects Upon the Reactivity of Molecules

ONE OF THE MOST IMPORTANT cornerstones in the framework of contemporary organic chemical thought is the knowledge that the reactions of compounds are largely determined by their functional groups. All carboxylic acids may be neutralized by base, essentially all esters may be saponified, most ketones may be converted to semicarbazones, and most monobromo compounds may ultimately be converted to the corresponding ethoxy compounds by treatment with sodium ethoxide. Of equal importance, however, is the realization that rate constants and positions of equilibria associated with the reactions of functional groups may be strongly dependent upon whatever else is present in the reacting molecules. Rates and equilibria are often markedly affected by changes in the carbon skeleton or by the introduction of additional substituents which themselves suffer no net change. Familiarly, chloroacetic acid is a stronger acid than acetic, the esters of mesitoic acid are much more slowly saponified than are those of benzoic, cyclohexanone reacts more rapidly and more completely with semicarbazide than does acetone, and the bromine atom in p-nitrobromobenzene is more rapidly displaced by ethoxide than is the bromine in bromobenzene.

In attempting to correlate structure and reactivity, we shall divide structural effects into three broad categories: inductive (or electrostatic) effects, resonance (or conjugation) effects, and steric effects. This division, although not based upon thermodynamics, is, by and large, congenial with the thinking of organic chemists. Moreover, at present it appears that the most promising

199

approach toward a simple quantitative treatment of the influence of structure on reactivity will be based on just such a division.[1]

It is to be emphasized that a given structural change may affect the *rate* of a reaction and its *position of equilibrium* in opposite directions; that is, it may slow down a reaction but allow it to go more nearly to completion. For example, if a methyl group is substituted for each of the three α-hydrogens in acetalde-hyde, the rate constant for semicarbazone formation is lowered by a factor of twenty at 25°, but the equilibrium constant for semicarbazone formation is increased by about 60 percent.[2] The semicarbazone of trimethylacetaldehyde is thus more stable to hydrolysis, for the semicarbazone of acetaldehyde, al-though formed more rapidly, is hydrolyzed 28 times as rapidly. Substitution of methyl groups for the α-hydrogens in this reaction has raised the value of $\Delta F^{\ddagger}$ but lowered the value of ΔF. It appears that equilibrium is much more quickly established in the system involving the light two-carbon aldehyde and its semicarbazone than in the system involving the more massive and bulky five-carbon aldehyde and its semicarbazone.

Inductive and Field Effects

The ionization of carboxylic acids has been more extensively studied than has any other type of organic chemical equilibrium.[3] For such reactions, any change in structure that will facilitate the removal of the H^+ ion from the acid molecule or hinder its return to the carboxylate anion should increase the ioniza-tion constant of the acid—that is, lower the free energy of ionization. (Analogous

[1] Before the 1950's, it was generally felt that attempts to link structure and reactivity, ex-cept for a number of very special cases, would meet one major obstacle. It seemed that al-though a structural formula, when interpreted in the light of modern concepts, would tell us much about potential-energy effects (bond energies, resonance energies, and dipole interac-tions), it would tell little about the kinetic energy of a reacting species (that is, about the oc-cupancy of the various possible rotational and vibrational energy levels) and about the degree of its solvation. Since both potential and kinetic energies change during ordinary reactions, it was felt that a structural change might result in predictable potential-energy effects which would be, however, offset by unpredictable kinetic energy or solvation effects. (See, for exam-ple, Hammett, *Physical Organic Chemistry*, McGraw-Hill Book Co., Inc., New York, 1940, pp. 69–80.)

In recent years, however, evidence has been accumulating showing that quantitative correlations may be made by considering independent contributions of inductive, resonance, and steric effects of substituents, then combining these appropriately to obtain an overall effect. This evidence has been reviewed by Taft in *Steric Effects in Organic Chemistry* (edited by Newman), John Wiley and Sons, Inc., New York, 1956, pp. 556–677. Such a division virtually ignores the difference between kinetic- and potential-energy effects; inductive, resonance, and steric effects each involve both potential- and kinetic-energy contributions which, at present, cannot generally be (and often need not be) disentangled.

[2] Westheimer, *J. Am. Chem. Soc.*, **56**, 1962 (1934).

[3] A recent and very detailed review of the effects of structure on acidity is given by Brown, McDaniel, and Haflinger in Braude and Nachod, *Determination of Organic Structures by Physical Methods*, Academic Press, Inc., New York, 1955, pp. 567–662. Dissociation constants quoted without reference within this chapter are taken largely from this source.

statements apply, of course, to other Brønsted acids.) Table 7-1 compares the pK values (in water at 25°) of a number of aliphatic acids to that of acetic acid (note once again that a large ionization constant corresponds to a small pK value).

Table 7-1. pK Values for Some Carboxylic Acids

Acid	pK	Acid	pK	Acid	pK
CH_3COOH	4.80	FCH_2COOH	2.66	$HOCH_2COOH$	3.83
$(CH_3)_3N^+\!\!-CH_2\!-COOH$	1.83	$ClCH_2COOH$	2.86	$N\!\equiv\!C\!-CH_2\!-COOH$	2.43
$H_3N^+\!\!-(CH_2)_4\!-COOH$	4.27	$Cl_2CHCOOH$	1.30	$HOOC\!-CH_2\!-COOH$	2.83
$^-O_2C\!-CH_2\!-COOH$	5.69	$Cl_3C\!-COOH$	0.65	$CH_3\!-CH_2\!-COOH$	4.88
$^-O_2C(CH_2)_4COOH$	5.41	$Cl\!-(CH_2)_2COOH$	4.0	$(CH_3)_3C\!-COOH$	5.05
				$HCOOH$	3.77

From the first column, we see the effect of introducing a charged substituent. As we would suspect merely from electrostatic considerations, a positive center such as $(CH_3)_3N^+$ or NH_3^+ eases the departure of the positive hydrogen ion from the —COOH group. The effect is large (almost a thousandfold increase in K_a) for $(CH_3)_3N^+\!\!-CH_2COOH$, in which the positive center lies close to the carboxyl group; it is much smaller (about a threefold increase in K_a) for $H_3N^+\!\!-(CH_2)_4\!-COOH$, in which the positive center is five atoms removed from the carboxyl group. This is again in harmony with our knowledge that electrostatic interactions become weaker as the distance between charges is increased.

Conversely, the introduction of a *negative* charge should *increase* the energy needed to remove an H^+ ion and should thus *weaken* the acid. Substitution of the —CO_2^- group for an α-hydrogen in acetic acid yields the hydrogen malonate ion, $^-O_2C\!-CH_2\!-COOH$. We must, however, be a little careful in comparing the strength of this acid with that of acetic, for the malonate ion has four equivalent basic sites whereas the acetate ion has only two.

In the absence of other effects, the malonate ion would, on a statistical basis alone, be *twice as strong a base* as the acetate ion; that is, the hydrogen malonate ion would be *half as strong an acid* as acetic acid. Actually, it is found to be about one eighth as strong, so the electrostatic effect here is in the "correct direction" but its magnitude is quite small. The comparison between malonic acid itself and the hydrogen malonate ion is more appropriate and much more striking.

By a statistical argument similar to that above, the two acids should differ in strength by a factor of 4 if other effects are absent. In truth, malonic acid is over four hundred times as strong an acid as the hydrogen malonate ion— that is, the ratio K_1/K_2 for malonic acid is 405. As would be expected, the ratio K_1/K_2 decreases as the distance between the carboxyl groups is increased; this ratio is 16.4 for succinic, 8.6 for glutaric, and 6.1 for azelaic acid (the nine-carbon dibasic acid).

Furthermore, the ratio $K_1/4K_2$ (note the statistical factor 4) may be taken as a measure of the electrostatic effect exerted by the negative —CO_2^- group at one end of a molecule on the arrival or departure of a H^+ ion at the other end. In a simple treatment based upon this principle, Bjerrum[4] equated the free-energy difference corresponding to $RT \ln K_1/4K_2$ to the classical electrostatic energy necessary for complete separation of a positive and a negative charge that are separated by a distance r in the molecule. This energy is inversely proportional to D, the dielectric constant of the medium lying between the charges, leading to Bjerrum's relationship,

$$RT \ln \frac{K_1}{4K_2} = \frac{Ne^2}{Dr} \qquad (1)$$

where e is the charge on the electron and N is Avogadro's number. There is some difficulty in selecting a suitable value for D; for if the dielectric constant for the pure solvent is used, the values of r calculated by equation (1) are over 30 percent less than may be accommodated by our present picture of molecular dimensions. A similar but more sophisticated treatment by Kirkwood and Westheimer[5(a)] recognizes that a sizable portion of the space between the centers of charge is occupied, not by molecules of solvent, but by the carbon chain of the acid. Insofar as a "microscopic dielectric constant" can be assigned to this carbon chain, it should be much nearer to the very low values (about 2) of the paraffin hydrocarbons than to the high value of the ionizing solvent (80 for water). Assuming (for mathematical simplicity) that a molecule acts as a homogeneous ellipsoidal cavity of low dielectric constant, surrounded by a homogeneous region of high dielectric constant, it is possible to estimate an "effective dielectric constant" having a value that depends somewhat upon the assumed shape of the molecular cavity but that, in any event, is considerably lower than the dielectric constant of the solvent. The Kirkwood-Westheimer treatment leads to more satisfactory values for r—the distance between the ends of the molecules—but still must be regarded as a relatively crude approximation since the molecules involved are obviously not true ellipsoids. It neverthe-

[4] Bjerrum, Z. physik. Chem., **106**, 219 (1923).
[5] (a) Kirkwood and Westheimer, J. Chem. Phys, **6**; 506, 513 (1938). (b) For further refinements in treatment, see Tanford, J. Am. Chem. Soc., **79**, 5348 (1957).

less expresses the important point that electrostatic effects are transmitted through the carbon chain (largely by electron polarization, p. 59) as well as through the solvent (largely by orientation polarization in the case of polar solvents).

This treatment also helps to account for the striking increase in the ratio K_1/K_2 as bulky alkyl groups are introduced between the —COOH groups in dicarboxylic acids.

	malonic	diethyl-malonic	succinic	tetramethyl-succinic	glutaric	β,β-di-n-propyl-glutaric
$\frac{K_1}{K_2} =$	734	121,000	19.2	6130	11.9	4180

Two effects appear to operate here. The first, and probably the most important, concerns dielectric constant. In malonic, succinic, and glutaric acids, much of the space between the —COOH groups on the ends of the molecules is occupied by sections of solvent molecules. In the alkylated acids, however, most of the space between —COOH groups is occupied by the alkyl groups on the chain. Thus, for the alkylated acids, the "low-dielectric-constant cavity" is fat, whereas for the nonalkylated acids it is thin. The —COOH groups in the alkylated acids interact through a medium of low dielectric constant, whereas those in the non-alkylated acids interact largely through a medium of high dielectric constant. Since electrostatic interaction is inversely proportional to the dielectric constant of the medium between interacting species, the acid-weakening action of a —COO⁻ group on a —COOH group at the other end of the molecule is more strongly transmitted in the alkylated acids. A second effect concerns steric crowding. Ordinarily a flexible molecule of a dicarboxylic acid in a solvent of high dielectric constant will tend to adopt the conformation (p. 73) in which the —COOH groups are as far from each other as possible. However, as crowding in the molecule is increased by the introduction of alkyl substituents, the —COOH groups become pushed somewhat closer together and the inter-action between them is increased. There is, in fact, good evidence that *hydrogen bonding* is of some importance in the monoanions of the alkylated diacids (p. 211).

A number of workers refer to electrostatic action transmitted through chains of atoms as **inductive effects** and electrostatic action transmitted either through empty space or through solvent molecules as **field effects,** but the experimental separation of these two "effects" has thus far proven difficult.[6]

Inductive (and field) effects may arise not only from ionic charges but also from the action of *dipoles* within the reacting molecule. In Chapter 2 it was pointed out that the nitrogen, oxygen, and lighter halogen atoms are,

[6] For an attempt in this direction, see Roberts and Moreland, *J. Am. Chem. Soc.*, **75,** 2167 (1953).

because of their greater measure of unscreened nuclear charge, better electron attractors (that is, are more electronegative) than the carbon and hydrogen atoms. When a more electronegative atom is substituted for hydrogen in a molecule, electron density is pulled toward this atom and away from the nearby atoms; and those atoms nearest the position of substitution will suffer the greatest induced polarization. If the molecule in question is an acid, this substitution will make it a stronger acid, just as would the introduction of a positive charge.

For example, the second column in Table 7-1 shows that the substitution of chlorine or fluorine for an α-hydrogen atom in acetic acid strengthens the acid, and the further substitutions of two and three chlorine atoms cause additional increases in acidity. Similarly, glycolic acid, $HO—CH_2—COOH$, in which the electronegative oxygen atom of the $—OH$ group has replaced an α-hydrogen of acetic acid, is almost ten times as strong an acid as the latter. The substitution of chlorine for a β-hydrogen in propionic acid also increases the acidity, but, as might be expected, the increment is much less than for α substitution since the electron attractor is farther away from the site of reaction. Electron shifts associated with inductive effects are sometimes indicated by arrowheads, attached to the bonds in structural formulas, and pointing in the direction toward which the electron density is shifted. The inductive effects of the chlorine atoms in dichloroacetic and β-chloropropionic acids may thus be represented,

showing schematically how the polarization is passed from one atom to another along the length of the chain. However, such representations fail to show (a) that the inductive effect falls off with distance from the primary electron attractor and (b) that a portion of the observed effect (just how much, we cannot be sure) is transmitted, not through the chain, but through the space outside the molecule—generally through molecules of solvent. This is especially so if the molecule is kinked or curled.

Increases in acidity also result when chain hydrogens are replaced with $—NO_2$, $—C{\equiv}N$, $—COOH$, $—COOR$, $—\underset{\underset{\textstyle H}{|}}{C}{=}O$, or $—\underset{\underset{\textstyle R}{|}}{C}{=}O$. Each of these functional groups is known from dipole-moment studies (Chap. 3) to have electron-withdrawing ability. Each contains an electronegative atom, doubly or triply bonded to a more positive atom that is, in turn, singly bonded to the

remainder of the molecule. Considering, for example, the acyl group, $O\!\!=\!\!C\!-$,
$\underset{R}{\mid}$

it will be recalled that one of the electrons associated with the carbonyl carbon
is a π electron (p. 19). This is more easily polarized than are the strongly
localized σ electrons comprising ordinary single bonds. The carbonyl oxygen
can thus withdraw electron density much more effectively from its neighboring
carbon (leaving the latter with a partial positive charge) than can the single-
bonded oxygen atoms in ethers and alcohols. We should therefore expect a
keto group to be more effective in boosting the strength of an acid than a similarly located hydroxide or alkoxide group. Analogous arguments may be applied to the additional functional groups listed above.[7] To express these arguments more briefly in the language of resonance, we may say that the character
of each of the functional groups involved is, to some extent, represented by the
"polar forms" listed below on the right:

$$-\overset{+}{N}\underset{O_-}{\overset{O}{\diagup\!\!\!\diagup}} \quad\longleftrightarrow\quad -\overset{++}{N}\underset{O_-}{\overset{O^-}{\diagup}}$$

$$-C\!\equiv\!N \quad\longleftrightarrow\quad -\overset{+}{C}\!=\!N^-$$

$$-C\underset{OH(\,OR)}{\overset{O}{\diagup\!\!\!\diagup}} \quad\longleftrightarrow\quad -\overset{+}{C}\underset{OH(\,OR)}{\overset{O^-}{\diagup}}$$

$$-C\underset{H(\,R)}{\overset{O}{\diagup\!\!\!\diagup}} \quad\longleftrightarrow\quad -\overset{+}{C}\underset{H(\,R)}{\overset{O^-}{\diagup}}$$

Note that in each of these "polar forms" the atom bearing a *positive* formal
charge is (in the absence of molecular coiling) closest to the remainder of the
molecule. Since we may imagine each of these atoms as a positive center,
withdrawing electron density from its neighbors, the resonance concept furnishes a rather vivid picture of the electron-attracting character of these functional groups.

Turning now to the electron-attracting abilities of alkyl groups, we find
them to be very nearly the same as that of the hydrogen atom. From the last

---

[7] The reader is reminded that the introduction of a second —COOH group into a carboxylic acid molecule boosts the acidity, not only because of its electron-attracting properties,
but also because of a statistical effect; that is, a dicarboxylic acid should be statistically twice
as likely to lose a proton as is a monocarboxylic acid.

column in Table 7-1 it can be seen that substituting methyl groups for all *three* α-hydrogens in acetic acid decreases the acidity, but merely by a factor of two; alkyl substitution in other acids generally results in similarly small decreases in acidity. If we push the site of substitution still nearer to the reaction center by replacing the nonacidic hydrogen of H—C—OH with a methyl group, we

$$\underset{\text{O}}{\overset{\|}{}}$$

lower the dissociation constant by a factor of about ten. It appears then that the methyl group (as well as other alkyl groups) is a slightly *poorer* electron withdrawer than the hydrogen atom. This "acid-weakening" character of the methyl group (in comparison with the hydrogen atom) has been recognized for many years and a number of structural explanations have been suggested.[8] None of these, in the opinion of the author, is fully convincing.

In contrast to alkyl substitution, replacement of an α-hydrogen in acetic acid by a vinyl or phenyl group *increases* the acidity (by a factor of about two in each case). It appears then that an unsaturated carbon atom is a better electron attractor (that is, more electronegative) than a saturated carbon atom —a conclusion that is in accord with considerable additional evidence. What appears to be the most satisfactory explanation of this difference[9] is based upon difference in bond hybridizations. Let us recall that the bonds to a saturated carbon atom are "hybrid bonds," formed from the combination of a single s and three p orbitals of the carbon atom (p. 18). On the other hand, a double-bonded carbon will have one of its p electrons participating in π-bond formation, with only two of its p electrons available for hybridization to form σ bonds. The bonds around the unsaturated carbon atom are consequently called "sp^2 hybrids." Now a spherically symmetrical $2s$ electron has the bulk of its charge density closer to the nucleus than does a dumbbell-shaped $2p$ electron. Similarly, an sp^2 hybrid bond should have the bulk of its charge density closer to the center of coordination than does an sp^3 hybrid bond (since the former is more like a pure s bond than the latter). This means that a carbon atom participating in

---

[8] Some workers (see, for example, Ingold, *Structure and Mechanism in Organic Chemistry*, Cornell University Press, Ithaca, 1953, p. 70) feel that the acid-weakening properties of the methyl group arise because this group is more *polarizable* than the hydrogen atom—that is, that its seven valence electrons do a slightly better job than the lone valence electron of hydrogen in satisfying the demand of the electronegative oxygen atoms in the —COOH group. This seems almost a paraphrase of the statement that the hydrogen atom is a slightly more powerful electron attractor than the methyl group, but Ingold suggests a subtle difference. In contrast to the chloro, cyano, and hydroxyl groups, which presumably have an "intrinsic polarity," alkyl groups exhibit polar effects only when under the influence of other polar groups within the molecule. However, the polar effect of a group is generally determined by a study of a molecule in which the group in question competes with one or more different groups for electron density; it is therefore doubtful that the distinction made by Ingold is experimentally meaningful.

[9] Walsh, *Discussions Faraday Soc.*, **2**, 18 (1947); Bartlett, *J. Chem. Ed.*, **30**, 29 (1953).

sp^2 bonding (an unsaturated carbon) is pulling in its electrons more efficiently than a carbon atom participating in sp^3 bonding (a saturated carbon). By an extension of this argument, a carbon atom bearing a triple bond should be an even stronger electron attractor.

By convention, groups which are more powerful electron attractors than the hydrogen atom are said to exhibit *negative* inductive ($-I$) effects, whereas those which are poorer electron attractors than hydrogen display *positive* inductive ($+I$) effects. Table 7-2 summarizes the inductive effects of the more usual substituent groups.

Table 7-2. Inductive Effects of Groups

$-I$ Groups (remove e⁻)			$+I$ Groups (give e⁻)
—NH₃⁺	—CHO	—OR	—CH₃
—NR₃⁺	—C=O	—SH	—CH₂R
—NO₂	|	—SR	—CHR₂
—C≡N	R	—CH=CH₂	—CR₃
—COOH	—F	—CR=CR₂	—C—O⁻
—COOR	—Cl	—C≡C—H	‖
	—Br		O
	—OH		

Although we have chosen to illustrate inductive effects of groups by comparing dissociation constants of acids, it must be understood that such effects influence virtually all heterolytic organic reactions. However, some care should be exercised in ascribing an observed change in reactivity to an inductive effect since other effects frequently become important. As we shall soon see, the reactivities of aromatic compounds are often influenced by conjugation, whereas the reactivities of many aliphatic compounds are influenced also by steric factors. (Indeed, there are a number of instances in which variations in reactivity are ascribed by one group of workers to inductive effects but by another group of workers, equally authoritative, to steric effects.) It appears, however, that inductive effects are relatively clear-cut in the reactions of *meta*-substituted benzene derivatives and those of relatively rigid alicyclic systems such as the derivatives of bicyclo(2.2.2)-octane (I).[6]

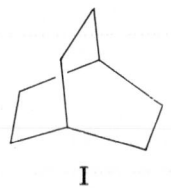

I

In spite of the difficulties in disentangling inductive effects from other influences, a number of relatively safe generalizations may be made. An electron-attracting group that boosts the acidity of an acid will, if substituted for a hydrogen atom of an amine molecule, withdraw electrons from the basic nitrogen, thus lowering its basicity. Likewise, such a substitution should reduce the formation constants of addition compounds formed by the amine with metal ions. In the extreme case, the fully fluorinated amine $(CF_3)_3N$ shows no basic properties at all.

By a similar argument, electronegative groups that ease the departure of H^+ from acids will make more difficult the departure of the negative CN^- ion from the cyanohydrin anion in the equilibrium,

$$R—CH—C\equiv N \rightleftharpoons RCHO + CN^- \qquad (2)$$
$$\underset{O_-}{|}$$

thus stabilizing the cyanohydrin anion with respect to the aldehyde.[10]

The same holds true with reaction rates, for substitution of electron-attracting or electron-repelling groups can strongly influence the equilibrium between reactants and activated complex.[11] A reaction between an electrophilic and a nucleophilic reagent will be accelerated by electron-attracting substituents on the electrophile (since these would tend to make it more electrophilic) but slowed down by electron-attracting substituents on the nucleophile (since these would tend to drain electron density away from the nucleophilic center). Thus, carbonyl-addition reactions are almost invariably accelerated when electronegative groups are substituted on the carbonyl compound, whereas nucleophilic displacements by amines are generally retarded by substitution of electronegative groups in the amine molecule. Substitution reactions of tertiary halides are almost always accelerated by electron-repelling substituents (which should ease the departure of the negative halide ion in the rate-determining ionizing step) and, conversely, are retarded by electron-attracting groups.[12]

[10] Lapworth and Manske, *J. Chem. Soc.*, **1928**, 2533. The more usual way of describing this effect is that electron-attracting groups on the aldehyde molecule increase the positive character of the carbonyl carbon, thus facilitating attack by a nucleophile. The nucleophile does not have to be negatively charged, but may be ammonia, hydroxylamine, or even water.

[11] A number of workers (see, for example, Ingold, *J. Chem. Soc.*, **1933**, 1120) prefer to differentiate inductive influences in reactants and products from those electronic shifts that occur in the activated complex as a result of the electrical demands of one reagent on another. The former are termed *inductive effects*, the latter *inductomeric effects*. We shall not make this distinction in subsequent discussions, but will group all such effects together simply as inductive effects.

[12] The same cannot, however, be said for substitution reactions of *primary* halides, for these generally proceed through a different type of activated complex in which the carbon atom at the substitution site is partially bonded to both the incoming and the leaving group. For these reactions, electron-attracting groups may, depending upon other circumstances, cause either an increase or decrease in rate. See, for example, Hine, *et al.*, *J. Am. Chem. Soc.*, **77**, 3886 (1955) and Ballinger, *et al.*, *J. Chem. Soc.*, **1955**, 3641.

In a complex reaction, the equilibrium constant for a rapid and reversible step preceding the rate-determining step generally becomes incorporated into the rate expression for the overall reaction. In such a case, the reaction may appear subject to inductive effects largely because of the influence of the inductive effect on a preliminary equilibrium. For example, the substitution of electron-attracting groups in the acyl portion $\left(\text{R---C---}\atop{\|\atop O}\right)$ of esters speeds up

their saponification;[13] the withdrawal of electron density from the carbonyl group facilitates attack by the OH^- ion, thus favoring the formation of anion III:

$$
\underset{}{R-\overset{O}{\overset{\|}{C}}-OEt} \overset{OH^-}{\rightleftharpoons} \left(\underset{\underset{III}{\overset{|}{O_-}}}{R-\overset{\overset{OH}{|}}{\underset{}{C}}-OEt}\right) \rightarrow R-\overset{O}{\overset{\|}{C}}-OH + OEt^- \qquad (3)
$$

On the other hand, substitution of electronegative groups generally slows down the acid-catalyzed hydrolyses of such carbonyl derivatives as imines, oximes, and hydrazones since, in these cases, the preliminary equilibrium involves attachment of a positive H^+ ion to the $C{=}N$ bond.

As we shall presently see, the most reliable estimate of inductive effects may be obtained by comparing the rates of acid- and base-catalyzed hydrolyses of substituted esters (p. 228).

Hydrogen Bonding and Acid Strength

The hydrogen bond (p. 28) may be regarded as a special type of short-range electrostatic interaction which becomes important only when the positive center (the hydrogen atom) and the negative center (an oxygen, nitrogen, or fluorine atom) lie within 2 Å of each other. Although it is reasonable to suspect that such interaction might affect the reactivities of, say, the nitro group in o-nitrophenol or the keto group in o-hydroxyacetophenone, we must turn to the comparison of acidity constants for the least equivocal examples of the chemical effects of the intramolecular hydrogen bond. A list of the dissociation constants of some substituted benzoic acids[14] follows.

---

[13] See, for example, Kindler, *Ann.*, **450**, 1 (1926); **452**, 90 (1927); **464**, 278 (1928); *Ber.*, **69**, 2792 (1936).

[14] These values, taken from Dippy, *Chem. Revs.*, **25**, 151 (1939), refer to aqueous solutions at 25° C.

$K \times 10^5$ 6.3   8.1   3.4

$K \times 10^5$ 105   2.9   5000

Note that the substitution of an —OH group *para* to the —COOH group in benzoic acid *lowers* the acidity by a factor of two, but that the substitution of an *ortho* hydroxy group *raises* the acidity sixteenfold. Furthermore, the substitution of two *ortho* hydroxy groups raises the acidity almost a thousandfold. Now it is well known that the substitution of almost *any* neutral group *ortho* to the —COOH group in benzoic acid causes an increase in acidity (p. 236), but for no other group are the effects of *ortho* substitution and *para* substitution so different as for the hydroxy group. Substitution of an *o*-CH$_3$O— group (which is a bit larger than a hydroxy group but otherwise very similar) results in less than a 30 percent increase in acidity. The difference is obviously that the methoxy group, unlike the hydroxy group, has no acidic hydrogens to participate in hydrogen bonding. In the hydrogen-bonded form of salicylic acid (IV), the positive (hydrogen) end of the phenolic hydroxyl group lies very near the —COOH group, pulling electron density away from the carboxyl hydrogen atom and easing its departure. The hydrogen bonding occurs also in the anion

IV   V   VI

V, the negative charge being spread over the six-membered ("chelate") ring that includes the hydrogen bridge, rather than being localized merely to the carboxylate group. In 2,6-hydroxybenzoic acid (VI) both phenolic —OH groups participate in hydrogen bonding; in the anion of this acid the negative charge is spread over *two* chelate rings. Note that in these cases the hydrogen bonding persists in the carboxylate anion as well as in the acid itself. In contrast, although intramolecular hydrogen bonding occurs in *o*-nitrophenol (as evidenced from its high volatility, p. 30), hydrogen bonding cannot occur in the *o*-nitrophenolate anion, and the acidity of this phenol is nearly the same as that of its *para* isomer.[15]

In a number of dicarboxylic acids such as maleic acid, VII, the —COOH

VII   VIII

groups are so situated that intramolecular hydrogen bonding may take place between the hydrogen atom of one —COOH group and the oxygen atom of the second. The first ionization constants of such acids, like the ionization constant of salicylic acid, should be "abnormally high"; but since the remaining acidic hydrogen atom of the mono anion (for example, anion VIII) is incorporated into a negatively charged cyclic system, the second ionization constant of such an acid should be "abnormally low." Thus, intramolecular hydrogen bonding should increase the ratio K_1/K_2, a ratio that is also, however, strongly influenced by ordinary inductive and field effects (p. 202). It has recently been suggested that the effect of intramolecular hydrogen bonding on the acidity of a dibasic acid may be estimated by comparing K_1 for the acid to K_E, the acidity constant of the monomethyl or monoethyl ester of the same acid (since the diacid and its monoester should be very similar except that hydrogen bonding cannot occur in the anion derived from the latter). Using this criterion, it can further be shown that for those dibasic acids in which hydrogen bonding is important, the factor by which such bonding raises the value of K_1 is, to a good approximation, $K_1/2K_E$.[16] This ratio is substantially greater than unity for diethylmalonic

---

[15] Brierglieb, *Naturwissenschaften*, **31**, 62 (1943).
[16] Westheimer and Benfey, *J. Am. Chem. Soc.*, **78**, 5309 (1956). The "2" in the denominator is a statistical factor; since the diacid has two acidic hydrogens but the ester only one, the diacid—in the absence of all other effects—would be just twice as strong an acid as the mono-

(16.0), tetramethylsuccinic (13.5), and maleic (5.3) acids but very nearly unity for malonic (1.8), succinic (1.06), and fumaric (1.0) acids.[17] We can appreciate that the *trans* configuration of fumaric acid does not allow the close approach of the —COOH groups that is necessary for intramolecular hydrogen bonding (as, for example, in structure VII). Such a close approach appears to be relatively rare in aliphatic dicarboxylic acids, except, presumably, in very "crowded" acids such as diethylmalonic, tetramethylsuccinic, and β,β-di-*n*-propylglutaric acids. In these cases, the formation of hydrogen-bonded structures is apparently favored because in this way the —COOH groups tend to be "pulled out of the way" of the bulky alkyl groups, increasing the freedom of motion (hence the entropy) in the remainder of the molecule.

Conjugation Effects

Important as the inductive effect is, it often fails badly if used to predict differences in reactivity among aromatic compounds. Considering only the inductive effect, for example, we might anticipate *p*-hydroxybenzoic acid to be a stronger acid than benzoic, whereas the reverse is found to be true. We might predict, using the inductive effect, that *m*-nitrophenol is a stronger acid than the *para* isomer, but, again, the opposite is true. Similarly, the inductive effect, by itself, cannot account for the very great difference in the basicities of aniline and benzylamine (benzylamine is the stronger base by a factor of 50,000).

It may be recalled, however, from the discussion of dipole moments (Chap. 3) that the transmission of electrical effects along the chain of σ bonds comprising an aliphatic molecule is very much different in character from the transmission of effects involving π electrons along the π bonds that comprise a conjugated system. In the first case, the inductive effect, a relay of electron polarization occurs but decreases sharply as one moves along the aliphatic chain away from the primary pole. In contrast, a disturbance of π-electron density at one atom in a conjugated system may become distributed over the "π-electron streamer" (p. 20) associated with the entire system, with those atoms far from the source of the disturbance being just as much affected as are the atoms close to it. This mode of transmission may be termed a **resonance** or **conjugation effect** since it is readily described using the language of resonance. For example, two resonance structures for nitrobenzene (IX and IX′) indicate that the substitu-

---

ester. The above authors present a more exact treatment which takes into account, not only the hydrogen bonding in the monoanion of the diacid, but also the (relatively small) differences in the degree of hydrogen bonding between the unionized form of the diacid and that of the monoester.

[17] See Ref. 3, pp. 624–625. The ionization constants of succinic and tetramethylsuccinic acids are compared to those of the respective monomethyl esters, whereas those for the remaining acids are compared to those of the respective monoethyl esters.

tion of a nitro group on a benzene ring results in withdrawal of π-electron density from the ring, especially from the *ortho* and *para* positions. In the same way, structures X and X' for the phenoxide ion indicate that the negative charge is not localized on the oxygen atom but also resides partially on the ring, again at the *ortho* and *para* positions.

The resonance effects of the —NO₂ and —O⁻ substituents may also be represented by curved arrows, pointing toward the direction in which π-electron density is shifted.

(In this notation the δ's represent fractional charges resulting from the indicated "shifts".) Both types of notation emphasize an important characteristic of resonance effects; they are transmitted largely to *alternate atoms* in the conjugated system. Resonance forms analogous to IX, IX', X, or X', which put the positive or negative charges in the *meta* position, cannot be drawn without including one or more unsatisfactory features in the structure.[18] While the difficulty in

[18] A structure such as XI, which places the negative charge of the phenoxide on the *meta*

XI

drawing such forms is consistent with the "alternating character" of the atoms forming a conjugated system, it cannot be considered an "explanation." (Indeed a similar alternating character may be predicted without consideration of resonance forms as such by using a different approach to the theoretical treatment of conjugated systems—the so-called *molecular orbital* method.[19(a)] A satisfactory explanation of this aspect of conjugation has not been given in nonmathematical language, although there have been several attempts.[19(b)]

Before considering the transmission of effects between substituents through conjugated systems, we should recall that the reactivities of a number of substituents are markedly altered when they themselves are attached to unsaturated carbon atoms. The —OH groups in phenols, for example, are more acidic than the —OH groups in alcohols. The *direction* of this effect is not surprising, for the phenyl group is known to be a slightly stronger electron attractor than the ordinary alkyl groups (p. 206). However, the *magnitude* of this effect seems far greater than would be expected on the basis of the inductive effect alone (for example, pK_a for phenol is about 10, pK_a for methanol is about 18), and it is currently felt that the acidity of phenol must also be boosted by a resonance effect. As structures X and X′ indicate, the negative charge on the phenolate ion is distributed over the benzene ring, whereas the negative charge on an alkoxide ion is localized at the oxygen atom. Since the phenolate ion is thus stabilized in a manner not possible for alkoxide ions, we would expect the loss of a hydrogen ion from phenol to occur more readily than the loss of a hydrogen ion from an alcohol. One may well wonder how much of the difference in acidity between phenols and alcohols is due to the inductive effect of the benzene ring and how much is due to the "resonance stabilization" of the phenoxide

---

position, is open to some objection because it depicts a bond between two nonadjacent carbons in a planar ring. The distance separating these two atoms is about 2.4 Å, far greater than the length of normal carbon-carbon bonds, and any "*trans*-annular" bonding action of this sort would be expected to be extremely weak.

We might also note that if the conjugated system is a five- or seven-membered ring

| XII | XIII | XIV |

(such as XII, XIII, or XIV) then *each atom in the ring* should be subject to similar resonance effects since two atoms separated by an odd number of atoms in one direction around the ring will be separated by an even number of atoms in the other direction.

[19] See, for example; (a) Coulson, *Valence*, Oxford University Press, Oxford, 1952, pp. 238–258; and Katellar, *Chemical Constitution*, Elsevier Publishing Co., Amsterdam, 1953, pp. 273–288; (b) Longuet-Higgins, *Proc. Chem. Soc.*, **1957**, 159; Dickens and Linnett, *Quart. Revs.*, **XI**, 310 (1957).

anion. In this case there is at present no experimental method for making a clear-cut separation of the two effects.

Similarly, the basicity of aniline falls below the basicities of the ordinary aliphatic amines by a factor of about 10^6. Here, the electron-attracting power of the phenyl group would be expected to lower the basicity of the aromatic amine, but, again, the effect is far too large to be attributed merely to an inductive effect. The unshared electrons responsible for the basicity of aromatic amines comprise part of the π-electron system that also includes the π electrons associated with the aromatic carbon atoms. Electron density, which, in ali- phatic amines, is localized on the nitrogen atom, becomes partially drained off into the regions above and below the plane of the benzene ring in aniline. As a result, the nitrogen atom in aniline assumes a partial positive charge (forms XV and XV′) and its basicity is greatly diminished. Saying this a little differ-

ently, the anilinium ion (pK_a 4.58) is a stronger acid than the ammonium ions derived from aliphatic amines (pK_a values lying between 10 and 11) because of delocalization of negative charge in the basic form in a manner prohibited for the acidic form. This argument corresponds closely to that which we have used to account for the acidity of phenols, but for anilinium ions we can say with more confidence how much of the enhanced acidity is due to the inductive effect and how much to the resonance effect. The pK_a values of the conjugate acids of dimethylaniline (XVI), benzoquinuclidine (XVII), and quinuclidine (XVIII) are given below:[20]

XVI	XVII	XVIII
pK_a 5.06	7.79	10.58

In XVII the basicity of the nitrogen atom is influenced by the inductive effect of the benzene ring, but since the bonds from the nitrogen atom are held far out of the plane of the benzene ring, conjugation effects should be very slight. Generally speaking, then (for we have not considered kinetic energy and en-

[20] Wepster, *Rev. trav. chim.*, **71**, 1159, 1171 (1952).

tropy effects), the inductive effect accounts for approximately 3 of the 5.5 pK units by which the basicities of aliphatic amines differ from those of aromatic amines.[21]

Perhaps the most striking difference between alkyl and aryl halides is the extreme slowness with which the aryl derivatives (except for nitro compounds) undergo nucleophilic substitution reactions under conditions where most alkyl halides react readily. Chlorobenzene, for example, survives for days in basic solutions at room temperature although thermodynamics predicts its hydrolysis. Since this is a kinetic, rather than a thermodynamic effect, it must be explained on the basis of the energy gap that separates the reactants ($C_6H_5Cl + OH^-$) from the activated complex. In chlorobenzene, the lobes of two of the unshared electrons on the chlorine atom lie perpendicular to the benzene ring; hence, these two electrons have become part of the π-electron system lying above and below the plane of the molecule, and the C—Cl bond (like the C—N bond in aniline and the C—O bond in phenol) assumes some double-bond character

---

[21] Similar arguments are sometimes invoked to explain why carboxylic acids are stronger acids than alcohols and why amides are weaker bases than amines. Carboxylate anions are stabilized by the distribution of negative charge over two oxygen atoms in the —COO⁻ group

, whereas a neutral amide molecule (but not its conjugate acid) is

stabilized by a similar delocalization . On the other hand, we might

suspect that the differences between carboxylic acids and alcohols (and between amides and amines) are due largely to the strong inductive effect of the carbonyl group. It is pertinent, however, that dimethyldihydroresorcinol ("dimedon," XIX) and methylketene dimer (XX) —both of them enols with a hydroxy group conjugated with a carbonyl group—show acidities

comparable to those of carboxylic acids. XIX is about one tenth as strong as acetic acid (von Schilling, Ann., **308**, 193 (1900)), whereas XX is about 25 times as strong (Woodward and Small, J. Am. Chem. Soc., **72**, 1297 (1950)). Since the keto groups in these compounds are sufficiently far from the hydroxyl groups so that the inductive effects may be considered relatively small, it seems that the high acidities in these cases are due largely to conjugation effects—that is, stabilization of the negative charges in the respective anions by distribution over conjugated systems. By inference, then, it is reasonable that conjugation effects are of comparable importance in carboxylic acids and amides.

$(XXI \leftrightarrow XXI')$.[22] To convert the chlorobenzene molecule to the activated complex for basic hydrolysis $(XXII \leftrightarrow XXII')$ requires a substantial expenditure of energy, for in such a process a π-electron system embracing seven atoms is cut down to one involving only five. The difficulty with which nucleophilic

XXI   XXI'   XXII   XXII'

substitution reactions on vinyl halides proceed may be similarly explained.

It thus appears that the —NH₂ and —Cl substituents, although capable of *withdrawing* electron density from saturated carbon chains by induction, are capable also of *supplying* π-electron density to conjugated systems. The same is true for the substituents —OH, —OR, —O—C—R, —F, and —Br; when any of these substituents is put on a conjugated system, resonance forms analogous to XXI and XXI' may be drawn for the resulting compound. On the other hand, the —NO₂, —C≡N, —COOH, —COOR, —C=O, —C=O substituents, each of which is associated with a negative inductive effect, also withdraw π-electron density from conjugated systems. When any of these groups is affixed to a conjugated system, structures analogous to IX and IX' may be drawn for the resulting compound.

Let us then (in analogy with the classification of inductive effects) designate those groups as $+R$ in character that, by resonance effects, *supply* electron density to conjugated systems, and those groups as $-R$ that *withdraw* electron density from such systems. Resonance effects (R effects) of the more usual groups are summarized in Table 7-3.[23]

---

[22] The partial double-bond character of the C—Cl bond in chlorobenzene is consistent with the reduced length of this bond, 1.69 Å (Brockway and Palmer, *J. Am. Chem. Soc.*, **59**, 2181 (1937)), as compared with the "normal" C—Cl bond length, 1.76 Å. Forms such as XXI and XXI' also help to account for the relatively low dipole moment of chlorobenzene (p. 66).

[23] As with inductive effects, a number of workers, particularly those of the "English school," distinguish between resonance effects present in ordinary chemical species and such effects present only in activated complexes. The former are termed *mesomeric*, the latter *electromeric* effects (see, for example, Ingold, Ref. 8, pp. 75–90). We shall, in the present text, group all such effects together simply as resonance or conjugation effects. Such effects have, in the past, been designated also as T effects (tautomeric effects). Since the differences between resonance and tautomerism are now well understood, such usage has become much less common.

Table 7-3. Resonance Effects of Groups

$+R, -I$ Groups	$-R, -I$ Groups	$+R, +I$ Groups
—F	—NO$_2$	—O$^-$
—Cl	—C≡N	—S$^-$
—Br	—CHO	—CH$_3$
—I	—C=O	—CR$_3$
—OH	$\quad\mid$	
—OR	R	
—O—C—R	—COOH	
$\qquad\parallel$	—COOR	
$\qquad$O	—CONH$_2$	
—SH	O	
—SR	$\mid$	
—NH$_2$	—S—R	
—NR$_2$	$\mid$	
—NH—C—R	O	
$\qquad\parallel$	—CF$_3$	
$\qquad$O		

Note that each of the $+R$ groups (except —CH$_3$ and —CR$_3$) is attached to the remainder of the molecule by an atom having *one or more unshared pairs* of electrons. The —CH$_3$ and —CR$_3$ groups exhibit very slight $+R$ effects, presumably as a result of hyperconjugation (**XXIII** ↔ **XXIII'**). In each of the

$$-R \text{ groups} \left(\text{except } -\overset{\displaystyle O}{\underset{\displaystyle O}{\overset{\mid}{\underset{\mid}{S}}}}-R \text{ and } -CF_3 \right), \text{ the atom closest to the remainder}$$

of the molecule is also multiple bonded to a more electronegative element (for

example, —N=O, —C=O, and —C≡N). The $-R$ character of the $-\overset{\displaystyle O}{\underset{\displaystyle O}{\overset{\mid}{\underset{\mid}{S}}}}-R$[24]

and —CF$_3$[25] groups has recently been established by the action of these groups in lowering the basicity of the —NH$_2$ group when situated *para* to it. Form **XXIV** (in which the sulfur atom has ten rather than eight valence electrons) has been proposed to account for the electron-attracting effect of the sulfone group, whereas form **XXV** (again a sort of "hyperconjugated" form) has been suggested to explain the $-R$ effect of the —CF$_3$ group.

[24] Bordwell and Cooper, *J. Am. Chem. Soc.*, **74**, 1058 (1952).
[25] Roberts, Webb, and McElhill, *ibid.*, **72**, 408 (1950).

CH₃

$$\text{XXIII} \longleftrightarrow \text{XXIII}' \qquad \text{XXIV} \qquad \text{XXV}$$

Generally, the best indications of the nature of the resonance effect of a substituent arise from the study of reactions in which that substituent is *para* to the reaction center in an aromatic system. Inductive effects are also present in such cases, but these are often relatively small since the substituent and the center of reaction are four carbons distant. When the substituent and the reaction center lie *meta* to each other, inductive effects are more evident. Here, due to the alternating nature of the atoms in a conjugated system, resonance effects become less, although they do not, as might be supposed, entirely disappear. (When the substituent is *ortho* to the reaction center, both inductive and resonance effects may operate strongly, but superimposed on these are proximity or steric effects that further complicate the interpretation of data.) We can now appreciate why *p*-hydroxybenzoic acid (*pK* 4.58)—in which the —COOH group feels the +*R* effect of the —OH group more strongly than its −*I* effect —is a weaker acid than benzoic acid (*pK* 4.20), whereas *m*-hydroxybenzoic acid (*pK* 4.08)—in which the importance of the two effects is reversed—is a slightly stronger acid than benzoic. Similarly, *p*-nitrobenzoic acid (*pH* 3.43) is a slightly stronger acid than its *meta* isomer (*pK* 3.45) since the −*R* effect of the —NO₂ group is more important in the *para* compound (even though the −*I* effect is less important). In *p*-fluorobenzoic acid (*pK* 4.14) the +*R* and the −*I* effects of the fluoro group nearly cancel each other, but in *p*-chlorobenzoic acid (*pK* 3.99) the intensity of the +*R* effect of the chloro group is much less. In general, *conjugation is more important for substituents involving first-row elements* (—F, —OH, —NH₂) than for substituents involving the heavier elements (—Cl, —Br, and —SH). The outer (2*p*) orbitals of the first-row elements are roughly the same size as the π orbitals associated with double-bonded carbon atoms, but the outer (3*p* and 4*p*) orbitals of the heavier elements are considerably larger; and orbital overlap, which is the basis for bonding action, is less effective. (There are, in fact, very few unequivocal examples of compounds having true multiple bonds involving elements other than carbon, oxygen, and nitrogen.)

Since the *p*-CH₃ group lowers the acidities of benzoic acid, phenol, and the anilinium ion appreciably more than does the m-CH$_3$ group, we may conclude that the electron-repelling action of this group operates through conjugation effects as well as through induction, this being perhaps the chief chemical justification for writing structures such as XXIII and XXIII'.

As with inductive effects, our preliminary discussion of resonance effects has been based upon the influence of substituents on acidities—mainly because of the large quantity of available data. It should be re-emphasized, however, that the resonance effects of substituents appear to influence practically all types of reactions in which the reaction center is attached to an aromatic system. This is true both for equilibria and reaction rates. Furthermore, if a reaction is aided by electron withdrawal due to induction, it should be aided also by electron withdrawal due to resonance.

The Hammett Equation[26]

Thus far, our considerations have been mainly qualitative. At present, however, there exist a number of quantitative (or almost quantitative) relationships between structure and reactivity. One of the oldest and most familiar of these is the *Hammett equation*, which relates structure to both equilibrium constants and rate constants for the reactions of *meta-* and *para*-substituted benzene derivatives.[27] Consider a series of aromatic compounds, each with the same reaction center present as a side chain, but each having, in addition, a different substituent situated *meta* or *para* to that reaction center—for example, a group of substituted benzyl chlorides. The Hammett relationship stipulates that the rate or equilibrium constant associated with the reaction of any one of these compounds (say the specific rate of hydrolysis of p-nitrobenzyl chloride) may be determined from the corresponding constant from the "parent compound" (benzyl chloride itself) if two parameters are known. The first parameter (σ) is characteristic only of the substituent (in this case the p-nitro group) and represents the ability of the group to attract or repel electrons by a combination of its I and R effects. The second parameter (ρ), characteristic of the reaction series at hand (in this case the hydrolyses of substituted benzyl chlorides), is a measure of the sensitivity of this type of reaction series to ring substitution. If k and k_0 are the rate constants for reaction of the substituted and unsubstituted compound, respectively, the Hammett equation may be written:

[26] (a) Hammett, *Physical Organic Chemistry*, McGraw-Hill Book Co., Inc., New York, 1940, pp. 184–199. (b) Jaffe, *Chem. Revs.*, **53**, 191 (1953).

[27] Modified forms of the Hammett equation have recently been found to apply also to naphthalene derivatives (Price and Michel, *J. Am. Chem. Soc.*, **74**, 3652 (1952)), and to certain alicyclic (Ref. 6) and heterocyclic (Elderfield and Siegel, *ibid.*, **73**, 5622 (1951)) derivatives.

$$\log\left(\frac{k}{k_0}\right) = \rho\sigma \tag{4}$$

[If equilibrium, rather than rate, constants are being considered, the term on the left is $\log (K/K_0)$.] Now the σ value for a substituent may be obtained most directly by measuring the effect of that substituent on the ionization constant of benzoic acid in water at 25°. σ is defined

$$\sigma = \log\left(\frac{K_{X-C_6H_4-COOH}}{K_{C_6H_5COOH}}\right) \tag{5}$$

where $K_{X-C_6H_4-COOH}$ and $K_{C_6H_5COOH}$ are the ionization constants for the substituted and unsubstituted benzoic acids, respectively. In effect, the ionization of benzoic acid has been arbitrarily chosen as a standard reaction type (for which ρ is fixed at unity), and σ is defined on the basis of this standard. A positive σ value for a substituent indicates that the substituent is a *stronger* electron attractor than hydrogen; substituents with negative σ values are *weaker* electron attractors than hydrogen. To obtain ρ for a given reaction series, it is necessary to measure rate or equilibrium constants for a number of compounds, each having the reaction center under consideration and each having a different ring substituent with a known σ value. The logarithms of the measured constants are plotted against the corresponding σ values, and the slope of the best straight line through the points on such a plot is the ρ value for the reaction series at hand (Ex. 6). Reactions with *positive* ρ values are *aided by electron withdrawal* from the benzene ring, whereas those with *negative* ρ values are made *more difficult by electron withdrawal*. The σ values for twenty of the more familiar substituents are listed in Table 7-4, and the ρ values for some typical reaction series are given in Table 7-5.

Table 7-4. Substituent Constants (σ values)[26(b)]

Group	σ_m	σ_p	Group	σ_m	σ_p	Group	σ_m	σ_p
—CH$_3$	−0.07	−0.17	—F	+0.34	+0.06	—NH—C—Ph (‖O)	+0.22	+0.08
—C$_2$H$_5$	−0.04	−0.15	—Cl	+0.37	+0.23	—COOH	+0.36	+0.27
—C$_6$H$_5$	+0.06	+0.01	—Br	+0.39	+0.23	—C—O$^-$ (‖O)	+0.10	+0.13
—CF$_3$	+0.42	+0.55	—I	+0.35	+0.28	—CHO	+0.38	+0.22
—OH	0.00	−0.46	—NO$_2$	+0.71	+0.78	—C—CH$_3$ (‖O)	+0.31	+0.52
—O$^-$	−0.71	−0.52	—NH$_2$	−0.16	−0.66	—CN	+0.68	+0.63
—OCH$_3$	+0.12	−0.27	—N(CH$_3$)$_3^+$	+0.91	+0.86			

Table 7-5. Reaction Constants (ϱ-values)[26(b)]

Reaction	ρ
1. Ionization of benzoic acids, water, 25° (eq)	1.000
2. Ionization of benzoic acids, ethanol, 25° (eq)	1.957
3. Ionization of phenols, water, 25° (eq)	2.113
4. Acidities of anilinium ions, water, 25° (eq)	2.767
5. Addition of HCN to benzaldehydes, ethanol, 20° (eq)	1.492
6. Ionization of triarylmethyl chlorides, SO_2, 0° (eq)	−3.974
7. Saponification of methyl benzoates, 60 percent acetone, 0° (rate)	2.460
8. Acid hydrolysis of ethyl benzoates, 60 percent EtOH, 100° (rate)	0.144
9. Hydrolyses of benzyl chlorides, 50 percent acetone, 60° (rate)	−1.688
10. Benzoylation of aromatic amines, benzene, 25° (rate)	−2.781
11. cis-trans isomerization of substituent azobenzenes, C_6H_6, 25° (rate)	−0.610
12. Reduction of nitrobenzenes with $SnCl_2$, water, 90° (rate)	1.149
13. Addition of HCN to benzaldehydes, ethanol, 20° (rate)	2.329
14. Side-chain bromination of acetophenones, water, 25° (rate)	0.417
15. Decomposition of substituted benzoyl peroxides, acetophenone, 80° (rate)	0.374

At the present time, substituent constants for over 110 different substituents have been calculated, and reaction constants for almost 400 different reaction series are known.[28] This means that about 44,000 rate and equilibrium constants of *meta-* and *para-*substituted benzene derivatives may in principle be calculated from only 510 parameters. Over 3000 of these constants have been measured and have been found to agree with the values predicted by the Hammett equation with a probable error of 15 percent (only 0.06 logarithmic units).

Two questions come to mind. First, why should the Hammett relationship hold at all? Second, why is it that this relationship does not also encompass the reactions of *ortho-*substituted benzene derivatives and those of aliphatic compounds as well? (As we shall see, similar, but less general, relationships may hold for these.) It will be recalled that log K_{eq} for a reaction is proportional to the standard free-energy change, ΔF^0, and that log k_{rate} for a reaction is proportional (from the arguments of the transition-state theory, p. 179) to the free energy of activation, $\Delta F^{\ddagger}$. If we are considering the equilibrium constants associated with a given reaction series, we may rewrite the Hammett equation

---

[28] In addition, the Hammett equation has been found to correlate such diverse data as half-wave potentials from polarographic reductions, infrared absorption frequencies, and nuclear magnetic resonance-absorption frequencies associated with the fluorine nuclei in substituted fluorobenzenes. These are summarized by Jaffe, Ref. 26b, p. 214.

as

$$\log K = \rho\sigma + \log K_0 \tag{6}$$

or, in terms of free-energy changes

$$-\Delta F = (RT\rho)\sigma - \Delta F_0 \tag{7}$$

(The ΔF values refer to standard free-energy changes, but the superscript zeros have been omitted for simplicity.) Now, for a given reaction series at a given temperature, T, ρ, and ΔF_0 are constants; equation (7) is therefore of the form $y = ax + b$. The free-energy changes associated with the reactions of the members of a series are thus *linearly related* to the respective σ values (and, from the definition of σ, linearly related to the standard free energies of ionization of the correspondingly substituted benzoic acids). If we are dealing with reaction rates, an analogous equation may be derived, this time expressing a linear relationship between the values of $\Delta F^{\ddagger}$ and the σ values.

In *meta-* and *para-*substituted benzene derivatives, the substituents are relatively rigid and lie far enough from the reaction center for us to feel safe in assuming that steric interaction between the substituent and reaction center is negligible. It appears that in most of such cases, substituents may affect reactivity, directly or indirectly, *solely by their ability to withdraw electrons from, or supply electrons to, the reaction site.* It is tempting, and in many cases it is correct, to assume that the change in ΔF^0 (or in $\Delta F^{\ddagger}$) resulting from the introduction of a substituent merely represents an increase or decrease in the classical electrostatic energy gap that separates the reactants from the products (or from the activated complex, if we are considering rate constants). Such an increase or decrease is presumably directly proportional to the electron-attracting or electron-repelling power of the substituent, as represented by its σ value. We must not forget, however, that a substituent, due to its electron-attracting ability, may also introduce kinetic energy effects; it may affect the vigor of molecular vibrations and rotations and is rather likely to alter the mode and degree of solvation of the species involved in the reaction. In order that the Hammett equation be applicable, it is necessary either that these kinetic energy effects be negligible or that they be proportional to potential-energy effects.[29]

It should now be clear why the Hammett equation, in its simple form, is not generally applicable to the reactions of *ortho-*substituted benzene derivatives. Here the substituents lie close to the reaction site and may influence the reaction both by their electron-attracting ability and steric interaction. In order

---

[29] It may be shown that the first of these conditions is fulfilled when substitution does not appreciably alter the value of ΔS^0 (or $\Delta S^{\ddagger}$) of a reaction, whereas the second condition is fulfilled simply if the change in ΔS^0 caused by substitution is proportional to the change in ΔF^0. For a detailed discussion of this problem, see Taft, "Separation of Polar, Steric, and Resonance Effects in Reactivity" in *Steric Effects in Organic Chemistry* (edited by Newman), John Wiley and Sons, Inc., New York, 1956, pp. 660–665.

that a linear relationship between free energies and substituents apply to these reactions, two conditions must hold. First, each *ortho* substituent must have what may be termed a "steric interaction capacity" which, like its electron-attracting ability, is independent of the reaction at hand (this is true in some cases).[30] Second, the sensitivity of reactions to steric effects must quantitatively parallel their sensitivity to electron withdrawal or supply (generally this is not true).

Similarly, it would be anticipated that the reactions of aliphatic compounds would *not* follow the Hammett equation, for even if the substituent is several carbons removed from the reaction site, the bending and twisting of the aliphatic chain might allow appreciable steric interaction between groups. On the other hand, it might be suspected that the reactions of relatively rigid alicyclic compounds may be correlated by a linear free-energy relationship similar to the Hammett equation. This has been found to be the case for reactions of derivatives of 4-substituted bicyclo[2.2.2]octane-1-carboxylic acid (**XXVI**).[6] For such compounds a new set of σ values must be used since there is

COOR

X

XXVI

no conjugation in the ring system, and all electron withdrawal or supply by the substituent must therefore occur by the inductive (or a combination of the inductive and field) effects. Moreover, the reactions of a number of aliphatic compounds that lack the rigidity of the bicyclo[2.2.2]octane system also follow linear free-energy relationships similar to the Hammett equation. For such compounds, the steric interactions present in the reactant molecules may be considerable, but such interactions also persist in the products and in the activated complex. Thus, the free energies of reaction or of activation, which rely wholly on *differences*, are not significantly affected. We see then that steric interaction is not a sufficient condition for failure of Hammett-like relationships; there must be sizable *variation* of such interaction during the progress of the reaction.

It would be well at this point to make a distinction between the two ways in which the resonance effect of a substituent may influence reactivity in the *para* (and *ortho*) positions. In *p*-nitrobenzoic acid, for example, the $-R$ effect of the nitro group is transmitted to the *para*-carbon atom of the ring by conjugation but must be relayed to the carboxyl carbon, and thence to the acidic —OH group, by induction (**XXVII**). On the other hand, in *p*-nitrophenol, the

[30] Taft, *J. Am. Chem. Soc.*, **75**, 4538 (1953).

acidic —OH group is in direct conjugation with the nitro group (XXVIII).

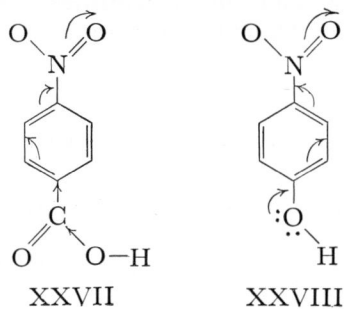

XXVII   XXVIII

In both cases the nitro group is acid strengthening, but, as might be expected, it is more effective in the second. The p-nitro group boosts the acidity of benzoic acid by a factor of 6 and should, according to the Hammett treatment, increase the acidity of phenol by a factor of about 36 (since ρ for this reaction is about 2). However p-nitrophenol is almost 600 times as strong an acid as phenol. Likewise the p-nitroanilinium ion is 4000 times as strong an acid as the anilinium ion although the simple Hammett treatment would predict it to be only about 125 times as strong; again, the —NO₂ group is in direct conjugation with the —NH₂ group in the basic form. Similar departures are generally observed for rates and equilibria of reactions involving derivatives of anilines or phenols and having, at the same time, $-R$ groups (Table 7-3) $para$ to the reaction centers. However, a rather good fit to the Hammett equation is achieved by assigning to each of these $-R$ groups a *second substituent constant*, which may be designated σ_p^c, the superscript c designating direct conjugation. These σ_p^c values (which may be evaluated, for example, from the acidities of the appropriate *para*-substituted anilinium ions) are greater than the normal σ values and are used only for the reactions of phenols, anilines, and their derivatives. They are listed in Table 7-6.[31]

[31] By a parallel line of reasoning, two substituent constants should be associated also with each $+R$ group in the *para* position. The first would apply to reactions of esters, acids, and carbonyl compounds (where there is direct conjugation between substituent and reaction center), the second to reactions of phenols, anilines, and their derivatives (where direct conjugation is absent). The substituent constants originally derived by Hammett for electron-repelling groups apply to the first class of reactions; it is likely that a set of σ_p^c values, applicable to reactions of anilines and phenols, would give a somewhat better fit to the Hammett equation for the latter class (see, for example, Hunig, *et al.*, *Ann.*, **579,** 87 (1953)). However, the substituent constants for the more usual electron-repelling groups tend to be small, and the errors introduced by adopting a single value for these are not serious enough to warrant widespread adoption of a double scale.

An even better fit to the Hammett equation (with, however, the introduction of additional parameters) may be obtained by assuming a *range* of σ values for certain substituents and choosing a value within the range that seems most appropriate for the reaction at hand (see Jaffe, Ref. 26(b), pp. 228–229). For a third approach to this problem see Taft, Ref. 29, pp. 576–583.

Table 7-6. Substituent Constants for Electron-attracting Groups to be Used for Reactions of Anilines, Phenols, and Their Derivatives[26(b)]

Group	σ_p^c	Group	σ_p^c
—NO$_2$	1.27	—C—CH$_3$ $\parallel$ O	0.87
—COOH	0.73	—CN	1.00
—CHO	1.13		

Recent work suggests that the Hammett equation may also apply to the specific rates of electrophilic substitution reactions on the benzene ring itself (aromatic chlorination, nitration, mercuration, etc.).[32] It appears that the specific rates of *meta*-substitution reactions may be correlated rather well using the ordinary σ_m values, but an additional set of substituent constants (designated σ_p^+ values, since the attacking reagent is generally a cation) must be used for *para* substitution. Conveniently (but as yet inexplicably), the σ_p^+ values may be estimated simply by subtracting 0.13 from the corresponding σ_p values (or from the σ_p^c values when these are available). Since the reaction site is on the benzene ring itself, rather than on a side chain, these substitution reactions are very sensitive to the presence of electron-attracting or electron-repelling groups; that is, the ρ values are unusually large (for example, ρ for aromatic chlorination in acetic acid is -10.1, whereas ρ for aromatic nitration in acetic anhydride is -6.5). This treatment is particularly useful for estimating the ratio of *meta* to *para* substitution in a given reaction; but in making such estimates it must be remembered that *meta* substitution, aside from polar effects, has a 2 to 1 statistical advantage over *para* substitution since there are two positions on a ring *meta* to a given substituent but only one position *para* to it.

The Brønsted catalysis law (p. 113),

$$\log k_{\text{cat.}} = a \log K_a + b \qquad (8)$$

which expresses the relationship between the acidity constant K_a for an acid and its catalytic constant $k_{\text{cat.}}$ for a given acid-catalyzed reaction, is also a linear free-energy relationship. On the basis of the transition state theory, equation (8) may be rewritten:

$$\Delta F^{\ddagger} = a\Delta F^0 + \left[RT \left(\log \frac{RT}{Nh} - b \right) \right] \qquad (9)$$

the expression in brackets being a constant at a given temperature. This is

[32] McGary, Okamoto, and Brown, *J. Am. Chem. Soc.*, **77**, 3037 (1955).

most easily explained if the mechanism of catalysis is

$$X \xrightarrow[\text{slow}]{\text{HA}} \begin{cases} XH^+ \xrightarrow[\text{fast}]{Y} \\ A^- \end{cases} \text{products}$$

for here, the catalytic constant is simply the rate constant for the slow step involving proton transfer (p. 189). Since the free energy of activation for this proton transfer is linearly related to the standard free energy of ionization of the acid, the change in $\Delta F^{\ddagger}$ caused by a structural alteration in HA is proportional to the corresponding change in ΔF^0 of ionization. Moreover, the proportionality constant, a, is found practically always to be *less than unity*. A structural change that lowers the free energy needed for *complete* proton removal (ionization of HA) will also lower the free energy needed for *partial* proton removal (formation of the activated complex $X \cdots H \cdots A$); but for partial proton removal, the effect will, as expected, be less.[33] The fact that the same constant, a, applies to all acids of a given series (for example, to all carboxylic acids or to all phenols) suggests that each of these acids forms an activated complex in which the degree of proton transfer to the substrate X is the same. It is further reasonable to suppose that as the Brønsted parameter a approaches unity, the proton transfer from HA to X in the transition state becomes more and more nearly complete.

Polar Effects in Aliphatic Compounds. The Taft Treatment[34]

The quantitative correlation between structure and reactivity for aliphatic compounds is simplest when (a) the reaction center is not part of a conjugated system and (b) when the degree of steric interaction between substituent and reaction site does not change appreciably as the reaction progresses. These are severe limitations; nevertheless, a number of aliphatic reaction series are known (and doubtless many more exist) where at least some members conform to these conditions. For such reactions, as for the reactions of *meta*- and *para*-substituted benzene derivatives, substituents influence rates and equilibria only through their electron-attracting abilities. It is not surprising, therefore, that rates and equilibria for such reactions obey a relationship which, at first glance, appears identical to the Hammett equation:

$$\log\left(\frac{k}{k_0}\right) = \sigma^* \rho^* \tag{10}$$

As in the Hammett equation, k is the rate constant (or equilibrium constant) for a particular member of the reaction series; k_0 is the corresponding constant

[33] For a detailed treatment of this topic, see Bell, *Acid-base Catalysis*, Oxford University Press, Oxford, 1941, p. 159.

[34] (a) Taft, *J. Am. Chem. Soc.*, **74**, 2729, 3120 (1952); **75**, 4231 (1953). (b) See also Ref. 29, pp. 586–629.

for the "parent compound" in the series (generally the methyl compound, since data are most readily available for these); ρ^* is the reaction constant, analogous to Hammett's ρ; and σ^* is the *polar substituent constant*, again representing the electron-attracting ability of the substituent being considered, this time as transmitted through an aliphatic chain. Unlike the σ constants, the values of σ^* are not defined in terms of dissociation constants of carboxylic acids since not all aliphatic acids obey equation (10) (probably because the larger substituents, irrespective of polarity, interfere with solvation of the carboxylate anion).

It appears, however, that a rather good σ^* value for a given substituent may be obtained by selecting an ester having that substituent *alpha* to the carbonyl group, then *comparing the specific rates for acidic and basic hydrolysis of that ester* (at the same temperature in the same solvent).[35] Taft then defines σ^*:

$$\sigma^* = \frac{1}{2.5}\left[\log\left(\frac{k}{k_0}\right)_B - \log\left(\frac{k}{k_0}\right)_A\right] \tag{11}$$

where the subscripts B and A refer respectively to basic and acidic hydrolysis and the k_0 values refer to the specific rates of corresponding hydrolyses of the acetate ester (the "parent compound"). The factor 2.5 is purely arbitrary, being introduced to put the Taft σ^* values on about the same scale as the Hammett σ values. To understand the basis for this definition, let us compare reaction series 7 and 8 in Table 7-5. We see that the rates of basic hydrolysis (saponification) of benzoic esters, of which series 7 is typical, are very sensitive to electron attraction or repulsion by substituents (that is, the ρ value for the series is high). However, the rates of acid hydrolysis, of which series 8 is typical, are *practically unaffected by electron attraction or repulsion*. The ρ values are close to zero; in series 8, for example, the rate of hydrolysis for the p-nitrobenzoic ester exceeds that for the p-methoxy ester only by about 12 percent. On the other hand, the rates of acid hydrolysis of *aliphatic* esters are strongly affected by substituents. Since there is no reason why these esters should be more susceptible to *polar* effects than are aromatic esters and since resonance effects cannot be transmitted along aliphatic chains, we may conclude that steric effects are intervening in the aliphatic series. With negligible polar and resonance effects, the ratio of k_A (the specific rate of acid hydrolysis for the substituted ester) to $(k_0)_A$ (the specific rate for the parent ester) then becomes a measure of the steric effect of the substituent, and log $(k/k_0)_A$ becomes a measure of the increment in $\Delta F^{\ddagger}$, arising as a result of this steric effect. Taft assumes that because the activated complex in a normal acid-catalyzed hydrolysis (**XXIX**) differs from that in base-catalyzed hydrolysis (**XXX**) only by the presence of two additional protons, *steric effects in the two types of hydrolyses should be virtually the same*. Since both polar and steric effects are important in base-catalyzed hy-

[35] This was apparently first suggested by Ingold, *J. Chem. Soc.*, **1930**, 1032.

$$
\left[\ R-\overset{\overset{\displaystyle O}{|}}{\underset{\underset{\displaystyle H\ \ H}{|}}{C}}\text{-------}\overset{\overset{\displaystyle H}{|}}{\underset{\underset{\displaystyle R'}{|}}{O}}\ \right]^{+} \qquad\qquad \left[\ R-\overset{\overset{\displaystyle O}{|}}{\underset{\underset{\displaystyle H}{|}}{C}}\text{------}\overset{}{\underset{\underset{\displaystyle R'}{|}}{O}}\ \right]^{-}
$$

XXIX   XXX

drolysis, the term $\log (k/k_0)_B$ is a measure of the increment in $\Delta F^{\ddagger}$ arising from a combination of both effects. The difference, $[\log (k/k_0)_B - \log (k/k_0)_A]$, is thus taken as a measure of the polar effect alone.[36]

A number of σ^* values are listed in Table 7-7; substituents having positive σ^* values are, by Taft's convention, stronger electron attractors than the methyl group. The ρ^* values for seven reaction series, which conform in part to the Taft relationship, are listed in Table 7-8. (Unless otherwise stated, these reactions are carried out in aqueous solution at 25° C.) Also included (designated n) is the number of members of each series found to give reasonably good agreement to the Taft equation. As with the Hammett equation, a positive ρ^* value signifies that the reactions constituting a series are facilitated by electron withdrawal.

The reaction series in Table 7-8 show a wide variation in type, but only a small number of compounds in each series are known to give good fits to the Taft equation. We may *not* assume that because certain members of a series give good agreement with equation (8), all members of that series will give good agreement. In very general terms, we may say that quantitative predictions of rate or equilibrium constants from equation (8) become less reliable as the steric requirements of the substituent increase and as the position of substitution draws near to the site of reaction. Nevertheless, it is difficult to say *a priori* whether or not the Taft equation will hold in a particular case. Although Taft lists σ^* values for over fifty substituents, reaction series including more than ten of these are rare. About twenty of these substituents have not been included in any reaction series as yet, and eight others have been included in only one series. Thus, the Taft relationship, although of considerable theoretical interest, is, at present, significantly less useful for predictive purposes than is the Hammett equation.[37] The Taft equation has also been extended to certain reactions

[36] It is not necessary that all σ^* values be obtained from measurements of the same type of ester, for it is found that the value of $\log (k/k_0)$ associated with a given substituent on the acyl group is, to a good approximation, independent of temperature, solvent, and the nature of the alkyl group as long as the polarity of the solvent is kept low.

[37] It is interesting that Taft's σ^* values have been found to be directly proportional to the substituent constants obtained from 4-substituted bicyclo-(2.2.2)-octane-1-carboxylic acids (p. 224). This is to be expected, for both sets of constants are measures of the electron-attracting capacities of substituents as transmitted through saturated systems. For a recent treatment relating the σ^* values to Hammett's σ constants, see Taft and Lewis, *J. Am. Chem. Soc.*, **80**, 2436 (1958).

Table 7-7. Polar Substituent Constants (Taft σ^* values) Aliphatic Series[29]

Group	σ^*	Group	σ^*	Group	σ^*
Cl_3C—	+2.65	$ClCH_2$—	+1.05	CH_3—	0.00
Cl_2CH—	+1.94	C_6H_5—	+0.60	C_2H_5—	−0.10
CH_3—C— $\overset{\|}{\underset{O}{}}$	+1.65	H—	+0.49	i-Pr—	−0.19
$C_6H_5C\equiv C$—	+1.35	$C_6H_5CH_2$—	+0.22	t-Bu—	−0.30

Table 7-8. Reaction Constants (Taft ϱ^* values) Aliphatic Series[29]

Reaction Series	ρ^*	n
1. $RCOOH + H_2O \rightleftharpoons RCOO^- + H_3O^+$ (eq)	+1.72	16
2. $RCOOH + Ph_2CN_2 \rightarrow R-\overset{\|}{\underset{O}{C}}-OCHPh_2 + N_2$ (rate, EtOH)	+1.18	12
3. $\left[(NH_3)_5Co-O-\overset{\|}{\underset{O}{C}}-R \right]^{++} + OH^- \rightarrow (NH_3)_5Co-OH^{++} + RCOO^-$ rate)	+0.79	7
4. $RCH_2OH + H_2SO_4 \rightarrow RCH_2-OSO_3H + H_2O$ (rate)	+4.60	5
5. $Ph-\overset{\|}{\underset{O}{C}}-CHR_2 + Br_2 \xrightarrow{OH^-} Ph-\overset{\|}{\underset{O}{C}}-CR_2Br + Br^-$ (rate)	+1.59	5
6. $RCH\overset{}{\underset{O}{\diagdown\diagup}}CH_2 + H_2O \xrightarrow{HClO_4} RCH-CH_3$ (rate, 0°) $\underset{OH}{}$	−1.83	5
7. $RCH_2Br + PhS^- \rightarrow RCH_2-S-Ph + Br^-$ (rate, MeOH, 20°)	−0.61	5

of *ortho*-substituted benzene derivatives, but here again, the paucity of data prevents a critical evaluation of its utility.

Steric Effects

Long before the nature of the inductive and resonance effects was understood, it was recognized that a substituent could influence a chemical reaction principally by its ability to occupy space. Esterification reactions are generally retarded by substituting alkyl groups for α- or β-hydrogens in the acid or in the alcohol, and the esters of such "hindered" acids or alcohols, once formed, are saponified with unusual slowness. The hydrolyses of *ortho*-substituted benzonitriles or benzamides are generally much slower than those of the corresponding *para*-substituted or unsubstituted compounds, and carbonyl-addition reactions of aliphatic ketones are severely inhibited by branching at the α positions. Such effects are often coclassified as *steric hindrance* phenomena; that is, situations where contact between reaction centers is made more difficult by interference of groups that do not otherwise participate. Although "steric hindrance" has, in the past, been used to account for a number of trends in reactivity that are now far more convincingly explained electronically, there remains a substantial body of chemical facts which are best explained with the aid of steric arguments. We should note also that, given the correct conditons, steric effects may accelerate, rather than retard, reactions. Moreover, although steric factors are most often considered in relation to reaction rates, equilibria too may be sterically affected.

To date, the most extensive investigations of steric effects on equilibria have been carried out by H. C. Brown and his co-workers.[38] Brown's conclusions are based largely on the dissociation constants of addition compounds formed by Lewis acids, such as trialkylborons, with amines.

$$R_3N{:}BR_3' \rightleftharpoons R_3N + BR_3'$$

Consider, for example, the adducts formed by $(CH_3)_3B$ with ammonia, methylamine, dimethylamine, and trimethylamine. The dissociation constants for these addition compounds (in the gaseous state at $100°$) are as follows:

	$H_3N : BMe_3$	$MeNH_2 : BMe_3$	$Me_2NH : BMe_3$	$Me_3N : BMe_3$
K	4.6	0.0350	0.0214	0.477

Recalling that methyl groups are slightly less effective electron attractors than hydrogen atoms (and are thus "base strengthening"), we are not surprised that substitution of a single methyl group for hydrogen in ammonia leads to a less dissociated complex and that substitution of a second methyl group decreases $K_{\text{diss.}}$ still further. One wonders, however, why substitution of a third methyl reverses the trend (this is also the case if H^+ is the reference acid). From the corresponding data for the adducts of the ethylated amines, we see

	$H_3N : BMe_3$	$EtNH_2 : BMe_3$	$Et_2NH : BMe_3$	$Et_3N : BMe_3$
K	4.6	0.0705	1.22	very large

that the substitution of only *two* ethyl groups reverses the trend set by the inductive effect. Furthermore, substitution of a single alkyl group for a hydrogen in ammonia can lower the stability of the adduct with trimethylboron if the alkyl group is sufficiently bulky (for example, $t\text{-}C_4H_9{-}$). Similarly, the stability of the pyridine-trimethylboron adduct is *increased* by substituting a methyl

---

[38] Brown and Johannesen, *J. Am. Chem. Soc.*, **75**, 16 (1953), and earlier papers in the series dating back to that by Brown, Schlesinger, and Cardon, *ibid.*, **64**, 325 (1942). For a brief, but critical, review of this work, see Hammond in *Steric Effects in Organic Chemistry* (edited by Newman), John Wiley and Sons, Inc., 1956, pp. 454–460.

group in the 3 or 4 position of the pyridine ring, but is *decreased* by methyl substitution in the 2 position. Substitution of methyl groups in both the 2 and 6 positions of pyridine prevents formation of a trimethylboron addition compound, even at −80°. It seems clear that the stabilities of these boron-nitrogen adducts are decreased when the alkyl groups of the amine "get in the way" of the alkyl groups of the boron compound; if there is too much interference, an adduct will not form at all. Conversely, quinuclidine (XVIII), in which the substituents on the nitrogen atom have been "tied back" so that they cannot interfere with the front-side approach of the boron compound, forms an extremely stable adduct with trimethylboron. Steric interaction between the groups on two different atoms, which arises during the formation of a bond between these atoms, is designated *front strain* ("*F* strain").

The surprisingly low basicities exhibited by trialkylamines (even, presumably, when the steric requirements of the acid are very slight) are more difficult to explain. Brown originally felt that the coordination of such an amine with an acidic species—that is, the formation of a fourth bond by nitrogen—requires that the alkyl groups of the amine be pushed back, close enough together so that they interfere with each other. Such steric interaction, designated *back strain* ("*B* strain"), was presumed to destabilize the addition compound, making the amine appear less basic than primary or secondary amines. Since, however, the bond angles about the nitrogen atoms in amines are now known to be nearly the same as the bond angles around the nitrogen atoms in trialkylammonium salts, the formation of a fourth bond by nitrogen should cause practically no change in steric interaction between the alkyl groups bound to nitrogen. Moreover, it has been found that the basicities of tertiary amines in water may be correlated with the Taft σ^* values of the alkyl groups,[39(a)] which presumably measure *only inductive effects*. Since we may thus conclude that steric factors do not significantly affect the base strengths of aliphatic amines in water, we may most logically attribute the low basicities of tertiary amines to solvation effects.[39(b)] More specifically, the conjugate acid of a tertiary amine, R_3NH^+, has only one N—H bond, whereas the conjugate acids of secondary and primary amines have, respectively, two and three N—H bonds. This means that a cation of the type R_3NH^+ is not as strongly solvated in a hydroxylic solvent as are cations $R_2NH_2^+$ and RNH_3^+, for solvation of such ions occurs mainly by hydrogen bonding through the N—H bonds:

$$\underset{\text{H}}{\overset{\text{H}}{\diagdown}}\text{O}\cdots\text{H}-\overset{+}{\text{N}}-$$

[39] (a) Hall, *J. Am. Chem. Soc.*, **79**, 5441 (1957). (b) Bell and Bayles, *J. Chem. Soc.*, **1952**, 1518.

Weak solvation of the ions derived from tertiary amines thus tends to diminish the basicity of these amines in water. On the other hand, the weak basicities of tertiary amines toward acids of moderate or large steric requirements (for example, toward Me_3B and i-Pr_3B) in nonaqueous media are probably due, at least in part, to F strain. Back strain may well enter the picture in accounting for the acidities of boron trialkyls, for with these the bond angles around the boron atom are near 120°. When the boron atom forms a fourth bond, these angles are reduced to near 110°, thus increasing steric interaction between the alkyl groups. However, front strain and the inductive effect also decrease the acidity in such cases, and separation of the three effects is, at present, not possible.

In the dissociation of substitution hexaphenylethanes to triphenylmethyl radicals ($Ar_3C{:}CAr_3 \rightleftharpoons 2Ar_3C\cdot$), the bond angles about the central carbons are increased from about 110° in the ethane to 120° in the radical. This dissociation relieves steric strain, not only because it eliminates interference between aryl groups on different carbon atoms, but also because it lessens interaction between aryl groups bound to the same carbon atom. We should then suspect that substituents that increase the steric requirements of the aryl group should increase the degree of dissociation of the ethane. Thus, at 25° in benzene, the dissociation constant for diphenyltetra-o-tolylethane (**XXXI**) is 1.50, whereas that for the tetra-p-tolyl compound (**XXXII**) is only 0.0013, a difference that is almost certainly due to the increased crowding in the *ortho* compound.[40]

XXXI   XXXII

This reaction is further discussed in Chapter 16.

Turning now from equilibria to rates, we may infer that steric effects will speed up a reaction if there is a decrease of crowding in going from the reactants to the transition state but will retard a reaction if the transition state is the more crowded. Most of the reactions subject to classical "steric hindrance" (for

[40] Marvel, Kaplan, and Himel, *J. Am. Chem. Soc.*, **63**, 1892 (1941).

example, the more usual types of esterifications, saponifications, and carbonyl-addition reactions) fall into the second category—that is, reactions in which the density of material around the reaction site is increased in the activated complex. However, the solvolyses of tertiary halides in water-alcohol mixtures generally proceed through preliminary loss of halide ion to form a carbonium ion. The bond angles around the halogen-bearing carbon increase from about 110° in the reactant to about 120° in the carbonium ion intermediate, and lie somewhere between these two values in the activated complex. This then is a case where the formation of the activated complex *releases* strain, and, as expected, the presence of bulky groups near the reaction site leads to increases in rate. The specific rate of solvolysis for the moderately crowded chloride XXXIII (at 25° in 80 percent ethanol) is over 21 times that for *t*-butyl chloride, whereas that for the very crowded chloride XXXIV is over 500 times as large as for *t*-butyl chloride.[41] These accelerations seem far greater than can be accounted

$$
\begin{array}{ccc}
\text{H}_3\text{C} & & \text{CH}_3 \\
\text{H}_3\text{C}-\text{C}-\text{CH}_2-\text{C}-\text{Cl} \\
\text{H}_3\text{C} & & \text{CH}_3
\end{array}
\qquad
\left[
\begin{array}{ccc}
\text{H}_3\text{C} & & \text{CH}_3 \\
\text{H}_3\text{C}-\text{C}-\text{CH}_2-\text{C} \\
\text{H}_3\text{C} & & \text{Cl}
\end{array}
\right]_2
$$

XXXIII   XXXIV

for merely on the basis of the slight inductive effects of the alkyl groups.

Although steric effects are easily visualized qualitatively, a fundamental quantitative treatment is a task of considerable magnitude. De la Mare and his co-workers[42] have recently proposed such a treatment for a relatively simple type of reaction—the exchange of Br⁻ for the bromine atom in alkyl bromides. At first glance, this may not seem to be a true chemical reaction at all, but its rate may be followed by using radioactive bromide ion in solution and measuring the speed in which radioactivity is incorporated into the organic bromide.

$$\text{*Br}^- + \text{RBr} \xrightarrow{\text{acetone}} \text{*Br}-\text{R} + \text{Br}^- \qquad \text{rate} = k_2(\text{*Br}^-)(\text{RBr}) \qquad (12)$$

Theoretical calculations were carried out, comparing energies and entropies of activation for exchange reactions in which the alkyl group was methyl, ethyl, *n*-propyl, *i*-propyl, *i*-butyl, *t*-butyl, and neopentyl. In each case, a transition state having the incoming and outgoing bromine atoms equidistant from the reaction center was assumed, and bond angles and bond lengths that minimized the free energy were chosen. The energy needed to build the transition state from the reactants may then be calculated, using relationships that have previously been derived for bond-stretching, bond-bending, and for nonbonding

[41] Brown and Berneis, *J. Am. Chem. Soc.*, **75**, 10 (1953).
[42] De la Mare, Fowden, Hughes, Ingold, and Mackie, *J. Chem. Soc.*, **1955**, 3196. This very detailed paper has been reviewed by Ingold, *Quart. Revs.*, **XI**, 1 (1957).

compression energies. Entropy changes in going from reactant to transition state may be calculated using quantum mechanical treatments for entropies of translation, rotation, and vibration. Such calculations are obviously complex, and we cannot describe them here, but we may note two conclusions that emerge. First, this work confirms the experimental observation that substituents in the β position are considerably more effective "steric hinderers" than α substituents. The energy of activation for the bromide exchange reaction on neopentyl bromide, $(CH_3)_3C—CH_2Br$, is estimated to be almost 5 kcal per mole greater than that for t-butyl bromide, $(CH_3)_3C—Br$, this energy difference corresponding to a difference of almost 4 powers of 10 in the specific rates of exchange for these two bromides. It can, in fact, be shown, using a scale model of the transition state, that hydrogen atoms belonging to β-methyl groups are better able to interfere with the bromine atoms than are hydrogen atoms belonging to α-methyl groups[43] (p. 276). Secondly, the quantum-mechanical relationships used to calculate changes in translational, rotational, and vibrational entropies (which are then combined to estimate entropies of activation) include the *masses* of the species involved, and any alteration of structure that increases the mass of a reactant or alters the distribution of mass will change its entropy. In particular, when the calculations for the transition state in halide-exchange reactions are carried out, it turns out that substitution of a heavy group for a hydrogen atom in the alkyl chain invariably results in a more negative entropy of activation.

Branching in the alkyl chain will decrease the rate of exchange, *even if the space-filling abilities of the substituent are ignored.* That portion of the effect of added masses which depends upon their weight but not their volume has been called by de la Mare and co-workers the *ponderal effect.* Since it is often in the same direction as the steric effect, we can see why it is so often included with the latter. Nevertheless, de la Mare's calculations show that insofar as entropies of activation for halide exchange in the higher alkyl halides differ from those for methyl halides, two thirds to three fourths of these entropy differences are ponderal rather than steric in origin.[44]

[43] Although the changes in energy and entropy of activation due to a change in steric factors generally effect the reaction rate in the same direction, this is not invariably so. The one outstanding exception is the case of bromide exchange in t-butyl bromide vs. that in methyl bromide. Here, the substitution of methyl groups for three α-hydrogens boosts the energy of activation (tending to decrease the rate) but leads also to a more positive entropy of activation (which, in itself, would tend to increase the rate). As in all such cases, the activated complex has assumed the structure that results in the smallest increase in *free energy.* The extra energy needed to stretch the C—Br bond more in the t-butyl reaction than in the methyl reaction is partially compensated for by the extra freedom associated with the activated complex in the former reaction. Nevertheless, the net steric effect of the substitution is strongly retarding.

[44] A typical case in which ponderal and steric effects are lumped together is a treatment by Taft (*J. Am. Chem. Soc.*, **75,** 4538 (1953); see also Ref. 29, pp. 642–655) of "steric effects" which is similar in nature to his handling of polar effects in aliphatic reaction series. In effect,

Steric Inhibition of Resonance

Resonance effects associated with a conjugated system are most pronounced when the atoms of such a system lie in a common plane; such effects fall off rapidly as departures from planarity increase. We have seen how steric inhibition of resonance affects dipole moments (p. 70), and we need not be surprised that it may affect rates and equilibria also. It has already been noted (p. 210) that essentially all *ortho* substituents boost the acidity constant of benzoic acid, a trend that cannot be due to ordinary steric effects since the steric requirements of the H^+ ion are negligible. However, it will be recalled that the —COOH group is a "$-R$ group"; contributions of structures such as XXXV and XXXV' result in transfer of π-electron density from the benzene ring to the —COOH group, thus tending to weaken its acidity. (Corresponding structures such as XXXVI may be drawn for the benzoate ion, but these are

XXXV   XXXV'   XXXVI

considerably less important because of the accumulation of negative charge on the carboxylate group.) However, *ortho* substituents will "get in the way" of the carboxyl oxygens unless the latter move out of the plane of the benzene ring, and when this happens, the acid-weakening resonance effect is greatly diminished.

On the other hand, since a nitro group substituted *para* to a phenolic hydroxide group greatly increases its acidity, again by a conjugation effect, we should expect that the acidity of the phenol may be lowered by pushing the nitro group out of the plane of the benzene ring by *ortho* substitution. Thus, of the two nitro-*m*-xylenols, XXXVII and XXXVIII, the latter is the weaker acid[45] even though the methyl groups (whose inductive effect would tend to weaken the acidity) are closer to the acidic —OH group in XXXVII. The nitro group in XXXVIII can exhibit its inductive effect, but its resonance effect is cut down. Similarly, N,N-dimethylpicramide (XXXIX) is a far

---

this treatment is largely confined to series in which chain length and degree of branching are varied, and fails when electronegative substituents are introduced near the reaction site. "Steric substituent constants" are assigned by Taft to the various alkyl groups by noting the effects of these groups on the rates of acid-catalyzed ester hydrolyses (p. 229), but such constants are more nearly measures of combined steric and ponderal effects.

[45] Wheland, *The Theory of Resonance*, John Wiley and Sons, Inc., New York, 1944, p. 195.

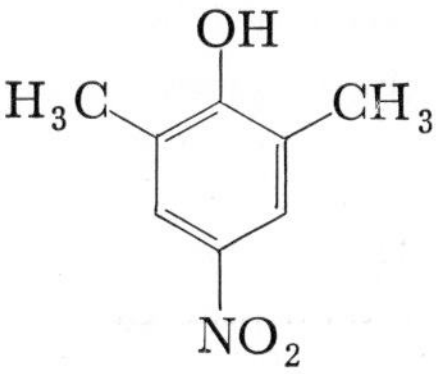

OH
H₃C — (ring with CH₃ and NO₂)

XXXVII
($pK_a = 7.16$)

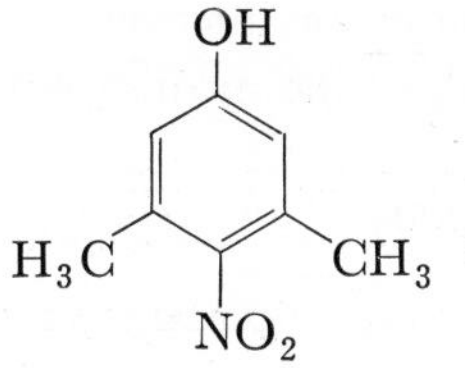

OH
(ring with H₃C, CH₃, NO₂)

XXXVIII
($pK_a = 8.24$)

stronger base than picramide itself (XL)[46] since the *o*-nitro groups in the former compound force the —NMe₂ group out of the plane of the benzene ring, in-

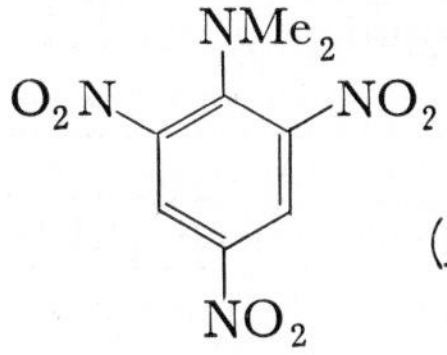

NMe₂
O₂N — (ring) — NO₂
(NO₂ at bottom)

XXXIX
($pK_a = -4.7$)

NH₂
O₂N — (ring) — NO₂
(NO₂ at bottom)

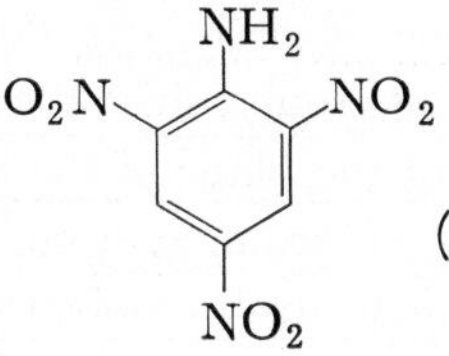

XL
($pK_a = -9.3$)

sulating the amino nitrogen from the electron-withdrawing resonance effects of all three nitro groups. In picramide, however, there is very little interference between the small —NH₂ group and the nitro groups *ortho* to it; departures from coplanarity are slight, and considerable π-electron density is drained off from the amino group to the nitro groups.

Similar effects appear with respect to reaction rates. Aromatic substitution reactions are generally accelerated by substituents which allow the charge originally associated with the attacking reagent to be spread over a large area, either in the activated complex or in a high-energy intermediate. Familiarly, the bromine atom in *p*-nitrobromobenzene is far more easily displaced by bases than is the bromine atom in bromobenzene, principally because the high concentration of negative charge originally centered at the attacking position in the base becomes redistributed in the intermediate XLI, not only over the

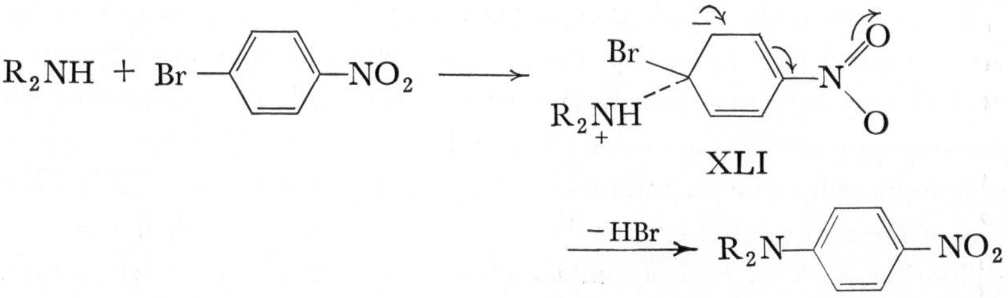

$$R_2NH + Br\text{—}\underset{}{\bigcirc}\text{—}NO_2 \longrightarrow$$

Br
R₂NH⁺ — (ring) — N(=O)O

XLI

$$\xrightarrow{-HBr} R_2N\text{—}\bigcirc\text{—}NO_2$$

benzene ring, but over the nitro group as well. Conversely, the benzene ring in dimethylaniline is attacked by electrophilic reagents (such as the benzenediazonium ion, $C_6H_5N_2^+$) far more rapidly than is benzene itself, largely because *p*-electron density from the amino nitrogen can shift into the π orbitals

[46] Hammett and Paul, *J. Am. Chem. Soc.*, **56**, 827 (1934).

of the benzene ring in the intermediate XLII to help accommodate the added positive charge. Thus, the nitro group has activated the benzene ring toward

XLII

nucleophilic substitution, whereas the dimethylamino group has activated it toward electrophilic substitution. Both of these are resonance effects whose magnitudes may be severely cut down by substitution of methyl groups *ortho* to the activating groups, since the latter, under such circumstances, would be pushed far out of the plane of the benzene ring. On this basis, we can see why displacements of bromide from the nitrobromo-*m*-xylene (XLIII) are far slower than from *p*-nitrobromobenzene.[47] A similar argument explains why the hindered amine, XLIV, does not react with diazonium compounds under conditions where dimethylaniline reacts readily.[48] Nucleophilic substitution on compound XLIII and electrophilic substitution on compound XLIV may be

XLIII

XLIV

said to be "hindered," but in both cases the effect is obviously very much different from classical "steric hindrance," since here there is no direct interference between the hindering groups (the methyls) and the attacking reagent.

The question as to whether hyperconjugation is also subject to steric hindrance is not easy to answer. Suppose, for example, that we substitute two methyl groups *ortho* to a substituent participating in hyperconjugation. Since hyperconjugation effects are relatively small, it should be difficult to disentangle effects supposedly due to inhibition of hyperconjugation from the inductive effects of the two methyl groups themselves. It has been noted, however, that the chloride XLV is hydrolyzed in aqueous acetone almost twice as rapidly as is the chloride XLVII.[49] Both hydrolyses are thought to proceed through carbonium ions, the ion XLVI derived from XLV presumably being stabilized

[47] Spitzer and Wheland, *J. Am. Chem. Soc.*, **62**, 2995 (1940).
[48] Friedlander, *Monatsh.*, **19**, 627 (1898).
[49] Baddeley and Gordon, *J. Chem. Soc.*, **1954**, 2190. For a more detailed discussion of steric inhibition of hyperconjugation, see Jaffe and Roberts, *J. Am. Chem. Soc.*, **79**, 391 (1957).

by hyperconjugation. Using molecular models, it is possible to show that al-

XLV   XLVI   XLVI'

XLVII

though both the five-membered ring in compound XLV and the seven-membered ring in compound XLVII are puckered, the latter ring is much more so.
The bond from C_α to the benzene ring lies much more nearly in the plane of
the benzene ring in XLV than in XLVII. It might then be argued that hyperconjugation in the carbonium ion derived from XLVII should be considerably
less important than in carbonium ion XLVI, and to the extent that the stability of the intermediate carbonium ion governs the rate of solvolysis, XLV
should react more rapidly than XLVII.

Interactions in Alicyclic Systems

Polar and steric effects of substituents that influence the reactivities of aliphatic
compounds, will, of course, be present in alicyclic compounds as well. However,
the operation of such effects, which depends largely upon how closely the substituents approach the reaction center under consideration, may be modified
by the geometry of the cyclic structure. Of the more usual ring systems, interpretation of the action of substituents should be most straightforward for derivatives of cyclobutane and cyclopentane. The cyclobutane ring appears to
be planar and the departures from planarity exhibited by the cyclopentane
ring are slight,[50] being at present of little chemical significance.

The reactions of cyclopropyl compounds are often strongly influenced by
the substantial *internal strain* present in the three-membered ring, for here the
C—C—C bond angles are only 60°, little more than one half their "preferred"
value, 109.5°. In particular, nucleophilic substitution reactions on the ring
carbons are unusually slow, for such reactions generally proceed through a transi-

[50] See, for example, Pitzer, *Science*, **101,** 672 (1945); also Aston in Ref. 3, pp. 546–548.

tion state in which the bonds about the carbon atom are opened out well beyond the normal tetrahedral angle,[51] a transition state which, however, is not possible for cyclopropyl compounds. Thus at 95° the hydrolysis of cyclo-propyl chloride is only $\frac{1}{300}$ as fast as that of cyclobutyl chloride and $\frac{1}{100}$ as fast as that of cyclopentyl chloride. Likewise, cyclopropyl bromide is unreactive towards iodide ion under conditions where the higher cycloalkyl bromides react readily. Furthermore, since the C—N—C bond angles in amines are ordinarily increased (although sometimes only slightly) when an acidic species forms a fourth bond to nitrogen, it is not surprising that the highly strained base, ethyleneimine (XLVIII), is a weaker base than alicyclic amines having the nitrogen atom as part of a four, five, or six-membered ring. The derivatives of

$$H_2C\text{———}CH_2$$

N

H

XLVIII

cyclohexane are of particular interest,[52] for among alicyclic compounds, it is the cyclohexyl system that is most frequently encountered. The cyclohexane ring is not planar but is known to assume a "zig-zag" or "chairlike" conformation (XLIX), in which each of the C—C—C bond angles is very close to

XLIX

L

axial bonds

LI

equatorial bonds

the normal value for tetrahedral carbon, 109.5°. Through the center of the cyclohexane ring a line may be drawn (AA' in structure L) which crystallographers would call a "six-fold axis of alternating symmetry." Six of the twelve bonds projecting from the cyclohexane ring are parallel to this axis and are thus termed *axial* bonds (L), whereas the remaining six bonds, which extend outward from the axis and make angles of 109.5° with that axis, are *equatorial*

[51] This is true whether the substitution is of the unimolecular (S_N1) or bimolecular (S_N2) type (see Chap. 8). The concept of internal strain ("*I* strain") has been developed largely by Brown and Gerstein (*J. Am. Chem. Soc.*, **72**, 2926 (1950)), who use it, with less striking success, to account for trends in activity among the larger-ring compounds.

[52] Detailed discussions of the geometry of cyclohexane derivatives are given by (*a*) Dauben and Pitzer in Newman, Ref. 29, pp. 13–35 and (*b*) Barton and Cookson, *Quart. Revs.*, **X**, 44, 1956.

bonds (LI). (Axial and equatorial positions are often abbreviated a and e.) It is to be emphasized that for 1,3 substitution, a pair of *cis* substituents may be *aa* or *ee*, whereas a pair of *trans* substituents may be *ae* or *ea*. For 1,2 and 1,4 substitution the reverse is true: *trans* substituents may be *aa* or *ee*, whereas *cis* substituents must be *ae* or *ea*. The two *conformations* of a given *cis-* or *trans*-substituted cyclohexane do *not* represent different forms separable under ordinary conditions, for the cyclohexane ring is flexible enough to "turn itself inside out," whereupon all bonds that were originally axial become equatorial and vice versa. This is best shown with a three-dimensional model.

Examination of models will reveal an additional feature of the cyclohexane ring that almost certainly would not be noticed from a planar projection. Any substituent except hydrogen (and possibly fluorine) in an axial position interferes with other axial hydrogen atoms, not those bound to adjacent carbons (for these are on the other side of the ring), but rather with those axial hydrogens bound to carbons in the 3-positions. As the substituent becomes bulkier, its preference for the equatorial position becomes stronger. Thus, for *t*-butyl-cyclohexane, it has been estimated that the conformation with the *t*-butyl group in the equatorial position is more stable than that with the *t*-butyl group in the axial position, the difference in energies being about 5.6 kcal per mole.[53] This means that at room temperature, only about 1 molecule in 10,000 will adopt the latter conformation. The very strong preference of the *t*-butyl group for an equatorial position results in "conformational purity," not only for *t*-butyl-cyclohexane, but also for derivatives of it. The 4-substituents must occupy equatorial positions when *trans* to the *t*-butyl group (LII) and axial positions when *cis* to this group (LIII). The reverse is true for 3-substituents (LIV and LV). Remembering that the axial positions are considerably more hindered

trans, ee	*cis, ea*	*trans, ea*	*cis, ee*
LII	LIII	LIV	LV

than the equatorial, we are not surprised that esters of *cis*-4-*t*-butylcyclohexanol (LIII, R = OH) are more slowly saponified than those of the *trans* isomer (LII, R = OH). On the other hand, with the esters of 3-*t*-butylcyclohexanol, the *trans* isomer (LIV, with the ester group in the axial position) is the more slowly saponified. For reactions where the bond connecting substituent "R" to the cyclohexane ring breaks, the opposite situation prevails. Since an axial

[53] Winstein and Holness, *J. Am. Chem. Soc.*, **77**, 5562 (1955).

substituent is more crowded than an equatorial one, the partial breakage of the bond to a substituent in the transition state will release more strain if the substituent is axial. We may then expect *steric acceleration* (p. 231) to assist breakage of bonds to axial substituents.[54]

As a final example of conformational effects, let us consider the acidities of alicyclic dicarboxylic acids, a number of which are listed in Table 7-9.

Table 7-9. Acidities of Alicyclic Dicarboxylic Acids[3]

	pK_1^a	pK_2^a	$K_1/4K_2$		pK_1^a	pK_2^a	$K_1/4K_2$
Cyclopropane-				Cyclohexane-			
1,2-*cis*	3.33	6.47	345	1,2-*cis*	4.34	6.76	66.7
1,2-*trans*	3.65	5.13	7.6	1,2-*trans*	4.18	5.93	14.0
Cyclobutane-				1,3-*cis*	4.10	5.46	5.8
1,3-*cis*	4.03	5.31	4.8	1,3-*trans*	4.31	5.73	6.5
1,3-*trans*	3.81	5.28	7.6				
				1,4-*cis*	4.44	5.79	5.5
Cyclopentane-				1,4-*trans*	4.18	5.42	4.3
1,2-*cis*	4.37	6.51	34.5				
1,2-*trans*	3.89	5.91	24.2				
1,3-*cis*	4.23	5.53	5.0				
1,3-*trans*	4.40	5.45	2.8				

As we have already seen (p. 202), the ratio $K_1/4K_2$ may be taken as a measure of the influence of the —COO^- group in the monoanion on the acidity of the remaining —COOH group. Since the carboxyl groups are generally closer to each other in a *cis*-dicarboxylic acid than in the corresponding *trans* isomer, we may expect this ratio to be larger for the *cis* diacid. The 1,3-cyclohexanedicarboxylic acids are seen to be exceptional, for with these the $K_1/4K_2$ ratio is the larger for the *trans* diacid. This is in agreement with measurements made on three-dimensional molecular models which show that for 1,3-substituted cyclohexanes, the substituents are slightly closer to each other when in the *trans* (*ae*) positions (LVI) than in the *cis* (*ee*) positions (LVII). However, similar measurements of 1,2-substituted cyclohexanes show that substituents in the *cis* (*ae*) positions (LVIII) *are the same distance from each other* as substituents

---

[54] For example, it has been found (Eliel and Ro, *J. Am. Chem. Soc.*, **79**, 5995 (1957)) that the *p*-toluenesulfonate group in *cis*-4-*t*-butylcyclohexyl *p*-toluenesulfonate (LIII, R = *p*-CH₃—C₆H₄—SO₃—) undergoes displacement by the $C_6H_5S^-$ ion almost 20 times as fast as the same group in the *trans* isomer. Similarly, the *p*-toluenesulfonate group is removed from the *cis* isomer in acetic acid at 50° over 2.5 times as rapidly as from the *trans* isomer (Ref. 53).

in the "preferred" *trans* positions—that is, both equatorial (**LIX**). Why, then, should the ratio $K_1/4K_2$ for the 1,2-*trans* diacid be so much less than the ratio for the *cis* isomer? It is likely that in this case, repulsion between carboxyl groups forces the *trans* acid and the anions derived from it to assume the conformation in which *both —COOH groups are axial* (**LX**) and as far from each other as possible—this despite the increase in crowding associated with that conformation.

It will also be noted that the ratio $K_1/4K_2$ is greater for *trans*-1,3-cyclobutanecarboxylic acid than for its *cis* isomer. This is not a conformational effect, for the distance between carboxyl groups is unquestionably greater in the *trans* diacid. However, the space between carboxyl groups in the *cis* diacid (**LXI**) is occupied chiefly by molecules of solvent (that is, by material of high dielectric constant), whereas the space between carboxyl groups in the *trans* diacid (**LXII**) is occupied largely by the cyclobutane ring (that is, a region of low dielectric constant). Since polar effects are more powerfully transmitted across material of low dielectric constant, the interaction between carboxyl groups is slightly more effective for the *trans* diacid despite the greater separation between the groups in this isomer. This argument is essentially the same as that used to account for the high $K_1/4K_2$ ratios for diethylmalonic and tetramethylsuccinic acids in contrast to the corresponding ratios for malonic and succinic acids (p. 203).

EXERCISES FOR CHAPTER 7

1. Predict which substituent in each of the following pairs has the more negative *I* effect (that is, which is the more powerful electron attractor):
   (a) —N(CH$_3$)$_2$ or —P(CH$_3$)$_2$?
   (b) —Si(CH$_3$)$_3$ or —Si(CH$_3$)$_2$?

(d) —NH_2 or —$N(CH_3)_3^+$?

(e) —COO^- or —COOH?

(f) —C=O or —C=CH_2?
$\quad\quad$|$\quad\quad\quad\quad$|
$\quad$ CH_3 $\quad\quad\quad$ CH_3

(g) —NH—C=O or —NH—C=$\overset{+}{N}(CH_3)_2$?
$\quad\quad\quad\quad$|$\quad\quad\quad\quad\quad\quad$|
$\quad\quad\quad$ CH_3 $\quad\quad\quad\quad\quad$ CH_3

(h) —NH_2 or —$NHSO_2CH_3$?

(i) —SO_2H or —SO_3H?

(j) Cyclopropyl or cyclopentyl?

(k) —C≡N or —CH_2NH_2?

(l) —SCH_3 or —Cl?

(m) —C≡C—CH_3 or —$N(CH_3)_2$?

2. Predict the direction of the inductive effect exhibited by each of the following substituents:

(a) —$\overset{+}{S}(CH_3)_2$

(b) —Se—CH_3

(c) —CH_2—C_6H_5

(d) —OAc

(e) —O—C$(CH_3)_3$

(f) —N=O

(g) —B$(C_6H_5)_2$

(h)

(i) —CH———CH_2
$\quad\quad\quad$\ /
$\quad\quad\quad\quad$ O

(j) —Si$(CH_3)_3$

(k) —HgCl

(l)

3. Intramolecular hydrogen bonding generally becomes important in the monoanion of a dibasic acid when the oxygen atom of the carboxylate group approaches to within about 2.0 Å of the hydrogen atom of the carboxyl group. On this basis, show that appreciable hydrogen bonding will occur in cases where the ratio $K_1/K_2 >$ 4000. Assume the effective dielectric constant of the medium to be 41, midway between the dielectric constant of water and that of aliphatic hydrocarbons.

4. Predict which acid in each of the following pairs is the stronger. Justify your choice in each case:

(a) $^+NH_3$—CH_2—CH_2—COOH or HO—CH_2—CH_2—COOH?

(b) Br_2CH—CH_2—COOH or CH_3—CHBr—COOH?

(c) $(CH_3)_2$C=CH—COOH or CH_2=CH—CH_2—COOH?

(d) H—C≡C—COOH or ?

(e) $CH_2(COOH)_2$ or HOOC—$\overset{\textstyle Cl}{\underset{\textstyle |}{CH}}$—$COO^-$?

(f) Dimethylmaleic acid or fumaric acid?

(g) CH_3—O—CH_2—CH_2—COOH or CH_3—S—CH_2—CH_2—COOH?

(h) C_6H_5—C—CH_2—COOH or C_6H_5—CH—CH_2—COOH?
$\quad\quad\quad\quad\quad$||$\quad\quad\quad\quad\quad\quad\quad\quad$|
$\quad\quad\quad\quad\quad$O$\quad\quad\quad\quad\quad\quad\quad\quad$OH

(i) CH_3SCH_2COOH or CH_3—$\overset{\textstyle O}{\underset{\textstyle \underset{\textstyle O}{|}}{\overset{|}{S}}}$—$CH_2COOH$?

(j) $n\text{-}C_4H_9\text{--}CH\text{--}CH_2\text{--}COO^-$ or $HOOC\text{--}C(CH_3)_2\text{--}C(CH_3)_2\text{--}COO^-$?

$\qquad\qquad\quad |$
$\qquad\qquad\; COOH$

(k)

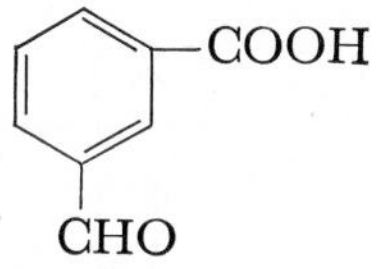

or

?

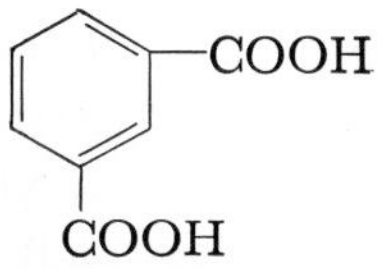

(l) Benzoic acid or *o*-methylmercaptobenzoic acid?

(m)

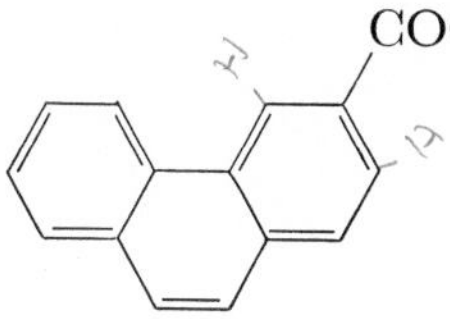

or

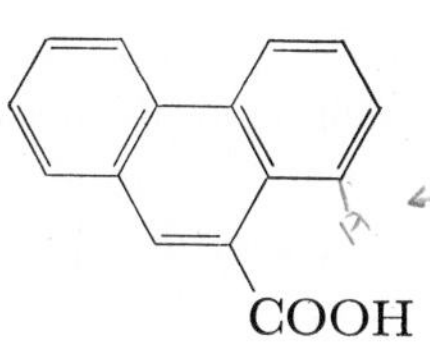

?

(n)

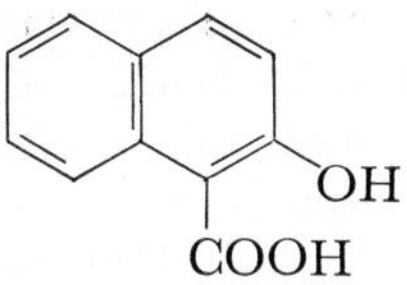

or

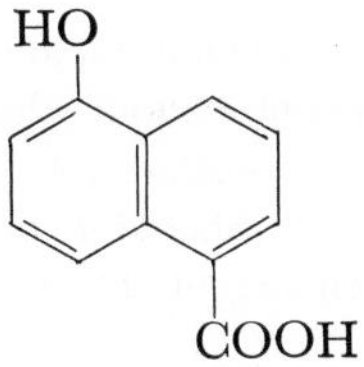

?

(o) *p*-Fluorobenzoic acid or *p*-chlorobenzoic acid?

(p)

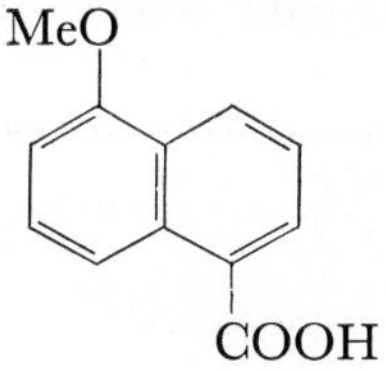

or

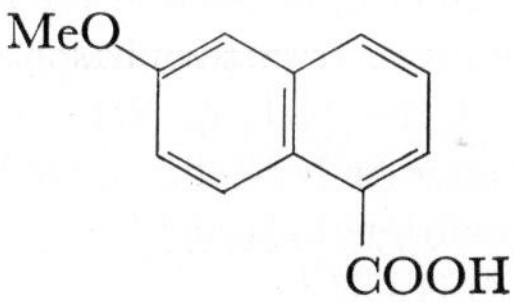

?

(q) 3-Fluoro-4-bromobenzoic acid or 3-bromo-4-fluorobenzoic acid?
(r) 2-Methyl-4-hydroxyacetophenone or 3-methyl-4-hydroxyacetophenone?
(s) $C_6H_5CH_2SeH$ or $p\text{-}CH_3\text{--}C_6H_4\text{--}SeH$?

(t)

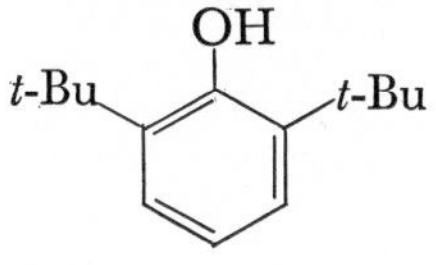

or

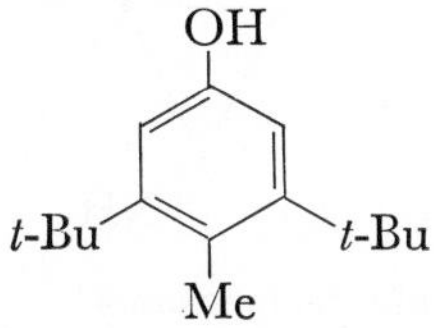

?

5. Decide whether each of the following are $+R$ or $-R$ groups, and justify your choice by drawing resonance structures for benzene rings substituted with these groups:

$$-S^-, \quad -P(CH_3)_2, \quad -N{=}O, \quad -CH_2\text{--}CH_2\text{--}\overset{+}{N}(CH_3)_3, \quad -N\text{--}C\text{--}NHCH_3, \quad \text{cyclo-}$$
$$\qquad\qquad\qquad\qquad\qquad\qquad\qquad\qquad\qquad\qquad\qquad\; \underset{S}{\overset{\|}{}}$$

$$\text{hexyl}, \quad -C\text{--}O^-, \quad -N{=}N\text{--}Ph, \quad -C{=}NH, \quad -SCN, \quad -SO_2NH_2, \quad -Si(CH_3)_3.$$
$$\qquad\;\; \underset{O}{\overset{\|}{}} \qquad\qquad\qquad\qquad\; \underset{NH_2}{|}$$

6. The following are the acidity constants (in water at 25°) for some substituted benzene-seleninic acids, $ArSeO_2H$:

Substituent	$K \times 10^5$	Substituent	$K \times 10^5$
none	1.6	m-NO$_2$	8.5
p-MeO—	0.89	p-Br	3.2
m-MeO—	2.2	p-C$_6$H$_5$O—	1.3
m-Cl	3.5		

(a) Show that equilibria for the reaction series

$$ArSeO_2H + H_2O \leftrightarrows ArSeO_2^- + H_3O^+$$

are governed by the Hammett equation, and calculate the ρ value for this series.
(b) Are the sign and magnitude of ρ about what you would expect? Explain.
(c) Calculate the dissociation constant for p-nitrobenzeneseleninic acid. (The observed value is 1.0×10^{-4}.) Should σ_p or σ_p^c be used in this calculation?
(d) Calculate the σ constant for the p-C$_6$H$_5$O— substituent.

7. Predict which base in each of the following pairs is the stronger if the reference acid is the proton, H^+. Indicate in which cases a reversal of order would result if triisopropylboron, $(i$-Pr$)_3$B, is taken as the reference acid.
(a) Trimethylamine or trimethylphosphine?
(b) NH$_2$—CH$_2$—CH$_2$—NH$_3^+$ or NH$_2$—CH$_2$—CH$_2$—NH$_2$?
(c) Ethylenediamine or N,N'-dimethylethylenediamine?
(d) Allylamine or trimethylamine?
(e) C$_6$H$_5$O$^-$ or C$_6$H$_5$CH$_2$O$^-$?
(f) CH$_3$NHCl or NH$_3$?

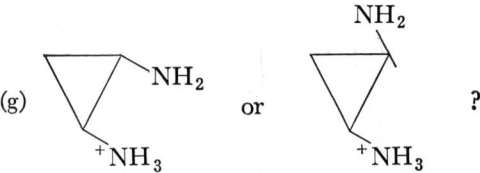

(g) ... or ... ?

(h) Aniline or *trans*-4-aminocyclohexanol?
(i) *m*-Aminobenzonitrile or *p*-aminobenzonitrile?
(j) *p*-Nitroaniline or 1-amino-4-nitronaphthalene?

(k) ... or ...

(l) *n*-Butylamine or diethylamine?

(m) Pyridine or N-methylpiperidine?

(n) 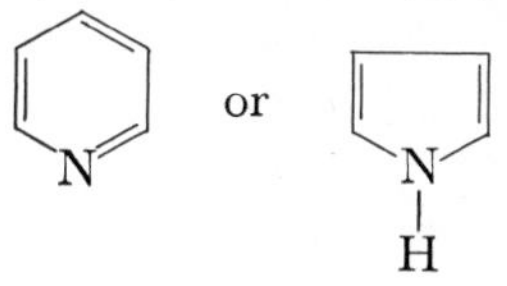 or ?

(o) 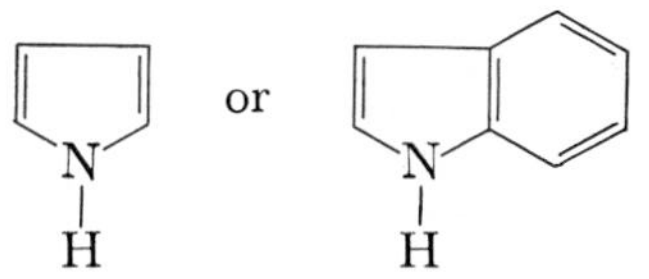 or ?

(p) 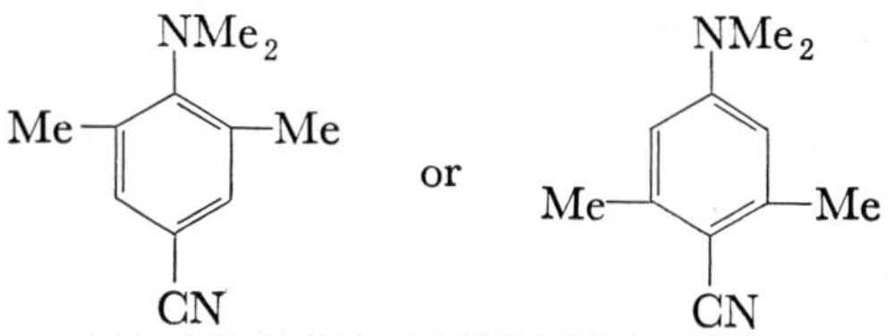 or ?

(q) 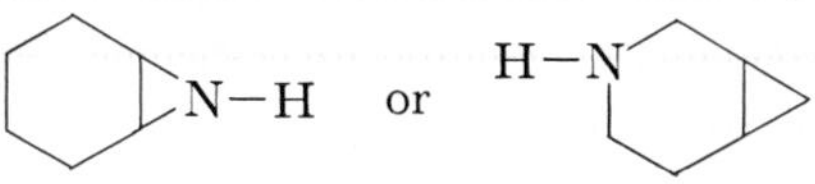 or ?

(r) 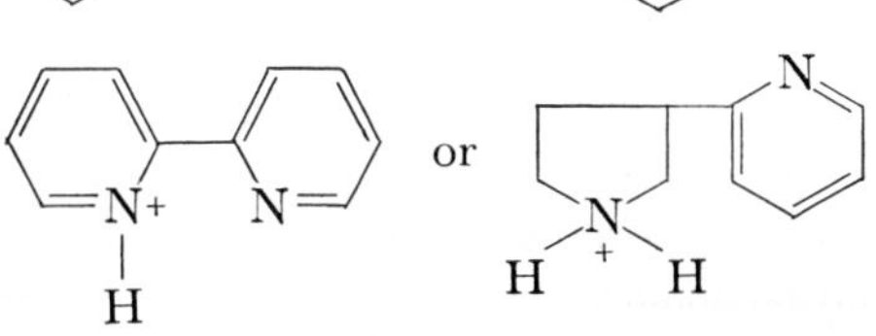 or ?

8. Predict the sign of the Hammett σ constant for each of the following substituents. Justify in each case.

$m\text{-}(CH_3)_2\overset{+}{S}\text{---}$, $m\text{-}C_2H_5O\text{---}$, $p\text{-}HO_2S\text{---}$, $m\text{-}HO\text{---}N{=}CH\text{---}$, $p\text{-}N{\equiv}C\text{---}CH_2\text{---}$,

$p\text{-}N{\equiv}C\text{---}S\text{---}$, $m\text{-}N{\equiv}C\text{---}S\text{---}$, $p\text{-}CH_3\overset{\overset{\displaystyle O}{\|}}{\underset{\underset{\displaystyle O}{\|}}{S}}\text{---}$, $m\text{-}NH_2\overset{\overset{\displaystyle}{}}{\underset{\underset{\displaystyle O}{\|}}{C}}\text{---}O\text{---}$, $p\text{-}(CH_3)_3Si\text{---}$,

$p\text{-}C_6H_5O\text{---}$.

9. Indicate, for each of the following reaction series, whether the ρ value is positive or negative or whether a decision cannot be made in the absence of further data:

(a) $ArPO_3H^- + H_2O \rightleftharpoons ArPO_3^= + H_3O^+$ (eq)

(b) $2ArCH_2NH_2 + Ag^+ \rightleftharpoons (ArCH_2NH_2)_2Ag^+$ (eq)

(c) $ArCH_3 + Cl_2 \overset{h\nu}{\rightarrow} ArCH_2Cl + HCl$ (rate)

(d) 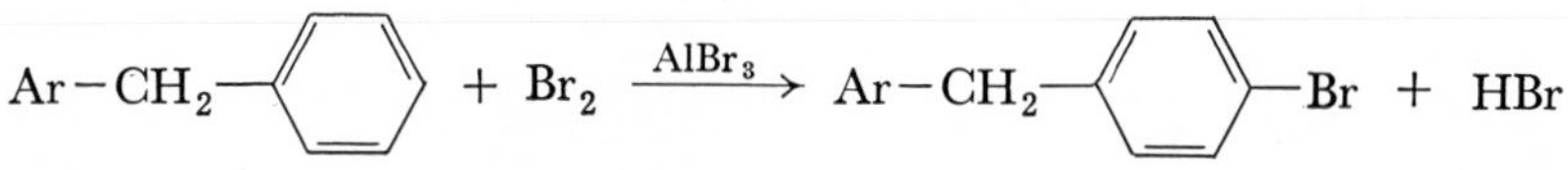 $Ar\text{---}CH_2\text{---}\bigcirc + Br_2 \overset{AlBr_3}{\longrightarrow} Ar\text{---}CH_2\text{---}\bigcirc\text{---}Br + HBr$

(rate)

(e) $Ar-\underset{\underset{O}{\|}}{C}-CH_3 + H_2 \xrightarrow{Ni} Ar-\underset{\underset{OH}{|}}{C}H-CH_3$ (rate)

(f) $ArCOOH + CH_3OH \xrightarrow{H^+} ArCOOMe + H_2O$ (rate)

(g) $ArCN + HS^- \rightarrow \left[Ar-\underset{\underset{S}{|}}{C}=NH \right]^-$ (rate)

(h) $ArSO_2Cl + C_6H_6 \xrightarrow{AlCl_3} ArSO_2C_6H_5 + HCl$ (rate)

(i) $Ar_2SeBr_2 \rightleftharpoons Ar_2Se + Br_2$ (eq)

(j) $ArO^- + C_2H_5Cl \rightarrow ArOC_2H_5 + Cl^-$ (rate)

(k) $ArCH_2F + OH^- \rightarrow ArCH_2OH + F^-$ (rate)

(l) $ArNH_2 + HNO_2 \xrightarrow{H^+} Ar-N\equiv N^+ + 2H_2O$ (rate)

10. Make rough sketches of the following, specifying whether the substituents are axial or equatorial:
    (a) *cis*-1,2-Dichlorocyclohexane
    (b) *cis*-1,3-Dichlorocyclohexane
    (c) *trans*-1,4-Dichlorocyclohexane
    (d) Disodium salt of *trans*-1,4-cyclohexanedicarboxylic acid
    (e) 1,2,3-Trichlorocyclohexane (all *cis*)
    (f) *trans*-Decalin
    (g) *cis*-Decalin

11. Explain each of the following:
    (a) *n*-Butyric acid is a slightly stronger acid than *i*-butyric acid.
    (b) Dissociation constants of carboxylic acids and phenols are much more sensitive to the dielectric constant of the solvent than are the dissociation constants of anilinium ions.
    (c) Cyclopentadiene is a stronger acid than benzene.
    (d) The ρ value correlating the specific rates of the hydrolyses of substituted benzamides is positive for base-catalyzed hydrolyses but negative for acid-catalyzed hydrolyses.
    (e) The ratio K_1/K_2 for 1,2-*cis*-cyclopropanedicarboxylic acid is raised by a factor of 600 by substituting two methyl groups for the hydrogens on the 3 positions.
    (f) Acetylacetone, $(CH_3-\underset{\underset{O}{\|}}{C}-)_2CH_2$, is a stronger acid than acetonylacetone,

    $CH_3-\underset{\underset{O}{\|}}{C}-CH_2-CH_2-\underset{\underset{O}{\|}}{C}-CH_3$.

    (g) A bromine atom raises the acidity of phenol more effectively when substituted in the *meta* than in the *para* position, but the reverse is true for the $CH_3-\underset{\underset{O}{|}}{\overset{\overset{O}{\|}}{S}}-$ substituent.

(h) When the dinitro compound, LXIII, is treated with base, the nitro group in the 1 position, although more "hindered," is more easily displaced than that at the 4 position.

LXIII

(i) Anthracene-9-carboxylic acid is six times as strong an acid in water as is anthracene-2-carboxylic acid.

(j) The loss of Cl⁻ from C_6H_5—$C(CH_3)_2Cl$ in aqueous alcohol is accelerated by a *p*-Cl substituent but retarded by an *o*-Cl substituent.

(k) The dissociation constant of benzoic acid is increased by a factor of 100 by an *o*-nitro substituent, but that of benzeneboronic acid, $PhB(OH)_2$, is increased only by a factor of 3 by a similar substitution.

(l) *trans*-2-Hydroxycyclohexanecarboxylic acid is a stronger acid than its *cis* isomer in water, but in ethanol the reverse is true.

Nucleophilic Substitution Reactions
in Aliphatic Systems

OF THE VARIOUS CLASSES of organic reactions (p. 120), nucleophilic substitution reactions on carbon have, to date, been studied most intensively.[1] The net change in such reactions may be described simply as follows: A basic reagent, using a pair of its electrons, forms a new bond to the carbon atom under attack, and one of the substituents originally bound to this carbon atom is freed, departing with the pair of electrons comprising the bond that has been broken. This very broad class includes many familiar and useful organic reactions, among them the Williamson ether synthesis,

$$\left[R\text{—}\ddot{\underset{\cdot\cdot}{O}}:\right]^{-} + R'\text{—}Br \longrightarrow R\text{—}O\text{—}R' + Br^{-}$$

the alkylations of amines and sulfides,

$$R_3N: + R'\text{—}Br \longrightarrow [R_3N\text{—}R']^{+} + Br^{-}$$
$$R_2\ddot{S}: + R'\text{—}I \longrightarrow [R_2S\text{—}R']^{+} + I^{-}$$

the synthesis and hydrolysis of alkyl halides,

$$Br^{-} + \left[R\text{—}O\underset{H}{\overset{H}{\diagup\diagdown}}\right]^{+} \longrightarrow Br\text{—}R + H_2O$$

[1] For detailed discussions of nucleophilic aliphatic substitution see: (a) Ingold, *Structure and Mechanism in Organic Chemistry*, Cornell University Press, Ithaca, 1953, pp. 306–418; (b) Hine, *Physical Organic Chemistry*, McGraw-Hill Book Co., Inc., New York, 1956, pp. 93–168; (c) Streitwieser, *Chem. Revs.*, **56**, 573–735 (1956).

$$H—\overset{\cdot\cdot}{\underset{\cdot\cdot}{O}}\mathord{:}^- + R—Br \longrightarrow H—O—R + Br^-$$

and the alkylations of sodiomalonic ester,

$$[(EtOOC)_2CH\mathord{:}]^- + R—Br \longrightarrow (EtOOC)_2CHR + Br^-$$

Mechanistic investigations have been centered largely about the reactions of alkyl halides. Among the other types of substrate that have been studied are trialkylsulfonium $(R'—SR_2^+)$ and tetraalkylammonium $(R'—NR_3^+)$ salts, and substituted ethylene oxides $\left(\begin{array}{c} R_2C{-}{-}{-}{-}CR_2' \\ \diagdown\diagup \\ O \end{array}\right)$. Also of considerable interest are

p-toluenesulfonate and p-bromobenzenesulfonate esters (often referred to as *tosylates* and *brosylates*); for the substitution reactions of these compounds, unlike those of the more usual esters, generally involve the breakage of an alkyl-oxygen bond, $R{-}O{-}\overset{\displaystyle O}{\underset{\displaystyle O}{\overset{|}{\underset{|}{S}}}}{-}Ar.$

In a great many nucleophilic substitutions, the attacking nucleophile is either water or the hydroxide ion. These are, of course, the familiar hydrolysis reactions. More generally, a substitution reaction in which the attacking nucleophile is the solvent is commonly known as a **solvolysis.**

Unimolecular and Bimolecular Substitution Reactions

By 1935 it had become evident, largely through the investigations of Hughes, Ingold, and co-workers,[2] that the more usual nucleophilic substitution reactions could proceed by what appear to be two distinctly different paths. In the first of these, the new bond is being formed at the same time the old bond is breaking, and in the transition state, the incoming group and the leaving group are both "half bonded" to the carbon atom being attacked. This is the path by which the basic hydrolysis of methyl iodide proceeds.

$$HO^- + CH_3I \rightarrow \left[\begin{array}{c} H \\ | \\ HO\cdots C\cdots I \\ \diagup\ \diagdown \\ H\quad H \end{array}\right] \rightarrow HO—CH_3 + I^-$$

reactants   transition state   products

(A more detailed description of the activated complex in this reaction is given in Chap. 5, p. 128). Such reactions are, in effect, *direct displacement reactions.*

[2] Hughes, Ingold, and Patel, *J. Chem. Soc.*, **1933**, 526; Hughes and Ingold, *ibid.*, 1571; Gleave, Hughes, and Ingold, *ibid.*, **1935**, 235, 244, 255.

In the second path, the bond to the leaving group is broken *before* the new bond is created, the reaction proceeding through an intermediate of somewhat the same nature as a free carbonium ion. (As we shall see, just how "free" this carbonium ion is constitutes an important question.) Reactions proceeding by this mechanism may thus be represented in two steps—for instance, for hydrolysis of *t*-butyl chloride,

$$(CH_3)_3C\!-\!Cl \xrightarrow{-Cl^-} (CH_3)_3C^+ \xrightarrow{+H_2O} (CH_3)C\!-\!OH + H^+$$

$$\text{reactant} \qquad\qquad \text{intermediate} \qquad\qquad \text{products}$$

This path is sometimes called the *dissociation, heterolysis,* or *carbonium-ion mechanism,* or the *solvolytic displacement.* Here, the leaving group is "pulled off" by the solvent, whereas in the direct displacement reaction, it is "pushed off" by the incoming nucleophile but still with the help of pulling action by the solvent. In the "dissociation mechanism," the initial step is generally the slow one.[3] Since the *molecularity* of a reaction has been defined as the number of chemical species that form new bonds or suffer the breakage of old bonds during the rate-determining step, we see that the direct displacement mechanism is *bimolecular,* whereas the "dissociation" mechanism is *unimolecular.* (Molecules of solvent doubtless participate in both types of reaction, but they do not suffer changes in covalence.) The two types of mechanism are often abbreviated, respectively, as the S_N2 (substitution-nucleophilic-bimolecular) and S_N1 (substitution-nucleophilic-unimolecular) mechanisms.

Speaking very broadly, nucleophilic substitutions on *primary* carbon atoms tend to proceed by the S_N2 mechanism, those on *tertiary* carbon atoms tend to proceed by the S_N1 mechanism, and those on *secondary* carbon atoms often constitute borderline cases. For the S_N1 mechanism, the activated complex in the slow (bond-breaking) step assumes some of the character of an ion pair; that is, its formation requires considerable separation of charge. Alkyl groups, as we have already observed (p. 205), are more effective electron releasers than hydrogen. Hence, we would expect the leaving group $:X$ (with its pair of bonding electrons) to depart more easily from $Alk_3C:X$ than from $Alk\!-\!CH_2:X$.[4] Aryl groups linked to the α-carbon are even more effective in facilitating uni-

<hr/>

[3] Recently evidence has been obtained that in a few S_N reactions proceeding through preliminary dissociation, the initial step is more rapid than the attack on the carbonium ion. See, for example, Gelles, Hughes, and Ingold, *J. Chem. Soc.*, **1954**, 2918, and Swain and Kreevoy, *J. Am. Chem. Soc.*, **77**, 1122 (1955). These, it is emphasized, are exceptional cases.

[4] Two additional effects may account, in part, for the ease of unimolecular substitution on tertiary carbon atoms. Since the tertiary carbon atom generally finds itself in more crowded surroundings than does a primary carbon atom, we may expect more relief from steric strain on expulsion of the leaving group from a tertiary carbon than from a primary carbon. Such unusually crowded halides as $(t\text{-Bu})_2(i\text{-Pr})C\!-\!Cl$ are known to undergo unimolecular solvolysis extremely rapidly (see, for example, Bartlett and Swain, *J. Am. Chem. Soc.*, **77**, 2801 (1955)).

Secondly, a carbonium ion (and presumably an activated complex having much of the character of a carbonium ion) should be stabilized by hyperconjugation involving structures

molecular substitution than are alkyl groups, for such groups stabilize the carbonium ion (and the carbonium-ion-like activated complex) by supplying π-electron density from the ring (II ↔ II').

$$\text{II} \qquad\qquad\qquad\qquad \text{II}'$$

The ease of both the S_N1- and S_N2-type reactions is affected by the polarity of the solvent. To predict the direction of such effects, we may use the principles given in Chapter 6 (p. 183). In doing so, however, it should be remembered that there are many cases in which a solvent may exert specific effects on a reaction, exclusive of its polarity. In making the following generalizations, we are therefore speaking broadly. Consider first the S_N1 reactions of alkyl halides and sulfonate esters. Activation in such reactions requires separation of unlike charge, and we would suspect that such reactions are more rapid in solvents of high dielectric constant (for instance, water and formic acid) than in solvents of low dielectric constant (ethanol, acetone, and dioxane). That, in general, is what we find. Similar reasoning may be applied to other nucleophilic substitution reactions, both of the S_N1 and S_N2 types, varying the "charge type" of the reactants. The results are summarized in Table 8-1.

One further reminder: For reactions in which ionic charge is created or destroyed during formation of the transition state, the effects of solvent polarity are much more striking than for reactions in which charge is merely dispersed during activation. Although quantitative correlations between solvent and reactivity will be discussed later in this chapter, the following comparison indicates the extent of the difference. It appears that the specific rates of substitution reactions in which the formation of the activated complex requires creation or destruction of charge will suffer changes of from 3 to 6 powers of 10 when

such as I'. Such hyperconjugation would be expected to be more important if there are three

$$\text{I} \qquad\qquad\qquad \text{I}'$$

alkyl groups on the α-carbon (that is, if the carbon atom is tertiary) than if there is only one alkyl group (that is, if the α-carbon is primary). Furthermore, forms such as I' suggest that the β-C—H bonds are loosened during the formation of the activated complex. Since normal C—H bonds are "looser" bonds than normal C—D bonds (p. 192), we might suspect that substitution of deuterium for β-hydrogen atoms should lower the extent of hyperconjugation slightly, thus retarding unimolecular substitution at the α-carbon atom. Such an effect has been observed (p. 285).

transferred from water to absolute ethanol. In contrast, S_N reactions for which activation requires only dispersal of charge are from 3 to 10 times as rapid in ethanol as in water.[5]

Table 8-1. Predicted Effects of Solvent Polarity on Rates of Nucleophilic Substitution Reactions[5(a)]

Type of Reaction	Requirements for Activation Process	Effect upon Rate of Increasing Dielectric Constant of Medium
$RX \rightarrow R^+X^-$ (S_N1)	Separation of unlike charges	Increase
$Y^- + RX \rightarrow YR + X^-$ (S_N2)	Slight dispersal of negative charge	Decrease
$Y: + RX \rightarrow Y:R^+ + X^-$ (S_N2)	Separation of unlike charges	Increase
$R_3S^+ \rightarrow R^+ + R_2S$ (S_N1)	Slight dispersal of positive charge	Decrease
$R_3S^+ + Y^- \rightarrow RY + R_2S$ (S_N2)	Partial neutralization of charge	Decrease
$R_3S^+ + R_3N \rightarrow R_2S + R_4N^+$ (S_N2)	Slight dispersal of positive charge	Decrease

It is interesting that a change in solvent may bring about marked alterations in the mechanism of a reaction. As we shall see, a number of the reactions of t-butyl halides that proceed by the S_N1 mechanism in aqueous alcohol will proceed by the S_N2 mechanism in acetone. Conversely, reactions of methyl halides that proceed by the S_N2 mechanism in aqueous alcohol may adopt the S_N1 mechanism in the more strongly ionizing solvent, formic acid.

Kinetics

Without giving the matter much thought, one might expect bimolecular substitution reactions to display simple second-order kinetics,

$$\text{rate} = k_2(\text{R}:X)(Y:) \tag{1}$$

and unimolecular substitution reactions to display simple first-order kinetics.

---

[5] (a) Examples of the solvent effects for S_N reactions of the various charge types are listed by Ingold, Ref. 1(a), pp. 347–350, and by Streitwieser, Ref. 1(c), p. 602. See also de la Mare, Keffek, and Salama, J. Chem. Soc., **1956**, 3686. (b) For examples of specific solvent effects (exclusive of dielectric constant, see Grim, Ruf, and Wolff, Z. physik. Chem., **B13**, 301 (1933); and Norris and Haines, J. Am. Chem. Soc., **75**, 1425 (1953).

$$\text{rate} = k_1(R:X) \tag{2}$$

Furthermore, one would anticipate that all S_N1 reactions of a given substrate would proceed at the same specific rate (as long as solvent, temperature, and ionic strength are kept constant), since all such substitutions should have the same rate-determining step—the initial bond breaking. Such a correspondence between order and molecularity is often, but by no means always, observed. Quite obviously, if the attacking reagent in an S_N2 substitution is a solvent molecule, the reaction will appear to follow first-order kinetics since the concentration of the solvent will not change significantly during the course of the reaction.

It is also important that a unimolecular substitution reaction will show substantial departures from first-order kinetics if the initial ionization step is significantly reversible—that is, if the reaction may be represented by the following sequence:

$$R:X \underset{k_r}{\overset{k_f}{\rightleftharpoons}} :X + R^+ \overset{:Y}{\underset{k'}{\rightarrow}} R:Y \tag{3}$$

we have already considered a substitution reaction of this type—the hydrolysis of benzhydryl chloride $(C_6H_5)_2CHCl$ (p. 170). Here, the concentration of the attacking reagent, water, was considered constant, and application of the steady state approximation gave the rate expression,

$$\text{rate} = \frac{d(RY)}{dt} = \frac{k_f(RX)}{1 + \dfrac{k_r(:X)}{k'}} \tag{4}$$

If the concentration of the attacking reagent $(:Y)$ varies during the reaction, the rate expression becomes

$$\text{rate} = \frac{k_f(RX)}{1 + \dfrac{k_r(:X)}{k'(:Y)}} \tag{5}$$

A rate expression such as equation (4) or (5) is very compelling evidence for a preliminary bond-breaking step—much more so than is the rate expression given in equation (2).[6] The overall rate of unimolecular substitution should,

---

[6] There is some objection to referring to the reaction represented by sequence (3) as unimolecular. The preliminary bond-breaking step *is* unimolecular; but although this may be the slow step, its rate does not in itself, determine the rate of the overall reaction. As is evident from equation (4), the rate of the overall reaction depends upon k_r and k' as well as k_f. Strictly speaking, for a complex reaction, one is on safest ground when one refers to the molecularity of individual steps only. We shall, however, continue to refer to all nucleophilic substitution reactions involving preliminary bond breaking in the substrate as "S_N1 reactions" since such terminology, although not completely correct, is extremely widespread, and since from the organic chemist's point of view, such reactions are very similar in nature to those S_N reactions in which the overall rate is the same as the rate of the preliminary bond-breaking step.

in the absence of other effects, be *decreased* by addition of nucleophile $:X$ from an outside source, for some of the added $:X$ should combine with R^+ present in solution, reversing the initial "dissociation" step. Since such an effect depends upon a simple shift in the equilibrium of the bond-breaking step, it is often called a *mass-law effect* and will be operative only if the added nucleophile is chemically the same as the fragment resulting from the initial bond breaking. Thus, we should expect that an alkyl bromide which hydrolyzes via the S_N1 path should be hydrolyzed more slowly if an ionic bromide is added to the reaction mixture, but not if an ionic chloride is added. (The reverse should be true for the hydrolysis of an alkyl chloride, and neither hydrolysis should be retarded by addition of an ionic nitrate or fluoride.) And that is not all; the mass-law effect should come into play even though no common ion is added; for as a substitution reaction proceeds, the concentration of the leaving group must increase. This means that a S_N1 reaction, during its early stage, may display first-order kinetics, but as the leaving group accumulates in solution, reversal of the bond-breaking step may become important. The reaction rate should lag farther and farther behind that predicted from the initial first-order rate constant, but the rate will fit an expression such as equation (4) nicely.

However, these mass-law effects are *not* observable for all S_N1 reactions. For example, the hydrolyses of $(C_6H_5)_3C$—Cl in "85 percent aqueous acetone,"[7] of benzhydryl chloride and bromide in 80 percent aqueous acetone,[8] and benzyl chloride in 61 percent by weight aqueous dioxane[9] are retarded by addition of excess "common ion," but the hydrolyses of t-butyl bromide in "90 percent aqueous acetone[10]" and s-butyl bromide in "75 percent aqueous alcohol[11]" are not.

The mass-law effect will not be observed for an S_N1 reaction if the ratio $\frac{k_r(:X)}{k'}$ in equation (4) or the ratio $\frac{k_r(:X)}{k'(:Y)}$ in equation (5) is very much less than unity. This will be the case if the carbonium-ion intermediate, R^+, is much more likely, under the reaction conditions employed, to combine with the attacking nucleophile than to revert back to the original reactant. In the hydrolysis reactions just cited, water molecules are, in effect, competing with halide ions for the carbonium ions formed in the initial ionization step. A carbonium ion, during its rather short lifetime, is surrounded by a "solvation cage," consisting largely of water molecules since water is a much more effective solvating agent than acetone, dioxane, or alcohol. Such a solvated carbonium

[7] Swain, Scott, and Lohmann, *J. Am. Chem. Soc.*, **75**, 136 (1953). Compositions of mixed solvents given in quotation marks refer to the relative *volumes* of pure solvents which are mixed; "85 percent aqueous acetone" is a mixture of 85 volumes of acetone to 15 volumes of water.

[8] Benfey, Hughes, and Ingold, *J. Chem. Soc.*, **1952**, 2488.

[9] Beste and Hammett, *J. Am. Chem. Soc.*, **62**, 2481 (1940).

[10] Bateman, Hughes, and Ingold, *J. Chem. Soc.*, **1940**, 960, 1014.

[11] Coburn, Grunwald, and Marshall, *J. Am. Chem. Soc.*, **75**, 5735 (1953).

ion will persist either until it pulls a water molecule out of its solvation cage (forming a molecule of the carbinol and causing the remainder of the cage to collapse), or until a halide ion pushes through the solvation cage to attack the positively charged carbon. The relatively unstable *t*-butyl and *s*-butyl carbonium ions, in which positive charge is concentrated over a small volume, will tend to destroy their solvation cages before an external halide ion can attack. As the stability, and hence the average lifetime, of the carbonium ion increases, reaction with such a halide ion (hence reversal of the ionization step) becomes more likely. Since such reversal is the basis of the mass-law effect, we see why *the importance of this effect increases as the intermediate carbonium ion becomes more stable.*

The competition between water molecules and halide ions for a carbonium-ion intermediate is somewhat one sided because of the favored position of water molecules in the solvation cage of the carbonium ion. If, however, the attacking reagent is not a component of the solvent, a closer competition (and, hence, a mass-law effect of greater magnitude) should result. This is the case for substitution reactions carried out in liquid SO_2. Thus, the rate of conversion of *m*-chlorobenzhydryl chloride to the corresponding fluoride

$$m\text{-Cl}\text{—}C_6H_4\text{—}CHPh\text{—}Cl + F^- \xrightarrow{SO_2} m\text{-Cl}\text{—}C_6H_4\text{—}CHPh\text{—}F + Cl^-$$

can be depressed by more than 99 percent by addition of excess chloride ion.[10]

On the other hand, as the bond making and bond breaking become more nearly contemporaneous—that is, as the substitution becomes more nearly bimolecular in character—the carbonium-ion intermediate may no longer be thought to have even a transitory existence, and the mass-law effect disappears.

In addition to the common-ion effect (and independent of it), substitution reactions are subject to the same *salt effects* that influence virtually all reactions involving ions (p. 185). If a reaction requires separation of positive and negative charge during formation of the transition state, it will be favored by high ionic strengths. If charge is partially neutralized or dispersed during formation of the transition state, the reaction will generally proceed more rapidly in solutions of low ionic strengths. Since these effects are in the same direction as the effects of dielectric constant, they need not be discussed here in detail. However, we should note that the magnitude of such salt effects depends, in part, upon the dielectric constant of the medium; for charges operate more effectively through media of low dielectric constants than through media of high dielectric constants. Consider, for example, the hydrolysis of 0.1 molar *t*-butyl bromide in aqueous acetone.[10] This reaction, as we have seen, shows no appreciable mass-law effect, but as the hydrolysis proceeds, the accumulation of H_3O^+ and Br^- ions increases the ionic strength. Since this hydrolysis requires separation of charge in the transition state, its specific rate will show an upward drift, the magnitude of which must necessarily increase throughout the course of the reaction. Moreover, as expected, the salt effect in "90 percent aqueous acetone" is significantly greater than that in "70 percent aqueous acetone." In the first (the less aqueous) of these solvent mixtures, the apparent first-order rate constant has risen by about 16 percent of its initial value when the reaction is four fifths complete; in the second of these mixtures, the corresponding increase is only about 7 percent.

In describing what we have chosen to regard as two distinct mechanisms for nucleophilic substitution, we have, quite naturally, tended to emphasize the extreme cases. However, it was noted that a number of such substitutions, particularly those on secondary carbon atoms, constitute what were noncommitally called "borderline cases." Many of these follow, to a rather good approximation, a rate law of the following type:

$$\text{rate} = k_1(\text{R}:X) + k_2(\text{R}:X)(:Y) \tag{6}$$

and it is perhaps natural to suppose that these borderline cases are simply reactions in which some of the individual acts of substitution are unimolecular and others are bimolecular. Yet, in a number of these cases, the rate data give an equally good fit to more complicated expressions that are consistent with a picture in which each of the individual acts of substitution in a given reaction is very nearly the same.[12(a)] In such intermediate mechanisms, the attacking reagent may be considered to approach the substrate and, either by ion-dipole or dipole-dipole interaction, to supply the "push" necessary for bond breaking in the substrate without actually colliding with it. Using such a picture, it may be shown (Ex. 12) that the rate should depend upon the concentration of attacking reagent but not be proportional to it. The question as to which picture of a borderline-type substitution reaction is more nearly correct is both important and difficult, and strong arguments exist in support of both sides.[12]

Attacking Reagents and Leaving Groups

That atom of a nucleophilic reagent which, during a substitution reaction on carbon, becomes bonded to the carbon atom may be conveniently designated as the "attacking atom." Because a nucleophile attacks by using a pair of its own electrons, we would suspect the most effective nucleophile to be the one whose attacking atom has the valence electrons most available for coordination. Since this seems, broadly speaking, to be the criterion for base strength, it is reasonable that the strongest bases should be the most effective reagents for

---

[12] For arguments that "borderline" S_N reactions proceed by a single mechanism rather than a combination of unimolecular and bimolecular mechanisms, see (a) Bird, Hughes, and Ingold, *J. Chem. Soc.*, **1954**, 634 and (b) Winstein, Grunwald, and Jones, *J. Am. Chem. Soc.*, **73**, 2300 (1951). For rather compelling arguments to the contrary, see (c) Gold, *J. Chem. Soc.*, **1956**, 4633.

nucleophilic substitution reactions. But basicity involves thermodynamic measurements whereas nucleophilic "pushing power" (or, as it is often called, *nucleophilicity*) generally involves reaction rates. Again, basicity most often refers to coordination with H^+, whereas nucleophilicity, as we use the term, involves coordination to carbon. Therefore, a correspondence between the order of basicities and the order of nucleophilicities among various reagents, although reasonable, is by no means axiomatic.[13]

Postponing for the present the discussion of the measurement of nucleophilicity, we may note that such a correspondence does exist; that is, the strongest bases generally, but not always, carry out displacement reactions most rapidly. Yet even this rough correspondence is subject to an important provision: it will hold only as long as we limit our considerations to *nucleophiles whose attacking atoms are in the same horizontal row in the periodic table*. In particular, it is most useful for groups of nucleophiles having the same attacking atom. Thus, for nucleophiles in which the attacking atom is oxygen, we may list, in order of decreasing nucleophilicity:

$$OH^- > OPh^- > CO_3^= > OAc^- > H_3C-\!\!\left\langle\!\!\bigcirc\!\!\right\rangle\!\!-SO_3^- >$$

$$Br-\!\!\left\langle\!\!\bigcirc\!\!\right\rangle\!\!-SO_3^- > H_2O > ClO_4^-$$

and for nucleophiles in which the attacking atom is nitrogen:

$$NH_2^- > NH_3 > N\!\!\left\langle\!\!\bigcirc\!\!\right\rangle \approx \left\langle\!\!\bigcirc\!\!\right\rangle\!\!-NH_2 > O_2N-\!\!\left\langle\!\!\bigcirc\!\!\right\rangle\!\!-NH_2$$

Keeping the charge type the same but varying the attacking atom gives the following sequence:

$$R_3C:^- > R_2N^- > RO^- > F^-$$

Such lists must be interpreted with care, for there are a number of cases known where the relative nucleophilicities of two reagents will be reversed as the substrate is changed. Occasionally such reversals may be rationalized by calling on steric effects,[14] but often there appears to be no satisfactory explanation. Next we may consider such series as F^-, Cl^-, Br^-, I^-, and OR^-, SR^-, SeR^-—that

[13] In some cases we may expect the same type of structure-reactivity equation (for instance, the Hammett or Taft equation) to apply to a set of bases with respect not only to their basicity constants, but also to the specific rates of their participation in S_N reactions. In such cases, the correlation between basicity and nucleophilicity is obviously not only qualitative but also quantitative.

[14] For example, triethylamine, as expected, reacts more rapidly with methyl iodide than does pyridine, but the order of nucleophilicities of the two amines is reversed in their reactions with isopropyl iodide (Brown and Eldred, *J. Am. Chem. Soc.*, **71**, 445 (1949)). The reaction between Et_3N and *i*-PrI thus appears to be severely retarded by "front strain" (p. 232) in the activated complex.

is, nucleophiles in which the attacking atoms are members of the same vertical group in the periodic table. Here, the *weaker* bases are derived from the *heavier* members of the series; yet these bases prove to be the most effective nucleophiles. Thus, we have, in the order of decreasing nucleophilicity,

$$I^- > Br^- > Cl^- > F^-$$
$$SeR^- > SR^- > OR^- \text{ and}$$
$$R_2Se > R_2S > R_2O$$

longest halide (I⁻) is weakest base but is strongest nucleophile

The reason for these trends is a matter that merits conjecture, especially since the stronger nucleophiles in these series tend to form the weaker bonds with aliphatic carbon atoms. It is sometimes suggested that the heavier members of these groups are more nucleophilic largely because their atoms are more *polarizable;* that is, the clouds of valence electrons about these atoms are most easily distorted by electrophilic centers. In visualizing the formation of the activated complex, we may imagine the electron cloud of the attacking atom to be pulled in toward the carbon atom under attack. (This is during the early stages of the reaction, before appreciable energy due to the formation of the new bond is released.) The more easily this electron cloud is distorted, the lower will be the activation energy required for substitution. Negative ions having the very polarizable sulfur atom free to attack (thiocyanate, thiosulfate, sulfite, and sulfide) would be expected to be (and are) especially effective nucleophiles. Similarly effective are the azide (N_3^-) and cyanide ions, in which the negative charge is distributed over more than one polarizable atom.

Yet polarizability can hardly be the entire story. If the attack is by an anion, solvation must also be considered. During the activation process, the solvation cage of the attacking nucleophile must be disrupted and a new "cage" built up around the activated complex. Any difficulty in breaking up the solvation cage of the attacking species must be reflected in an increase in the activation energy for substitution, hence in a decrease in reaction rate. Now, it is well known that the solvation energies of ions increase as their charge to size ratios increase; that is, it takes more energy to "desolvate" (partially or wholly) a small ion than a large one having the same charge. Thus, the relatively low nucleophilicities of reagents with small attacking atoms are due, at least in part, to the difficulty in removing molecules of solvent from the attacking site.[15]

[15] Edwards (*J. Am. Chem. Soc.*, **76**, 1540 (1954)) has shown that the nucleophilicities of a number of reagents are closely related to their oxidation potentials (that is, to the half-cell potentials for the reaction, $2X^- \rightarrow X_2 + 2e^-$). This correlation suggests that the same factors should govern both properties. It may be shown (see, for example, Gould, *Inorganic Reactions and Structure*, Henry Holt and Co., New York, 1955, p. 207) that the species X^- is easily oxidized to X_2 if: (*a*) the X—X bond energy is high; (*b*) the ionization potential of X^- is low; (*c*) the solvation energy of X^- is low; and (*d*) the solvation entropy of X^- is high. Of these four factors, the *ionization potential* of X^- (which is a measure of the availability of electrons from X^-) and its *solvation energy* tend to be most important. Since we have already agreed that these two factors also govern the nucleophilicity of X^-, it is not surprising that this correlation exists.

It is to be emphasized that the specific rate of a nucleophilic substitution will *not* depend markedly on the nucleophilicity of the attacking reagent if the substitution proceeds by a carbonium-ion mechanism. In fact, for those $S_N 1$ reactions in which the dissociation step is essentially irreversible, the specific rate should be independent of the attacking reagent. Thus, *t*-butyl bromide in nitromethane undergoes substitution by a number of reagents, among them chloride ion, bromide ion, pyridine, and water. The specific rates for these reactions are very nearly the same although the products are, of course, different.[16] Even if the dissociation step in an $S_N 1$ reaction is significantly reversible, the *initial* rate should be independent of the identity of the substituting agent. During the later stages of the reaction, the substituting agent may influence the overall reaction rate, depending upon how successfully it can compete with the leaving group for the carbonium ion formed in the initial step. A very effective nucleophile will lower the value of the fraction $\dfrac{k_r(:X)}{k'(:Y)}$ in equation (5), thus tending to eliminate the downward drift in the apparent first-order rate constant as the reaction proceeds. But there is a limit; no matter how effective a nucleophile the attacking reagent is, it obviously cannot make the overall reaction faster than the initial bond breaking without changing the reaction mechanism.

Turning now to the leaving group, $:Y$, we may note that the activation process, both in bimolecular and unimolecular substitution, requires a stretching of the $C:Y$ bond. To be an effective leaving group, a substituent should be bound to the carbon atom with a relatively weak bond. Moreover, a rather good negative correlation exists between the basicities and the "departing tendencies" of substituents. *The less basic the substituent, the more easily it is pulled off by solvent or pushed off by an attacking nucleophile.* The following groups are thus arranged in order of the ease with which they are displaced from aliphatic carbon atoms:

$$-NR_2 < -OH \approx -OR < -NR_3^+ < -OAc \approx -F <$$

$$-Cl < -Br < -I < -OSO_2 - \underset{}{\bigcirc} - CH_3 < -OSO_2 - \underset{}{\bigcirc} - Br$$

(Again, there may be individual cases where the order of "departing abilities" of two substituents may be reversed when attacking reagent, alkyl group, or solvent is changed.) Although the $-OH$ and $-OR$ groups are generally not displaced from aliphatic carbon atoms, these groups are converted in strongly acid solution to $-OH_2^+$ and $-O-R^+$. In these, the added proton draws the

$$\underset{\displaystyle H}{\overset{\displaystyle |}{}}$$

[16] Bunton, Greenstreet, Hughes, and Ingold, *J. Chem. Soc.*, **1954**, 647. De la Mare, Hughes, Ingold, and Pocker, *J. Chem. Soc.*, **1954**, 2930.

electrons of the alkyl-oxygen bond toward the oxygen atom, greatly facilitating departure of the substituent. Thus, alcohols and ethers may be converted to alkyl bromides by HBr although they are inert to Br^- in neutral solutions. Similarly, although displacement of the $-N(CH_3)_2$ group from aliphatic carbon is ordinarily not possible, the "leaving efficiency" of this group may be very much increased when it is methylated to $-N(CH_3)_3^+$.

It is interesting that iodide, besides being a very powerful nucleophile, is a very effective leaving group. This at first seems to be an inconsistency, and one may ask, "If a C—I bond is so easily broken, why is such a bond so readily *formed* in displacement reactions?" In answering this, we should note once more that the activation process for breaking a bond involves *stretching* that bond; it is here that the low C—I bond energy (57 kcal per gram bond) facilitates reaction. On the other hand, for a reaction in which a new C—I bond is being formed, bond formation has barely begun in the activated complex; and the energy of the bond-to-be is not nearly so important in determining the activation energy as are the ease of polarization and the ease of desolvation which make the iodide ion such an effective attacking reagent. The dual ability of iodide to attack and depart readily in nucleophilic displacements makes it an effective catalyst for other such displacements. Thus, addition of small amounts of iodide to an aqueous solution of methyl bromide accelerates the hydrolysis of the latter,[17] since, in addition to the ordinary slow reaction of water with CH_3Br, the following series of more rapid reactions may occur

$$I^- \xrightarrow{CH_3Br} \begin{cases} CH_3I \\ Br^- \end{cases} \xrightarrow{H_2O} \begin{cases} H^+I^- \\ CH_3OH \end{cases} \xrightarrow{CH_3Br} \begin{cases} CH_3I \\ Br^- \end{cases} \xrightarrow{etc.}$$

The net result of this reaction series is the destruction of methyl bromide while the iodide is continually being used, then regenerated.

The identity of the leaving group in an S_N2 reaction should obviously affect the reaction rate (that is, an alkyl chloride, bromide, and toluenesulfonate should undergo substitution reactions at different rates), and if more than one attacking nucleophile is present, the leaving group may also influence the relative amounts of products formed. With an S_N1 reaction, the leaving group will likewise determine the reaction rate, but it should *not* influence the ratio of products formed, for the formation of the new bond must presumably wait until the leaving group is removed from the reaction site. A mixture of products, the composition of which is independent of the leaving group, is an excellent indication that the unimolecular mechanism is operating, just as is a substitution rate which is independent of the identity of the attacking group. For example, let us compare the reactions of benzhydryl chloride, $(C_6H_5)_2CHCl$, and

[17] Moelwyn-Hughes, *J. Chem. Soc.*, **1938**, 779.
[18] Church, Hughes, and Ingold, *J. Chem. Soc.*, **1940**, 966.

benzhydryl bromide, $(C_6H_5)_2CHBr$, with 90 percent aqueous acetone which is also 0.10 molar in sodium azide, NaN_3.[18] The products in both cases are benzhydrol, $(C_6H_5)_2CH—OH$, formed in the attack by the water, and benzhydryl azide, formed in the attack by the very nucleophilic azide ion. Although the bromide is found to react 33 times as rapidly as the chloride (at 50°), the mixtures of products resulting from the two reactions have, to within experimental error, the same composition (66 percent hydrol and 34 percent azide).

When the carbonium-ion intermediate in an S_N1 reaction has one or more β-hydrogen atoms, another type of reaction may become important. Instead of undergoing substitution, the carbonium ion may undergo *elimination* of a hydrogen ion, forming an olefin.[19]

$$\diagdown \!\! \underset{\diagup}{CH} \!\! - \!\! \underset{\diagdown}{\overset{+}{C}} \!\! \diagup \quad \xrightarrow{-H^+} \quad \underset{\diagup}{\diagdown} C \!\! = \!\! C \underset{\diagdown}{\diagup}$$

Since the laws of chance governing the fate of a given carbonium ion do not depend upon the mode of origin of the ion, the ratio of the olefin to the substitution product (but not the specific rate of formation of each) in an S_N1 reaction should be independent of the leaving group. This is often, but not invariably, the case. Typically, both *t*-butyl iodide and *t*-butyl bromide undergo solvolysis in aqueous ethanol at 25°. Although the iodide is destroyed almost three times as rapidly as the bromide, the mole fraction of *i*-butene in the mixture of products (0.13) is the same for both halides.[20] With *t*-butyl chloride, which is destroyed about $\frac{1}{43}$ as rapidly as the bromide under the same conditions, the mole fraction of olefin in the product rises to 0.17. While this difference is small, it seems larger than the experimental error, and similar small differences have been observed for the *t*-amyl halides. Although the question must be considered an open one, it appears at present that nonparticipating ions may influence (albeit only slightly) the relative rates of the possible reactions of a carbonium ion in solution.

Furthermore, if more than one olefin is obtained from a given carbonium ion, the ratio of olefins in the product should also be independent of the source of the carbonium ion. We shall see in Chapter 12 that this is the case.

Stereochemistry

It has already been noted that in a direct displacement reaction, the incoming group hits the carbon atom under attack on one side while the leaving group

---

[19] When a substitution reaction is accompanied by elimination, any kinetic study based upon the rate of appearance of the free leaving group in solution is, in effect, following the combined rate of substitution and elimination reactions. The same is true of a study of solvolysis based upon the rate of appearance of H^+.

[20] Cooper, Hughes, and Ingold, *J. Chem. Soc.*, **1937**, 1280; **1948**, 2038.

departs from the opposite side. This process, known as the **Walden inversion,** is said to turn the molecule "inside out," a description that is best understood if we examine a case in which four different groups are attached to the carbon atom under attack.

Note that the section $U\!-\!\underset{V}{\overset{T}{C}}\!-$ of the substrate is converted to its mirror image,

$-\underset{V}{\overset{T}{C}}\!-U$, as a result of the reaction, and that if T, U, and V represent different substituents, the mirror images cannot be superimposed. In short, the configuration about the carbon atom has become *inverted* during the course of the displacement reaction.

Since we obviously cannot see the individual acts of molecular substitution, how can we be sure that this inversion occurs? It might at first seem that if a dextrorotatory reactant yields a levorotatory product (or vice versa), then inversion has taken place; that is, a change in direction of rotation indicates an inversion of configuration about the asymmetric carbon atom. Although this is very often true, there are a significant number of cases known where an alteration of an optically active molecule may reverse the direction of rotation even though the configuration about the asymmetric atom remains unchanged.[21]

[21] For example, acetylating the amino group and ethylating the carboxyl group in dextrorotatory alanine, CH_3—$CH(NH_2)$—$COOH$, yield a levorotatory ester, although neither of these structural changes should affect the configuration about the asymmetric carbon atom. Even more disturbingly, the mere conversion of lactic acid, CH_3—$CH(OH)$—$COOH$, to its anion reverses the direction of rotation.

The correlation between configuration and direction of rotation can be made somewhat more reliable by comparing not only the molecular rotations for the compounds under consideration, but also the *changes* in rotation when temperature, solvent, concentration, and wavelength of polarized light are varied. A further degree of reliability is obtained by comparing changes in rotation when the compounds under consideration are subjected to similar alterations in structure which must not, however, alter the configurations about the centers of asymmetry (acylation of amino groups, esterification of —COOH groups, etc.). See, for example, Freudenburg and co-workers, *Ber.*, **56**, 193, (1923); **60**, 2447 (1927); **61**, 1083, (1928); **64**, 703, (1931).

Nevertheless, in the absence of other information, conclusions that have been based upon such comparisons, however reliable they may be, cannot be regarded as certain. Moreover, such comparisons leave unanswered the frequently important question as to how *optically pure* a product is in comparison with the reactant—that is, just how much racemization has taken place during the reaction.

Since direction of rotation is thus a useful, but by no means conclusive, indication of relative configuration, we must turn to more rigorous methods to demonstrate that every act of direct displacement in a given reaction is accompanied by inversion of configuration.

Two important groups of experiments unequivocally established this for a number of direct displacement reactions, and the assumption that *all* direct displacement reactions invert, when further applied to many additional groups of reactions, has led to no significant inconsistencies. Let us consider a single example[22] from nearly a dozen reaction series investigated by Kenyon, Phillips, and their co-workers. In these, an optically active alcohol (with the alpha-carbon asymmetric) is converted to its enantiomorph. (In the following series, the α values designate the specific rotation for each of the compounds at 5461 Å and 23° C.)

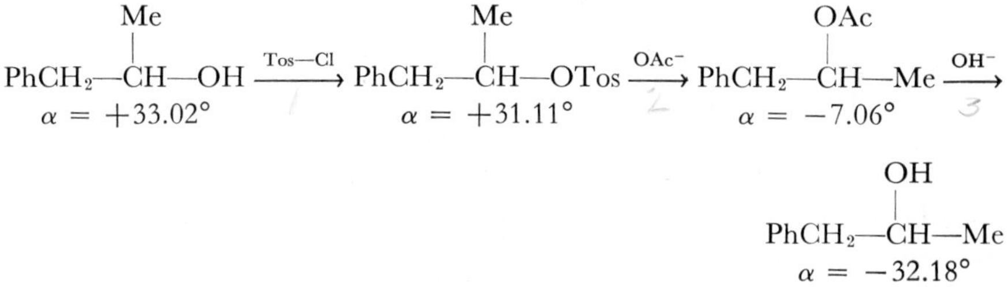

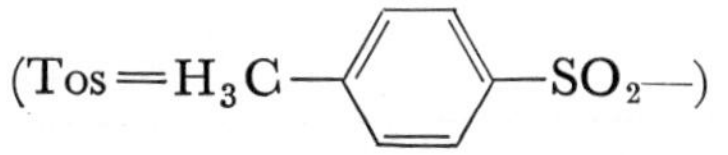

$$
\begin{array}{ccc}
\text{Me} & \text{Me} & \text{OAc} \\
| & | & | \\
\text{PhCH}_2\text{—CH—OH} \xrightarrow{\text{Tos—Cl}} & \text{PhCH}_2\text{—CH—OTos} \xrightarrow{\text{OAc}^-} & \text{PhCH}_2\text{—CH—Me} \xrightarrow{\text{OH}^-} \\
\alpha = +33.02° & \alpha = +31.11° & \alpha = -7.06°
\end{array}
$$

$$
\begin{array}{c}
\text{OH} \\
| \\
\text{PhCH}_2\text{—CH—Me} \\
\alpha = -32.18°
\end{array}
$$

$$(\text{Tos} = \text{H}_3\text{C} - \!\!\!\bigcirc\!\!\!- \text{SO}_2\text{—})$$

Since the resulting carbinol has a rotation opposite in sign but nearly equal in magnitude to that of the original carbinol, an inversion of configuration at the asymmetric carbon atom must have occurred in one of the three steps. In the first step—the conversion of the alcohol to the tosylate—the reaction takes place at the *oxygen* of the —OH group rather than at the asymmetric carbon; the configuration about the carbon must therefore remain unchanged here. The third step is the basic hydrolysis of an ester; since it is now known that such reactions ordinarily[23] involve breakage of the acyl-oxygen, rather than the

alkyl-oxygen bond $\left(\text{that is, } -\overset{\diagdown}{\text{C}}\text{—O—}\overset{|}{\underset{\text{O}}{\text{C}}}\text{— rather than } -\overset{\diagdown}{\underset{\diagup}{\text{C}}}\text{—O—}\underset{\text{O}}{\text{C}}\text{—}\right)$, the

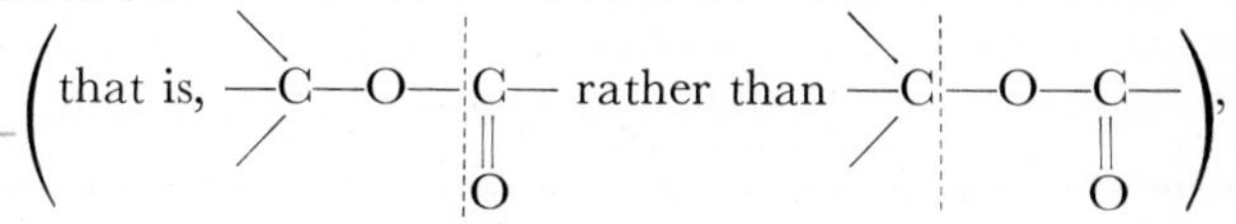

---

[22] Phillips, *J. Chem. Soc.*, **1923**, 44. See also papers by Kenyon, Phillips and co-workers, *J. Chem. Soc.*, **1923**, 64; **1925**, 399, 2552; **1926**, 2052; **1933**, 173; **1935**, 1072, 1663; **1936**, 303.

[23] It might be supposed that inclusion of the word "ordinarily" substantially weakens the argument given; for, we may ask, how do we know that this hydrolysis is of the "ordinary" rather than the "extraordinary" type? In actuality, we know enough about ester hydrolysis at present to say that considerable confidence that those esters which undergo saponification with alkyl-oxygen breakage are of a few very specialized types (see Chap. 9). Moreover, for any particular ester, the position of bond breaking may be independently confirmed by carrying out the saponification in water "labeled" with heavy oxygen (p. 145).

configuration about the asymmetric carbon atom remains unaltered in this step. The inversion must therefore have taken place in the second step, the displacement of tosylate by acetate. The same conclusion arises from a number of similar Kenyon-Phillips cycles, and it can be likewise shown that the displacement of TosO⁻ by EtO⁻ results in inversion of configuration. It is significant, however, that if such cycles are applied to carbinols having a phenyl group alpha to the asymmetric carbon, the resulting carbinol has a rotation opposite in sign to that of the original carbinol, *but the magnitude of its rotation has fallen substantially;* that is, considerable racemization has accompanied the substitution of acetate for tosylate. Such substitutions, however, no longer display second-order kinetics.

A second set of experiments of considerable fundamental interest employs optically active alkyl halides, again with the α-carbon atom asymmetric.[24]

When, for example, *d*-2-iodooctane, $CH_3\overset{\overset{\displaystyle I}{\mid}}{-}CH-C_6H_{13}$, is added to a solution containing free iodide ion, the organic iodide undergoes racemization. Furthermore, the rate of racemization is proportional to the concentration of I^-. Iodide ions are quite obviously attacking the *d*-iodide molecules, forming new C—I bonds and breaking old ones.

$$d\text{-}C_8H_{17}I + I^- \rightarrow l\text{-}C_8H_{17}I + I^-$$

Dextrorotatory molecules are being converted to levorotatory molecules in some or all of these displacements (without further evidence, we cannot decide which). When half of the original *d* molecules have been so inverted, the solution will have become optically inactive and any further acts of displacement will bring about no change in specific rotation; for at that point in the reaction, a *d* molecule will be just as likely to be attacked as will be an *l* molecule. But this exchange of iodine between inorganic and organic iodide may be observed in another way. If *radioactive* iodide is used in solution, the iodide exchange will result in incorporation of radioactive iodine atoms in the organic iodide. The fraction of radioactive iodine in the iodooctane will increase until it becomes equal to the fraction of radioactive iodine in the inorganic iodide. Now if *every* displacement of iodide by iodide results in inversion, the rate of racemization should be just *twice* the rate of iodide exchange (as indicated by transfer of radioactive iodine); this must be so, for a given group of molecules of *d*-iodooctane will be *completely* racemized when just half of them have been inverted— that is, when exchange has proceeded half way to completion. The ratio of racemization to exchange in this case has been found to be 1.93 ± 0.16. In similar halide exchange experiments with α-phenylethyl bromide and α-bromo-

[24] Hughes and co-workers, *J. Chem. Soc.*, **1935**, 1525; **1936**, 1173; **1938**, 209.

propionic acid, using radioactive bromide, the corresponding ratios have been found to be 1.82 ± 0.19 and 2.03 ± 0.12.[25] In these displacements then, as in the Kenyon-Phillips cycles, *virtually every act of bimolecular substitution entails inversion of configuration.* Moreover, at present, this principle, is thought to apply to *all* S_N2 reactions on carbon.

With the S_N1 mechanism, the story should be different. Suppose that a substitution on an asymmetric carbon atom proceeds through a free carbonium

$$\text{ion,} \left[T\!-\!C \overset{\textstyle U}{\underset{\textstyle V}{\diagup}} \right]^+,$$ and suppose further that the bonds to the electron-deficient

carbon atom lie in a single plane. We should then expect such a reaction to be accompanied by *complete racemization* (unless, of course, there were an additional asymmetric center not at the reaction site), for the carbonium-ion intermediate, having a plane of symmetry, should not give rise to an optically active product (p. 149).

Complete or almost complete racemization *is* sometimes observed in S_N1 reactions. For example, the hydrolysis of optically active α-phenylethyl chloride, $CH_3\!-\!CHPh\!-\!Cl$, in 80 percent aqueous acetone proceeds with about 97 percent racemization.[26] *p*-Methoxybenzhydryl hydrogen phthalate (III) is one of a special group of esters that suffer alkyl-oxygen bond breakage on hydrolysis and solvolysis. If an optically active form of this ester is dissolved in methanol, unimolecular solvolysis occurs and the methyl ether resulting (IV) is racemic.[27]

III, active   + MeOH ⟶

IV, racemic

[25] The extent of halide exchange at any desired time may be determined by diluting the reaction mixture with water, extracting the organic iodide with a nonpolar solvent, then measuring the radioactivity of the nonaqueous phase. The handling of data in both the exchange experiments and the racemization experiments is complicated slightly by the reversibility of the displacement reaction, and the exchange experiment is complicated further by the slow decay of the radioactive iodine. For a brief summary of the treatment of data in these experiments see Hammett, *Physical Organic Chemistry*, McGraw-Hill Book Co., Inc., New York, 1940, pp. 164–165.

[26] Hughes, Ingold, and Scott, *J. Chem. Soc.*, **1932**, 1232.

[27] Balfe, Doughty, Kenyon, and Poplett, *J. Chem. Soc.*, **1942**, 605. For similar examples, see: Balfe, *et. al.*, **1946**, 797; **1951**, 376; Davies and White, *ibid.*, **1952**, 3300.

More commonly, however, S_N1 reactions are found to lead to a combination of inversion and racemization; that is, *the product has a configuration opposite to that of the reactant, but its optical purity is substantially less.* Typically, when optically active 2-bromooctane is dissolved in 60 percent aqueous ethanol, it is converted to a mixture of 2-octanol and its ethyl ether. Some inversion has occurred in the formation of both of these products, but both are about two thirds racemized.[28] Yet we must be careful in interpreting such an experiment, for as the reaction proceeds, Br^- is formed, and this can racemize the starting material (just as I^- can bring about the racemization of 2-iodooctane by iodide exchange). Racemization due to bromide exchange is negligible near the beginning of the reaction when (Br^-) is very small, but it becomes important near the half-way point in the solvolysis. It is possible (although the mathematical treatment is a little complex) to estimate the specific rate of bromide exchange by following both the appearance of H^+ volumetrically and the disappearance of optical activity polarimetrically during the course of the reaction. After corrections are made for racemization due to bromide exchange, it turns out that, aside from this effect, there is 32 percent racemization in the formation of the alcohol and 26 percent racemization in the formation of the ether. Similarly, in the

$$(CH_3)_2CH—(CH_2)_3—\overset{\overset{\displaystyle CH_3}{|}}{\underset{\underset{\displaystyle Cl}{|}}{C}}—C_2H_5$$

V

solvolysis of the tertiary chloride V in aqueous ethanol, 70 to 80 percent racemization is observed.[29] (Here, interpretation of the results is straightforward, for this alkyl chloride is not appreciably racemized by S_N2-type chloride exchange.) Likewise, when the optically active tosylates VI and VII are treated with acetic acid, the corresponding inverted acetates are obtained, but 10

$$C_2H_5—\overset{\overset{\displaystyle CH_3}{|}}{CH}—OTos \qquad\qquad t\text{-Bu}—CHPh—OTos$$

VI   VII

[28] Hughes, Ingold, and Masterman, *J. Chem. Soc.*, **1937**, 1196. The optical purity of the ether may be determined by comparing the product from this reaction with the ether formed in the reaction of 2-bromobutane with OEt^- in absolute ethanol. In the latter solution, the substitution is unmistakably bimolecular in character and may be assumed to proceed with almost 100 percent inversion. The optical purity of the alcohol is determined by comparing the product obtained with 2-octanol that has been resolved by conventional methods.

[29] Hughes, Ingold, Martin, and Meigh, *Nature*, **166**, 679 (1950).

percent racemization is observed in the first case[30] and 90 percent racemization in the second.[31]

The persistence of optical activity in the products from many reactions that are unmistakably S_N1 in character indicates that the intermediate, though it may be electron deficient, is not satisfactorily described as a carbonium ion unless definite restrictions as to its freedom are recognized. It is sometimes said that the carbonium-ion intermediate may be *shielded by the leaving group* so that the incoming reagent is more likely to attack the ion on the "unshielded" side than on the "shielded" side. In effect, the carbonium ion, although it is itself symmetric, may, at the moment of attack, be in an asymmetric environment. Furthermore, the shield is not stationary; just after the bond breaking has occurred, the leaving group lies close to the newly formed carbonium ion, but as the carbonium ion grows older, the leaving group recedes and its shielding action becomes less and less efficient. The longer the "lifetime" of the carbonium ion, the more nearly free it can become before it is attacked by the entering group. On this basis, we would expect those substrates that give the most stable carbonium ions to undergo the greatest degree of racemization in their substitution reactions. This is what we find.

Although such a picture of the S_N1 reaction is easily visualized, we have found it necessary to use in our description the terms "carbonium-ion lifetime" and "shielding efficiency." These terms represent quantities that are not easily defined. An alternate description, which is most readily applied to solvolyses, has recently been suggested.[32] It is proposed that solvolytic substitution reactions proceed through an intermediate VIII that has much of the character of an ion pair.[33] The intermediate VIII may then react in one of two ways. The

| substrate | VIII | | IX |

bonds about the carbon atom in VIII may "rehybridize," expelling the leaving group and forming the inverted product; or an additional molecule of solvent can replace the leaving group $X:$, converting VIII into IX, the solvated free carbonium ion. Since IX has a plane of symmetry, it must yield racemic prod-

[30] Kenyon, Phillips, and Pittman, *J. Chem. Soc.*, **1935**, 1072.

[31] Winstein and Morse, *J. Am. Chem. Soc.*, **74**, 1133 (1952).

[32] Streitwieser, Ref. 1(c), p. 641. See also Doering and Zeiss, *J. Am. Chem. Soc.*, **75**, 4733 (1953).

[33] Description of VIII as an ion pair is appropriate only if the leaving group, $:X$, is negatively charged. If $:X$ is uncharged, VIII is simply an aggregate of the carbonium ion, leaving group, and solvent, held together by ion-dipole interaction.

ucts. This picture allows the degree of racemization to be expressed in terms of concepts that have been rigorously defined. The ratio of inversion to racemization should be equal to the ratio k_i/k_r, the relative rates of the competing reactions by which intermediate VIII is consumed. This interpretation, however, leaves unanswered the important question, "What is the nature of the process by which VIII is converted to IX?"

In discussing the stereochemistry of nucleophilic substitution reactions, we should not overlook a number of special cases in which *net retention of configuration* is observed. In the predominant product resulting from such reactions, the configuration about the reaction center is *the same* as that in the substrate. (In such cases, some degree of racemization may also occur.) In order that a compound react in this manner, there must be, in addition to the leaving group, a nearby substituent, often called a **neighboring group,** which has nucleophilic character. This group may intervene in the substitution reaction, not only affecting the stereochemical outcome, but also increasing the rate and, in many cases, bringing about molecular rearrangements. Neighboring group reactions are discussed at some length in Chapter 14; here we are interested only in stereochemical matters. The classic example of neighboring-group participation is encountered in the basic hydrolysis of the α-bromopropionate ion, CH_3—$CHBr$—COO^-.[34] If an optically active form of this ion is hydrolyzed in very concentrated base, the lactate ion, CH_3—$CHOH$—COO^-, which is formed has, as may be expected, an inverted configuration; here, a direct displacement reaction has occurred. However, if the hydrolysis is carried out in dilute base, the lactate is formed with *retention* of configuration. In the latter reaction, there are *two* acts of substitution at the asymmetric carbon, the first bringing about an inversion, the second bringing about an inversion of the original inversion. It appears that the slow step of the hydrolysis in dilute base is the breaking of the C—Br bond, rapidly followed by formation of an α-lactone, X (first inversion), after which the lactone is broken by water (second inversion).[35]

$$X$$

[34] Cowdrey, Hughes, and Ingold, *J. Chem. Soc.*, **1937,** 1208.

[35] The rate law for the reaction will not tell whether the formation of the three-membered ring occurs at the same time as the breakage of the C—Br bond or whether the C—Br bond is broken first, since in either case the reaction should exhibit first-order kinetics. It has been shown, however; that the reaction shows a positive salt effect (see Grunwald and Winstein,

A more recent example of neighboring-group participation is the reaction of *trans*-2-acetoxycyclohexyl brosylate (XII) with acetate in glacial acetic acid.

$$Me-C(=O)-O \quad \xrightarrow{-OBs^-} \quad Me-^+C(O^-) \quad \xrightarrow{+OAc^-} \quad Me-C(=O)-O$$

| XII | XIII | XIV |

$$(\,OBs = -OSO_2-\!\!\langle\ \rangle\!\!-Br\,)$$

As shown, a second acetoxyl group replaces the brosylate group. The product is not the *cis*-diacetate (which we would expect if acetate ion attacked the ring on one side while the brosylate ion departed from the other), nor is it a mixture of the *cis*- and *trans*-diacetates with the former predominating (which we would expect if the brosylate ion initially departed, leaving a "free" carbonium ion). Instead, the chief product is the *trans*-diacetate (XIV), indicating that the acetoxy group, like the carboxylate group, *is capable of preserving the configuration about a neighboring carbon atom while the latter is subject to nucleophilic attack.*[36] The proposed intermediate is the cyclic carbonium ion XIII, which may suffer either at carbon-1 or carbon-2. In either case, the *trans*-diacetate should result. (However, if the starting material is optically active, the resulting diacetate should be, and is observed to be, racemic.)

J. Am. Chem. Soc., **70**, 841 (1948)), suggesting that the formation of the activated complex requires separation of unlike charge rather than dispersal of charge; that is, that ionization of the C—Br bond is the slow step.

Since the α-lactone proposed as an intermediate has never been isolated and, more particularly, since attempts to prepare α-lactones have failed, some workers (see, for example, Ingold, Ref. 1 (*a*), p. 384) prefer to regard the intermediate in this reaction as a type of "zwitter-

$$^-O \quad \diagdown \quad \begin{array}{c} H \\ | \\ O=C \longrightarrow \overset{+}{C} \diagup \\ \diagdown \\ Me \end{array} \quad XI$$

ion" (XI) in which an electrostatic bond from the carboxylate group holds the carbonium ion in the correct configuration for subsequent attack by water. At the present time, the lack of a method for distinguishing between the lactone and zwitterion intermediate makes this question largely a semantic one.

Finally, it should be noted that if the α-lactone intermediate is to account for the overall retention of configuration, its hydrolysis must involve cleavage of the alkyl-oxygen bond rather than the acyl-oxygen bond. Such cleavage is different from that observed for ordinary esters (Chap. 9) but similar to that sometimes observed for β-lactones.

[36] Winstein, Hess, and Buckles, *J. Am. Chem. Soc.*, **64**, 2780, 2787, 2796 (1942). Winstein, Grunwald, and Ingraham, *ibid.*, **70**, 821 (1948).

Removal of the Leaving Group. Reactions in Nonpolar Solvents

A negatively charged leaving group, whether it arises from an S_N1- or S_N2-type reaction, is ordinarily solvated. Negative ions are most effectively solvated by hydroxyl-containing compounds (which operate through the formation of hydrogen bonds), and this is one of the chief reasons why the vast majority of S_N reactions of halides and sulfonate esters are carried out in solvents consisting wholly or partially of water, alcohols, or carboxylic acids. When the hydroxylic solvent is present in very large excess, ordinary kinetic studies cannot, of course, detect its participation in a reaction. To obtain what is hoped will be a better picture of the role played by such a solvent we may transfer the reaction to a relatively inert solvent (such as benzene or CCl_4) and note the effect of adding small measured amounts of a hydroxylic solvent in which the reaction is known to occur readily. However, we should exercise considerable reserve in applying conclusions based upon the study of a reaction in a nonpolar solvent to the "same reaction" in a large excess of hydroxylic solvent; for the reaction environments in the two cases must be very different. Any phenomenon involving ions in a polar solvent may suffer modification when transferred to a nonpolar solvent, since single ions cannot exist in appreciable concentrations in the latter but are associated to ion pairs, triplets, and higher aggregates.

Consider the reaction between methyl bromide and pyridine in benzene. This is accelerated by adding small quantities of alcohols or phenols,[37] although the reaction will proceed at a measurable rate in their absence. Moreover, the more acidic hydroxylic compounds (for example, p-nitrophenol) are the more effective catalysts, presumably because they form the stronger hydrogen bonds to the departing bromide ion. In a manner of speaking, the added molecules of alcohol or phenol are "pulling" at the bromide while the nitrogen of the pyridine molecule is "pushing" at the methyl carbon, and for this reason the catalyzed reaction is sometimes said to proceed by a "push-pull" mechanism.[38]

The reactions of triphenylmethyl chloride in benzene are of considerable interest. This chloride undergoes chloride exchange with such benzene-soluble ionic chlorides as $Bu_4N^+Cl^-$ and $(C_{18}H_{37})_2NMe_2^+Cl^-$ at a rate independent of the concentration of chloride,[39] indicating that, as in polar solvents, the rate-

---

[37] (a) Swain and Eddy, J. Am. Chem. Soc., 70, 2989 (1948). (b) Pocker, J. Chem. Soc., 1957, 1279.

[38] This reaction and, by inference, a number of similar reactions were formerly said also to be "termolecular," largely because early data (Ref. 37(a)) indicated that they were third order—that is, first order each in attacking reagent, substrate, and "pulling reagent." On the basis of more recent and more complete data by Pocker (Ref. 37(b)), it now appears that such reactions are, in general, of no particular integral order with respect to added alcohol and phenol although they are indeed first order in both attacking reagent and substrate. It therefore seems adequate to describe these as S_N2 reactions, proceeding with the help of pulling action by alcohol or phenol.

[39] (a) Swain and Kreevoy, J. Am. Chem. Soc., 77, 1122 (1955). (b) Hughes, Ingold, Mok,

determining step in such exchange is simply the ionization:

$$Ph_3CCl \rightarrow Ph_3C^+ + Cl^-$$

On the other hand, the methanolysis of Ph_3CCl in benzene is *first order in methanol*, provided the concentration of methanol is very low (below 0.001 M), and the methanolysis is *considerably slower* than chloride exchange.[40] Here, then, it appears that the reaction of the Ph_3C^+ ion with methanol is slow, compared both to the ionization and to its reversal—that is, that the methanolysis sequence is

$$Ph_3CCl \underset{fast}{\overset{fast}{\rightleftharpoons}} Ph_3C^+Cl^- \xrightarrow[slow]{MeOH} Ph_3C\!-\!OMe + HCl$$

which would be consistent with the observed rate law.

At higher concentrations of methanol, the kinetic picture seems to change, for here the reaction order with respect to (methanol) rises from unity to well over 2. Thus suggests the involvement of one or two additional molecules of alcohol in the activated complex, and, once again, it may be supposed that these serve to pull at the chloride while the first methanol molecule attacks the phenylated carbon.

$$Ph_3C\!-\!Cl + MeOH \underset{fast}{\overset{fast}{\rightleftharpoons}} Ph_3C^+\ ^-Cl \cdot\cdot H\!-\!OMe \xrightarrow[slow]{MeOH}$$

$$\begin{array}{c} Me \quad_+\quad H \\ \diagdown \quad \diagup \\ O \\ | \\ Ph_3C \qquad + Cl^- + HOMe \end{array}$$

There is another way in which the "pulling action" in halide substitutions may be intensified. Dipositive mercury and unipositive silver are known to be unusually electrophilic toward halide ions (aside from F^-), and the substitution reactions of a number of alkyl halides are markedly accelerated by the addition of silver or mercuric compounds—a "catalysis" quite obviously due to electrophilic "pull" by these heavy metal ions. However, the kinetics of such catalyzed reactions may become quite complex. In the course of a reaction

---

Patai, and Pocker, *J. Chem. Soc.*, **1957**, 1265. (This paper summarizes the conclusions arising from work described in four papers immediately preceding it.)

[40] Swain and Pegues, *J. Am. Chem. Soc.*, **80**, 812 (1958). The rate law proposed by these authors is different from that proposed by Hughes *et al.*, (Ref. 39(b)), whose data indicate that this methanolysis becomes zero order, rather than first order, in MeOH at low concentrations of the latter. This important discrepancy is a reflection of the difficulty in carrying out kinetic studies in this system. The methanolysis is strongly catalyzed by HCl produced (not only by the reaction itself, but also by traces of moisture). Swain and Pegues attempt to minimize this difficulty by carrying out the methanolysis in the presence of a number of tertiary amines, showing also (in the opinion of the present author, satisfactorily) that these amines do not significantly affect the methanolysis.

catalyzed by Ag^+, an insoluble silver halide will generally precipitate; and since this halide is itself often a catalyst, the reaction will take on the complications typical of heterogeneous reactions. With Hg^{2+}, difficulties arise from the multiplicity of species formed by dipositive mercury in the presence of halide (Hg^{2+}, HgX^+, HgX_2, HgX_3^- and HgX_4^{2-}). However, if the constants governing the various mercuric-halide equilibria are known, kinetic treatments are possible.[41] Silver- or mercury-catalyzed substitution reactions, with but few exceptions, have much of the character of S_N1 reactions (although since an additional species is participating in the reaction, they are, in the strict sense, bimolecular). Like S_N1 reactions, they occur most readily with tertiary halides and least readily with primary halides; and like S_N1 reactions, substitution at an asymmetric carbon is attended by partial racemization, although, in the absence of neighboring-group effects (p. 270), there is net inversion of configuration. Thus such reactions may be considered to pass through an electron-deficient intermediate which, as in the case of S_N1 reactions, we represent as a carbonium ion.

$$R{-}X \xrightarrow[\text{slow}]{Ag^+} AgX + R^+ \xrightarrow[\text{fast}]{Y:} RY$$

and

$$RX \xrightarrow[\text{slow}]{HgX_2} HgX_3^- + R^+ \xrightarrow[\text{fast}]{Y:} RY$$

In a similar manner, carbonium ions may be generated from alkyl halides by the action of electrophilic metal chlorides in inert solvents. On this basis, we can see why optically active α-phenylethyl chloride is racemized by action of $SnCl_4$ in CCl_4.[42]

$$d\text{-MeCHPhCl} \xrightarrow{SnCl_4} SnCl_5^- + \left[CH_3{-}C \begin{array}{c} Ph \\ \diagup \\ \diagdown \\ H \end{array} \right]^+ \xrightarrow{SnCl_5^-} d,l\text{-MeCHPhCl}$$

Steric Effects

We have already pointed out (and it will bear repetition) that atoms become more crowded in the formation of the activated complex in an S_N2 reaction but become *less crowded* during activation in an S_N1 reaction. Therefore, S_N2 reactions should be far more effectively hindered by the presence of bulky groups. In fact, S_N1 reactions would be expected to be subject to *steric acceleration* (p. 234) if they exhibit steric effects at all. The most straightforward conclusions concerning steric hindrance should arise from examining the influence

---

[41] Roberts and Hammett, *J. Am. Chem. Soc.*, **59**, 1063 (1937); Benfey, *ibid.*, **70**, 2165 (1948); Oae and VanderWerf, *ibid.*, **75**, 2724 (1953).

[42] Heald and Gwyn-Williams, *J. Chem. Soc.*, **1954**, 362.

of *alkyl substitution* on reaction rates, since the inductive effects of alkyl groups, although by no means negligible, are generally much smaller than those associated with other substituents (p. 205). For S_N reactions, we should be particularly interested in the effects of successive substitution at positions α and β to the reaction site; for it is now recognized that substitution at the γ position and at positions still farther removed have, except for special cases, only slight effects on reactivity.

One of the simplest possible nucleophilic substitutions is the replacement of one halogen by another in an alkyl halide (the so-called "Finkelstein reaction").[43]

$$RX + Y^- \rightarrow RY + X^- \qquad S_{N_2}$$

Such a reaction can be followed kinetically, even if the attacking and leaving groups are chemically the same, since radioactive isotopes of chlorine, bromine, and iodine have been available for some years. The reaction series of greatest interest to us are

R = Me, Et, *i*-Pr, *t*-Bu (successive substitution of CH_3 groups for α-hydrogens);
and
R = Et, *n*-Pr, *i*-Bu, *neo*-Pe (Me_3C—CH_2—)
    (successive substitution of CH_3 groups for β-hydrogens)

In comparing rates of reactions of halides in these series, we must be sure that each halide reacts by the same mechanism. The reactions are therefore carried out in the poorly ionizing solvent, dry acetone, in which even the *t*-butyl halides undergo substitution by the S_N2 mechanism. Relative specific rates (with k_2 for the methyl halide in each series set at unity) for two types of halide exchange are given in Table 8-2. We should remember that these trends are not due solely to steric effects. When the reactivities of molecules having different masses are being compared, *ponderal* effects must enter the picture. These, it will be remembered (p. 235), depend exclusively upon the *distributions of masses* in the reactants and in the activated complex. These effects operate appreciably only on the entropies of activation, almost invariably decreasing the rates of reactions of heavier compounds in comparison to lighter compounds. Ponderal effects that cannot yet be measured must be estimated theoretically.[43(b)] Thus far, calculations have been reported only for the bromide-bromide exchange reaction; these show, for example, that the bromide exchange of *t*-butyl bromide is retarded ponderally by a factor of about 10 (as compared to the reaction of

---

[43] (a) Studies prior to 1953 on steric effects in Finkelstein reactions have been summarized by Ingold, Ref. 1(a), pp. 403–418. (b) Further extensive work is described by de la Mare and co-workers in eight additional papers, *J. Chem. Soc.*, **1955**, 3169–3236. (c) For a recent summary, see Ingold, *Quart. Revs.*, **XI**, 1 (1957).

Table 8-2. Relative Rate Constants for S_N2 Halide Exchanges in Acetone (25°)

R =	Cl⁻ + RI → RCl + I⁻	Br* + RBr → RBr⁻ + Br⁻
Me	1.00	1.00
Et	0.089	0.013
i-Pr	0.0028	1.4×10^{-4}
t-Bu	—	3.9×10^{-5}
n-Pr	0.053	0.0085
i-Bu	0.0034	4.4×10^{-4}
neo-Pe	1.2×10^{-6}	2×10^{-7}

methyl bromide) and that in neopentyl bromide the exchange is retarded ponderally by a factor of about 100.

It is also likely that inductive effects play a small part in determining the relative rates in the "α series" above (Me, Et, i-Pr, and t-Bu), but not in the "β-series" (Et, n-Pr, i-Bu, and neo-Pe). It is difficult to say a priori how large such effects are, but de la Mare and co-workers[43(b)] estimate that each α-methyl group inductively retards bromide-bromide exchange by a factor of about 5. While the magnitude (and, perhaps, even the direction) of this effect may be open to question, it is obvious that inductive effects, like ponderal effects, account for only a small measure of the observed differences in rate (6 to 7 powers of 10) recorded in Table 8-2.

Figure 8-1 is a sketch of the activated complex for the S_N2 bromide-exchange reaction of 2-bromobutane (chosen because it has both α- and β-methyl groups). We see that the configuration about the carbon atom under attack is such that the α-methyl group tends to be held out of the way of the very large bromide ion but that substantial overlap is possible with the β-methyl group. If there is only one β-methyl group, as in n-propyl bromide, this inter-

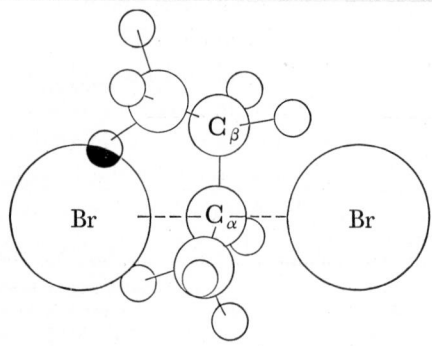

Fig. 8-1. Activated Complex in S_N2 Bromide Exchange.

ference may be avoided by rotating the C_α—C_β bond, thus pushing the β-methyl group "out of the way" of the bromide ions. If there are two β-methyl groups, both will try to avoid interfering with the bromide ions, and serious restrictions will be placed upon the freedom of rotation of the carbon-carbon bonds in the transition state. These restrictions in freedom correspond to a more negative entropy of activation, which corresponds, in turn, to the low rate of substitution that is observed.[44] With three β-methyl groups (neopentyl bromide) there is no way in which such interference may be avoided; the reaction requires attack by one of the small number of very energetic Br$^-$ ions in solution and therefore it will be very slow indeed. Neopentyl halides are, in fact, extremely inactive toward nucleophilic reagents in bimolecular substitutions. (They will react at moderate rates, albeit with extensive rearrangement, under conditions that favor unimolecular substitution.) Broadly speaking, the trends which we have discussed for halide exchanges are observed for other series of S_N2 reactions.

Bimolecular substitutions may also be retarded when the steric requirements of the attacking reagent become excessive. We may show this by selecting a series of amines or alkoxide bases having varying degrees of branching and using these as attacking reagents toward a common substrate. Below, for example, are listed the relative specific rates[45] (in nitrobenzene at 25°) for the reaction of some substituted pyridines with methyl iodide:

---

[44] Until recently it was felt that the substitution reactions of n-propyl halides were slightly slower than those of ethyl halides because the restrictions on bond rotation in the transition state for the propyl compounds were significantly greater than those for ethyl compounds. (See, for example, Denbar and Hammett, *J. Am. Chem. Soc.*, **72**, 109 (1950)). However, the calculations by de la Mare and co-workers (Ref. 41(b), p. 3232) suggest that differences in activation entropies between the ethyl and propyl compounds are ponderal, rather than steric, in origin.

[45] Brown, Gintis, and Podall, *J. Am. Chem. Soc.*, **78**, 5376 (1956).

Substitution of a methyl group in the 4-position of the pyridine ring *increases* the rate, for the electron-repelling effect of the methyl group has made the nitrogen atom more nucleophilic. However, substitution of a methyl group in the 2-position, or, more particularly, methyl groups in the 2- and 6-positions *retards* the substitution. This effect is obviously steric in origin, pointing to interference between the hydrogen atoms of the ring methyl and those in the substrate (Fig. 8-2). Moreover substitution of the very bulky *t*-butyl group in the 2-position lowers the rate of substitution by a factor of 5000.

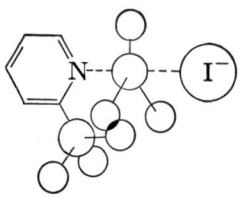

Fig. 8-2. Activated Complex in the Pyridine-Methyl Iodide Reaction.

Similarly, quinuclidine (XV) has been found to react with methyl iodide over 50 times as rapidly as triethylamine.[46] The two amines have similar

XV

basicities toward H^+, but in quinuclidine the substituents on the nitrogen atom are held back, allowing no steric interference with the substrate. The difference is even more striking if a more hindered substrate is used. With isopropyl iodide, quinuclidine reacts over 700 times as rapidly at Et_3N.

Let us turn now to unimolecular substitution. To begin with, we can do little more than speculate as to the *steric* effects of α-alkyl substituents in the substrate. We are, of course, very much aware that such substituents greatly accelerate S_N1-type reactions, for it is the presence or absence of alkyl groups on the α-carbon that determines whether we are dealing with a reaction on a primary, secondary, or tertiary carbon. Yet, we cannot say how much of this accelerative effect is to be attributed to induction, how much to hyperconjugation, and how much, if any, to steric acceleration. With β substitution the picture

[46] Brown and Eldred, *J. Am. Chem. Soc.*, **71**, 445 (1949).

is a little clearer. Successive incorporation of alkyl groups at the β position generally results in small, and apparently nonsystematic, accelerations of S_N1 reactions until the substrate becomes very crowded indeed, whereupon reaction rates increase sharply, possibly by several powers of 10. Thus substitution of one, two, and three methyl groups for β-hydrogens in t-butyl bromide increases the solvolysis rate in 80 percent aqueous ethanol at 25° by 78, 22, and 68 percent, respectively.[47] However, the solvolyses of such crowded chlorides as XVI and XVII appear to be several thousand times as fast as that of t-BuCl under the same conditions.[48] Although the fact that rearrangements accompany the solvolyses of the very crowded halides has led to some apprehension,[49] it would

seem that we almost certainly have here an example of *steric acceleration;* that is, a reaction in which formation of the transition state eases the crowding that prevailed in the reactant and which therefore is assisted by a maximum of crowding in the reactant.

Substitution reactions on cyclic systems were discussed briefly in the preceding chapter (p. 241), but there is one type of cyclic system that merits special consideration. Compounds such as apocamphyl tosylate (XVIII) and 1-iodotrypticine (XIX) (p. 280) with leaving groups on "bridgehead" carbon atoms are especially inactive to nucleophilic substitution, *both by the unimolecular and bimolecular mechanisms.* Tosylate XVIII is inert to lithium iodide in boiling acetone (a powerful S_N2-type reagent), and the corresponding chloride is inert both to silver nitrate (an S_N1-type reagent) at 160° and to concentrated alcoholic

[47] Ingold, Ref. 1(a), p. 414.

[48] Bartlett and Swain, *J. Am. Chem. Soc.,* **77,** 2801 (1955). Unfortunately, this portion of the picture, which is most interesting, is also most difficult to study, for the solvolyses of such halides as XVI and XVII are attended by extensive molecular rearrangement. Even the preparation of pure samples of XVI and XVII is a formidable task, for treatment of the corresponding carbinols with HCl yields, in addition to the desired chlorides, one or more additional chlorides formed by molecular rearrangements. Since the experiments of Bartlett and Swain were carried out on mixtures of chlorides and since each chloride in the mixture may have been reacting in more than one manner, the rate constants obtained should be accepted with reserve, although we may still be quite sure that each of the chlorides in each of the mixtures reacted many times as rapidly as t-butyl chloride.

[49] See, for example, Bartlett, *J. Chem. Ed.,* **30,** 22 (1953), and Ingold, Ref. 1(a), p. 417. Streitwieser, Ref. 1(c), pp. 709–710, also discusses this problem.

KOH (an S_N2-type reagent).[50] Iodide XIX, and the corresponding bromide also, are unreactive to concentrated alcoholic NaOH, Na_2S, and silver nitrate in boiling ethanol,[51] being thus inert both to S_N1- and S_N2-type reagents.

| XVIII | XIX | XX |

The striking lack of reactivity of compounds of this type shows how necessary it is that the bonds to a carbon atom on which a nucleophilic substitution is occurring have substantial freedom of motion. In XVIII and XIX the bonds to the α-carbon atoms are held rigidly in place by the cyclic structures. Since Walden inversions about such carbon atoms cannot occur, S_N2 reactions at these carbons are virtually impossible.

S_N1 reactions are presumed to proceed through carbonium ions. Such ions are most stable when the three bonds to the positive carbon atom lie in the same plane, and their stability falls off sharply as departures from coplanarity increase. The bonds to the bridgehead carbons in XVIII and XIX are obviously not coplanar, and even an approach to coplanarity is prohibited by the rigidity of the bicyclic systems. While it is not impossible to convert such compounds to carbonium ions, such ions should be of very high energy and should form very infrequently. One would then predict that, with persistence, it should be possible to force such compounds as XVIII and 1-bromobicyclo(2.2.2)-octane (XX) (in which the bicyclic system is slightly more flexible) to undergo S_N1 reactions, although extremely sluggishly. Actually XX reacts very slowly with aqueous $AgNO_3$ to give the corresponding alcohol,[52] but the more rigid trypticyl halides (for example, XIX) will not react, even under the most severe forcing conditions.

Structure and Reactivity; Further Considerations

Thus far a number of relationships between structure and reactivity have emerged in our discussion of nucleophilic substitutions. We have learned that S_N1 reactions are accelerated by α-alkyl substituents, and, more strikingly, by

[50] Bartlett and Knox, *J. Am. Chem. Soc.*, **61**, 3184 (1939).
[51] Bartlett and Lewis, *J. Am. Chem. Soc.*, **72**, 1005 (1950); Bartlett and Greene, *ibid.*, **76**, 1088 (1954).
[52] Doering, Levitz, Sayigh, Sprecher, and Whelan, *J. Am. Chem. Soc.*, **75**, 1008 (1953).

α-aryl and α-vinyl substituents; but that S_N2 reactions are retarded by α-alkyl substituents and also by β-alkyl substituents. We have learned that the rate of an S_N2 reaction may generally be increased by increasing the basicity of the attacking reagent, that the rate of an S_N1 reaction is necessarily independent of the attacking reagent, but that both types of reaction are accelerated if the basicity of the leaving group is decreased. With respect to the reactions of halides and sulfonate esters, we have learned that S_N1 reactions are favored by increasing the ionizing power of the solvent, but that the solvent effects in an S_N2 reaction will depend upon the charge on the attacking group. Finally, we have learned that S_N2 reactions are completely prohibited and S_N1 reactions very seriously retarded if the leaving group is attached to a bridgehead carbon.

The accelerative effect of an α-aryl group on an S_N1 reaction has been attributed to the ability of the benzene ring to stabilize the partial positive charge in the carbonium-ion-like transition state by delocalization (XXI′). We should then expect, and we find, that substituents on the benzene ring which further increase the effective length of the conjugated system, either by electron donation (XXII) or by hyperconjugation (XXIII) will further facilitate unimolecular substitution. Attempts have been made to put the accelerative

(or retarding) effects of substituents on a more quantitative basis. The Hammett equation (p. 220) has been applied to the alcoholyses of ring-substituted benzhydryl chlorides and triphenylmethyl chlorides,[53] but with only moderate success. However, it has been shown that the rates of hydrolysis of ring-substituted α-phenylethyl chlorides in 90 percent aqueous acetone can be correlated by a Hammett-like relationship, using, instead of the ordinary σ values, Brown's σ^+ values (p. 226).[54] It is interesting that this should be so, for the σ^+ values are intended for reactions in which the transition state is positively charged.

The accelerating action of α-halogens and α-alkoxide groups on unimolecular substitution may be similarly explained. Again, π-electron density

[53] See, for example, Altscher, Baltzly, and Blackman, *J. Am. Chem. Soc.*, **74**, 3649 (1952). For further references, see Jaffe, *Chem. Revs.*, **53**, 205 (reactions 99–102a) (1953).
[54] Brown and Okamoto, *J. Am. Chem. Soc.*, **79**, 1913 (1957).

drifts from the halogen or oxygen atom toward the partially positive carbon atom in the activated complex, stabilizing the latter.

$$\left[:\overset{..}{\underset{..}{Cl}}:CR_2^+ \cdots X^- \longleftrightarrow :\overset{..}{\underset{..}{Cl}}::CR_2 \cdots X^- \right] \text{ and}$$

$$\left[R:\overset{..}{\underset{..}{O}}:CR_2^+ \cdots X^- \longleftrightarrow R:\overset{+}{\underset{..}{O}}::CR_2 \cdots X^- \right]$$

As with the reactions of substituted benzene derivatives (p. 218), the "$+R$" effects of the halogen and alkoxide substituents are opposed by their respective "$-I$" effects, (that is, electron withdrawal by induction), which, if present alone, would be expected to retard carbonium ion formation.[55] If a halogen or alkoxide substituent is attached to a β-carbon, its conjugative effect may no longer operate but its inductive effect may persist. Therefore such substituents, except for cases involving neighboring-group participation (Chap. 14) will *retard* unimolecular substitutions.

Perhaps the most useful generalization concerning the relationship of structure to ease of unimolecular substitution reactions is this. In forming the activated complex, the leaving group has begun to depart with its pair of bonding electrons; the reaction will therefore be facilitated by any feature that increases the electron density at the carbon constituting the reaction site. We obviously cannot apply this rule to bimolecular substitutions, for electron density is being supplied to the reaction site by the attacking reagent at the same time that electron density is being removed by the leaving group. For any particular reaction, we cannot compare the quantity of electron density that has been supplied with that which has been removed at the instant the system passes through the transition state. We therefore cannot say whether the carbon at the reaction site is more positive or more negative in the activated complex than in the reactant; consequently an S_N2 reaction might be accelerated or retarded by electron-rich substituents on the substrate.

However, this much is certain; if, bound to the α-carbon, there is a group that can delocalize *either* positive or negative charge, such a group should facilitate bimolecular substitution, irrespective of the extent of bond making and bond breaking that has transpired in the transition state. Both the phenyl and vinyl groups are of this type.

---

[55] Although insufficient data have been obtained to allow a clear decision, it appears that, unlike the heavier halogens, the $-I$ effect of the α-fluoro group outweighs its $+R$ effect insofar as these effects influence unimolecular substitution. It has been found, for example (Hine and Lee, *J. Am. Chem. Soc.*, **74**, 3182 (1952)), that PhCF$_2$Br loses Br$^-$ in 50 percent aqueous acetone less than one fifth as rapidly as does PhCH$_2$Br. This is in contrast to the effect of the *p*-F substituent on reactions of benzene derivatives, where, it will be remembered, (p. 219) the $+R$ and $-I$ effects of fluorine nearly cancel, resulting in a very small σ constant for this substituent. We must remember, however, that in reactions of benzene derivatives, a *p*-fluoro substituent is *six atoms removed* from the site of reaction, and its inductive effect has been very much diminished, whereas in the case we are discussing, the fluoro substituent is only *one atom removed* from the reaction site.

$$\left[\begin{array}{c}\overset{+}{\underset{/}{\text{C}}}\text{—}\hspace{-0.3em}\bigcirc \longleftrightarrow \overset{}{\underset{/}{\text{C}}}\hspace{-0.3em}=\hspace{-0.3em}\bigcirc_{+}\end{array}\right] \text{ or } \left[\begin{array}{c}\overset{-}{\underset{/}{\text{C}}}\text{—}\hspace{-0.3em}\bigcirc \longleftrightarrow \overset{}{\underset{/}{\text{C}}}\hspace{-0.3em}=\hspace{-0.3em}\bigcirc^{-}\end{array}\right] \text{ and}$$

$$\left[\begin{array}{c}\overset{+}{\underset{/}{\text{C}}}\text{—CH}\hspace{-0.3em}=\hspace{-0.3em}\text{CH}_2 \longleftrightarrow \overset{}{\underset{/}{\text{C}}}\hspace{-0.3em}=\hspace{-0.3em}\text{CH}\text{—}\overset{+}{\text{CH}}_2\end{array}\right] \text{ or } \left[\begin{array}{c}\overset{-}{\underset{/}{\text{C}}}\text{—CH}\hspace{-0.3em}=\hspace{-0.3em}\text{CH}_2 \longleftrightarrow \overset{}{\underset{/}{\text{C}}}\hspace{-0.3em}=\hspace{-0.3em}\text{CH}\text{—}\overset{-}{\text{CH}}_2\end{array}\right]$$

Hence, both benzyl and allyl derivatives undergo S_N2 reactions more readily than saturated compounds of an otherwise similar nature. Roughly speaking, the S_N2 reactions of allyl compounds are ten to one hundred times as rapid as those of the corresponding ethyl compounds at or near room temperature, whereas those of benzyl compounds are one to several hundred times as rapid.[56]

By noting the effect of electron-attracting and electron-donating substituents on the rate of S_N2 reactions of benzyl derivatives, we should be able to determine whether the carbon atom under attack in a particular type of reaction acquires a partial positive or partial negative charge in the activated complex. To date, too few reaction series have been studied in this way to allow a definite conclusion, but for benzyl halides it appears that the α-carbon atom will become more positive in the transition state (that is, the reaction will be retarded by electron-withdrawing groups) if the attacking reagent is uncharged. If, however, the attacking reagent is negatively charged (OR^-, OH^-, I^-, etc.), the α-carbon becomes more negative in the transition state and the reaction is facilitated by electron withdrawal. This is reasonable, for the activated complex in the attack by a neutral molecule has much of the character of an ion pair;

$$Y: \;+\; \text{ArCH}_2X \longrightarrow \left[\begin{array}{c}\text{Ar}\\ |\\ Y\text{---}\overset{+}{\underset{/\backslash}{\text{C}}}\text{---}X^-\\ \text{H}\;\;\text{H}\end{array}\right] \longrightarrow \left[Y\text{—CH}_2\text{Ar}\right]^+ \;+\; X^-$$

whereas if both the attacking and leaving group are negatively charged, it is not surprising that some of the excess negative charge permeates the region between these groups.

The incorporation of an α-carbonyl, α-carbethoxy, or α-cyano group into the substrate *accelerates* bimolecular substitution. This rate enhancement is sometimes quite striking, as in the halide exchange reaction of alkyl chlorides

[56] For recent compilations, see Streitwieser, Ref. 1(c), pp. 584, 585, 591.

with KI in acetone. The following relative rate constants (n-PrCl $= 1.00$, $T = 50°$) have been observed:[57]

	ClCH$_2$COOEt	ClCH$_2$COPh	ClCH$_2$COCH$_3$	ClCH$_2$CN
$\dfrac{k}{k_{\text{PrCl}}}$	1600	100,000	33,000	2800

This effect is surprisingly consistent, being independent of the charge on the attacking reagent. Of a number of explanations that have been suggested, perhaps the most satisfactory is as follows:[58] It is proposed that there is appreciable attraction between the electron-rich attacking reagent and the electron-deficient carbon of the carbonyl (or cyano) group. Put a little differently, there should be significant overlap between the bond-forming p orbital of the attacking atom and the electron-deficient π orbital of the carbonyl carbon. This interaction constitutes partial bond formation between the attacking atom and the carbonyl carbon (XXIV'), and helps to stabilize the activated complex, thus speeding up the substitution. On the other hand, if there is a non-

XXIV   XXIV'

participating halogen atom bound to the α-carbon atom in the substrate, it should *repel* the attacking reagent (since both species are electron rich), thus lowering the stability of the activated complex and retarding the bimolecular substitution.[59] By the same argument, we would predict that an α-oxygen atom, as in an alkoxy or acyloxy group, would also retard S_N2 reactions. Although less than a dozen cases have been reported, it appears that here our predictions are seriously wrong, for these groups are found to increase the rates of such substitutions, sometimes by several powers of ten.[57,60] The following, for example, are relative rate constants (n-BuCl $= 1$, $T = 50°$) for chloride-iodide exchange in acetone:

	MeO—CH$_2$Cl	AcO—CH$_2$Cl	PhCOO—CH$_2$Cl
$\dfrac{k}{k_{\text{BuCl}}}$	900	270	60

[57] Conant, Kirner, and Hussey, *J. Am. Chem. Soc.*, **47**, 488 (1925).
[58] See (a) Bartlett, in Gilman's *Organic Chemistry*, Vol. III, John Wiley and Sons, Inc., New York, 1953, p. 35; (b) Streitwieser, Ref. 1(c), pp. 597–601.
[59] Hine, Thomas, and Ehrenson, *J. Am. Chem. Soc.*, **77**, 3886 (1955).
[60] Ballinger, de la Mare, Kohnstam, and Prestt, *J. Chem. Soc.*, **1955**, 3641; Kirner, *J. Am. Chem. Soc.*, **48**, 2945 (1926).

The rate-enhancing action of α-oxygen atoms has been rationalized in several ways, but none appears to be completely convincing.[61]

Somewhat surprisingly, S_N1 reactions may be substantially retarded by substitution of deuterium atoms for hydrogen atoms at one or more β-carbons. Typically, the following deuterated compounds undergo solvolysis more slowly than the corresponding nonlabeled compounds by the factors indicated.[62]

$$\frac{k_D}{k_H}$$

	Cl	Cl	Cl
	$(CD_3)_2\overset{|}{C}CD_2CH_3$	$Me_2\overset{|}{C}CD_2CH_3$	$Me_2CD-\overset{|}{C}(CH_3)_2$
$\dfrac{k_D}{k_H}$	0.43	0.71	0.78

	Br	OTos
	$EtCD_2-\overset{|}{C}H-CD_3$	$EtCD_2-\overset{|}{C}H-CD_3$
$\dfrac{k_D}{k_H}$	0.72	0.64

These isotope effects suggest that somehow the β-hydrogen atoms are involved in the rate-determining ionization step. Since the observed effects are relatively small and since we know that the C—H bonds are not broken in S_N reactions, we may infer that the effects arise from stretching of the β-C—H bonds in the activated complex. This fits in with our feeling that an aliphatic carbonium ion, and an activated complex having some of the character of such an ion, may be stabilized by hyperconjugation in which the β-C—H bonds assume some degree of "no-bond" character (XXV—XXV'). Since β-C—D

$$\left[\begin{array}{cc} \overset{H}{\underset{|}{}} & \overset{H^+}{} \\ -\overset{|}{C}-\overset{|}{C}{}^{+}\cdots X^- & \leftrightarrow -C{=}C\cdots X^- \\ | \quad | & | \\ \mathbf{XXV} & \mathbf{XXV'} \end{array} \right]$$

bonds are somewhat "tighter" bonds than β-C—H bonds (p. 192), we should expect substitution of deuterium for β-hydrogen to lower the extent of stabilization by hyperconjugation in the activated complex, boost the energy of activation, and thus retard the reaction. Similarly, the solvolysis of chloride XXVI

---

[61] For example, Streitwieser (Ref. 1(c), p. 600) suggests that this acceleration occurs because the oxygen atom bound to the α-carbon helps to stabilize the activated complex by dispersing the partial positive charge on this carbon by conjugation. This reason seems closely similar to that used to explain the accelerating effect of the alkoxide group on S_N1 reactions (p. 282), and should be applicable only if the α-carbon has acquired an additional measure of positive charge during activation. In the view of the present author, this condition is not always fulfilled, particularly if the attacking reagent is an anion.

[62] The first three compounds were solvolyzed in 80 percent ethanol at 25° (see Shiner, *J. Am. Chem. Soc.*, **75**, 2925 (1953); **76**, 1603 (1954)). The last two compounds were solvolyzed in formic acid at 98° (see Lewis and Boozer, *ibid.*, **76**, 791 (1954)). For a more detailed approach to this problem, see Streitwieser, Jagow, Fahey, and Suzuki, *ibid.*, **80**, 2326 (1958).

in acetic acid at 50° occurs only nine tenths as rapidly as that of the corresponding nonlabeled chloride, suggesting that hyperconjugated structures of the type XXVII stabilize the transition state in this solvolysis.[63] As expected, the

corresponding deuterium isotope effect for S_N2 reactions is much smaller. The specific rate of reaction of i-PrBr with NaOEt is only 13 percent larger than that for the same reaction of $(CD_3)_2CHBr$.[64] This difference may be due merely to a ponderal effect.

Allylic Halides. Allylic Rearrangement and Internal Return

It has been remarked that a carbonium ion derived from ionization of an allylic substrate may be represented by a pair of structures (XXVI ↔ XXVI'),

indicating that the positive charge is distributed over a π-orbital embracing three carbon atoms (XXVII), rather than being localized on the α-carbon. In a substitution reaction proceeding through such a carbonium ion, the incoming nucleophile may attack either at the γ- or the α-carbon. If attack is at the α-carbon an "ordinary substitution product," of course, results, but if the attack is on the γ-carbon, the reaction becomes an **allylic rearrangement.** In the latter case, the double bond shifts and the incoming group takes a position two carbons removed from that originally occupied by the leaving group.[65]

Typically, the solvolysis of crotyl chloride (XXVIII) in "50 percent aqueous acetone" (with a little $CaCO_3$ added to remove the HCl formed) yields a mixture of two isomeric alcohols.[65]

---

[63] Lewis and Coppinger, *J. Am. Chem. Soc.*, **76**, 4495 (1954).

[64] Shiner, *J. Am. Chem. Soc.*, **74**, 5285 (1952).

[65] For a recent review of allylic rearrangements, see deWolfe and Young, *Chem. Revs.*, **56**, 784–801 (1956). Included in this are accounts of a number of unpublished experiments by Young and co-workers, to which reference is made in the present text.

$$CH_3-CH=CH-CH_2Cl \xrightarrow[47°]{\text{water-acetone}} \begin{cases} CH_3-CH=CH-CH_2OH \quad (56 \text{ percent}) \\ \\ CH_3-CH-CH=CH_2 \qquad (44 \text{ percent}) \\ \quad\quad | \\ \quad\quad OH \end{cases}$$

XXVIII

Similarly, if the same chloride is solvolyzed in boiling ethanol (again in the presence of $CaCO_3$), a mixture of the two corresponding ethyl ethers is obtained, 91 percent of which is the ether of crotyl alcohol and 9 percent the rearranged ether, $CH_3-CH-CH=CH_2$.[65] Now, if the solvolysis of α-methylallyl chloride,

$\quad\quad\quad\quad\quad |$
$\quad\quad\quad\quad OEt$

$CH_3-CHCl-CH=CH_2$, proceeds through the same carbonium ion intermediate as does crotyl chloride, we would expect to get the same pair of products (and in the same proportions) from both solvolyses, since the fate of an intermediate species should be independent of its mode of birth. In actuality, the pairs of products obtained from the two isomeric chlorides are the same, *but the ratio of products varies.* Of the mixture of alcohols from the hydrolysis of α-methylallyl chloride in water-acetone, 43 percent (rather than 56 percent) is crotyl alcohol (that is, the so-called *product spread* for the solvolysis of this pair of halides is 13 percent). Likewise, of the mixture of ethers resulting from the ethanolysis of this chloride, 53 percent (rather than 91 percent) is ethyl crotyl ether; that is, the product spread is 38 percent. As a rule, similar variations are also observed in the compositions of mixtures obtained from other pairs of isomeric allylic halides. Moreover, such variations are consistent in character; a mixture resulting from the solvolysis of a primary halide has a greater proportion of "primary product" and less "nonprimary product" than has the mixture resulting from the solvolysis of the isomeric nonprimary halide. Thus, in the solvolysis of such a pair of isomeric halides, it appears either that the intermediates in the two cases differ in some respect or that the solvolysis of one or both halides is proceeding partially by some other path that circumvents the common intermediate. Significantly, the product spread in such a pair of solvolyses may generally be reduced by increasing the ionizing power of the medium, and further reduced by addition of Ag^+.

The interpretation of these facts depends upon how we wish to regard borderline substitutions (p. 258). If we take the view that they are reactions in which some of the individual acts of substitution are unimolecular and the others bimolecular, we may consider the solvolyses of allylic halides as competitions between direct displacement by solvent (in which there should be no rearrangement) and substitution via preliminary ionization (in which rearrangement may occur). We may reduce the extent of bimolecular substitution by increasing the ionizing power of the solvent or by adding an electrophilic catalyst. In doing so, the extent of solvolysis through preliminary ionization is increased; in the extreme case, the solvolysis may become completely unimolecular in character, and the product spread should disappear.[66] The ratio of products then represents the relative rates of solvent attack at the α and γ positions of the carbonium-ion intermediate.

In referring to such a "carbonium ion" we must not forget that it is not a free cation, but rather that it constitutes part of an ion pair. At present, it appears that this type of ion pair is somewhat unusual, having the halide ion located equidistant (or nearly equidistant) from the α- and γ-carbons (XXIX). The evidence for such an arrangement stems largely from a phenome-

$$\begin{array}{c} \text{H}_3\text{C} \\ \diagdown \gamma \\ \text{CH} \cdots \text{Cl} \\ \diagup \\ \text{CH} = = = = \text{CH}_2 \ \alpha \end{array}$$

XXIX

non, first reported in 1951, now called **internal return**.[67] When α,α-dimethylallyl chloride (XXX) is subjected to solvolysis, either in acetic acid[67] or in aqueous ethanol,[68] a portion of the halide becomes converted to its isomer, γ,γ-dimethylallyl chloride (XXXI).

$$\text{CH}_2 = \text{CH} - \text{C}(\text{CH}_3)_2\text{Cl} \xrightarrow[\text{(or H}_2\text{O-EtOH)}]{\text{HOAc}} (\text{CH}_3)_2\text{C} = \text{CH} - \text{CH}_2\text{Cl}$$

XXX XXXI

+ solvolysis products

The rate of the isomerization is proportional only to the concentration of the original allylic chloride. This at first suggests that the isomerization might be due to a rapid attack of Cl⁻ on a carbonium ion that is formed in a slow step; but if this were the case, the solvolyses reactions themselves would exhibit mass-law effects (p. 256) when carried out in the presence of extra Cl⁻. No such effects have been observed. Moreover, when the isomerization is carried out in the presence of excess radioactive Cl⁻, it is found that the isomerization proceeds much more rapidly than the incorporation of labeled Cl⁻ into the organic molecule. Evidently, the Cl⁻ that departs from the α-carbon atom is,

---

[66] For example, no significant product spread is observed in the hydrolyses of $Me_2C=CHCH_2Cl$ and $Me_2CClCH=CH_2$ in water or in the acetolyses of these two chlorides in dry acetic acid in the presence of AgOAc (see Ref. 65, p. 795). Note that the ionization mechanism is further favored in these cases, since one of the carbon atoms that helps accommodate the positive charge in the carbonium ion is tertiary.

[67] Young, Winstein, and Goering, *J. Am. Chem. Soc.*, **73**, 1958 (1951).

[68] de la Mare and Vernon, *J. Chem. Soc.*, **1954**, 2504.

more often than not, the Cl⁻ that becomes bound to the γ-carbon atom in the same molecule; that is, a chlorine is more likely to change its location in a given molecule than to break free and become equilibrated with Cl⁻ in solution. Intermediate **XXXII** is consistent with this evidence, for in this ion pair the Cl⁻ has taken a position favorable for the required migration.

$$\begin{array}{c} \text{Cl} \\ \diagup \diagdown \\ {}^{\gamma}\text{CH}_2 \\ \diagup \quad \diagdown \\ \text{CH} \!=\!=\!=\!=\! \text{C} \overset{\displaystyle\diagup \text{CH}_3}{\underset{\alpha \quad \diagdown \text{CH}_3}{}} \end{array}$$

XXXII

Granted that allylic *isomerizations* proceed through a "bridged" ion pair such as **XXIX**, what is the evidence that *solvolyses* (with and without allylic rearrangement) pass through the same intermediate? Let us, for an instant, suppose the contrary—that solvolyses of allylic halides proceed through some intermediate other than **XXXII**, perhaps a solvated carbonium ion. Whatever the nature of this intermediate, its formation requires separation of unlike charge, just as does the formation of **XXIX** and **XXXII**. It should therefore be formed more readily in dry EtOH (dielectric constant 24) than in dry HOAc (dielectric constant 6); as expected, the solvolyses of chlorides **XXX** and **XXXI** are somewhat faster in ethanol than in acetic acid. But, it has been observed that the isomerization of **XXX** to **XXXI** does *not* take place in dry ethanol.[68] It is difficult to believe that this is because the "bridged" ion-pair intermediate, **XXXII**, cannot be formed in dry ethanol even though it is formed in dry acetic acid and in wet ethanol. Rather, it seems much more likely that **XXXII** is also formed in dry ethanol, *but that very shortly after its formation it is converted by ethanol to one of the two possible isomeric ethyl ethers*—that is, that solvolysis in dry ethanol has proceeded through **XXXII**. We may also then infer that solvolysis in wet ethanol and in acetic acid proceeds through **XXXII**, for there seems no reason why the bridged ion pair should be destroyed in dry ethanol but not in other hydroxylic solvents. It is appreciated that this evidence is indicative rather than conclusive. The question is by no means closed.

Internal return has been observed in a number of additional systems, among them the derivatives of 4-methylcyclohexene.[69] For example, if one of the enantiomorphs of the *p*-nitrobenzoate **XXXIII** is dissolved in 80 percent aqueous acetone, it undergoes a combination of internal return and hydrolysis. Both of these reactions proceed through the symmetric bridged ion pair, **XXXIV**. Therefore, the products from both reactions must be racemic. In

[69] Goering and co-workers; *J. Am. Chem. Soc.*, **77**, 1129, 5026, 6249 (1955).

this case, the rate of racemization due to internal return is very nearly half the rate of solvolysis. On the other hand, when the corresponding chloride (*trans*-5-methyl-3-chlorocyclohexene) is solvolyzed in acetic acid, the rate of racemization is over four times the rate of solvolysis. As expected, internal return may compete with solvolysis most effectively in solvents that are only weakly nucleophilic.

From the discussion of allylic rearrangements thus far, it might be suspected that such arrangements may occur only through ionization. This was thought to be the case until 1949–1951, during which period it was shown that there are a number of substitution reactions of allylic compounds, *distinctly bimolecular in character* but nevertheless involving allylic rearrangement.[70] One such reaction is that between diethylamine and α-methylallyl chloride, first order in both reagents, yielding the crotylammonium derivative, XXXV.

This rearrangement is not due to a preliminary isomerization of the starting chloride, for although the chloride is known to isomerize, it undergoes the observed substitution reaction far more rapidly. Furthermore, the reaction is not a normal displacement followed by a rearrangement of the ammonium salt, $CH_2{=}CH{-}CHCH_3{-}\overset{H}{\underset{\,}{N}}Et_2^+Cl^-$; for this salt is known to be stable under the reaction conditions used. The most reasonable interpretation of the facts is indicated in the equation above. The attacking reagent attacks the γ-carbon, pushing π-electron density from the β—γ bond to the α—β bond as the chloride ion is pulled off by solvent. This mode of attack is often referred to as an *ab-*

[70] (a) Kepner, Winstein, and Young, *J. Am. Chem. Soc.*, **71**, 115 (1949); (b) Young, Webb, and Goering, *ibid.*, **73**, 1036 (1951); (c) England and Hughes, *Nature*, **168**, 1002 (1951).

normal bimolecular displacement or *S_N2′ reaction.*[71] It is generally observed when bimolecular substitution at the α position of an allyl derivative (but not at its γ position) is seriously retarded by steric hindrance.

By carrying out this type of reaction on cyclohexene derivatives, it is possible to show that the entering group comes in and the leaving group departs from the *same side* of the substrate molecule. (This is, of course, in contrast to the stereochemical situation in an ordinary *S_N2* reaction.) For example, ordinary bimolecular substitution on the 2,6-dichlorobenzoate of the hindered cyclohexenol XXXVI is virtually prohibited sterically, but the *S_N2′* reaction (using piperidine or sodiomalonic ester as an attacking reagent) takes place

easily.[72] As shown, the attacking reagent comes in *cis* to the leaving group. On the basis of the limited data now available, it appears that the *cis* relationship between the entering and leaving groups in the *S_N2′* reaction is general. However, no completely satisfying explanation for this stereochemistry seems to have appeared, although there have been a number of attempts.[70(b),72]

Epoxides[73]

Epoxides $\left(\text{C--------C derivatives} \right)$ are of some interest as substrates in

nucleophilic substitutions, for in these there are two possible reaction sites that, for unsymmetrical epoxides, are nonequivalent. Ether linkages are ordinarily not broken by the more usual nucleophilic reagents, but the highly strained three-membered epoxide ring is exceptional in this respect. The most straight-

[71] For a review of the *S_N2′* reaction, see de Wolfe and Young, *Chem. Revs.*, **56**, 769–784 (1956).

[72] Stork and White, *J. Am. Chem. Soc.*, **78**, 4609 (1956).

[73] For reviews on the ring opening of epoxides see (a) Winstein and Henderson in Elderfield's *Heterocyclic Compounds*, Vol. 1, John Wiley and Sons, Inc., New York, 1950, pp. 22–46, (b) Eliel in Newman's *Steric Effects in Organic Chemistry*, John Wiley and Sons, Inc., New York, 1956, pp. 106–114.

forward mechanism for the opening of the epoxide ring is closely analogous to ordinary bimolecular substitution.

$$CH_3O:^- + H_2C \overset{\diagup}{\underset{O}{\diagdown}} CHMe \longrightarrow CH_3O:CH_2-CH-O^-\ ^{74}$$
$$\underset{Me}{|}$$

$$SCN^- + H_2C \overset{\diagup}{\underset{O}{\diagdown}} CH-CH_2Cl \longrightarrow NCS:CH_2-CH \overset{O^-}{\underset{CH_2Cl}{\diagdown}}\ ^{75(a)}$$

$$C_6H_5CH_2NH_2 + H_2C \overset{\diagup}{\underset{O}{\diagdown}} CH-C_6H_5 \longrightarrow C_6H_5CH_2\overset{+}{N}H_2-CH_2-CHPh-O^-\ ^{75(b)}$$

Like the direct displacement mechanism, this mode of ring opening is favored by very nucleophilic attacking reagents and by the absence of alkyl substituents on the carbon atom under attack. As indicated, if one of the carbons in the ethylene oxide ring is less substituted than the other, attack will occur preferentially (sometimes exclusively) at the less substituted carbon.

Openings of epoxide rings may be acid catalyzed. In these, the conjugate acid

$$\left(\overset{\diagdown}{\underset{\diagup}{C}} \overset{|}{\underset{|}{\diagdown}} O\text{---}H \right)^+$$

is involved. The ring-opening step may be unimolecular

or it may be bimolecular.

The ring opening of ethylene oxide itself with HCl and HBr has been found to exhibit a third-order rate law,[76]

[74] Reeve and Sadle, J. Am. Chem. Soc., **72**, 1251 (1950).
[75] (a) Nichols and Ingham, ibid., **77**, 6547 (1955). (b) Browne and Lutz, J. Org. Chem., **17**, 1187 (1952).
[76] Brønsted, Kilpatrick, and Kilpatrick, J. Am. Chem. Soc., **51**, 428 (1929).

$$\text{rate} = k_3(\text{oxide})(\text{H}^+)(\text{halide}^-) \qquad (7)$$

clearly consistent with the second of these mechanisms and inconsistent with the first (in which the nucleophile attacks *after* the rate-determining step). Moreover, a number of acid-catalyzed epoxide openings proceed with almost complete *inversion of configuration* at the carbon atom under attack—a stereochemical situation generally considered typical of direct displacement reactions. In one of the simplest of such cases, the acid-catalyzed methanolysis of cyclopentene oxide (XXXVII) yields only *trans*-2-methoxycyclopentanol (XXXVIII), whereas if the reaction passed through a carbonium ion, both *cis* and *trans* isomers would be formed.[77]

$$\xrightarrow[\text{H}_2\text{SO}_4]{\text{MeOH}}$$

XXXVII   **XXXVIII**

On the other hand, it now appears that the acid-catalyzed hydrolyses of simpler epoxides in water almost certainly proceed through carbonium-ion intermediates.[78] Although we might suspect that the rate law for such reactions could not tell us whether or not water is involved in the rate-determining step (since water is present in large excess), careful study of the kinetics of these hydrolyses in strong acid shows that their rates are proportional, not to (H_3O^+), but rather to Hammett's h_0 function. We have already seen that such a dependence indicates that the activated complex for the rate-determining step consists of the substrate, a proton, *but nothing else* (p. 190); this strongly suggests a unimolecular slow step.

The entropies of activation for such hydrolyses point to the same conclusion. It is interesting that $\Delta S^{\ddagger}$ values for acid-catalyzed breakage of C—O bonds tend to fall rather sharply into two ranges: (a) from -20 to -25 cal per degree, and (b) from 0 to $+10$ cal per degree. From independent evidence it is believed that the activated complexes for hydrolyses in the first group (hydrolyses of ordinary esters and γ-lactones) involve just one molecule of water. The transition states for hydrolyses in the second group (which includes simple acetals and sucrose) are thought (again from independent evidence) to involve *no* water. This distinction is reasonable, for the mere loosening of a C—O bond should not greatly affect the freedom of motion in a system, but removing a water molecule from the solvent and linking it to a single molecule of the substrate will impose severe restrictions on its randomness, resulting in a sizable

---

[77] Winstein and Henderson, *J. Am. Chem. Soc.*, **65**, 2196 (1953). For additional examples of stereospecificity in acid-catalyzed epoxide-ring openings, see Browne and Lutz, Ref. 73(b).

[78] Pritchard and Long, *J. Am. Chem. Soc.*, **78**, 2663, 2667, 6008 (1956); **79**, 2362 (1957).

decrease in entropy. Now, the $\Delta S^{\ddagger}$ values for the hydrolyses of the simpler epoxides have been found[78] to lie between -3 and -6 cal per degree, suggesting that these reactions proceed through transition states involving *no water molecule*. However, the fact that these $\Delta S^{\ddagger}$ values actually lie between the two ranges given above would make us rather reluctant to accept this conclusion were it not for other evidence.

When the opening of an epoxide ring proceeds through a carbonium ion, we should expect the ring to break preferentially at the *most highly substituted carbon atom;* for, as we have repeatedly noted, secondary and tertiary carbons are better able to tolerate a positive charge than are primary carbons. This means that the reaction of an unsymmetric epoxide with a given nucleophile may yield mainly one product in the absence of acid, but mainly another with acid present. We have, for example, seen that the reaction of methoxide with propylene oxide and that of benzylamine with styrene oxide yield secondary alcohols (attack at primary carbon) under basic conditions. Yet, under acidic conditions, these same pairs of reagents yield mainly primary alcohols, for the ring opens more easily at the secondary carbon atoms.

$$EtOH \quad + H_2C\underset{\diagdown\ O\ \diagup}{\text{————}}CHMe \xrightarrow{H^+} HO\text{—}CH_2\text{—}CHMe\text{—}OEt \text{ (mostly)}[74]$$

$$PhCH_2NH_2 + H_2C\underset{\diagdown\ O\ \diagup}{\text{————}}CHPh \xrightarrow{H^+}$$

$$HO\text{—}CH_2\text{—}CHPh\text{—}NHCH_2Ph \text{ (mostly)}[75(b)]$$

The Internal Nucleophilic Substitution $(S_N i)$ Mechanism

One of the more usual methods of converting alcohols to alkyl chlorides is treatment with thionyl chloride, $SOCl_2$. This reaction has been shown to proceed through an alkyl chlorosulfite (XXXIX), an ester that, with care, can be isolated and shown to decompose upon heating to the alkyl chloride and SO_2.[79]

$$ROH + SOCl_2 \rightarrow R\text{—}O\overset{\overset{\textstyle O}{|}}{\text{—}S}\text{—}Cl \xrightarrow{\text{heat}} RCl + SO_2$$
$$\text{XXXIX}$$

This substitution is almost unique in that it sometimes (but not always) results in retention of configuration about the α-carbon atom, even though no neighboring groups are involved. However, if the reaction is carried out in the presence of amines (as is sometimes done in the laboratory in order to remove the

[79] (a) Bartlett and Herbrandson, *J. Am. Chem. Soc.*, **74**, 5971 (1952). (b) Lewis and Boozer, *ibid.*, **74**, 308 (1952); **75**, 3182 (1953).

HCl formed), the substitution proceeds with *inversion* of configuration. These facts suggest that the chlorosulfite (**XXXIX**) decomposes through a cyclic intermediate, **XL**. As shown, the intermediate **XL** may break down in a sort

$$\begin{array}{ccc} \searrow \\ \diagup C-O-S-Cl \\ \underset{O}{|} \end{array} \longrightarrow \quad \overset{+}{\diagup}C \cdots \overset{O}{\underset{Cl}{\diagdown}} S-O \overset{Cl^-}{\underset{Cl^-}{<}} \quad \overset{ret}{\nearrow} \quad \diagup C-Cl + SO_2 \\ \overset{inv}{\searrow} \quad Cl-C\diagup + SO_2 + Cl^-$$

XL

of "internal return" reaction, forming the chloride with retention of configuration; or, if excess Cl^- is present, an ordinary displacement reaction may take place, forming the alkyl chloride with inversion. The latter reaction occurs when the reaction is carried out in the presence of base; for the HCl formed in the initial condensation of alcohol and $SOCl_2$ is converted to the nucleophilic Cl^- ion. We strongly suspect that intermediate **XL** is an ion pair with a partial positive charge on the α-carbon, for the reaction resulting in retention exhibits certain of the characteristics of S_N1 reactions. It is retarded when deuterium atoms are substituted for β-hydrogens,[79(b)] and it takes place most readily when phenyl groups are bound to the α-carbon.[80] Furthermore, the chlorosulfites of primary alcohols[81] or alcohols in which the α-carbon is at a bridgehead[50] do not decompose to yield alkyl chlorides at all. Since the substitution takes place through a type of "internal return" reaction, we often refer to it as an S_Ni (substitution-nucleophilic-internal) *reaction.*[82] The same type of mechanism seems to apply also to the decomposition of secondary chlorocarbonates.[83] As with

$$\begin{array}{ccc} \searrow \quad O \\ \diagup C-O-\overset{\|}{C}-Cl \end{array} \longrightarrow \quad \overset{+}{\diagup}C \cdots \overset{\bar{O}}{\underset{:Cl:}{\diagdown}} C=O \overset{Cl^-}{\underset{Cl^-}{<}} \quad \overset{ret}{\nearrow} \quad \diagup C-Cl + CO_2 \\ \overset{inv}{\searrow} \quad Cl-C\diagup + CO_2 + Cl^-$$

chlorosulfites, inversion, rather than retention, prevails if the reaction is carried out in an excess of amine.

[80] Cowdrey, Hughes, Ingold, Masterman, and Scott, *J. Chem. Soc.*, **1937**, 1252.

[81] Whitmore and Rothrock, *J. Am. Chem. Soc.*, **54**, 4341 (1932).

[82] The reaction of HNO_2 with certain cyclic amines and the reaction of PCl_5 with certain cyclic carbinols may take place through an S_Ni mechanism (Huckel and co-workers, *Ann.*, **540**, 250 (1939); **543**, 198 (1940), as may the reaction of HBr with phenylalkyl carbinols at low temperatures (Levene and Rothen, *J. Biol. Chem.*, **127**, 237 (1939)). At present these seem to be exceptional cases. As yet, only two reagents, thionyl chloride and phosgene, may be considered as generally useful for bringing about S_Ni reactions, and even with these, conditions must be carefully controlled.

[83] (a) Houssa and Phillips, *J. Chem. Soc.*, **1932**, 108, 1232. (b) Wiberg and Shryne, *J. Am. Chem. Soc.*, **77**, 2774 (1955).

With allylic systems, another mode of reaction is possible—internal substitution with allylic rearrangement (which we may abbreviate S_Ni').

$$RCH{=}CH{-}CH_2{-}O{-}S{-}Cl \rightarrow \underset{\underset{O}{|}}{\overset{CH}{\underset{R-CH}{\nearrow}}}\overset{}{CH_2} \rightarrow R{-}CH{-}CH{=}CH_2$$

$$+ \quad SO_2$$

This is, in fact, a much more favorable reaction path for allyl chlorosulfites than the ordinary S_Ni reaction. The study of the reactions of substituted allyl chlorosulfites is not easy, for although allyl chlorosulfite itself has been characterized, the substituted allyl chlorosulfites have not. They must, therefore, be prepared on the spot from the alcohol and $SOCl_2$, a reaction yielding HCl along with the desired ester. In a polar solvent, HCl will be partially ionized, and in the presence of Cl^-, the chlorosulfite may conceivably react by five mechanisms: S_N1, S_N2, S_N2', S_Ni, and S_Ni'. However, if the reaction is carried out in dry ether, in which dry HCl is known to be unionized,[84] the first three of these mechanisms may be assumed to be unimportant.[85] Under these conditions it is found that γ-methylallyl alcohol (crotyl alcohol) is converted only to α-methylallyl chloride, whereas the α-substituted alcohol is converted only to the γ-substituted chloride, that is, in both cases S_Ni' reaction predominates to the virtual exclusion of the S_Ni reaction.

$$CH_3{-}CH{=}CH{-}CH_2{-}OH \xrightarrow{\text{SOCl}_2,\ \text{ether}} CH_3{-}\overset{Cl}{\underset{H}{\overset{|}{\underset{|}{C}}}}{-}CH{=}CH_2$$

$$CH_3{-}\underset{\underset{OH}{|}}{CH}{-}CH{=}CH_2 \rightarrow CH_3{-}CH{=}CH{-}CH_2{-}Cl$$

Substitution Reactions of Ambident Nucleophiles[86]

Just as allyl derivatives and epoxides are of special interest because they may undergo nucleophilic substitution at more than one site, such nucleophiles as the nitrite and cyanide ions and the anion of acetoacetic ester

[84] Bushwell, Rodebush, and Roy, *J. Am. Chem. Soc.*, **60**, 2528 (1938).

[85] Young and co-workers, *J. Am. Chem. Soc.*, **77**, 4182 (1955); *Science*, **117**, 473 (1953).

[86] (a) For a discussion of this subject, together with references to earlier work see Kornblum, Smiley, Blackwood; and Iffland, *J. Am. Chem. Soc.*, **77**, 6269 (1955). (b) See also Brandstrom, *Arkiv for Kemi;* **6**, 155 (1953); **7**, 81 (1954).

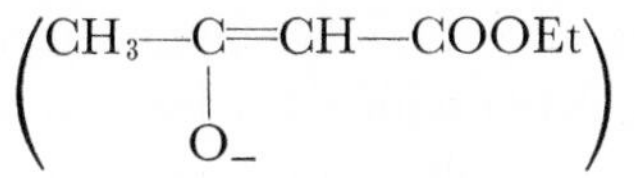

$$\left(\begin{array}{c} CH_3-C=CH-COOEt \\ | \\ O_- \end{array} \right)$$

are of interest because they contain more than one atom that may function as an attacking atom. These reagents are sometimes said to be *ambident*, signifying that they may attack with "either tooth." It has, for example, been recognized for many years that alkyl bromides ordinarily form nitriles ($R-C\equiv N$) when treated with NaCN but yield predominantly isonitriles ($R-N\equiv C$) when treated with AgCN. The reactions of alkyl iodides, either with NaNO$_2$ or AgNO$_2$, yield mixtures of nitroalkane (RNO$_2$) and alkyl nitrite ($R-O-N=O$), but the proportion of the latter is invariably greater from the reaction with AgNO$_2$. In the past it was thought that these differences arose because the silver ion somehow modified the nature of the attacking reagent, but it now seems much more likely that the influence of the silver is due to its interaction with the substrate.

More particularly, it appears that as the substitution reaction acquires an increasing degree of "S_N1 character," the incoming nucleophile tends to attack with its most electronegative atom, but if the reaction acquires more of the character of a bimolecular substitution, the incoming group attacks with a less electronegative atom. Since the Ag$^+$ ion, and even sparingly soluble silver salts, aid in the formation of a carbonium ion by removing the halide from the substrate (p. 274), the action of silver salts favors attack by the nitrogen atom of the CN$^-$ ion and by the oxygen atom of the NO$_2^-$ ion. There is considerable evidence (much of it pertaining to the reactions of AgNO$_2$) to support this conclusion. For example, those alkyl halides giving the highest ratios of nitroalkane to alkyl nitrite on treatment with silver nitrite are primary halides (for which substitution reactions have the least "S_N1-like character"); those halides giving the largest nitrite:nitro ratio are tertiary halides (for which substitutions have the greatest degree of "S_N1-like character"). Furthermore, the nitrite:nitro ratio in a given reaction can be increased by transferring the reaction from a less polar to a more polar solvent. When *n*-heptyl iodide is treated with silver nitrite in ether, the nitrite to nitro ratio in the resulting product is 1:8, but when the reaction is carried out in acetonitrile, the ratio rises to 2:5. Treatment of benzyl bromide with silver nitrite yields a mixture of products in which the nitro compound predominates over the nitrite ester by a ratio of about 2:1; but if a methoxy group is introduced on the *para* position of the benzene ring, the positive charge in the carbonium ionlike transition state is stabilized (p. 281), and nitrite ester becomes the predominant product, again by a ratio of about 2:1. On the other hand, if the positive charge in the transition state is "destabilized" by a *p*-nitro group, the nitro:nitrite ratio in the product rises to about 10:1.

The story is much the same for other ambident reagents. Treatment of the silver salt of α-pyridone (XLI) with ethyl iodide yields an O-ethyl derivative (XLII); but if the potassium salt is used, an N-ethyl derivative (XLIII) results.[87] Similar effects may be observed in the absence of univalent silver if the

reagents are judiciously chosen. The anion of aceotoacetic ester (XLIV) attacks ordinary primary halides (whose substitution reactions are generally bimolecular) yielding C-alkyl derivatives (XLV); but the same anion attacks the α-chloro ether (XLVI) (whose substitution reactions in ethanol are unimolecular) to yield an O-alkyl derivative (XLVII)[88]

The rationalization of these contrasts in the behavior of ambident anions (which the reader may or may not find fully convincing) is as follows. In an S_N1 reaction, the incoming nucleophile, if an anion, attacks the carbonium-ion intermediate largely because of the gain in electrostatic stability resulting from the neutralization of charge. It will be to the advantage of the carbonium ion to approach the anion near the spot where the latter *has its highest concentration of negative charge*. Since excess negative charge is heaviest on the most electronegative atom, the new bond should form at this atom. On the other hand, in a direct displacement reaction, a section of the solvation shell about the attacking reagent must be disrupted and the formation of the new bond initiated while the leaving group is still partially bound to the carbon atom under attack. Since the solvation shell is thickest about the atom having the highest concentration of negative charge, less reorganization of solvent molecules will be necessary if the solvation shell in the region of the less electronegative atom is disrupted. Hence, bond formation at this atom is favored. In effect, then, the most nucleophilic site in an ambident anion is the least electronegative atom having an unshared electron pair.

[87] Von Pechmann and Baltzer, *Ber.*, **24,** 3148 (1891); Rath, *Ann.*, **489,** 107 (1931).
[88] Simonsen and Storey, *J. Chem. Soc.*, **95,** 2106 (1909).

Attempted Correlations of Substitution Rates. The Swain and Winstein-Grunwald Equations

The problem of quantitative correlation of nucleophilic substitution rates has aroused the interest of a number of workers. What, in general, is desired is the tabulation of a series of constants ("parameters") associated with the various substrates, attacking reagents, and solvents, which would, in principle, allow the *a priori* calculation of the specific rate of attack by any reagent on any substrate in any solvent. The most ambitious treatment of this sort seems to be that proposed by Swain,[89] who pictured all S_N reactions, irrespective of mechanistic type, as resulting from the combination of a "pushing" and "pulling" action. The "pull" may be exerted by one or more solvent molecules or by an added Lewis acid (for example, Ag^+ or $SnCl_4$); in all cases the pulling agent is acting in an electrophilic capacity. The "push" in an S_N2 reaction is exerted by the entering group. In an S_N1 reaction it is exerted by the solvent, but may become very feeble in cases where the carbonium ion intermediate is unusually stable. In a "borderline substitution" the push may be exerted by the incoming group, by the solvent, or by a combination of these. In all cases, the pushing reagent is acting in a nucleophilic capacity. We may then represent an S_N reaction on substrate $R:X$ schematically, and very generally, as

$$N: \; + \; R(:X) \; + \; E \xrightarrow[\text{determining}]{\text{rate-}} \Big[N:\text{---}R \; + \; X\text{---}E \Big] \longrightarrow \begin{array}{l} \text{final} \\ \text{products} \end{array}$$

where $N:$ and E are the pushing and pulling reagent, respectively. (Note that we have not specified the number of molecules of $N:$ or E, nor the nature of the bonding in $N:\text{---}R$ and $X:\text{---}E$.)

The Swain treatment stipulates, in effect, that the nucleophilic "push" and the electrophilic "pull" associated with a substitution reaction make independent contributions to its free energy of activation, and that if we select a substitution reaction of a given substrate in a given solvent, we may calculate its specific rate, k, if we know the solvolysis rate, k_0, of the *same* substrate in a standard solvent. (The standard solvent chosen by Swain, in agreement with a related treatment by Winstein, p. 302, was 80 percent aqueous alcohol.) The Swain relationship is

$$\log \frac{k}{k_0} = ns_n + es_e \tag{8}$$

where n is a *nucleophilicity parameter* associated with reagent $N:$, e is an *electro-*

---

[89] Swain, *J. Am. Chem. Soc.*, **70**, 1119 (1948); Swain and Scott, *ibid.*, **75**, 141 (1953); Swain, Mosely, and Bown, *ibid.*, **77**, 3727, 3731 (1955).

philicity parameter associated with reagent E, s_n is the sensitivity of the reaction under consideration to nucleophilic push, and s_e is the sensitivity of this reaction to electrophilic pull.

The Swain equation, like the Hammett equation (p. 220) and the Taft equation (p. 227), is a *linear free-energy relationship*. Since four parameters, rather than two, are involved, four points of reference must be arbitrarily chosen. By selecting solvolysis in 80 percent aqueous alcohol as a "standard reaction," we are automatically fixing two of these; n and e for this reagent are 0.00. The remaining two points of reference become fixed upon choosing a "reference substrate" for which both s_n and s_e are given the value 1.00.[90] t-Butyl chloride was chosen as this standard.[91] It then becomes necessary to obtain n values for as many nucleophilic reagents as possible, e values for as many electrophilic reagents as possible (polar solvents will have both an n and an e value), and s_n and s_e values for as many substrates as possible. From rate data on 152 *solvolyses* involving 25 substrates and 17 solvent systems, values for 78 Swain parameters giving the "best fit" to equation (11) were calculated (a task better carried out with an electronic calculator rather than with a slide rule). A number of typical Swain parameters are listed in Tables 8-3 and 8-4. With these, and others not included, rates of solvolyses within the scope of this treatment may be estimated with a probable error of 0.12 in the logarithm, even though the rate of solvolysis of a given substrate may change by several powers of 10 when transferred from one solvent to another.

The orders of electrophilicities and nucleophilicities given in Table 8-3 are, qualitatively at least, not greatly different from what we would expect. How-

---

[90] In Swain's 1955 papers, only *solvolysis* reactions were considered; that is, reactions in which N: is the same as E. This limitation would ordinarily prevent evaluation of the various parameters associated with the reagents and substrates. In fact, it may easily be shown that no matter how many data were obtained, evaluation of the Swain parameters would require solving x simultaneous equations in $x + 2$ unknowns. For this reason, Swain made two additional assumptions, fixing s_n/s_e for methyl bromide as 3.0 and s_n/s_e Ph$_3$C—F as $\frac{1}{3}$. (It will be recalled that in substitution reactions of MeBr, the push tends to be considerably more important than the pull, whereas the reverse is true for such reactions of triphenylmethyl halides.) There is, of course, no guarantee that the two magnitudes have anything but qualitative significance.

[91] Swain's assumption that $s_n = s_e$ for t-BuCl has subsequently proved to be a relatively unwise one. Recent experiments by Doering and Finkelstein (described by Streitwieser, Ref. 1(c), p. 642) show that the observed variation in rates of solvolysis of t-BuCl in various solvents closely parallels the observed variation is solvolysis rates of bromide XLVIII which is struc-

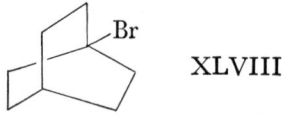 **XLVIII**

turally protected from backside attack (p. 280). Since nucleophilic "push" cannot be important in the solvolysis of XLVIII, it can scarcely be important in the solvolysis of t-BuCl.

ever, some of the individual s_n and s_e values in Table 8-4 are not in accord with chemical experience. Benzhydryl chloride is listed as being more sensitive to electrophilic pull than is triphenylmethyl fluoride, whereas both benzhydryl chloride and t-butyl chloride, are listed as being *more* sensitive to nucleophilic push than are methyl, ethyl, and n-butyl bromides. Inconsistencies of this kind lead one to doubt the theoretical validity of the Swain equation, despite its usefulness for predictive purposes.

Table 8-3. Electrophilic and Nucleophilic Reagent (Solvent) Parameters in the Swain Treatment

Solvent	e	n
HCOOH	+6.53	−4.40
97.5 percent Ac₂O, 2.5 percent HOAc	+5.34	−8.77
H₂O	+4.01	−0.44
HOAc	+3.12	−4.82
80 percent EtOH	0.00	0.00
MeOH	−0.73	−0.05
EtOH	−1.03	+0.53
90 percent acetone	−1.52	−0.53

Table 8-4. Nucleophilic Susceptibility and Electrophilic Susceptibility Substrate Parameters in the Swain Treatment

Substrate	s_n	s_e	s_n/s_e
Triphenylmethyl fluoride	0.37	1.12	0.33
Benzhydryl chloride	1.24	1.25	0.99
t-Butyl chloride	1.00	1.00	1.00
i-Propyl bromide	0.90	0.58	1.55
Benzyl tosylate	0.69	0.39	1.77
Ethyl bromide	0.80	0.36	2.22
n-Butyl bromide	0.77	0.34	2.26
Methyl bromide	0.81	0.27	3.00

The Swain treatment has also been applied to a series of S_N2 reactions in water (in which case the es_e term in equation (8) remains a constant). The attempted correlation, applied to such substrates as benzyl chloride and ethyl tosylate and to such nucleophiles as CN⁻, I⁻, N₃⁻, and OH⁻, appears subject to a serious limitation. *The type of atom under attack must not vary;* that is, a given set of n values derived from substitution reactions on saturated carbons does not, in general, apply to substitutions on sulfur, mercury, or even on unsaturated carbon.[92]

On the other hand, for a group of substitution reactions that are essentially insensitive to nucleophilic push, the Swain equation may, in principle, be simplified to

$$\log \frac{k}{k_0} = es_e \tag{9}$$

Actually, the relationship

$$\log \frac{k}{k_0} = Ym \tag{10}$$

which, except for symbols, is identical to (9), was proposed by Winstein and Grunwald,[93] five years before the presentation of the Swain equation. As in the Swain treatment, 80 percent alcohol was chosen as the reference solvent and t-BuCl as the reference substrate (for which m was fixed as 1.00). The Y value (which Winstein prefers to regard as a measure of *ionizing ability*) for any solvent is thus obtained by comparing the specific rate of solvolysis of t-BuCl in this solvent to that for its solvolysis in 80 percent ethanol. The m value for a given substrate could be obtained by measuring the specific rates of solvolysis of that substrate in a number of solvents of known Y values, plotting their logarithms, and drawing the best straight line through the experimental points (Ex. 10). The Winstein-Grunwald equation (10) gives a satisfactory correlation of the rates of solvolysis of a few tertiary halides and secondary sulfonate esters, and attempts have been made to apply it also to secondary halides. Here, agreement is good for solvolyses in various mixtures of the same two solvents, but is much poorer if reactions in a number of different solvents are being compared. In other words, if we take the Y values obtained from the study of the solvolysis of t-BuCl in various solvents and solvent mixtures and plot them against the logarithms of the specific solvolysis rates of, say, benzhydryl chloride in these same solvents, the points are badly scattered. Those for 20, 40, 60, and 80 percent ethanol lie on one line; those for the various water-dioxane mixtures lie on a different line; and those for water-acetic acid mixtures lie on still a third line. If equation (10) were to apply rigorously to benzhydryl chloride, all points should lie on the same line.

It has recently been shown[94] that the Winstein-Grunwald equation may be applied to a large number of substrates if, to each substrate there is assigned

[92] For a discussion of this phase of the problem, see Edwards, *J. Am. Chem. Soc.*, **76**, 1540 (1954).

[93] Winstein and Grunwald, *J. Am. Chem. Soc.*, **70**, 846 (1948); Winstein, Grunwald, and Jones, *J. Am. Chem. Soc.*, **73**, 2700 (1951).

[94] Winstein, Fainberg, and Grunwald, *J. Am. Chem. Soc.*, **79**, 1597, 1602, 4151, 5937 (1957).

not a single m value, but a series of m values, one for each solvent pair. Typically, the m value for benzhydryl bromide has been fixed at 1.69 for HOAc—H_2O mixtures, 0.91 for water-acetone mixtures, and 0.95 for water-dioxane mixtures. While such an expedient improves the correlation, it obviously makes the treatment less useful, for it greatly increases the number of parameters that must be determined experimentally.

The partial failure of equation (10) when applied to secondary halides is to be expected, for the applicability of this relationship should be limited to substitutions in which nucleophilic push contributes little or none of the driving force of the reaction. While this may be true of the solvolysis of tertiary halides, it is not, as we have seen, true for secondary halides. Moreover, the Winstein-Grunwald relationship assumes that every act of ionization of the substrate results in an act of solvolysis—that is, that there is no "internal return" (p. 288). This is much more likely to be the case in nucleophilic solvents such as alcohols than in carboxylic acids. What is perhaps surprising about the Winstein-Grunwald relationship when applied to a large range of solvents is not that its success is limited, but rather that it yields any measure of correlation at all.

Long-lived Carbonium Ions

The carbonium ions considered thus far have short lives; evidence for their intervention in reactions is largely kinetic and stereochemical. However, a number of carbonium ions are known which may exist for extended periods of time in favorable surroundings. Triarylmethyl carbonium ions (Ar_3C^+) are especially stable, and may be formed simply by the ionization of triarylmethyl halides in polar solvents which should not, however, react with the ions. It has long been known, for example, that solutions of such halides in liquid SO_2 conduct electric current,[95(a)] and that the observed relationships between conductivity and concentration are typical of a weak electrolyte.[95(b)] These halides are, as a rule, *partially ionized* in liquid SO_2 to ion pairs (which do not contribute to the conductivity), and the ion pairs are, at moderate concentrations, *partially dissociated* to ions (which do contribute).

$$Ar_3C\text{—}Cl \underset{\text{liquid } SO_2}{\rightleftharpoons} Ar_3C^+Cl^- \rightleftharpoons Ar_3C^+ + Cl^-$$

Triarylmethyl *perchlorates*, on the other hand, appear to be completely ionized in this solvent, but, once again, the resulting ion pairs are only partially dissociated.

$$Ar_3C\text{—}OClO_3 \xrightarrow[\text{(complete)}]{\text{liquid } SO_2} Ar_3C^+ClO_4^- \rightleftharpoons Ar_3C^+ + ClO_4^-$$

[95] (a) Walden, *Ber.*, **35**, 2018 (1902); Gomberg, *ibid.*, **35**, 2403 (1902). (b) Ziegler, Wollschitt, and Mathes, *Ann.*, **479**, 90, 111 (1930).

Now the dissociation constants of the perchlorates have been found to be independent of the nature of the aryl groups,[95(b)] and it may be supposed that this is also true for solutions of the triarylmethyl halides. On this basis, the different conductivities exhibited by solutions of the various triarylmethyl chlorides merely reflect differences in their degrees of *ionization*. As may be expected, ionization is favored by *p*-alkyl and *p*-phenyl groups on the benzene rings and is hampered by the *p*-chloro groups.[96] Indeed, the *p*-methoxy derivative, XLIX, appears to be very nearly completely ionized in SO_2 at 0°. On the other

XLIX

hand, benzhydryl halides (diarylmethyl halides) do not conduct measurably in SO_2.

Triarylmethyl derivatives may also be ionized in less polar solvents, but if dissociation of the ion pairs and higher aggregates is slight, ionization will not be readily detectable by conductimetric studies. It may, however, be detectable spectrophotometrically, for the spectrum associated with a carbonium ion is modified to only a slight degree when that ion is incorporated into an ion pair. Thus, it has been shown that carbonium salts are formed when triarylmethyl chlorides are treated with a number of Lewis acids in aromatic solvents; for example,

$$Ph_3C—Cl + SnCl_4 \text{ (in benzene)} \rightarrow Ph_3C^+SnCl_5^- \quad [97(a)]$$

The solutions formed in these reactions exhibit spectra closely akin to those of the corresponding triarylmethyl perchlorates in SO_2; moreover, evaporation of these solutions yields salts that retain the spectra typical of the carbonium ions, indicating that carbonium ions may also exist in the solid state. The spectrum of the triphenylcarbonium ion is also exhibited by solutions of triphenyl carbinol in concentrated sulfuric acid;[98(a)] the observed "four-fold freezing-point depres-

[96] Bartlett, Lichtin, and Glazer, *J. Am. Chem. Soc.*, **73**, 5530, 5537 (1951).
[97] (a) Sharp and Sheppard, *J. Chem. Soc.*, **1957**, 674. (b) Bayles, Evans, and Jones, *ibid.*, **1957**, 1020.
[98] (a) Hantzsch, *Z. physik. Chem.*, **61**, 257 (1908). (b) Hammett and Deyrup, *J. Am. Chem. Soc.*, **55**, 1900 (1933).

sion" (p. 99) observed for such solutions[98(b)] indicates that conversion to the carbonium ion is very nearly complete.

$$Ph_3C—OH + 2H_2SO_4 \longrightarrow Ph_3C^+ + H_3O^+ + 2HSO_4^-$$

(4 moles of particles per mole Ph₃COH)

Maximum resonance stabilization of the triphenylcarbonium ion would presumably be achieved if all three benzene rings and the central carbon atom were coplanar. However, it may readily be shown by use of scale models that such a structure would involve considerable steric interference between the *ortho* hydrogens of one benzene ring and those of another. Thus, one or more of the benzene rings must be twisted out of the plane containing the three bonds to the central carbon atom. It is currently believed, largely on the basis of spectral evidence,[98(a),99(a)] that all three rings are so twisted. If this is so, the ion may exist in the symmetric "propellerlike" conformation, L, or in the unsymmetric conformation, LI, or may be an equilibrium mixture of both.[99(b)]

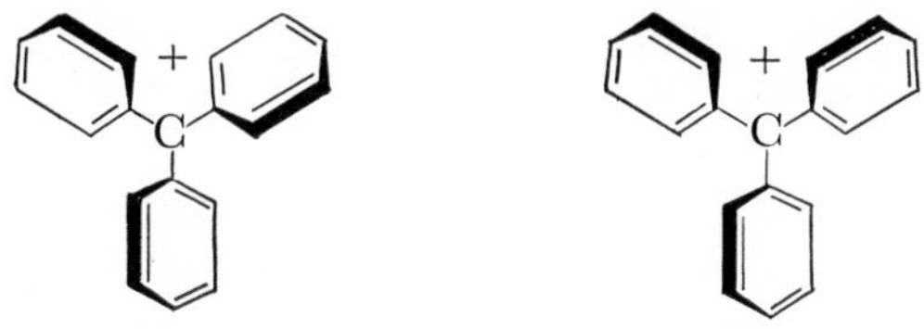

L   LI

In addition to triarylcarbonium ions, a number of additional long-lived carbonium ions are known. Three of the more interesting of these are shown below.

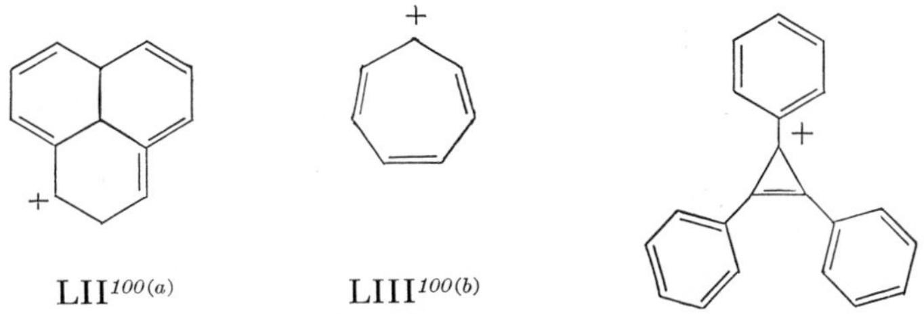

LII[100(a)]   LIII[100(b)]   LIV[100(c)]

For each of these, a number of resonance structures may be drawn, showing that in all three cases the positive charge is spread over a number of atoms rather than being confined to a single atom.

[99] (a) Deno, Jaruzelski, and Schriesheim, J. Org. Chem., **19**, 155 (1954). (b) For spectral evidence that certain triarylcarbonium ions may consist of a mixture of both forms, see Lewis, Magel, and Lipkin, J. Am. Chem. Soc., **64**, 1774 (1942).
[100] (a) Pettit, Chem. and Ind., **1956**, 1306. (b) Doering and Knox, J. Am. Chem. Soc., **76**, 3203 (1954). (c) Breslow, J. Am. Chem. Soc., **79**, 5318 (1957).

EXERCISES FOR CHAPTER 8

1. Decide which reagent in each of the following pairs is the more nucleophilic. Justify your choice in each case.

(a) NH_2^- or NH_3?

(b) Urea or thiourea?

(c) Nitrite or nitrate?

(d) HPO_4^{2-} or HPO_3S^{2-}?

(e) Phenol or ethanol?

(f) Acetic anhydride or *n*-propyl alcohol?

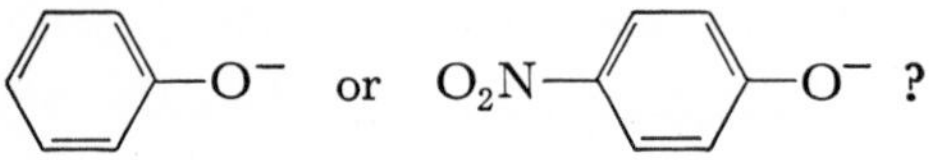

(h) $(CH_3)_3B$ or $(CH_3)_3P$?

(i) $(EtOOC)_2CH:^-$ or $^-:CH_2COOEt$?

(j) SH^- or Cl^-?

(k) $(C_6H_5)_2O$ or C_6H_5Cl?

(l) N_3^- or F^-?

(m) Benzene or mesitylene?

(g)

2. Decide which reagent in each of the following pairs reacts more rapidly with sodium ethoxide in ethanol:

(a) $CH_2=CHCl$ or $CH_2=CH-CH_2Cl$?

(b) Me_2S or $Me_3S^+I^-$?

(c)

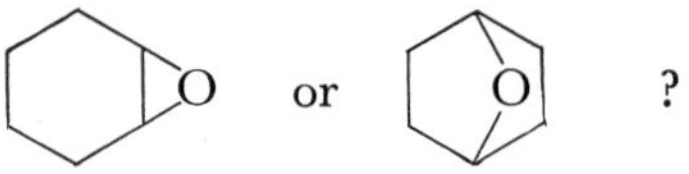

(d)

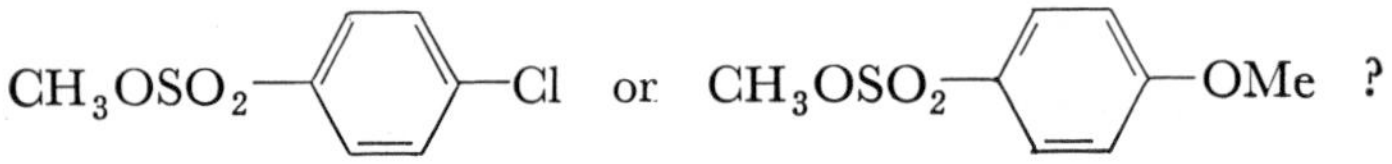

(e) CCl_4 or $SiCl_4$?

(f)

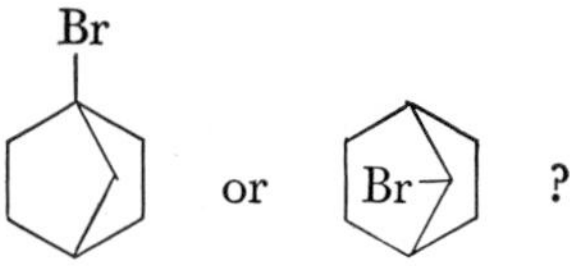

(g) Methyl chloride or dimethyl sulfate?

(h)

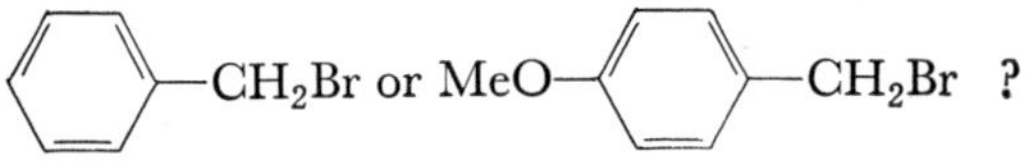

(i)

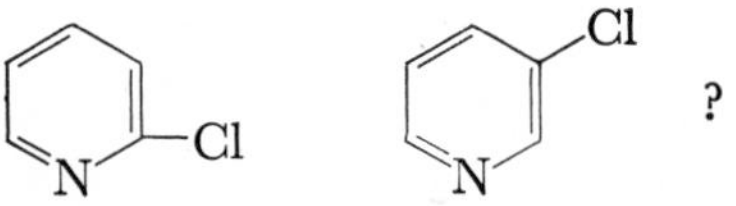

3. Decide which reagent in each of the following pairs reacts more rapidly with LiI in acetone:

(a) *n*-BuBr or *t*-BuBr?

(b) $Ph-C-CH_2Br$ or

$\quad\quad\ \ \overset{\|}{O}$

$Ph-C-CH_2CH_2Br$?

$\quad\quad\ \ \overset{\|}{O}$

(c) EtBr or EtOTos?

(d) 1-Chloro-2-methylbutane or 2-chlorobutane?

(e)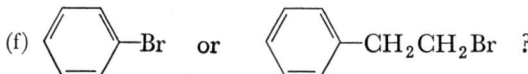

(f) ⬡—Br   or   ⬡—CH$_2$CH$_2$Br ?

(g) Cyclobutyl bromide or cyclopentyl bromide?

(h) ClCH$_2$CH$_2$Br or CH$_3$CHClBr?

(i) *cis*- or *trans*-4-*t*-butylcyclohexyl bromide?

4. Suggest routes for the following conversions: (R = 2-octyl)

(a) *D*-ROH to *L*-RN(CH$_3$)$_3^+$Br$^-$

(b) *D*-ROH to *D*-RNH$_2$

(c) *D*-ROAc to *L*-RCOOH

(d) *D*-RNH$_2$ to *L*-ROAc

(e) *D*-RSH to *L*-ROTos

(f) *D*-ROH to *D*-RCH$_2$OH

(g) *D*-CH$_3$CHBr—CHO to
    D-CH$_3$CH(OAc)—COOH

5. Decide which reagent in each of the following pairs reacts more rapidly with AgOAc in acetic acid:

(a) *n*-PrBr or *i*-PrBr?

(b) *t*-BuBr or *t*-Bu—CH$_2$Br?

(c) ⬡—CH$_2$Cl   or   ⬡—CH$_2$Cl ?

(d) (CH$_3$)$_3$CBr or (C$_2$H$_5$)$_2$C(CH$_3$)Br?

(e) CH$_3$OCH$_2$Cl or CH$_3$OCH$_2$CH$_2$Cl?

(f) CH$_2$=C(CH$_3$)CH$_2$Cl or CH$_3$CH=CH—CH$_2$Cl?

(g) (CH$_3$)$_2$CDBr or CH$_2$D—CH(CH$_3$)—Br?

(h) [benzene ring with COOH and COOC(CH$_3$)$_3$]   or   [O$_2$N-substituted benzene ring with COOH and COOC(CH$_3$)$_3$]   ?

(i) Cyclopropyl bromide or cyclobutyl chloride?

(j) [decalin with Br]   or   [norbornane with Br] ?

(k) (CH$_3$)$_3$COC(=O)—⬡—Br   or   (CH$_3$)$_3$COSO$_2$—⬡ ?

(l) [naphthalene with NO$_2$ and CH(CH$_3$)Br]   or   [naphthalene with O$_2$N and CH(CH$_3$)Br] ?

(m) 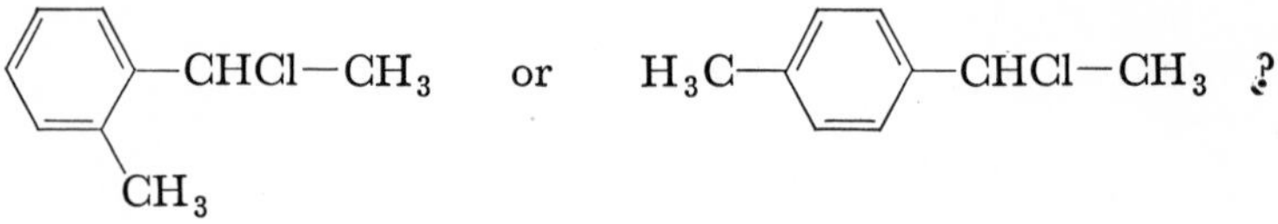 —CHCl—CH$_3$ or   H$_3$C——CHCl—CH$_3$?

(n) 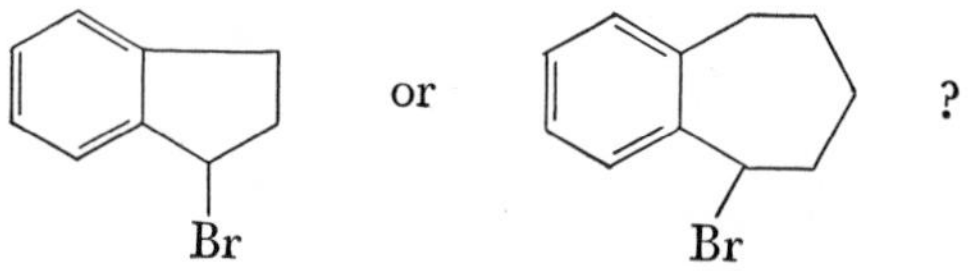   or   ?

(o) *cis*- or *trans*-2-Acetoxycyclohexyl brosylate?

6. Suggest mechanisms for the following reactions:

(a) *i*-PrBr + anhydrous HCOOH → *i*-PrO—$\overset{\overset{\textstyle O}{\textstyle \|}}{C}$H

(b) *i*-PrBr + Me$_3$N $\xrightarrow{\text{acetone}}$ *i*-Pr—NMe$_3^+$Br$^-$

(c) 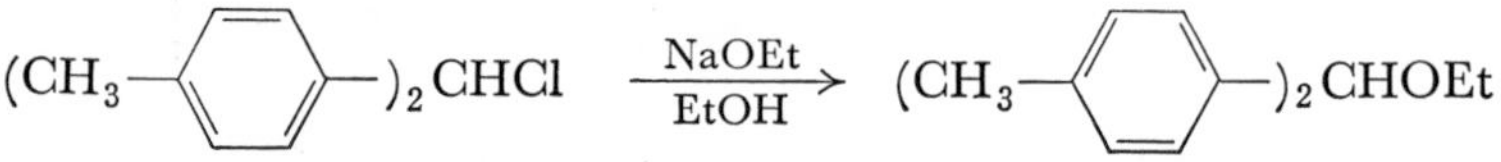 (CH$_3$——)$_2$CHCl $\xrightarrow[\text{EtOH}]{\text{NaOEt}}$ (CH$_3$——)$_2$CHOEt

(d) MeOH + HBr → CH$_3$Br

(e) Et$_3$N + Me$_3$S$^+$ → Et$_3$N(CH$_3$)$^+$ + Me$_2$S (in alcohol)

(f) D-PhCHBr—COOH + Ag$_2$O → D-PhCH(OH)—COOH + AgBr (in aqueous alcohol)

(g) D-MeCHOH—Et + SOCl$_2$ + 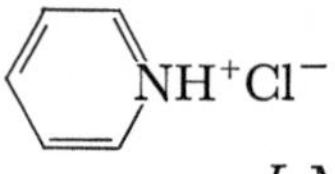 NH$^+$Cl$^-$ $\xrightarrow{\text{dioxane}}$

L-MeCHCl—Et + SO$_2$

(h) 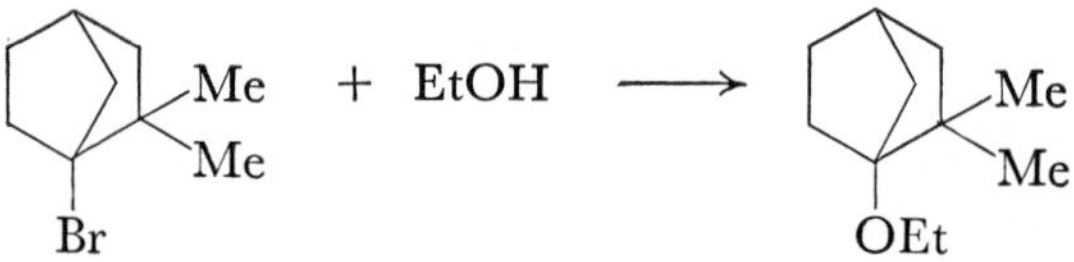 Me + EtOH ⟶ Me

(i) D-CH$_3$—CHCl—Hx $\xrightarrow[\text{benzene}]{\text{TiCl}_4}$ *racemic*-CH$_3$—CHCl—Hx (Hx = *n*-C$_6$H$_{13}$-)

(j) CH$_3$CH—CH$_2$ $\xrightarrow[\text{SO}_3^{2-}]{\text{HSO}_3^-}$ CH$_3$—CH—CH$_2$OH (in water)
    \O/ |
                                    SO$_3$H

(k) D-Ph—CHMe—OCOCl $\xrightarrow{\text{heat}}$ D-Ph—CHMe—Cl + CO$_2$ (no solvent)

(l) CH$_2$=CH—CH(CH$_3$)Br + LiBr $\xrightarrow{\text{acetone}}$ CH$_3$CH=CH—CH$_2$Br

(m) Ph$_3$C—Cl + PhCH$_2$OH $\xrightarrow{\text{benzene}}$ Ph$_3$C—OCH$_2$Ph + HCl

(n) CH$_3$CH=CH—CH$_2$Br + Na$^+$CH(COOEt)$_2^-$ $\xrightarrow{\text{EtOH}}$ CH$_3$—CH—CH=CH$_2$
                                                                          |
                                                                    CH(COOEt)$_2$

(o) 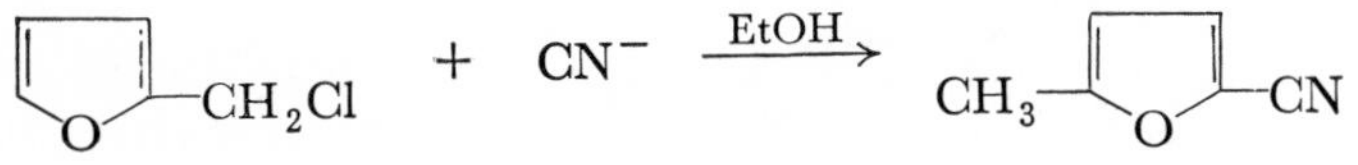 [furan ring with —CH$_2$Cl] $+$ CN$^-$ $\xrightarrow{\text{EtOH}}$ CH$_3$—[furan ring]—CN

(p) EtO—CH—Cl $+$ CH$_3$COCH$_2$COCH$_3$ $\xrightarrow[\text{EtOH}]{\text{OEt}^-}$ CH$_3$—C=CH—COCH$_3$
$\quad\quad\;\;|$
$\quad\quad$ Me

$\quad\quad\quad\quad\quad\quad\quad\quad\quad\quad\quad\quad\quad\quad\quad\quad\quad$ O$_-$ CH—OEt
$\quad\quad\quad\quad\quad\quad\quad\quad\quad\quad\quad\quad\quad\quad\quad\quad\quad\quad\quad\quad$ |
$\quad\quad\quad\quad\quad\quad\quad\quad\quad\quad\quad\quad\quad\quad\quad\quad\quad\quad\quad\quad$ Me

(q) 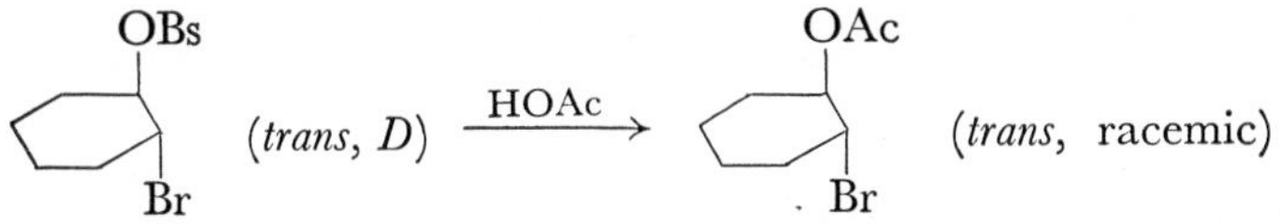 [cyclohexane with OBs and Br, (trans, D)] $\xrightarrow{\text{HOAc}}$ [cyclohexane with OAc and Br] (trans, racemic)

(r) 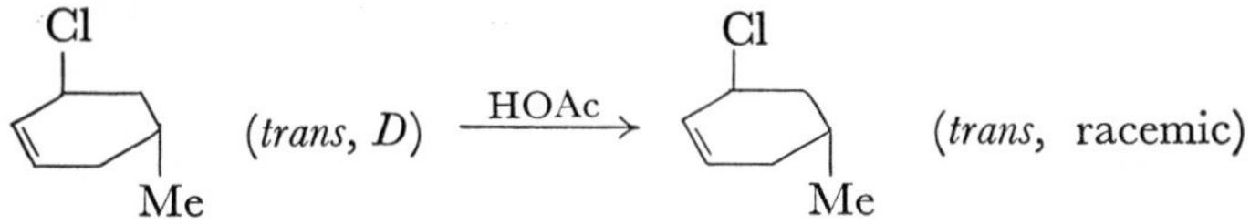 [cyclohexene with Cl and Me, (trans, D)] $\xrightarrow{\text{HOAc}}$ [cyclohexene with Cl and Me] (trans, racemic)

(s) 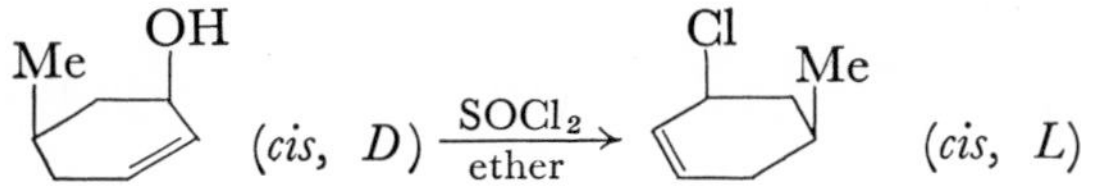 [cyclohexene with Me, OH, (cis, D)] $\xrightarrow[\text{ether}]{\text{SOCl}_2}$ [cyclohexene with Cl, Me] (cis, L)

7. Predict whether each of the following reactions proceeds with inversion or retention of configuration at the asymmetric carbon atom, and indicate whether substantial racemization is to be expected:

(a) i-BuI $+$ NaOAc $\xrightarrow{\text{alcohol}}$ i-BuOAc

(b) 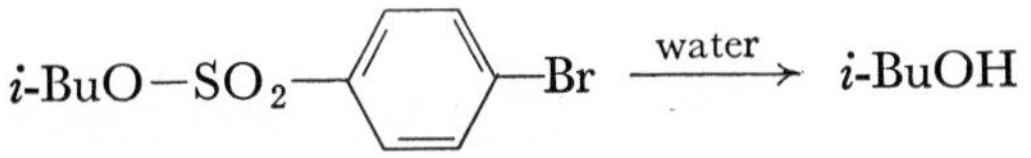 i-BuO—SO$_2$—[benzene ring]—Br $\xrightarrow{\text{water}}$ i-BuOH

(c) Ph—CH—Br $\xrightarrow[\text{HOAc}]{\text{AgOAc}}$ Ph—CH—OAc
$\quad\quad\;\;|$ $\quad\quad\quad\quad\quad\quad\quad\quad\quad$ |
$\quad\quad$ CH$_3$ $\quad\quad\quad\quad\quad\quad\quad\quad$ CH$_3$

(d) Ph—CH—Br $\xrightarrow[\text{24 hours (acetone)}]{\text{excess LiI}}$ Ph—CH—I
$\quad\quad\;\;|$ $\quad\quad\quad\quad\quad\quad\quad\quad\quad\quad\quad\quad\quad$ |
$\quad\quad$ Me $\quad\quad\quad\quad\quad\quad\quad\quad\quad\quad\quad\quad$ Me

(e) i-Bu—O—C—Ph $+$ OH$^-$ $\rightarrow$ i-BuOH $+$ PhCOO$^-$
$\quad\quad\quad\quad\;\;||$
$\quad\quad\quad\quad\;\;$ O

(f)

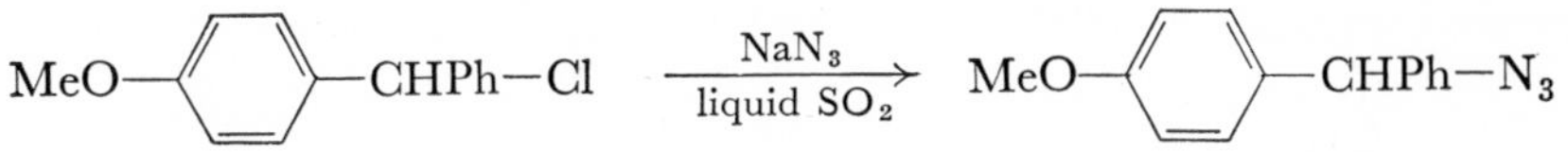

MeO—[benzene ring]—CHPh—Cl $\xrightarrow[\text{liquid SO}_2]{\text{NaN}_3}$ MeO—[benzene ring]—CHPh—N$_3$

(g) CH$_3$—C—OH $\xrightarrow[\text{dioxane}]{\text{HBr}}$ CH$_3$CHD—Br
$\quad\quad\;\;|$
$\quad\quad$ (H above, D below)

$\quad\;\;$ H
$\quad\;\;|$
(g) CH$_3$—C—OH $\xrightarrow[\text{dioxane}]{\text{HBr}}$ CH$_3$CHD—Br
$\quad\quad\;\;|$
$\quad\quad$ D

(h) $CH_3-CH=CH-CH\begin{smallmatrix}CH_3\\\\Cl\end{smallmatrix}$ $\xrightarrow{\text{aqueous acetone}}$ $CH_3-CH=CH-CH(CH_3)-OH$

(i) $Ph-\underset{\underset{OTos}{|}}{\overset{\overset{CH_3}{|}}{C}}-COOH + HCO_3^- \xrightarrow{\text{water}} Ph-\underset{\underset{OH}{|}}{\overset{\overset{CH_3}{|}}{C}}-COOH$

(j)

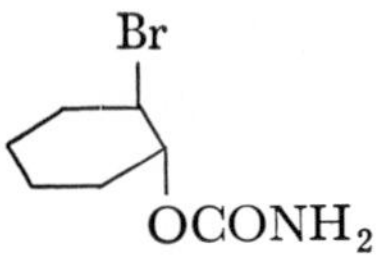

$\xrightarrow[\text{EtOH}]{OEt^-}$?   (note two asymmetric carbon atoms)

(k)

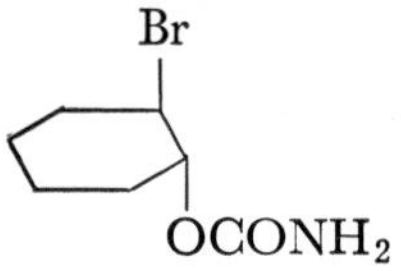

$\xrightarrow[\text{EtOH}]{AgNO_3}$?

8. Predict the product, or mixture of products, in each of the following reactions:
   (a) Benzyl tosylate treated with aqueous lithium iodide
   (b) $CH_3-CH=CH-CH_2OH$ + aqueous HCl →
   (c) $Ph_2CHCl \xrightarrow[\text{NaNO}_3]{\text{aqueous acetone}}$
   (d) γ-Bromovaleric acid treated with Ag_2CO_3 in aqueous ethanol

(e) $Ph-CH\underset{\underset{O}{\diagdown\diagup}}{-}CH-$⟨benzene ring⟩$-OMe \xrightarrow[\text{MeOH}]{H_2SO_4}$

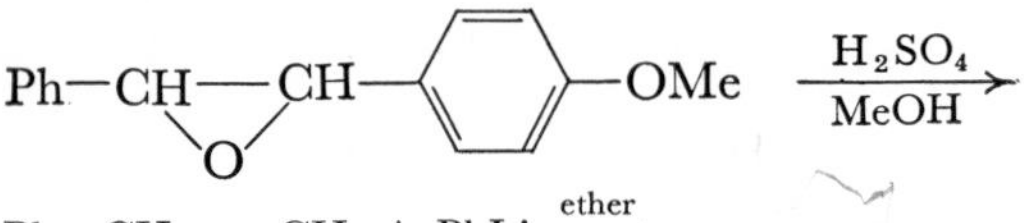

(f) $Ph-CH\underset{\underset{O}{\diagdown\diagup}}{-}CH_2 + PhLi \xrightarrow{\text{ether}}$

(g)

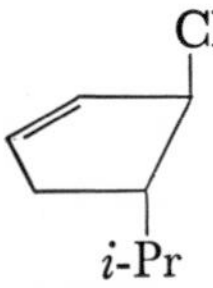

$+$ $(CH_3)_3N$ $\xrightarrow{\text{acetone}}$

(h)

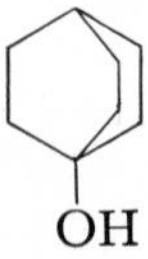

$+$ $SOCl_2$ $+$ Et_3N $\longrightarrow$

(i) $PhC\underset{\underset{O}{\|}}{-}N=C\underset{\underset{SH}{|}}{-}SMe + EtI \xrightarrow[\text{EtOH}]{OEt^-}$

(j) $HCNHPh \underset{\underset{O}{\|}}{} + EtI + Ag_2O \xrightarrow{\text{EtOH}}$

(k)

Me

+ SOCl$_2$ $\xrightarrow{\text{ether}}$

OH

9. Aside from its acid- and base-catalyzed hydrolyses, ethylene oxide undergoes slow hydrolysis in aqueous solutions buffered at pH 6 to 8 with a rate independent of pH. Two mechanisms have been suggested for this reaction:

(1) $H_2O + H_2C$——CH_2 $\xrightarrow{\text{slow}}$ $H_2\overset{+}{O}$—CH_2—CH_2O^- $\xrightarrow{\text{fast}}$ $HOCH_2CH_2OH$, and

O

(2) $H^+ + H_2C$——CH_2 $\underset{}{\overset{\text{eq}}{\rightleftarrows}}$ $\left[H_2C$————$CH_2 \right]^+$ $\xrightarrow[\text{slow}]{OH^-}$ $HOCH_2CH_2OH$

O

O
|
H

(a) Show that both proposed mechanisms should lead to the same rate law—that is, that both are consistent with a rate independent of pH.

(b) It has been found (Pritchard and Long, J. Am. Chem. Soc., **78**, 6008 (1956)), that the hydrolysis is about 10 percent faster in H_2O than in D_2O. Heavy water is known to be about half as strong an acid as ordinary water and about one third as strong a base. Which of the proposed mechanisms is in better agreement with the observed (small) isotope effect? Explain.

10. Given the following rate constants for the solvolyses of t-BuCl and t-BuBr in the solvents listed (25°):

Solvent	80% EtOH	100% EtOH	40% EtOH	MeOH	70% MeOH	HOAc	80% Me$_2$C=O
$k_{BuCl} \times 10^6$	9.2	0.097	1300	0.75	98	0.21	2.0
$k_{BuBr} \times 10^4$	3.4	0.057	350	0.34	31	0.10	1.1

(a) Calculate Y values for each of the solvents.
(b) Estimate m for the solvolyses of t-BuBr.

11. Explain each of the following:
(a) The rates of hydrolysis of alkyl bromides (0.1 molar) in 0.01 N NaOH are in the order: t-BuBr > MeBr > EtBr > i-PrBr.
(b) BF$_3$ accelerates the unimolecular substitution reactions of alkyl fluorides but not those of alkyl chlorides. The reverse is true for AgF.
(c) The ethanolysis of benzhydryl chloride is accelerated by addition of small quantities of water, but there is no significant increase in the ratio Ph$_2$CHOH/Ph$_2$CHOEt in the product.
(d) Triphenylmethyl chloride reacts more rapidly with p-nitrobenzyl alcohol in benzene than with p-methylbenzyl alcohol.
(e) An aqueous solution of the optically active salt LV yields, upon standing, the ester LVI, in which just *half* of the R groups have been racemized.

LV → LVI + (with COO⁻Na⁺ product)

$(R = PhO - \bigcirc - CHPh -)$

(f) The relative specific rates of unimolecular solvolysis of the following chlorides in ethanol are

$$HC\equiv C - CMe_2 - Cl = 1.0 \qquad MeC\equiv C - CMe_2Cl = 2000$$
$$H_2C= CH - CMe_2Cl = 10{,}000$$

(g) Treatment of substituted anisoles with HI yields CH_3I and a substituted phenol, rather than CH_3OH and a substituted iodobenzene.

(h) Br^- is displaced by the S_N2 mechanism more rapidly from CH_2BrCl than from CH_2Br_2.

(i) The second-order reaction between p-nitrobenzyl bromide and LiCl in 10 percent aqueous dioxane is accelerated when the water content is raised to 30 percent, but is retarded if the water content is increased further to 50 percent.

(j) The rate of racemization of chloride LVII exceeds its rate of solvolysis in acetic acid, but the rate of racemization of brosylate LVIII equals its rate of solvolysis.

(k) A β-CH_3O group generally retards the hydrolysis of an alkyl chloride, but with a β-CH_3S group its acceleration is sometimes spectacular.

12. Consider a description proposed by Bird, Hughes, and Ingold,[12(a)] intended to apply to both types of limiting substitution mechanisms and to borderline cases as well. Suppose that for any substitution reaction there is a volume v (which we may call a "critical-reaction volume") that surrounds each molecule of substrate. Suppose further that if one or more molecules of attacking reagent are within this volume, there is a significant probability of reaction, but, if not, there is a negligible probability of reaction. For S_N2 reactions this volume is very small, for S_N1 reactions this volume is much larger, for borderline cases this volume is of an intermediate magnitude.

(a) Show that if there are n reagent particles in a solution of volume V, the probability of finding at least one particle in the critical reaction volume v is

$$1 - \left(1 - \frac{v}{V}\right)^n$$

(This calculation is very much like the calculation of the probability of drawing at least one queen from a full deck of playing cards in x independent attempts.)

(b) Note that $v \ll V$ and that n is very large. Show that the rate of reaction may be represented by the expression,

$$\text{rate} = K(RX)(1 - e^{-Nvc})$$

where (RX) is the concentration of the substrate, K is a proportionality constant, c is the concentration of the attacking reagent, and N is Avogadro's number.

$$\left(\text{Hint: } \log_e x = (x - 1) - \frac{1}{2}(x - 1)^2 + \frac{1}{3}(x - 1)^3 \cdots \right)$$

(c) Show that the reaction will appear to be first order (independent of c) if v is large, but second order if v is small.

$$\left(\text{Note: } e^x = 1 + x + \frac{x^2}{2} + \frac{x^3}{3} + \cdots \right)$$

(d) Assume that a reaction may be regarded as first order if the term Ke^{-Nvc} (which represents the departure of the rate from that corresponding to first-order kinetics) is less than 1 percent of K. Show that on this basis, a reaction will appear to be first order when the critical reaction volume is more than *five times* the average volume of solution per molecule of attacking reagent.

(e) Assume that a reaction may be regarded as second order if $KNvc$ (the specific rate corresponding to second order kinetics) is within 1 percent of $K(1 - e^{-Nvc})$. Show that on this basis, the reaction will appear to be second order when the critical reaction volume, v, is less than $\frac{1}{50}$ of the average volume of solution per molecule of attacking reagent.

Reactions of Carboxylic Acids

and Esters

Formation and Hydrolysis of Esters. Plurality of Mechanism[1]

THERE ARE A NUMBER of paths by which esterifications and ester hydrolyses may proceed. The hydrolysis of esters, like ring opening in epoxides (p. 291), may involve bond breakage at one of two possible sites. In many instances, the *acyl-to-oxygen* bond breaks $\left(\text{R—C}\!\!\mid\!\!\text{—O—R}\right)$; but sometimes it is the *alkyl-to-oxygen* bond that breaks $\left(\text{R—C—O—}\!\mid\text{R}\right)$. In the first case, ester hydrolysis is a nucleophilic substitution (—OH for —OR) at the acyl carbon; in the second, the reaction may be regarded as a nucleophilic substitution (—OH for $\left.-\text{O—C—R}\right)$ at an alkyl carbon. It should therefore not surprise us that either of these reactions may, like the reactions considered in the preceding chapter, proceed either by a *unimolecular* or a *bimolecular* mechanism. Furthermore, as with the opening of epoxide rings, ester hydrolysis may occur through *attack on the ester itself* (in basic or neutral solution) or, alternatively, through *attack on its conjugate acid*, $\text{R—C—O}\overset{+}{\underset{\text{O}}{\big/}}\overset{\text{R}}{\underset{\text{H}}{\big\backslash}}$ (in acid solution). In view of these three mechanistic dichotomies, we can visualize eight (2^3) possible mechanisms for ester

[1] For a review of this topic, see Day and Ingold, *Trans. Faraday Soc.*, **37**, 686 (1941).

hydrolysis; to date *six* of these have been observed. A corresponding set of eight mechanisms may be proposed for the reverse reaction, esterification, but since esterifications are almost invariably carried out in acid solutions, we need consider only four of these. To date, *three* different esterification mechanisms have been observed. We may describe the various paths for esterification and hydrolysis, using a shorthand notation proposed by Ingold,[2] in which the letters *B* or *A* stipulate whether the substrate itself or its conjugate acid is attacked, the symbols *AC* and *AL* indicate whether acyl-oxygen or alkyl-oxygen bond breakage occurs, and the numbers "1" and "2" refer to the molecularity of the rate-determining step. Thus, a $B_{AC}2$ hydrolysis is a bimolecular reaction involving acyl-oxygen bond breakage, carried out in a basic (or possibly in a neutral) medium. The possible mechanisms for esterification and ester hydrolysis are summarized in Table 9-1. The reader is reminded that a carboxylic acid in a basic medium is converted to a carboxylate ion, $RCOO^-$, which, because of its negative charge, is not subject to nucleophilic attack by alcohols or their conjugate bases. *Esterifications in basic media are therefore not observed.*

Ester Saponification. The $B_{AC}2$ Mechanism

$R - \overset{O}{\overset{\|}{C}} + O - R'$ $2 = bimolecular$
                       $= 2° order$

It has long been known that the basic hydrolyses (saponifications) of ordinary esters are second-order reactions.[3] The transition states in these reactions may then be assumed to contain one molecule of ester and one OH^- ion; that is, the reactions are *bimolecular*. The site at which the ester molecule is broken is, as we have seen (p. 145), established by experiments using water enriched in O^{18}. When an alkali metal hydroxide is dissolved in "labeled" water, the OH^- ions quickly become labeled also, because of the very rapid transfer of protons $H_2O \rightleftharpoons H^+ + \overset{..}{O}H^-$ between H_2O^{18} and OH^-. The hydrolysis of *n*-amyl acetate (and, presumably, $NaOH \rightleftharpoons Na^+ + OH^-$ of other simple esters as well) in such O^{18}-enriched solutions yields an "unlabeled" alcohol but a "labeled" carboxylate anion.

$$O^{18}-H^- + \quad \overset{O}{\underset{Me}{\overset{\|}{\underset{|}{C}}}}-O-Am \xrightarrow{S_N2 \ displacement} HO^{18}-\overset{O}{\overset{\|}{\underset{Me}{C}}} + OAm^- \longrightarrow$$

$$\left[O^{18}-\overset{O}{\overset{\|}{\underset{Me}{C}}} \right]^- + AmOH \quad (Am=\textit{n-}C_5H_{11}-)$$

[2] Ingold, *Structure and Mechanism in Organic Chemistry*, Cornell University Press, Ithaca, 1953, p. 754.
[3] Warder (*Ber.*, **14**, 1361 (1881)), obtained the rate law for saponification of ethyl acetate in one of the very early kinetic studies on organic systems.

Table 9-1. Mechanisms for Esterification and Ester Hydrolysis

Type	Remarks
$B_{AC}2$	Very common; includes almost all basic ester hydrolyses (saponifications)
$A_{AC}2$	Very common; includes acid hydrolyses of esters of primary and most secondary alcohols, and most ordinary esterification reactions
$B_{AC}1$	Not observed to date
$A_{AC}1$	Rare; some esterifications and hydrolyses in concentrated solutions of very strong acids are of this type
$B_{AL}2$	Extremely rare; observed only for hydrolyses of β-lactones in the absence both of strong base and strong acid
$A_{AL}2$	Not observed to date
$B_{AL}1$ $A_{AL}1$	Apparently quite general for the hydrolysis of esters of tertiary alcohols and those secondary alcohols that yield the most stable carbonium ions (for example, benzhydrol and α-methylallyl alcohol). Not generally observed for hydrolysis in concentrated bases

clearly pointing to acyl-oxygen breakage.[4] A mechanism consistent both with the rate law and the observed site of bond-breakage is

$$
HO^- + \underset{R}{\overset{O}{\underset{\|}{C}}}-OR' \xrightarrow{\text{slow}} \left[HO-\underset{R}{\overset{O}{\underset{|}{C}}}-OR' \right]^- \xrightarrow{\text{fast}} HO-\underset{R}{\overset{O}{\underset{\|}{C}}} + OR'^- \xrightarrow{\text{fast}} \begin{cases} RCOO^- \\ R'OH \end{cases}
$$

$$I$$

The overall reaction is irreversible. Although the first, and very probably the second, steps are reversible, the final step is not.

Now a question concerning anion I comes to mind, "Is this an intermediate or merely an activated complex?" To answer this, let us consider another group of experiments involving labeled oxygen,[5] this time present in the acyl group

[4] Experiments intended to establish acyl-oxygen fission have been carried out on the esters of such alcohols as α-methylallyl alcohol and neopentyl alcohol—alcohols which yield carbonium ions known to undergo rearrangement. (See, for example, Norton and Quayle, J. Am. Chem. Soc., **62**, 1170 (1940).) Since saponification of such esters yields unrearranged products, it is assumed that the free carbonium ions are not intermediates. The interpretation of such experiments is not as clear cut as is that of the experiments in O^{18}-enriched water. What they show is that either acyl-oxygen fission occurs, or that if alkyl-oxygen fission occurs, it is bimolecular.

[5] Bender, J. Am. Chem. Soc., **73**, 1626 (1951).

of the ester,

$$\overset{\overset{\displaystyle O^{18}}{\displaystyle \|}}{R-C}-O-R'.$$

Suppose ethyl, isopropyl, or *t*-butyl benzoate, labeled at the benzoyl oxygen, is subjected to saponification in ordinary water, but the reaction is stopped before completion and the unreacted ester reisolated. It is then found that the O^{18} *content of the unreacted ester has decreased.* Depending upon the ester, the rate of O^{18} loss is from one tenth to one third the rate of saponification. The sequence below suggests how this oxygen exchange can occur:

[handwritten margin note: O^{18} loss is less than amt of hydrolysis.]

[reaction scheme, with handwritten annotations "exchange of O^{18} in ester"]

Since, in the exchange reaction, the labeled oxygen must depart as O^*H^-, the lifetime of anion I must be sufficient to allow a significant chance for its isomerization to anion II, which may break up in the required manner. Since the existence of an activated complex is only momentary, anion I must instead be an intermediate.

Two further consequences arise from the presently accepted mechanism for saponification. In forming the intermediate I we are increasing the density of negative charge at the reaction center. Therefore, saponification should be facilitated by groups that will withdraw some of the excess negative charge (that is, by electron-attracting substituents). This should be true whether such substituents are located on the alkyl or acyl portion of the ester. Moreover, in forming intermediate I, we are increasing the extent of crowding; therefore, we should expect saponification to be subject to *steric retardation*. Both steric and polar effects are in the expected direction. The following relative saponification rates[6] are illustrative of polar effects:

[handwritten margin note: acyl substituents]

	CH_3COOMe	$CH_2ClCOOMe$	$CHCl_2COOMe$
$\dfrac{k}{k_{MeOAc}}$	1.0	761	16,000

	$(COOMe)_2$	CH_3COOEt	$CH_3-\overset{\overset{\displaystyle O}{\displaystyle \|}}{C}-COOEt$
$\dfrac{k}{k_{MeOAc}}$	170,000	0.60	10,000

[handwritten: ET denotes]

[6] These, and many others, have been compiled in Hammett's *Physical Organic Chemistry*, McGraw-Hill Book Co., Inc., New York, 1940, pp. 211–212. They refer to reactions in water at 25°.

[handwritten: $K = \dfrac{p d c t s}{reactants}$ ∴ higher K value or higher ratio of K's indicates shift to right.]

Similarly, the three reaction series—the saponification (a) of methyl esters of substituted benzoic acids, (b) of the ethyl esters of these acids, and (c) of the benzoates of substituted phenols[7]—exhibit Hammett ρ values that are positive. Thus, as predicted, these saponifications are accelerated by such substituents as —Cl, —Br, and —NO$_2$ (both on the alkyl and acyl sections of the molecule), and are retarded by such substituents as —CH$_3$, —NH$_2$, and p-CH$_3$O—. Benzoates are, in general, saponified more slowly than acetates or even propionates. This observation may cause some surprise since the phenyl group is generally considered a more *effective electron attractor* than the methyl and ethyl groups. But it should be remembered that the benzene ring, despite its $-I$ effect, is conjugated with a carbonyl group in a benzoate, and may donate π-electron density to it through conjugation;

whereas conjugate effects of this sort are absent in aliphatic esters.

With respect to steric effects, we may consider the following two series:[8]

	CH$_3$COOEt	C$_2$H$_5$COOEt	(CH$_3$)$_2$CHCOOEt	(CH$_3$)$_3$CCOOEt
$\dfrac{k}{k_{\text{EtOAc}}}$	1.0	0.47	0.10	0.011

and

	CH$_3$CH$_2$OAc	(CH$_3$)$_2$CHCH$_2$OAc	(CH$_3$)$_3$CCH$_2$OAc	(C$_2$H$_5$)$_3$CCH$_2$OAc
$\dfrac{k}{k_{\text{EtOAc}}}$	1.0	0.70	0.18	0.031

Although it might be argued that the progressive drop in saponification rate with successive methyl substitution, in the first series, is due, at least in part, to the electron-repelling action of the methyl groups, this cannot be said about the second series because here the structural alterations are too far (four atoms removed) from the reaction site. The decrease in rate in this case must be largely steric in origin.

Esterification and Acid-catalyzed Hydrolysis of the Most Usual Type. The $A_{AC}2$ Mechanism

The most obvious difference between the basic hydrolysis of esters and their acid-catalyzed hydrolysis is that the latter is *experimentally reversible*, its reversal

[7] See, for example, Tommila and Hinshelwood, *J. Chem. Soc.*, **1938**, 1801.
[8] The data for the ethyl esters were obtained by Kindler, *Ber.*, **69B**, 2792 (1936); they refer to reactions in 88 percent ethanol at 30°. The data on the acetates are reported by Newman in *Steric Effects in Organic Chemistry*, John Wiley and Sons, Inc., 1956, p. 220; they refer to reactions in 70 per cent dioxane at 20°.

being the acid-catalyzed esterification reaction. Some of the earliest experiments demonstrating the phenomena of equilibrium and reversibility in chemistry were, in fact, concerned with esterification and ester hydrolysis.[9] Now an important feature of reversible reactions is that the mechanism of the reverse reaction is known with as much certainty as is the mechanism of the forward reaction. This is a consequence of the so-called *principle of microscopic reversibility*, which stipulates that if a system is at equilibrium and if there are a number of (necessarily reversible) steps occurring, then the total number of molecular systems participating in a given step per unit time must be the same as the total number of systems participating in the reverse of this step. More particularly, *if a given sequence of steps constitutes the favored mechanism for the forward reaction, the reverse sequence of these steps constitutes the favored mechanism for the reverse reaction.*[10] Thus, if we determine the mechanism for acid hydrolysis, we automatically establish the mechanism for acid-catalyzed esterification.

Let us first consider evidence similar to that upon which our proposed mechanism for saponification is based. Hydrolyses of ethyl hydrogen succinate (III)[11] and the cyclic ester, γ-butyrolactone (IV),[12] in H_2O^{18} establish acyl-

$$HOOC-CH_2CH_2-C-OEt + H_2O^{18} \xrightarrow{H^+}$$
$$\underset{O}{\|}$$

III

$$HOOC-CH_2-CH_2-C-O^{18}H + EtOH$$
$$\underset{O}{\|}$$

$$\text{(IV)} + H_2O^{18} \xrightarrow{H^+} HO-CH_2-CH_2-CH_2-C-O^{18}H$$
$$\underset{O}{\|}$$

IV

oxygen cleavage; whereas experiments with $Ph-C-OEt$ (with $\underset{O_{18}}{\|}$) in acid suggest that

acid-catalyzed hydrolysis (and, consequently, esterification) passes through an intermediate having a lifetime long enough to allow appreciable oxygen ex-

---

[9] Berthelot and Saint Gilles, *Ann. Chim.*, **65**, 385 (1862); **68**, 225 (1863). Guldberg and Waage, *J. prakt. Chem.*, **19**, 69 (1879).

[10] This principle is stated without proof, since a more detailed consideration of it would require statistical arguments that cannot be presented here. For a rigorous discussion, the student with theoretical inclinations is referred to Tolman s *Statistical Mechanics*, Oxford University Press, Oxford, 1938. p. 163. The principle is, of course, obvious for a one-step reversible reaction, since an activated complex having minimum free energy should be most favored, both for the forward and reverse reactions. For reactions having several steps, however, the argument becomes more complex.

[11] Datta, Day, and Ingold, *J. Chem. Soc.*, **1939**, 838.

[12] Long and Friedman, *J. Am. Chem. Soc.*, **72**, 3692 (1950).

change with the solvent.[13] That the rates of acid-catalyzed hydrolyses are proportional both to (H+) and (ester) has long been recognized, but the kinetic participation of water is more difficult to demonstrate when the latter is a major component of the system. Rates of hydrolyses carried out in acetone with measured amounts of water have been shown[14] to be very nearly proportional to (H_2O), but we must use reserve in interpreting experiments of this sort, since what is observed may conceivably be a rate increase due to an increase in solvent polarity as water is added. However, it is possible, by a close examination of the dependence of rate on acidity, to decide for this reaction whether water is involved in the transition state for the slow step; for, it will be recalled, if the activated complex consists merely of a molecule of ester and a hydrogen ion, the reaction rate should be proportional to Hammett's h_0 function;

$$\text{rate} = k(RCOOR')h_0 \tag{1}$$

whereas if a water molecule is also involved, the rate should be proportional to the hydronium-ion concentration (p. 190).

$$\text{rate} = k(RCOOR')(H_3O^+) \tag{2}$$

A distinction cannot be made in dilute aqueous solutions where h_0 approaches (H_3O^+), but the two quantities are measurably different at acid concentrations greater than 1.0 molar. In such acidic solutions, the rates of hydrolyses of the more usual esters[15(a)] and of γ-butyrolactone, (IV),[15(b)] have been found to be very nearly proportional to (H_3O^+). On the other hand, the rates of hydrolyses of β-propiolactone,

$$\begin{array}{c} CH_2\text{—}C\text{=}O \\ | \qquad | \\ CH_2\text{—}O \end{array}$$

, and β-butyrolactone,

$$\begin{array}{c} Me\text{—}CH\text{—}C\text{=}O \\ | \qquad | \\ CH_2\text{—}O \end{array}$$

,

are proportional to h_0;[16] but it may be assumed that the β-lactones, because of strain associated with the four-membered rings, behave abnormally.

The mechanism for ordinary acid-catalyzed hydrolyses (and esterifications) must then meet the following requirements: (1) all steps must be significantly reversible; (2) acyl-oxygen bond breakage must occur; (3) the transition state in the hydrolysis must consist of a molecule of ester, a molecule of water, and an H+ ion; and (4) the reaction must pass through an intermediate that can survive long enough to allow oxygen exchange with the solvent. The following mechanism, involving the conjugate acids of both the ester and the carboxylic acid, fits these conditions:[11]

[13] Bender, *J. Am. Chem. Soc.*, **75**, 5986 (1953).

[14] Friedmann and Elmore, *J. Am. Chem. Soc.*, **63**, 864 (1941).

[15] (a) Duboux and de Sousa, *Helv. Chim. Acta*, **23**, 1381 (1940); Bell, Dowding, and Noble, *J. Chem. Soc.*, **1955**, 3106; Chmiel and Long, *J. Am. Chem. Soc.*, **78**, 3326 (1956). (b) Long, Dunkle, and McDevit, *J. Phys. Chem.*, **55**, 829 (1951).

[16] Long and Purchase, *J. Am. Chem. Soc.*, **72**, 3267 (1950).

$$R-\overset{+}{\underset{O}{C}}-\overset{R'}{\underset{H}{O}} \quad \underset{-H_2O,\ fast}{\overset{+H_2O,\ slow}{\rightleftharpoons}} \quad \left[R-\underset{\underset{H}{\overset{|}{O}}\ \overset{|}{R'}}{\overset{\overset{O}{||}}{C}}-O\overset{H}{\underset{H}{\cdots}} \right]^+ \quad \underset{+R'\ OH,\ slow}{\overset{-R'\ OH,\ fast}{\rightleftharpoons}} \quad R-\underset{O}{\overset{+}{C}}-O\overset{H}{\underset{H}{\cdots}} \ +\ R'OH$$

V

As required, the active intermediate, V, is a complex of ester, water, and H$^+$.
Assuming that shifts of protons from one oxygen atom to another may be very
rapid, we may represent the oxygen exchange accompanying acid-catalyzed
hydrolyses as

$$\left[R-\underset{H\ \ R'}{\overset{\overset{*}{O}\ \ H}{C}}-O \right]^+ \quad \underset{\text{very rapid}}{\longrightarrow} \quad \left[R-\underset{H\ \ R'}{\overset{H\ \ H}{\overset{*}{O}}}-O \right]^+ \quad \rightleftharpoons \quad R-\underset{O}{\overset{+}{C}}-\overset{R'}{O}\underset{H}{} \ +\ H_2O^*$$

If the ester is dissolved in an alcohol, R″OH, and acid is added, the original
ester, RCOOR′, is converted to a second, RCOOR″, with an alkyl group
derived from the alcohol. This is the familiar *ester interchange* reaction; it almost
certainly proceeds through intermediate VI, which is identical to V except that
an R″OH group has replaced an HOH group.

$$\left[\underset{H\ \ \ R\ \ \ H}{\overset{R''\ \ \ O\ \ \ R'}{O-\overset{|}{C}-O}} \right]^+$$

VI

In acid-catalyzed hydrolysis, ester interchange, and esterification, the bond
angle about the acyl carbon is reduced from near 120° to near 109° during the
rate-determining step, and steric crowding is thereby increased. We should then
expect these reactions to be subject to steric retardation, just as is saponification.
Moreover, intermediate V differs from the corresponding saponification intermediate I only by the presence of two protons; and this is true also for the
respective transition states leading to these intermediates. Since the steric
requirements of two protons may be considered negligible, it is very likely that
acid-catalyzed hydrolysis, esterification, and saponification are subject to
virtually the same steric effects. Polar influences, however, should be much
less important for the acid-catalyzed reactions than for saponification, for the
rate of an $A_{AC}2$ reaction is jointly controlled by two factors *that respond differently*

to polarity. Such a reaction will be accelerated if the conversion of the substrate to its conjugate acid is made more complete (this will be facilitated by electron-repelling groups), but it will also be accelerated if the protonated substrate coordinates more readily with the displacing reagent (this will be facilitated by electron-attracting groups). If we are considering reactions in very acidic media where virtually all of the substrate will be converted to its conjugate acid, we may be reasonably sure that the $A_{Ac}2$ reaction will be accelerated by electron-attracting groups, but we are far more often interested in reactions in only moderately acidic solutions, and here we cannot safely predict the direction of polar effects (although we may expect their magnitudes to be small). The reasonably successful Taft treatment of polar and steric effects (p. 227) is based upon the assumption that polar effects in the acid hydrolyses of the usual esters are negligible. Typically, the specific rate of hydrolysis of ethyl *p*-nitrobenzoate (in "60 percent alcohol" at 100°) exceeds that of ethyl *p*-methoxybenzoate by only 12 percent,[17] whereas the specific rate of esterification of *p*-methoxybenzoic acid (in MeOH at 25°) exceeds that for *p*-nitrobenzoic acid by about 70 percent.[18]

As an example of steric effects in $A_{Ac}2$ reactions, let us consider the esterification rates of a number of aliphatic acids. The following are a few of the many relative specific rates that have been determined (MeOH, 40°):[19]

	CH₃COOH	n-C₃H₇COOH	(CH₃)₃CCOOH
$\dfrac{k}{k_{HOAc}}$	1.0	0.51	0.037

	(CH₃)₃CCH₂COOH	$(CH_3)_3C{-}\overset{\overset{\displaystyle CH_3}{\textstyle \vert}}{C}H{-}COOH$
$\dfrac{k}{k_{HOAc}}$	0.023	0.00062

	(CH₃)₃C—C(CH₃)₂—COOH	Et₃C—COOH
$\dfrac{k}{k_{HOAc}}$	0.00013	0.00016

	(i-Pr)₂CHCOOH	$(CH_3)_3C{-}\overset{\overset{\displaystyle Et}{\textstyle \vert}}{C}H{-}COOH$
$\dfrac{k}{k_{HOAc}}$	<10⁻⁴	<10⁻⁴

The sharp decrease in rate with the increasing chain branching suggests the combination of steric and ponderal effects which we have already discussed in regard to the halide-exchange reaction (p. 275). As with the latter, β-alkyl

[17] Timm and Hinshelwood, *J. Chem. Soc.*, **1932**, 55.
[18] Hartman and Gassmann, *J. Am. Chem. Soc.*, **62**, 1559 (1940).
[19] Loening, Garrett, and Newman, *J. Am. Chem. Soc.*, **74**, 3929 (1952).

substituents are significantly more effective "steric hinderers" than α-alkyl substituents.[20] Thus, incorporation of three α-methyl groups into acetic acid lowers the esterification rate by a factor of 27, but incorporation of three β-methyl groups into propionic acid lowers the rate by a factor of 36. More spectacularly, if the methyl groups in trimethylacetic acid are replaced with ethyl groups (thus effectively adding three β-carbons), the esterification rate is lowered by a factor of 230. In extreme cases, di-isopropylacetic acid and α-t-butylbutyric acid, both of which have four β-methyl groups, are esterified too slowly to measure.

Very nearly the same idea may be expressed somewhat differently using the Newman *rule of six*,[21] which says, in effect, that those atoms which are most effective in providing steric hindrance to addition are separated from the attacking atom in the transition state by a chain of four atoms. This means that if either the attacking atom or the carbonyl oxygen is designated "1," the "blocking atom" will be in the "6" position (Fig. 9-1). If the acid is assumed to have a coiled structure with normal bond lengths and bond angles, it is possible to show, using molecular models, that an atom in the 6-position is much more likely to draw close to the path of the attacking reagent than is an atom in, say, the 5- or 7-position. If there are only a few (3 or 6) atoms in the 6-positions, they may be moved out of the way of the attacking nucleophile by rotation about the C_3—C_4 bond; but if there are 9 or 12 atoms in the 6-positions, it becomes increasingly difficult to twist the acid chain into a permissible conformation while avoiding close interaction with the 1-position. Of the acids whose esterification rates are listed on page 322, the final two have 12 hydrogen atoms in the 6-positions, and the four preceding these have 9 each. Although t-butylacetic acid is esterified more rapidly than we would predict, the trend is otherwise quite definite.

[20] It might appear that the effectiveness of β-alkyl substituents in steric hindrance may be rationalized in the same way for esterifications as for halide-exchange reactions, that is, carboxylic acid molecules, like alkyl halide molecules, are chains which are bent or coiled so that hydrogens on β-alkyl groups block the path of the attacking reagent more effectively than those on α-alkyl groups (see Fig. 8-1). While such an explanation may not actually be wrong, the description of these two reactions in similar language masks important differences. Because of the different conventions in nomenclature, the atom under attack in a halide-exchange reaction *is* the α-carbon, but that under attack in esterification *is adjacent to* the α-carbon. Therefore, a hydrogen on a β-methyl group in a halide-exchange reaction is separated from the attacking atom in the activated complex by *three* atoms, but in an esterification, it is separated by *four* atoms. Moreover, the configuration of bonds about the carbon atom under attack is different for the two types of transition state. Thus, except in a rather broad sense, the stereochemical situations in the two types of reactions are dissimilar.

[21] Newman, *J. Am. Chem. Soc.*, **72**, 4783 (1950). In its original form, this rule tended to emphasize the importance of the 1,6 relationship between the blocking atom and the carbonyl oxygen, although this oxygen does not suffer attack. What is more important, in the opinion of the present author, is interaction between the blocking atom and the incoming nucleophile. It should also be noted that the rule is intended to apply only to reactions in which the configuration about the atom under attack is tetrahedral in the transition state.

The esterification of benzoic acid is retarded by introducing a substituent *ortho* to the —COOH group, and (unless unusually severe conditions are employed) virtually prevented by a pair of substituents at the 2- and 6-positions. This is doubtless a steric effect, for it is observed whether the substituents are electron attracting or electron repelling. Typically, an o-C_2H_5 group lowers the rate of esterification (methanol, 15°) of benzoic acid by a factor of 5, whereas an o-NO_2 group lowers it by a factor of 32.[22] Both 2,4,6-tribromobenzoic and 2,4,6-trimethylbenzoic acids are resistant to esterification under the usual conditions (although, as we shall soon see, the latter may be easily esterified by employing the correct tactics). The nature of these "*ortho* effects" is readily understood if we recall (p. 236) that substituents *ortho* to the —COOH group

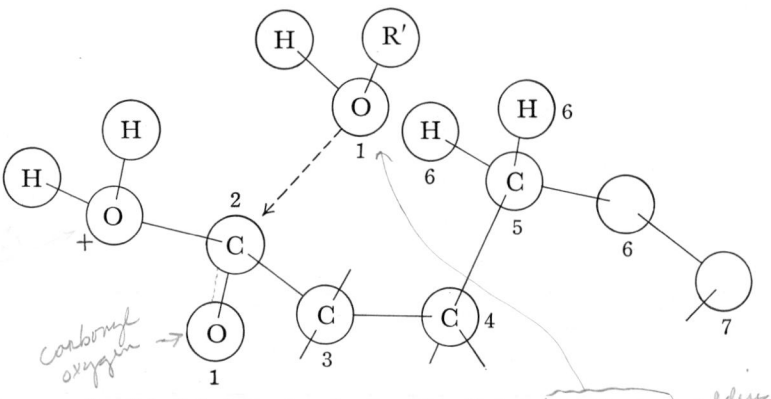

Fig. 9-1. Coiled Structure for Transition State in Esterification.

force the latter well out of the plane of the benzene ring. Although we know somewhat less about the geometric details of esterification than those of nucleophilic displacement, we feel reasonably certain that the attack on an unsaturated function (and this includes the $-\overset{+}{\underset{\textstyle OH}{C}}\overset{\textstyle OH}{}$ group) occurs from a direction *perpendicular to the plane defined by that group.* As shown in Figure 9-2, if there is one substituent, X, *ortho* to the protonated carboxyl group, the incoming alcohol molecule can attack only by route A; if two *ortho* substituents are present, this route is also closed.

Since the reactants in acid-catalyzed ester hydrolyses are very similar in nature to those in esterification, and since the transition states for the two reactions are almost identical, we would expect steric effects in ester hydrolysis to be very nearly the same as those in esterification. A close parallelism has indeed

[22] Sudborough and Turner, *J. Chem. Soc.*, **101**, 237 (1912).

been observed.[23] Furthermore, since the specific rates of esterification and hydrolysis vary in almost exactly the same manner as the structure of the substrate is modified, the ratio of these specific rates—the equilibrium constant for esterification—should undergo very little variation with structure. This is also known to be the case.[24] Structural modifications that cause decreases of several powers of ten in the esterification rate change the equilibrium constant by less than 20 percent.

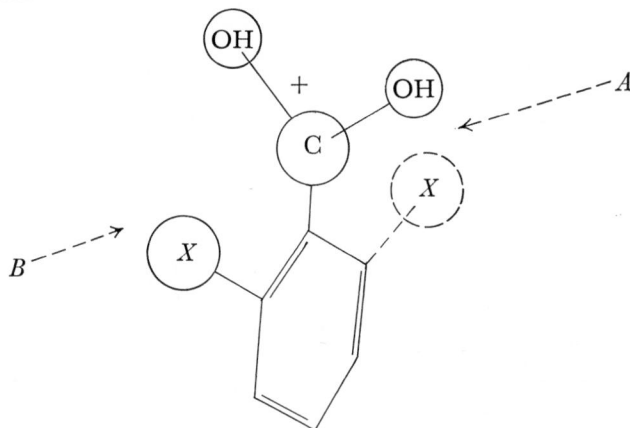

Fig. 9-2. Steric Hindrance in Esterification of ortho-substituted Benzoic Acids.

Reactions Proceeding Through Acylium Ions. The $A_{AC}1$ Mechanism

Mesitoic acid (2,4,6-trimethylbenzoic acid) is stubbornly resistant to attempted esterifications under ordinary conditions, but it may be easily esterified by dissolving it in concentrated sulfuric acid, then pouring the resulting solution into cold methanol.[25] Conversely, the methyl ester of this acid, which can be saponified only with extreme difficulty, may be hydrolyzed simply by dissolving in concentrated H_2SO_4 and diluting this solution with ice water.[26] Apparently, concentrated sulfuric acid has converted mesitoic acid and its ester to intermediates that are far more readily attacked than are the respective conjugate acids—intermediates in which the "blocking effectiveness" of the ortho-methyl groups has been greatly decreased. The mesitoyl cation, VII, should be such an intermediate, for the $-\overset{+}{C}{=}O$ group is linear and lies in the plane of the benzene ring; attacking reagents may approach the carbonyl carbon perpendicular to the plane of the ring, essentially without hindrance. Indeed, we have already

[23] Smith et al., J. Am. Chem. Soc., **63**, 1556 (1940); **63**, 3465 (1941).
[24] See, for example, Branch and McKittrick, J. Am. Chem. Soc., **45**, 321 (1923).
[25] Newman, J. Am. Chem. Soc., **63**, 2431 (1941).
[26] Treffers and Hammett, J. Am. Chem. Soc., **59**, 1708 (1937).

seen (p. 99) that cryoscopic determinations of the number of particles per "molecule" of mesitoic acid or ester in concentrated sulfuric acid indicate that both solutes yield just this cation—an ion that, upon dilution with water or alcohol, should once more form the parent acid or ester. The nearly

VII

complete conversion of an acid or ester to an acylium ion is only rarely observed, for such an ionization apparently requires both steric assistance (that is, a very crowded —COOH or —COOR group) and stabilization of the positive charge by electron-donating groups. (Yet, such groups should not be too effective as electron donors lest the molecule suffer sulfonation.) Thus, 2,4-dimethylbenzoic acid and 2,4,6-tribromobenzoic acid are not measurably converted to their respective acylium ions in 100 percent H_2SO_4, whereas 2,6-dimethylbenzoic acid is only partially converted.[27] However, it should not be assumed that because conversion of an acid or an ester to its acylium ion is not detectable cryoscopically, none occurs. A reaction involving the slow and incomplete formation of an acylium ion is, in fact, far more suited to kinetic study than are the interconversions of mesitoic acid and its esters in the manner just described (for in these, the rate of conversion is generally governed by the delay in adding a third reagent to a mixture of the remaining two). A kinetic study of the hydrolyses of methyl benzoate and methyl p-toluate in sulfuric acid containing small amounts of water suggests that these reactions proceed through acylium ions.[28] These hydrolyses are first order in ester but independent of

[27] Interestingly, isopropylidinemalonic ester, VIII, which, as shown, is somewhat similar structurally to mesitoic ester, can be largely converted to an acylium ion in 100 percent sul-

VIII

furic acid. Like mesitoic esters, it cannot be hydrolyzed by the usual methods, but it may be converted to its half ester in 65 percent yield by dissolving it in 100 percent H_2SO_4, then adding the solution to cold water. (See Corey, J. Am. Chem. Soc., 74, 5902 (1952).)

[28] (a) Experiments by Graham and Hughes, reported by Ingold, Ref. 2, p. 771. (b) See also Leisten, J. Chem. Soc., 1956, 1572.

$$PhCOOMe \underset{fast}{\overset{H^+}{\rightleftharpoons}} Ph-\overset{+}{\underset{\underset{H}{O}}{C}}\overset{Me}{\diagup}O \xrightarrow[slow]{H_2SO_4} Ph-\overset{+}{C}=O + \xrightarrow[fast]{H_2O} Ph-\overset{+}{\underset{\underset{H}{O}}{C}}\overset{H}{\diagup}O$$

the concentration of added water (when the latter is kept below 1.0 M). The half lives for these reactions at 20° are 7.7 hours (for PhCOOMe) and 2.0 hours (for p-$CH_3C_6H_4COOMe$); hence the concentration of acylium ion at any point in the reaction is far too small to be detected cryoscopically.

Evidence of a different sort indicates that the $A_{Ac}1$ mechanism operates in the hydrolyses of β-lactones in strongly acid solutions (but not, as we shall presently see, in weakly acid solutions). The hydrolyses of β-propiolactone and its homolog, β-butyrolactone, in 2 to 5N H_2SO_4 or $HClO_4$ occur with acyl-oxygen cleavage; for if H_2O^{18} is used, almost no O^{18} enters the β-OH group of the resulting acid.[29] Unlike γ-lactones (and presumably ordinary esters also), the rates of hydrolysis of β-lactones are proportional to Hammett's h_0 function,[16] a proportionality that, we have learned, indicates that the activated complex in the slow step consists only of a molecule of substrate and a proton. The following mechanism is thus consistent with the known facts about this hydrolysis:

$$\underset{O-C=O}{\overset{\overset{\beta}{CH_2}\overset{\alpha}{CH_2}}{|\quad|}} \overset{H^+}{\underset{K}{\overset{fast, eq}{\rightleftharpoons}}} \underset{\underset{\underset{H}{+}}{O-C=O}}{\overset{CH_2CH_2}{|\quad|}} \xrightarrow[k_1]{slow} HO-CH_2CH_2-\overset{+}{C}=O \xrightarrow[fast]{H_2O}$$

$$HO-CH_2CH_2-\overset{*H}{\underset{\underset{H}{O}}{C}}\overset{}{\diagdown}O \quad (3)$$

$$rate = k_1(LH^+) = k_1K(L)(H^+)\frac{\gamma_{H^+}\gamma_L}{\gamma_{LH^+}} = k'(L)a_{H^+}\frac{\gamma_L}{\gamma_{LH^+}} = k'(L)h_0$$

(L = lactone)

As with hydrolysis of methyl benzoate in concentrated sulfuric acid, the rate of reaction is simply the rate of unimolecular breakage of the acyl-oxygen bond.

Further Substitution Reactions on Acyl Carbon Atoms. The Formation and Hydrolysis of Amides

We have now examined just half of the known mechanisms for ester hydrolysis: those involving substitution on the acyl carbon. Before taking up the remaining mechanisms, which involve substitution on the alkyl carbon, let us consider a number of additional reactions that are, in essence, attacks on acyl-carbon atoms. These are, in some respects, surprisingly similar to the ester hydrolyses so far described. For example, much of what has been said concerning the usual

[29] Olson and Hyde, *J. Am. Chem. Soc.*, **63**, 2459 (1941).

modes of ester hydrolysis (by the $B_{AC}2$ and $A_{AC}2$ mechanisms) may also be applied to the hydrolysis of amides. The following similarities stand out:

(a) Rates of basic and acid hydrolysis of many amides at *moderate concentrations* of acid and base have been found to be proportional, respectively, to (amide) $\times$ (OH⁻) and (amide) $\times$ (H⁺).[30]

(b) The hydrolyses of N-substituted amides necessarily involve acyl-nitrogen, rather than alkyl-nitrogen, bond breakage. If this were not so, alcohols, rather than amines, would be formed in such solvolyses.

(c) The basic hydrolysis of Ph—C—NH₂ in ordinary water is accompanied
$$\underset{\text{O}_{18}}{\overset{\|}{}}$$

by the loss of O^{18} to the solvent,[31] just as are the saponifications of acyl-labeled benzoates (p. 317), demonstrating the existence of an intermediate (IX) having a sufficiently long lifetime to allow proton exchange between oxygen atoms.

(d) Both acidic[32(a)] and basic[32(b)] hydrolyses of amides are subject to steric retardation by bulky groups, just as are the hydrolyses of esters.

(e) The *basic* hydrolysis of amides is accelerated by electron-attracting groups, as is the saponification of esters, but polar effects in the *acid* hydrolyses of amides are slight.[30,32(a)]

In line with these similarities, it seems likely that the basic hydrolysis of amides proceeds as follows:

$$\text{HO}^- + \underset{\text{R}}{\overset{\text{O}}{\overset{\|}{\text{C}}}}\text{—NHR}' \underset{\text{slow}}{\rightleftharpoons} \left[\underset{\text{R}}{\overset{\text{O}}{\overset{|}{\text{HO—C}}}}\text{—NHR}'\right]^{-} \overset{\text{fast}}{\rightarrow}$$
$$\text{IX}$$

$$\underset{\text{R}}{\overset{\text{O}}{\overset{\|}{\text{HO—C}}}} + \text{NHR}'^- \overset{\text{fast}}{\rightarrow} \begin{cases} \text{RCOO}^- \\ \\ \text{R}'\text{NH}_2 \end{cases}$$

and that acid hydrolysis takes the path:

$$\underset{\overset{\|}{\text{O}}\ \text{H}}{\overset{\text{H}}{\overset{|}{\text{R—C}}}}\overset{+}{\underset{}{\text{N}}}\text{—R}' \underset{\text{slow}}{\overset{\text{H}_2\text{O}}{\rightarrow}} \left[\underset{\overset{|}{\text{O}}\ \text{H}}{\overset{\text{O H}}{\text{R—C—N—R}'}}\right]^{+} \overset{\text{fast}}{\rightarrow} \begin{cases} \underset{}{\overset{\text{O}}{\overset{\|}{\text{R—C}}}}\text{—OH}_2^+ \\ \text{R}'\text{NH}_2 \end{cases} \overset{\text{fast}}{\rightarrow} \begin{cases} \text{RCOOH} \\ \text{R}'\text{NH}_3^+ \end{cases}$$
$$\text{X}$$

[30] See, for example, Reid, *Am. Chem. J.*, **21**, 284 (1899).
[31] Bender, Ginger, and Kemp, *J. Am. Chem. Soc.*, **76**, 3350 (1954); **77**, 348 (1955).
[32] (a) Reid, *Am. Chem. J.*, **24**, 397 (1900). (b) Cason, et al., *J. Org. Chem.*, **18**, 1129 (1953).

The overall reactions in both cases are virtually irreversible: the first because of the conversion of the acid to its anion, the second because of the conversion of the amine (or ammonia) to its conjugate acid.

In concentrated acid solutions, rates of amide hydrolysis are found to pass through a maximum and the value of the hydrogen ion concentration corresponding to this peak is, in general, different for each amide.[33(a)] This maximum appears to correspond to the point where virtually all of the amide is converted to its conjugate acid, and further addition of strong acid merely serves to "tie up" the water present in the solvation shells of H^+ and the anion, decreasing the quantity of "free" water available for attack at the carbonyl carbon.

The observed rate law for the basic hydrolyses of N-methylanilides,[33(b)]

$$\text{rate} = k_2(\text{OH}^-)(\text{anilide}) + k_3(\text{OH}^-)^2(\text{anilide})$$

suggests that these hydrolyses are occurring by *two* paths. The second-order term corresponds to the ordinary hydrolysis through an intermediate analogous to IX, whereas the third-order term probably results from hydrolysis proceeding through conjugate base XI, the concentration of which is proportional to $(\text{OH}^-)^2$.

One additional feature deserves mention. During the acid hydrolysis of amides there is *inappreciable oxygen exchange* between solvent and substrate[31] (a situation different from that observed during the acid hydrolysis of esters). This means that the breakup of cation X to form amine $R'NH_2$ is much more rapid than the transfer of protons from one oxygen atom to another in X and its breakup to form water. In fact, aside from analogy, there is no significant evidence at present that cation X is an actual intermediate. It may merely be an activated complex.

Amines do not ordinarily react with acids in solution to form amides

[33] (a) Krieble and Holst, *J. Am. Chem. Soc.*, **60**, 2976 (1938); Edward and Meacock, *J. Chem. Soc.*, **1957**, 2000. (b) Beichler and Taft, *J. Am. Chem. Soc.*, **79**, 4927 (1957).

(although such reactions are known at elevated temperatures). Instead, the preparation of amides is most often carried out by treating an ester, an acid anhydride, or an acyl halide with an amine or with ammonia. The formation of amides from acyl halides is often very rapid and in other ways unsuited for convenient kinetic studies, and the reactions of anhydrides with amines (perhaps with less justification) have, until very recently, also been slighted. The conversions of esters to amides have been investigated by a number of workers and it is now recognized that these are very similar in character to ester saponifications and basic hydrolyses of amides. They are accelerated by electron-attracting groups,[34] retarded by bulky groups,[35] necessarily involve acyl-oxygen cleavage, and their kinetics (with suitable interpretation) suggest bimolecular rate-determining steps. Unlike basic hydrolyses of amides and esters, however, the conversions of esters to amides are reversible, and may thus be represented as follows:

prep of amides similar to

$$
RNH_2 + \underset{\underset{R'}{|}}{\overset{\overset{O}{\|}}{C}}-OR''
\underset{fast}{\overset{slow}{\rightleftharpoons}}
\underset{\underset{H\ \ R'}{|\ \ |}}{R-\overset{\overset{H\ \ O^-}{|\ \ |}}{N}\overset{+}{-}C-OR''}
\underset{fast}{\overset{fast}{\rightleftharpoons}}
\underset{\underset{R'\ H}{|\ \ |}}{RNH-\overset{\overset{O^-}{|}}{C}-\overset{+}{O}-R''}
\underset{slow}{\overset{fast}{\rightleftharpoons}}
$$

$$
\text{XII} \qquad\qquad \text{XIII}
$$

$$
RNH-\underset{\underset{R'}{|}}{\overset{\overset{O}{\|}}{C}} + R''OH
$$

The "suitable interpretation," mentioned parenthetically above, may become necessary because the ester is attacked, not only by the amine, but also by the conjugate base of the amine, RNH^-. Although this anion should be present in low concentration, it is far more nucleophilic than the amine itself and, molecule for molecule, it should be a much more efficient attacking reagent. For example, the rate law for the conversion of $PhCH_2COOMe$ to $PhCH_2CONH_2$, using ammonia in methanol,[36] suggests that ammonia and the amide ion are competing for the ester molecules in the initial step. It may be shown (Ex. 3) that such a competition leads to a rate expression having two terms, the first proportional to (NH_3), the second proportional to $(NH_3)^{3/2}$.

When an ester is converted to an amide in an aqueous solvent, appreciable hydrolysis may accompany amidization, for although water is less nucleophilic

[34] Gorvin, J. Chem. Soc., 1945, 732.
[35] Miller et al., J. Am. Chem. Soc., 70, 1946 (1948); 71, 1245 (1949); 72, 5635 (1950); 75, 1150 (1953).
[36] Betts and Hammett, J. Am. Chem. Soc., 59, 1568 (1937).

than the vast majority of amines, it is present in large excess. Of particular interest are the reactions of esters with *tertiary* amines; here the intermediate XIV (analogous to XII) cannot be converted to an amide, for this requires loss of a proton from the nitrogen atom and a tertiary amine has no proton to lose. In this case, intermediate XIV may decompose into its parent ester and amine, or it may lose OR''^- to form an N-acylammonium ion:

$$R_3N + R'COOR'' \rightleftharpoons R_3\overset{+}{N}-\underset{\underset{\text{XIV}}{R'}}{\overset{\overset{O^-}{|}}{C}}-OR'' \xrightarrow{-OR''^-} \underset{\substack{\text{N-acylammonium} \\ \text{ion}}}{R_3\overset{+}{N}-\overset{\overset{O}{\|}}{C}-R'} \xrightarrow{H_2O} \begin{cases} R_3N \\ R'COOH \\ R''OH \end{cases}$$

Now, N-acylammonium ions derived from tertiary amines are very readily hydrolyzed. Hence it is quite possible that if the departure of OR''^- is sufficiently rapid compared to the reversal of the original association step, the overall reaction (which is simply an ester hydrolysis) will be faster than hydrolysis of the ester through direct attack by a water molecule. As pointed out in the preceding chapter, an effective leaving group must be only weakly basic—that is, it should be the conjugate base of a relatively strong acid. We would thus expect the amine-catalyzed ester hydrolysis to take place most readily if $R''OH$, the alcohol or phenol from which the ester is derived, is unusually acidic. It has, in fact, been shown that the hydrolyses of the esters of *p*-nitrophenol and 2,4-dinitrophenol are strikingly catalyzed by such amines as trimethylamine, quinoline, pyridine, and the picolines.[37] Typically, *p*-nitrophenyl acetate is hydrolyzed about twenty times as fast in 0.01 M aqueous Me_3N and four times as fast in 0.01 M 4-picoline as in pure water. These hydrolyses are *not* due to the presence of OH^- in such solutions, for the observed catalyses are not affected by addition of the conjugate acids of the respective tertiary amines (which would lower the concentration of OH^- in solution but leave the concentration of amine unchanged). The heterocyclic base, imidazole, XV, is a particularly effective catalyst; for the hydrolysis in 0.01 M aqueous imidazole is almost 100 times as fast as in pure water. In this case, the N-acetyl derivative may lose a proton from the second nitrogen of the imidazole ring, yielding N-acetylimidazole, XVI, which may be detected spectroscopically (λ_{max} at 245 mμ). The latter is considerably more stable than N-acylammonium ions, and it is possible to alter the kinetic characteristics of the reaction by using a large excess of imidazole; for then intermediate XVI is formed rapidly and its hydrolysis becomes the rate-determining step. These amine-catalyzed hydrolyses

[37] Bender and Turnquest, *J. Am. Chem. Soc.*, **79**, 1652, 1656 (1957).

are important because of the possibility that they may constitute relatively simple models for hydrolysis reactions catalyzed by such enzymes as α-chymotrypsin and papain. Indeed, the imidazole ring (a section of the amino acid, histidine) has been proposed as a vital part of the active catalytic sites in these enzymes.[37,38]

Hydrolysis and Alcoholysis of Acyl Chlorides

Along with the substitution reactions on the acyl-carbon atoms of acids, esters, and amides, we should consider such reactions on the acyl carbons of acid halides. Our glimpse will be brief, however, for these reactions, in many ways, resemble the substitution reactions of alkyl halides described in the preceding chapter.[39] As with alkyl halides, a duality of mechanism and a range of borderline cases are recognized. In the alcoholyses of substituted benzoyl chlorides, for example, both extreme mechanisms appear to operate within the same reaction series.[40] Reaction rates for monosubstituted benzoyl chlorides follow a trend typical of those bimolecular nucleophilic substitutions in which the bond-making process governs the activation energy; specifically, the reaction is accelerated by substitution of halo and nitro groups in the benzene ring but retarded by substitution of a p-CH$_3$ group. In line with this trend, we would expect the alcoholysis of mesitoyl chloride to be extremely slow, both because of electron repulsion by the three methyl groups, and because of steric hindrance by those methyls in the 2- and 6-positions. Since this alcoholysis is, on the contrary, "immeasurably fast," we may safely assume that the S_N1 mechanism

[38] Doherty and Vaslow, J. Am. Chem. Soc., **74,** 931 (1952).

[39] The reactions of acid anhydrides are, in a number of respects, similar in character to those of acid chlorides. However, considerably less quantitative data exists on the former group of reactions and they will not be discussed here. For recent work on acid anhydrides, see papers by Gold and co-workers, Trans. Faraday Soc., **44,** 506 (1948), J. Chem. Soc., **1953,** 1406, 1409, 1416, by Berliner and Altschul, J. Am. Chem. Soc., **74,** 4110 (1952), and by Denney and Greenbaum, ibid., **79,** 3701 (1957).

[40] Norris and co-workers, J. Am. Chem. Soc., **57,** 1415, 1420 (1935); **61,** 1418 (1939).

has taken over; for reactions proceeding by this mechanism are subject to steric assistance and to acceleration by electron donation. Similarly, the hydrolysis of mesitoyl chloride in 95 percent aqueous acetone is also unimolecular, for its rate is not affected by addition of hydroxide ions.[41]

It further appears that, as with some alkyl halides, the solvolyses of acyl chlorides may undergo a change in mechanism as the polarity of the solvent is changed. The relative rates of solvolysis of the following p-substituted benzoyl chlorides, for example, suffer an almost complete reversion in order as the reaction is transferred from 40/60 ethanol-ether (dielectric constant 13) to 50/50 water-acetone (dielectric constant 53).[42] Note that in the alcohol-ether

Table 9-2. Effect of Solvent Changes on Relative Solvolysis Rates of p-Substituted Benzoyl Chlorides

Medium	D	Relative Solvolysis Rates				
		p-NO$_2$	p-Br	H	p-CH$_3$	p-CH$_3$O
40% EtOH + 60% Et$_2$O	13	32	2.5	1	0.47	0.25
Pure EtOH	22	22	2.1	1	0.70	0.81
50% H$_2$O + 50% Me$_2$C=O	52	12	0.92	1	2.9	30

mixture, the trend in reactivities is much the same as that observed for the saponification of esters and the basic hydrolysis of amides—typical bimolecular processes. When the reactions are transferred to 100 percent ethanol, the p-methoxy compound moves into the borderline region, since it now reacts more rapidly than the p-methyl compound. In 50/50 water-acetone, the solvolysis of only the p-nitro compound appears to have retained its bimolecular character. The hydrolyses of the remaining acyl chlorides have become distinctly "S_N1-like," and are now subject to acceleration by electron-donating groups.

The kinetic study of the hydrolyses and alcoholyses of acyl halides is not as straightforward as might be desired, for one must select a solvent rather carefully in order to determine the role of the attacking reagent. If a reaction is carried out in media containing water or alcohol as a major component, the rate law may be noncommittal on this point. On the other hand, if the reaction is carried out in a nonpolar solvent, adding measured quantities of alcohol or water, the kinetic order is often masked by the medium effects arising as a result

[41] Brown and Hudson, *J. Chem. Soc.*, **1953**, 3352.
[42] Brown and Hudson, *J. Chem. Soc.*, **1953**, 883.

of adding a polar liquid to a nonpolar one.[43] To date, the most informative kinetic results have been obtained from experiments in ether. The ethanolyses of acetyl chloride[43(a)] and p-nitrobenzoyl chloride[44] in ether have been found to be second order in ethanol over a large concentration range. Thus, the activated complex in these reactions may be presumed to consist of a molecule of acyl chloride, *two* molecules of alcohol, and an unknown number of molecules of ether. Recalling Swain's proposal that both "push" and "pull" are necessary in many (if not all) nucleophilic substitutions (p. 299), we are tempted to picture one of the alcohol molecules as attacking the carbonyl carbon while the other pulls at the chlorine atom through hydrogen bonding.

$$
\begin{array}{c}
\text{H} \qquad \text{R} \\
\diagdown \qquad \diagdown \\
\text{O} \ + \ \text{C--Cl ---- H--OEt} \ \longrightarrow \\
\diagup \qquad \| \\
\text{Et} \qquad \text{O}
\end{array}
\qquad
\begin{array}{c}
\text{H} \qquad \text{R} \\
\diagdown + \diagup \\
\text{O--C} \ + \ \left[\text{Cl ---- HOEt} \right]^{-} \\
\diagup \qquad \| \\
\text{Et} \qquad \text{O}
\end{array}
$$

Before assuming such a mechanism to be general, however, one would like to know whether similar rate laws govern the reactions between other acyl chlorides and other alcohols and whether, in particular, a molecule of phenol (which should form stronger hydrogen bonds to chlorine than does alcohol) can replace a molecule of alcohol in the transition state when the reaction is carried out in the presence of both phenol and alcohol.

The Claisen Condensation

The Claisen condensation is related to the saponification and "amidization" of esters. In saponification, a hydroxide ion attacks the acyl carbon of the ester; in "amidization," an amine or its conjugate base attacks. In the Claisen condensation, the attacking reagent is a *carbanion*, obtained by removal of a slightly acidic hydrogen from a ketone, a nitrile, or, most often, from another molecule of ester. In the cyclic counterpart of the Claisen condensation, the *Dieckmann reaction*, the acyl carbon of a —COOR group is attacked by a negatively charged carbon somewhere else in the same molecule, forming a new C—C bond and a new ring.

---

[43] Typically, the rate of ethanolysis of acetyl chloride in CCl_4 depends upon the concentration of ethanol, but the reaction *cannot be said to be any particular order in ethanol.* "Apparent orders" with respect to ethanol may be obtained by plotting the logarithms of the instantaneous rates against the logarithms of ethanol concentrations, then measuring the slope of the resulting curve, but such "apparent orders" are found to vary from about three in dilute solutions to unity in more concentrated solutions. See (a) Hudson and Saville, *J. Chem. Soc.*, **1955**, 4121. Similarly, the "apparent order" with respect to water of the hydrolysis of benzoyl chloride in water-acetone mixtures has been found to vary from two in 70 percent acetone to near seven in 50 percent acetone; see (b) Hudson and Archer, *J. Chem. Soc.*, **1950**, 3259.

[44] Ashdown, *J. Am. Chem. Soc.*, **52**, 269 (1930).

$$-\underset{\underset{O}{\parallel}}{C}-\overset{R}{\underset{\vdots}{C}}:^- \;+\; \underset{\underset{O}{\parallel}}{C}-OR' \;\longrightarrow\; -\underset{\underset{O}{\parallel}}{C}-\underset{\vert}{C}-\overset{R}{C} \;+\; OR'^- \quad \text{(Claisen)}$$

$$-\underset{\underset{O}{\parallel}}{C}:^- \quad \underset{\underset{O}{\parallel}}{C}-OR \;\longrightarrow\; -\underset{\vert}{C}-\underset{\underset{O}{\parallel}}{C} \;+\; OR^- \quad \text{(Dieckmann)}$$

An important requirement for the Claisen condensation is that carbanions be available, at least in small concentration. Although the factors favoring the stability of carbanions are not to be discussed until the following chapter, we might note here the evidence that carbanions are present in significant quantities in solutions in which the Claisen condensation is occurring. It is now well recognized that esters, ketones, and nitriles having one or more α-hydrogen atoms undergo hydrogen exchange at the α-position when dissolved in "labeled" ethanol, C_2H_5OD, containing NaOEt,[45] indicating the existence of the following mobile equilibria:

$$H-\underset{\vert}{C}-\underset{\underset{O}{\parallel}}{C}- \;+\; OEt^- \;\rightleftharpoons\; {}^-:\underset{\vert}{C}-\underset{\underset{O}{\parallel}}{C}- \;+\; EtOH,$$

and

$$ {}^-:\underset{\vert}{C}-\underset{\underset{O}{\parallel}}{C}- \;+\; EtOD \;\rightleftharpoons\; D-\underset{\vert}{C}-\underset{\underset{O}{\parallel}}{C}- \;+\; OEt^- $$

[handwritten margin note: lability of α H in presence of ET O⊖ (Ethoxide ion) Exchange of D° for H⊕]

Furthermore, optically active esters of the type $\overset{R}{\underset{R'}{\diagdown\!\!/}}\overset{*}{C}H-COOEt$ are racemized by ethoxide ion,[46] the asymmetry of the α-carbon atom presumably being lost in the carbanion, $\overset{R}{\underset{R'}{\diagdown\!\!/}}\overset{\cdot\cdot}{C}{}^-\!-COOEt.$

Having established the existence of carbanions in the reaction mixture, we may write (provisionally) for the Claisen condensation a mechanism very similar to that for ester saponification and that for the formation of amides. Thus, for the formation of acetoacetic ester,

$$CH_3-COOEt + OEt^- \rightleftharpoons {}^-:CH_2-COOEt + EtOH$$

[45] See, for example, Brown and Eberly, *J. Am. Chem. Soc.*, **62**, 113 (1940).
[46] Kenyon and Young, *J. Chem. Soc.*, **1940**, 216.

$$\underset{\underset{CH_3}{|}}{EtO-\overset{\overset{O}{\|}}{C}} + \ ^-:CH_2COOEt \rightleftharpoons \left[\underset{\underset{CH_3}{|}}{EtO-\overset{\overset{O}{|}}{\underset{|}{C}}-CH_2COOEt}\right]^- \rightleftharpoons$$

XVII

$$EtO^- + \underset{\underset{CH_3}{|}}{\overset{\overset{O}{\|}}{C}-CH_2COOEt}$$

$$\underset{\underset{O}{\|}}{CH_3-\overset{}{C}-CH_2-COOEt} + OEt^- \rightleftharpoons \left[\underset{\underset{O}{\|}}{CH_3-\overset{}{C}-\overset{\cdot\cdot}{C}H-COOEt}\right]^- + EtOH$$

Here, we cannot say whether anion XVII is a true intermediate or merely an activated complex. (Moreover, experiments in which the acyl oxygen is "labeled" cannot answer this question, for even if XVII were long lived, there is no path by which the acyl oxygen can exchange with solvent oxygen.) Note that in the final step, the product, acetoacetic ester, is converted by base to its anion. Since this β-ketoester is almost as strong an acid as phenol, this conversion should be nearly complete if an excess of ethoxide (which is a somewhat stronger base than OH$^-$) is used. The success of the Claisen condensation, as it is usually carried out, depends upon this final step which removes the desired keto ester from the reaction site; for this condensation is known to be reversible,[47] and if the final proton transfer could not occur, the equilibrium involved would allow only a small degree of conversion. Ethyl isobutyrate is not appreciably converted to keto ester XVIII by sodium ethoxide since the latter has no

$$2(CH_3)_2CH-COOEt \underset{MsMgBr \text{ or } Ph_3CNa}{\overset{OEt^-}{\longrightarrow}} (CH_3)_2CH-\overset{\overset{O}{\|}}{C}-C(CH_3)_2-COOEt + EtOH$$

XVIII

α-hydrogen atoms and therefore cannot be converted to an anion by NaOEt. However, as indicated, the preparation of XVIII *can* be carried out using a stronger base than ethoxide, such as sodium triphenylmethide, Na$^+$CPh$_3^-$, or mesitylmagnesium bromide, XIX (which, although a Grignard reagent, is too

(MsMgBr, XIX)

---

[47] See, for example, Kutz and Adkins, *J. Am. Chem. Soc.*, **52**, 4391 (1930).

hindered to undergo the typical Grignard addition reactions).[48] The use of these very strong bases assists the reaction in two ways. The removal of the very weakly acidic α-hydrogen from isobutyric ester is accelerated, and, what is more important, the resulting keto ester is partially converted to the anion $^-$:CMe$_2$—C—CMe$_2$—COOEt, by removal of a γ-*hydrogen*, with the resulting

$$\underset{O}{\overset{||}{}}$$

favorable effect on the equilibrium.

The Cleavage of β-Diketones

The basic cleavage of β-diketones is essentially a reversal of the Claisen condensation, for here an OH$^-$ or OR$^-$ ion attacks an acyl carbon, displacing a carbanion. Let us compare the following cleavages, for which rate laws have been determined.[49]

$$\text{HO}^- + \underset{\underset{Me}{|}}{\overset{\overset{O}{||}}{C}} - \underset{\underset{Me}{|}}{\overset{\overset{Me}{|}}{C}} - \underset{}{\overset{\overset{O}{||}}{C}} - \text{Me} \rightarrow \text{HO} - \underset{\underset{Me}{|}}{\overset{\overset{O}{||}}{C}} + \ ^-\text{:}\underset{\underset{Me}{|}}{\overset{\overset{Me}{|}}{C}} - \underset{}{\overset{\overset{O}{||}}{C}} - \text{Me} \rightarrow \begin{cases} \text{CH}_3\text{COO}^- \\ \text{Me}_2\text{CH} - \underset{\overset{||}{O}}{C} - \text{Me} \end{cases}$$

XX

$$\text{EtO}^- + \underset{\underset{Me}{|}}{\overset{\overset{O}{||}}{C}} - \text{CH}_2 - \overset{\overset{O}{||}}{C} - \text{Me} \rightleftharpoons \text{EtO} - \underset{\underset{Me}{|}}{\overset{\overset{O}{||}}{C}} + \ ^-\text{:CH}_2 - \overset{\overset{O}{||}}{C} - \text{Me}$$

The first of these reactions, rendered irreversible because of the formation of the acetate ion in the final step, takes place readily, and its rate is simply proportional to (OH$^-$) × (diketone).[49(a)] The second cleavage of acetylacetone is slower, although we should perhaps expect the opposite, reasoning that the additional methyl groups in the first diketone should retard the attack, both sterically and inductively. Moreover, the kinetics of the second reaction appear to *depend upon whether the diketone or the ethoxide ion is in excess*. If the diketone is in excess, the reaction rate is proportional to added ethoxide but independent of added diketone, whereas if ethoxide is in excess, the reaction is first order in diketone but zero order in ethoxide.[49(b)] This relationship suggests that the rate of cleavage is proportional to the concentration of some species formed by *a very nearly complete reaction between one mole each of ethoxide and diketone*. In this case

[48] For discussions of the Claisen condensation with isobutyric esters and other similarly unreactive esters, see, for example, Spielman and Schmidt, *J. Am. Chem. Soc.*, **59**, 2009 (1937), and Renfrow and Hauser, *ibid.*, **60**, 463 (1938).

[49] (a) Pearson and Mayerle, *J. Am. Chem. Soc.*, **73**, 926 (1951). (b) Pearson and Sandy, *ibid.*, **73**, 931 (1951).

the number of moles of this species would be determined by whichever of the two reagents is *not in excess*. Immediately the conjugate base of acetylacetone

$$\left(CH_3-\underset{\underset{O}{\|}}{C}-\overset{\cdot\cdot}{\underset{}{C}H}-\underset{\underset{O}{\|}}{C}-CH_3 \leftrightarrow CH_3-\underset{\underset{O_-}{|}}{C}=CH-\underset{\underset{O}{\|}}{C}-CH_3 \right) \text{ comes to mind, and}$$

the kinetic picture is consistent with a mechanism in which the rate-determining step is the reaction of the anion with a molecule of solvent. Yet this cannot be, for dimethylacetylacetone, XX, which cannot lose a proton in the same way, reacts *more rapidly* than acetylacetone (both with EtO⁻ and OH⁻). Let us, however, recall a fundamental limitation of kinetic studies: they cannot tell us whether the rate-determining step in a reaction sequence involves one group of reactants or a second group in rapid equilibrium with the first. In particular, the anion XXI is in equilibrium with the diketone and ethoxide, and a reaction rate proportional to the concentration of XXI is necessarily proportional to the product (OEt⁻) × (diketone):

$$CH_3-\underset{\underset{O}{\|}}{C}-CH_2-\underset{\underset{O}{\|}}{C}-CH_3 + OEt^- \rightleftharpoons CH_3-\underset{\underset{O_-}{|}}{C}=CH-\overset{\overset{O}{\|}}{C}-CH_3 + EtOH$$

XXI

$$K_{eq} = \frac{\text{anion}}{(\text{diketone})(\text{OEt}^-)}$$

and,

$$\text{rate} = k(\text{anion}) = k'(\text{diketone})(\text{OEt}^-) \qquad (4)$$

The rate law is thus equally consistent with a rate-determining attack by ethoxide on the diketone.

$$EtO^- + \underset{\underset{Me}{|}}{\overset{\overset{O}{\|}}{C}}-CH_2-\overset{\overset{O}{\|}}{C}-Me \xrightarrow{\text{slow}} EtO-\underset{\underset{Me}{|}}{\overset{\overset{O}{\|}}{C}} + :CH_2-\overset{\overset{O}{\|}}{C}-Me \xrightarrow[\text{fast}]{EtOH}$$

EtOAc + Me₂C=O + EtO⁻

The kinetic complications arise because these two species may react in an alternate way—that is, by simple proton transfer. This is why acetylacetone is cleaved much more slowly than dimethylacetylacetone, XX. In the latter compound, the alternate reaction path, which greatly lowers the concentrations of the reacting species in the cleavage reaction, is closed.

For an unsymmetrical β-diketone, $R-\underset{\underset{O}{\|}}{C}-CH_2-\underset{\underset{O}{\|}}{C}-R'$, two modes of cleavage, leading to two different acids (or esters), are possible. If the substrate exists very largely in the keto (rather than in one or both of the enol) forms, the preferred position of attack is easily predicted; for a nucleophilic OH^- or OR^- ion will be most likely to attack the *more electrophilic* of the two carbonyl groups. The acid RCOOH should be formed in preference to R'COOH if R— is a stronger electron attractor than R'—; this is equivalent to saying that the cleavage should yield, as the principal product, the *stronger of the two possible acids* (or its ester).[50(a)] When considerable enolization of the diketone occurs, the situation becomes more complicated, for, although there is only one possible enolate anion, there are two possible enols: R—C=CH—C—R' and

$$\underset{\text{OH}}{|} \qquad \underset{\text{O}}{\|}$$

R—C—CH=C—R'. Since, it appears, attack takes place on a keto (rather

$$\underset{\text{O}}{\|} \qquad \underset{\text{OH}}{|}$$

than on an enol) carbon atom, the first of these two forms shown is protected from attack at the carbon adjacent to R— but not adjacent to R'—, whereas the reverse is true for the second form. Thus, the mode of attack will depend not only on the electrophilicities of the carbonyl groups in the keto form, but also on the relative amounts of the two enol forms present in the reaction mixture. If substituent R— favors enolization more than does R'—, then R'—COOH will tend to be formed rather than R—COOH. Thus the cleavage of benzoylacetone, $PhCOCH_2COCH_3$, yields mainly acetic acid,[50(b)] rather than the stronger acid, benzoic acid. This is in line with our knowledge that a phenyl group promotes enolization more effectively than a methyl group (Chap. 10).

Esterifications and Hydrolyses Proceeding Through Carbonium Ions. The $A_{AL}1$ Mechanism[51]

Returning now to ester hydrolysis and esterification, let us consider the acid-catalyzed hydrolyses of the esters of tertiary alcohols. If we apply to such esters the same types of tests that, for the esters of primary and most secondary alcohols, indicate or suggest acyl-oxygen cleavage, we obtain different answers. The acid hydrolysis of *t*-butyl acetate in H_2O^{18} yields *labeled t*-butyl alcohol, establishing, in this case at least, *alkyl-oxygen cleavage*.[52]

---

[50] (a) Bradley and Robertson, *J. Chem. Soc.*, **1926**, 2356; (b) Kutz and Adkins, *J. Am Chem. Soc.*, **52**, 4036 (1930).

[51] For a review of alkyl-oxygen cleavage in ester hydrolyses and related reactions, see Davies and Kenyon, *Quart. Revs.* **IX**, 203 (1956).

[52] Bunton, Comyns, and Wood, *Research*, **4**, 383 (1951). In this hydrolysis, the acetic acid resulting is also labeled with O^{18}, but this may be shown to be due to rapid exchange with water. To complete the argument, it must be shown that the *t*-butyl alcohol also does not become labeled through exchange with water. These authors show that although such an exchange does occur, it is a much slower reaction than the hydrolysis under consideration.

$$(CH_3)_3C\!-\!O\!-\!\underset{\underset{O}{\|}}{C}\!-\!CH_3 + H_2O^{18} \xrightarrow{H^+} (CH_3)_3C\!-\!O^{18}\!-\!H + CH_3COOH$$

from alcohol

A similar, but more definite, conclusion arises from the acid-catalyzed hydrolysis of the optically active acetate, XXII. The resulting carbinol, XXIII, is almost completely racemized.[53] This shows not only that alkyl-oxygen cleavage

$$(CH_3)_2CHCH_2CH_2CH_2\!-\!\underset{\underset{Me}{|}}{\overset{\overset{Et}{|}}{C}}\!-\!O\!-\!\underset{\underset{O}{\|}}{C}\!-\!CH_3 \xrightarrow[\text{water dioxane}]{H^+}$$

XXII (active)

$$i\text{-}C_6H_{13}\!-\!\underset{\underset{Me}{|}}{\overset{\overset{Et}{|}}{C}}\!-\!OH + CH_3COOH$$

90 percent (racemized)

XXIII

has occurred, but also that the reaction is unimolecular—that is, that it proceeds

through the carbonium ion, $i\text{-}C_6H_{13}\!-\!\underset{\underset{Me}{|}}{\overset{\overset{Et}{|}}{C^+}}$. If it were bimolecular—that is, a

direct displacement of acetate by water—inversion of configuration about the asymmetric carbon, rather than racemization, should occur. Assuming that acetate XXII and *t*-butyl acetate are representative esters of tertiary alcohols, we may represent the acid-catalyzed hydrolysis of esters in this class as follows:

$$R'\!-\!\underset{\underset{O}{\|}}{\overset{\overset{H}{|}}{\underset{+}{C}}}\!-\!O\!-\!CR_3 \underset{+R'COOH, \text{ fast}}{\overset{-R'COOH, \text{ slow}}{\rightleftharpoons}} R_3C^+ \underset{-H_2O, \text{ slow}}{\overset{+H_2O, \text{ fast}}{\rightleftharpoons}} R_3C\!-\!\overset{+}{\underset{\diagdown H}{O}}{\diagup}^H$$

Although the reaction is represented as being reversible, esterifications of tertiary alcohols are seldom carried out in the manner indicated. However, the esterification of the optically active secondary alcohol, 2-octanol, using sulfuric acid in a large excess of acetic acid, appears to take place, at least in part, by the $A_{AL}1$ mechanism, for extensive racemization accompanies this reaction.[54]

Both the $A_{AC}1$ and the $A_{AL}1$ mechanisms are, quite naturally, facilitated by strongly acidic solvents, but the structural features within the ester which favor the two mechanisms are different. The breakage of the acyl-oxygen bond

[53] Bunton, Hughes, Ingold, and Meigh, *Nature*, **166**, 679 (1950).
[54] Hughes, Ingold, and Masterman, *J. Chem. Soc.*, **1939**, 840.

to form an acylium ion $\left(\begin{array}{c} O \\ \| \\ R-C{:}\overset{..}{O}{:}R' \\ {+}\quad | \\ H \end{array} \right)$ is favored by the presence of electron-

attracting substituents in R' and electron-repelling substituents in R, whereas the reverse is true if the alkyl-oxygen bond is to be broken, forming a carbonium

ion $\left(\begin{array}{c} H \\ | \\ R-C-O{:}R'^{+} \\ \| \quad\quad {..} \\ O \end{array} \right)$. Bearing this in mind, we can rationalize (although we

probably would not have predicted) the order of the hydrolysis rates for alkyl benzoates in concentrated sulfuric acid.[55]

$$(CH_3)_3C-OBz > (CH_3)_2CH-OBz > CH_3-OBz > CH_3CH_2-OBz$$

The hydrolysis of methyl benzoate in concentrated sulfuric acid proceeds, as we have noted (p. 326), by the $A_{Ac}1$ mechanism. Ethyl benzoate is apparently hydrolyzed via the same route, since the substitution of an electron-repelling methyl group for an α-hydrogen in the alkyl section of the molecule decreases the hydrolysis rate by about 50 percent. But the substitution of two, and, more particularly, three methyl groups for α-hydrogens in the alkyl section *boosts* the reaction rate again. The trend is, of course, very much like that for the basic hydrolyses of the corresponding alkyl bromides (p. 311, Ex. 11a), and strongly suggests a change in mechanism; that is, *i*-propyl and *t*-butyl benzoates are hydrolyzed via the $A_{AL}1$ mechanism (where electron-repelling substituents in the alkyl group aid reaction), rather than via the $A_{Ac}1$ mechanism (where such substituents inhibit the reaction). In line with this supposition we are not surprised to learn that the electron-attracting *p*-nitro group *retards* the hydrolysis of ethyl benzoate by a factor of 63, whereas the same group *accelerates* the hydrolysis of *i*-propyl benzoate by a factor of 200.[55(b)]

The intervention of alkyl-oxygen cleavage in the reactions between esters and alcohols may be detected without difficulty by simply identifying the products. Acyl-oxygen cleavage in such reactions would result in ester interchange (p. 321), but if alkyl-oxygen cleavage occurs, the ester is converted instead to an ether and a carboxylic acid.

$$ \begin{array}{c} {+} \\ R-C-O-R' \\ \| \quad | \\ O \quad H \end{array} \rightarrow \left\{ \begin{array}{l} R'^{+} \xrightarrow{R''OH} R'-O-R'' + H^{+} \\[2mm] R-COOH \end{array} \right. $$

In this manner *t*-butyl benzoate and triphenylmethyl acetate, when treated

[55] (a) Kuhn, *J. Am. Chem. Soc.*, **71**, 1575 (1949); (b) Leisten, *J. Chem. Soc.*, **1956**, 1572.

with methanolic HCl, have been found to yield, respectively, t-BuOMe and Ph$_3$COMe, together with the respective parent acids.[56]

Alkyl-Oxygen Cleavage in Neutral and Basic Media. The $B_{AL}1$ and $B_{AL}2$ Mechanisms

The unimolecular cleavage of esters at the alkyl-oxygen bond is, in essence, an S_N1 reaction in which the carboxylate ion is the leaving group. On this basis, we may predict a number of characteristics of this mechanism: (a) It should be observed only for those esters in which the alkyl group forms a *relatively stable carbonium ion*—that is, esters of tertiary alcohols and certain special secondary alcohols such as benzhydrols and α-substituted allyl alcohols. (b) It should be facilitated by electron-repelling substituents on the alkyl group (which would stabilize the carbonium ion intermediate), and by electron-attracting substituents on the acyloxy group (which would tend to ease the departure of the latter). (c) Aside from an expected positive salt effect, the rates of reactions proceeding by the $B_{AL}1$ mechanism should not be increased by addition of OH⁻. (d) The rate constant should be subject to decrease by the mass-law effect (p. 256) as the reaction progresses. (e) This mechanism should be favored by media of high dielectric constant; in particular, the rates of such reactions carried out in aqueous acetone, aqueous alcohol, or aqueous dioxane should depend upon the concentration of water but should not be proportional to it. (f) This mechanism should not be subject to steric hindrance. (g) When such reactions occur at an asymmetric carbon atom, extensive racemization should occur. (h) Finally, when an ester of a substituted allyl alcohol is hydrolyzed by this mechanism, partial allylic rearrangement (p. 286) should be observed.

The stereochemical studies of reactions proceeding by the $B_{AL}1$ mechanism have, to date, been concerned largely with the half esters of phthalic acid (these, besides being esters, are acids and may generally be resolved directly, using the conventional basic resolving agents). For example, the hydrolyses of the optically active half esters, XXIV, XXV, and XXVI, in dilute aqueous NaOH yield the corresponding racemic alcohols, and XXIV also yields a racemic alcohol in 10N NaOH.[57] Again, the stereochemical results point both to unimolecularity and alkyl-oxygen cleavage. If, however, half esters XXV or XXVI are hydrolyzed in concentrated base, the resulting alcohols are formed with retention of configuration, indicating that the more usual $B_{AC}2$ mechanism has taken over. Indeed, it is quite likely that hydrolysis by both mechanisms is occurring in dilute base, but that hydrolysis by the $B_{AL}1$ mechanism is so fast that the alternate

---

[56] (a) Cohen and Schneider, *J. Am. Chem. Soc.*, **63**, 3382 (1941). (b) Bunton and Wood, *J. Chem. Soc.*, **1955**, 1522.

[57] Kenyon *et al.*, *J. Chem. Soc.*, **1936**, 85, 576; (b) **1942**, 605; (c) **1946**, 803, 807.

mechanism is difficult or impossible to detect. As the concentration of base is progressively increased, hydrolysis by the $B_{AC}2$ mechanism is necessarily accelerated, but that by the $B_{AL}1$ mechanism is very nearly unaffected, and the rate of the former may overtake, then pass, the rate of the latter.[58] (With half ester XXIV, which forms an exceptionally stable carbonium ion, $B_{AL}1$ hy-

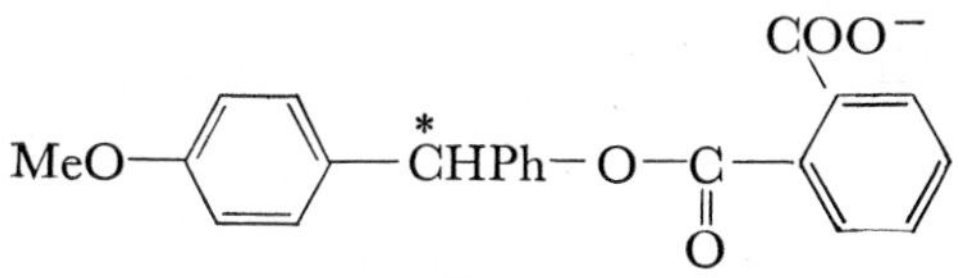

XXIV

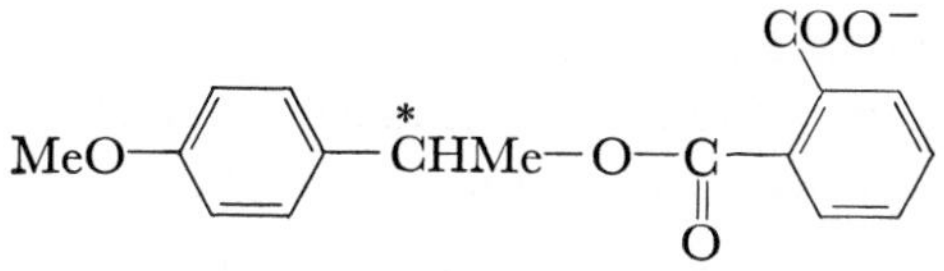

XXV

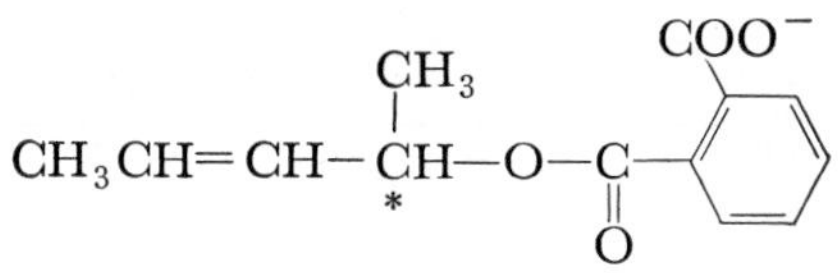

XXVI

drolysis is presumably so rapid that it predominates even in concentrated base.) We may likewise understand why the half ester XXVII, when hydrolyzed in concentrated base in aqueous methanol, yielded its parent alcohol, but why, when treated with dilute base in the more polar solvent water, it yielded both its parent alcohol and the isomer formed by allylic rearrangement.[59]

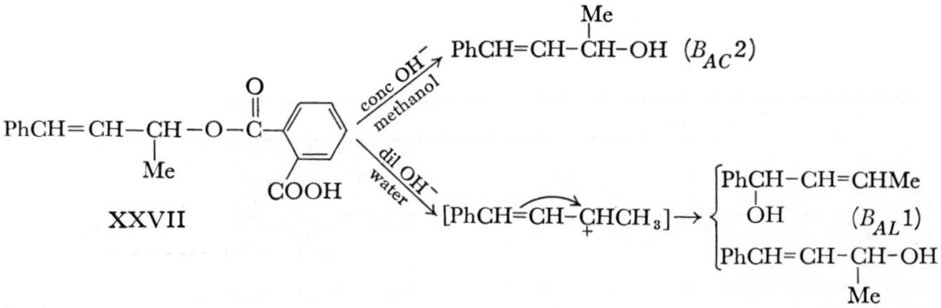

[58] This explanation would be on firmer ground if it were shown that when the hydrolysis product is racemic, the rate of hydrolysis is very nearly independent of (OH⁻); that when the hydrolysis occurs with retention of configuration, it is first order in OH⁻; and that in the concentration range where racemization is partial, the rate of hydrolysis varies with (OH⁻), but by less than a first-order dependence. To the knowledge of the present author, such experiments have not, as yet, been described.

[59] Kenyon, Partridge, and Phillips, *J. Chem. Soc.*, **1937**, 207.

As has been indicated, alkyl-oxygen heterolysis of esters in alcoholic solutions leads to etherification of the solvent rather than ester interchange. Thus, triphenylmethyl benzoate reacts with ethanol (in methyl ethyl ketone) to yield the expected ether,

$$Ph_3C \!-\! O \!-\! \underset{\underset{O}{\|}}{C} \!-\! Ph \xrightarrow{-PhCOO^-} Ph_3C^+ \xrightarrow{EtOH} Ph_3C\!-\!O\!-\!Et \ + \ H^+$$

Aside from a small salt effect, the rate of this reaction is not increased by the addition of sodium ethoxide, demonstrating unimolecularity.[60] Similar alkylations have been reported for ammonia,[57(c)] p-thiocresol,[61] hydrogen peroxide,[62] and other nucleophiles, using esters that undergo the $B_{AL}1$ cleavage. In each of these cases, an optically active acid phthalate yields racemic products.

Bimolecular alkyl-oxygen fission (the $B_{AL}2$ mechanism) in the hydrolysis of *carboxylic* esters is extremely uncommon. It appears that the only unequivocal example to date is the hydrolysis of β-butyrolactone, XXVIII, at pH values

[60] Hammond and Rudesill, *J. Am. Chem. Soc.*, **72**, 2769 (1950).
[61] Dabby, Davies, Kenyon, and Lyons, *J. Chem. Soc.*, **1953**, 1541.
[62] Davies and White, *J. Chem. Soc.*, **1952**, 3300.

between about 2 and 8. In strongly basic solution, this cyclic ester undergoes saponification by the $B_{AC}2$ mechanism; and, as we have seen (p. 327), hydrolysis in strongly acid solutions proceeds by the less ordinary $A_{AC}1$ mechanism. Hydrolysis in H_2O^{18} at extreme pH values thus yields β-hydroxybutyric acid with essentially *no* O^{18} *in the* β-OH *group*,[29] but at intermediate pH values, this hydroxyl group in the resulting acid *is* labeled. It might appear that here we are simply observing another example of $B_{AL}1$ hydrolysis, but for one additional observation: hydrolysis at intermediate pH values results in *inversion of configuration* about the β-carbon;[63] that is, the resulting hydroxy acid is the enantiomorph of that resulting from hydrolysis in strong base or in strong acid.

$$H_2O^* + D\text{-} \quad \begin{array}{c} H_3C \quad\quad H \\ \diagdown \quad \diagup \\ C\text{---}CH_2 \\ | \quad\quad | \\ O\text{---}C\!\!=\!\!O \end{array} \longrightarrow L\text{-} \quad \begin{array}{c} H \quad\quad Me \\ \diagdown \quad\quad | \\ O^*\text{---}C\text{---}CH_2\text{---}C\text{---}O^- \\ \diagup_+ \quad | \quad\quad \| \\ H \quad\quad H \quad\quad O \end{array} \longrightarrow$$

$$L\text{-}\ HO^*\text{---}CHMe\text{---}CH_2\text{---}COOH$$

XXVIII

It is likely that β-propiolactone is also hydrolyzed by this mechanism at intermediate pH values, but the absence of the stereochemical criterion in this case makes us less certain.[64]

It has been remarked that alkyl-oxygen cleavage in ester hydrolysis is favored by electron-attracting groups or atoms in that section of the molecule derived from the acid. Since such groups invariably increase the strength of acids, a rather good rule of thumb (not without exception) is that esters of the strongest acids are most likely to suffer alkyl-oxygen bond breakage in hydrolysis. This is consistent with our knowledge that the alkyl esters of sulfonic acids, in most of their ordinary displacement reactions, undergo cleavage of the alkyl-oxygen bond rather than the S—O bond. Similarly, it has been shown that the basic hydrolyses of a number of alkyl nitrates,[65] sulfates,[66] and chromates[67] (that is, esters of strong acids) take place, at least in part, with alkyl-oxygen cleavage. On the other hand, esters of somewhat weaker acids—for example, alkyl nitrites,[68] phosphates,[69] and hypochlorites[67]—undergo basic hydrolysis with alkyl-oxygen bonds intact.

[63] Olson and Miller, *J. Am. Chem. Soc.*, **60**, 2687 (1938).

[64] See, however, Bartlett and Rylander, *J. Am. Chem. Soc.*, **73**, 4273 (1951). For another possible example of the $B_{AL}2$ mechanism, the reaction between methyl benzoate and sodium methoxide to yield dimethyl ether, see Bunnett, Robinson, and Pennington, *ibid.*, **72**, 2328 (1950).

[65] Cristol, Frenzus, and Shadan, *J. Am. Chem. Soc.*, **77**, 2512 (1955).

[66] Burwell and Holmquist, *ibid.*, **70**, 878 (1948); **74**, 1462 (1952).

[67] Anbar, Dostrovsky, Samuel and Yoffe, *J. Chem. Soc.*, **1954**, 3603.

[68] Allen, *J. Chem. Soc.*, **1954**, 1869.

[69] Blumenthal and Herbert, *Trans. Faraday Soc.*, **41**, 611 (1945).

Decarboxylation

Almost any carboxylic acid, RCOOH, can be made to suffer decarboxylation if it is treated severely enough (provided, of course, that it is not first destroyed in some other way). However, the decarboxylation of an acid should occur most readily if, within group R—, there is a *strongly electron-attracting substituent* such as —NO_2, —CCl_3, —C≡N, or —C=O. This is to be expected, for a

decarboxylation is ordinarily a heterolysis in which group R— departs *with an electron pair* $\left(\text{R}-\text{C}-\text{O}^- \rightarrow \text{R:}^- + \text{O}=\text{C}=\text{O} \right).$

One of the first decarboxylations to be studied kinetically was that of acetoacetic acid.[70]

$$CH_3-C-CH_2-COOH \rightarrow CH_3-C-CH_3 + CO_2$$

This reaction, as well as the closely related decomposition of α,α-dimethyl-acetoacetic acid into methyl isopropyl ketone and CO_2,[71] follows a rate law of the following type:

$$\text{rate} = k\,(\text{keto acid}) + k'\,(\text{keto-acid anion}) \tag{5}$$

This suggests that there are two distinct modes of decarboxylation, neither of which involves the enol form of the acid or its salt (since α,α-dimethylaceto-acetic acid cannot exist in an ordinary enol form). It seems likely that the two terms in the rate law correspond simply to unimolecular decompositions of the keto acid (equation 6) and its anion (equation 7), respectively. There is one minor difficulty: with both keto acids, k (for the keto acid itself) is much greater than k' (for the anion), whereas one would expect the proton on the —COOH group to inhibit, rather than to accelerate, decarboxylation. It is likely, there-fore, that there is a partial transfer of the carboxyl proton, through intra-molecular hydrogen bonding, XXIX, to the keto group, where it should aid decarboxylation.

$$CH_3-C-CH_2-C-O^- \xrightarrow[\text{slow}]{-CO_2} \left[CH_3-C-CH_2^- \leftrightarrow CH_3-C=CH_2 \right] \tag{6}$$

XXX

$$\xrightarrow[\text{fast}]{+H_2O} (CH_3)_2C=O + OH^-$$

[70] Widmark, *Acta med. Scand.*, **53**, 393 (1920); *Chem. Abstr.*, **15**, 2763 (1921).
[71] Pederson, *J. Am. Chem. Soc.*, **51**, 2098 (1929); **58**, 240 (1936).

$$H_3C-\overset{\overset{\displaystyle ..}{\overset{\displaystyle O:}{\|}}}{C}\overset{\displaystyle ----H-O}{\underset{\displaystyle CH_2}{\diagdown}}C=O \xrightarrow{\text{slow}} CH_3-\overset{\overset{\displaystyle OH}{|}}{C}\underset{\displaystyle CH_2}{\diagdown} + \overset{\overset{\displaystyle O}{\|}}{C}=O \xrightarrow{\text{fast}}$$

$$(CH_3)_2\,C=O + CO_2 \,(7)$$

XXIX	XXXI

Furthermore, the intermediate anion **XXX** or the enol **XXXI** may be "trapped" by carrying out the decarboxylation in the presence of bromine or iodine. Here, the reaction product is a monobromo or monoiodoketone, but the rate at which the keto acid disappears is unchanged. The halogenation does *not* occur before the decarboxylation step (for if it did, the rate of decarboxylation would change); nor does it occur after the final formation of the ketones, for it may be shown that these are not halogenated under decarboxylation conditions. Since halogenation occurs after the decarboxylation and before the formation of the ketone, it must be a reaction of a short-lived intermediate—almost certainly enol **XXXI**, or anion **XXX**, or both.

$$CH_3-\underset{\underset{\displaystyle O}{\|}}{C}-CH_2:^- + Br_2 \xrightarrow{\text{fast}} CH_3-\underset{\underset{\displaystyle O}{\|}}{C}-CH_2Br + Br^-$$

$$CH_3-\underset{\underset{\displaystyle OH}{|}}{C}=CH_2 + Br_2 \xrightarrow{\text{fast}} CH_3-\underset{\underset{\displaystyle O}{\|}}{C}-CH_2Br + HBr$$

On this basis, we can understand why bicyclic β-keto acids in which the —COOH group is bound to a "bridgehead" carbon (for example, camphenonic acid, **XXXII**) may be decarboxylated only with extreme difficulty.[72] The

XXXII	XXXIII

hypothetical enol **XXXIII** that would presumably result from the decarboxylation of acid **XXXII** may be drawn on paper, but a scale model of this enol, having the correct bond angles, cannot be constructed, even with pushing and twisting. The reader will recall that the four atoms attached to the pair of double-bonded atoms must lie very nearly in a common plane—a requirement clearly incompatible with this bicyclic ring system, since one of these four atoms in **XXXIII** is the carbon atom of the methylene bridge that must be pulled

[72] This, and a number of similar cases, are described by Fawcett, *Chem. Revs.*, **47**, 219 (1950).

far out of the plane of the remaining three. (This is a case covered by *Bredt's rule*, which stipulates that except for very large ring systems introduction of a double bond at the bridgehead of bicyclic systems is prohibited.[73]) Since acid XXXII cannot, except with rearrangement, yield the necessary enol or an enolate ion intermediate, it resists decarboxylation.

The rates of decarboxylation of a number of additional acids are proportional to the concentrations of the respective carboxylate ions, and, in the absence of evidence to the contrary, we may assume that these anions undergo heterolysis to a carbanion and CO_2 in the same manner as the anions of acetoacetic and α,α-dimethylacetoacetic acids. Among these acids are α-nitroacetic and α-nitroisobutyric acids,[74] dibromomalonic acid,[75] phenylpropiolic acid (Ph—C≡C—COOH),[76] the trihaloacetic acids,[76,77] and 2,4,6-trinitrobenzoic acid.[78] In the first three of these cases, the carbanion intermediates have been "trapped" with Br_2 (as with the β-keto acids). With none of these is the rate of decarboxylation of the acid itself appreciable; but malonic acid, for which a hydrogen-bonded structure analogous to XXIX may be drawn, decomposes almost ten times as rapidly as its monovalent anion.

Furthermore, a number of nitrogen-containing acids exist that undergo

---

[73] Bredt, *Ann.*, **437**, 1 (1924). This rule does not apply to systems such as XXXIV in which one of the bridges is merely a covalent bond. Neither does it apply to systems having bridges with five or more atoms, for these are sufficiently flexible to conform to the geometry of the double bond without excessive strain in the ring. Thus, keto acid XXXV decarboxylates readily at 250° in quinoline (Prelog, *et al.*, *Helv. Chim. Acta*, **31**, 92 (1948); **32**, 1284 (1949)), although the enol derived from it has a double bond at a bridgehead.

XXXIV

XXXV

[74] Pederson, *J. Phys. Chem.*, **38**, 559 (1934).

[75] Muus, *ibid.*, **39**, 343 (1935); **40**, 121 (1926).

[76] Fairclough, *J. Chem. Soc.*, **1938**, 1186.

[77] Verhoek, *et al.*, *J. Am. Chem. Soc.*, **56**, 571 (1934); **72**, 299 (1950).

[78] Verhoek, *J. Am. Chem. Soc.*, **61**, 186 (1939).
The easy decarboxylation of 2,4,6-trinitrobenzoic acid constitutes a further indication that the rate-determining step in the decarboxylation is a unimolecular splitting of the carboxylate ion. A decarboxylation that is first order in carboxylate ion is consistent with such a mechanism, but it does not demand such a mechanism. Such a rate law is also consistent with a mechanism in which the rate-determining step is the attack of an OH^- ion on the carboxyl group of the free acid; for, as was pointed out (p. 338), the concentration of the anion is directly proportional to the product (acid) $\times$ (OH^-). However such a bimolecular mechanism for decarboxylation should be subject to steric hindrance, and 2,4,6-trinitrobenzoic acid, in which the —COOH group is shielded from outside attack should undergo decarboxylation slowly or not at all. Since this is not the case, the bimolecular decarboxylation mechanism for this acid is untenable, and unless this acid is an exception, other decarboxylations with similar rate laws may also be assumed to be unimolecular.

first-order decarboxylation themselves but form anions that do not.[79] Typical
of these are quinaldic acid (XXXVI) and thiazole-2-carboxylic acid (XXXVIII).
Since these acids are in equilibrium with their respective zwitterions (XXXVI'
and XXXVIII', respectively), kinetics alone does not tell us which form of the
acid is undergoing decarboxylation. Since, however, the dipolar ion XXXIX
(which cannot tautomerize to a "non-zwitterionic" form analogous to XXXVI)
is found to undergo decarboxylation readily, it seems very likely that for the
other acids also, it is the zwitterion that is being decarboxylated. This is as it

should be, for an added positive charge on the carboxylate group should hinder
decarboxylation, but an added positive charge on the remainder of the molecule
should aid decarboxylation. Here again, the anionlike intermediate XXXVII
may be trapped, this time by addition of an aldehyde or ketone.[79a] Decar-

boxylation should take place even more readily if the $-\overset{\text{N}}{\underset{\|}{\text{C}}}-$ group is situated
beta to the —COOH group; for in this case, decarboxylation of the zwitterion
results directly in neutralization of charge.

[79] (a) Hammick, Brown, et al., J. Chem. Soc., **1937**, 1724; **1939**, 809; **1949**, 173, 659, 2577.
(b) Schenkel, et al., Helv. Chim. Acta, **31**, 942 (1948); **33**, 16 (1950).

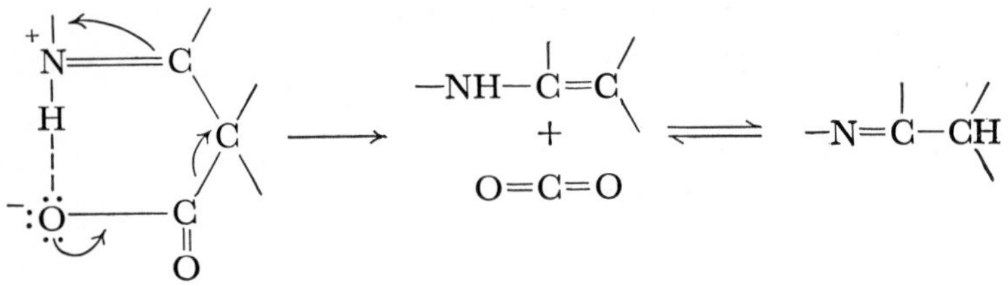

$$-NH-\underset{|}{C}=\underset{\diagdown}{C} + O=C=O \rightleftharpoons -N=\underset{|}{C}-CH$$

2-Quinolylacetic acid, XL, and 2-thiazolylacetic acid, XLI (shown as the zwitterions), are acids of this type and are somewhat more easily decarboxylated than acids XXXVI and XXXVIII.[79] Similarly, we see why primary (but not

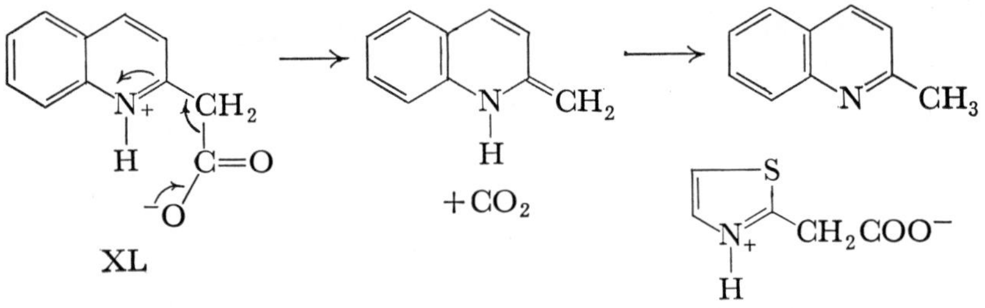

XL

+CO$_2$

XLI

secondary or tertiary) amines may catalyze the decarboxylation of β-keto acids.[80] The keto group is converted by the amine to an imine $\left(\underset{\diagup}{\overset{\diagdown}{C}}{=}N{-}\right)$ linkage, and the resulting β-amino acid (for example, XLII) presumably

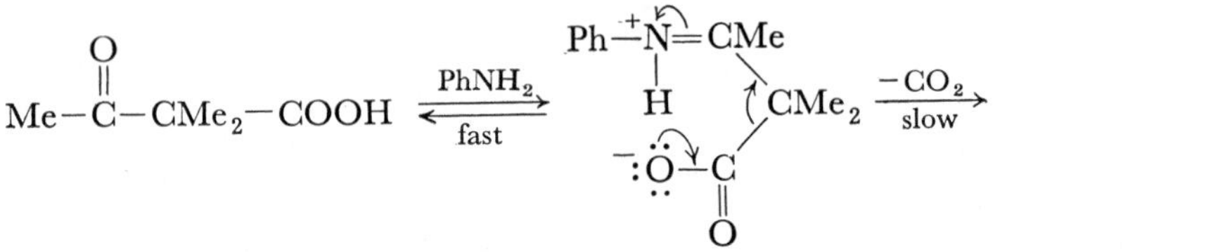

$$Me-\underset{\overset{\|}{O}}{C}-CMe_2-COOH \underset{fast}{\overset{PhNH_2}{\rightleftharpoons}}$$

XLII

$$\overset{H_2O}{\underset{fast}{\longrightarrow}} \begin{cases} PhNH_2 \\ Me-\underset{\overset{\|}{O}}{C}-\underset{\overset{|}{H}}{C}Me_2 \end{cases}$$

$$Ph-NH-\underset{|}{C}=CMe_2$$

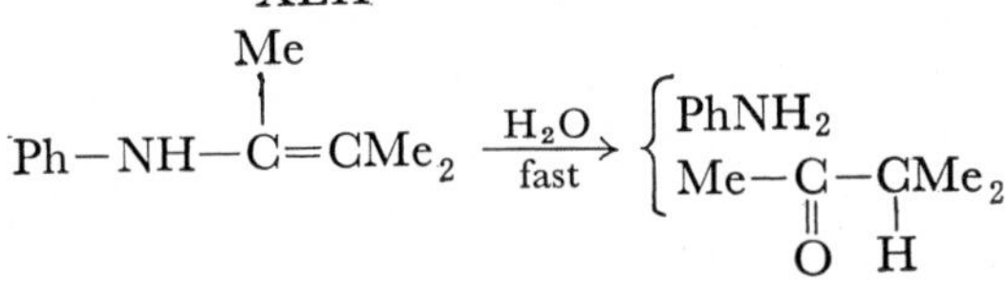

undergoes decarboxylation more rapidly than the original keto acid. In the example shown, the decarboxylation of α,α-dimethylacetoacetic acid is found to be over ten times as fast in 0.05 molar aniline as in water. A comparison between the intermediates for the catalyzed (XLII) and uncatalyzed (XXIX) reactions indicates why this should be so. Since the imino nitrogen is far more

[80] Pederson, J. Am. Chem. Soc., **60**, 595 (1938).

basic than the keto oxygen, the transfer of a proton from the —COOH group (a process assisting decarboxylation) is virtually complete for the imino-acid intermediate but only partial for the keto acid.

A rather different mode of catalysis, involving such heavy metal ions as Cu^{2+}, Fe^{3+}, and Mn^{2+}, has been found to be effective in the decarboxylations of the *dibasic* keto acids: acetonedicarboxylic acid

$$\left(\begin{array}{c} \text{HOOC—CH}_2\text{—C—CH}_2\text{—COOH} \\ \| \\ \text{O} \end{array}\right),^{81(a)}$$

oxaloacetic acid,

$$\left(\begin{array}{c} \text{HOOC—CH}_2\text{—C—COOH} \\ \| \\ \text{O} \end{array}\right),^{81(b)}$$ and dimethyloxaloacetic

acid

$$\left(\begin{array}{c} \text{HOOC—CMe}_2\text{—C—COOH} \\ \| \\ \text{O} \end{array}\right).^{81(c)}$$ From the study of the Cu^{2+}-catalyzed

decarboxylation of the third of these acids, a rather clear-cut mechanistic picture emerges. The decarboxylation product in this case is the salt of monoacid

$$(CH_3)_2CH\overset{\displaystyle O}{\overset{\displaystyle \|}{—C}}—COOH,$$ showing that the —COOH group adjacent to the —CMe$_2$- linkage has been lost. Both —COOH groups appear to be necessary for the Cu^{2+}-catalyzed reaction, since Cu^{2+} does *not* significantly catalyze the decarboxylations of acetoacetic acid or the monoester of dimethyloxaloacetic acid (both of which have only one carboxyl group). Furthermore, since catalysis by Cu^{2+} is most effective at that pH where the dianion of the substrate predominates, we may assume that anion to be the reactive form in catalysis. It thus appears that the reaction proceeds through chelate XLIII, in which the electrophilic Cu^{2+} ion assumes a role analogous to that of the labile proton in the decarboxylations of β-imino acids. Here, the intervention of the copper eno-

XLIII   XLIV

[81] (a) Prue, *J. Chem. Soc.*, **1952**, 2331. (b) Speck, *J. Biol. Chem.*, **178**, 315 (1949). (c) Steinberger and Westheimer, *J. Am. Chem. Soc.*, **73**, 429 (1951). These metal-ion catalyses are of some interest to the biochemist since the catalytic action of enzymes in promoting decarboxylations of these acids is often enhanced by the same metal ions that catalyze their decarboxylations in the absence of enzymes. See, for example, Vennesland, Gollub, and Speck, *J. Biol. Chem.*, **178**, 301 (1949); and (c) above.

late, XLIV, can be demonstrated without a "trapping reagent," since this enolate is unusually stable, and its formation and destruction can be followed spectrophotometrically.[81(c)]

The decarboxylations of an additional class of acids, β,γ-unsaturated acids, are formally quite similar to those of β-keto acids and β-imino acids. This can best be seen by comparing XLV below to structures XLII and XXIX. (Note the shift of the double bond, leading to rearrangement.) Such decarboxylations

$$\text{XLV} \xrightarrow[>200°]{\text{heat}}$$

XLV

require rather severe conditions, for here the acid cannot exist in a zwitterionic form (as can β-imino acids), nor can there be appreciable proton transfer by intramolecular hydrogen bonding at the γ-carbon. It is also likely that the decarboxylations of α,β-unsaturated acids take the same path—that is, that these acids first arrange to β,γ-unsaturated acids; for it has been shown that a number of α,β-unsaturated acids are in mobile equilibrium with the corresponding β,γ-unsaturated acids at temperatures necessary for the decarboxylations, provided that interconversion between the two requires transfer of only a proton.[82]

$$R-CH_2-CH=CR'-COOH \underset{}{\overset{200°}{\rightleftharpoons}} R-CH=CH-CHR'-COOH \rightarrow$$
$$R-CH_2-CH=CHR' + CO_2$$

Thus, what appears to be a decarboxylation without rearrangement is instead a pair of rearrangements, the second, in a sense, nullifying the first. We should then expect those α,β-unsaturated acids that cannot rearrange by a proton shift to β,γ-unsaturated acids to undergo decarboxylation only with great difficulty. Indeed the acid $(CH_3)_3C-CH=CH-COOH$ remains unchanged after 2 hours' heating at 300°.[83]

Like nucleophilic substitutions, decarboxylations display a duality of reaction mechanism. The large majority of decarboxylations are unimolecular, but a number of bimolecular decarboxylations are now known. These are, in effect, displacements of the carboxyl group (without its pair of bonding electrons) by a proton—that is, S_E2 reactions—and almost always take place in strongly acid solutions. Such reactions generally occur at unsaturated carbon

[82] Linstead, et al., J. Chem. Soc., **1925**, 616; **1929**, 2153; **1930**, 1603.
[83] Arnold, Elmer, and Dodson, J. Am. Chem. Soc., **72**, 4359 (1950).

$$Sv\text{H}^+ + \begin{matrix} \backslash \\ \text{C}-\text{COOH} \\ | \\ \text{C} \\ / \backslash \end{matrix} \xrightarrow{\text{slow}} \begin{matrix} \\ \text{H}-\text{C}-\text{C} \\ | \\ \text{C}^+ \\ / \backslash \end{matrix} \overset{\text{O}}{\underset{\text{O}-\text{H}}{\diagdown}} \xrightarrow{\text{fast}} \begin{matrix} \\ \text{H}-\text{C} \\ | \\ \text{C} \\ / \backslash \end{matrix} + \overset{\text{O}}{\underset{\text{O}}{\text{C}}} + \text{H}^+$$

$(Sv = \text{solvent})$

XLVI

atoms; for in such cases, the new C—H bond may form without necessity for simultaneous breakage of the old C—C bond. We should expect them to be first order both in carboxylic acid and in H$^+$, and they should be favored by electron-donating substituents and aromatic rings bound to the β-carbon, since such groups should stabilize the intermediate carbonium ion, XLVI (and, presumably, also the transition state leading to XLVI). The decarboxylations, for example, of acids XLVII,[84(a)] XLVIII,[84(b)] and XLIX,[84(c)] in strongly acid solutions, appear to be bimolecular.

XLVII   **XLVIII**   **XLIX**

The Decarboxylation of Silver Salts with Halogens

Silver salts of carboxylic acids may be converted to alkyl or aryl halides by treatment with elemental bromine or iodine in an inert solvent. In this, the so-called *Hunsdiecker reaction*, CO$_2$ is evolved, but the reaction is related in only a formal sense to the decarboxylation reactions that we have thus far considered. There is strong evidence that the Hunsdiecker reaction usually (although perhaps not always) proceeds by a mechanism involving free radicals.[85] The initial step in the reaction is heterogeneous (for the silver salt is generally not appreciably soluble in the solvent used) and we will not attempt to speculate as to its intimate details. The net result of this step, however, is that only a portion of the halogen is precipitated as a silver halide. If care is taken to keep the mixture cold so that further steps in the transformation do not occur, an equal quantity of halogen in solution may be shown to have strong oxidizing properties, being capable of oxidizing *two* equivalents of added reducing agent per gram-atom of halogen. If an olefin be added to the mixture at this point, a

[84] (a) Johnson and Heinz, *J. Am. Chem. Soc.*, **71**, 2913 (1949). (b) Schenkel and Schenkel-Rudin, *Helv. Chim. Acta*, **31**, 514 (1948). (c) Schubert, *J. Am. Chem. Soc.*, **71**, 2693 (1949).

[85] For a brief survey of this evidence, see Johnson and Ingham, *Chem. Revs.*, **56**, 250 (1956).

halogen atom becomes affixed to one double-bonded carbon, whereas the carboxylate anion becomes affixed to the other.[86] In short, the halogen in such solutions has "positive" character—much like the halogens in hypohalites— and such solutions are generally considered to contain acyl hypohalites of the type

$$R-\overset{O}{\underset{}{\overset{\|}{C}}}-O-Br \text{ and } R-C-O-I,$$

although no pure acyl hypobromites or hypoiodites have, as yet, been isolated.

$$R-COO^-Ag^+ + Hal_2 \xrightarrow{-AgHal} \left[R-\overset{O}{\overset{\|}{C}}-O-Hal \right] \rightarrow R-Hal + CO_2$$

The decompositions of the "hypohalites" in solution to form CO_2 and alkyl or aryl halides exhibit a number of features typical of free-radical reactions (Chap. 16). They are promoted by radiation[87] and exhibit induction periods.[88] In addition, the "side products" arising from such reactions can be easily explained by only assuming the intervention of free radicals. For example, when silver benzoate is treated with Br_2 in CCl_4, the expected product, bromobenzene, is formed, but appreciable quantities of chlorobenzene and $BrCCl_3$ may also be isolated.[89] These products point to the following reaction sequence:

$$Ph-COOAg + Br_2 \rightarrow Ph-\overset{O}{\underset{}{\overset{\|}{C}}}-O-Br \rightarrow$$

$$\begin{cases} Ph\cdot & \xrightarrow{CCl_4} PhCl + CCl_3\cdot \xrightarrow{Br_2} BrCCl_3 \\ Br\cdot \\ CO_2 \end{cases}$$

When the Hunsdiecker reaction is carried out on silver picolinate (L) in hot nitrobenzene, 2,2'-dipyridyl is one of the products, strongly suggesting the pyridyl radical as an intermediate.[90]

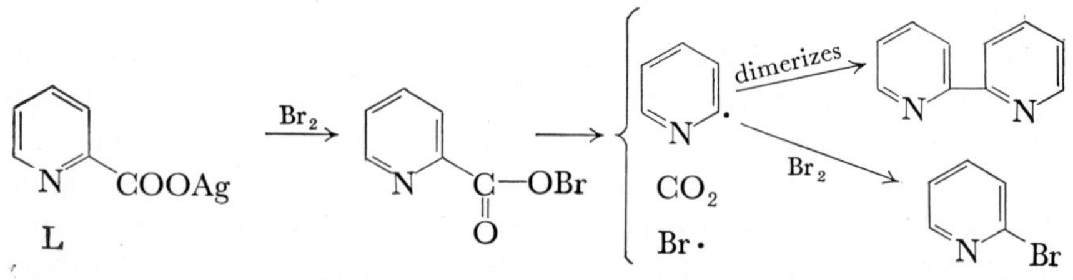

[86] See, for example, Edwards and Hodges, *J. Chem. Soc.*, **1954**, 761.
[87] Bockemuller and Hoffman, *Ann.*, **519**, 165 (1935). Wieland and Fischer, *Ann.*, **446**, 49 (1926).
[88] Conley, *J. Am. Chem. Soc.*, **75**, 1148 (1953).
[89] Dauben and Tilles, *J. Am. Chem. Soc.*, **72**, 3185 (1950).
[90] Kuffner and Russo, *Monatsh.*, **85**, 1097 (1954).

Similarly, bibenzyl is obtained when silver trifluoroacetate is treated with bromine in toluene;[91] the following reaction sequence is indicated:

$$CF_3COOAg \xrightarrow{Br_2} CF_3-\underset{\underset{O}{\|}}{C}-O-Br \rightarrow$$

$$\begin{cases} Br\cdot \\ CF_3\cdot \\ CO_2 \end{cases} \xrightarrow{PhCH_3} HBr + PhCH_2\cdot \xrightarrow{dimerizes} \begin{matrix} Ph-CH_2 \\ | \\ Ph-CH_2 \end{matrix}$$

At present, then, the most satisfactory mechanism for the Hunsdiecker reaction (barring the initial formation of the acyl hypohalite, about which we know very little), is simply

$$R-\underset{\underset{O}{\|}}{C}-O-Br \rightarrow \begin{cases} R\cdot \\ Br\cdot \\ CO_2 \end{cases} \xrightarrow{Br_2} \begin{cases} RBr \\ Br\cdot \end{cases} \xrightarrow{RCOOBr} Br_2 + CO_2 + R\cdot \xrightarrow{etc.}$$

If this mechanism is correct, we should expect the silver salt of an optically active acid—in which the α-carbon is asymmetric—to yield, upon treatment with halogen, a racemic halide; for the radical $R-\overset{R'}{\underset{R''}{C}}\cdot$ should be symmetric

(p. 149). Virtually complete racemization has indeed been observed when the Hunsdiecker reaction is carried out on n-Bu—$\overset{*}{C}$HEt—COOAg,[92(a)] PhCH$_2$—$\overset{*}{C}$HEt—COOAg[92(b)] and Et-$\overset{*}{C}$HMe—COOAg.[92(c)]

It is interesting that the silver salts LI and LII, having bridgehead carboxylate groups, readily undergo the Hunsdiecker reaction.[93] If the proposed

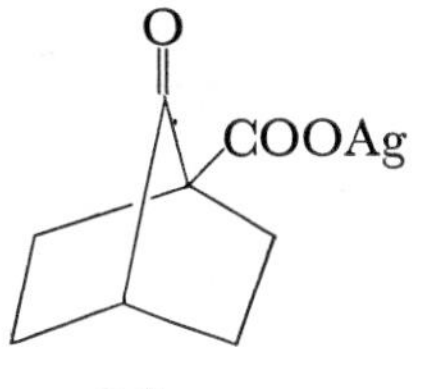

LI 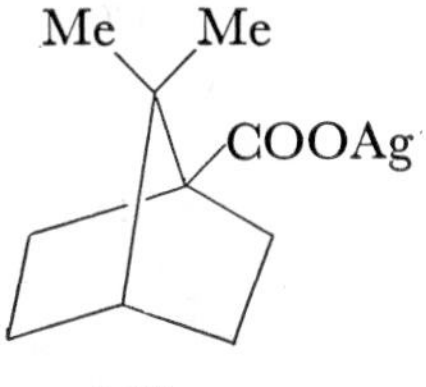   LII 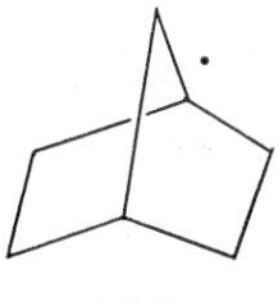   LIII

[91] Haszeldine and Sharpe, J. Chem. Soc., **1952**, 993.

[92] (a) Arnold and Morgan, J. Am. Chem. Soc., **70**, 4248 (1948). (b) Bell and Smyth, J. Chem. Soc., **1949**, 2372. (c) Heintzeler, Ann., **569**, 102 (1950). (d) What appears to be an exceptional case has been described by Arcus, Campbell, and Kenyon, J. Chem. Soc., **1949**, 1510. Here the reaction of D-Me—CHPh—COOAg with bromine is reported to yield a bromide with 43 percent inversion of configuration. To the extent that these results are correct, an alternate mechanism for the Hunsdiecker reaction must be considered. However, a more recent attempt to repeat this conversion (Cason, Kalm, and Mills, J. Org. Chem., **18**, 1670 (1953)) yielded none of the expected MeCHPh—Br.

[93] Wilder and Winston, J. Am. Chem. Soc., **75**, 5370 (1953); Cope and Synerholm, ibid., **72**, 5228 (1950).

mechanism is correct, both reactions should proceed through an intermediate such as **LIII**, in which the unpaired electron is situated at a "bridgehead carbon." Since the bonds to such a carbon atom cannot lie in a common plane (p. 280), we may conclude that coplanarity of the bonds to a "tervalent carbon atom" is a far less compelling requirement for free radicals than for carbonium ions.

EXERCISES FOR CHAPTER 9

1. Predict which member in each of the following pairs is hydrolyzed more rapidly in dilute NaOH. Assume equal concentrations in each case.
   (a) Ethyl benzoate or ethyl p-nitrobenzoate?
   (b) p-Nitrophenyl acetate or p-methoxyphenyl acetate?
   (c) Ethyl benzoate or ethyl lactate?
   (d) Ethyl acetate or acetamide?
   (e) Ph—CMe$_2$—CHMe—COOEt or Ph—CHMe—CMe$_2$—COOEt?
   (f) *trans-t*-Butylcarbethoxycyclohexane or the *cis* isomer?
   (g) Ethyl α-naphthoate or ethyl β-naphthoate?
   (h)

   (i) β-Propiolactone or δ-valerolactone?

2. Predict which substrate in each of the following pairs is hydrolyzed more rapidly. Assume equal concentrations in each case.
   (a) (*t*-BuO)$_2$CrO$_2$ or (Ph$_3$C—O—)$_2$CrO$_2$ in water?
   (b) β-Butyrolactone in water or in 6N NaOH?
   (c) Benzoyl bromide or benzoyl chloride in 50/50 water ethanol?
   (d) β-Propiolactone or α-chloro-β-propiolactone in HOAc-OAc⁻ buffer?
   (e) Methyl nitrite or *n*-propyl nitrite in water?

(f)

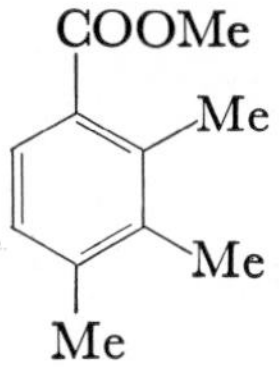

COOMe / Me / Me / Me

or

COOMe / Me / Me / Me

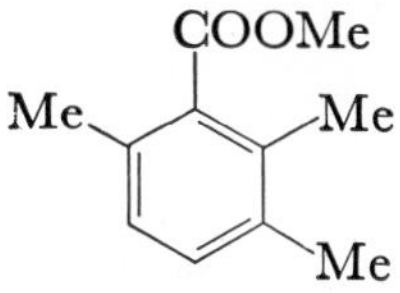

in conc H_2SO_4 ?

(g) n-Propyl benzoate or n-propyl p-toluate in conc H_2SO_4?

(h) CH_3—C—O—C—CCl_2—CMe_3 or CH_3—C—O—C—$CHCl$—CMe_3 in water?
    ‖ ‖   ‖ ‖
    O O   O O

(i) CH_3—C—O—C—CCl_2—CMe_3 or CH_2Cl—C—O—$CCCl_2CMe_3$ in water?
   ‖ ‖   ‖ ‖
   O O   O O

(j) i-Propyl benzoate or i-propyl p-toluate in conc H_2SO_4?

3. (a) The conversion of $PhCH_2COOEt$ to $PhCH_2CONH_2$ by ammonia in methanol is accelerated by addition of NaOMe but retarded by addition of NH_4Cl. Explain.

(b) The rate law for this reaction (in the absence of added NaOMe or NH_4Cl) is

$$rate = k(RCOOEt)(NH_3) + k'(RCOOEt)(NH_3)^{3/2}$$

Show that this rate law is consistent with a competition between ammonia and the amide ion, NH_2^-, in attacking the ester. Assume that $NH_2^- < OMe^-$ in this solution, and note that the MeO^- present arises from the equilibrium,

$$NH_3 + MeOH \rightleftharpoons NH_4^+ + MeO^-$$

4. Suggest mechanisms for the following reactions:

(a) CH_3—O—N=O + $OH^- \rightarrow CH_3OH + NO_2^-$

(b) $PhCOOH + H_2O^{18} \rightarrow Ph$—C—OH + H_2O
              ‖
              O_{18}

(c) 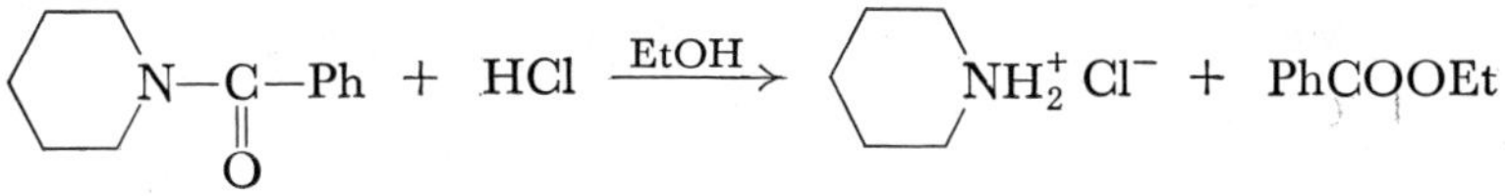 ⬡N—C—Ph + HCl $\xrightarrow{EtOH}$ ⬡NH_2^+ Cl^- + $PhCOOEt$
     ‖
     O

(d) 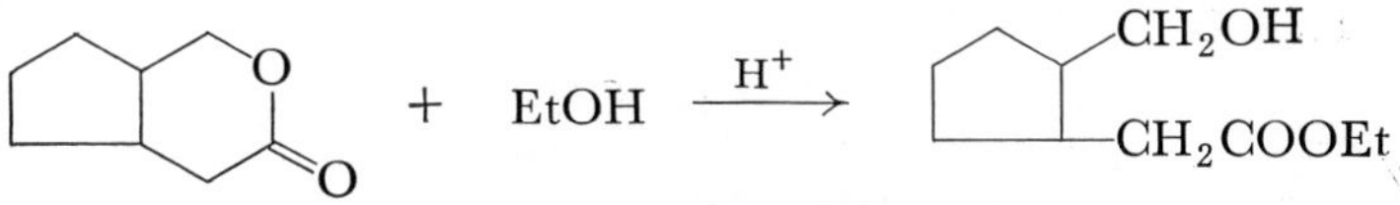 (bicyclic diketone) + EtOH $\xrightarrow{H^+}$ (cyclopentane)—CH_2OH / —CH_2COOEt

(e) HO—C—CH_2—CH_2—$COOEt$ + liquid $NH_3 \rightarrow$
   ‖
   O

          NH_4^+ ^-O—C—CH_2—CH_2—$CONH_2$
                ‖
                O

(f) 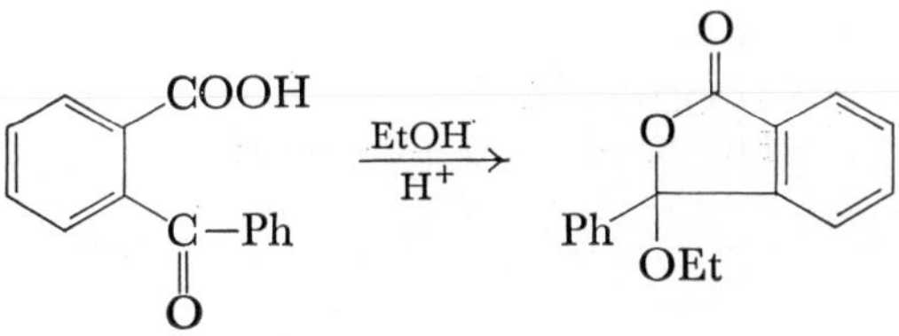 (benzene)—COOH / —C—Ph $\xrightarrow{EtOH}{H^+}$ (structure with Ph, OEt, O)
       ‖
       O

(g)

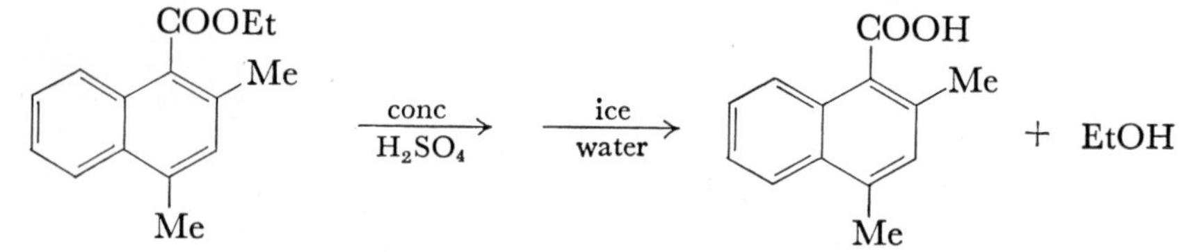

$$\xrightarrow[\text{H}_2\text{SO}_4]{\text{conc}} \xrightarrow[\text{water}]{\text{ice}}$$

+ EtOH

(h)

+ conc H_2SO_4 $\longrightarrow$

+ $MeO-SO_3H$

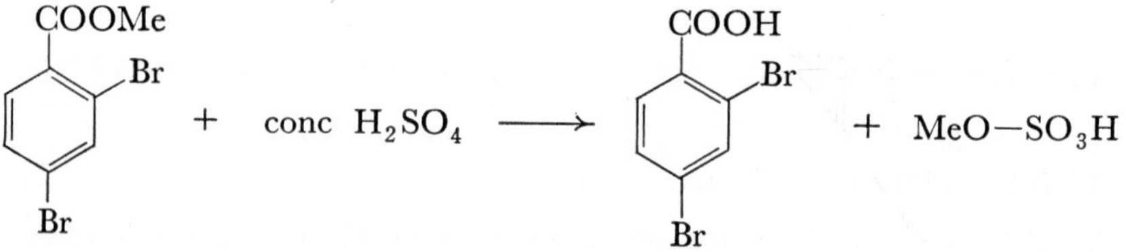

(i) $Ac_2O + EtOH \xrightarrow{Et_3N} CH_3COOEt + Et_3NH^+OAc^-$

(This reaction proceeds much more slowly in the absence of amine.)

(j) $(EtOOC)_2 + CH_2(CH_2COOEt)_2 \xrightarrow{OEt^-}$

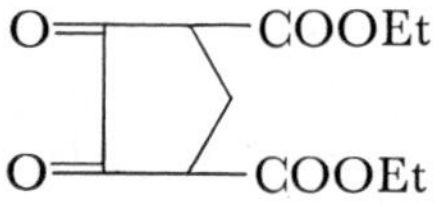

(k)

$-COOEt$ + EtOD $\xrightarrow{OEt^-}$ $D-$ $-COOEt$ + EtOH

(l) $Ph_2CHOAc + H_2O \xrightarrow{H^+} Ph_2CHOH + AcOH$

(m)

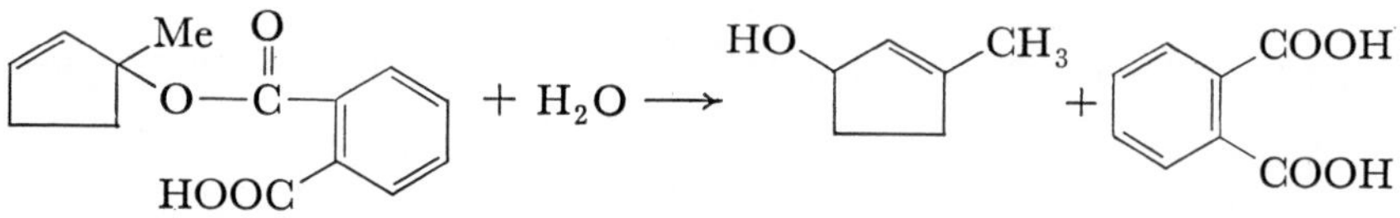

+ $H_2O \longrightarrow$

+

(n)

+ conc $OH^- \longrightarrow$

$Ph-O-$ $-CHPh-O^-$ +

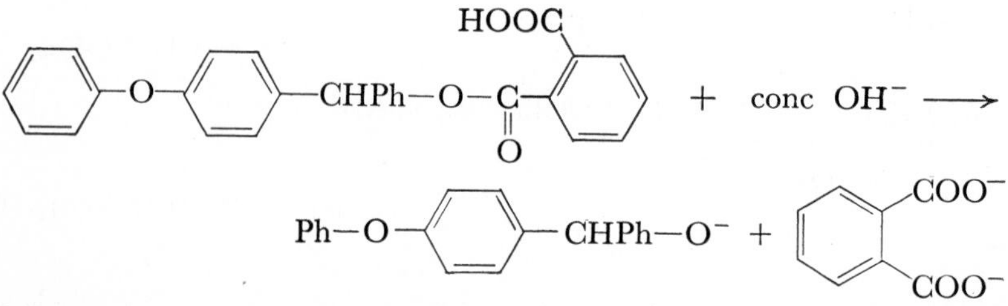

(o) $B(OMe)_3 + H_2O \rightarrow B(OH)_3 + MeOH$

(p) $(EtOOC)_2 + CH_3CH=CH-COOEt \xrightarrow{OEt^-}$

$EtOOC-C-CH_2-CH=CH-COOEt + EtOH$
$\quad\quad\quad\overset{\|}{O}$

(q) $PhC{-}CMe_2{-}COOEt + CH_3COOEt \xrightarrow{OEt^-}$
$\overset{\|}{O}$

$$PhCOOEt + CH_3{-}\overset{\|}{\underset{O}{C}}{-}CMe_2{-}COOEt$$

(r)

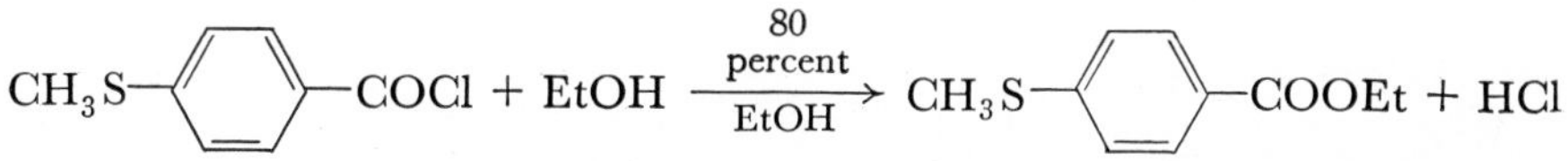

$CH_3S{-}\langle\bigcirc\rangle{-}COCl + EtOH \xrightarrow[EtOH]{\overset{80}{percent}} CH_3S{-}\langle\bigcirc\rangle{-}COOEt + HCl$

(s)

$N{\equiv}C{-}\langle\bigcirc\rangle{-}COCl + EtOH \xrightarrow{ether} EtOOC{-}\langle\bigcirc\rangle{-}CN + HCl$

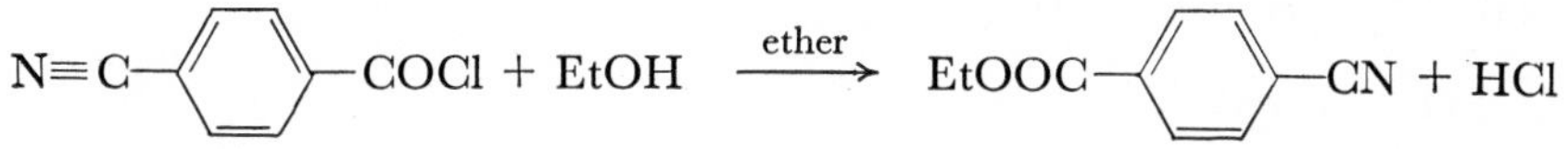

(t) $(HOOC{-}CH_2{-})_2C{=}O + CuCO_3 + H_2O \rightarrow$
$$CO_2 + CH_3\overset{\|}{\underset{O}{C}}CH_2COOH + Cu^{2+}$$

(u) $\langle N\bigcirc\rangle{-}CH_2COOH \xrightarrow[water]{heat} \langle N\bigcirc\rangle{-}CH_3 + CO_2$

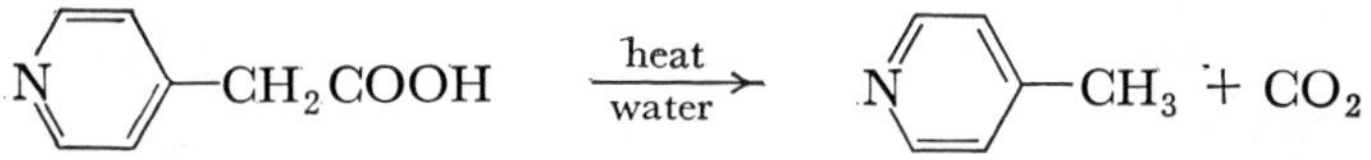

(v) $PhCH_2{-}\underset{\underset{NH_2}{|}}{CH}{-}COOH + OAc^- \xrightarrow{water, PhCHO}$
$$PhCH_2CH_2NH_2 + CO_2 + OAc^- + PhCHO$$

(w) $Ph{-}\underset{\underset{OH}{|}}{CH}{-}COOAg + Br_2 \rightarrow PhCHO + AgBr + CO_2 + HBr$

(x)
$$\underset{}{\overset{COOH}{\underset{OH}{\langle\bigcirc\rangle}}} \xrightarrow[Cl_3CCOOH]{HBr} \overset{OH}{\langle\bigcirc\rangle} + CO_2$$

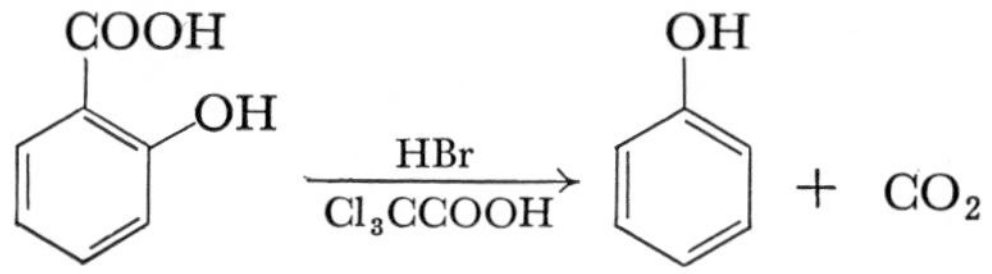

(y)
$$\begin{matrix} Me \\ \diagdown \\ \quad C{-}CH_2 \\ \diagup \, | \quad | \\ Me \quad O{-}C{=}O \end{matrix} \xrightarrow[heat]{H_2O} CO_2 + Me_2CH{=}CH_2$$

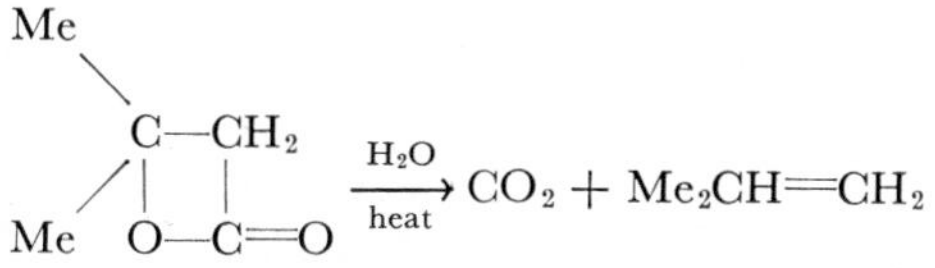

(z)

$$d\text{-}R{-}O{-}\overset{}{\underset{O}{C}}{\langle\bigcirc\rangle}^{COOH} \xrightarrow{H_2O} \begin{matrix} d, l\text{-}R{-}O{-}\overset{O}{\overset{\|}{C}}{-}\langle\bigcirc\rangle \\ d\text{-}R{-}O{-}\overset{O}{\overset{\|}{C}}{-}\langle\bigcirc\rangle \end{matrix} + \langle\bigcirc\rangle\overset{COOH}{\underset{COOH}{}}$$

$$(R{=}MeO{-}\langle\bigcirc\rangle{-}CHPh{-})$$

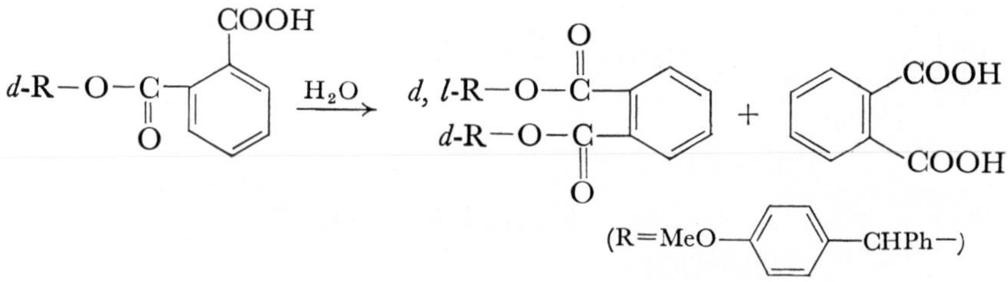

5. Predict the products:

(a) $CH_3SH + AcOH + PhSO_3H \xrightarrow{ether}$

(b)

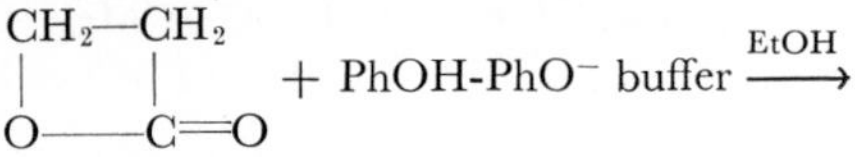

$$\begin{array}{c} CH_2\!\!-\!\!CH_2 \\ | \qquad | \\ O\!\!-\!\!-\!\!C\!\!=\!\!O \end{array} + \text{PhOH-PhO}^- \text{ buffer} \xrightarrow{EtOH}$$

(c)

$+ \; CN^- \xrightarrow{EtOH}$

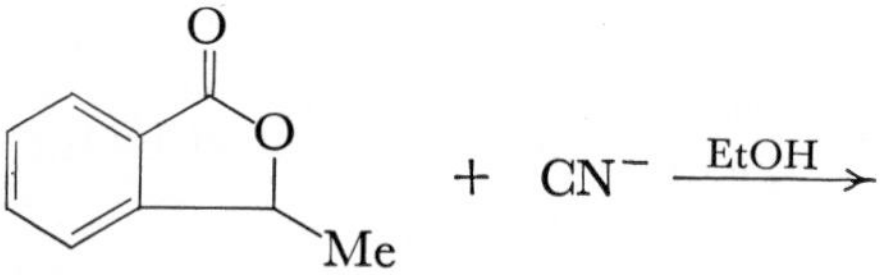

(d)

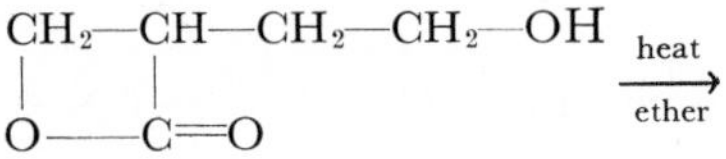

$$\begin{array}{c} CH_2\!\!-\!\!CH\!\!-\!\!CH_2\!\!-\!\!CH_2\!\!-\!\!OH \\ | \qquad | \\ O\!\!-\!\!-\!\!C\!\!=\!\!O \end{array} \xrightarrow[\text{ether}]{\text{heat}}$$

(e)

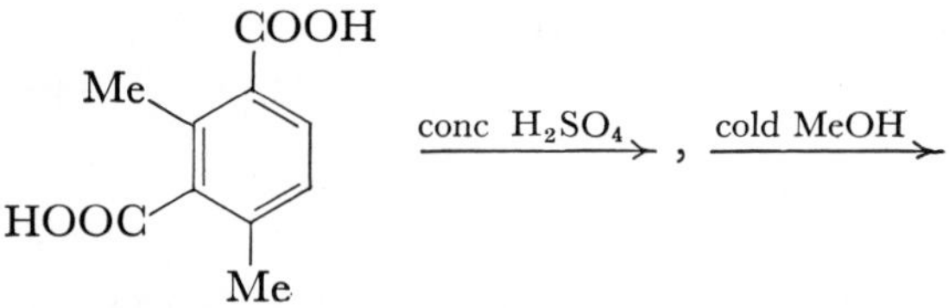

$\xrightarrow{\text{conc } H_2SO_4} , \xrightarrow{\text{cold MeOH}}$

(f) AcO——$NO_2 + H_2O + $ $\longrightarrow$

(g) $NaNO_2 + MeO$——$CHPh\!-\!O\!-\!\underset{\underset{O}{\|}}{C}$— $\xrightarrow{EtOH}$

(h) —$CHMe\!-\!O\!-\!\underset{\underset{O}{\|}}{C}$— $+ PhSO_2^- \xrightarrow{EtOH}$

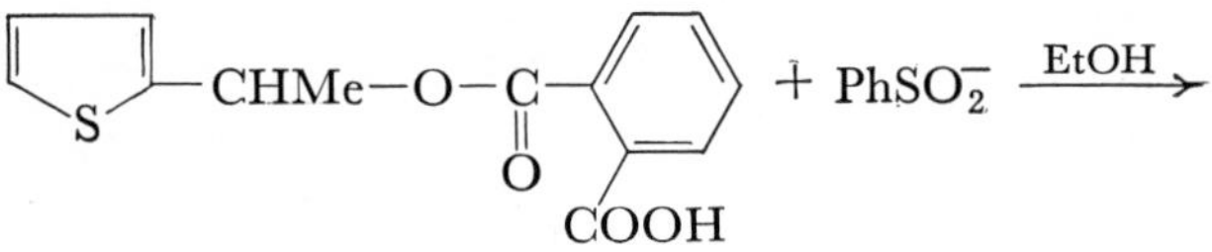

(i) 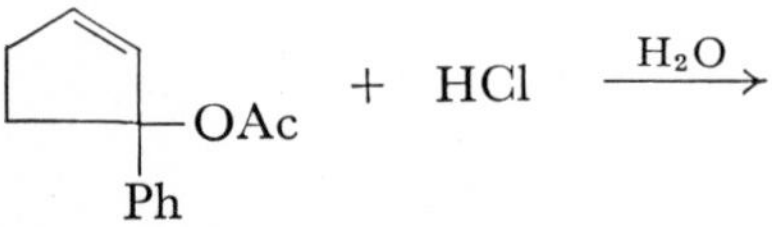 $+ \; HCl \xrightarrow{H_2O}$

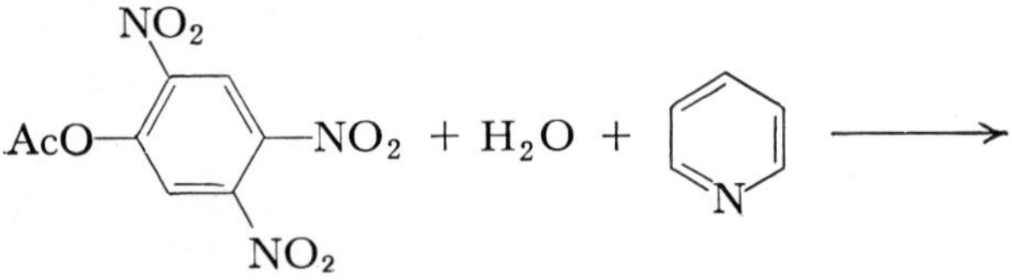

(j) 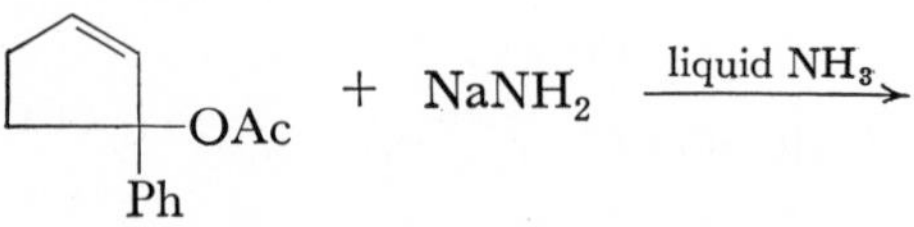 $+ \; NaNH_2 \xrightarrow{\text{liquid } NH_3}$

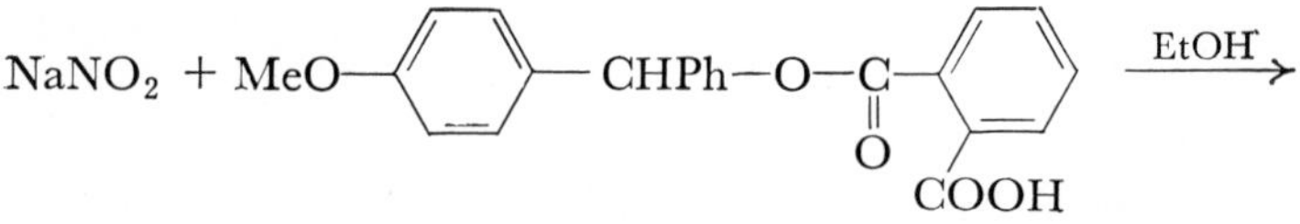

(k) 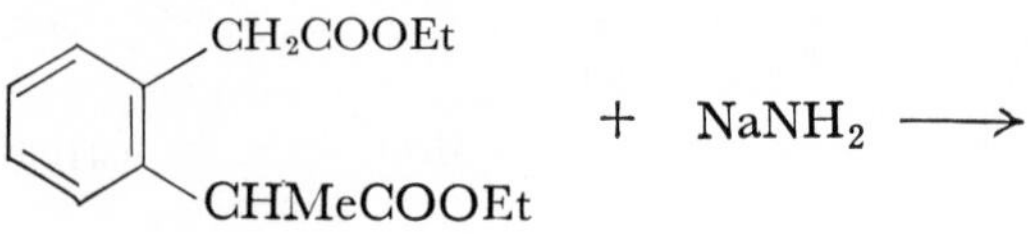 $+ \; NaNH_2 \longrightarrow$

(l)

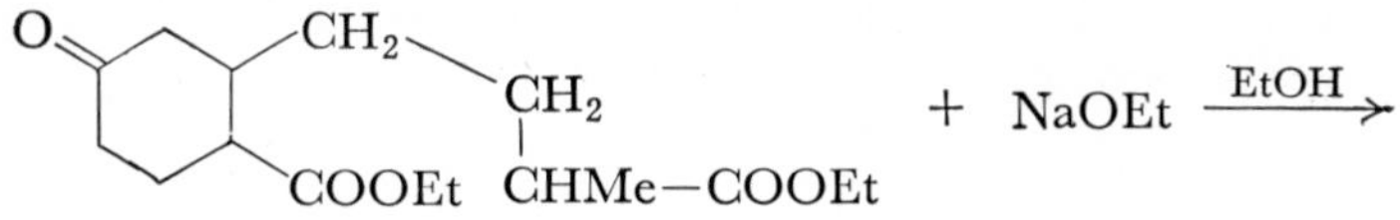

$+$ NaOEt $\xrightarrow{\text{EtOH}}$

(m) 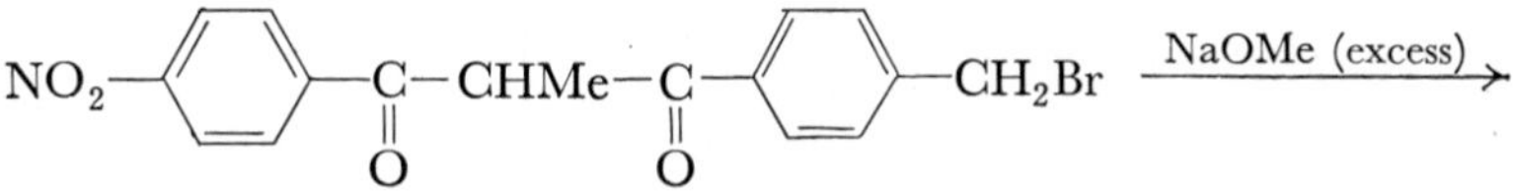 NO_2—⟨⟩—$\underset{O}{\overset{||}{C}}$—CHMe—$\underset{O}{\overset{||}{C}}$—⟨⟩—$CH_2Br$ $\xrightarrow{\text{NaOMe (excess)}}$

(n)

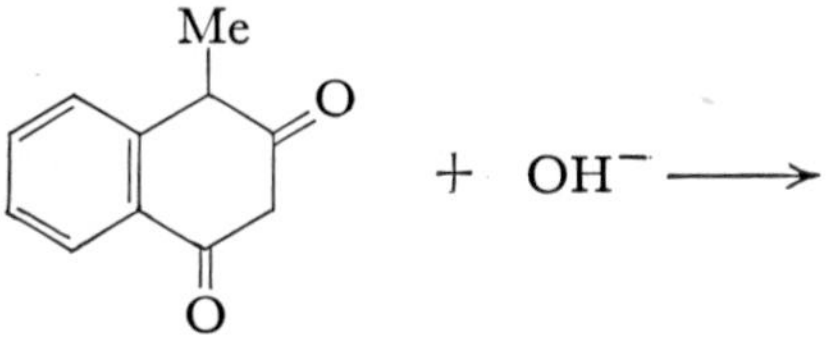

$+$ OH$^-$ ⟶

(o) i-Pr—O—NO_2 + OEt$^-$ $\xrightarrow{\text{EtOH}}$

(p)

$\xrightarrow[275°]{\text{heat}}$

(q)

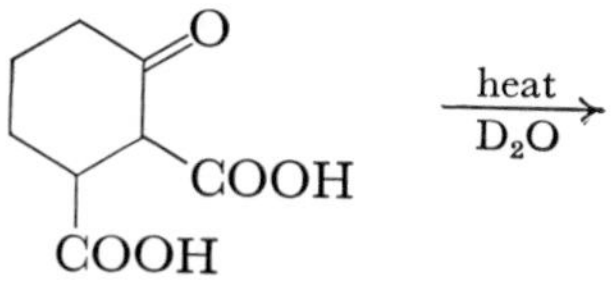

$\xrightarrow[D_2O]{\text{heat}}$

(r)

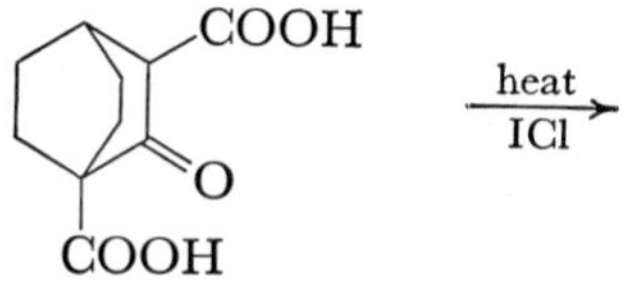

$\xrightarrow[ICl]{\text{heat}}$

(s)

$+$ $PhNH_2$ ⟶

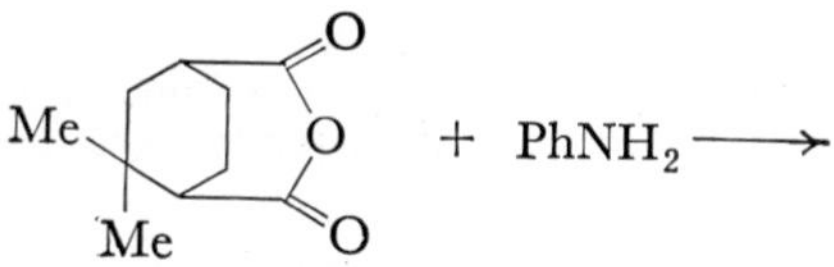

(t) HOOC—CH_2—$\overset{O}{\overset{||}{C}}$—$CMe_2$—COOH + Cu^{2+} $\xrightarrow[\text{heat}]{H_2O}$

(u) Ph—CH—NHAc + Br_2 $\xrightarrow{CCl_4}$
 |
 COOAg

6. Two mechanisms are to be considered for the reaction of an amine RNH_2 with benzoic anhydride (see Denney and Greenbaum, Ref. 39). In both, the initial step is the attack of the amine on the carbonyl group, forming an adduct,

Ph—$\underset{O}{\overset{||}{C}}$—O—$\underset{O}{\overset{||}{C}}$—Ph + RNH_2 ⇌ Ph—$\underset{O}{\overset{||}{C}}$—O—$\underset{\underset{+}{NH_2R}}{\overset{O^-}{\overset{|}{C}}}$—Ph

The conversion of the adduct to the observed products, an amide and a carboxylate ion, may then proceed by one of the following two paths:

$$
\text{Path 1: Ph—C—O—C—Ph} \underset{k_2}{\overset{k_1}{\rightleftharpoons}} \text{Ph—C—O}^- + \text{C—Ph} \xrightarrow[-H^+]{k_3}
$$

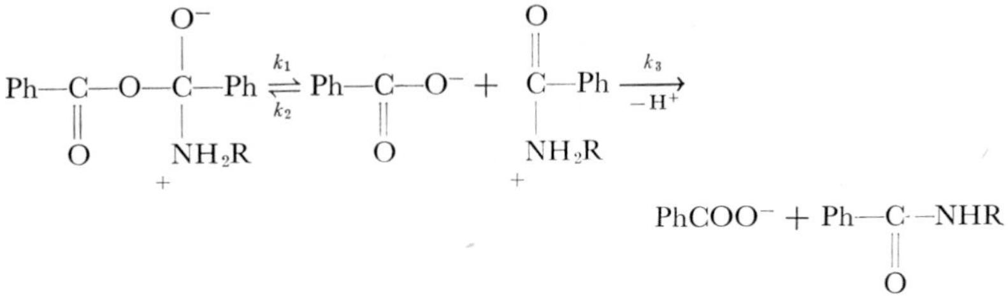

with the O^-, O and NH_2R substituents on the respective carbons.

$$
\text{PhCOO}^- + \text{Ph—C—NHR}
$$

$$
\text{Path 2: Ph—C—O—C—Ph} \xrightarrow[k_4]{RNH_2} \text{RNH}_3^+ + \text{Ph—C—O—C—Ph} \xrightarrow{k_5}
$$

$$
\text{Ph—C—O}^- + \text{Ph—C}
$$
with NHR substituent.

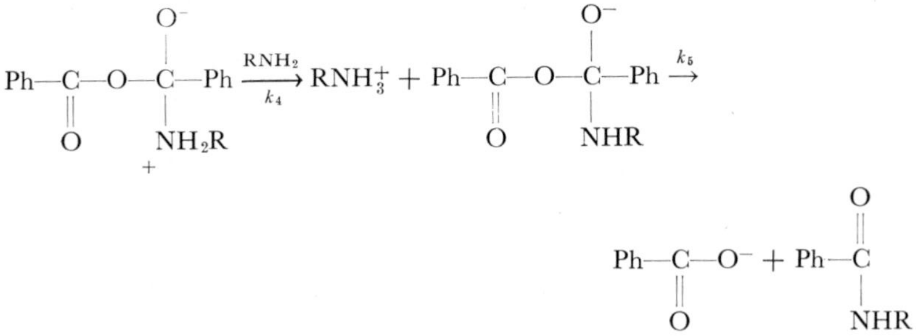

(a) Benzoic anhydride having just one carbonyl group labeled with O^{18},

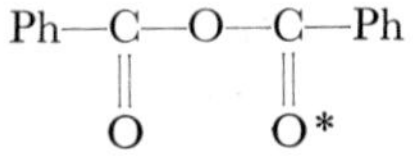

$$
\text{Ph—C—O—C—Ph}
$$
with O and O^* carbonyls

$$
\overset{O^*}{\underset{\|}{}}
$$

is prepared from Ph—C—Cl and PhCOOAg. This singly labeled anhydride is treated with NH_3 at $-33°$. *One half* of the labeled oxygen is found in the benzamide formed. With which of the two mechanisms above is this consistent?

(b) When the anhydride, labeled as above, is treated with aniline in ether, only one third of the labeled oxygen is found in the amide, the remaining two thirds being in the benzoate. With which of the two mechanisms above is this consistent? Explain.

(c) When the experiment in (b) is repeated, using aqueous acetone as a solvent, about 45 percent of the labeled oxygen is found in the benzanilide. Account for the variation in behavior as the solvent is changed.

(d) The results of an experiment using a deuterated cyclohexylamine, $C_6H_{11}ND_2$, in ether are essentially the same as those for aniline in ether, but if nonlabeled cyclohexylamine, $C_6H_{11}NH_2$, is used, about 40 percent of the labeled oxygen is found in the amide. Explain.

(e) If labeled p-nitrobenzoic benzoic anhydride, O_2N—⟨benzene ring⟩—C—O—C—Ph, with O^* and O carbonyls,

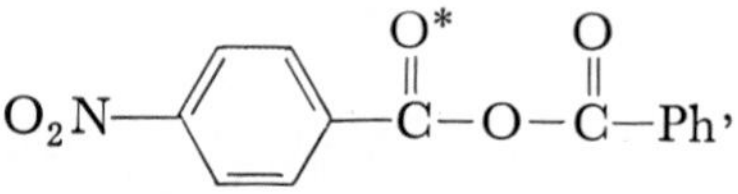

is treated with aniline in ether, 53 percent of the labeled oxygen is found in the *p*-nitrobenzanilide. Account for the difference between the behavior of this anhydride and unsubstituted benzoic anhydride in part (b).

7. Predict which acid in each of the following pairs is more readily decarboxylated under the conditions specified:
   (a) α-Nitropropionic acid or β-nitropropionic acid (heat in water)?
   (b) α-Nitropropionic acid or α-aminopropionic acid (heat in dilute base)?
   (c)

   or   (heat in aqueous acetate-acetic acid buffer) ?

   (d) CH_3—C≡C—COOH or Ph_2C=C—COOH (heat in 2N NaOH)?
   |
   H

   (e) 4-Pyridylacetic acid or 2-pyridinecarboxylic acid (heat in quinoline)?
   (f) Ph—CH=CH—CH_2COOH or CH_3CH=CH—CH_2COOH (heat in absence of solvent)?
   (g) Trichloroacetic acid or 2-pyridylacetic acid (heat in 6N NaOH)?

(h)

   or   (heat with aniline in water) ?

   (i) CH_3—C—CH_2—C—CH_2—COO⁻ or CH_3—C—C—CH_2—COO⁻ $(Cu(OAc)_2$
           ‖   ‖   ‖ ‖   in water)?
           O   O   O O
   (j) 2,6-Dimethylbenzoic acid or 2,6-dibromobenzoic acid (in conc H_2SO_4)?
   (k) Ph—CH=CMe—COOH or MeCH=CPh—COOH (heat in conc H_2SO_4)?
   (l) PhCH=CMe—COOH or MeCH=CPh—COOH (heat alone)?

8. Explain each of the following:
   (a) $(n\text{-}Pr)_2$CH—COOH is esterified more rapidly than is *i*-Pr—CHEt—COOH.
   (b) The conversion of ethyl acetate to N-methylacetamide with methylamine in methanol is retarded by addition of ammonium acetate.
   (c) Ester hydrolysis by the $B_{AL}2$ mechanism is practically never observed.
   (d) The incorporation of β-alkyl groups in a carboxylic acid not only raises the energy of activation for its esterification, but also lowers the entropy of activation.
   (e) 2,6-Dimethylbenzonitrile may be hydrolyzed with alkali to 2,6-dimethylbenz-amide, but this amide is extremely difficult to hydrolyze with alkali to the carboxylate salt.
   (f) *p*-Me—C_6H_4—COOMe is hydrolyzed more rapidly than PhCOOMe in concentrated H_2SO_4, but the reverse is true in dilute H_2SO_4.
   (g) Exchange of O^{18} with water is more nearly complete in the saponification of CH_3—C—OMe than in the saponification of CH_3—C—OPh.
                 ‖   ‖
                 O*   O*

(h) The rates of hydrolysis of alkyl acetates in 1N HCl lie in the order:

$$t\text{-Bu}— > \text{Me}— > \text{Et}— > i\text{-Pr}—$$

(i) The saponification of p-NH_2—C_6H_4—COOEt is accelerated by incorporating a methyl group *meta* to the —COOEt group but retarded by a methyl group *ortho* to the —COOEt group.

(j) 2,4,6-Trimethoxybenzoic acid cannot be esterified in the same way as mesitoic acid.

(k) A mixture of Ph—COOEt, Me_2CH—COOEt, and $NaCPh_3$ in ether yields the keto ester Ph—C—CMe_2—COOEt after standing a short time, but yields the
$$\overset{\|}{O}$$
keto ester Me_2CH—C—CMe_2COOEt after standing several days.
$$\overset{\|}{O}$$

(l) Acid LIV undergoes decarboxylation much more slowly upon heating in H_2SO_4 than does acid LV.

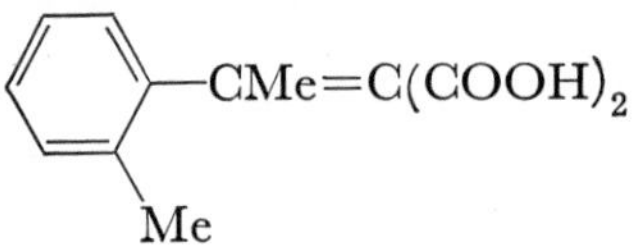

LIV 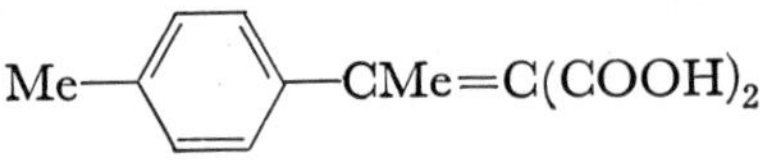   LV

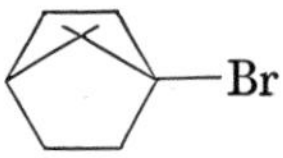

LVI 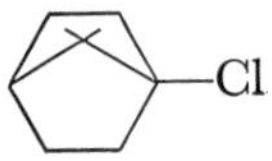   LVII

(m) Silver salt LII (p. 355) yields a mixture of bromide LVI and chloride LVII when treated with bromine in CCl_4, but yields only LVI when the reaction is carried out in hexane.

(n) The basic hydrolysis of $CF_3CONHPh$ is not first order in OH^-, but tends toward a limiting value at high hydroxide concentrations, the observed rate law being

$$\text{rate} = \frac{k_2(OH^-)(\text{amide})}{1 + K(OH^-)}$$

Carbanions and Enolization

THE C—H BOND is relatively strong and its polarity is ordinarily very slight. The removal of a proton from a —C—H linkage to form a *carbanion*, —C:⁻, should therefore be difficult; indeed, a hydrogen atom bound to a carbon may, in most cases, be considered to have negligible acidity. This need not be so if one or more strongly electron-attracting groups lie near the C—H bond under consideration, or, more particularly, if removal of the hydrogen ion leaves a carbanion in which the negative charge may be spread over a number of atoms rather than being confined to a single carbon. Given one or both of these conditions, conversion to a carbanion may be significant, and, as we shall see, a number of important reactions may proceed through carbanion intermediates.

Ionization of Carbon-Hydrogen Bonds and Prototropy

If dilute sodium hydroxide is added to a solution of a β-diketone (such as acetylacetone), to a β-keto ester (such as acetoacetic ester), or to an aliphatic nitro compound (such as nitromethane), an equimolar quantity of base is consumed, indicating a neutralization. Unlike the conventional neutralizations, however, these reactions are *not immeasurably fast*, for each involves the breakage of a C—H bond and requires appreciable activation energy. In each of these cases, ionization of the C—H bond is favored both by the presence of adjacent electron-attracting substituents $\left(\diagup C{=}O, \text{ —COOEt, or —NO}_2 \right)$ and by the delocalization of negative charge in the resulting anion.

$$CH_3\text{—}C\text{—}CH_2\text{—}C\text{—}CH_3 \xrightarrow{-H^+} \left[CH_3\text{—}C\text{—}\overset{..}{\overset{-}{C}}H\text{—}C\text{—}CH_3 \leftrightarrow \right.$$

$$CH_3\text{—}C\text{=}CH\text{—}C\text{—}CH_3 \leftrightarrow CH_3\text{—}C\text{—}CH\text{=}C\text{—}CH_3 \left.\right]$$

$$CH_3\text{—}C\text{—}CH_2\text{—}C\text{—}OEt \xrightarrow{-H^+} \left[CH_3\text{—}C\text{—}\overset{..}{\overset{-}{C}}H\text{—}C\text{—}OEt \leftrightarrow \right.$$

$$CH_3\text{—}C\text{=}CH\text{—}C\text{—}OEt \leftrightarrow CH_3\text{—}C\text{—}CH\text{=}C\text{—}OEt \left.\right]$$

$$CH_3\text{—}N \xrightarrow{-H^+} \left[{}^-\!:CH_2\text{—}N \leftrightarrow CH_2\text{=}N \right]$$

The original diketone, keto ester, or nitro compound may be regenerated by acidifying the solution of the respective anion; but in the third case, the conversion of anion to nitroalkane is slow and may be shown to proceed through an isomeric intermediate—a so-called *aci*-nitroalkane, $CH_2\text{=}N\overset{\diagup OH}{\diagdown O}$—which is very much more acidic and less highly colored than the original nitroalkane.

The nitro-*aci*-nitro pair constitutes an example of **tautomerism**—that is, the coexistence of two (or more) compounds that differ from each other only in the position of one (or more) mobile atoms and in electron distribution.[1] It is also an example of the more specific phenomenon of **prototropy**—that is, tautomerism in which interconversion between forms may be achieved (at least in thought) merely by the shift of a hydrogen ion and a redistribution of electron density. As previously pointed out, both acetylacetone and acetoacetic ester, represented above as their *keto forms*, may also exist in tautomeric forms— the *enols*, $CH_3\text{—}C\text{=}CH\text{—}C\text{—}CH_3$ and $CH_3\text{—}C\text{=}CH\text{—}COOEt$.[2] (For both of

---

[1] For detailed treatments of tautomerism see (*a*) Wheland, *Advanced Organic Chemistry*, John Wiley and Sons, Inc., New York, 1949, pp. 580–646; (*b*) Ingold, *Structure and Mechanism in Organic Chemistry*, Cornell University Press, Ithaca, N.Y., 1953, pp. 473–529; and (*c*) Thomson, *Quart. Revs.*, **X**, 27 (1956).

[2] Additional tautomeric forms of these compounds, such as $CH_2\text{=}C\text{—}CH_2\text{—}C\text{—}CH_3$ and

$CH_3\text{—}C\text{—}CH\text{=}COEt$, are conceivable, but there is no convincing evidence that they exist

these keto-enol pairs, interconversion between the forms is far more rapid than between the forms of nitromethane under comparable conditions.) Furthermore, a sample of acetylacetone, acetoacetic ester, or nitromethane will, unless special precautions are taken, consist of an equilibrium mixture of the two respective tautomeric forms.

Since those compounds forming the most stable carbanions are, with a few exceptions, those which exist in tautomeric forms, the question of carbanion stability is tied in with the phenomenon of prototropy. The prototropic forms of a compound (let us say a ketone, ke, and an enol, en) necessarily have a common conjugate base. Any attempt to determine the acid strength of form ke, using the conventional method of measuring the pH of a partially neutralized solution, will give instead an apparent ionization constant, K_{app}, which is related to the ionization constant of the keto form, K_{ke}, by the equation:

$$K_{ke} = K_{app} \frac{(ke) + (en)}{(ke)} \tag{1}$$

Thus, K_{app} will approach K_{ke} when the keto form is present in much larger concentration than the enol; but even if the mixture is 90 percent enol, the apparent equilibrium constant will differ from the acidity constant of the ketone only by a factor of 10.

Table 10-1. Apparent Acidity Constants for Some Acids in Which the C—H Bond Undergoes Ionization

Acid	pK_a	Acid	pK_a
$CH_2(CN)_2$	11.2	CH_3—C—CH_2—C—CH_3 (O, O)	9.0
CH_3—C—CHMe—C—CH_3 (O, O)	11.0	CH_3—C—CH_2—C—CF_3 (O, O)	4.7
CH_3—C—CH_2COOEt (O)	10.7	$CH_2(NO_2)_2$	3.6
CH_3—NO_2	10.2	$HC(NO_2)_3$	<1
CH_3—C—CH_2—C—Ph (O, O)	9.4	$HC(SO_2CH_3)_3$	<1

Table 10-1 lists the apparent pK_a values (water, 25°) for some representative "*pseudo acids*"—that is, acids in which a C—H bond slowly undergoes

in measurable amounts and rather good reasons that they should not. The observed enols should exist as *cis* and *trans* forms, but due to the mobile keto-enol equilibria, the two forms of each enol should be rapidly interconverted and therefore isolable only with great difficulty, if at all.

ionization.[3] All but the last of these may exist in tautomeric forms, and to change the given values to actual pK_a values, the concentrations of the individual tautomeric forms in solution must be known (p. 376). In each case, however, the predominating form of the acid in aqueous solution is that listed, so the apparent pK_a values are only slightly greater than the values corrected for tautomerism. It is to be noted that the relative strengths of these acids are governed in part by the same factors that determine the strengths of the more ordinary acids in which the acidic hydrogen is derived from an O—H bond. For example, substitution of three electron-attracting fluorine atoms for terminal hydrogens in acetylacetone boosts its acidity by a factor of 20,000. Conversely, substitution of a methyl group on the center carbon of this diketone lowers its acidity by a factor of about 100, an effect due partially to the electron-repelling action of this group and partially to steric inhibition of resonance in the anion (as described on p. 378). More subtly, acetoacetic ester, in which one of the carbonyl groups is bound to an —OEt group, is only one fiftieth as strong an acid as acetylacetone. Since this carbonyl group acquires electron density as a result of conjugation within the ethoxy group (I′), it can absorb a smaller measure of negative charge from the negative carbon in the anion (I″) and is thus less effective in stabilizing the anion. As with carboxylic acids and phenols, the nitro group is more strongly acid strengthening than are the acetyl and cyano

groups; indeed, the three nitro groups attached to a single carbon in trinitromethane make it a strong acid. The bicyclic diketone II is not appreciably more acidic than ordinary monoketones (for which pK_a values approach 19 or 20), since the conjugation-stabilized anionic form of II would have a double bond at a "bridgehead," in violation of Bredt's rule (p. 348).[4]

II

[3] These apparent pK_a values have been compiled by Pearson and Dillon, *J. Am. Chem. Soc.*, **75**, 2439 (1953). See this paper for additional references.
[4] Bartlett and Woods, *J. Am. Chem. Soc.*, **62**, 2933 (1940).

The sulfonyl group $\left(-\overset{\overset{\displaystyle O}{|}}{\underset{\underset{\displaystyle O}{|}}{S}}- \right)$ is also strongly acid strengthening, a large

part of its electron-attracting action being due to its inductive effect. It is also likely that a sulfur atom bound to a carbon from which a proton has been removed can absorb some of the negative charge into one of its outer d orbitals, thus stabilizing the resulting anion. This type of delocalization is often represented by structures such as III′, in which the sulfur atom has "expanded its

| III | III′ | IV | V |

valence shell" since, by classical count, it now shares 10 electrons. However, we should not expect the C=S "double bond" (which involves both d and p orbitals) in III′ to be a replica of an ordinary double bond between first-row elements (which involve only p orbitals). In particular, the requirement that all atoms attached to a double-bonded pair must lie in or near a common plane no longer holds. Thus, the trisulfone IV, unlike the diketone II, is strongly acidic, presumably because anion V, despite the "double bond" at the bridgehead, is an acceptable structure.[5]

We must turn away from hydroxylic solvents if we wish to study the acidities of such very weak acids as acetophenone, phenylacetylene, and triphenylmethane, for the anions derived from these acids are such strong bases that they may not exist in appreciable concentrations in water or alcohol. (Such very weak acids may generally be converted to their conjugate bases by treatment either with a very active metal or with the alkali metal derivative of a still weaker acid—for example, butylsodium.) Absorption spectroscopy is a useful tool for comparing acidities, for the spectrum of a carbanion is different from that of its parent acid (especially when conjugation effects in the two species are different), and the concentration of both the acid and its anion in a given

[5] Doering and Levy, *J. Am. Chem. Soc.*, **77**, 509 (1955). In the opinion of the present author, the evidence for a C=S "double bond" in anions derived from sulfones is not as strong as that which applied to sulfonium salts (see, for example, p. 372). It may, in fact, be argued, that the acidity of IV is due almost wholly to the combined inductive effect of three sulfone groups adjacent to the bridgehead carbon, although this does not explain why IV is an appreciably weaker base than H—C(SO$_2$CH$_3$)$_3$. In any event, the question is a difficult one and merits further investigation.

solution may generally be estimated. If one weak acid, HA, is dissolved in an inert solvent containing the alkali metal derivative of a second weak acid, say $Na^+A'^-$, protons will slowly be transferred from HA to A'^-, and eventually equilibrium will prevail.

$$HA + A'^- \rightleftharpoons A^- + HA'$$

By measuring the concentrations of the four species involved in this equilibrium, we can compare the acidities of HA and HA', just as we might compare the acidities of two indicators (p. 103). Comparisons of this sort, which have been carried out for solutions in ether and liquid ammonia, have only an approximate significance, for the activity coefficients of the various species are unknown. We may not yet, in good conscience, put these acids on the same quantitative scale as those studied in water or alcohol. However, experiments such as those described enable us to list the following weak acids (and many others) in order of decreasing acidity:[6]

$$EtOH > Ph - \underset{\underset{O}{\|}}{C} - CH_3 > Ph - C \equiv CH \geqslant$$

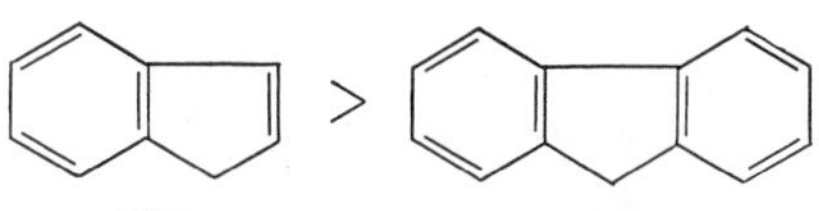

VI   VII

$$> Ph_3CH > Ph_2CH_2$$

A benzene ring adjacent to a C—H linkage facilitates the ionization of this bond by its capacity to absorb negative charge in the resulting carbanion (VIII ↔ VIII'); however, it is not as effective in this respect as a carbonyl group (Ex. 8a). A carbanion may acquire an extra measure of stability if its parent acid contains a cyclopentadiene ring (for example, indene, VI, and fluorene, VII). In such cases, the negative charge is distributed over each car-

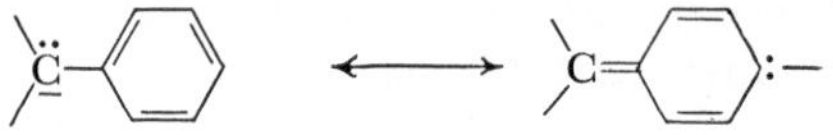

VIII   VIII'

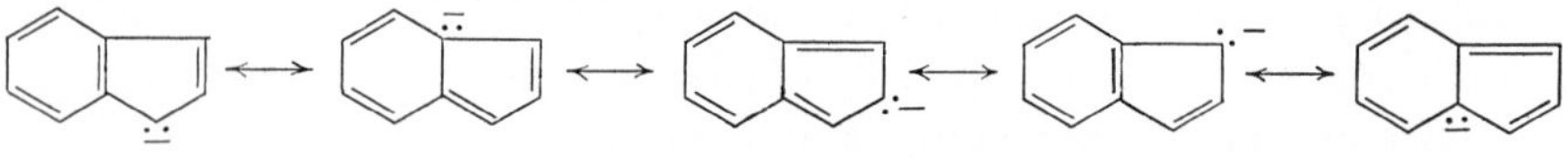

IX

bon in the five-membered ring, as well as over the six-membered ring(s), as shown below in the canonical forms of anion IX. Although there are three benzene rings adjacent to the C—H linkages in trypticine (X), this hydrocarbon

[6] Conant and Wheland, *J. Am. Chem. Soc.*, **54**, 1212 (1932).

is not appreciably more acidic than ordinary aliphatic hydrocarbons.[7] Again,

forms such as **XI** (analogous to **VIII'**), which might be expected to stabilize the trypticide anion, are prohibited by Bredt's rule.

Although the alkali-metal derivatives of hydrocarbons are ionized in ether, they are, as might be expected, largely nondissociated in that solvent; that is, they exist mainly as ion pairs and other ionic aggregates.[8] They appear to be strong electrolytes in liquid ammonia,[9] with which, however, they react slowly—for example,

$$Ph_3C^- + NH_3 \rightarrow Ph_3CH + NH_2^-$$

Another indication that a compound forms carbanions, although perhaps to a small extent, is the conversion of C—H bonds to C—D bonds when the compound is dissolved in D_2O or OD-labeled alcohol under basic conditions (or, alternately, the conversion of C—D bonds to C—H bonds when the deuterium-labeled compound is dissolved in ordinary water or alcohol). We have seen, for example, that hydrogen exchange at the α-carbon of esters in the Claisen condensation suggests the existence of a carbanion intermediate in this reaction (p. 335). Similarly, hydrogen exchange may be shown to occur at the α-carbon atoms in most ketones, aldehydes, nitroalkanes, nitriles, and sulfones under basic conditions, and often in neutral solutions as well. It also has been shown that a number of the trihalomethanes ($HCCl_3$, $HCBr_3$, $HCBr_2F$, and others) undergo hydrogen exchange in basic solutions,[10] showing that these too are in equilibrium with carbanions.

$$HCX_3 \xrightarrow{-H^+} CX_3^- \xrightarrow{D_2O} DCX_3 + OD^-$$

The trimethylsulfonium ion, $(CH_3)_3S^+$, readily undergoes hydrogen exchange

[7] Bartlett and Lewis, *J. Am. Chem. Soc.*, **72**, 1005 (1950).
[8] Swift, *J. Am. Chem. Soc.*, **60**, 1403 (1938); Keevil and Bent, *ibid.*, **60**, 193 (1938).
[9] Kraus and Kahler, *J. Am. Chem. Soc.*, **55**, 3537 (1933).
[10] (a) Sherman and Bernstein, *J. Am. Chem. Soc.*, **73**, 1376 (1951). (b) Hine, *et al.*, *ibid.*, **76**, 827 (1954); **78**, 479, 3337 (1956); **79**, 1406 (1957).

under similar conditions.[11] Here, the intermediate is not actually a carbanion, but rather a sort of zwitterion, **XII**, in which a partial neutralization of charge is possible by electron drift from the carbon atom into the d orbitals of the sulfur atom (**XII′**).

$$CH_3 \overset{+}{\underset{\underset{CH_3}{|}}{S}} CH_3 \xrightarrow{-H^+} \left[\overset{-}{:}CH_2 \overset{+}{\underset{\underset{CH_3}{|}}{S}} CH_3 \leftrightarrow CH_2 {=} \overset{..}{\underset{\underset{CH_3}{|}}{S}} CH_3 \right]$$

$$\text{XII} \qquad\qquad \text{XII′}$$

(Note that in form **XII′**, the sulfur atom is associated with ten, rather than eight, valence electrons.) Hydrogen exchange is similarly rapid for the cyclic sulfonium ion **XIII**, suggesting again that a carbon-sulfur bond having considerable double-bond character may exist at the bridgehead of a bicyclic system. The tetramethylammonium ion, however, undergoes hydrogen exchange in

XIII

basic solutions exceedingly slowly; the "zwitterion," $^-:CH_2 \overset{+}{N}(CH_3)_3$, cannot be stabilized by a form analogous to **XII′**, since nitrogen cannot expand its valence shell beyond eight electrons.[11]

Base- and Acid-catalyzed Halogenations of Ketones

The bromination or iodination of almost any enolizable ketone in the position adjacent to the carbonyl group is accelerated by addition of bases. Such bases are not catalysts in the strictest sense of the word, for they are stoichiometrically consumed. Nevertheless, these base-promoted halogenations are kinetically similar to reactions subject to general base catalysis, since if several bases are present, the rate law will contain several terms, one for each base (p. 112). For simplicity, let us first consider a system in which the action of only one base, $B:$, is significant—for example, the bromination of acetone, promoted by OH^-.[13] The rate of this reaction is proportional to the concentrations of ketone and base, but is *independent of the concentration of bromine*. This means that although bromine is consumed in the overall reaction, *it becomes involved after completion*

[11] Mamalis and Rydon, *J. Chem. Soc.*, **1955**, 1049.
[12] Doering and Hoffmann, *J. Am. Chem. Soc.*, **77**, 521 (1955).
[13] Bell and Longuet-Higgins, *J. Chem. Soc.*, **1946**, 636.

of the rate-determining step. The rate laws for the chlorination[13] and iodination[14] of acetone in the presence of hydroxide are the same as for its bromination; moreover a given basic solution of acetone reacts at the same rate with chlorine or iodine as with bromine. Clearly, the three halogenations have the same rate-determining step, the transition state of which contains acetone, an OH^- ion, and an indeterminate number of solvent molecules. A very simple mechanism fulfilling these conditions comes to mind:

$$CH_3—C—CH_3 \underset{slow}{\overset{OH^-}{\rightleftharpoons}} \left[^-{:}CH_2—C—CH_3 \leftrightarrow CH_2{=}C—CH_3 \right] \overset{X_2}{\underset{fast}{\rightarrow}}$$

$$XCH_2—C—CH_3 + X^-$$

Here X may be Cl, Br, or I, and the "indeterminate number of solvent molecules" is taken as zero. If the mechanism proposed for acetone also applies to the bromination of the optically active ketone XIV, a given basic solution of this ketone should undergo racemization in the absence of bromine at the same rate that it would undergo bromination in the presence of bromine; for the presumed rate-determining step in the bromination reaction (the conversion of ketone to carbanion XV) destroys the asymmetry. Although the rates of

bromination and racemization have not been compared in water, they have been found to be the same in aqueous acetic acid (with acetate ion added as the base).[15] And that is not all; since the concentration of anion XV is small, its rate of destruction should equal its rate of formation, once the initial step is under way. If anion XV is generated in D_2O in the absence of bromine, it will soon be destroyed by reaction with solvent, incorporating a deuterium atom at the α position. Again, the deuteration and racemization have a common rate-determining step and should therefore take place at the same rate,

[14] Bartlett, *J. Am. Chem. Soc.*, **56**, 967 (1934).
[15] Hsu and Wilson, *J. Chem. Soc.*, **1936**, 623.

provided reaction conditions (solvent, basicity, and temperature) are the same. It has, in fact, been found that the rates of racemization and deuteration of ketone XIV are, within experimental error, equal in D_2O-dioxane mixtures in the presence of NaOD.[16]

The halogenations of enolizable ketones are also accelerated by acids, and the characteristics of the acid-catalyzed reactions are somewhat the same as those promoted by base. Such reactions have been found to be subject to *general acid catalysis;*[17(a)] their rates are proportional to the concentrations of ketone and added acid, but *independent of the concentration of halogen;*[17(b)] the rate of halogenation of a ketone with an asymmetric α-carbon atom is the same as its rate of racemization in the absence of halogen;[17(c)] and the rates of acid-catalyzed bromination and deuteration of a given ketone are the same in heavy water.[17(d)] Again, we may conclude that bromination, iodination, racemization, and deuteration proceed through a common intermediate, formed in a common rate-determining step. Since we are now considering reactions in acid solutions, we may be quite certain that this common intermediate is *not* the conjugate base of the ketone; it is far more likely to be the enol form, XVI, of the substrate.

$$H-\overset{|}{\underset{|}{C}}-\overset{|}{C}=O \underset{\text{fast}}{\overset{HA}{\rightleftharpoons}} H-\overset{|}{\underset{|}{C}}-\overset{|}{C}=O\cdot\cdot HA \underset{\text{slow}}{\overset{B:}{\longrightarrow}} H-\overset{|}{\underset{|}{C}}-\overset{|}{C}=O\cdot\cdot H-A\rightarrow B:H+\overset{|}{C}=\overset{|}{C}-OH+A^-$$

$$\text{XVI}$$

$$\text{then, }\overset{|}{\underset{|}{C}}=\overset{|}{C}-OH \xrightarrow[\text{fast}]{\text{Hal}_2 \text{ or } D_2O} \text{halogenation or deuteration} \qquad (2)$$

$$\text{XVI}$$

Note that the enolization is not simply a "proton jump" from the α-carbon to the carbonyl oxygen atom (for this would allow no role for the acid catalyst). Of the several items of evidence pointing to the rapidity of the initial step,[18] the most convincing is the very rapid oxygen exchange that ketones undergo when dissolved in aqueous acidic solutions,[19] an exchange that may be studied using H_2O^{18}. The oxygen exchange reaction of acetone, for example, is many times as fast as its acid-catalyzed bromination under similar conditions. Now this exchange, whatever its detailed mechanism may be, almost certainly proceeds through the hydrogen-bonded complex $(CH_3)_2C=O \cdot \cdot HA$, the same type of intermediate as that proposed for acid-catalyzed enolization. Since the

[16] Hsu, Ingold, and Wilson, *J. Chem. Soc.*, **1938**, 78. The deuteration of ketone XIV in heavy water and its racemization in ordinary water would be expected (and are found) to proceed at slightly different specific rates; for the strength of a given base is slightly different in the two solvents, and their solvation characteristics are not identical.

[17] (a) Dawson *et al.*, *J. Chem. Soc.*, **1926**, 2282, **1928**, 2844; **1929**, 1884. (b) Zucker and Hammett, *J. Am. Chem. Soc.*, **61**, 2791 (1939). (c) Bartlett and Stauffer, *ibid.*, **57**, 2580 (1935). (d) Rietz, *Z. physik. Chem.*, **179**, 119 (1937).

[18] See, for example, Hammett and Pfluger, *J. Am. Chem. Soc.*, **55**, 4079 (1933); and Zucker and Hammett, *ibid.*, **61**, 2785 (1939).

[19] Cohn and Urey, *J. Am. Chem. Soc.*, **60**, 679 (1938).

overall exchange reaction cannot proceed any more rapidly than any individual step, we may conclude that the formation of the complex, if it is indeed a step in the exchange reaction, is likewise many times as fast as the enolization.

This ketone-acid association (which, if the acid is sufficiently strong, amounts to the formation of the conjugate acid of the ketone, $H-\overset{|}{\underset{|}{C}}-\overset{+}{\underset{|}{C}}-OH$) draws electron density away from the α-C—H bond toward the carbonyl group, facilitating the removal of the α-hydrogen by a basic species. The role of the base (designated noncommittally as B:) in sequence (2) may be played by a molecule of solvent, or, if the solvent is hydroxylic, by a hydrogen-bonded aggregate of solvent molecules. If other basic species are present in appreciable quantity, these may also attack the hydrogen-bonded acid-ketone complex formed in the initial step and the rate law for enolization will contain one or more terms of the type $k_{cat.}$(ketone)$(HA)(B)$. In a solution such as an aqueous acetate-acetic acid buffer, the rate law becomes even more complex, since there are three acids (H_3O^+, HOAc, and H_2O) and three bases (OH^-, OAc^-, and H_2O) which may participate. The rate law for the iodination (hence the enolization) of acetone, applicable over a large range of buffer compositions, is[20]

$$\text{rate} = (\text{acetone})[k_1 + k_2(H_3O^+) + k_3(HOAc) + k_4(OH^-)$$
$$+ k_5(OAc^-) + k_6(HOAc)(OAc^-)] \quad (3)$$

(For a given solution, only two or three of these terms may be significant.) Each of the terms may be considered to represent the action of a different acid, or base, or both; for example, the term containing k_2 represents the action of the acid H_3O^+ and the base H_2O (which does not appear in the kinetic expression), whereas the term containing k_6 represents the action of the acid HOAc and the base OAc^-. Terms containing $(H_3O^+)(OH^-)$, $(H_3O^+)(OAc^-)$, and $(HOAc)(OH^-)$ seem, at first glance, to be missing, but they are hidden in the terms containing k_1, k_3, and k_5, respectively. Each of these three terms, because of the mobile equilibria involved, represents the combined action of two acid-base pairs.[21] for example, the term containing k_3 represents the action of both the HOAc—H_2O and the H_3O^+—OAc^- couples.

At this point it may occur to the reader that the mechanism just considered for acid-catalyzed enolization (which we may refer to as a *concerted* mechanism), reopens the question of enolization promoted by base; for sequence (2) obviously becomes a base-induced enolization if HA is the solvent and B: is its conjugate base. In contrast to the mechanism proposed on page 373 (which, because it yields the enolate anion, may be called the *carbanion mechanism*), sequence (2) yields the enol itself. In the carbanion mechanism, the base attacks

[20] Dawson and Spivey, *J. Chem. Soc.*, **1930**, 2180.
[21] Swain, *J. Am. Chem. Soc.*, **72**, 4578 (1950).

without help from an acidic species, whereas in the concerted mechanism, as its name implies, simultaneous action by both acid and base are necessary (although the acid arrives at the reaction site first). Kinetics offers no choice if the "acid," which comprises the chief difference between the two possible transition states, is one or more solvent molecules. The question is certainly not settled, but as we shall presently see, the relations between structure and reactivity in base-promoted enolization are significantly different from those in acid-catalyzed enolization, suggesting that, at least in some cases, different mechanisms operate.

Keto-enol Equilibria

While considering the details of the enolization process under various conditions we must not lose sight of one fact; the conversion of ketone to enol or to enolate ion, whatever the mechanism may be, is much slower than the halogenation of the enol. This means that if we quickly titrate an equilibrium mixture of ketone and enol with Br_2, we should observe an end point when all of the enol, but practically none of the ketone, is brominated. (The bromine color at the end

Table 10-2. Enol Content in Some Ketones, Diketones, and Keto Esters[22]

Compound	Percent Enol	Compound	Percent Enol
CH_3—C—CH_3 ‖ O	0.00025	Ph—C—CH_2—C—CH_3 ‖ O ‖ O	99
cyclohexanone	0.02	1,3-cyclohexanedione	95
CH_3—C—CH_2—C—CH_3 ‖ O ‖ O	80	CH_3—C—C—CH_3 ‖ O ‖ O	0.0056
CH_3—C—CH—C—CH_3 ‖ O │ Me ‖ O	33	1,2-cyclopentanedione	99
CH_3—C—CH_2—COOEt ‖ O	7.5	1,2-cyclohexanedione	40
CH_3—C—CH(i-Pr)—COOEt ‖ O	5	$CH_2(COOEt)_2$	0.1

[22] For more extensive data on keto-enol equilibria, including the composition of equilibrium mixtures in the gas phase and in various solvents, see Wheland, Ref. 1(a), pp. 600–611, and Hammond in *Steric Effects in Organic Chemistry*, edited by Newman, John Wiley and Sons, Inc., New York, 1956, pp. 446–453.

point should, however, slowly fade as the remaining ketone is converted into enol and the latter brominated.) It is thus possible to estimate, by selective bromination, the quantity of enol in a keto-enol mixture, although the determination as described is rather unsatisfactory in practice unless it is modified in one of several ways, which do not, however, alter its essential principle.[23] The ketones, diketones, and keto esters listed in Table 10-2 exist as mixtures of tautomers in which the enol content may be as low as a fraction of a percent or, in other cases, may approach immeasurably close to 100 percent. The enol contents given refer to equilibrium mixtures at 25° in the absence of solvent.

The first four entries in this table emphasize the striking difference between the extent of enolization in mono- and diketones. Incorporation of a second carbonyl group, in the *beta* position to the first, increases the length of the conjugated system in the enol form from three to five atoms,[24]

$$\left[\begin{array}{c} | \quad | \\ -C=C-OH \end{array} \longleftrightarrow \begin{array}{c} \overset{-}{\ddot{}} \ | \quad \overset{+}{|} \\ -C-C=OH \end{array} \right] \quad vs. \quad \left[\begin{array}{c} O \ H-O \\ \| \quad | \\ C \quad C \\ \diagdown C \diagup \\ | \end{array} \longleftrightarrow \begin{array}{c} \overset{-}{O} \ H-\overset{+}{O} \\ | \quad \| \\ C \quad C \\ \diagdown C \diagup \\ | \end{array} \right]$$

but this effect almost certainly accounts only for a portion of the observed difference. Intramolecular hydrogen bonding (XVII) occurs in the enol forms of

XVII

most acyclic β-diketones and β-keto esters, but obviously cannot occur in the keto forms. Since the energies of most O—H · · · O hydrogen bonds lie near

[23] In a procedure developed by Meyer (*Ber.*, **45**, 2843 (1912); **47**, 826 (1914)), an excess of bromine is added to the equilibrium mixture, and the bromine not consumed after a very short time is destroyed by addition of β-naphthol. The resulting mixture is treated with KI, which reacts with the α-bromoketone (formed by bromination of the enol), yielding iodine

$$\begin{array}{c} | \quad | \\ CBr-C=O + H^+ + 2I^- \rightarrow \end{array} \begin{array}{c} | \quad | \\ CH-C=O + Br^- + I_2 \end{array}$$

and the iodine formed is titrated with thiosulfate. For an even more elegant procedure, which can be adapted to measurement of very small quantities of enol, see Schwarzenbach and Wittwer, *Helv. Chim. Acta*, **30**, 657, 669 (1947).

[24] Replacement of a methyl group by a phenyl group in acetylacetone or acetoacetic ester results in an extension of the conjugated system in the enol form to include the benzene ring also, an effect which should (and does) increase the degree of enolization.

6 kcal per mole, we may expect hydrogen bonding, when present, to stabilize the enol form with respect to the keto by about this figure. In the absence of other effects, this would favor the enol in the equilibrium by about 4 powers of 10. Such hydrogen bonding loosens the O—H bond and allows somewhat more electron density to shift from the hydroxyl oxygen of the enol into the remainder of the conjugated system. As a result, the polarity of the enol is lowered; and, indeed, in practically all cases where a diketone or a keto ester has been separated into tautomeric forms, the enol has been found to be the more volatile, hence, presumably, the less polar form (although hydroxyl compounds as a class are commonly considered to be more polar than carbonyl compounds).

The atoms forming an effectively operating conjugated system should, as we have repeatedly seen, lie in or near a common plane. Therefore any structural feature that hinders the coplanarity of the
$$-\overset{|}{\underset{\underset{O}{\|}}{C}}-\overset{}{\underset{\underset{OH}{|}}{C}}=\overset{|}{C}-$$
group should decrease the stability of the enol form and lower the degree of enolization. A scale model of XVII shows that group R and group R' will interfere with each other when either is as large as or larger than a methyl group unless the model is twisted so that the planarity of the conjugated system is destroyed. We thus see why incorporation of a methyl group in the 3-position of acetylacetone (XVII, R' = CH₃) lowers the degree of enolization, in this case by over 50 percent. The effect appears to be less for acetoacetic ester, for in the preferred conformation of the terminal —COOEt substituent (p. 74), the

XVIII

bulky ethyl group is far removed from substituent R' (XVIII). Nevertheless, substituents R and R' may still interfere, and the isopropyl derivative of acetoacetic ester is appreciably less enolized than acetoacetic ester itself.[25]

[25] In contrast to the effect of alkyl substitution on the methylene group of acetylacetone, substitutions on the *methyl* groups of this diketone *increase* the degree of enolization (Hammond, Ref. 23, p. 447). It has been suggested that the preferred conformation of the keto form of β-diketones is XIX, in which the carbonyl oxygen atoms are as far apart as possible. This conformation becomes much less favorable, however, when the R groups are bulky enough

XIX   XX

On the other hand, when the ends of the enol form of a diketone are tied back into a ring, the intramolecular rotations—which, in an acyclic structure result in large departures from planarity—are prohibited. This being the case, the enol becomes stabilized and the degree of enolization increased. Thus, the 1,3-cyclohexanedione derivative, dimedon (XXI), exists almost completely as the enol form XXII, in which all carbon atoms in the ring except C$_5$ are coplanar. (This predominance of enol is all the more striking since the geometry of the ring system prohibits intramolecular hydrogen bonding.)

XXI   XXII

Cyclization has a most remarkable influence on the degree of enolization of α-diketones. Diacetyl, CH_3—C—C—CH_3, exists almost exclusively as the

keto form whereas 1,2-cyclopentanedione is almost 100 percent enolized. This is almost certainly a conformational effect. In the most stable conformation of biacetyl (XXIII), the C=O dipoles are pointing in opposite directions with the negative oxygen atoms as far from each other as possible. Because of the rigidity of the cyclopentane ring, however, the two carbonyl dipoles in 1,2-

XXIII   XXIV   XXV

cyclopentanedione lie at an angle of only about 65°, and the compound adopts the enol form (XXV), presumably in an attempt to relieve this electrostatically unsatisfactory situation. In 1,2-cyclohexanedione, the larger ring is somewhat more flexible and the predominance of the enol form therefore not as great.

Cyclization appears to favor enolization for monoketones also; for example, the fraction of the enol form in liquid cyclohexanone is almost 100 times that in liquid acetone. No convincing explanation, consistent with the magnitude of the effect, seems to have been presented.

---

to interfere with each other (for example, when R is *i*-Pr or *t*-Bu). Rather than adopt the electrostatically unfavorable conformation, XX, the diketone will generally prefer to tautomerize to the enol.

Since, as we have remarked, the keto form of a diketone or keto ester is almost invariably more polar than the enol form, we need not be surprised that the enol:keto ratio for a given pair of tautomers at equilibrium in solution depends markedly on the polarity of the solvent, and that this ratio tends to be greatest in the least polar solvents. Acetoacetic ester is typical of many tautomeric materials for which such a dependence has been observed; the following figures represent the enol contents at equilibrium for dilute solutions of this keto ester in various solvents (at 18°).[26]

Solvent	H_2O	HOAc	EtOH	Benzene	Hexane	Pure ester
Percent enol	0.4	5.7	10.5	16.2	46.4	7.7

Structure and Rate in Enolization

The rate of enolization of a ketone, or, more precisely, the rate of its conversion to the enol-enolate system may be obtained by measuring its rate of halogenation or rate of deuterium exchange, or if the carbon bearing the acid hydrogen is asymmetric, its rate of racemization. The rates of numerous enolizations (and related prototropic shifts such as nitro to *aci*-nitro conversions) have been determined under a variety of conditions and in a number of solvents. Typical values (for reactions in water at 25°) are recorded in Table 10-3.[27] These reactions were carried out in the absence of added acid or base, being therefore first order. It is evident that the stronger acids tend to enolize more rapidly than the weaker. This is not surprising, for any structural feature that serves to stabilize the enolate anion (extended conjugation, coplanarity, or the presence of electron-attracting groups) would be expected to stabilize a transition state in which the α-hydrogen is in the process of being removed. Yet there are enough discrepancies to remind us that the correlation between the two types of phenomenon is only a rough one. Acetoacetic ester enolizes about 2000 times as rapidly as nitromethane although the compounds have nearly equal acidities; an α-bromo group boosts the rates of enolization of acetylacetone and malonic ester but decreases that of benzoylacetone; benzoyltrifluoroacetone, Ph—C—CH₂—C—CF₃, enolizes only one half as rapidly as acetylacetone

$$\text{Ph—C—CH}_2\text{—C—CF}_3$$
$$\;\;\;\;\;\;\|\;\;\;\;\;\;\;\;\;\;\;\;\|$$
$$\;\;\;\;\;\;O\;\;\;\;\;\;\;\;\;\;\;O$$

---

[26] Meyer, *Ann.*, **380**, 212 (1911). Since the polarity of a solution of a ketone or keto ester changes as more and more solute is added, the enol:keto ratio of a given material in a given solvent will also depend on the *concentration*. More particularly, as the solution becomes more concentrated, the enol:keto ratio will approach that existing in the absence of solvent. Typically, acetoacetic ester in a 1-percent solution in CS_2 is 39 percent in the enol form; that in an 82-percent solution in CS_2 is 8 percent in the enol form; and the pure ester is 7.7 percent in the enol form. (See Meyer and Kappelmeier, *Ber.*, **44**, 2718 (1911).)

[27] Rate data for proton transfer from a number of ketones, esters, sulfones, and nitroalkanes have been compiled by Pearson and Dillon, Ref. 3. See also Eidinoff, *J. Am. Chem. Soc.*, **67**, 2027 (1945); and Reid and Calvin, *ibid.*, **72**, 2948 (1950).

Table 10-3. Rate Data for Ionization of Acids Involving C—H Bond Breakage

Acid	k_1 (min^{-1})	Acid	k_1
$CH_2(NO_2)_2$	50	CH_3—C—CH—COOEt ‖ | O Et	4.5×10^{-4}
CH_3—C—CH_2—C—CH_3 ‖ ‖ O O	1.0	CH_3NO_2	2.6×10^{-6}
CH_3—C—CHBr—COOEt ‖ O	0.36	CH_3—C—CH_2Cl ‖ O	3.3×10^{-6}
CH_3—C—CH_2—COOEt ‖ O	0.072	CH_3—C—CH_3 ‖ O	2.8×10^{-8}

although its acidity constant is about 70 times as great. Moreover, in the nitro-alkane series the *weaker acids appear to enolize the more rapidly* (although differences within the series are small.[28] Apparently those substituents that show strong electron-withdrawing power by induction are, in general, relatively more effective in stabilizing the anion than the activated complex leading to it. Thus nitro compounds and trifluoromethyl ketones, almost without exception, undergo tautomerization more slowly than nonhalogenated ketones, diketones, or β-keto esters of comparable acidity.

The rates of conversion of haloforms to their carbanions constitute a puzzling series, for deuterium-exchange experiments[29] indicate that the heavier

$$HCX_3 + B: \rightleftharpoons B:H^+ + CX_3^-$$

haloforms (which one would expect to be less acidic) are the more reactive. The following relative rate constants (water, 0°) for base-catalyzed hydrogen transfer illustrate the trend:

Haloform	$DCCl_2F$	$DCCl_3$	$DCBr_2Cl$	$DCBr_3$	DCI_3
$\dfrac{k}{k_{DCCl_3}}$	0.019	1.0	31.0	121	130

These figures bring to mind an equally disturbing trend in the rates of decarboxylation of the anions of trihaloacetic acids (CX_3COO^-) where, once again,

[28] Maron *et al.*, *J. Am. Chem. Soc.*, **60**, 2558 (1938); **65**, 212 (1943). Pearson and Dillon, *ibid.*, **72**, 3574 (1950).

[29] Hine, Burske, Hine, and Langford, *J. Am. Chem. Soc.*, **79**, 1406 (1957). In this case, the exchange of hydrogen between deutero-haloforms, DCX_3, and ordinary water was studied. The conclusions resulting from these experiments should also apply to ordinary haloforms, since the hydrogen isotope effect, although sizable, probably remains very nearly constant throughout the series.

the derivatives of iodine react most rapidly, and those of fluorine least rapidly.[30] The activated complexes in the two types of reaction have one obvious feature in common: the CX_3 group has assumed considerable carbanion character (p. 346) in both. It thus appears that a CX_3^- anion (and an activated complex leading to it) is most stable if X is iodine and least stable if X is fluorine, but explanations to account for this trend have not been convincing. One suspects that because the halogens (except fluorine) may "expand their valence shells," the C—X bonds in each of these anions (except CF_3^-) have some double-bond

character (XXVI ↔ XXVI'), being in this respect similar to the $^-:\overset{|}{\underset{|}{C}}-\overset{+}{\underset{|}{S}}-$

bond in the sulfonium derivative XII (p. 372). Nevertheless, why this double-

$$\left[X-\overset{\overset{\displaystyle X}{|}}{\underset{\displaystyle \cdot\cdot}{C}}-X \right]^- \longrightarrow \left[:\overset{\cdot\cdot}{X}=\overset{\overset{\displaystyle X}{|}}{\underset{\displaystyle \cdot\cdot}{C}}-X \right]^-$$

$$\text{XXVI} \qquad\qquad \text{XXVI}'$$

bond character should be more important for the CI_3^- ion than for the CCl_3^- ion (if indeed it is) is a baffling point.

Returning now to more familiar ground, let us reconsider the base-catalyzed bromination of ketones. In the absence of "complicating effects" we should expect the rate of such brominations to fall when an electron-repelling alkyl group is substituted for an α-hydrogen. This has been found to be the case, for example, in the acetate-catalyzed bromination of acetophenone; here, the substitution of a single methyl for a hydrogen in the acetyl group of the ketone results in a 6-fold decrease in specific rate (at 75°), whereas substitution of two such methyls results in a 33-fold decrease.[31] Furthermore, in the

halogenation of an unsymmetric ketone (for example, $RCH_2-\overset{\overset{\displaystyle O}{||}}{C}-CHR_2'$) the alpha carbon bearing the fewer alkyl groups (in this case, the one on the left) should be preferentially attacked.[32] Conversely, substitution of an electron-attracting halogen atom for an α-hydrogen in a ketone should accelerate its further halogenation. On this basis, we may understand why the major product from the base-promoted bromination of acetone (with the ketone in large

excess) is the unsymmetrical tribromo compound, $CH_3-\overset{\overset{\displaystyle O}{||}}{C}-CBr_3$. The mono-bromo compound first formed is more readily brominated than acetone itself, and the dibromo compound is still more readily brominated. Thus, the forma-

[30] See, for example, Brown, *Quart. Revs.*, 5, 134 (1951).
[31] Evans and Gordon, *J. Chem. Soc.*, **1938**, 1434.
[32] Cardwell, *J. Chem. Soc.*, **1951**, 2442.

tion of the tribromo compound takes place in a series of steps, the slowest of which is the enolization of acetone itself.

The picture changes markedly when we turn to acid-catalyzed halogenations—reactions whose rates are determined by acid-catalyzed enolizations. Here, the substitution of alkyl groups for α-hydrogens *accelerates* halogenation, whereas α-halo substituents retard it. As a consequence, we often find that an unsymmetric ketone suffers halogenation (or any other enolization-controlled reaction) mainly at one position in strong acid and at another position in base. In the following four ketones, for example, the letters a and b designate the favored positions of attack under acidic and basic conditions:

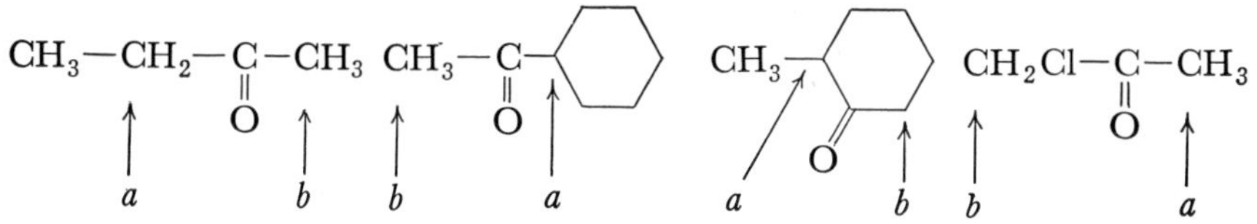

Similarly, when acetone is brominated in the presence of strong acid rather than in base, the monobromo derivative becomes isolable; for under these conditions, it enolizes more slowly than in acetone itself.

The change in structure-reactivity relationships as an enolization reaction is transferred from basic to acidic solutions suggests (although it does not demand) a change in mechanism. To account for the accelerating action of α-alkyl groups on acid-catalyzed enolization, we may remind ourselves that an alkyl group adjacent to a C=C double bond stabilizes the latter by about 2.5 kcal per mole, an effect which is generally attributed to hyperconjugation,

$$\left(RCH_2-C=C- \leftrightarrow H^+CHR=C-\overset{..}{C}- \right).$$ Since a C=C double bond is being

formed in an acid-catalyzed enolization, it is reasonable that the process should be aided by α-alkyl groups. This explanation, however, obviously has a hollow ring unless we can explain why the inductive action of α-alkyl groups, which presumably is important in acid-induced enolization, suddenly becomes unimportant in the presence of a basic catalyst. In this regard, we may assume that the breakage of the α-C—H bond, which requires a good portion of the activation energy necessary for a base-induced enolization, is facilitated in the presence of acid; for here the —C=O group has been converted either to a

$-\overset{+}{\underset{|}{C}}$—OH linkage or a $-\underset{|}{C}$=O $\cdots$ HA linkage, and electron density has

been pulled away from the α-C—H bonds, weakening them. In acid, then, breakage of the C—H bond becomes less of a problem than the reorganization of charge around the α-carbon atom in forming the double bond, and factors that control the ease of breakage of this bond likewise become less important.[33]

Although inductive effects overshadow hyperconjugation in base-induced enolizations, it is still possible to show that the latter exist. In hyperconjugation, as we ordinarily consider it, a double bond is stabilized by the "loosening" of a C—H bond adjacent to it; and if such a C—H bond is replaced by a somewhat "tighter" C—D bond, hyperconjugative effects diminish slightly (see, for example, p. 285). Thus, replacement of the four β-hydrogen atoms in phenyl cyclopentyl ketone, yielding the deuterated ketone, XXVII, lowers the rate for acid-catalyzed enolization (HCl in HOAc) by 20 percent, and since the same

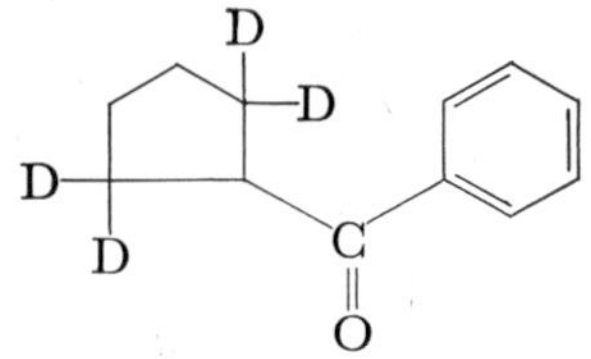

XXVII

isotope effect arises in the acetate-catalyzed enolization of this ketone, we may conclude that hyperconjugation also operates here.[34] It has been suggested[34] that we have here evidence that a concerted, rather than a carbanion, mechanism (p. 374) for base-catalyzed enolization is operating. For it may be argued that hyperconjugation should not significantly stabilize an anion such as XXVIII or a transition state leading to it, since the high concentration of negative charge on the carbonyl group in hyperconjugated structure XXVIII'' would be expected to make this a very unstable structure. Although this argument is interesting, it is indicative, rather than conclusive.

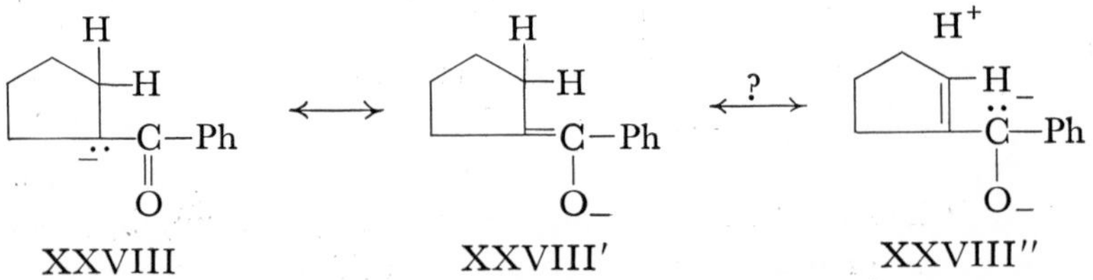

XXVIII   XXVIII'   XXVIII''

The Concerted and the Carbanion Mechanisms for Tautomerism

The mechanistic ambiguity which we have noted for base-promoted enolization does not apply to all base-accelerated tautomerizations. A rather clear

---

[33] The retarding action of α-halo substituents in acid-catalyzed enolizations may be more directly explained. Since such substituents are electron attracting, they reduce the basicity of the ketone, thus lowering the equilibrium concentration of its conjugate acid—the active intermediate in the enolization.

[34] Emmons and Hawthorne, J. Am. Chem. Soc., 78, 5593 (1956).

decision is possible, for example, in the conversion of the β,γ-unsaturated nitrile, XXIX, to its α,β-unsaturated isomer, XXX. If this reaction is initiated in EtOD in the presence of OEt$^-$, but the unconverted starting material is reisolated while the reaction is still in its early stages, considerable deuterium

| XXIX | XXXI | XXX |

may be found in nitrile XXIX; this indicates not only that the isomerization proceeds through anion XXXI, but also that this anion, once formed, is more likely to revert back to nitrile XXIX than proceed to nitrile XXX.[35]

An equally clear decision is possible (although the answer in this case is different) for the tautomerization of such imines as XXXII to the isomeric imines—for example, XXXIII. Here, if the reaction is carried out in EtOD,

| XXXII | XXXIII |

the rate of isomerization is found to be equal to the rate at which deuterium enters the imine (at least in the early stages of the reaction), and if the reaction is carried out on an optically active imine, Ph—$\overset{*}{\text{C}}$HMe—N=CPh$_2$, the rate of isomerization is also equal to the rate of racemization.[36] The observed correspondence in rates may be interpreted in one of two ways. The isomerization may proceed through a carbanion intermediate, Ph—$\overset{\cdot\cdot}{\text{C}}$Me—N=CPh$_2$, which is converted almost completely to imine XXXIII, in which case the isomerization would be very nearly irreversible; or alternately, this reaction may proceed by a concerted attack of the acid EtOH (or EtOD) and the base OEt$^-$ on the imine (note that, according to this mechanism, each removal of a hydrogen

from the "left" side of the molecule is accompanied by an addition of a hydrogen

[35] Ingold, de Salas, and Wilson, *J. Chem. Soc.*, **1936**, 1328.

[36] Perez Ossorio and Hughes, *J. Chem. Soc.*, **1952**, 426. (b) de Salas and Wilson, *ibid.*, **1938**, 319.

to the "right" side). The first possibility, the formation of a carbanion and its irreversible destruction, is eliminated by our knowledge that the *isomerization is reversible* (K_{eq} 0.47 at 85°);[37] hence we may conclude that the concerted mechanism operates for this reaction. If the reaction were irreversible, neither alternative could, on the basis of the evidence quoted, be excluded. Indeed the base-catalyzed bromination of ketones is, as we have emphasized, mechanistically ambiguous, largely because of its approach to irreversibility.

By using similar methods of investigation, it should be possible to obtain information concerning the paths of a number of additional tautomerizations—for example:

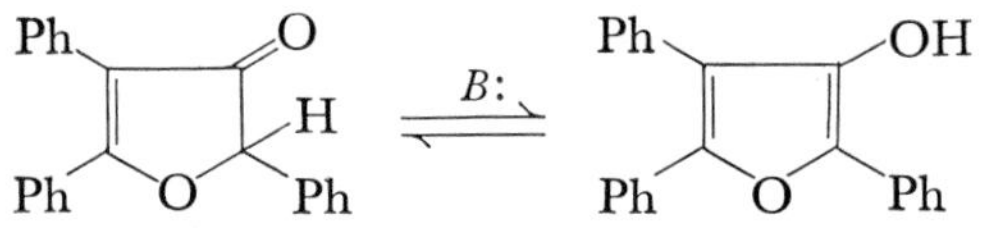

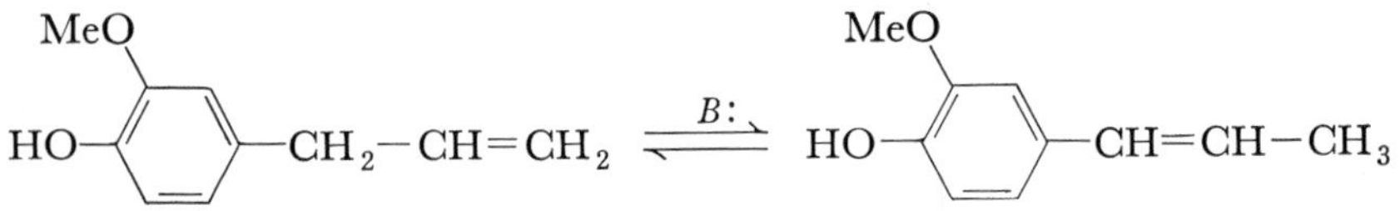

Yet, although the literature of tautomerism is extensive, there remain many tautomeric conversions for which we cannot say which, if either, of these mechanisms applies. One rule of thumb is, however, of some use: For relatively acidic substances in strongly ionizing solvents, tautomerization is likely to involve initial dissociation of a proton, whereas if the acidity of the substance, or the ionizing power of the solvent, are lowered, the concerted mechanism becomes more likely.

Carbanion Character in the Phenoxide and Pyrrolyl Anions

The conjugate base of a ketone, a keto ester, or a nitroparaffin is, as has been emphasized, generally formed by ionization of a C—H bond. Since, however, the negative charge is not confined to a carbon atom or group of carbon atoms, but is instead spread over a conjugated system including an oxygen atom as well, it may be argued that such anions are not "true carbanions" in the same sense as is, say, the triphenylmethide ion, $Ph_3C:^-$. The definition of a "true carbanion," is, like many definitions, somewhat arbitrary; but, regardless of definition, such conjugate bases obviously have much of the character of carb-

[37] Hsu, Ingold, and Wilson, *J. Chem. Soc.*, **1933**, 1493; **1934**, 93; **1935**, 1774.

anions; that is, they are anions in which a significant concentration of negative charge lies on one or more carbon atoms. On this basis, there are other anions that, although not generally formed by ionization of a C—H bond, also have unmistakable carbanion character. The most important of these are the conjugate bases of phenol and pyrrole; *ambident* reagents (p. 296) in which the carbon atoms, as well as the more electronegative oxygen or nitrogen atoms, are nucleophilic. Indeed these anions are often represented as resonance hybrids in which one or more of the individual structures have negatively charged carbons.

The phenoxide ion displays carbanion character, for example, in its reactions with bromine, with CO_2 (the Kolbe reaction), and with chloroform (the Reimer-Tiemann reaction); for in each of these reactions, the attacking atom is carbon rather than oxygen.

Similarly, in the carboxylation and ethylation of the pyrrolyl anion (**XXXIV**), the attacking atom in the ring is carbon, rather than nitrogen.

Geometry of Carbanions

We have noted on several occasions that the bonds about the tervalent carbon of a free carbonium ion, $-\overset{|}{\underset{|}{C}}{}^{+}$, prefer to lie in a common plane and that, as a consequence, the conversion of an asymmetric carbon atom to a positive carbon during the progress of a reaction results in a racemic product (unless other centers of asymmetry are present in the reactant). It then may be asked whether the same situation applies to carbanion intermediates, but here a satisfactory answer is more difficult to obtain. The suggested correspondence between base-catalyzed racemization of a ketone and carbanion formation (p. 373), which, at first thought, would seem to imply that carbanions (like carbonium ions) may not be asymmetric, is not of help here. Aside from the ambiguity in mechanism (which might mean that free carbanions do not intervene at all here), it must be remembered that the anion, if formed, would be in mobile equilibrium with the enol, in which the asymmetry of the α-carbon is surely destroyed.

$$-\overset{|}{\underset{*}{C}}H-\overset{|}{C}- \xrightarrow[\text{slow}]{B:} \left[-\overset{|}{\underset{..}{C}}-\overset{|}{C}- \right] \underset{BH:,\text{fast}}{\overset{BH^{+},\text{fast}}{\rightleftharpoons}} -\overset{|}{C}=\overset{|}{\underset{OH}{C}}- \quad \text{(symmetric)}$$

In all probability however, the carbanion, if formed, *is* symmetric, not necessarily because it is a carbanion, but rather because it is part of a conjugated system that should be planar. The same is true for such carbanions as the conjugate bases of triphenylmethane and indene; for in these also, the carbon atom from which the hydrogen is removed becomes part of a conjugated system (p. 370). If we then narrow our inquiry to the geometry of carbanions that are *not* stabilized by conjugation, we may be left with no problem at all, for it is doubtful that such carbanions exist. We would be most likely to find them in the alkyl derivatives of the very basic metals—for example, alkylsodium and alkylpotassium compounds; but such compounds, unless the alkide portion is stabilized by conjugation, appear to be insoluble in all solvents except those with which they react.[38] Thus, if carbanions are present in such compounds, they are incorporated into a crystal network, the detailed structure of which is unknown.

[38] Alkylsodium compounds dissolve in diethylzinc (and presumably in other alkylzinc derivatives) to give conducting solutions; but here again, it is extremely likely that a chemical reaction occurs—for example,

$$C_2H_5Na + (C_2H_5)_2Zn \rightarrow Na^+ + (C_2H_5)_3Zn^-$$

For a brief discussion of this problem see Sidgwick, *Chemical Elements and Their Compounds*, Oxford University Press, Oxford, 1950, pp. 277–279.

Stereochemical studies with such organometallic derivatives will tell us little about the geometry of the "free" carbanion, since there is no reason to suppose that the carbanions present (if indeed they are present) in such networks have the same configurations as the corresponding solvated carbanions.[39] At any rate, there is little point in speculating about the geometry of a carbanion that is not stabilized by conjugation until such a carbanion can be demonstrated to exist.

The Aldol Condensation and Related Reactions

The most important group of reactions proceeding through carbanion intermediates are base-catalyzed aldol condensations, including such variations as the Knoevenagel and Perkin reactions. Our present picture of the aldol condensation is rather similar to that of the Claisen condensation (p. 334); for in both, the characteristic step involves the attack of a carbanion on a $C=O$ group.

$$-\overset{\overset{\text{O}}{\|}}{\text{C}}-\overset{\overset{\text{H}}{|}}{\text{C}}-\text{H} \underset{BH^+}{\overset{B:}{\rightleftharpoons}} -\overset{\overset{\text{O}}{\|}}{\text{C}}-\overset{\overset{\text{H}}{|}}{\text{C}}:^- \quad \text{(XXXV)} \quad \text{(carbanion formation)}$$

$$-\overset{\overset{\text{O}}{\|}}{\text{C}}-\overset{\overset{\text{H}}{|}}{\text{C}}:^- + \overset{\overset{\text{O}}{\|}}{\text{C}}-\text{R} \rightleftharpoons -\overset{\overset{\text{O}}{\|}}{\text{C}}-\overset{\overset{\text{H}}{|}}{\underset{\text{R}}{\text{C}}}-\overset{\overset{\text{O}^-}{|}}{\underset{\text{R}}{\text{C}}}-\text{R} \underset{B:}{\overset{BH^+}{\rightleftharpoons}} -\overset{\overset{\text{O}}{\|}}{\text{C}}-\overset{\overset{\text{H}}{|}}{\underset{\text{R}}{\text{C}}}-\overset{\overset{\text{OH}}{|}}{\underset{\text{R}}{\text{C}}}-\text{R} \quad \begin{matrix}\text{(addition and}\\\text{proton transfer)}\end{matrix}$$

XXXV $\qquad\qquad\qquad\qquad\qquad\qquad\qquad\qquad\qquad$ XXXVI

$$-\overset{\overset{\text{O}}{\|}}{\text{C}}-\overset{\overset{\text{H}}{|}}{\text{C}}-\overset{\overset{\text{OH}}{|}}{\underset{\text{R}}{\text{C}}}-\text{R} \xrightarrow{-H_2O} -\overset{\overset{\text{O}}{\|}}{\text{C}}-\text{C}=\overset{}{\underset{\text{R}}{\text{C}}}-\text{R} \quad \text{(dehydration; does not always occur)}$$

XXXVI

As with the Claisen condensation, the overall reaction is reversible, but in practice, it is often pushed to completion by destruction (dehydration) of the condensation product, XXXVI. A number of bases (designated above as $B:$),

---

[39] It has been reported (Letsinger, *J. Am. Chem. Soc.*, **72**, 4842 (1950)) that optically active 2-iodooctane can be converted to the corresponding lithium compound and thence to the corresponding carboxylic acid at low temperatures with partial retention of optical activity. If the reactions of alkyllithium compounds could be shown to proceed through carbanion intermediates, the conversion described would indicate that a carbanion could retain optical activity and is therefore nonplanar. However, alkyllithium derivatives are known to be typical covalent compounds, and there is no strong evidence that their reactions involve carbanions. The conversion of optically active chlorides and bromides having asymmetric α-carbon atoms to Grignard reagents, thence to carboxylic acids, has been shown to proceed with very nearly complete racemization (Goering and McCarron, *ibid.*, **80**, 2291 (1958)).

have been found useful, among them hydroxide and alkoxide ions, amines, and carboxylate ions. Let us consider the reaction sequence as represented above (aside from the final step, which is not actually part of the condensation itself). There are six individual steps (three forward and three reverse), and since the apparent rate law will depend upon the relative magnitudes of the various rate constants, we might expect a number of rate laws for specific condensations. However, there are simplifying assumptions that can be made. The third step, in which a proton is transferred to an oxygen atom from another oxygen atom, may be assumed to be much faster than either of the steps preceding it. Further-more, the rate constants for the first two steps and the respective back reactions must have values that prohibit the collection of significant quantities of anion **XXXV** in solution; for the concentration of this carbanion is generally observed to remain small. There are two kinetically simple, limiting cases. In the first, carbanion formation is very slow, hence rate determining; in the second, car-banion formation is rapid but its reversal is also rapid. If the latter is so, we have the familiar situation in which a slow step is preceded by a rapid equilibrium. The rate law becomes

$$\text{rate} = k(\text{carbanion})(R_2C{=}O) = kK_{eq} \frac{\left(\overset{\overset{\textstyle O}{\|}}{-C}-CH_2-\right)(B\!:)(R_2C{=}O)}{(BH^+)} \quad (4$$

(If $B\!:$ is the conjugate base of the solvent, (BH^+) in the denominator vanishes.) A typical condensation in this category is the hydroxide-catalyzed self-condensa-tion of acetaldehyde when the concentration of the aldehyde exceeds 1 molar.

$$CH_3CHO \underset{\xleftarrow{\hspace{1cm}}}{\xrightarrow{OH^-,\ slow}} {:}CH_2CHO \xrightarrow[fast]{CH_3CHO} \underset{\underset{CH_3}{|}}{CH_2{-}\overset{\overset{\textstyle CHO}{|}}{C}{-}\overset{\overset{\textstyle H}{|}}{}{-}O^-} \xrightarrow[fast]{H_2O} \underset{\underset{CH_3}{|}}{CH_2{-}\overset{\overset{\textstyle CHO}{|}}{CH}{-}OH}$$

(aldol)

At high concentrations of acetaldehyde, the condensation is first order in alde-hyde, whereas if the initial carbanion formation were rapid and reversible, the reaction should, as indicated in equation (4), be second order in aldehyde.[40] The reaction is also, at least to a good approximation, first order in hydrox-ide.[40(a)] Furthermore, if the formation of the carbanion were significantly reversible, the condensation, when carried out in D_2O, should yield an aldol with C—D bonds, and, if the reaction were halted in the early stages, the un-reacted aldehyde should likewise have C—D bonds. This test has also been

[40] For kinetic studies of the aldol condensation of acetaldehyde, see (a) Bell, *J. Chem. Soc.*, **1937**, 1637; (b) Bell and Smith, *ibid.*, **1958**, 1691; (c) Broche and Gilbert, *Bull. Soc. chim. France*, **1955**, 131.

applied and the reaction has been found to be accompanied by practically *no C—D bond formation*, either in the product or in the unreacted aldehyde, thus confirming the conclusions drawn from the observed rate law.[41]

On the other hand, the formation of the carbanion may be rapid and reversible, but its subsequent attack on the carbonyl group relatively slow. This is the case, for example, for the ethoxide-catalyzed condensation of benzaldehyde with acetophenone,[42] and for the hydroxide-catalyzed condensation of

$$
CH_3—\underset{\underset{O}{\|}}{C}—Ph \underset{\text{EtOH, fast}}{\overset{\text{OEt}^-, \text{fast}}{\rightleftharpoons}} {}^-:CH_2—\underset{\underset{O}{\|}}{C}—Ph \underset{\text{slow}}{\overset{\text{PhCHO}}{\longrightarrow}} Ph—\underset{\underset{O_-}{|}}{\overset{\overset{H}{|}}{C}}—CH_2—\underset{\underset{O}{\|}}{C}—Ph \underset{\text{fast}}{\overset{H^+}{\rightarrow}}
$$

$$
Ph—\underset{\underset{OH}{|}}{\overset{\overset{H}{|}}{C}}—CH_2—\overset{\overset{O}{\|}}{C}—Ph
$$

malonic ester with formaldehyde,[43] both of these reactions exhibiting rate laws

$$
H_2C=O + CH_2(COOEt)_2 \overset{OH^-}{\longrightarrow} H_2C—\underset{\underset{OH}{|}}{CH(COOEt)_2}
$$

corresponding to equation (4). Much the same picture is appropriate for the base-catalyzed self-condensation of acetone, but here the evidence is of a less direct sort (Ex. 3). It is also possible that the concentration of the carbanion may be kept small, *both* by reversal of its formation and addition to the C=O group, with the two modes of destruction occurring at comparable rates. The rate law then becomes somewhat more complex but may readily be derived using the steady-state approximation (Ex. 4). This is the situation, for example, with the aldol concentration of acetaldehyde at *low* aldehyde concentrations.[40(c)] As the concentration of aldehyde decreases, the attack by the carbanion on the C=O group becomes less likely and its destruction by solvent assumes significance. At such concentrations, the reaction is accompanied by deuterium exchange at the α-hydrogens if carried out in D_2O.[40(b)]

In the familiar *Perkin reaction*, a carbanion derived from an acid anhydride condenses with benzaldehyde or a substituted benzaldehyde to yield a cinnamic acid derivative. The base necessary for removal of the proton may be an amine, a salt of a weak inorganic acid (phosphate, carbonate, etc.), or, more usually, the salt of the carboxylic acid related to the anhydride.

[41] Bonhoeffer and Walters, Z. physik. Chem., 181A, 441 (1938).
[42] Coombs and Evans, J. Chem. Soc., 1944, 1295.
[43] Welch, J. Chem. Soc., 1931, 653.

Complications may occur if the carboxylate ion used as the base and the anhydride participating are derived from different acids, for carboxylate interchange is known to occur readily between anhydride and salt.[44]

Under such conditions, a mixture of two cinnamic acids, $PhCH=CR-COOH$ and $PhCH=CR'-COOH$, will result.

The *Michael reaction* differs somewhat from the base-catalyzed aldol condensation; for in it a carbanion attacks a $C=C$ bond in conjugation with a $C=O$ bond, instead of attacking the $C=O$ bond itself. (As already pointed out on page 117, such $C=C$ bonds, unlike "ordinary" $C=C$ bonds, are electrophilic.) Two frequently used carbanion sources are malonic ester, $CH_2(COOEt)_2$, and cyanoacetic ester, $EtOOC-CH_2-CN$. Typically,

XXXVII

[44] Hauser and Breslow, *J. Am. Chem. Soc.*, **61**, 786 (1939). For studies pertinent to the mechanism of the Perkin reaction, see Kalnin, *Helv. Chim. Acta*, **11**, 977 (1928); Breslow and Hauser, *J. Am. Chem. Soc.*, **61**, 793 (1939); Buckles and Bremer, *ibid.*, **75**, 1487 (1953).

The product from the initial addition, the enolate ion, XXXVII, is rapidly converted to the corresponding keto form, and the overall reaction is often viewed merely as an addition of the ester to the C=C double bond. The conversions of both malonic and cyanoacetic esters to their anions by base are known to be rapid.[3] It is very likely therefore that for Michael reactions involving these esters, the rate-determining step is the second—the formation of the new C—C bond (although this has not yet been demonstrated kinetically). The reaction is reversible,[45] and as was the case with the Claisen condensation (p. 334), the maximum possible yield is governed by the basicity of the reaction mixture. In the Claisen condensation, it will be recalled, the product was a *stronger* acid than the reactant and the reaction could therefore be pushed toward completion by a large excess of base. With the Michael condensation, the product is a *weaker* acid than the reactant (since a C—H bond has been converted to a C—C bond); hence a large excess of base will favor the reactant. It follows then, that although some base is needed to get the Michael reaction under way, a high yield of product requires that the basicity of the reaction mixture be kept relatively low.

When both of the double-bonded carbons are bound to benzene rings (for example, as in α-phenylcinnamic ester, XXXVIII), the Michael reaction fails, presumably because the structure has been stabilized by incorporation of the otherwise reactive double bond into an extended conjugated system (XXXVIII').

XXXVIII   XXXVIII'

A compound having two or more C=C double bonds in conjugation with a carbonyl group (for example, the unsaturated ester, XXXIX) may, in principle, undergo the Michael reaction in several different ways. As shown, the carbanion may attack at either the β or δ position; moreover, in the case of δ attack, two products are possible depending upon whether the proton becomes bound to the α- or γ-carbon in the final product. As seen, ester XLI is the only

[45] Ingold and Perren, *J. Chem. Soc.*, **121**, 1414 (1922).

$$\underset{\substack{\delta \quad \gamma \quad \beta \quad \alpha \quad \| \\ \text{CH}_2=\text{CHCH}=\text{CHCOMe}}}{}$$

XXXIX

(β attack)

$$\underset{\substack{\text{CH(COOEt)}_2 \\ | \\ \text{CH}_2=\text{CHCHCH}=\text{COMe} \\ | \\ \text{O}_-}}{} \xrightleftharpoons{\text{BH}^+} \underset{\substack{\text{CH(COOEt)}_2 \\ | \\ \text{CH}_2=\text{CHCHCH}_2\text{COMe} \\ \| \\ \text{O}}}{}$$

XL

(δ attack)

$$\underset{\substack{\text{CH}_2\text{CH}=\text{CHCH}=\text{COMe} \\ | \qquad\qquad | \\ \text{CH(COOEt)}_2 \qquad \text{O}_-}}{} \xrightleftharpoons{\text{BH}^+}$$

$$\begin{cases} \underset{\substack{\text{CH(COOEt)}_2 \qquad \text{O} \\ | \qquad\qquad\qquad \| \\ \text{CH}_2\text{CH}_2\text{CH}=\text{CHCOMe}}}{} & \text{(XLI)} \\[2ex] \text{and/or} \\[2ex] \underset{\substack{\text{CH}_2\text{CH}=\text{CHCH}_2\text{COMe} \\ | \qquad\qquad\qquad \| \\ \text{CH(COOEt)}_2 \qquad \text{O}}}{} & \text{(XLII)} \end{cases}$$

one of the three possible products that retains the —C=C—C=O conjugated system. Hence, it is not surprising that this ester is the predominant product.[46(a)] On the other hand, if a phenyl group is put into the δ position (that is, if the reaction is carried out using PhCH=CH—CH=CH—COOEt), the chief product is formed by β attack; for only in this product would the ⬡—CH=CH— conjugated system be retained.[46(b)] The γ,δ double bond may also be stabilized by hyperconjugation since reaction of MeCH=CMe—CH=CH—COOEt with sodiomalonic ester proceeds by β, rather than by δ attack. In the preceding discussion, we have assumed implicitly that of several possible products, the *most stable* will predominate—that is, that the course of the reaction is *thermodynamically controlled*. This is by no means the case for all organic reactions; often a given product will predominate because it is formed *more rapidly* than the others—that is, the reaction may be *kinetically controlled*. However, in the case of the Michael condensation, as it is usually carried out, thermodynamic control of products is to be expected; for the steps are reversible and the reaction mixture is generally allowed to come to equilibrium before being "worked up."

The Benzoin Condensation

The condensation of two benzaldehyde or substituted benzaldehyde molecules has long been known to be catalyzed by cyanide ion, but not by any of the more usual stronger bases.

$$\text{Ar—CHO} + \text{Ar}'\text{—CHO} \xrightarrow{\text{CN}^-} \underset{\substack{\| \quad | \\ \text{O} \quad \text{OH}}}{\text{Ar—C—CH—Ar}'}$$

[46] (a) Farmer and Mehta, *J. Chem. Soc.*, **1931**, 1904. (b) Vorlander and Groebel, *Ann.*, **345**, 206 (1906).

(HCN, $Hg(CN)_2$, and nitriles are ineffective as catalysts). Without knowing of the specific cyanide catalysis, we would be likely to regard the benzoin condensation as similar to the aldol condensation, with the anion derived from a benzaldehyde molecule ($Ph—\bar{C}=O$) attacking the $C=O$ group of a second molecule. But we have no evidence that the hydrogen of a —CHO group is significantly acidic; certainly it is not sufficiently acidic to be removed by such a weak base as CN^-. However, the cyanide ion can boost the acidity of this hydrogen markedly by converting the aldehyde to the conjugate base of a cyanohydrin (that is, an α-hydroxynitrile), the α-hydrogen then becoming similar in character to the α-hydrogens of nitriles or esters. This conversion is known to occur readily under the conditions necessary for the benzoin condensation. The rate

law for the formation of benzoin itself (which is generally presumed to be typical of reactions of this type) has been found to be.[47]

$$\text{rate} = k(\text{PhCHO})^2(\text{CN}^-) \tag{5}$$

telling us that the activated complex in the rate-determining step contains two molecules of aldehyde and a cyanide ion. We then may conclude that carbanion XLIV, once formed, attacks the $C=O$ group of a second molecule of benzaldehyde, yielding anion XLV—a cyanohydrin which should be easily converted to

benzoin itself. Since the overall condensation is reversible,[48] each step must be

[47] Stern, Z. physik. Chem., **50**, 513 (1905).
[48] Buck and Ide, J. Am. Chem. Soc., **53**, 2784 (1931).

reversible. The rate law by itself does not tell us whether (c), (d), or (e) is the rate-determining step, but we may assume that (d)—a transfer of a proton between oxygen atoms—is not. Furthermore, (e) is simply the reverse step in a ketone-cyanohydrin interconversion, a reaction in which, for simple cases, equilibrium is known to be very rapidly established.[49] Thus, if the mechanism proposed above is correct, step (c) is almost certainly rate determining.[50]

The limitations of the benzoin condensation are of some interest.[51] When the strongly electron-donating —NMe_2 group is substituted *para* to the —CHO group in benzaldehyde, the reaction fails. Due to conjugation (XLVI ↔

XLVI'), the carbonyl group acquires additional electron density; that is, it becomes less electrophilic. As a result, steps (a) and (c), both of which involve addition of an anion to the carbonyl group, are hindered. Apparently, however, the effect of the —NMe_2 group on initial cyanohydrin formation is less important than is its effect on the rate-determining condensation step (c); for if a mixture of benzaldehyde and *p*-dimethylaminobenzaldehyde (XLVI) is treated with NaCN, the "mixed benzoin," XLVII (but not the isomeric mixed benzoin), is formed. In the mechanism proposed, the carbonyl group on the final product is that involved in the initial cyanohydrin-anion formation; we may therefore conclude that the cyanohydrin anion formed from *p*-dimethylamino-benzaldehyde may add to benzaldehyde, but that the cyanohydrin anion derived from benzaldehyde will not add to XLVI itself. The benzoin condensation is also inhibited by strongly *electron-attracting* groups; *p*-bromobenzaldehyde forms a benzoin slowly and incompletely, and *p*-nitrobenzaldehyde does not undergo the benzoin condensation. Both of these aldehydes readily form cyanohydrins,[49] but in the anions corresponding to XLIV, electron density has been pulled away from the attacking carbon atom, making it a far less effective attacking site. The *p*-nitro group is particularly effective in this respect for here the nitro group and the attacking carbon are in conjugation (XLVIII ↔

[49] See, for example, Baker, *et al.*, *J. Chem. Soc.*, **1942**, 191; **1949**, 1089.
[50] See, however, Wiberg, *J. Am. Chem. Soc.*, **76**, 5371 (1954).
[51] This topic has been reviewed by Ide and Buck in *Organic Reactions*, Vol. IV (edited by Adams), John Wiley and Sons, Inc., New York, 1948, p. 269.

XLVIII'). On the other hand, o-nitrobenzaldehyde undergoes the benzoin condensation; presumably because the conjugation between the —NO₂ group

and the —C group, which prohibits the condensation of the *para* isomer,

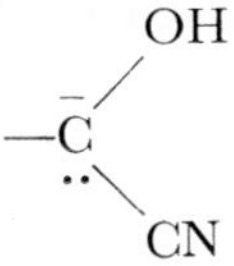

is rendered ineffective in the anion of the *ortho* isomer (XLIX) because coplanarity between the two groups is no longer possible.

It is now known that certain thiazolium and imidazolium salts (having cations such as those shown below) also act as catalysts for the benzoin condensation.[52] Here, it appears that the condensation proceeds through an intermediate

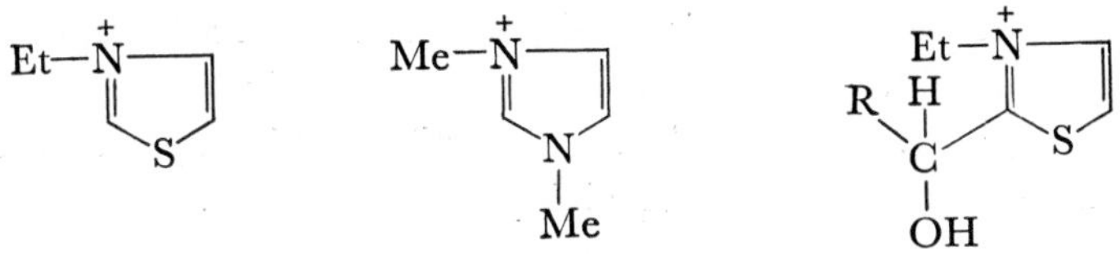

adduct of the type L, in which the α-hydrogen, like that in a cyanohydrin, has been rendered acidic by the strongly electron-withdrawing character of the ring.[52(b)]

Hydrolysis of Haloforms

The basic hydrolyses of chloroform, bromoform, and other trihalomethanes are of considerable current interest because of the evidence that these reactions proceed not only through carbanions but also through intermediates having *bivalent carbon*—that is, carbon atoms with only *two* covalent bonds. It should be recalled that methylene chloride, CH_2Cl_2, is hydrolyzed by base much more slowly than is methyl chloride, and we should therefore expect chloroform to be hydrolyzed still more slowly. However, the hydrolysis of chloroform is a relatively fast reaction, leading us to suspect that the hydrolyses of the three halides do not proceed by the same mechanism (although all three reactions are first order in halide and first order in base).[53(a)(b)] The abnormally high reactivity of chloroform toward OH⁻ does not extend to all other nucleophiles; it reacts very slowly, for example, with the thiophenolate ion, PhS⁻, which is weakly

---

[52] (a) Ugai, et al., *J. Pharm. Soc. Japan*, **63**, 269 (1943); (b) Breslow, *J. Am. Chem. Soc.*, **80**, 3719 (1958).
[53] (a) Petrenko-Kritchenko and Opotsky, *Ber.*, **59**, 2131 (1926). (b) Hine, *J. Am. Chem. Soc.*, **72**, 2438 (1950). (c) For studies of the basic hydrolyses of other trihalomethanes, see Hine, et al., *J. Am. Chem. Soc.*, **76**, 827 (1954); **78**, 479 3337 (1956); **79**, 1406 (1957); **80**, 819, 824 (1958).

basic but generally considered strongly nucleophilic (p. 260). However, if chloroform is treated with a solution containing both the OH⁻ and the PhS⁻ ions, the reaction is rapid and the product is phenyl orthothioformate, HC(SPh)$_3$.[53(b)] The high reactivity of chloroform thus requires the presence of a strong base and, in view of the base-catalyzed hydrogen exchange that is observed to occur between haloforms and hydroxylic solvents (p. 381), it seems very likely that the hydrolysis of chloroform proceeds through the Cl$_3$C:⁻ carbanion, even though only small quantities of this anion exist in solution at a given instant. Furthermore, the fact that the hydrogen exchange reaction is much faster than the basic hydrolysis[29] indicates that this carbanion is formed rapidly and reversibly in the attack by OH⁻ on the haloform.[54] Thus, most of the Cl$_3$C:⁻ anions formed are reconverted to chloroform, but some react further, ultimately yielding the observed hydrolysis products, carbon monoxide and formate. Although we know little about the final stages in the hydrolysis of the trichloromethide anion, it seems rather clear that this ion first loses Cl⁻ to form *carbon dichloride*, CCl$_2$, an intermediate containing bivalent carbon.

$$\text{HCCl}_3 \underset{\text{fast}}{\overset{\text{OH}^-}{\rightleftharpoons}} \text{Cl}_3\text{C:}^- \underset{\text{slow}}{\overset{-\text{Cl}^-}{\longrightarrow}} \text{CCl}_2 \xrightarrow{\text{further hydrolysis}} \text{CO} + \text{HCOO}^-$$

If the initial steps in the hydrolysis are those indicated, the reaction may be said to proceed by an *α-elimination mechanism*—that is, a mechanism in which a hydrogen atom and a chlorine atom are detached from the *same* carbon. In the far more usual β-elimination reactions, atoms are lost from *adjacent* carbons. A similar sequence may be written for the reactions of haloforms with alkoxides in alcoholic media, for these alcoholyses are also unexpectedly fast.[55] Since species containing bivalent carbon are unusual (although not unknown), we should be reluctant to suppose that carbon dihalides intervene in such reactions if the evidence were not rather convincing. In the first place, it may be argued that the hydrolysis of the Cl$_3$C:⁻ ion is much more likely to occur by loss of a Cl⁻ ion than by direct displacement of Cl⁻ by OH⁻. With chloroform, such a displacement is very slow, and it should be even slower for the conjugate base of chloroform since there is electrostatic repulsion between the reacting ions. Secondly, the basic hydrolysis of chloroform in the presence of iodide yields appreciable quantities of HCCl$_2$I, a product that is *not* formed at a significant rate by displacement of chloride by iodide (in neutral solution) and therefore is almost certainly not formed by such a displacement on Cl$_3$C:⁻ (in basic

---

[54] The basic hydrolysis of DCF$_2$Br is, however, not accompanied by deuterium exchange (Hine and Langford, *J. Am. Chem. Soc.*, **79**, 5497 (1957)). It appears that this haloform is converted to CF$_2$ by a concerted process

$$\text{HO}^- + \text{HCF}_2\text{Br} \rightarrow [\text{HO} \cdot \cdot \text{H} \cdot \cdot \text{CF}_2 \cdot \cdot \text{Br}]^- \rightarrow \text{HOH} + \text{CF}_2 + \text{Br}^-$$

analogous to the *E*2 process for β elimination (Chap. 12).

[55] Hughes and Preling, reported by Ingold, Ref. 1(b), p. 330; Hine and Tanabe, *J. Am. Chem. Soc.*, **80**, 3002 (1958).

solution). Again, it is far more likely that this product is formed by reaction of iodide on neutral CCl_2.

The best evidence for carbon-dihalide intermediates arises, however, from experiments in which such species are "trapped" before they can be further hydrolyzed or solvolyzed; as may be supposed, such dihalides are extremely reactive. Like the methylene "diradical," CH_2 (Chap. 16), they add to double bonds, forming cyclopropane derivatives. Thus, when chloroform is treated with base in the presence of cyclohexene, the bicyclic dichloride, LI, is formed.[56(a)] Similarly, the action of t-BuO$^-$ on bromoform in the presence of 2-butene yields dibromide LII.[56(b),57]

It also seems likely that the condensation of chloroform with phenols in basic media (the Reimer-Tiemann reaction, p. 387) proceeds through CCl_2, since, once again, direct attack of phenoxide on the chloroform molecule with displacement of chloride would be expected to be very slow.

Organometallic Compounds

We have already seen that solutions of the sodium and potassium derivatives of such hydrocarbons as triphenylmethane, cyclopentadiene, and indene contain carbanions, although in nonpolar solvents such carbanions exist almost exclusively as ion pairs and higher aggregates. Carbanions probably exist also in the solid state in the sodium and potassium derivatives of the lower hydrocarbons. The reactions that these metallic derivatives undergo are similar in nature

[56] (a) Doering and Hoffmann, J. Am. Chem. Soc., 76, 6162 (1954). (b) Skell and Garner, ibid., 78, 3409 (1956). Note that the addition is stereospecific; that is, if trans-2-butene is used, the methyl groups in the product are trans, whereas if the cis-olefin is used, the methyl groups in the product are cis.

[57] At present it is not completely clear whether carbon dihalides have zero or two unpaired electrons per molecule. For consideration of this question, see Skell and Garner, J. Am. Chem. Soc., 78, 5430 (1956). See also Chap. 13.

to those of the more usual organometallics, and it is perhaps not surprising that the reactions of Grignard reagents and organolithium compounds are often represented as involving anions also. Thus, the reactions of, say, methyllithium are sometimes depicted as reactions of the methide ion.

$$H_3C^{\bar{:}} + O{=}C{=}O \longrightarrow H_3C-C\overset{O^-}{\underset{O}{\diagdown}}$$

$$H_3C^{\bar{:}} + \overset{CH_2-CH_2}{\underset{O}{\diagup}} \longrightarrow H_3C-CH_2-CH_2-O^-$$

$$H_3C^{\bar{:}} + Br-Hg-Br \longrightarrow H_3C-Hg-Br + Br^-$$

It is possible that, in some cases, the reactions of organolithium compounds and Grignard reagents do indeed proceed through preliminary ionization to a carbanion (although this has not yet been demonstrated), but this is certainly not true in all instances and is probably not true in most. Where a carbanion $R:^-$ is an intermediate, we should expect the reagents RNa, RLi, and RMgBr to yield the same product (or the same mixture of products) on reaction with a given electrophile. Of the many cases where such a correspondence is *not* observed, the following three are typical:

$$(i\text{-Pr})_2\,C{=}O \overset{i\text{-PrLi}}{\underset{i\text{-PrMgBr}}{\Longleftarrow}} \begin{array}{l} (i\text{-Pr})_3\,C-OH \ \ ^{58c} \\ (i\text{-Pr})_2\,CHOH \ + \ CH_3CH{=}CH_2 \end{array}$$

$$CO_2 \overset{(CH_2{=}CH)_2CHMgBr}{\underset{(CH_2{=}CH)_2CHNa}{\Longleftarrow}} \begin{array}{l} (CH_2{=}CH-)_2\,CH-COOH \ \ ^{58b} \\ CH_2{=}CH-CH{=}CH-CH_2-COOH \end{array}$$

$$Ph_2C{=}NPh \overset{PhLi}{\underset{PhMgBr}{\Longleftarrow}} \begin{array}{l} Ph_3C-NHPh \ \ ^{58c} \\ CHPh-NHPh \end{array}$$

It thus appears that the reactions of organolithium compounds and Grignard

^{58} (a) Young and Roberts, *J. Am. Chem. Soc.*, **66**, 1444 (1944). (b) Paul and Tchelitchev, *Compt. rend.*, **224**, 1118 (1947). (c) Gilman and Kirby, *J. Am. Chem. Soc.*, **55**, 1265 (1933).

reagents involve the entire molecule (or more than one entire molecule) of the organometallic.

The majority of the reactions of organolithium compounds appear to be too fast for convenient kinetic study, but the limited and not too satisfactory data available indicate that the activated complexes in such reactions contain a single molecule of RLi. The reactions of organolithium compounds with ketones and with alkyl halides are first order in RLi and first order also in the reagent undergoing attack. The rate law for the reaction with ketones[59] suggests that it proceeds through an addition compound such as LIII, which decomposes to the observed product, the alkoxide LIV; and it is possible that other "addition

$$\underset{R}{\overset{R}{\diagdown}}C=O + R'-Li \longrightarrow \underset{R}{\overset{R}{\diagdown}}\underset{\overset{|}{\underset{\text{LIII}}{}}}{\overset{R'-Li}{\overset{|}{C=O}}} \longrightarrow \underset{R}{\overset{R}{\diagdown}}\underset{\overset{|}{\underset{\text{LIV}}{}}}{\overset{R'}{\overset{|}{C-O-Li}}}$$

reactions" of organolithium compounds proceed by analogous paths. The manner in which organolithium derivatives attack alkyl halides (RLi + R'X → R—R' + LiX) is not clear, but scattered experiments indicate that during such reactions the alkyl group from the halide assumes *considerable carbonium-ion character*. Thus, the reaction of n-butyllithium with optically active *sec*-butyl bromide yields an almost completely racemic octane.[60]

$$\textit{n-}\text{BuLi} + \text{Et}\!-\!\overset{*}{\underset{\underset{\text{Me}}{|}}{\text{CH}}}\!-\!\text{Br} \rightarrow \textit{n-}\text{Bu}\!-\!\underset{\underset{\text{Me}}{|}}{\overset{\overset{\text{Et}}{|}}{\text{CH}}} + \text{LiBr}$$

(racemic)

Moreover, phenyllithium reacts with α-methylallyl chloride to give the same mixture of allylic isomers (in very nearly the same proportions) as result from the reaction of γ-methylallyl chloride,[61] a situation bringing to mind the hydrolyses of very active allylic halides (p. 286), where, it will be recalled, the intercession of an allylic carbonium ion was indicated.

$$\begin{array}{c}\text{MeCH}=\text{CH}-\text{CH}_2\text{Cl} \overset{PhLi}{\searrow} \\ \\ \text{MeCH}-\text{CH}=\text{CH}_2 \overset{}{\underset{PhLi}{\nearrow}} \\ \underset{\text{Cl}}{|} \end{array} \left[\underset{\text{MeCH}\!-\!\text{CH}\!-\!\text{CH}_2}{\bigcirc\quad\bigcirc\quad\bigcirc}\right]^{+} \rightarrow \begin{cases} \text{PhCH}_2-\text{CH}=\text{CH}-\text{CH}_3 \\ \qquad (90 \text{ percent}) \\ \text{Ph}-\text{CHMe}-\text{CH}=\text{CH}_2 \\ \qquad (10 \text{ percent}) \end{cases}$$

[59] Swain and Kent, *J. Am. Chem. Soc.*, **72**, 518 (1950).
[60] Zook and Goldey, *J. Am. Chem. Soc.*, **75**, 3975 (1953).
[61] Cristol, Overhults, and Meek, *J. Am. Chem. Soc.*, **73**, 813 (1951).

The following mechanism, in which one molecule of the lithium compound acts as a Lewis acid, seems consistent with the facts:

$$R'-X + Li-R \xrightarrow{\text{slow}} \begin{cases} R'^+ & \xrightarrow[\text{fast}]{R-Li} R'-R + Li^+ \\ X:Li:R^- \end{cases}$$

In contrast, the reaction of an organosodium derivative with an optically active alkyl chloride (having an asymmetric α-carbon) generally yields an optically active hydrocarbon. Although we cannot be sure, it seems very likely that inversion of configuration about the asymmetric carbon has occurred during the attack by the carbanion.[62] In a typical case,[62(a)]

$$Na^+Ph_2CH^- + D\text{-}CH_3\overset{*}{C}HPhCl \rightarrow L\text{-}Ph_2CH-\underset{\underset{Me}{|}}{\overset{\overset{Ph}{|}}{C}}H \text{ (probably)} + NaCl$$

Concerning the mechanisms of reactions of Grignard reagents, we can do little more than speculate, for the Grignard reagent, which is often blandly designated as "$RMgX$," is now known to consist of a number of different species in solution. In addition to $RMgX$, evidence has been obtained for the existence of R_2Mg, MgX_2, MgX^+, R_2MgX^-, and polymeric species, in a solution that would ordinarily be employed as that of a "single Grignard reagent."[63(a)] In view of these complexities, the assumption that $RMgX$ is the only active species (or even that it is the most active species) in a solution of a Grignard reagent takes a great deal for granted.[63(b)] Moreover, any kinetic study of the reaction of a Grignard reagent must be very carefully devised so that there is no ambiguity concerning the species whose disappearance is being followed. Thus, aside from experimental difficulties, rate studies of Grignard reactions offer vexing interpretive problems.

One point, however, seems quite certain, in a number of cases the addition of a Grignard reagent to a carbonyl group requires *two* molecules of magnesium-containing species. There are a number of instances known[64] where careful admixture of "equivalent" quantities of ketone and Grignard reagent yields a

[62] (a) Bergmann, *Helv. Chim. Acta*, **20**, 590 (1937). (b) For further examples, see Letsinger, et al., *J. Am. Chem. Soc.*, **70**, 406 (1948); **73**, 2373 (1951); and LeGoff, Ulrich, and Denney, *ibid.*, **80**, 622 (1958). (c) The stereochemistry of the reactions of alkyl sodium derivatives with alkyl bromides and, more particularly, with alkyl iodides is complicated by the possibility of metal-halogen interchange before displacement, and extensive racemization is often observed. See, for example, Brink, Lane, and Wallis, *J. Am. Chem. Soc.*, **65**, 943 (1943).

[63] (a) Schlenk and Schlenk, *Ber.*, **62**, 920 (1929); Evans and Pearson, *J. Am. Chem. Soc.*, **64**, 2865 (1942); Noller and Raney, *ibid.*, **62**, 1749 (1940). (b) For recent evidence that the active species in (at least some) Grignard solutions is R_2Mg, see Mosher and Leffler, *J. Am. Chem. Soc.*, **78**, 4959 (1956), and Dessy, et al., *ibid.*, **79**, 3476 (1957).

[64] See, for example, Gilman and Jones, *J. Am. Chem. Soc.*, **62**, 1243 (1940).

precipitate, which, upon treatment with water, yields the ketone once more. Generally in such cases, the addition takes place in the usual manner if *excess* Grignard reagent is employed. Thus it appears very likely that one molecule of a magnesium-containing species (which we may designate for convenience as $RMgX$) acts as a Lewis acid. Here, the electrophilic magnesium atom is bound to the oxygen of the carbonyl group, pulling electron density from the carbon and making it more susceptible to attack by a second "molecule of $RMgX$":

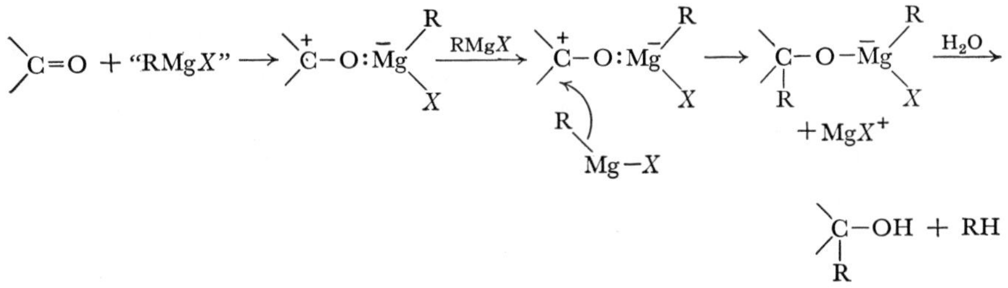

If this sequence is, in the main, correct, the addition reaction should proceed with a single equivalent of $RMgX$, provided an additional Lewis acid is added to perform the coordinating function in the initial step. It has indeed been shown that a number of additions of Grignard reagents to C=O groups are facilitated by addition of anhydrous $MgBr_2$, a typical Lewis acid.[65]

The reader is doubtless aware that there are several ways in which the reactions between ketones and Grignard reagents may "go astray." With a branched ketone or a branched Grignard reagent (or both), the ketone may be reduced to the corresponding carbinol while the alkyl group of the Grignard is converted to an olefin. Isotopic studies have shown that this reaction involves a transfer of a β-hydrogen from Grignard to ketone.[66] It is probable that this reduction proceeds through a cyclic activated complex, LIV, similar in nature to that thought to be involved in the Meerwein-Ponndorf (aluminum iso-

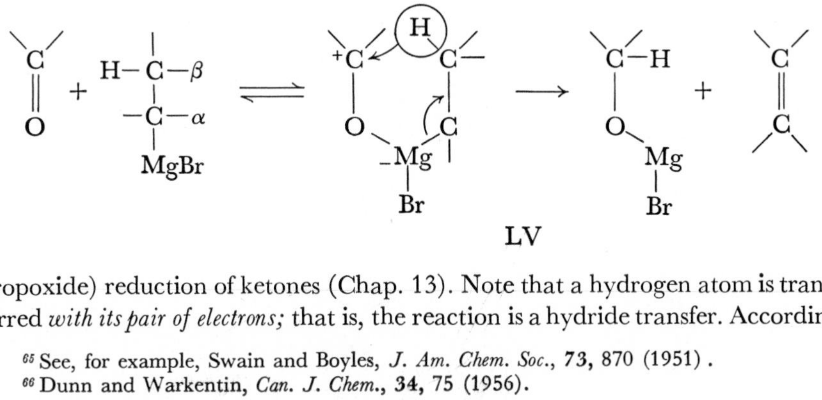

LV

propoxide) reduction of ketones (Chap. 13). Note that a hydrogen atom is transferred *with its pair of electrons;* that is, the reaction is a hydride transfer. According

[65] See, for example, Swain and Boyles, *J. Am. Chem. Soc.,* **73,** 870 (1951).
[66] Dunn and Warkentin, *Can. J. Chem.,* **34,** 75 (1956).

to this mechanism, a molecule of Grignard reagent must become coordinated with the oxygen atom of the ketone in order to transfer its β-hydrogen to the carbonyl group. This being the case, the reduction reaction should be inhibited by addition of a Lewis acid to the reaction mixture; for any ketone molecules coordinating with the added Lewis acid would be unavailable for coordination to RMgX. But the addition reaction of Grignards is, as we have seen, *facilitated* by such Lewis acids as $MgBr_2$ and MgI_2. We should then expect that in cases where both addition and reduction occur, the addition of anhydrous magnesium halides will increase the extent of addition but decrease the extent of reduction, and this is what is found. Thus, in the reaction of *n*-propylmagnesium bromide with diisopropyl ketone, the ratio of addition to reduction is 0.48 in the absence of added MgI_2, but rises to 2.5 when excess MgI_2 is added.[65]

EXERCISES FOR CHAPTER 10

1. Predict which member in each of the following pairs is the stronger acid. Justify your choice in each case.

(a) CH_3NO_2 or *n*-PrNO₂?

(b) $CH_2\left(\!\!\begin{array}{c}O\\ \|\\ -S-Ph\\ \|\\ O\end{array}\!\!\right)_2$ or $CH_2\left(-S-Ph\right)_2$?

(c) CH_3—⟨ ⟩—$CHPh_2$ or Ph_2CHCH_2Ph ?

(d) Methyl acetoacetate or acetoacetamide?

(e) $CH_3COCH_2COCH_2F$ or $CH_3COCHFCOCH_3$?

(f) or ?

(g) $O_2S$$SO_2$ or ?

(h) or ?

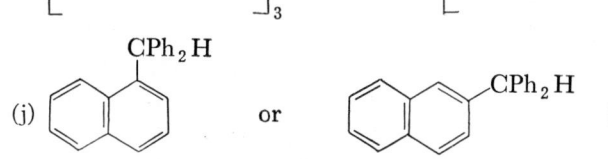

(i) $\left[\begin{array}{c} \end{array}\right]_3$ CH or $\left[\begin{array}{c} \end{array}\right]_3$ CH ?

(j) [naphthalene with CPh₂H] or [naphthalene with CPh₂H] ?

(k) Me₂Se or Me₂O?

(l) [structure] or [structure] ?

2. Predict which member in each of the following pairs is the more extensively enolized. Justify your choice in each case.
   (a) $CH_3COCH(i\text{-}Pr)COCH_3$ or $i\text{-}PrCH_2COCH_2COCH_3$?
   (b) 1,2-Cycloheptanedione or 1,3-cycloheptanedione?
   (c) Cyclopentanone or diethyl ketone?

(d) [structure] or [structure] ?

(e) [structure] or [structure] ?

(f) Benzoylacetone in toluene or in nitrobenzene?

(g) [structure] or [structure with C—CH₃] ?

(h) $PhCH_2COCH_3$ or $PhCHMeCOCH_3$?

(i) [structure] or [structure] ?

(j) or ?

(k) or ?

(l) or ?

(m) or ?

3. The position of equilibrium in the hydroxide-catalyzed aldol condensation of acetone is such that the forward reaction (ketolization) is much less easily studied than the reverse reaction (deketolization).

$$Me_2C-CH_2-C-CH_3 \text{ (ketol)} \xrightarrow{\text{OH}^-} 2Me_2C=O$$
$$\qquad | \qquad\quad ||$$
$$\qquad OH \qquad O$$

The rate law for deketolization is

$$\frac{-d(\text{ketol})}{dt} = k(\text{ketol})(\text{OH}^-)$$

(a) Show that this rate law indicates that the conversion of acetone to its conjugate base is a rapid reversible reaction, but that the conjugate base condenses with a second acetone molecule slowly. (Note that according to the principle of microscopic reversibility, the steps in the deketolization are the reverse of the steps in the ketolization.)

(b) Which do you think would proceed more rapidly (given the same concentration of base): the ketolization of acetone or its base-catalyzed bromination?

4. Consider the mechanism for the base-catalyzed aldol condensation (p. 390),

(a) Assuming that the concentration of the enolate ion (formed in the initial step remains small and constant, and that the third step (proton transfer) is very rapid, apply the steady state approximation to show that the rate of formation of the condensed product is

$$\text{rate} = \frac{k_1\left(\begin{array}{c}\text{O}\\\parallel\\\text{—C—CH}_2\text{—}\end{array}\right)(B\text{:}) + k_{-2}\left(\begin{array}{cc}\text{O} & \text{O}^-\\\parallel & |\\\text{—C—CH—CR}_2\end{array}\right)}{\dfrac{k_{-1}(BH^+)}{k_2(R_2C\text{=}O)} + 1}$$

(b) Assume further that for a reaction carried out in water in its early stages,

$$\left(\begin{array}{ccc}\text{—C—CH—CR}_2\\\parallel \quad | \quad |\\\text{O} \quad\ \ \text{O}_-\end{array}\right)$$

is negligibly small. Show that if $k_2(R_2C\text{=}O) \gg k_{-1}(BH^+)$ (that is, if essentially all the anion is converted to aldol when formed), the rate law above becomes a simple second-order rate law.

(c) Show that if $k_{-1}(BH^+) \gg k_2(R_2C\text{=}O)$ (that is, if the formation of the carbanion is rapid and reversible), the rate equation above becomes a simple third-order rate law.

5. Suggest mechanisms for the following conversions:

(a)

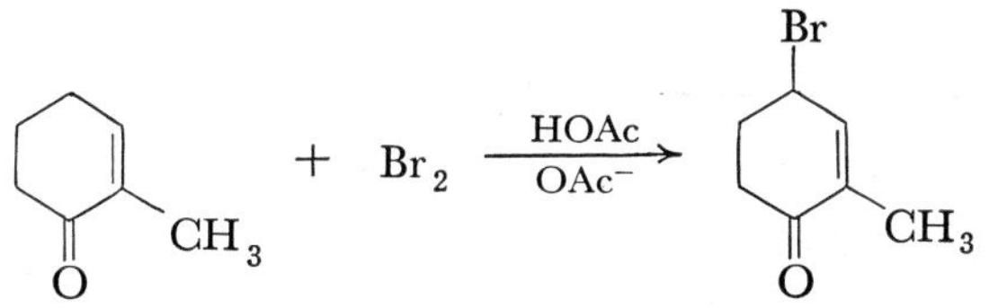

(b) $(CH_3)_2C\text{=}O + H_2O^{18} \xrightarrow{\text{HOAc}} (CH_3)_2C\text{=}O^{18} + H_2O$

(c) 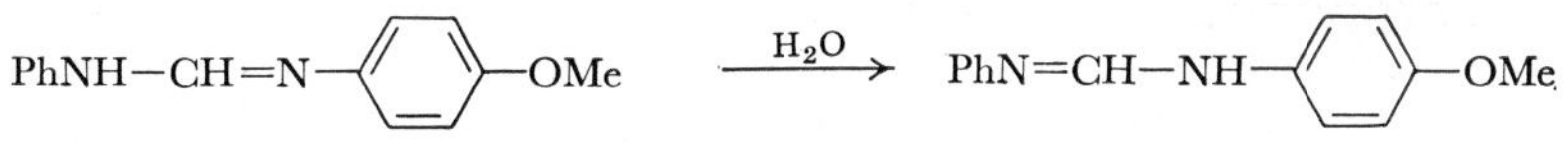 $PhNH\text{—}CH\text{=}N\text{—}\boxed{}\text{—OMe} \xrightarrow{H_2O} PhN\text{=}CH\text{—}NH\text{—}\boxed{}\text{—OMe}$

(d) 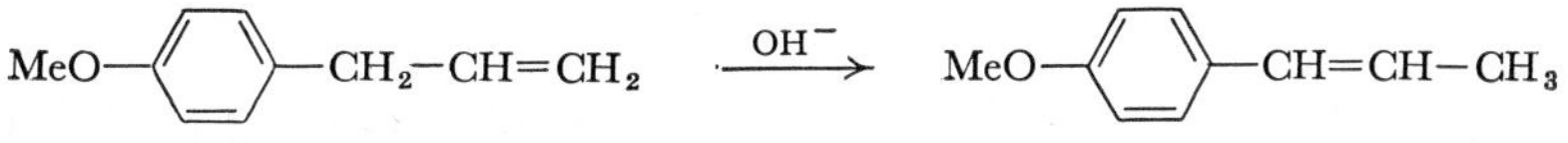 $MeO\text{—}\boxed{}\text{—}CH_2\text{—}CH\text{=}CH_2 \xrightarrow{OH^-} MeO\text{—}\boxed{}\text{—}CH\text{=}CH\text{—}CH_3$

(e) 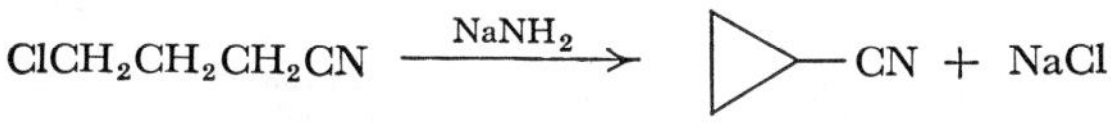 $ClCH_2CH_2CH_2CN \xrightarrow{NaNH_2} \triangleright\text{—CN} + NaCl$

(f) $Me_2C\text{=}O + I_2 + OD^- \xrightarrow{D_2O} DCI_3 + CH_3C\begin{array}{c}\text{O}^-\\\diagdown\\\diagup\\\text{O}\end{array}$

(g) 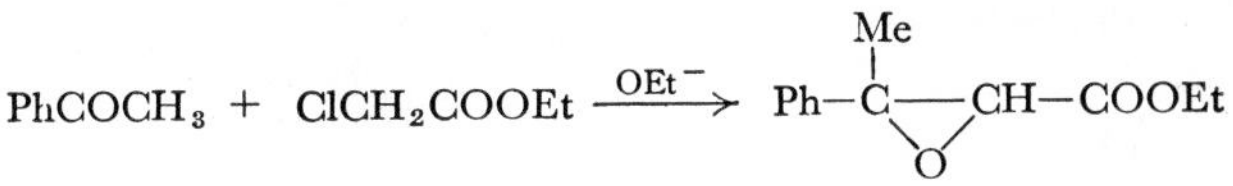 $PhCOCH_3 + ClCH_2COOEt \xrightarrow{OEt^-} Ph\text{—}\overset{\displaystyle Me}{\underset{\displaystyle O}{\text{C}}}\text{—CH—COOEt}$

(h)

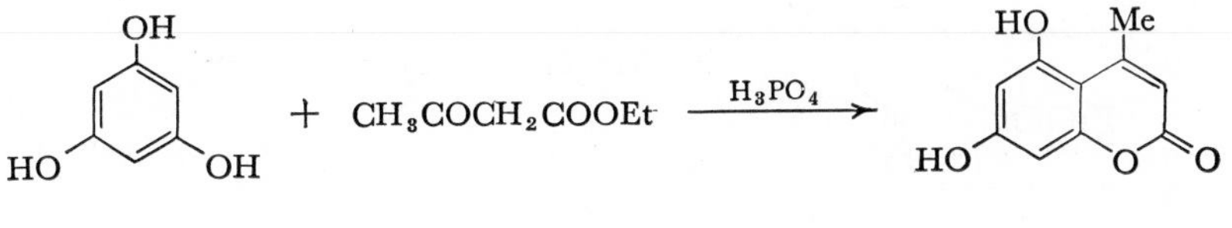

(i) $2CH_3COCH_2COOEt \xrightarrow[I_2]{OEt^-} \begin{matrix} CH_3COCHCOOEt \\ | \\ CH_3COCHCOOEt \end{matrix} + I^-$

(j) $+ HCCl_3 \xrightarrow{OH^-}$

(k) $3Me_2C=O \xrightarrow{H_2SO_4}$

(l) $CHBr(COOEt)_2 + HI \rightarrow I_2 + CH_2(CCOEt)_2 + HBr$

(m) $PhCOCH_3 + D_2O \xrightarrow{\text{(pyridine—OH)}} PhCOCH_2D + DOH$

(n) $HCCl_3 + PhS^- \xrightarrow{OH^-} HC(SPh)_3 + Cl^-$

(o) $CBr_4 + OH^- + CH_3CH=CHCH_3 \rightarrow Me\text{—}CH\underset{CBr_2}{\diagdown\diagup}CH\text{—}Me + OBr^-$

(p) $PhMgBr + PhCH=CH\text{—}COCH_3 \rightarrow \xrightarrow{H_2O} Ph_2CHCH_2COCH_3$

(q) $(CH_2=CH\text{—})_2CHNa + CO_2 \rightarrow \xrightarrow{H_2O} CH_2=CH\text{—}CH=CH\text{—}CH_2\text{—}COOH$

(r) $Ph_2C=NPh + PhMgBr \longrightarrow \xrightarrow{H_2O}$

(s) $\begin{matrix} C(COOEt)_2 \\ \| \\ CH\text{—}CH(COOEt)_2 \end{matrix} + \begin{matrix} CN \\ | \\ CH_2COOEt \end{matrix} \xrightarrow{OEt^-}$

$CH_2(COOEt)_2 + \begin{matrix} CN \\ | \\ C=CH\text{—}CH(COOEt)_2 \\ | \\ COOEt \end{matrix}$

6. Predict the products, justifying your guess in each case:

(a) $+ OEt^- \longrightarrow$

(b) $+ Me_3N + I_2 \longrightarrow$

(c)

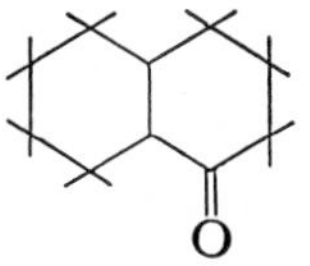

$+ \ D_2O \ + \ DCl \ \longrightarrow$

(d) $PhCH_2COCH_3 + OAc^- + ICl \xrightarrow{HOAc}$

(e) $PhCHMe\!-\!\overset{\displaystyle O}{\underset{\displaystyle \|}{C}}\!-\!CH_2\!-\!CH_3 + Br_2 \xrightarrow[EtOH]{OEt^-}$

(f)

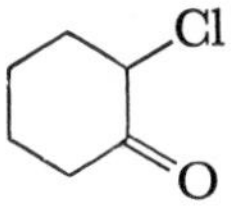

$+ \quad Cl_2 \quad \xrightarrow[HOAc]{OAc^-}$

(g)

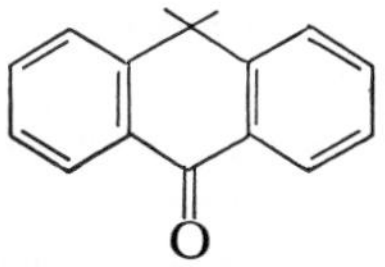

$+ \quad OEt^- \quad \xrightarrow{EtOH}$

(h) $CH_3\!-\!\underset{\underset{\displaystyle O}{\displaystyle \|}}{C}\!-\!\underset{\underset{\displaystyle Br}{\displaystyle |}}{C}Me\!-\!COOEt + OH^- \rightarrow$

(i) $PhCH_2COCH_3 + PhCHO \xrightarrow{OEt^-}$

(j)

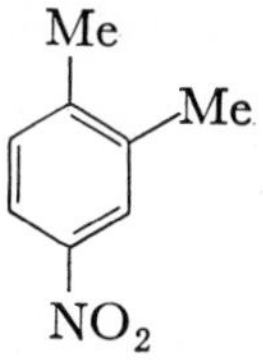

$+ \quad OEt^- \quad \xrightarrow{EtOD}$

(k) $CH_3\!-\!(CH\!=\!CH\!-\!)_3COOEt + CH_2(COOEt)_2 \xrightarrow{OEt^-}$

(l) 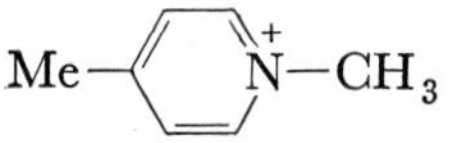 $Me\!-\!\langle\ \rangle\!-\!\overset{+}{N}\!-\!CH_3 + PhCHO \xrightarrow{OEt^-}$

(m)  $MeO\!-\!\langle\ \rangle\!-\!CHO + PhCHO \xrightarrow{CN^-}$

(n) $(CH_3)_4P^+ + D_2O \xrightarrow{OD^-}$

(o)

$Na^+ + HCCl_3 \xrightarrow{OH^-}$

(p)

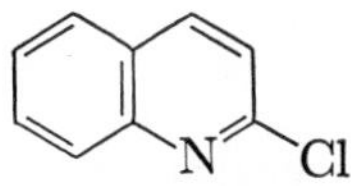

$+ \quad PhLi \quad \longrightarrow$

(q) $(C_2H_5)_2CHMgBr + (C_2H_5)_2C\!=\!O \rightarrow$

(r) $CH_3CH\!=\!CH\!-\!\underset{\underset{\displaystyle O}{\displaystyle \|}}{C}\!-\!CH_3 + PhLi \rightarrow$

(s)

$+$ CH_3Li $\longrightarrow$

7. In the Mannich reaction, a compound having a labile C—H bond, an aldehyde, a primary or secondary amine, and the ammonium ion derived from the amine react to form a so-called Mannich base (LV).

$$-\overset{|}{\underset{|}{C}}-H + RCHO + HNR_2 \xrightarrow{NR_2H_2^+} -\overset{H}{\underset{|}{\overset{|}{C}}}-\overset{|}{\underset{R}{\overset{|}{C}}}-NR_2 + H_2O$$

LV

Propose a mechanism for the Mannich reaction consistent with the following observations:

(a) The reaction conditions used are often significantly milder than those needed to carry out an aldol condensation between the first two reactants.

(b) Generally, when the aldol condensation product from the first two reactants is prepared independently and is treated with the amine, the Mannich base, if it forms at all, forms more slowly than when the three components are mixed.

(c) The reaction is third order overall, first order in each of the three components.

(d) The reaction is inhibited in strongly basic and strongly acidic solutions.

(e) Reactions requiring the collisions of three molecular species in solution within a very short time interval are generally extremely slow.

8. Explain the following:

(a) The C=O group in $-\overset{O}{\overset{||}{C}}-\overset{|}{C}H-$ is more effective in increasing the acidity of the α-hydrogen than is the benzene ring in C_6H_5-CH-.

(b) Tri(o-tolyl)methane is less acidic than tri(p-tolyl)methane.

(c) The hydrogen exchange between 2-picoline and water is far more rapid than that between 3-picoline and water.

(d) When $ICH(COOEt)_2$ is treated with HI, elemental iodine is formed.

(e) The α-methylation of ketones with methyl iodide is much more effectively catalyzed by dimethylamine than by trimethylamine.

(f) The base-catalyzed bromination of ketone LVI is far slower than that of ketone LVII.

LVI

LVII

LVIII

(g) The basic hydrolysis of CBr_4 yields CO and $HCOO^-$ (the same products as result from the basic hydrolysis of $HCBr_3$), and OBr^-. The rate of hydrolysis is, however, much less than that for $HCBr_3$.

(h) The preferred position of attack in the bromination of 3-methylcyclohexanone is the same in acidic as in basic media. With isopropylcyclohexyl ketone, the preferred positions of attack are different in the two media.

(i) The attack of $Na^+CH(COOEt)_2^-$ on $CH_3\overset{7}{CH}=CH\overset{5}{CH}=CH\overset{3}{CH}=CHCOOMe$ occurs at carbon 3 or carbon 7 but not at carbon 5.

(j) When a Grignard reagent can undergo both 1,2 addition and 1,4 addition to an α,β-unsaturated ketone, addition of $MgBr_2$ to the reaction mixture generally lowers the ratio of 1,4 to 1,2 addition.

(k) The effect described in (j) is not observed in the reaction of PhMgBr with ketone LVIII although both 1,2 and 1,4 addition occur.

(l) There is a linear free-energy relationship (that is, a Brønsted-catalysis-law relationship) between the rates of amine-catalyzed bromination of nitroethane in water and the basicities of the amines in chlorobenzene, but no such relationship exists between bromination rates and basicities of the amines in water.

(m) When $PhCHMe-N=CPh_2$ and NaOEt are added to EtOH enriched with EtOD, the rate of enrichment of the imine with deuterium is at first equal to its net rate of isomerization to $PhCMe=N-CHPh_2$, but as the reaction proceeds, the rate of deuterium enrichment runs ahead of the net rate of isomerization.

(n) Cation LIX, unlike cation LX, is ineffective as a catalyst in the benzoin condensation.

LIX   LX

CHAPTER 11

Electrophilic and Nucleophilic
Substitutions in Aromatic Systems

Aromaticity

BENZENE MAY BE SAID to be the great grandfather of all aromatic compounds. In the development of our present ideas concerning aromaticity, this hydrocarbon played a unique and immensely important role;[1] for once the essential nature of the benzene ring was understood, the behavior of other aromatic compounds could be interpreted, for the most part, with little difficulty. To many chemists, in fact, the term "aromatic compound" is synonymous with "benzene derivative" (since even such fused-ring hydrocarbons as naphthalene and anthracene are actually benzene derivatives). But a number of heterocyclic systems have long been known which exhibit behavior sufficiently similar to that of benzenoid compounds so that they too may be classified as "aromatic"; the most familiar of these are thiophene, pyrrole, pyridine, and quinoline. There are, in addition, certain nonbenzenoid compounds of more recent vintage that, at least in some respects, may be considered aromatic.

Of the various criteria for aromaticity which have been suggested, two seem the most useful. The first is *resonance energy*. This quantity, it will be recalled, may generally be obtained from the heat of combustion or heat of hydrogenation, and tells us how much more stable a compound is than a second (hypo-

---

[1] The early attempts to propose a suitable single structure for benzene, and the revision of structural thinking which eventually became necessary due to the failure of these attempts, constitute an interesting and important chapter in the history of structural organic chemistry, which, however, will not be re-told here. See, for example, (a) Wheland, *Advanced Organic Chemistry*, John Wiley and Sons, Inc., New York, 1949, pp. 102–124, 387–414, (b) Ingold, *Structure and Mechanism in Organic Chemistry*, Cornell University Press, Ithaca, 1953, pp. 156–168, (c) Lachmann, *The Spirit of Organic Chemistry*, Macmillan, New York, 1899, Chap. 3.

thetical) compound having the same set of bonds as the first but without the cyclic conjugated system (p. 37). The resonance energies of pyridine, pyrrole, and thiophene, for example, are each close to 25 kcal per mole—comparable with the value for benzene (36 kcal per mole) and at the same time much greater than the resonance energies of conjugated but noncyclic dienes ($<$5 kcal per mole) which may be regarded as nonaromatic.

A second feature pointing to aromaticity in a compound is its tendency to undergo *substitution* reactions with a number of reagents that ordinarily simply "add across the double bond" in olefins. The most familiar and important of such reagents are electrophilic in character. Thus Cl_2 or $HOCl$ will chlorinate benzene derivatives with displacement of H^+ but generally convert olefins to dichloroalkanes or chlorohydrins; similarly, HBr adds to the $C{=}C$ double bond of a number of olefins, but with aromatic compounds only substitution (hydrogen exchange) occurs. Concentrated sulfuric acid, which ordinarily converts aromatic compounds to sulfonic acids, often converts olefins to alkyl hydrogen sulfates instead:[2]

$$RCH{=}CHR + H_2SO_4 \rightarrow RCH_2{-}CHR{-}OSO_3H$$

The reluctance of aromatic compounds to undergo addition reactions is, like their resonance energies, a reflection of the extra stability associated with cyclic conjugated systems; for in addition reactions these systems are destroyed whereas in substitution reactions they are preserved.

As with other effects related to conjugation, aromaticity requires that the atoms comprising the conjugated system lie in or near a common plane. We might expect the hydrocarbon cyclooctatetrene (I) to exhibit aromatic properties since, at first glance, it appears to be a "benzenelike" ring with eight instead of six members. However, if the molecule were planar, with each of the bond angles in the ring the same, these angles would be 135°, that is, 15° greater than the C—C—C bond angles in "normal" conjugated systems. It is not surprising therefore that the cyclooctatetrene molecule has been found not to be planar, but rather "tub shaped" (II).[3] Four of the bonds are 1.34 Å

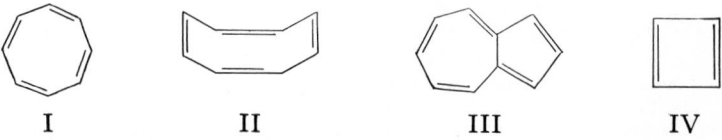

I II III IV

[2] Norris and Joubert, *J. Am. Chem. Soc.*, **49**, 873 (1927).

[3] The structure has been determined using x-ray diffraction (Kaufman, Fankuchen and Mark, *Nature*, **161**, 165 (1948)). An alternate "crownlike" structure has been proposed on the basis of spectral studies (Lippincott *et al.*, *J. Am. Chem. Soc.*, **73**, 3370 (1951), and electron-diffraction studies (Bastiansen *et al.*, *Nature*, **160**, 128 (1947)). Nevertheless, the bulk of evidence at present appears to favor the "tub" form. At any rate, the molecule is assuredly not planar.

(about the length of ordinary double bonds), whereas the remaining four are 1.54 Å, the length of ordinary single bonds. Moreover, with respect to its chemistry, the compound has been found to be nonaromatic. Its resonance energy is about 5 kcal per mole,[4] and it does not undergo the usual aromatic substitution reactions (although its tendency to rearrange in the presence of electrophiles prevents our classifying it as a "typical nonaromatic polyene").

The observed lack of aromaticity is in accord with the nonplanar structure, but there is some theoretical basis for the belief that even if the molecule were planar, it would not have properties akin to those of benzene. A quantum-mechanical treatment of conjugated cyclic systems indicates that the unusual stability which we term "aromaticity" should exist only for rings associated with $(4n + 2)$ π electrons, where n is an integer; that is, that rings having 6, 10, and 14 π electrons may be aromatic (provided they are planar) whereas those with 4, 8, and 12 may not.[5] Without the supporting calculations, which will not be reproduced here, such a result is necessarily accepted on faith, even though it looks a little like a rule of numerology. However, it is of less practical than theoretical interest for, aside from azulene (III) and its derivatives, very nearly all actual systems falling within its scope involve just six π electrons or may be broken down into six-electron units which "share edges."[6] Thus, excluding a few very unusual compounds, the characteristic structural feature of aromatic systems may be taken to be the π-electron sextet. With benzene and pyridine, each atom in the ring supplies a single π electron to the sextet; whereas with furan, thiophene, and pyrrole, the "hetero atom" supplies two π electrons and the four carbon atoms one π electron each. The "π-electron sextets" in pyridine and pyrrole may be represented schematically as shown in Figure 11-1. Note that pyridine has an extra pair of p electrons (in the shaded orbital) with which it may coordinate with an acid without disrupting the "aromatic sextet"; whereas with pyrrole, in which both π electrons of nitrogen have been incorporated into the sextet, this is not possible. Thus, pyridine coordinates much more readily with acids (that is, is a much stronger base) than pyrrole.

Removal of a proton from cyclopentadiene yields the cyclopentadienide

[4] Springall, White, and Cass, *Trans. Faraday Soc.*, **50**, 815 (1954).

[5] Hückel, *Z. Electrochem.*, **43**, 752, 857 (1937), Craig, *J. Chem. Soc.*, **1951**, 3175. For brief summaries of this question in nonmathematical terms, see Longuet-Higgins, *Proc. Chem. Soc.*, **1957**, 157; and Wheland *Resonance in Organic Chemistry*, John Wiley and Sons, Inc., New York, 1955, pp. 134–149.

[6] Such aromatics as naphthalene and anthracene (having, respectively, 10 and 14 π electrons) may obviously be broken down into edge-sharing benzene rings. Such fully conjugated cyclic polyenes as cyclodecapentaene, $C_{10}H_{10}$, and cyclododecahexaene, $C_{12}H_{12}$, have probably not yet been prepared, and, in any event, are almost certainly not planar molecules. Moreover, despite many attempts, cyclobutadiene, IV, has likewise not yet been prepared.

For descriptions of aromatic compounds that cannot readily be broken down into six-electron units, see Boekelheide and Vick, *J. Am. Chem. Soc.*, **78**, 653 (1956); and Pettit, *Chem. and Ind.*, **1956**, 1306.

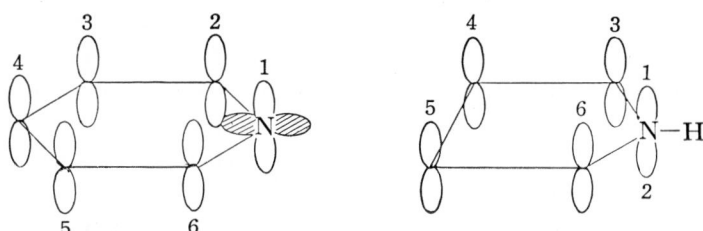

Fig. 11-1. π-Electron Sextets in Pyridine and Pyrrole

anion (V), whereas removal of a H:⁻ ion from cycloheptatriene (in principle) yields the cycloheptatrienylium cation (tropylium ion),[7] which is, however, in

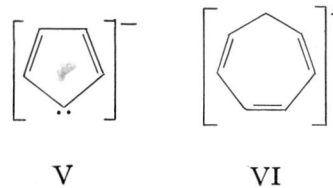

V VI

practice obtained in a different manner (see below). Since both of these ions have six π electrons in a cyclic system ($5 + 1$ in anion V, and $7 - 1$ in cation VI), we might expect to find aromaticity in both. But it is a little difficult to know where to look; for the reactions which these ions undergo are very much different from those of ordinary aromatic systems in which the rings bear no net charge. Moreover, the resonance energies of the ions cannot be determined in a straightforward manner. Nevertheless, it does appear that these ions are significantly more stable than other carbanions and carbonium ions. The *tropylium ion*, which results when tropylium chloride or bromide is dissolved in alcohol or water,[7] is probably the most stable carbonium ion yet prepared; for although the ion is eventually converted to ditropyl ether in water or ethyl tropyl ether in alcohol, solutions containing it may be studied without undue difficulty, although at a not too leisurely pace. Infrared studies indicate that the cyclic species in such solutions is planar and that all of the carbon-carbon bonds have the same length,[8] thus being consistent with an "aromatic cation" in which six π electrons are distributed evenly over a π orbital embracing seven atoms at the corners of a regular heptagon.

The special stability of the cyclopentadienide ion, V, and substituted cyclopentadienide ions was discussed in the preceding chapter (p. 370) where it was seen that cyclopentadiene and its derivatives exhibited unusually high acidities. However, these carbanions will not undergo electrophilic substitutions with those reagents that carry out substitution reactions on benzene and thio-

[7] Doering and Knox, *J. Am. Chem. Soc.*, **76,** 3203 (1954).
[8] Fateley and Lippincott, *J. Am. Chem. Soc.*, **77,** 249 (1955).

phene. As we shall presently demonstrate, the active intermediates in most of such substitution reactions are cations (for example, Br^+, NO_2^+, and $R\overset{+}{-}C=O$), and such cations would tend merely to form a new covalent bond with the cyclopentadienide ions, yielding a neutral (but nonaromatic) product. But there is a group of compounds, closely related to the cyclopentadienide ion, that is unquestionably aromatic in character. These compounds are the *ferrocenes*, in which an iron atom is "sandwiched" between two cyclopentadiene rings.[9] The simplest member of the series, ferrocene itself (dicyclopentadienyl-iron, VII) may be prepared by the treatment of $FeCl_2$ with cyclopentadienyl-

VII

sodium; it may be considered to be a pair of parallel $C_5H_5^-$ anions from which enough π-electron density has been drained toward the central Fe^{2+} ion to allow formation of two very strong π bonds.[10] Ferrocene undergoes Friedel-Crafts-type alkylations and acylations in much the same way as do benzene, thiophene, and naphthalene, and also undergoes attack by the benzenediazonium ion in the same way as do the more reactive of the usual aromatics. Ferrocene has not yet been halogenated or nitrated directly, for its iron atom is readily oxidized to the "+3 state," yielding the so-called ferricinium ion, $(C_5H_5)_2Fe^+$.

Azulene (III) and its derivatives may be nitrated, halogenated, and made to undergo Friedel-Crafts acylations and alkylations, but the reaction conditions must be mild, for the azulene ring system is readily destroyed.[11] In addition to taking azulene as an example of a "ten π-electron aromatic system," it may be regarded as a combination of a tropylium cation and a cyclopentadienide anion sharing a "common edge." Such a view is consistent with the rather high

[9] For summaries of the chemistry of ferrocene and related compounds, see Pauson, *Quart. Revs.*, **9**, 391 (1955); and Fischer, *Angew. Chem.*, **67**, 475 (1955). Cyclopentadiene forms "sandwich compounds," structurally similar to ferrocene, with a large number of different transition metals. However, with the exception of the ruthenium compound $(C_5H_5)_2Ru$, these are far less stable than ferrocene and its derivatives, and little is known concerning their chemistry.

[10] The nature of the hybridization of orbitals about the iron atom in ferrocene is still an open question. See Moffitt, *J. Am. Chem. Soc.*, **76**, 3386 (1954) and Dunitz and Orgel, *Nature*, **171**, 121 (1953).

[11] Anderson, Nelson, and Tazuma, *J. Am. Chem. Soc.*, **75**, 4980 (1950); **77**, 6321 (1955). For a review of the chemistry of the azulenes, see Gordon, *Chem. Revs.* **50**, 127 (1952).

dipole moment of azulene (p. 64) and with its tendency to undergo electrophilic substitution on the five-membered (the more negative) ring, rather than on the seven-membered (the more positive) ring.[11]

An additional interesting cyclic system having some aromatic character is found in the *sydnones*,[12] a set of compounds so named because they were first studied at the University of Sydney. The available electrons in the sydnone

$$Ph-N\overset{CH_2-COOH}{\underset{N=O}{\diagdown}} \xrightarrow{-H_2O} Ph-\overset{+}{N}\overset{CH=C-O^-}{\underset{N-O}{\diagdown}}$$

$$VIII \qquad\qquad\qquad\qquad IX$$

ring of N-phenylsydnone (IX), a compound prepared by the dehydration of N-nitroso-N-phenylglycine (VIII), are represented schematically in Figure 11-2. Once again, six π electrons are associated with the heterocyclic ring. It is thus not surprising that the sydnone ring undergoes halogenation[12(b)] and nitration[12(c)]

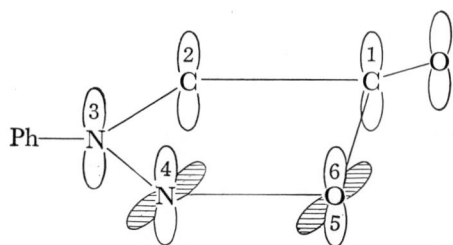

Fig. 11-2. N-Phenylsydnone

at the hydrogenated carbon. Additional electrophilic substitution reactions (for example, acylation and sulfonation) on the sydnone system have not as yet been reported, but only a few attempts seem to have been made.

At this point it may be asked why electrophilic-substitution reactions, which are so rare in aliphatic systems, become much more commonplace in aromatic chemistry. In the great majority of such reactions, the leaving group is the proton, and the reaction then requires the breakage of a rather strong C—H bond. The activation energy, which must be supplied largely by the attacking electrophile, is necessarily high, and there is, moreover, no particular reason why an electrophile should attack a relatively nonpolar C—H bond of an aliphatic compound. With aromatic substrates, however, there is one important circumstance that favors electrophilic substitution. *The attacking elec-*

[12] (a) For a review of the chemistry of the sydnones, see Baker and Ollis, *Quart. Revs.*, **XI,** 15 (1957). See also (b) Earl, *Rec. Trav. chim.*, **75**, 1080 (1956), and (c) Baker, Ollis, and Poole, *J. Chem. Soc.*, **1950**, 1542.

trophile may form a new bond before the old bond breaks, and the energy that becomes available when the new bond forms may be used to help bring about the breakage of the old bond. We might then anticipate that the attack on an aromatic system by an electrophile A^+ will pass through an intermediate (or a transition state) of the type X, in which both the attacking species and the leaving group are bound to the substrate. An intermediate analogous to X in an aliphatic

substitution would have five bonds to a single carbon atom and is therefore prohibited.

With nucleophilic substitutions, the tables are turned, for these are much more common among aliphatic compounds. The bonds between carbon and the more effective leaving groups (for example, C—Br, C—I, and C—OTos) tend to be weak and are considerably more polar than C—H bonds. The polarities of such bonds favor the initial nucleophilic attack on the carbon, whereas the weakness of the bonds eases the departure of the leaving group. However, when such a leaving group (which we may represent generally as $—\ddot{Y}:$) is attached to a benzene ring, one of its p orbitals lies parallel to the π orbitals of the ring. The resulting conjugation allows electron density to drift from $—\ddot{Y}:$ into the ring

(XI ↔ XI′), lowering the polarity of the C—Y bond and allowing it to assume some double-bond character. Clearly then, this conjugation should decrease the ease of nucleophilic substitution at the carbon atom bound to group $—\ddot{Y}:$; for that carbon has become less positive and the C—Y bond has been strengthened. Moreover, as has already been pointed out (p. 217), attachment of a second nucleophile to this carbon (as is necessary in the transition state for substitution) cuts down the π-electron system from seven atoms to five. Thus, although nucleophilic substitutions on aromatic substrates have long been known, they generally require much more severe conditions than those on aliphatic substrates. They occur most readily when the electron density in the aromatic system is diminished by the presence of one or more strongly electron-attracting groups (most often nitro groups).

In considering electrophilic aromatic substitution, we shall devote our attention largely to nitration, halogenation, sulfonation, and the Friedel-Crafts reaction. The mechanisms of other electrophilic substitutions, among them hydrogen exchange,[13(a)]

$$ArH + D^+ \rightleftharpoons ArD + H^+$$

diazo coupling,[13(b)]

$$ArH + Ar'N_2^+ \rightarrow Ar\!-\!N\!=\!N\!-\!Ar' + H^+$$

and bromodesulfonation,[13(c)]

$$ArSO_3H + Br_2 + H_2O \rightarrow ArBr + Br^- + H^+ + H_2SO_4$$

have also been investigated. However, despite some interesting differences in detail, these reactions appear, at present, to follow the broad patterns set by the more usual aromatic substitutions.

Nitration. The Nitronium Ion

Of the various types of electrophilic-substitution reactions, nitration currently presents the clearest mechanistic picture. As has been hinted several times in earlier chapters, the attacking electrophile in nitration is often (but, as we shall see, not always) the nitronium ion, NO_2^+. Since this cation is not found in the ordinary "store-room reagents," we should first make sure that it exists before apprehending it as the culprit in nitrations. The most convincing evidence arises from the structure determination (by x-ray crystallography) of solid NO_2-ClO_4[14(a)] and N_2O_5.[14(b)] The first of these compounds was found to contain the familiar ClO_4^- ion, and the second was found to contain the NO_3^- ion; but, in addition, both were found to contain what appeared to be the same *linear triatomic species*. From the stoichiometry of these compounds, this species must be the NO_2^+ ion, and the compounds may be represented, respectively, as $NO_2^+ClO_4^-$ and $NO_2^+NO_3^-$. Other nitronium salts, all necessarily derived from very strong acids, are now known, among them $NO_2^+FSO_3^-$, $(NO_2^+)_2S_2O_7^{2-}$, and $(NO_2^+)_2S_3O_{10}^{2-}$.[15] Although complete structure determinations of these com-

[13] (a) Gold and Satchell, *J. Chem. Soc.*, **1955**, 3622; **1956**, 2743, 3911; *Quart. Revs.*, **IX**, 51 (1955); Comyns, *et al.*, *J. Am. Chem. Soc.*, **78**, 3989 (1956). (b) Wistar and Bartlett, *ibid.*, **63**, 413 (1941); Hauser and Breslow, *ibid.*, **63**, 418 (1941). (c) Cannell, *ibid.*, **79**, 2927 (1957).

[14] (a) Cox, Jeffrey, and Truter, *Nature*, **162**, 258 (1948). (b) Grison, Ericks, and de Vries, *Acta Cryst.*, **3**, 290 (1950).

[15] Goddard, Hughes, and Ingold, *J. Chem. Soc.*, **1950**, 2559. The latter two nitronium compounds are salts of the polysulfuric acids $H_2S_2O_7$ and $H_2S_3O_{10}$. These acids are found in fuming sulfuric acid.

pounds have not been reported, spectral evidence indicates that each assuredly contains the nitronium ion; for the Raman spectrum of each shows a line at Raman frequency 1400 cm^{-1}, a line that is also found in the Raman spectra of NO_2ClO_4 and N_2O_5,[16(a)] and in the Raman spectra of mixtures of concentrated nitric and sulfuric acids.[16(b)] Some ionic or molecular species must be common to each of the solid compounds and must also be present in the mixture of acids. Since the anions are different in each case, we may conclude that the cation is the same—that is, that these materials, like NO_2ClO_4 and N_2O_5, contain the NO_2^+ ion.

Finally, cryoscopic measurements show that nitric acid in solutions of concentrated sulfuric acid exhibits a ν-factor (p. 98) of very nearly 4,[17] indicating that sulfuric acid reacts with nitric acid in the same way as with triphenylcarbinol, breaking off a hydroxyl group as water, then converting it to H_3O^+.

$$HNO_3 + 2H_2SO_4 \rightarrow NO_2^+ + H_3O^+ + 2HSO_4^- \qquad (\nu = 4)$$

Having established the existence of the nitronium ion, we should next clarify its role in substitution reactions. The nitrations, in concentrated sulfuric acid, of such aromatic compounds as nitrobenzene, benzoic acid, and benzenesulfonic acid have long been known to exhibit second-order kinetics—first order each in aromatic substrate and in "added nitric acid."[18] In 90 to 100 percent sulfuric acid, virtually all of the nitric acid has been converted to NO_2^+. Therefore, for these solutions, the reaction may also be said to be first order in nitronium ion. For example, for nitration of nitrobenzene,

$$\text{rate} = k(PhNO_2)(\text{``HNO}_3\text{''}) = k(PhNO_2)(NO_2^+) \qquad (1)$$

This rate law is obviously consistent with an activated complex containing the substrate and one nitronium ion, but it does not demand it, for these kinetics would also be observed if the attacking reagent were any species having a concentration (large or small) that remains proportional to (NO_2^+) during the course

---

[16] (a) Millen, J. Chem. Soc., **1950**, 2600, 2606. (b) Medard, Compt. rend., **199**,1615 (1934). Furthermore, Millen found that the species responsible for the line at Raman frequency 1400 cm^{-1} possesses no other "Raman-active" modes of vibration. The selection rules for Raman spectroscopy stipulate that this can be so only if the responsible species is diatomic or if it is symmetric, linear, and triatomic (as is CO_2). The nitronium ion is, as we have seen, an ion of the latter type.

[17] Gillespie, et al., Nature, **158**, 480 (1946); J. Chem. Soc., **1950**, 2473, 2493. The small apparent deviation from the fourfold value of ν is discussed in the latter two papers.

[18] (a) Martinsen, Z. physik. Chem., **50**, 385 (1904); **59**, 605 (1907). Relatively nonpolar aromatics such as benzene, toluene, and chlorobenzene are only slightly soluble in sulfuric acid, and their rates of nitration are generally controlled by the rates at which they dissolve. Anisole and phenol are more soluble, but are nitrated too rapidly for convenient kinetic measurements in concentrated H_2SO_4. (b) Martinsen's results have since been confirmed by a number of workers; see, for example, Westheimer and Kharasch, J. Am. Chem. Soc., **68**, 1871 (1946).

of the reaction (for example, HNO_3, $H_2NO_3^+$, NO_2HSO_4). Moreover, this rate law tells us little about how the attacking species is formed.

Thus it is clear that sulfuric acid, despite its value as a solvent in preparative nitrations, complicates the mechanistic picture. More detailed information has been obtained by the study of nitrations in the organic solvents, acetic acid and nitromethane, in which such aromatics as benzene, toluene, and xylene are easily soluble. Moreover, the nitrations of such compounds in these solvents proceed at rates that may be conveniently measured. To minimize complications due to the water formed in the reaction, a large excess of nitric acid is often used, although this makes the determination of the kinetic role of HNO_3 more difficult.[19] Under these conditions, aromatic substrates (aside from amines and phenols, which comprise a special problem) fall into three categories, based upon three different modes of kinetic behavior.

The rates of nitration of such aromatics as p-dichlorobenzene and ethyl benzoate (that is, compounds which, in classical terms, undergo nitration "with difficulty") are, as may be expected, proportional to the concentration of substrate. Since nitric acid is present in large excess, it does not appear in the kinetic expression, and these nitrations are *pseudo-first order*.

For aromatics that are "more active" than benzene (for example, toluene, the xylenes, p-chloroanisole), nitration rates are independent of the concentration of substrate. With nitric acid in large excess, these nitrations are *pseudo-zero order*. Their rates remain constant during the progress of a given nitration and suddenly drop to zero when all the substrate is consumed. Moreover, the nitration rate for each of the compounds in this category is the same in a given nitrating mixture.

Thirdly, as we might anticipate, there are a number of aromatics of intermediate activity which may be considered "borderline cases." Benzene and the monohalobenzenes, for example, exhibit pseudo orders between 0 and 1 in nitration, that is, their rates depend upon the concentration of the substrate but are not directly proportional to it. In this intermediate region, certain of the nitrations may be made to follow either pseudo-first- or pseudo-zero-order rate laws (but generally not both) by suitable adjustment of the reagent concentrations.

One may now ask, "Do these kinetic differences reflect differences in mechanism?" The answer is almost certainly "no"; for although three categories are listed above for descriptive convenience, we observe, in perspective, a continuous range of kinetic behavior. It is far more likely that a single mechanism operates for the substrates in all three "categories" and that the observed kinetic differences arise from differences in the relative rates of the individual steps within a common reaction sequence. For nitrations having rates inde-

[19] Ingold, *et al.*, *J. Chem. Soc.*, **1938**, 929; **1950**, 2400; *Nature*, **158**, 448 (1946).

pendent of the substrate concentration, the substrate must not become involved in the reaction sequence until after the slow step; the slow step must then be the formation of an active intermediate (that is, the attacking electrophile) with which the substrate then reacts very rapidly. This means that the attacking species is neither nitric acid itself nor its conjugate acid $H_2NO_3^+$ (the formation of which from HNO_3 should be very rapid since it requires only a proton transfer between oxygen atoms) but *is* almost certainly the NO_2^+ ion, the formation of which from HNO_3 or $H_2NO_3^+$ requires the breakage of a N—O bond.

It is possible, however, by using a less reactive aromatic, to slow down the step in which electrophilic attack occurs so that this attack becomes rate determining. The formation of NO_2^+ would then become the more rapid step; however, this ion may not accumulate in solution, for solutions of nitric acid in organic solvents are known from other evidence to contain only small quantities of NO_2^+. The formation of NO_2^+ must then be reversible. The rate of nitration in such cases is proportional to (NO_2^+)(substrate); and (NO_2^+) remains nearly constant since it is in equilibrium with a constant concentration of HNO_3. Pseudo-first-order kinetics are therefore observed. If we represent the sequence of steps in nitration as follows:

$$2HNO_3 \underset{\text{reversal}}{\overset{\text{formation (2 steps)}}{\rightleftharpoons}} \begin{cases} NO_2^+ \xrightarrow[\text{attack}]{\text{ArH}} ArNO_2 + H^+ \\ NO_3^- \\ H_2O \end{cases}$$

we may summarize the conclusions thus far as follows: if the "attack" step is much faster than the "reversal" step, pseudo-zero-order kinetics are observed; whereas if the opposite is true, pseudo-first-order kinetics are observed. Finally, it may be shown, using the steady state treatment (Ex. 2c), that when the "attack" and "reversal" steps have comparable rates, the nitration will exhibit an intermediate nonintegral order that will depend upon the concentrations of the reagents.

As indicated in the sequence above, the formation of the nitronium ion proceeds in two distinguishable steps rather than a single step. We may draw this conclusion by noting the action of added nitrate on the pseudo-zero-order nitrations; for nitrate greatly retards these reactions but does not alter their kinetic character.[19] Suppose that the nitronium ion were formed from HNO_3 in a single step.

$$2HNO_3 \rightleftharpoons NO_2^+ + NO_3^- + H_2O$$

If this were so, the action of nitrate in reversing the formation of NO_2^+ would slow down the reaction (as is observed). However, NO_3^- and the substrate would be competing for NO_2^+, and the reaction rate should be increased by increasing the concentration of substrate, since in doing so we make it a more effective competitor for NO_2^+. Furthermore, added water should be about as effective as added nitrate in retarding the formation of NO_2^+, hence in retarding the nitration. But the rates of nitration of toluene, ethylbenzene, and the xylenes are, as we have emphasized, independent of the concentration of substrate, whether or not additional nitrate has been added; and the retarding action of water, although observable, is far less than that of nitrate. We must conclude then that the formation of the nitronium ion from nitric acid does *not* occur in a single step.

The following two-step process for the formation of nitronium ion is in reasonable accord with the kinetic data:

$$2HNO_3 \rightleftharpoons \begin{cases} H_2NO_3^+ \rightleftharpoons NO_2^+ + H_2O \\ NO_3^- \end{cases}$$

Here again the nitrate ion retards the overall reaction by reversing the initial step, but there is no longer any competition between nitrate and substrate, since the former reacts with $H_2NO_3^+$ whereas the latter reacts with NO_2^+. By increasing the concentration of substrate we merely increase the quantity of material that remains waiting to consume the small supply of NO_2^+ as it is generated, and the nitration rate is, as observed, unaffected.[20]

The process of nitration requires not only the attachment of the nitro group to the substrate, but also the breakage of a C—H bond and the departure of a proton. Earlier in the chapter it was suggested that nitrations (as well as other electrophilic substitutions) occur much more readily in aromatic than in aliphatic systems because the new bond may form before the old bond breaks; that is, the bond-making and bond-breaking steps are not contemporaneous. This has been demonstrated, not by classical kinetics, but by experiments chosen to show the absence of hydrogen isotope effects in nitration.[21] In our initial consideration of isotope effects (p. 194) it was noted that deuterated nitrobenzene, $C_6D_5NO_2$, is nitrated at the same rate as ordinary nitrobenzene (in H_2SO_4—HNO_3 mixtures),[21(a)] showing that replacement of a C—H bond with a C—D bond in nitrobenzene does not affect the activation energy for attack by NO_2^+. Moreover, returning to nitrations in organic solvents, we find that substitution of deuterium or tritium for "light" hydrogen in benzene, toluene, or naphthalene does not retard the nitrations of these compounds; this observation is of little value, however, for here the formation of NO_2^+, rather than its attack on the aromatic, is known to be rate determining. In these cases hydrogen-isotope effects (or their absence) are best demonstrated by "competi-

[20] Since addition of water obviously tends to reverse the formation of the nitronium ion, it may be asked why water is so much less effective than nitrate ion in retarding the nitration. This question is perhaps best answered by considering the algebraic form of the rate law (see Ex. 2a).

[21] (a) Gold and Hawes, *J. Chem. Soc.*, **1951**, 2102. (b) Bonner, *et al., ibid.*, **1953**, 2605; Lauer and Noland, *J. Am. Chem. Soc.*, **75**, 3689 (1953). (c) Melander, *Arkiv Kemi*, **2**, 213 (1950).

tion" experiments in which a C—H and a C—D (or C—T) bond in equivalent positions are allowed to compete for NO_2^+ as it is generated. For example, when benzene that has been "labeled" at just one position with tritium (C_6H_5T) is mononitrated, just one sixth of the tritium atoms are removed. Similarly, when toluene labeled in an *ortho* position with tritium (XII) is nitrated, just half of the

ortho-hydrogens in the resulting o-nitrotoluene are labeled.[21(c)] These experiments, together with similar ones involving deuterium-substituted aromatics,[21(b)] show that a C—T bond (or a C—D bond) is just as likely to be broken during nitration as is a C—H bond in an equivalent position, telling us that, as with nitrobenzene, substitution of heavy for light hydrogen at a given position does not affect the activation energy for substitution by NO_2^+ at that position. But we have emphasized that the stretching of a C—T bond or a C—D bond is significantly more difficult than the stretching of an equivalent (but necessarily "looser") C—H bond. We may therefore infer that the activation process in the attack of NO_2^+ at a C—H bond involves very little, if any, stretching of that bond, and that the C—NO₂ bond is, as we suspected, very nearly formed before the C—H bond begins to break. Nitration by NO_2^+ thus proceeds through a

cationic species, $\left[Ar \begin{smallmatrix} \nearrow NO_2 \\ \searrow H \end{smallmatrix} \right]^+$, and if we assume that the H⁺ ion cannot depart

on its own but must be pulled off by some basic species in solution, we must admit that this cation exists in solution long enough to allow approach and attack of the base—that is, that it is an intermediate, rather than an activated complex. The following sequence then summarizes our present picture of the usual mechanism for aromatic nitration:[22]

$$HNO_3 \underset{H^+}{\rightleftharpoons} H_2NO_3^+ \underset{-H_2O}{\rightleftharpoons} NO_2^+ \xrightarrow{ArH} \left[Ar \begin{array}{c} NO_2 \\ \diagup \\ \diagdown \\ H \end{array} \right]^+ \xrightarrow[\text{fast}]{B:} ArNO_2 + BH^+$$

Nitrous Acid and Its Derivatives in Nitration

Aromatic nitrations are, as we have seen, generally retarded by addition of nitrate. We should therefore expect that any substance which rapidly forms nitrate when added to a nitrating mixture will likewise lower nitration rates. Nitrous acid, is, for example, known to be almost completely ionized in concentrated HNO_3, not as an acid, but rather as a base.[23]

$$O{=}N{-}OH + HNO_3 \rightleftharpoons [O{\equiv}N]^+ + H_2O + NO_3^-$$

A similar equilibrium exists in solutions of nitric acid in organic solvents, but the degree of ionization is slight (most of the nitrous acid having been converted either to N_2O_4 or NO_2, neither of which is of direct concern here). At any rate, we need not be surprised that nitrations, both in pure nitric acid and in organic solvents, are generally decelerated by addition of nitrous acid (or nitrites), this action being similar to that which would result from the addition of almost any base. The inhibition of nitration is particularly marked at high concentrations of nitrous acid, for here a second pair of equilibria assumes some importance.

$$2HNO_2 \rightleftharpoons N_2O_3 + H_2O \rightleftharpoons NO^+ + NO_2^- + H_2O$$

Now the nitrite ion, like the nitrate ion, can reverse the formation of $H_2NO_3^+$, a necessary intermediate in the formation of NO_2^+.

$$H_2NO_3^+ + NO_2^- \rightleftharpoons HNO_2 + HNO_3 \rightleftharpoons N_2O_4 + H_2O$$

HNO$_3$ to NO_2^+ is incomplete, being less than 1 percent in 85 percent H_2SO_4. There is still some question, however, as to why nitration rates decrease in very concentrated solutions of sulfuric acid. With such substrates as nitrobenzene, anthraquinone, and benzoic acid, this decrease may be attributed, at least partly, to the conversion of the substrates to their respective conjugate acids, which would be expected to undergo attack less readily than the substrates themselves (see Gillespie, *J. Chem. Soc.*, **1950**, 2542). Moreover, in going from 90 percent to 100 percent H_2SO_4, we are increasing the polarity of the medium, and by the arguments on page 184, we would expect a decrease in rate for those nitrations in which the rate-determining step is the attack of the positive NO_2^+ on an uncharged molecule of substrate. An earlier suggestion (see, for example, Bennett, *et al.*, *J. Chem. Soc.*, **1947**, 474) that the decrease in nitration rates is due to a lowering in very concentrated sulfuric acid of (HSO_4^-), which is necessary for removal of a proton from the reaction site, is no longer tenable since the absence of a hydrogen-isotope effect in nitration shows that proton removal is not a significant part of the activation process.

[23] Goulden and Millen, *J. Chem. Soc.*, **1950**, 2620.

Moreover, since the nitrite ion is a stronger base than the nitrate ion, it is more efficient in lowering the concentration of $H_2NO_3^+$, and is thus a more efficient nitration inhibitor than is nitrate. Kinetic studies of nitration in the presence of both large and small quantities of tripositive nitrogen have been carried out, and the data are in reasonably good accord with the two modes of inhibition described above[24] (Ex. 3).

Having considered the anticatalytic effect of nitrous acid on a number of nitrations, the reader may be disturbed to learn (if he is not already aware) that nitrous acid actually *accelerates* the nitration of such very active aromatic compounds as mesitylene, phenol, anisole, and aromatic amines. Such substrates are known to undergo *nitrosation* by nitrous acid, and the resulting nitroso compounds are, in turn, known to be very rapidly oxidized by nitric acid to the corresponding nitro compounds.[25]

$$\text{ArH} \xrightarrow[-\text{H}_2\text{O}]{\text{HNO}_2} \text{Ar}-\text{N}=\text{O} \xrightarrow[\text{fast}]{\text{HNO}_3} \text{ArNO}_2 + \text{HNO}_2$$

The kinetics of the nitrations of p-chloroanisole, p-nitrophenol, and mesitylene in solutions containing both nitrous and nitric acids point clearly to this additional mode of nitration—that is, nitration through prior nitrosation.[26] The rate laws consist of two terms, the first corresponding to the "ordinary" zero-order nitration by NO_2^+ (which, as we have seen, is inhibited by HNO_2), the second term being first order each in substrate and added HNO_2.[27] In concentrated nitric acid, and, more particularly, when pains are taken to eliminate nitrous acid and the oxides of nitrogen from the reaction mixture, nitration through nitrosation assumes little or no importance. In more dilute nitric acid (the nitration medium often used for very active compounds), in the presence of significant quantities of nitrous acid, this mode of nitration can be made to predominate, although nitration by the nitronium ion cannot be eliminated entirely. Insofar as the "nitrosation-oxidation" sequence can be distinguished kinetically from the nitration by NO_2^+, the former appears to follow the rate law (in acetic acid),

---

[24] Hughes, Ingold, and Reed, *J. Chem. Soc.*, **1950**, 2400.

[25] See, for example, Westheimer and Schramm, *J. Am. Chem. Soc.*, **70**, 1782 (1948) and Viebel, *Ber.*, **63**, 1577 (1930).

[26] Bunton, *et al.*, *J. Chem. Soc.*, **1950**, 2628.

[27] The kinetic study of the nitrations of phenol itself, the cresols, and anisole itself presents some difficulty. Independent of their nitration, these compounds are oxidized by nitric acid with the formation of nitrous acid. Since the latter acts as a catalyst in the nitration, the reaction appears to be autocatalytic. During a given "run," the concentrations of two of the reagents (HNO_3 and the substrate) decrease as a result of three independent reactions (oxidation, nitration, and oxidation of the nitroso compound), whereas the concentration of the catalyst increases. Complications due to the oxidation reaction can be avoided, preserving at the same time the HNO_2-catalyzed nitration reaction, by the use of somewhat less active aromatics such as the haloanisoles or the nitrophenols.

$$\text{rate (of nitrosation)} = \left[k + \frac{k'}{(\text{NO}_3^-)} \right] (\text{ArH})(\text{"HNO}_2\text{"}) \tag{2}$$

where ("HNO$_2$") represents the total concentration of species that can be titrated as tripositive nitrogen (present here very largely as N$_2$O$_4$). The form of this expression indicates that there are *two* attacking species in the nitrosation, each having a concentration proportional to that of N$_2$O$_4$.[28] It therefore seems likely that these two attacking species are N$_2$O$_4$ itself (corresponding to k) and the nitrosonium ion, NO$^+$ (corresponding to k'). The latter is generated from N$_2$O$_4$ in the following equilibrium:

$$\text{N}_2\text{O}_4 \rightleftharpoons \text{NO}^+ + \text{NO}_3^-$$

and its concentration should therefore be inversely proportional to (NO$_3^-$). The nitrosation rate is apparently independent of the activity of water in solution, indicating that attack of substrate either by HNO$_2$ or H$_2$NO$_2^+$ is not of importance (Ex. 3). The oxide N$_2$O$_3$ is likewise excluded (in this case) as the nitrosating agent, for its action would give rise to a term second order in ("HNO$_2$").

It may be asked why the phenomenon of nitration through nitrosation has been observed almost exclusively with the more reactive aromatic compounds and not with, say, nitrobenzene or the halobenzenes. To answer this, we should remember: (a) that the NO$^+$ ion is a much weaker acid and therefore a much less powerful reagent in electrophilic substitution reactions than is the NO$_2^+$ ion; and (b) that substantial quantities of NO$^+$ may exist in solutions in which all but tiny amounts of NO$_2^+$ are destroyed (for example, nitrous acid in moderately concentrated nitric acid). Now the nitrations of very reactive aromatics are generally carried out in solutions in which (NO$_2^+$) is very small since otherwise polynitration will become troublesome; however, if nitrous acid is present in such solutions, much may be converted to NO$^+$ and N$_2$O$_4$, and nitrosation assumes importance, not because these are efficient reagents but because they are available. If a less reactive aromatic is treated with the same nitration mixture, neither nitration nor nitrosation may occur at an appreciable rate. But by raising the acidity of the mixture and decreasing its water content, it is possible to boost (NO$_2^+$) greatly, while at the same time (NO$^+$) and (N$_2$O$_4$) are increased only slightly (since tripositive nitrogen exists largely in these forms already in less acidic mixtures). Thus, under conditions where attack by NO$_2^+$ of a relatively unreactive aromatic compound proceeds at a significant rate, attack by NO$^+$ may still be very slow, and attack by N$_2$O$_4$ (which is even less electrophilic than NO$^+$) will be slower still. When this is the case, nitronium attack becomes the only important path for nitration.

In addition to the two types of mechanism that we have considered, aromatic nitration may proceed in less usual ways. Nitrations with nitrogen

[28] Blackall, Hughes, and Ingold, *J. Chem. Soc.*, **1952**, 28.

pentoxide, acetyl nitrate (NO_2OAc), and benzoyl nitrate (NO_2OCOPh) in non-polar solvents have been described,[29(a)] and there is some evidence which indicates (although it does not prove) that the $H_2NO_3^+$ cation is a nitrating agent in HNO_3—$HClO_4$—H_2O mixtures.[29(b)]

Reactivity and Orientation in Electrophilic Substitution

During our discussion of nitration, we have described some aromatics as being "reactive" and others as "less reactive," referring simply to the rates at which they are attacked by a given electrophilic species (in this case NO_2^+ or NO^+). It might seem that we could arrange a group of aromatic compounds in the order of their reactivities merely by measuring their nitration rates under similar conditions, but this will not work for compounds undergoing pseudo-zero-order nitrations; for here the observed rate of nitration is the rate of formation of the nitronium ion. For these, competition experiments (p. 172) prove useful. Two (or more) substrates in a single solution compete for the NO_2^+ ion as it is formed, and from the ratio of the various nitration products, the relative (but not the absolute) specific rates of attack by the nitronium ion may be calculated.[30] The results of a few of such comparisons are listed.[31(a)]

	PhNO$_2$	PhCOOEt	PhBr	PhCl	PhF	PhCH$_2$Cl	PhH	PhCH$_3$	PhOH
$\dfrac{k}{k_{C_6H_6}}$	$<10^{-4}$	0.0037	0.03	0.03	0.15	0.30	1.0	25	1000

These values need not be considered at length here, for, qualitatively speaking, they reflect combinations of the inductive and resonance effects of substituents as discussed in Chapter 7. The activation process involves the attachment of the positive NO_2^+ ion to an "electron-rich" site in the ring. Therefore, nitration is facilitated by electron-releasing substituents such as alkyl groups but retarded by electron-attracting substituents (for example, —NO$_2$ and —COOEt). Similar statements may be made for other types of electrophilic-substitution reactions. When the I and R effects of a substituent are in *opposite* directions (as in the case with the halogens and the —OH,—NR$_2$, and

---

[29] (a) Gold, et al., J. Chem. Soc., 1950, 2452. (b) Halberstadt, Hughes, and Ingold, ibid., 1950, 2441.

[30] The applicability of this method requires only that the individual steps in which the competing substrates are attacked be of the same order (in this case unity) with respect to substrate. It does not require that the apparent rate laws for the overall reactions be the same. However, straightforward interpretation of the results is possible only if there is a single mechanism of attack for each of the substrates.

[31] (a) Taken largely from experiments by Ingold, et al., J. Chem. Soc., 1931, 1959; 1938, 905, 918; 1948, 575. No more than two significant figures are listed here since the reaction conditions were not the same in all competition experiments. (b) For a treatment (both theoretical and empirical) of relative reactivities of polycyclic aromatic hydrocarbons in nitration, see Dewar, Mole, and Warford, J. Chem. Soc., 1956, 3581. A useful (but rough) rule of thumb is that the reactivity of fused-ring hydrocarbons increases as the number of rings increases.

—SR groups) we cannot predict, in the absence of further information, whether that substituent will activate or deactivate the ring, but Hammett's σ value for the substituent will generally tell the tale. Thus the halogen atoms, which have positive σ values, are deactivating, whereas the —OH and —NR$_2$ substituents, which have negative σ values, are activating.

An important and related question is that of *orientation* in aromatic substitution, for an aromatic ring may generally be attacked in two or more different and nonequivalent positions. As with reactivity, we shall base our discussion of orientation on nitration reactions, bearing in mind that the arguments we use may be applied equally well to other types of electrophilic substitutions. Primarily, we are interested in explaining why some substituents (among them the —OH, —OR, and —NR$_2$ groups, and the alkyl and halo substituents) will direct incoming electrophiles predominantly to the *ortho* and *para* positions, whereas other substituents (among them the —NO$_2$, —CN, and —COOEt groups) direct such electrophiles to the *meta* position. This is a problem involving relative rates, for, in actuality, a given electrophile will attack *all* available positions of an aromatic ring, but reactions at the "favored" sites are more rapid than those at the less active positions. Of the activated complexes resulting from attack at each of the available positions, *the complex having the lowest energy is that associated with the "favored" position for attack.* As we have seen, the activated complex in aromatic nitration is intermediate in character between the substrate and the intermediate cation XIV; we may then represent this complex as XIII. However, to avoid the inconvenience of working with structures having

XIII

XIV

partial bonds, we shall discuss the orientation problem in terms of the energies of the various possible cation intermediates. This procedure is not entirely free from objection,[31(b)] but the conclusions reached will not be significantly different from those that would be based upon consideration of the activated complexes themselves.

Our first example is anisole. Representative structures for each of the possible cation intermediates are shown as follows:

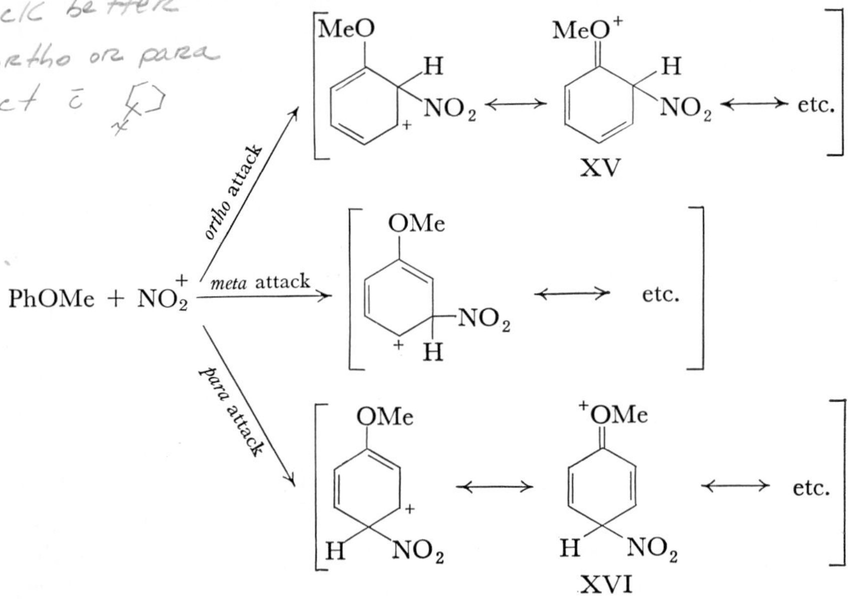

attack better in ortho or para attack ē (handwritten margin note)

PhOMe + NO₂⁺

ortho attack → XV

meta attack → etc.

para attack → XVI

Two additional structures, of importance comparable to those shown, may be drawn for each intermediate, but these do not affect the argument. Of the structures above, **XV** (for *ortho* attack) and **XVI** (for *para* attack) are of greatest interest in the present discussion. Try as we may, we cannot draw a structure analogous to either of these two for *meta* attack, this difficulty being a consequence of the "alternating character" of the atoms comprising a conjugated system. (As we have previously noted, this "alternating character" is readily described, although not in any sense "explained," using the language of resonance.) In the intermediate for *meta* attack, therefore, the positive charge carried in by the NO_2^+ ion must remain on the benzene ring until the proton departs, completing the substitution reaction. On the other hand, with *ortho* or *para* attack, π-electron density drifts from the electron-rich oxygen atom into the ring, dispersing the positive charge, and lowering the energy both of the intermediate and the transition state leading to it. We may thus conclude that in the nitration of anisole, attack should take place more readily at the *ortho* and *para* positions than at the *meta* position, although we cannot say, on the basis of this simplified picture, whether it is the *ortho* or the *para* position that is the more reactive. Analogous arguments may be used to account for *ortho-para* direction by halogen atoms and by the —OH, —OCR, and —NHCR groups. In each

$$\overset{\|}{O} \qquad \overset{\|}{O}$$

of these substituents, the atom bound to the ring has at least *one unshared and available pair of electrons*, and in each case electron density from this pair drifts into the ring to help disperse the positive charge carried in by the electrophile attacking either at the *ortho* or *para* position. *Ortho-para* direction by alkyl substituents may be explained in a similar way. Here, it may be argued, the intermediate cation (and the activated complex leading to it) may be stabilized by such hyperconjugated structures as XVII′ and XVIII′, which, again, are not possible for intermediates in *meta* attack.[32]

$$XVII \longrightarrow XVII'$$

$$XVIII \longrightarrow XVIII' \qquad XIX$$

There are a few, less usual, oxygenated substituents, among them the

$$-\overset{O}{\underset{..}{\overset{|}{I}}}-O \quad \text{and} \quad -\overset{\overset{O}{\|}}{\underset{\underset{O}{|}}{\overset{..}{S}}}-OH$$

groups, which constitute special cases. Although the atoms by which these groups are attached to the ring have unshared electron pairs, they also bear positive formal charges and tend therefore to withdraw electron density from, rather than supply it to, the benzene ring. In this respect,

[32] The *t*-butyl group is also *ortho-para* directing in nitration, suggesting again that hyperconjugated structures such as XIX (having C—C rather than C—H hyperconjugation) may contribute to the cationic intermediate. However, the ratio of *ortho* + *para* attack to *meta* attack in the nitration of *t*-butyl benzene is about 10 (Cohn, *et al.*, *Nature*, **169**, 291 (1952)), whereas in the nitrations of ethylbenzene and isopropylbenzene, the corresponding ratio is far greater (although the difficulty in analyzing for minute quantities of the *meta* isomers in the presence of large quantities of the *ortho* and *para* isomers prevents precise evaluation of the ratios in these cases). It appears then that, in comparable cases, C—C hyperconjugation, although not negligible, is significantly less important than C—H hyperconjugation.

The question of hyperconjugation has been complicated by a finding by Swain and co-workers (*J. Am. Chem. Soc.*, **79**, 505 (1957)), that $C_6H_5CD_3$ is nitrated at almost exactly the same specific rate as "ordinary" toluene. If we are correct in our original assumption (p. 285) that the importance of C—H hyperconjugation may be decreased by substitution of deuterium for hydrogen, we would have to conclude that hyperconjugation is a negligible factor in stabilizing the transition state in the *ortho* or *para* nitration of toluene. It is possible, however, that this assumption was too broad and that the effect of isotopic substitution on hyperconjugation is more subtle than we at present suppose.

they resemble the nitro group, and like the latter, they direct incoming electrophiles predominantly to the *meta* position.

The —NH$_2$ and —NR$_2$ groups are special cases of a different sort. Although they themselves are strongly *ortho-para* directing, they are converted, in the acidic media necessary for nitrations, to the —NH$_3^+$ and —NR$_2$H$^+$ groups, which are just as strongly *meta* directing. We may account for the *meta*-directing character of these positively charged substituents (and of such substituents as —SR$_2^+$, —PR$_3^+$, and —SeR$_2^+$ as well) by considering, as we did for the nitration of anisole, representative structures for the possible nitration intermediates, which, for this group of compounds, must be doubly charged.

Two additional structures, comparable in importance to that shown, may be drawn for the intermediate in *meta* attack, and one additional structure may be drawn for the intermediates in both *ortho* and *para* attack, but none of these affects the argument. Directing our attention to structures XX and XXI, we see that in both of these, the *positive charges are situated on adjacent atoms*. This feature lowers the stabilities of these structures; for, electrostatically speaking, a polyatomic dipositive ion is most stable when the positively charged atoms are as far removed from each other as possible. In the language of resonance, the contributions of structures XX and XXI to their respective intermediates must be small; this is equivalent to saying that in *ortho* and *para* attack, the positive charge carried in by the NO$_2^+$ group is not distributed over the benzene ring but tends to be concentrated over a small area opposite the —NH$_3^+$ substituent. In contrast, however, none of the three structures contributing to the intermediate for *meta* attack is analogous to **XX** or **XXI**; none has positive charges located on adjacent atoms. In this intermediate, therefore, the incoming positive charge may spread itself far more evenly about the ring than is possible for *ortho* or *para* attack and, as a consequence, this intermediate (and the activated complex leading to it) is the most stable of the three.[33]

By a similar argument, any substituent attached to the benzene ring by an atom bearing a positive charge should likewise be *meta* directing. Even if the positively charged atom is one position removed from the benzene ring, the effect of the pole may be transmitted inductively to the junction between ring and side chain, causing *meta* orientation. Thus, the —CH$_2$NMe$_3^+$ and the —CH$_2$SMe$_2^+$ substituents are *meta* directing (although —CH$_2$—CH$_2$—NMe$_3^+$ and —CH$_2$—PMe$_3^+$ are not[34]). We may use very similar reasoning to account for the *meta*-directing action of the nitro group, for the nitrogen atom in this

group bears a positive formal charge $\left(\text{that is, } -\overset{+}{\text{N}} \underset{\text{O}_-}{\overset{\text{O}}{\diagdown}} \right)$, and therefore

structures **XXII** and **XXIII**, for the intermediates in *ortho* and *para* nitration of nitrobenzene, are open to the same objection as structures **XX** and **XXI**. This question may be viewed in a somewhat different light, this time considering

XXII   XXIII   XXIV   XXIV'   XXIV''

the electron distribution in the substrate itself. We have noted on a number of occasions that the nitro group withdraws electrons from the benzene ring, and

[33] An alternative explanation for the *meta*-directing character of the —NH$_3^+$ group and similar positively charged substituents is that such groups withdraw electron density inductively from the ring carbon to which they are attached, creating a partial positive charge at that site. This charge is then relayed to the *ortho* and *para* positions, deactivating them preferentially; that is,

(See, for example, Ingold, Ref. 1(b), p. 248). Such an explanation requires that an electron deficiency due purely to the inductive effect be distributed over the ring to alternate carbons in much the same way as electron deficiencies due to resonance effects.

[34] Baker and Moffitt, *J. Chem. Soc.*, **1930**, 1722; Ingold, Shaw, and Wilson, *ibid.*, **1928**, 1280.

as is shown by structures XXIV′ and XXIV″, this electron withdrawal is most marked at the *ortho* and *para* positions. Since an electrophile tends to seek out the site of highest electron density, it will tend to attack preferentially at the *meta* position, where electron density has been depleted least, rather than at the *ortho* or *para* positions. Completely analogous considerations apply to the —COOH, —COOEt, —CHO, $-\overset{|}{\underset{R}{C}}$=O, and —C≡N groups, all of which

are *meta* directing in electrophilic substitutions.[35]

We have chosen to discuss orientation in aromatic substitution in terms of the manner in which substituents affect, either by induction or resonance, the distribution of electron density in the substrate and in the activated complex. We have ignored kinetic-energy effects, implying either that they are negligible or that they parallel the electronic (potential-energy) effects described. These are the same conditions that we proposed earlier in justifying the success of the Hammett equation (p. 220), which stipulates that the comparative ability of a given substituent to attract electrons from, or supply them to, a reaction site on a side chain may be expressed by a single parameter, independent of the nature of the reaction occurring at the side chain. It now may be asked whether a similar statement holds true if the reaction occurs, not on the side chain, but rather on the ring itself. If the answer is "yes," and if, as we have implied, kinetic-energy effects quantitatively parallel potential energy effects (or are negligible in comparison to them), a Hammett-like equation should apply to aromatic substitution reactions also. A recent compilation by Brown and co-workers[36] indicates that the Hammett treatment, with but slight modi-

---

[35] The predominant position of substitution in a number of aromatic molecules (both benzenoid and nonbenzenoid) may be predicted by the following rule: Of the various intermediates resulting from attack at each of the possible sites, the intermediate corresponding to the favored site of attack will be that having the *largest number of acceptable canonical forms*. Although this rule is based on oversimplified reasoning, and although the inclusion of the word "acceptable" introduces a certain element of arbitrariness, the rule is surprisingly useful. We have, for example, listed three contributing structures for the cationic intermediate in the *meta* nitration of anisole, but four structures each for the intermediate in *ortho* and *para* nitration. Ignoring structures of higher energy, such as XXV, the rule, as stated, predicts *ortho* and

XXV

para nitration. In the nitration of nitrobenzene, however, the intermediate for *meta* nitration has three contributing forms, but those for *ortho* and *para* nitration have but two (if we consider structures XX and XXI "unacceptable"). This rule also correctly predicts the predominant positions of nitration in naphthalene and thiophene (Ex. 1).

[36] Brown and Okamoto, *J. Am. Chem. Soc.*, **79**, 1913 (1957); McGary, Okamoto, and

fication, may indeed be used to correlate the rates of electrophilic substitution on the benzene ring. The Hammett-Brown equation,

$$\log\left(\frac{k}{k_0}\right) = \rho\sigma^+ \qquad (3)$$

is very nearly the same as the Hammett equation itself, and the symbols have similar significance. The k values, however, refer to the specific rate of substitution at a *single site;* thus for use in this equation, the observed specific rate for a reaction of benzene must be divided by 6 (since there are 6 equivalent positions in benzene) and, for the same reason, the rate constant for *meta* attack on a mono-substituted benzene derivative must be divided by 2. The notation σ^+ indicates that the attacking reagent is cationic. Equation (3) is applicable to *meta* and *para* substitution, but not generally to *ortho* substitution, suggesting that in ring substitution, as in side-chain reactions, *ortho* substituents often introduce steric effects which are unrelated to their polar character. The σ^+ values chosen by Brown for *meta* substituents are virtually the same as Hammett's σ constants, but this is not true for *para* substituents. Below are compared the σ^+ and σ constants of some typical substituents (for the *para* position):

	—OCH$_3$	—CH$_3$	—C(CH$_3$)$_3$	—F	—Cl	—Br	—I	—NO$_2$
σ_p^+	−0.76	−0.31	−0.25	−0.07	+0.11	0.15	0.13	0.78
σ_p	−0.27	−0.17	−0.20	+0.06	0.23	0.23	0.28	0.78

Aside from the nitro group (the only "$-R$" substituent for which a reliable value of σ_p^+ is at present available), all σ_p^+ constants appear to be significantly *more negative* than the respective σ_p constants. Since a highly negative value of σ is, by the Hammett convention, associated with effective donation of electron density *from* the substituent, we may infer that, compared to *meta* substituents, "$+R$" *para* substituents are more powerful electron donors during substitution on the benzene ring than during reactions on side chains. This is obviously because a substituent is in *direct conjugation* with a ring carbon in the *para* position (XXVI) but not, except under special circumstances (p. 225), with a side chain attached to this carbon (XXVII):

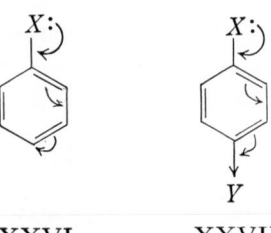

XXVI   XXVII

Brown, *ibid.*, **77**, 3043 (1955). At present, much less data (less than 50 rate constants) support the Hammett-Brown treatment of aromatic substitution that support the applicability of the original Hammett equation to side-chain reactions (over 3000 rate and equilibrium constants).

For aromatic substitutions to which the Hammett-Brown treatment applies, ρ values (which measure the sensitivity of the various reaction series to changes in the polarity of the substituent) lie between -4 and -10. These are much greater than the ρ values for the vast majority of side-chain reactions, in which one or more atoms may "shield" the reaction site from electrical disturbances in the ring. Typically, the replacement of a $-NO_2$ group by a $-OCH_3$ group boosts the rate of ring bromination by a factor of about 10^{15}, whereas a similar replacement in p-substituted ethyl benzoates lowers the rate of saponification by a factor of only 100.

There is no evident reason why this treatment should be confined in its use to substitution reactions in which the departing group is H^+. Indeed, the rate constants for the acid cleavage of substituted phenyltrimethylsilanes (equation 4)[37] and those for the brominolysis of substituted benzeneboronic acids (equation 5)[38] may be correlated satisfactorily by the Hammett-Brown equation.

$$ArSiMe_3 + H^+ \xrightarrow[\text{MeOH} + H_2O]{\text{HClO}_4} ArH + SiMe_3^+[\xrightarrow{H_2O} (Me_3Si)_2O] \qquad (4)$$
$$\rho_{50°} = -4.59$$

$$ArB(OH)_2 + Br^+ \xrightarrow[\text{H}_2O]{\text{HOAc}} ArBr + B(OH)_2^+[\xrightarrow{H_2O} B(OH)_3] \qquad (5)$$
$$\rho_{25°} = -4.30$$

and it is likely that this correlation will be found to extend to additional reaction series.

The *ortho* to *para* Ratio

Much of our discussion up until now suggests that the availability of electron density is the same at the position *para* to a given substituent as at the positions *ortho* to this substituent. If this were so, and if other effects were absent, we should expect the ratio of *ortho* to *para* isomers resulting from all electrophilic aromatic substitutions on mono-substituted benzenes to be 2.00 since there are two positions *ortho*, but only one *para*, to any single substituent. In actuality, this ratio is practically never observed, for there are good reasons why it should not be. First and most obvious, the *para* carbon is in a more favorable position for attack than is the carbon *ortho* to the substituent, for the substituent acts as a shield which blocks a portion of the volume through which the attacking group might otherwise pass. This steric effect, which should lower the *ortho* to *para* ratio, is detectable for small substituents and becomes quite important in the event the substituent is bulky. The activated complex for the *ortho* nitration of ethyl-

[37] Eaborn, *J. Chem. Soc.*, **1956**, 4858.
[38] Kuivila, *et al.*, *J. Am. Chem. Soc.*, **74**, 5068 (1952); **77**, 4838 (1955).

benzene is sketched in Figure 11-3 (the departing hydrogen is partially hidden

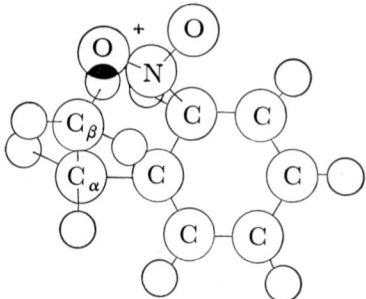

Fig. 11-3. Steric Hindrance in *ortho* Nitration of Ethylbenzene

by the attacking nitrogen atom). In the conformation shown, there is interference between one of the hydrogens on the β-carbon and the attacking NO_2^+ ion. This interference may be eliminated by rotation of the ethyl group about the bond that links the α-carbon to the ring, but when we limit the number of possible conformations in which the substrate may react, we lower the probability of reaction. As expected, *ortho* substitution becomes still more difficult with further branching at C_α. The following ratios then speak for themselves:[39]

	PhCH$_3$	PhCH$_2$CH$_3$	PhCH(CH$_3$)$_2$	PhC(CH$_3$)$_3$
o:*p* ratio in nitration	1.57	0.93	0.48	0.22

Similarly, we should expect the *ortho* to *para* ratio to be less if the attacking group is bulky than if it is small. Typically, the chlorination of chlorobenzene (in which the attacking reagent is probably Cl^+) yields a mixture of dichlorobenzenes in which the *ortho* to *para* ratio is about 0.7. Its nitration (in which the attacking reagent is the more bulky NO_2^+ ion) yields an *ortho* to *para* ratio of about 0.4. Finally, the *ortho* to *para* ratio resulting from the sulfonation of the same substrate (here the attacking reagent is probably the still more bulky SO_3 molecule) is less than 0.01. Similar trends have been observed in the substitution reactions of such aromatics as toluene, bromobenzene, and phenol.[40]

Sometimes we must reckon with the inductive effect. It has been emphasized that the intensity of this effect decreases sharply with distance from the "primary pole" (in contrast to resonance effects, which are transmitted mainly to alternate atoms in a conjugated system with no significant decrease in intensity with distance). Thus, irrespective of resonance effects, the electron density at the positions *ortho* to an electron-attracting group must be less than that *para* to this group. The difference, which depends upon the magnitude of the inductive effect of the group, should be reflected in a preference by the

[39] Brown and Bonner, *J. Am. Chem. Soc.*, **76**, 605 (1954).

[40] For a compilation of data relating to this question, see Holleman, *Chem. Revs.*, **1**, 218 (1925).

attacking electrophile for the *para* position. Thus, the *ortho* to *para* ratio resulting from the nitration of fluorobenzene is 0.14; that resulting from the nitration of chlorobenzene (in which the directing group is less electronegative) is 0.43. For nitrations of bromo- and iodobenzene, the ratios are 0.61 and 0.70, respectively.[40,41] This trend is clearly in line with the inductive effects of the respective halo substituents and would probably be even more pronounced if steric effects did not operate in the opposite direction. A similar trend appears in the series below,[39,42] in which the steric and inductive effects presumably reinforce each other:

	PhCH$_3$	PhCH$_2$Cl	PhCHCl$_2$	PhCCl$_3$
o:p ratio in nitration	1.57	0.75	0.53	0.23

By an extension of this reasoning, we would expect the *ortho* to *para* ratio in the nitration of such compounds as benzaldehyde, benzoyl chloride, and nitrobenzene to be very low; for, aside from their resonance effects, the —CHO, —COCl, and —NO$_2$ substituents have strongly negative inductive effects, and the steric requirements of each of these groups are by no means negligible. But this is not the case at all, for the *ortho* to *para* ratios from these compounds are found to be large—about 2 for the nitration of benzaldehyde, about 10 for ethyl benzoate and benzonitrile, and about 20 for nitrobenzene and benzoic acid.[40,43] Quite obviously, one or more additional effects which we have hitherto overlooked are activating the *ortho* position or deactivating the *para* position (or both). It has been suggested that such groups as —CHO, —COOH, and —NO$_2$ facilitate nitration at the *ortho* position (in comparison to that at the *para* position) by dipole-dipole interaction with the incoming nitronium ion (for example, XXVIII and XXIX).[44] However, this effect cannot be solely

| XXVIII | XXIX | XXX |

responsible for the high *ortho* to *para* ratios in these nitrations, for a similarly high ratio is obtained from the nitration of benzonitrile. Here because of the

[41] Sandin and Williams, *J. Am. Chem. Soc.*, **69**, 2747 (1947). It is possible, by carrying out the nitration in concentrated HNO$_3$ at 0°, to decrease the *ortho* to *para* ratio resulting from the nitration of iodobenzene to 0.52, a value less than that for the nitration of bromobenzene (0.59) under the same conditions. The reason for this reversal of order is not clear.

[42] Holleman, *et al.*, *Rec. trav. chim.*, **33**, 1 (1914); Ingold, *et al.*, *J. Chem. Soc.*, **1931**, 1959; **1949**, 575.

[43] Baker, *et al.*, *J. Chem. Soc.*, **1927**, 836; **1928**, 436; **1931**, 314. The figures quoted are approximate, for the *o:p* ratios in these cases are rather sensitive to reaction conditions.

[44] Hammond, Modic, and Hedges, *J. Am. Chem. Soc.*, **75**, 1388 (1953).

linearity of the —C≡N group, the positive end of the NO$_2$ dipole is far removed from the negative end of the C≡N dipole, and dipole-dipole interaction analogous to the type indicated in XXVIII and XXIX would be negligible. Indeed, the lack of *independent* evidence that such interaction exists, even in "favorable cases" suggests that the high $o:p$ ratios in the nitrations which we are considering are best explained in a different manner.[45]

Let us compare, for example, the canonical forms of nitrobenzene, XXIV′ and XXIV″, which depict, in the language of resonance, the depletion of electron density at the *ortho* and *para* positions. The question as to which of these

XXIV′   XXIV″

forms is the more important is a quantum-mechanical one and cannot be answered reliably by inspection. It appears, however, that XXIV″ (the so-called "*para*-quinoid" structure) has a significantly lower energy than XXIV′ (the so-called "*ortho*-quinoid" structure), although this difference seems never to have been explained satisfactorily in nonmathematical language.[46] On this basis, electron density is more effectively depleted at the *para* position than at the *ortho*, and *ortho* substitution should predominate over *para* (with *meta* substitution predominating over both *ortho* and *para*). Similar reasoning may be applied to the nitrations of benzoic acid, acetophenone, and benzonitrile.

Extending the argument to such *activated* aromatics as anisole, we may reconsider structures XV and XVI. Both depict the stabilization of the cationic

XV   XVI

[45] For a different type of argument that these high *ortho* to *para* ratios are the result of *para* deactivation, rather than *ortho* activation, see Ingold, *Ref*. 1(b), pp. 261–264.

[46] For a theoretical treatment of this question, see Dewar, *J. Chem. Soc.*, **1949**, 643. A number of workers have compared structures XXIV′ and XXIV″ to *o*-quinone and *p*-quinone, respectively, noting that of the latter pair of compounds the *para* structure is, again, the more stable (toward reduction), and implying that the greater stabilities of the *para* structures in both cases are somehow fundamentally related. It should be noted, however, that the reduction potential of a quinone in solution depends upon a number of factors other than the electron structure of the quinone itself, and the similarity between the two effects may be merely fortuitous.

intermediate in nitration by the drift of negative charge from the methoxide oxygen to the ring. Here, the intermediate for *ortho* nitration (XV) is of the *ortho*-quinoid type, whereas that for *para* nitration (XVI) is of the *para*-quinoid type. If the *para*-quinoid structure is again considered the more stable, we may infer that just as "−R" groups *deactivate* the *para* position more than the ortho, "+R" groups *activate* the *para* position more than the *ortho*. But the direction of this effect is the same as that of the steric effect, and often the same as that of the inductive effect, the three effects are difficult to separate. In a typically perplexing case, the *ortho* to *para* ratio resulting from the nitration of phenol is close to $\frac{2}{3}$.[40] The difference between this value and the "statistical value" of 2.0 almost certainly cannot be attributed solely to the steric effect, for the steric requirements of the —OH group are very modest. However, we cannot say at present just how much the *ortho* to *para* ratio is lowered by the inductive effect of the —OH group, and how much it is lowered by the tendency of the activated complex to approximate a *para*-quinoid (rather than an *ortho*-quinoid) structure.

Halogenations

In analogy with the picture of aromatic nitration which has been presented, we would expect the most effective species in aromatic halogenations to be the electron-deficient *halogenonium* ions, $:Cl:^+$, $:Br:^+$, and $:I:^+$. However, unlike the nitronium ion, these ions have not been characterized in salts, nor have they been detected in solution by physical methods.[47] Nevertheless, there is strong kinetic evidence that such cations participate in many (but certainly not all) aromatic halogenations.

Consider, for example, the chlorination of aromatic compounds in acidic solutions of HOCl (with Ag^+ added to remove chloride, which, when present, introduces mechanistic complications). As with nitrations in nitromethane, the rate law depends upon the reactivity of the substrate.[48] With relatively un-

---

[47] The appreciable conductivity of liquid iodine (Rabinovitsch, *Z. physik. Chem.*, **119**, 82 (1926)), is sometimes taken as evidence for its ionization into I^+ and $I^-\cdot xI_2$, but this conductivity appears to be metallic, rather than ionic, in character since it decreases with increasing temperature.

Salts of *substituted* halogenonium ions such as XXXI, XXXII, and XXXIII are known

XXXI   XXXII   XXXIII

(see, for example, Sandin and Hay, *J. Am. Chem. Soc.*, **74**, 274 (1952)), but these ions are not electron deficient in the same sense as are the simple halogenonium ions.

[48] (a) de la Mare, Hughes, and Vernon, *Research*, **3**, 192, 242 (1950). (b) Swain and Ketley, *J. Am. Chem. Soc.*, **77**, 3410 (1955).

reactive (but water soluble) aromatics such as nitrophenols and anisolesulfonic acids, chlorinations are third order,

$$\text{rate} = k(\text{ArH})(\text{HOCl})(\text{H}^+) \tag{6}$$

but with more reactive substrates (for example, phenol and anisole) the reactions become very nearly zero order in substrate—that is, second order overall.

$$\text{rate} = k(\text{HOCl})(\text{H}^+) \tag{7}$$

The observed duality in kinetics suggests that the steps in chlorination are analogous to those comprising the usual nitration mechanism. For aromatics which are chlorinated in accordance with rate law (6), the activated complex in the rate-determining step in which the ring is attacked consists of a molecule of substrate and either a $Cl \overset{+}{\underset{}{-}} O \overset{H}{\underset{H}{\diagdown}}$ ion or a Cl^+ ion. Since the interconversion between the two cations is probably far more rapid than the attack of either ion on the aromatic ring, kinetics alone cannot direct a choice. Suppose, however, that a much more active substrate is used. The specific rate at which the ring is attacked becomes much greater, and the attacking species may be consumed very nearly as rapidly as it is generated. The rate of the overall reaction then becomes essentially equal to the rate at which the attacking reagent, $ClOH_2^+$ or Cl^+, is formed from HOCl and H^+, the chlorination proceeds according to rate law (7), and we may expect to find a number of active aromatic substrates which are chlorinated at the same rate in a given solution.

The fact that a number of aromatic chlorinations are observed to follow rate law (7) strongly suggests that the attacking reagent in such cases is Cl^+, rather than $ClOH_2^+$. For it is very unlikely that the formation of $ClOH_2^+$ from HOCl and H_3O^+ (a proton transfer between two oxygen atoms) could be slow enough to be the rate-determining step in a chlorination reaction. Furthermore, it appears that chlorinations which follow rate-law (7) proceed more *rapidly* in D_2O than in H_2O.[48(b)] This is strong evidence against a rate-determining proton transfer, for D^+ transfers are known almost invariably to be slower than proton transfers under comparable circumstances. Thus, for chlorinations following rate law (7), the rate-determining step is the breakage of the Cl—O bond in $ClOH_2^+$. The analogy with nitration is virtually complete; and we may summarize the mechanism for chlorination in acidified HOCl as follows:

$$\text{HOCl} \underset{(1)}{\overset{\text{H}^+,\ \text{fast}}{\rightleftharpoons}} \text{ClOH}_2^+ \underset{(2)}{\rightleftharpoons} \text{Cl}^+ \underset{(3)}{\overset{\text{ArH}}{\longrightarrow}} \left[\text{Ar} \overset{\text{H}}{\underset{\text{Cl}}{\diagdown}} \right]^+ \underset{(4)}{\overset{-\text{H}^+,\ \text{fast}}{\longrightarrow}} \text{ArCl}$$

XXXIV

As with nitration, the apparent rate law will depend upon how step (3) and the reversal of step (2) compare in rate.[49] The intervention of the cationic intermediate XXXIV could be demonstrated by showing the absence of a kinetic hydrogen isotope effect in step (3)—the attack on the ring. This has not as yet been done for aromatic chlorination, but experiments similar to those described for nitration (p. 423) have shown that the hydrogen-isotope effect in aromatic bromination is negligible.[21(c),50(c)]

Kinetic studies of aromatic bromination in acidified solutions of $HOBr^{50}$ indicate that here also the attacking reagent is a halogenonium ion (in this case $:Br:^+$). However, we should remind ourselves that the halogenation conditions which we have been discussing are *not* the usual ones used in preparations, for aromatic brominations and chlorinations are ordinarily carried out using elemental bromine or chlorine, often in the presence of a Lewis acid such as zinc chloride, aluminum chloride, or ferric chloride. It has been suggested by some authors[51] that the function of such an acid is the heterolysis of the halogen molecule (for example, $Br_2 + ZnCl_2 \rightleftharpoons Br^+ + ZnCl_2Br^-$), prior to the attack on the substrate by the halogenonium ion. However, there seems little, if any, reliable evidence that such a heterolysis takes place at ordinary temperatures, and it is far more likely that the attacking species is the *diatomic halogen molecule itself.* If this is the case, the Lewis acid must await the formation of a complex between substrate and halogen molecule before assisting in the breakage of the bond between the halogen atoms. At present, then, the most likely mechanism for such halogenations appears to be

$$ArH \underset{fast}{\overset{X_2}{\rightleftharpoons}} ArH \cdot X_2 \xrightarrow[slow]{ZnCl_2,\ AlBr_3,\ etc.} \left\{ \begin{bmatrix} Ar \overset{\diagup H}{\underset{\diagdown X}{}} \end{bmatrix}^+ \atop ZnCl_2X^-,\ AlBr_3X^-,\ etc. \right\} \xrightarrow[fast]{-H^+} ArX$$

in which the rate-determining step is a simultaneous nucleophilic "push" by the substrate and an electrophilic "pull" by the catalyst on opposite ends of the halogen molecule with heterolytic breakage of the X—X bond. Recent kinetic studies[52] of such halogenations are consistent with this mechanism, for there

[49] The higher chlorination rate in D_2O may be explained in terms of the initial equilibrium. Since D_2O is a weaker base than H_2O (Wynne-Jones, *Trans. Faraday Soc.*, **32**, 1397 (1936)), a greater concentration of the conjugate acid of hypochlorous acid may exist in a given acidified solution of HOCl in heavy water than in the corresponding solution in ordinary water.

[50] See, for example, (a) Wilson and Soper, *J. Chem. Soc.*, **1949**, 3376; (b) Derbyshire and Waters, *ibid.*, **1950**, 564; (c) de la Mare, *et al.*, *ibid.*, **1957**, 131, 923, 3004.

[51] See, for example, Alexander, *Ionic Organic Reactions*, John Wiley and Sons, Inc., New York, 1950, p. 249.

[52] (a) It has been found, for example (Keefer and Andrews, *J. Am. Chem. Soc.*, **78**, 255, 4549 (1956)), that brominations of a number of aromatic hydrocarbons in acetic acid, catalyzed

appear to be no cases where a halogenation of this sort is zero order in substrate (which would be a symptom of the preliminary conversion of X_2 to a more reactive form).

It is not necessary that the role of electrophilic catalyst in halogenations be assumed by a metallic halide. Interhalogens, such as ICl[53(a)] and IBr[52(b)], and iodine itself[53(b)] may act in a similar capacity, and the same is true for HCl, carboxylic acids, and even water.[53(a)] However, the pulling action of water is feeble and becomes effective only for the more active substrates. The participation by water molecules in brominations carried out in bromine water cannot be demonstrated kinetically, but it has been shown that brominations in glacial acetic acid may be strikingly accelerated by small amounts of added water.[54]

It should be clear that a halogenonium ion, X^+, when it can be generated, is a more powerful halogenating agent than the corresponding halogen molecule, X_2, since halogenation with the latter requires an extra measure of activation energy to break the $X\text{---}X$ bond. Since ---OH is known to be a far poorer "leaving group" than the less basic halide ions (p. 261), we should expect the hypohalous acids, $X\text{---}OH$, to be even less powerful halogenating agents than the respective halogen molecules, $X\text{---}X$. Indeed, it has been found that the hypohalous acids, unless converted to their own conjugate acids, $X\text{---}OH_2^+$, will halogenate, at appreciable rates, only the most electron-rich aromatics. The phenoxide ion, for example, is chlorinated at a readily measurable rate with HOCl, the reaction exhibiting simple second-order kinetics.[55]

$$C_6H_5O^- + HOCl \rightarrow ClC_6H_4O^-\text{(3 isomers)} + H_2O$$
$$\text{rate} = k_2(\text{PhO}^-)(\text{HOCl}) \tag{8}$$

This reaction is accelerated strikingly by addition of HCl, for this acid reacts with HOCl to form Cl_2, which, we have remarked, is a more effective chlorinating agent.

$$HOCl + HCl \rightleftharpoons Cl_2 + H_2O$$

Elemental iodine is a less powerful halogenating agent than are chlorine

---

by $ZnCl_2$, are first order each in substrate, in bromine, and in $ZnCl_2$. See also (b) Yeddanapalli and Gnanapragsam, J. Chem. Soc., **1956**, 4934, and (c) Tsuruta et al., J. Am. Chem. Soc., **74**, 5996 (1952); **76**, 994 (1954).

[53] (a) Keefer and Andrews, J. Am. Chem. Soc., **78**, 5623 (1956); **79**, 5169 (1957). (b) Price and Arntzen, ibid., **60**, 2837 (1938). Aromatic iodinations with ICl, in the absence of other electrophilic catalysts, should be second (or higher) order in ICl, since this reagent is acting in a dual capacity; one molecule attacks the ring while one (or more) additional molecules "pull" the chloride off of the attacking molecule. Halogenations with IBr are more complex, since this interhalogen is appreciably dissociated into I_2 and Br_2 at room temperature and above; this compound acts primarily as a brominating agent, not, as one might suspect, an iodinating agent.

[54] Keefer and Andrews, J. Am. Chem. Soc., **78**, 3637 (1956).

[55] Soper and Smith, J. Chem. Soc., **1926**, 1582.

and bromine, for the metal halides usually used as halogenation catalysts co-ordinate only weakly with iodine, and their "pulling power" is of little avail. Aromatic iodinations in organic solvents are often carried out instead with iodine monochloride, ICl,[53(a),56] although iodinations with iodine itself are possible in the presence of $AgClO_4$[57(a)] since univalent silver is unusually elec-trophilic toward iodide.[57(b)] Elemental iodine has also been used for iodinations of phenols and aromatic amines in aqueous media, but for these reactions there is strong evidence that the attacking reagent is either I^+ or IOH_2^+, rather than I_2 or I_3^-. The iodination of aniline in the presence of base and excess iodide was discussed in an earlier chapter (p. 176), where it was shown that a rate law

$$\text{rate} = \frac{k(B:)(PhNH_2)(I_3^-)}{(I^-)^2} \tag{9}$$

could be interpreted as

$$\text{rate} = k'(PhNH_2)(B:)(I^+) \tag{10}$$

(For each additional base, $B:$, present in solution, an additional term may be added.) Rate law (10) immediately suggests an activated complex consisting of a molecule of base, a molecule of aniline, and an I^+ (or IOH_2^+) ion, but there are two additional interpretations possible, based upon alternate forms of the rate law, as follows:

$$\text{rate} = k''(PhNH_3^+)(B:)(HOI) \tag{11}$$

and

$$\text{rate} = k'''(PhNH_2)(B:H^+)(HOI) \tag{12}$$

The transition state suggested by expression (11), which implies attack upon the anilinium ion, may be excluded on chemical grounds; for the $-NH_3^+$ group is strongly *meta* directing, whereas iodination of aniline yields mainly the *p*-iodo compound. Expression (12) is not so easily disposed of, for it implies a mechanism similar to that which we have proposed for halogenations in organic solvents:

$$PhNH_2 + HOI \xrightleftharpoons{\text{fast}} H_2N\text{—}\langle\ \rangle \cdot IOH \xrightarrow[\text{slow}]{HB^+} \left[H_2N\text{=}\langle\ \rangle\text{<}^I_H\right]^+ \xrightarrow[\text{fast}]{-H^+} H_2N\text{—}\langle\ \rangle\text{—}I$$
$$+HOH + B: \tag{13}$$

while expression (10) suggests the following mechanism:

$$H_2N\text{—}\langle\ \rangle + I^+ \xrightleftharpoons[\text{eq}]{\text{fast}} \left[H_2N\text{=}\langle\ \rangle\text{<}^I_H\right]^+ \xrightarrow[\text{slow}]{B:} H_2N\text{—}\langle\ \rangle\text{—}I + B:H^+ \tag{14}$$

XXXV

[56] Lambourne and Robertson, *J. Chem. Soc.*, **1947**, 1167; Andrews and Keefer, *J. Am. Chem. Soc.*, **79**, 1412 (1957).

[57] (*a*) Birkenbach and Goubeau, *Ber.*, **66B**, 1280 (1933); **67B**, 917 (1934). (*b*) Craig, *et al.*, *J. Chem. Soc.*, **1954**, 332.

To distinguish between these two mechanisms, we may note that the rate-determining step in sequence (14) involves breakage of a C—H bond in the ring, whereas that in (13) does not. Thus, if (13) is correct, iodination of ring-deuterated anilines should proceed at very nearly the same rate as that of ordinary aniline, whereas if (14) is correct there should probably be a kinetic hydrogen-isotope effect. Although this test has apparently not yet been applied to aniline, it has been applied to the iodination of phenol in buffered aqueous media, for which the kinetic picture is very similar to that for aniline.[58] It has thus been found[59] that 2,4,6-trideuterophenol is iodinated at only one fourth the rate of unlabeled phenol, strongly suggesting a mechanism analogous to sequence (14) for the iodination of phenol, and, by implication, mechanism (14) itself for the iodination of aniline. It would be interesting to see whether the hydrogen-isotope effect in iodinations persists in nonpolar solvents where the existence of intermediate XXXV is more precarious.

Virtually nothing of what has been said regarding chlorination, bromination, or iodination may also be applied to fluorination; for it is certain now that the reactions of elemental fluorine with aromatic compounds, except perhaps at very low temperatures, proceed through *free fluorine atoms*, formed in a preliminary homolytic cleavage of F_2 molecules.[60] These reactions are additions, rather than substitutions, and lead to fluorinated cyclohexane derivatives. The very low F—F bond energy (about 37 kcal per mole) favors conversion of F_2 into atoms; whereas the very high ionization potential of the fluorine atom (about 100 kcal per mole greater than for chlorine) renders the formation of the :F:$^+$ ion in chemical systems impossible. Furthermore, fluorinations with hypofluorous acid, HOF, have not been carried out, since neither this acid nor its salts have been prepared.

Sulfonation

The intimate details of aromatic sulfonation reactions are, at present, known with much less certainty than those for nitration, chlorination, and bromination. There is little doubt, however, that sulfonation, like halogenation and nitration, may proceed by more than one mechanism, depending chiefly on the medium used. The most likely attacking reagent for sulfonations carried out in concentrated sulfuric acid (containing small amounts of water) appears to be the SO_3 molecule or its "solvate," $H_2S_2O_7$ (that is, $SO_3 \cdot H_2SO_4$). This guess is based largely on studies of the effect of added water on aromatic sulfonations, which

[58] Berliner, *J. Am. Chem. Soc.*, **73**, 4307 (1951).

[59] Grovenstein and Kilby, *J. Am. Chem. Soc.*, **79**, 2792 (1957).

[60] For a review of the reactions of elemental fluorine with organic compounds, see Bigelow, *Chem. Revs.*, **40**, 51 (1947).

indicate that sulfonation rates are inversely proportional to the *square of the concentrations of added water.*[61] Suppose that the added water reacts very nearly completely with the sulfuric acid that is present in excess.

$$H_2O + H_2SO_4 \rightarrow H_3O^+ + HSO_4^-$$

Neglecting autoprotolysis of sulfuric acid, the concentrations of both the H_3O^+ and HSO_4^- ions should be equal to the concentration of added water. Furthermore both of these ions are produced when SO_3 is formed from H_2SO_4; hence, we may write the equilibrium constant for the reaction as follows:

$$2H_2SO_4 \rightleftharpoons SO_3 + H_3O^+ + HSO_4^-; \quad K = \frac{(SO_3)(H_3O^+)(HSO_4^-)}{(H_2SO_4)^2} \quad (15)$$

telling us that if the concentration of unionized H_2SO_4 can be kept very nearly constant and if activity coefficients may be neglected, then the concentration of SO_3 should be inversely proportional to the product $(H_3O^+)(HSO_4^-)$ or to $(H_2O)^2_{added}$. If a single molecule of SO_3 is involved in the rate-determining step, the sulfonation rate should likewise be, as is observed, inversely proportional to $(H_2O)^2_{added}$. On the other hand, it may be shown (Ex. 5) that if the attacking species were $H_3SO_4^+$, HSO_3^+, S_2O_6, or $H_2S_3O_{10}$ (all of which may be present in concentrated sulfuric acid),[62] the rate of sulfonation would show a different type of dependence on $(H_2O)_{added}$. The answer appears unequivocal until we remind ourselves that in the concentration range studied (92 to 99 percent H_2SO_4) the concentration of unionized sulfuric acid is by no means constant[63] and that the activity coefficients of one or more of the species in equation (15) may change significantly in going from 92 to 100 percent H_2SO_4.[64] Thus, there exists the disturbing possibility that the rate data, when corrected for both of these trends, will approximate a rate law pointing to attack by a different species. Analysis of rate data for sulfonations in fuming sulfuric acid[65] is similarly difficult, due largely to the plurality of readily interconvertible species present in such solutions. However if SO_3 is the attacking reagent for sulfonations in 92 to 100 percent sulfuric acid, it is also very likely to be at least one of the attacking reagents for sulfonations in fuming sulfuric acid.

There are two additional features of the sulfonation reaction that must be accommodated by any proposed mechanism. First, aromatic sulfonation, as has

[61] Cowdrey and Davies, *J. Chem. Soc.*, **1949**, 1471. Similar (as yet unpublished) studies by Davenport and Hughes have been reported by Ingold, Ref. 1(b), p. 299.

[62] Gillespie, *J. Chem. Soc.*, **1950**, 2516.

[63] Deno and Taft, *J. Am. Chem. Soc.*, **76**, 244 (1954).

[64] These objections are essentially those expressed by Gold and Satchell, *J. Chem. So .*, **1956,** 1635. However, on the basis of a more complex treatment, these authors also suggest (although with reserve) that the most likely attacking species in such sulfonations in the SO_3 molecule.

[65] Brand, *J. Chem. Soc.*, **1950**, 1004.

long been known, is reversible in polar solvents. Secondly, aromatic sulfonation exhibits a pronounced kinetic hydrogen-isotope effect,[21(c)] suggesting that the C—H bond in the ring undergoes breakage in the rate-determining step. We may then represent the mechanism for sulfonation as

$$\text{ArH} + \text{SO}_3 \underset{\text{fast}}{\overset{\text{fast}}{\rightleftharpoons}} \left[\begin{array}{c} \text{H} \\ / \\ {}^{+}\text{Ar} \\ \backslash \\ \text{SO}_3^{-} \end{array} \right] \underset{\text{slow}}{\overset{\text{slow}}{\rightleftharpoons}} \text{ArSO}_3^{-} + \text{H}^{+} \overset{\text{fast}}{\rightleftharpoons} \text{ArSO}_3\text{H}$$

XXXVI

In accordance with the observed isotope effect, the rate-determining step in the forward reaction is the breakage of the Ar—H bond. If we assume the first step to be fast, its reversal must also be fast since intermediate XXXVI does not accumulate. Since one of the steps in the reverse reaction (desulfonation) must be slow and since the ionization of the sulfonic acid is very fast, the slow step here must also be the second. Note also that the evidence so far available does not tell us whether adduct XXXVI is an intermediate or merely an activated complex in a one-step reversible substitution.[66]

Friedel-Crafts Reactions[67]

The Friedel-Crafts reaction, the alkylation or acylation of an aromatic ring in the presence of such catalysts as $AlCl_3$, BF_3, $SnCl_4$, or I_2, is not an easy reaction to study quantitatively. Such condensations are usually sensitive to traces of moisture and are often accompanied by isomerization of the product or by polymerization. Moreover, the "catalytic halide" may form addition compounds with the aromatic substrate, with the alkylating or acylating reagent, with the products, or with combinations of these, and some of these adducts take part in the Friedel-Crafts reaction, whereas others do not. Finally, many Friedel-Crafts reactions are heterogeneous, and these do not lend themselves to straightforward kinetic treatment. Although olefins, alcohols, and (in special cases) esters and ethers may serve as alkylating agents, and although acylations may be carried out with esters, anhydrides, and carboxylic acids, we shall consider mainly the more usual Friedel-Crafts reagents—, alkyl and acyl halides. These are generally used in conjunction with the halides of aluminum, tin, or zinc; but for quantitative studies, use of the anhydrous halides of gallium

[66] Aromatic substitution with SO_3 in nitrobenzene has been found to be *second* order in SO_3 (Hinshelwood, *et al.*, *J. Chem. Soc.*, **1939**, 1372, **1944**, 469, 649). It is not known as yet whether this represents the reaction of a dimer of SO_3 or attack by SO_3 at two points in the reaction sequence.

[67] For a recent and critical discussion of the Friedel-Crafts reaction, see Baddeley, *Quart. Revs.*, **VIII**, 355 (1954).

is sometimes preferable, for with these, undesirable side reactions are often minimized.

The function of the metal halide is to loosen or break the carbon-halogen bond in the alkyl or acyl halide, making the latter reagent more electrophilic and therefore a more effective attacking reagent for the aromatic compound.

$$R-X + AlBr_3 \rightarrow \overset{\delta+}{R}\cdots X\cdots \overset{\delta-}{AlBr_3} \quad \text{or} \quad R^+XAlBr_3^-$$

The chlorides and bromides of aluminum[68(a)] and gallium[68(b)] are known to form polar addition compounds with many (although not all) alkyl and acyl halides. Typically, the addition of anhydrous aluminum bromide to a solution of ethyl bromide in cyclohexane causes a striking increase in the apparent dipole moment of the solute,[69] although aluminum bromide itself has no dipole moment. Such solutions appear to conduct the electric current feebly,[68(a)] with aluminum migrating to the anode. Furthermore, if aluminum bromide having radioactive bromide is dissolved, along with unlabeled ethyl bromide, in an inert solvent, the radioactive bromide is found to enter the ethyl bromide.[68(c)] These observations are consistent with the formation of a polar complex, $Et-Br:AlBr_3$; this is ionized to an unknown degree into the ion pair $Et^+AlBr_4^-$, which is, in turn, slightly dissociated into $Et^+ + AlBr_4^-$. Halide exchange is more rapid for secondary and tertiary halides but slower for methyl halides, these differences being in line with what we observed in Chapter 8—that a carbonium ion becomes more stable as branching at the α-carbon increases.

In Friedel-Crafts reaction mixtures where the concentration of carbonium ions (in ion pairs) is significant, it is likely that this ion is an attacking species and possible that it is the only important attacking species. Kinetics does not tell us whether the alkylating species is the complex $RX:AlX_3$ or the ion-pair $R^+AlX_4^-$; but it does assure us that if the alkylating species is the ion pair, then the formation of this ion pair cannot be rate determining. For if the ionization were the rate-determining step, the alkylation rates of a series of aromatics with a given alkylating mixture would be independent of the concentration and identity of the aromatic; whereas alkylations in the presence of $GaCl_3$,[70(a)] $AlCl_3$,[70(b)] and $AlBr_3$[70(c)] have been found to be first order in the aromatic, and

[68] (a) See, for example, Wertyporoch, et al., Ber., **64B**, 1357, 1369 (1931); **66B**, 1232 (1933). (b) Brown, et al., J. Am. Chem. Soc., **75**, 6275 (1953); **78**, 6247 (1956); Wong and Brown, J. Inorg. Nucl. Chem., **1**, 402 (1955). (c) Fairbrother, J. Chem. Soc., **1941**, 293; **1937**, 503.
[69] Fairbrother, Trans. Faraday Soc., **37**, 763 (1941).
[70] (a) Ulich and Heyne, Z. Elektrochem., **41**, 509 (1935). (b) Brown and Grayson, J. Am. Chem. Soc., **75**, 6285 (1953). (c) Jungk, Smoot, and Brown, ibid., **78**, 2185 (1956). (d) Smoot and Brown, ibid., **78**, 6245 (1956). In the experiments described in this paper, the aromatic was kept in large excess, so the kinetic order with respect to this reactant could not be determined. However, the fact that alkylations of benzene (with benzene in excess) are much slower than the corresponding alkylations of toluene (with toluene in excess) tells us that the two alkylations do not have a common rate-determining step.

this is probably also true for alkylations catalyzed by GaBr$_3$.[70(d)] Alkylations catalyzed by AlCl$_3$ and AlBr$_3$ in the slightly polar solvents nitrobenzene and 1,2,4-trichlorobenzene are first order also in catalyst and in alkylating agent,

$$\text{rate} = k(\text{ArH})(\text{Al}X_3)(\text{R}X) \tag{16}$$

This rate law is consistent with attack on ArH either by RX:AlX_3 or by R$^+$AlX_4^-, since the concentrations of both of these are proportional to (RX)(AlX_3). However, it excludes attack by free R$^+$ ions, since the concentration of R$^+$ is proportional to $\sqrt{(\text{R}X)(\text{Al}X_3)}$. Moreover, if the attacking reagent were the free carbonium ion, the ratio of products (for example, the *ortho* to *para* ratio from alkylation of a monosubstituted benzene) should be the same whether RCl, RBr, or RI is the alkylating agent; this, likewise, is not what is found.[71]

The mechanism of Friedel-Crafts alkylations in nonpolar solvents is, at present, obscure. It has been found that alkylations in benzene catalyzed by GaBr$_3$ are *second order* in catalyst,[70(d)] but there is no guarantee that this is true for other solvents or for other catalysts.[72] It would not be surprising however if alkylations, like some aromatic halogenations in nonpolar solvents, require "pulling action" by more than one molecule of Lewis acid.

The familiar skeletal rearrangements that occur during Friedel-Crafts alkylations may be assumed to arise from alkyl shifts or hydride shifts in the carbonium ion while the latter exists as a portion of an ion pair. (Carbonium-ion rearrangements are known to occur under a variety of conditions and will be discussed at some length in Chap. 14.) Since we know that, in general, secondary and tertiary carbonium ions are more stable than primary, we need not be surprised that alkylation of benzene with neopentyl chloride yields *t*-amylbenzene (XXXVII). Similarly, alkylation with primary chloride XXXVIII yields mainly the rearranged hydrocarbon XXXIX.[73] It is, however, somewhat

$$\underset{\overset{|}{\underset{\text{Me}}{\text{Me}}}}{\overset{\overset{\text{Me}}{|}}{\text{Me}-\text{C}-\text{CH}_2\text{Cl}}} \xrightarrow{\text{AlCl}_3} \underset{\overset{|}{\underset{\text{Me}}{\text{AlCl}_4^-}}}{\overset{\overset{\text{(Me)}}{\diagdown}}{\text{Me}-\text{C}-\text{CH}_2^+}} \rightleftharpoons \underset{\overset{|}{\underset{\text{Me}}{\text{AlCl}_4^-}}}{\overset{\overset{\text{Me}}{|}}{\text{Me}-\overset{+}{\text{C}}-\text{CH}_2}} \xrightarrow{\text{PhH}} \underset{\overset{|}{\underset{\text{Me}}{}}}{\overset{\overset{\text{Ph Me}}{|\ |}}{\text{Me}-\text{C}-\text{CH}_2}}$$

XXXVII

$$\text{Me}_3\text{C}-\text{CH}_2-\text{CH}_2\text{Cl} \xrightarrow{\text{AlCl}_3} \underset{\overset{|}{\underset{\text{H}}{\text{AlCl}_4^-}}}{\overset{\overset{\text{(H)}}{\diagdown}}{\text{Me}_3\text{C}-\text{C}-\text{CH}_2^+}} \rightleftharpoons \underset{\overset{|}{\underset{\text{H}}{\text{AlCl}_4^-}}}{\overset{}{\text{Me}_3\text{C}-\overset{+}{\text{C}}-\text{CH}_3}} \xrightarrow{\text{PhH}} \text{Me}_3\text{C}-\text{CHPh}-\text{CH}_3$$

XXXVIII   XXXIX

[71] Brown and Jungk, *J. Am. Chem. Soc.*, **77**, 5586 (1955).

[72] Ulich and Heyne, Ref. 70(a), report for example, that alkylations in CS$_2$ in the presence of gallium chloride are first order in catalyst. However, the work is not highly precise, and these authors seem to have ignored the fact that the catalyst exists in this solvent chiefly as Ga$_2$Cl$_6$. A reinvestigation of the kinetics of such alkylations might be profitable.

[73] Schmerling and West, *J. Am. Chem. Soc.*, **76**, 1917 (1954).

disturbing to find examples where alkylation with a *tertiary* halide yields a product derived from a secondary carbonium ion—for example, alkylation with chloride XL to give product XLI[73]. To account for the rearrangement in

$$
\text{MeCH}_2\text{—CMe}_2\text{Cl} \xrightarrow{\text{AlCl}_3} \underset{\underset{\text{H}}{|}}{\overset{\text{(H)}}{\text{Me—C—CMe}_2^+}} \rightleftharpoons \overset{+}{\text{Me—}}\overset{\overset{\text{H}}{|}}{\text{CH—CMe}_2} \xrightarrow{\text{PhH}} \underset{\text{(mainly)}}{\overset{\overset{\text{Ph}}{|}}{\text{Me—CH—CMe}_2\text{H}}}
$$

$$\text{AlCl}_4^- \qquad\qquad \text{AlCl}_4^-$$

XL $\qquad\qquad\qquad\qquad\qquad\qquad\qquad\qquad\qquad\qquad$ XLI

this direction, we should recall that a secondary carbonium ion, besides being less stable than a tertiary, is also more reactive. Therefore, if we assume that the two carbonium ions are allowed to reach equilibrium, we may represent the interconversions involved in the "skeletal rearrangement" as follows:

$$
\begin{array}{ccccc}
\text{secondary} & \rightarrow & \text{secondary carbonium ion} & \rightleftharpoons & \text{tertiary carbonium ion} & \leftarrow & \text{tertiary} \\
\text{halide} & & \text{(small equil conc)} & & \text{(larger equil conc)} & & \text{halide} \\
& & \Big\downarrow \begin{smallmatrix}\text{PhH}\\\text{fast}\end{smallmatrix} & & \Big\downarrow \begin{smallmatrix}\text{PhH}\\\text{slower}\end{smallmatrix} & & \\
& & \text{"secondary" product} & & \text{"tertiary" product} & &
\end{array}
$$

As may be seen, the ratio of "secondary" product to "tertiary" product depends not only upon the relative stabilities of the carbonium ions, but also upon the rates with which these ions react (as ion pairs) with the aromatic substrate. On the other hand, there seem to be a number of substrates that are so reactive they consume the carbonium ion originally formed, before the latter has a chance to undergo significant isomerization. Thus, alkylation of mesitylene with *n*-PrBr yields 91 percent of the *n*-propyl product under conditions where alkylation of benzene yields only 21 percent of the *n*-propyl product.[70(d)]

Having implied that isomerization requires ionization of the alkylating agent whereas alkylation itself does not, we may expect the milder catalysts that stretch the R—X bond without completely breaking it to bring about alkylation without isomerization. It appears that ferric chloride is a catalyst of this type, although it is often difficult to determine whether a bond has been broken or merely loosened in solution. At any rate, Friedel-Crafts alkylations of benzene with chlorides XXXVIII and XL in the presence of FeCl₃ yield unrearranged products,[73] whereas rearrangement predominates in the presence of AlCl₃.

Friedel-Crafts acylations[74] are similar in a number of respects to alkylations. Here, the attacking electrophile is an *acylium ion*, R—$\overset{+}{\text{C}}$=O, a type of carbonium ion which we have already encountered in our discussion of esterification (p. 325). Besides being formed from the action of aluminum halides and

[74] For recent quantitative studies of Friedel-Crafts acylations, see: Brown and Jensen, *J. Am. Chem. Soc.*, **80**, 2291, 2296 (1958); Denney and Klemchuk, *ibid.*, **80**, 3285 (1958).

other Lewis acids on acyl halides, such cations exist in high concentrations in solutions of acid anhydrides in concentrated sulfuric acid, [75(a)] or may be formed by the action of a soluble silver salt (for example, $AgClO_4$) on an acyl halide in a polar but nonhydroxylic solvent such as nitromethane.[75(b)]

$$(RCO)_2O + 2H_2SO_4 \rightarrow R{-}\overset{+}{C}{=}O + R{-}\overset{O}{\overset{\|}{C}}{-}\overset{+}{O}H_2 + 2HSO_4^-$$

$$RCOCl + Ag^+ \rightarrow R{-}\overset{+}{C}{=}O + AgCl$$

Solutions of either type are effective acylating agents.

Acylations, unlike alkylations, are not accompanied by rearrangement of the attacking electrophile, but are subject to a different complication. In some cases, especially when "R" of the $R{-}\overset{+}{C}{=}O$ ion is highly branched, decarbonylation (loss of carbon monoxide) occurs.[76] Trimethylacetyl chloride, for example, behaves in this way:

$$Me_3C{-}\overset{O}{\overset{\|}{C}}{-}Cl{:}AlCl_3 \Longrightarrow [Me_3C{\overset{\frown}{-}}\overset{+}{C}{=}O]^+ \longrightarrow Me_3C^+ + C{\equiv}O \xrightarrow{ArH} ArCMe_3$$
$$+AlCl_4^- \qquad\qquad +AlCl_4^-$$

This is a "side reaction," and, as is the case with rearrangements during alkylation, it may be minimized by using a very reactive substrate. For the more reactive the substrate, the more likely it is to be attacked by the acylium ion before the latter undergoes decarbonylation. Given similar conditions, the reactions of trimethylacetyl chloride and aluminum chloride with the three aromatics, benzene, toluene, and anisole result in yields of CO of about 90, 50, and 10 percent, respectively.[76]

It is of interest that Friedel-Crafts acylations require somewhat more than stoichiometric amounts of electrophilic catalysts, whereas alkylations proceed nicely in the presence of much smaller amounts. The product of an acylation is a ketone which is itself basic and which may inhibit the reaction in one of two ways. It may "tie up" the catalyst, thus preventing the ionization of the acylating agent, or, alternately, it may "tie up" the acylium ion, preventing its attacking the ring. More recently, halide exchange experiments have shown[77] that ketones, when added to Friedel-Crafts reaction mixtures, do not prevent ionization of the acyl halide. Therefore we may conclude that, in the absence

[75] (a) Gillespie, J. Chem. Soc., **1950**, 2997. It has been found, for example, that the *ν*-factor for acetic anydride in concentrated sulfuric acid is near 4. (b) Burton and Praill, *ibid.*, **1951**, 522, 726.

[76] See, for example, Rothstein and Saville, J. Chem. Soc., **1949**, 1946.

[77] Baddeley and Voss, J. Chem. Soc., **1954**, 418.

of substantial amounts of catalyst, the action of the acylium ion, rather than that of the catalyst, is blocked. The competition between the ketone and the substrate for the acylium ion may thus be represented as follows:

$$
R\overset{O}{\underset{\|}{C}}{-}Cl\!:\!AlCl_3 \;\rightleftharpoons\; R\overset{O}{\underset{\|}{C}}{}^{+}\,AlCl_4^{-}
\begin{cases}
\xrightarrow{\;ArH\;} \;\begin{matrix} R \\ \diagdown \\ \end{matrix} \overset{Ar}{}C{=}\ddot{O}\!:\!AlCl_3 + HCl \quad \text{(desired products)} \\[2em]
\xrightarrow{\;ArCOR\;} \left[R\overset{O}{\underset{\|}{C}}\!:\!\ddot{O}{=}C\overset{Ar}{\underset{R}{\diagdown}} \right]^{+} \; AlCl_4^{-}
\end{cases}
$$

(not possible when $Ar{-}\overset{O}{\underset{\|}{C}}{-}R$ is coordinated with $AlCl_3$)

It is probable that if the substrate is sufficiently reactive, acylation may occur through attack by $R{-}\overset{O}{\underset{\|}{C}}{-}Cl\!:\!A$ (where A is a Lewis acid) without prior ionization of the latter. Thus, the acylation of anisole in the presence of iodine[78] almost certainly proceeds through the complex $R{-}\overset{O}{\underset{\|}{C}}{-}Cl\!:\!I_2$ rather than the ion pair $R{-}\overset{+}{C}{=}O\;ClI_2^{-}$; for although there is evidence that the ClI_2^{-} anion might exist,[79] it is, at best, extremely unstable under ordinary conditions.

Nucleophilic Aromatic Substitution. The Bimolecular Mechanism[80]

The duality of mechanism which we have considered with respect to nucleophilic aliphatic substitution (Chap. 8) also extends to aromatic systems. The two most familiar types of aromatic substrates that undergo such substitutions under nondrastic conditions are nitrohalobenzenes and diazonium salts, typical reactions of which are shown:

$$
O_2N{-}\!\!\left\langle\!\!\bigcirc\!\!\right\rangle\!\!{-}Cl \;+\; R_2NH \;\longrightarrow\; O_2N{-}\!\!\left\langle\!\!\bigcirc\!\!\right\rangle\!\!{-}NR_2H^{+} \;+\; Cl^{-}
$$

$$
\left\langle\!\!\bigcirc\!\!\right\rangle\!\!{-}N_2^{+} \;+\; H_2O \;\longrightarrow\; \left\langle\!\!\bigcirc\!\!\right\rangle\!\!{-}OH_2^{+} \;+\; N_2
$$

[78] Kaye, Klein and Burlant, *J. Am. Chem. Soc.*, **75**, 745 (1953).

[79] von Kiss and Urmanczy, *Z. anorg. Chem.*, **202**, 189 (1931).

[80] (a) Nucleophilic aromatic substitution has been reviewed by Bunnett and Zahler, *Chem. Revs.*, **49**, 273 (1951). (b) See also: Hine, *Physical Organic Chemistry*, McGraw-Hill Book Co., Inc., New York, 1956, pp. 365–373; Ingold, Ref. 1(b), pp. 798–815; Bunnett, *Quart. Revs.*, **12**, 1 (1958).

Studies of reactions of the first type leave little doubt that they are bimolecular in character, whereas certain reactions of the second type are just as unmistakably unimolecular.

Second-order kinetics have been observed for many substitution reactions of *p*-nitrochlorobenzene, 2,4-dinitrochlorobenzene, and the corresponding bromo compounds,[81] and the reactions of a given substrate are fastest with the most basic nucleophiles. While these observations strongly indicate bimolecularity, they do not demand a mechanism analogous to the direct displacement mechanism in aliphatic systems in which bond making and bond breaking are synchronous. For, if the reaction center is an aromatic, rather than an aliphatic, carbon, an attacking nucleophile, like an attacking electrophile, may form a new bond *before* the old bond breaks. Indeed, as we have already suggested (p. 237), a nitro group *ortho* or *para* to the position under attack facilitates the reaction by dispersing the negative charge brought in by the attacking group before departure of the leaving group (XLII ↔ XLII').

$$\text{XLII} \qquad\qquad \text{XLII}'$$

For evidence in support of this picture, consider the specific rates at which 2,4-dinitro compounds of type XLIII react with piperidine:[82]

XLIII

$$(-X=-\text{Cl},-\text{Br},-\overset{\displaystyle O}{\underset{\displaystyle O}{\overset{|}{\underset{|}{S}}}}-\text{Ph},-\overset{\displaystyle O}{\underset{\displaystyle O}{\overset{|}{\underset{|}{S}}}}-\text{Ph})$$

If the breakage of the C—X bonds were important in the activation process for these substitutions, the chloro compound should react much more slowly than the bromo compound (since a C—Cl bond is more difficult to break than a

---

[81] See, for example, the methanolysis of 2,4-dinitrochlorobenzene (Reinheimer, *et al.*, *J. Am. Chem. Soc.*, **79**, 1263 (1957)), and the exchange of 2,4-dinitrobromobenzene with radioactive bromide (Le Roux, *et al.*, *J. Chem. Soc.*, **1945**, 586). There is some evidence that the rate laws for the reactions of 2,4-dinitrochlorobenzene with a number of amines contain a third-order term (that is, second order in base), as well as a second-order term; see, for example, Ross, Peterson, and Finkelstein, *J. Am. Chem. Soc.*, **79**, 6547 (1957); **80**, 2447, 5319 (1958). For an opposing view on this question, see Bunnett and Pruitt, *J. Elisha Mitchell Sci. Soc.*, **73**, 297 (1957).

[82] Bunnett, Garbisch, and Pruitt, *J. Am. Chem. Soc.*, **79**, 387 (1957).

C—Br bond), and the —SOPh and —SO$_2$Ph derivatives should react at very different rates. It is found, however that the chloro, bromo, and —SOPh derivatives *react at almost exactly the same rate*, and the —SO$_2$Ph compound reacts about two thirds as fast as these. Moreover, the activation energies for the four substitutions are very nearly equal, telling us that the *activation process in the four cases is substantially the same* and not affected by the nature of substituent *X*. It is likely, therefore, that the activation energy required in these substitutions is utilized in desolvating the piperidine molecule, in redistributing electric charge in the benzene ring and about the attacking nitrogen atom, and in pushing the C—*X* bond out of the plane of the ring, but *not* in breaking the C—*X* bond. It might also be noted that the corresponding substitution reaction on 2,4-dinitrofluorobenzene is about 750 times as fast as those on the chloro and bromo compounds (whereas if breaking of the C—F bond in the activation process were important, the fluoro compound should react more slowly). In line with the picture we have presented, it may be inferred that the strong electron-attracting power of the fluorine atom lowers the electron density at the center of reaction so that attack by the piperidine molecule becomes somewhat more favorable energetically.

We may next ask whether a species such as XLII is an intermediate or merely an activated complex. The isolation of salts having anions that are very probably analogous to XLII indicates that at least in some cases, and possibly in all, XLII is an intermediate. The most familiar of such salts is XLV, formed by the action of KOEt on 2,4,6-trinitroanisole (XLIV). As is indicated,

this salt appears identical to the salt formed under similar conditions from KOMe and 2,4,6-trinitrophenetole (XLVI); on acidification, both products yield the same mixture of trinitroethers.[83] Similar salts have not yet been prepared from the reactions of nitrohalobenzenes, and it may be that, because of the greater effectiveness of the halide ions as leaving groups, such salts are too unstable to be isolated.

There are, as may be expected, groups other than the —NO$_2$ group that facilitate nucleophilic substitution in the *ortho* and *para* positions. The —COCH$_3$,

[83] Meisenheimer, *Ann.*, **323**, 205 (1902).

—CN, and —$\overset{\overset{O}{\|}}{\underset{\underset{O}{\|}}{S}}$—CH$_3$ groups are in this category, but each is a far less potent

activator than the nitro group. The relative rate constants for the reactions of the following substituted bromobenzenes with piperidine (in benzene at 99°) are typically illustrative of the greater effectiveness of the nitro group.[84]

| $\dfrac{k}{k_{\mathrm{BrC_6H_4NO_2}}}$ | 1 | 0.013 | 0.031 | 0.053 |

In addition, the diazonium group, —N≡N+, is an effective activator for nucleophilic substitution, although this group is itself so easily displaced that quantitative studies of substitutions activated by it are difficult. There are, however, many instances where a nitro or halo substituent, *ortho* or *para* to the diazonium group in a diazo salt is displaced during a reaction that is intended to alter only the diazonium group.[85]

As is seen from structure XLII′, the action of the nitro group in facilitating nucleophilic substitution requires that the bond linking this group to the ring assume some double-bond character and therefore that the nitro group lie in or near the plane of the benzene ring. The nitro group becomes a much more feeble "activator" when it is forced out of the plane of the ring. We have already noted (p. 238) that 2-nitro-5-bromo-*m*-xylene (LI) undergoes substitution reactions much more slowly than *p*-nitrobromobenzene simply because the methyl groups sterically prohibit the approach to planarity that is necessary for effective

[84] Bunnett and Levitt, *J. Am. Chem. Soc.*, **70**, 2778 (1948).
[85] For example, treatment of the diazonium chlorides XLVII and XLVIII with ethanol (a reaction that ordinarily results merely in removal of the diazonium group by reduction) yields predominantly products XLIX and L, respectively, resulting from displacement of Br⁻ and NO₂⁻ by Cl⁻.

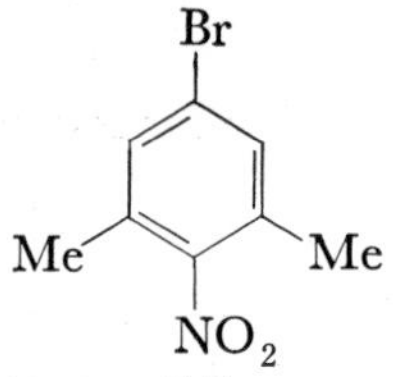

LI 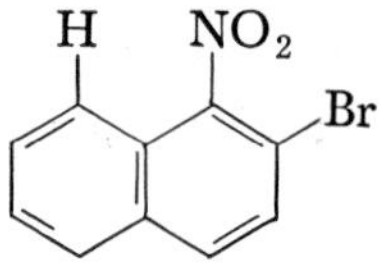   LII 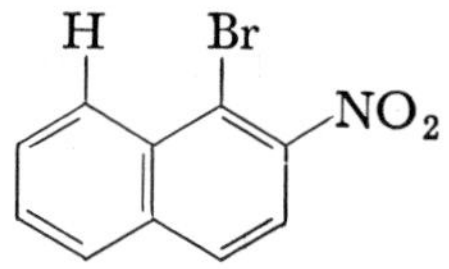   LIII

activation by the nitro group. A similar effect boosts the activation energy for the reaction of 1-nitro-2-bromonaphthalene (LII) with piperidine; $\Delta H\ddagger$ for this reaction has been found to be 12.3 kcal as compared to a $\Delta H\ddagger$ of 10.4 kcal for the same reaction of the 1-bromo-2-nitro isomer (LIII).[86] Here it is the so-called *peri* hydrogen (shown in the figure) that interferes with coplanarity of the nitro group in LII. On the same basis we may understand why the nitro group in the 1 position of compounds LIV and LV is more easily displaced than that in the 4 position, even though the former, classically speaking, is "hindered." In both of these compounds, the 4-nitro substituent may facilitate

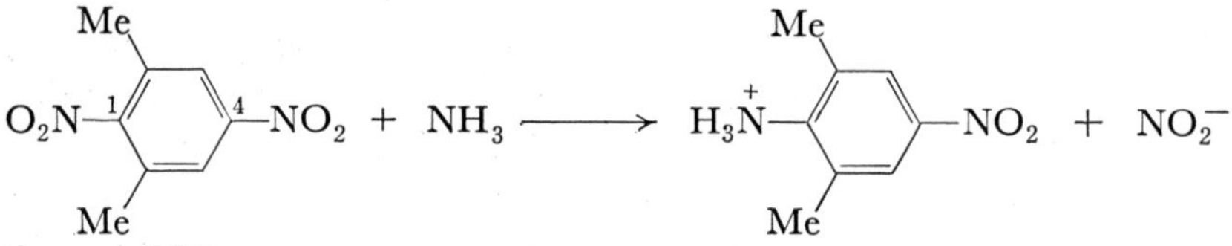

LIV

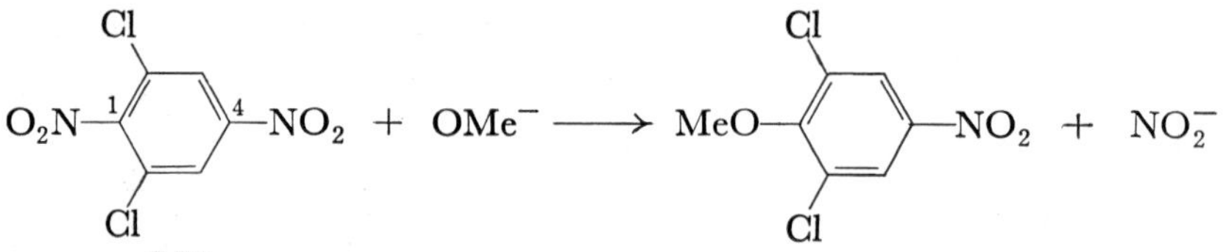

LV

displacement of the 1-nitro substituent, but the latter, because it is kept out of the plane of the ring, may not facilitate displacement of the 4-nitro substituent.[88]

[86] Berliner, Quinn, and Edgerton, *J. Am. Chem. Soc.*, **72**, 5305 (1950).
[87] (a) Ibbotsen and Kenner, *J. Chem. Soc.*, **123**, 1260 (1923). (b) Holleman, *Rec. trav. chim.*, **39**, 435 (1920).
[88] Displacement of the 1-nitro substituent in compounds LIV and LV is subject to less steric hindrance than might be supposed; for in the activated complex for such substitution, the incoming and leaving groups are well out of the plane of the ring with the two *ortho* substituents "sandwiched" between them. Using scale models it may be shown that unless the incoming group or the *ortho* substituents (or both) are excessively bulky, there is little steric interference in the transition state.

The Reactions of Diazonium Salts. The Aromatic S_N 1 Reaction

The formation of diazonium salts was discussed briefly in an earlier chapter (p. 175), where it was shown that the kinetic picture suggested the following sequence of steps:

$$2HNO_2 \underset{eq}{\overset{fast}{\rightleftharpoons}} N_2O_3 \xrightarrow[slow]{ArNH_2} \begin{cases} Ar\overset{+}{N}H_2\!-\!N\!=\!O \xrightarrow{fast} \longrightarrow ArN_2^+ + H_2O \\ \\ NO_2^- \end{cases}$$

with the detailed nature of the steps following the slow step still in doubt. Once formed, aromatic diazonium salts react with a host of different nucleophiles under a wide variety of conditions, the nucleophile attaching itself to the ring, and the diazonium group departing as N_2. Many of these reactions, particularly those carried out in basic solutions or in nonpolar media, proceed by free-radical mechanisms; certain of these will be treated in Chapter 16. On the other hand, the reactions of diazonium salts in acidic polar media are often heterolytic in character, and a number of these provide us with what is, at present, the only important group of examples of the S_N1 reaction on the aromatic ring.

The evidence for unimolecularity is much the same as that discussed for aliphatic systems. The decompositions of substituted benzenediazonium chlorides in water are first order[89] and, aside from solvent and salt effects, their rates are not affected by added alcohol or added chloride. Nevertheless, these reagents partially divert the product from a phenol to an aromatic ether or substituted chlorobenzene. We thus may infer that the rate-determining step in these conversions is the bond breaking in the diazonium ion, followed by a rapid combination with the attacking nucleophile which determines the identity of the product.

$$ArN_2^+ \xrightarrow[\substack{slow \\ \text{rate determining}}]{-N_2} Ar^+ \begin{array}{l} \xrightarrow{HOH} ArOH + H^+ \\ \xrightarrow{MeOH} ArOMe + H^+ \\ \xrightarrow{Cl^-} ArCl \end{array}$$

product determining

Moreover, in analogy with aliphatic S_N1 reactions, we should expect electron-withdrawing substituents in the benzene ring to retard the overall reaction and electron-donating groups to accelerate it. Accordingly we are not surprised that

[89] (a) Moelwyn-Hughes and Johnson, *Trans. Faraday Soc.*, **36**, 948 (1940); (b) Crossley, *et al.*, *J. Am. Chem. Soc.*, **62**, 1400 (1940); (c) DeTar and Ballentine, *ibid.*, **78**, 3916 (1956). (d) Under irradiation, decompositions of diazonium salts in solution proceed also via a free-radical path; see, for example, Boudreaux and Boulet, *ibid.*, **80**, 1588 (1958).

the specific rates of decomposition of the m-Cl and p-NO$_2$ substituted benzene-diazonium salts are, respectively, $\frac{1}{24}$ and $\frac{1}{240}$ of that for the parent salt (in water at 29°), whereas the m-CH$_3$ and m-OH groups *boost* the specific rate of decomposition (by factors of 4.5 and 12, respectively).[89(b)] It is, however, somewhat disturbing to find that the p-OH and p-CH$_3$O groups greatly reduce the rates of decomposition of aromatic diazonium salts. Here, it appears that because of direct conjugation between the —N$_2^+$ group and the —OH or —OMe group (LVI ↔ LVI'), the bond linking the N$_2^+$ group to the ring acquires

$$\left[R\ddot{O}-\!\!\left\langle\bigcirc\right\rangle\!\!-\overset{+}{N}\!\!\equiv\!\!N\!: \;\longleftrightarrow\; R\overset{+}{\ddot{O}}\!\!=\!\!\left\langle\bigcirc\right\rangle\!\!=\!\!\overset{+}{N}\!\!=\!\!\ddot{N}\!: \right] \qquad \overset{+H}{\underset{H}{H-C}}\!\!=\!\!\left\langle\bigcirc\right\rangle\!\!=\!\!\overset{+}{N}\!\!=\!\!\ddot{\bar{N}}\!:$$

LVI   LVI'   LVII

some double-bond character, and therefore becomes more difficult to break. Likewise, p-toluenediazonium chloride decomposes more slowly than the benzenediazonium salt, presumably because hyperconjugation (LVII) strengthens the C—N bond in the tolyl compound.

It is emphasized that the kinetic work on the reactions of diazonium salts in polar media has been concerned in the main with attack by weakly nucleophilic species—that is, H$_2$O, Cl$^-$, and alcohols. It is quite probable that if studies were extended to reactions with more effective nucleophiles (for example, I$^-$, CN$^-$, PhS$^-$, and SCN$^-$), bimolecularity would be observed. In fact, it has recently been found that the addition of the moderately strong nucleophile, Br$^-$, to a solution of p-nitrobenzenediazonium ion not only diverts some of the product to p-nitrobromobenzene, but also accelerates the heterolysis of the diazonium salt. In this case, the rate of decomposition is equal to the sum of two terms,

$$\frac{d(\mathrm{N_2})}{dt} = k_1(\mathrm{ArN_2^+}) + k_2(\mathrm{ArN_2^+})(\mathrm{Br^-}) \tag{17}$$

the second term corresponding to direct displacement of N$_2$ by the bromide ion.[90] The more usual way of replacing an aromatic diazonium group with bromide (or with chloride or cyanide) involves reaction with the cuprous complex CuBr$_2^-$ (or with CuCl$_2^-$ or Cu(CN)$_2^-$), the familiar *Sandmeyer reaction*. This reaction, which is thought at present to proceed through a free-radical mechanism, is discussed in Chapter 16.

The von Richter Rearrangement

The reaction of *meta*- and *para*-nitrohalobenzenes with aqueous alcoholic KCN above 150° results predominantly in loss of the nitro group as NO$_2^-$ (rather than

[90] Lewis and Hinds, *J. Am. Chem. Soc.*, **74**, 304 (1952).

displacement of the halogen atom) and the acquisition of a carboxyl group. This reaction is often called the *von Richter rearrangement*, for it was this worker who found that the position taken by the incoming carboxyl group was *not* the same as that vacated by the nitro group.[91(a)] More specifically, the reaction of a *p*-nitrohalobenzene yields a *meta* compound, whereas the reaction of a *m*-nitrohalobenzene yields a mixture of *ortho* and *para* compounds.

The migration of a cyano group is not involved here, for *meta*- and *para*-halobenzonitriles do not rearrange. What might appear to be the most reasonable mechanism is

LVIII

Yet this mechanism cannot be completely correct, for halobenzonitriles related to the "rearranged" acid cannot be hydrolyzed under the reaction conditions employed. Moreover, the amide related to the final acid, when prepared independently, likewise resists hydrolysis under von Richter conditions.

[91] (a) von Richter, *Ber.*, **8**, 1418 (1875). For more reactant studies of this reaction, see: (b) Holleman, *Rec. trav. chim.*, **24**, 194 (1905); (c) Bunnett, Cormack, and McKay, *J. Org. Chem.*, **15**, 481 (1950); (d) Bunnett and Rauhut, *ibid.*, **21**, 944 (1956).

A more acceptable (but still tentative) mechanism is as follows:[91(d)]

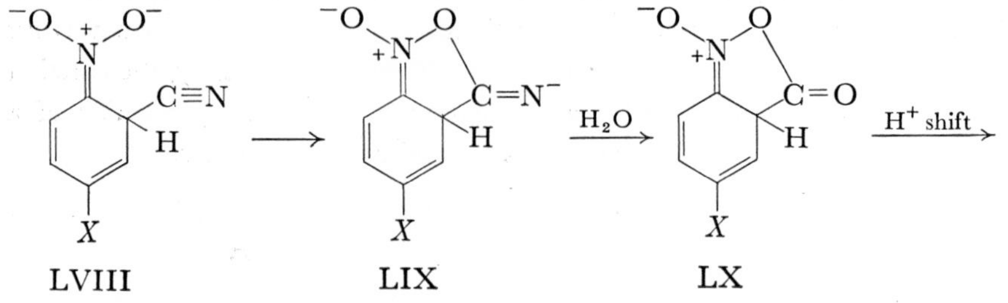

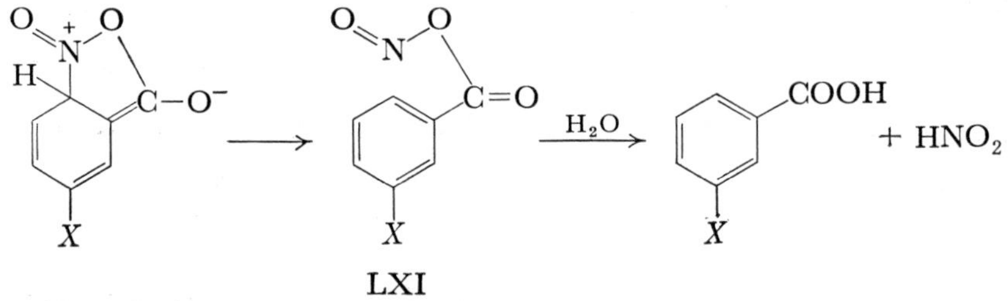

LVIII   LIX   LX

LXI

Once again it is proposed that the initial intermediate is adduct LVIII, formed by attack of CN⁻ on the electron-deficient ring carbon *ortho* to the nitro group. It is further suggested that the nitro group assists the hydrolysis of the cyano group, possibly by formation of the cyclic anion, LIX. As shown, the resulting species LX is tautomeric with the substituted benzoyl nitrite, LXI, which is, in turn, readily hydrolyzed to the resulting carboxylic acid. This scheme is an interesting one, but further investigation is obviously desirable.

Aminations of "Nonactivated" Aryl Halides. Benzynelike Intermediates

Aryl halides having no activating group such as —NO₂ or —CN may be converted to arylamines using metallic amides (for example, $NaNH_2$ or $LiNEt_2$). However, it is now clear that the mechanism by which these conversions generally proceed is very different from the substitution mechanisms that have thus far been considered. Indeed, these reactions are not simple substitutions at all but are instead combinations of *elimination* (of the hydrogen halide) and *addition*. As indicated, the intermediate in such a sequence is a substituted *benzyne*, LXII, a species of unusual interest since, despite many attempts, no compound having a triple bond in a six-membered ring (or, for that matter, in a three-, four-, or five-membered ring) has been isolated.[92] For this reason, we would be very

[92] Ideally, in an acetylenic derivative, the two triple-bonded carbons and the two atoms singly bound to these carbons should lie in a straight line. Such an arrangement, or even a reasonable approach to it, is obviously impossible when the triple bond is incorporated into a

skeptical of the existence of an intermediate such as LX if the evidence in its favor were not quite compelling.

$$(18)$$

The sequence above suggests that the aminations of aryl halides should be accompanied by rearrangement, but that these rearrangements need not be complete (as in the von Richter reaction). Such rearrangements have long been known to occur.[93] Furthermore, the entering nitrogen atom should not be found further than one carbon atom away from the position of the departing halogen atom; that is, *ortho*-substituted halobenzenes should not give rise to *para*-substituted arylamines. This also is observed. Typically, treatment of *o*-chlorotoluene with KNH_2 in liquid ammonia yields a mixture of *o*- and *m*-toluidines (but no *p*-isomer); similar treatment of *p*-chlorotoluene yields a mixture of *m*- and *p*-toluidines (but no *o*-isomer); and treatment of *m*-chlorotoluene yields a mixture of all three toluidines.[94(a)]

For reactions in which only one benzyne intermediate is possible, sequence (18) demands that the ratio of isomeric amines in the mixture of products be independent of the nature of the halogen atom that departs in the elimination step. This has been shown to be the case for the mixtures of amines resulting from the action of NH_3 and KNH_2 on the *o*-halotoluenes[94(a)] and also for the mixture of α- and β-naphthylpiperidines resulting from the action of piperidine

four-, five-, or six-membered ring. The bond lengths or the bond angles (or both) in cyclobutyne, cyclopentyne, and cyclohexyne would be very different from their "normal" values, and compounds containing such rings would be expected to be extremely unstable.

[93] See, for example, Haeussermann, *Ber.*, **33**, 939 (1900); **34**, 38 (1901); and Gilman, *et al.*, *J. Am. Chem. Soc.*, **67**, 3491 (1945); **68**, 143 (1946); **70**, 3945 (1948).

[94] (a) Roberts, Vaughan, Carlsmith, and Semenow, *J. Am. Chem. Soc.*, **78**, 611 (1956). (b) Roberts, Semenow, Simmons, and Carlsmith, *ibid.*, **79**, 601 (1956).

and sodamide on α-chloro-, α-bromo-, and α-iodonaphthalenes.[95] Moreover, if the benzyne intermediate is symmetric, the incoming nitrogen atom should be just as likely to attack at the position from which the halogen atom departed as at the adjacent position. In this regard we have already pointed out (p. 144) that when chlorobenzene having the 1-carbon labeled (LXIV) is treated with KNH_2 in liquid ammonia, almost exactly 50 percent rearrangement (actually

LXIV   48 percent   52 percent

52 percent rearrangement) occurs.[96] Finally, if sequence (18) represents the correct path for amination, halobenzenes having no *ortho* hydrogens should not undergo amination unless reaction conditions are made sufficiently severe so that direct displacement of the halogen may occur. It has, in fact, been found that bromodurene (LXV), bromomesitylene (LXVI), and 2-bromo-3-methyl-anisole (LXVII) are inert toward KNH_2 in liquid ammonia,[94(b),97] although steric hindrance to attack on the ring should not be prohibitive.[88]

LXV   LXVI   LXVII

None of the observations concerning the aminations of halobenzenes will, when taken alone, prove the intervention of the benzyne intermediate, but, when taken together, they comprise a rather convincing case. Furthermore, we now have evidence that benzyne intercedes as an intermediate in other reactions, for this species apparently is a powerful "dienophile" in the Diels-Alder reaction. Thus, if *o*-bromofluorobenzene is treated with lithium or magnesium in the presence of furan[98(a)] or anthracene,[98(b)] products are isolated that may be rationalized most easily by assuming a Diels-Alder condensation with benzyne, which, in turn, results from dehalogenation of the starting material.

[95] Bunnett and Brotherton, *J. Am. Chem. Soc.*, **78**, 6265 (1956). Here, the intermediate is presumably naphthalyne, LXIII.

[96] The slight departure from 50 percent rearrangement (a kinetic isotope effect) is not unexpected, for reactions at C^{14}-labeled positions are generally known to be slightly slower than those at unlabeled positions. See Ropp, *Nucleonics*, **10**, 22 (1952).

[97] Benkeser and Buting, *J. Am. Chem. Soc.*, **74**, 3011 (1952).

[98] (a) Wittig and Pohmer, *Angew. Chem.*, **67**, 348 (1955). (b) Wittig and Ludwig, *ibid.*, **68**, 40 (1956).

The elimination-addition (benzyne) mechanism is an important one for the substitution reaction of "nonactivated" aryl halides, but there is evidence that substitution by direct displacement (the S_N2 reaction) may occur as well. For example, although α-chloro-, α-bromo-, and α-iodonaphthalene yield the same mixture of naphthylpiperidines on treatment with piperidine and sodamide, the α-fluoro compound yields *much more of the unrearranged product* than do the other three halides.[93] This suggests that α-fluoronaphthalene is reacting by both the benzyne and S_N2 mechanisms, whereas the heavier halides react almost exclusively by elimination-addition. This is not surprising, for we have seen that aryl fluorides undergo S_N2 reactions much more easily than aryl chlorides, bromides, and iodides (p. 454). On the other hand, fluorides are known to be converted to benzynes only with difficulty[94(b)] (presumably because such a conversion requires the breaking of a C—F bond with considerable double-bond character).

The basic hydrolyses of halobenzenes and halotoluenes are negligibly slow at room temperature, but occur readily at 250 to 350°. It has recently been shown[99] these hydrolyses may, depending upon reaction conditions, proceed by the S_N2 mechanism, by the "benzyne mechanism," or by a combination of the two. Thus, *p*-bromotoluene is hydrolyzed by 1 N NaOH at 340° largely by the benzyne mechanism (50 percent rearrangement), and at 250° by both mechanisms simultaneously (22 percent rearrangement); whereas *p*-iodotoluene is hydrolyzed at 250° almost completely by direct displacement (less than 3 percent rearrangement). Chlorobenzene, with the chlorinated carbon labeled, has been shown to be hydrolyzed by both mechanisms at 340°; for among the resulting phenol molecules, 58 percent are labeled at the hydroxylated carbon with only 42 percent labeled at the positions *ortho* to it. (As we have seen, the amination of chlorobenzene, which proceeds entirely by the benzyne mechanism, yields a slight excess of rearranged product.)

[99] Bottini and Roberts, *J. Am. Chem. Soc.*, **79**, 1458 (1957).

It should be emphasized that the benzyne mechanism may operate only in the presence of strong base, since only strong bases can remove protons from the benzene ring. Thus, p-bromotoluene, when treated with aqueous sodium acetate at 340° yields p-cresol but none of the *ortho* or *meta* isomer,[99] indicating that the destruction of the halide has, in this solution, occurred only by the S_N2 mechanism.

EXERCISES FOR CHAPTER 11

1. Predict the position most likely to be taken by the incoming nitro group in the mono-nitration of each of the following. Justify your choice in each case.

(a) $C_6H_5CF_3$
(b) Thiophene
(c) Naphthalene
(d) C_6H_5SCN
(e) $C_6H_5SeO_2H$

(f)

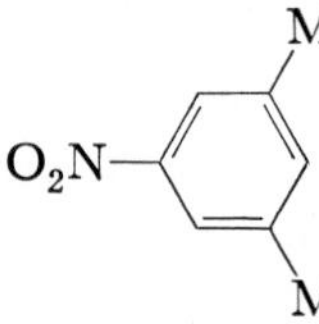

(g) 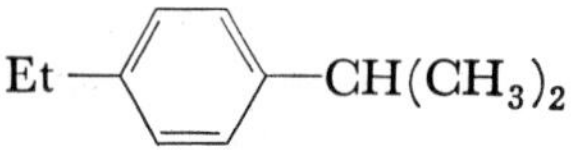 Et—⟨⟩—$CH(CH_3)_2$

(h) 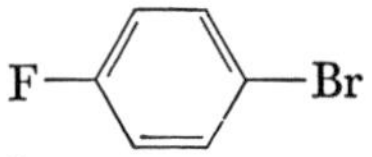 F—⟨⟩—Br

(i)

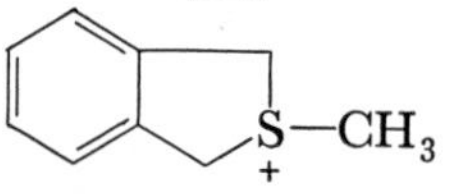

(j)

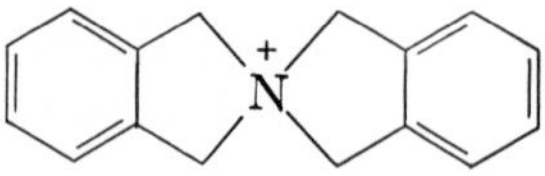

(k)

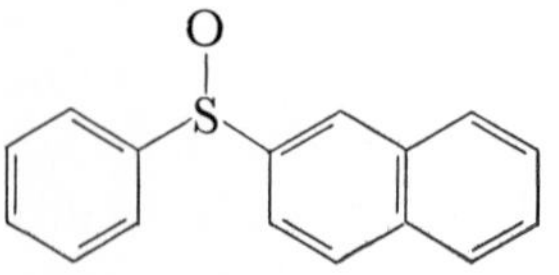

(l)

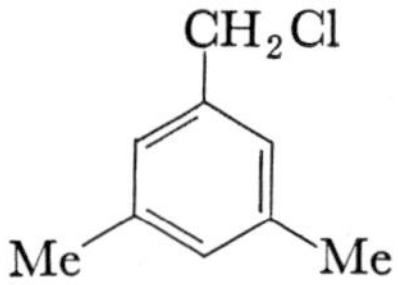

(m)

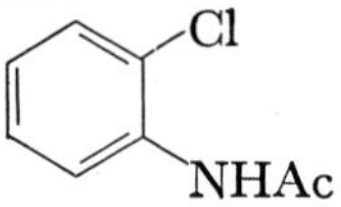

(n)

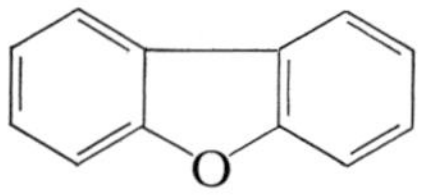

(o)

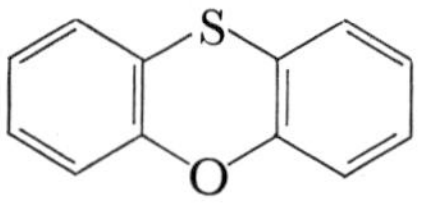

(p)

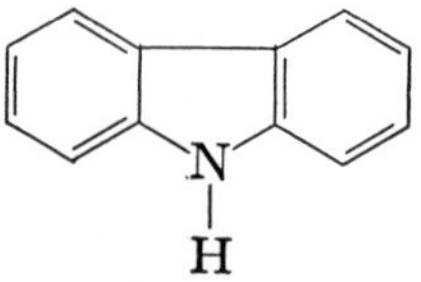

(q) biphenyl

(r)

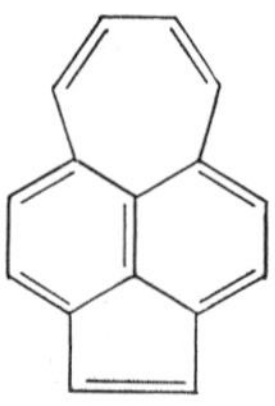

2. Consider the presently accepted mechanism for aromatic nitration:

$$2HNO_3 \underset{k_{-1}}{\overset{k_1}{\rightleftharpoons}} H_2NO_3^+ + NO_3^-$$

$$H_2NO_3^+ \underset{k_{-2}}{\overset{k_2}{\rightleftharpoons}} NO_2^+ + H_2O$$

$$NO_2^+ + ArH \xrightarrow[k_3]{} \left[Ar \overset{NO_2}{\underset{H}{\diagup}} \right]^+ \xrightarrow[k_4]{(fast)} ArNO_2 + H^+$$

(a) Assuming that, very shortly after the beginning of the reaction, the concentration of NO_2^+ reaches a steady state value, show that the reaction rate is given by the expression:

$$\text{rate} = \frac{\dfrac{k_1}{k_{-1}} (HNO_3)^2}{(NO_3^-) \left[\dfrac{k_{-2}(H_2O)}{k_3(ArH)} + 1 \right]}$$

(b) Assume that k_1 and k_{-1} are large (that is, that the first step is readily reversible) and that the concentrations of nitric acid, water, and nitrate ion remain nearly constant during the course of the reaction. Show that the rate law in (a) predicts a nitration rate very nearly independent of (ArH) when the attack by NO_2^+ on ArH is much faster than its return to $H_2NO_3^+$. Show also that if the attack by NO_2^+ on ArH is much slower than its return to $H_2NO_3^+$, the nitration rate becomes proportional to (ArH).

(c) Show that if the rate of attack by NO_2^+ is comparable to its rate of reconversion to $H_2NO_3^+$, the nitration rate will depend on (ArH) but will not be directly proportional to it.

(d) Show that if both (NO_3^-) and (H_2O) are small, doubling (NO_3^-) will be far more effective in retarding nitration than will doubling (H_2O).

(e) For the nitration of a very reactive aromatic, show that a large increase in (H_2O) will result in a transition from pseudo-zero- to pseudo-first-order kinetics.

3. Consider the inhibition of nitration by HNO_2. Assume that this inhibition occurs by the action of NO_3^- generated in the reaction:

$$HNO_2 + HNO_3 \rightleftharpoons NO^+ + H_2O + NO_3^-$$

(a) Assume further that the concentration of nitrate in such a solution may be estimated by adding (NO_3^-) present in the solution, before HNO_2 is added, to the concentration of nitrate generated by addition of HNO_2. Show that the rate of nitration in the presence of HNO_2 is

$$\text{rate} = \frac{(\text{rate})_0}{1 + a \sqrt{(\text{``}HNO_2\text{''})}}$$

where $(\text{rate})_0$ is the nitration rate in the absence of HNO_2, a is a constant, and ("HNO_2") is the total concentration of tripositive nitrogen present very largely as N_2O_4.

(b) According to (a), a plot of $(\text{rate}_0/\text{rate}$ vs. $\sqrt{(\text{``}HNO_2\text{''})}$ should give a straight line of slope a. It is found, however, that at small concentrations of added nitrous acid, this plot is "concave downward"—that is, that the ratio $(\text{rate})_0/\text{rate}$ is closer to unity than would be predicted by the expression in (a). Explain.

(c) Consider the additional mode of inhibition of nitration by HNO_2 in the presence of moderate concentrations of water. This presumably occurs by the action of small amounts of NO_2^- with $H_2NO_3^+$:

$$NO_2^- + H_2NO_3^+ \rightleftharpoons HNO_2 + HNO_3$$

Assume that the NO_2^- arises from N_2O_3, which is, in turn, generated from N_2O_4:

$$2N_2O_4 + H_2O \rightleftharpoons N_2O_3 + 2HNO_3$$
$$N_2O_3 \rightleftharpoons NO^+ + NO_2^-$$

and assume also that most NO^+ present in solution is generated from N_2O_4

$$N_2O_4 \rightleftharpoons NO^+ + NO_3^-$$

Show that (NO_2^-) is very nearly proportional to $(\text{``}HNO_2\text{''})^{3/2}$, and that if this mode of inhibition is considered to augment additively the inhibition by NO_3^- discussed in (a), then the rate of nitration may be approximated by the expression:

$$\text{rate} = \frac{(\text{rate})_0}{1 + a\,(\text{``}HNO_2\text{''})^{1/2} + b\,(\text{``}HNO_2\text{''})^{3/2}}$$

(d) Show that the rate law for nitrosation in nitric acid (equation 2) is consistent with attack by NO^+ or N_2O_4, but inconsistent with attack by HNO_2, $H_2NO_2^+$, or N_2O_3.

4. The rates of aromatic sulfonations is concentrated sulfuric acid containing small amounts of added water are inversely proportional to the square of the concentration of added water. Show that this is consistent with attack by SO_3 or $H_2S_2O_7$, but not with attack by $H_3SO_4^+$, HSO_3^+, or S_2O_6.

5. The *para* to *meta* ratio resulting from the nitration of toluene with acetyl nitrate in acetic acid is 8.5.
   (a) Estimate ρ for aromatic nitration in this medium.
   (b) Estimate the *para* to *meta* ratio resulting from the nitration of anisole under similar conditions. (Ignore nitration via nitrosation.)

6. Propose mechanisms for each of the following conversions:
   (a) $HNO_3 + H_2O^{18} \rightarrow H_3O^+ + [O_2NO^{18}]^-$
   (b) $N_2O_5 + C_6H_6 \xrightarrow{CCl_4} PhNO_2 + HNO_3$
   (c) $C_6H_6 + DCl \xrightarrow{AlCl_3} C_6H_5D + HCl$
   (HCl and $AlCl_3$ do not react in the absence of other substances.)

(d) $PhNH_2 \xrightarrow{HNO_2} \xrightarrow{\alpha-\text{naphthol}}$

(e) 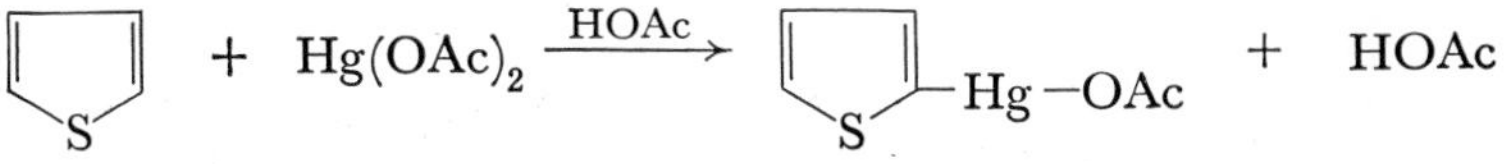 + Hg(OAc)$_2$ $\xrightarrow{\text{HOAc}}$ + HOAc

(f)

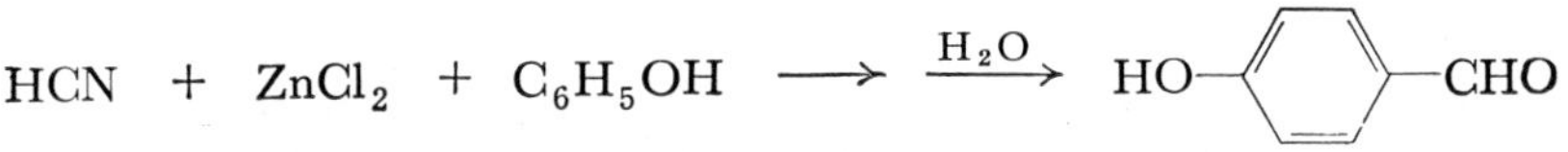

HCN + ZnCl$_2$ + C$_6$H$_5$OH $\longrightarrow$ $\xrightarrow{\text{H}_2\text{O}}$ HO—⟨ ⟩—CHO

(g) I$_2$O$_5$ + C$_6$H$_6$ + conc H$_2$SO$_4$ $\longrightarrow$ ⟨ ⟩—IO$_2$

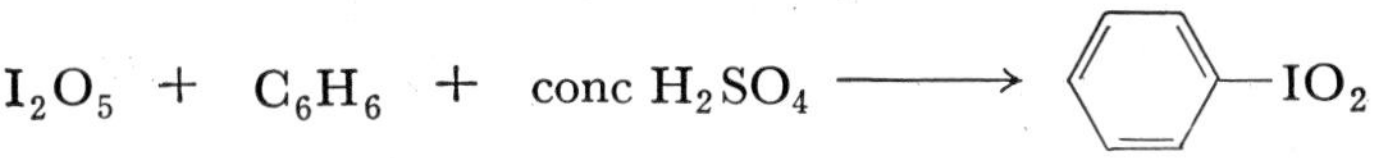

(h) C$_6$H$_6$ + fuming H$_2$SO$_4$ $\longrightarrow$ ⟨ ⟩—SO$_2$—⟨ ⟩

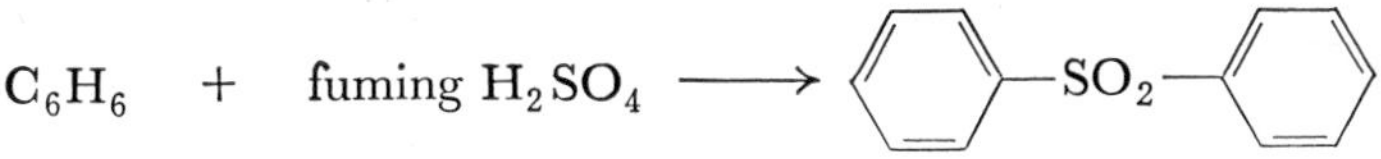

(i) IBr + C$_6$H$_5$OMe $\longrightarrow$ Br—⟨ ⟩—OMe + HI

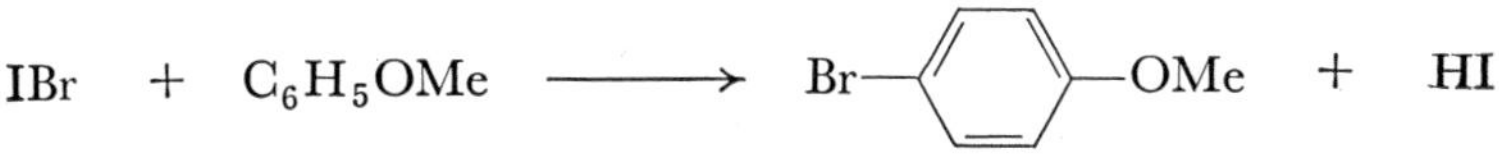

(j) 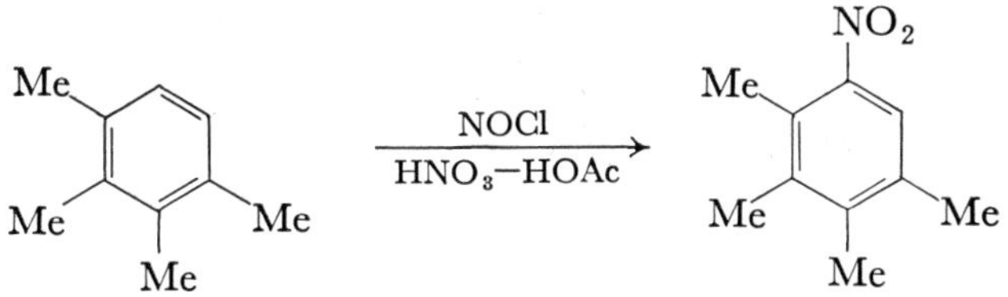 $\xrightarrow[\text{HNO}_3-\text{HOAc}]{\text{NOCl}}$

(k) t-Bu—C$_6$H$_5$ + Br$_2$ $\xrightarrow{\text{AlBr}_3}$ C$_6$H$_5$Br + Me$_2$C=CH$_2$ + HBr

(l) 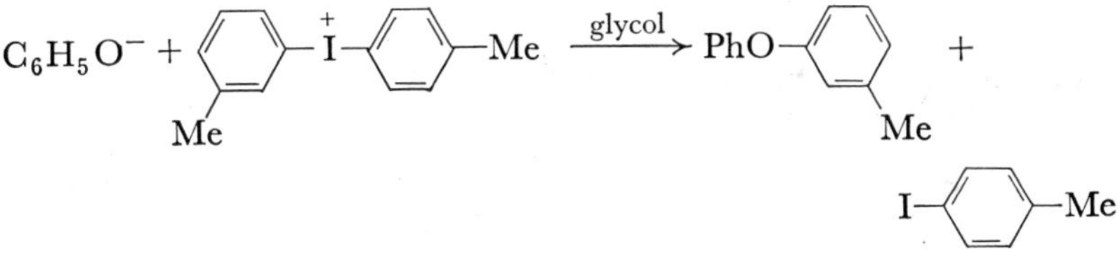 C$_6$H$_5$O$^-$ + $\xrightarrow{\text{glycol}}$ PhO— +

I—⟨ ⟩—Me

(m) + H$_2$SO$_4$ $\longrightarrow$

(n) C$_6$H$_5$O—C—CH$_3$ $\xrightarrow{\text{AlCl}_3}$ HO—⟨ ⟩—C—CH$_3$
        ‖   ‖
        O   O

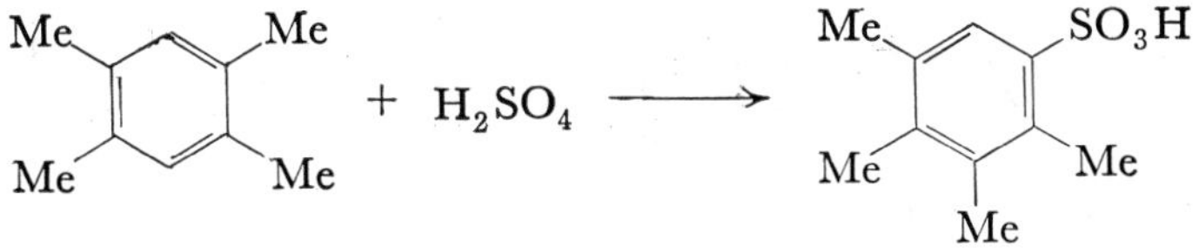

(o) + AlBr$_3$ $\xrightarrow{\text{HBr}}$

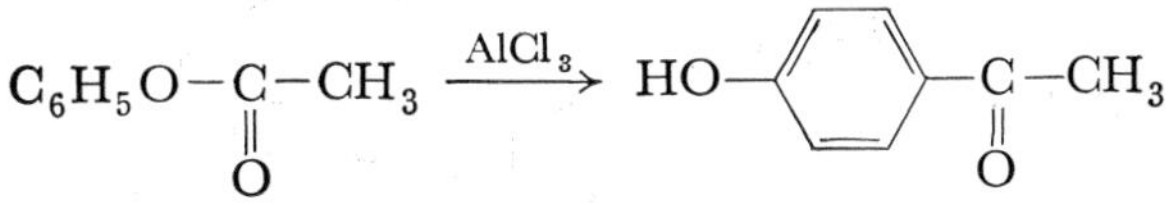

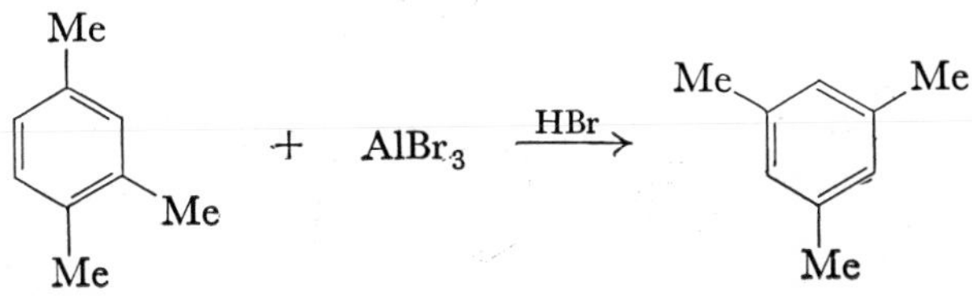

(p) $CH_3\underset{\underset{O}{\|}}{C}$—⟨benzene⟩—$(CH_2)_4 Cl$ $\xrightarrow{AlCl_3}$ indane with $CH_3\underset{\underset{O}{\|}}{C}$ and Me

(q) H_2N—, NO_2, MeO—, NO_2 benzene $+ HNO_2 \xrightarrow{H_2O}$ O_2N—, N_2^+, HO—, OMe benzene

(r) Me—, NO_2, $\underset{\underset{O}{\|}}{\overset{O}{S}}$, OH diaryl sulfone $\xrightarrow{OH^-}$ Me—⟨—SO_2^-—⟩—O—⟨—NO_2⟩

(s) Ac, tetralin $\xrightarrow[HCl]{AlCl_3}$ Ac, Me indane

(t) HO—⟨—⟩—Br $\xrightarrow[melt]{NaOH}$ ^-O—⟨—⟩—O^- $+$ Br^-

(u) Me—⟨—⟩, Br $+ KNH_2 \xrightarrow{ether}$ ⟨Me⟩—$\underset{H}{N}$—⟨Me⟩ $+$ Br^-

(v) $CH_3\underset{\underset{O}{\|}}{C}$—⟨—⟩—$CH_2CH_2CH_2\underset{\underset{Me}{|}}{CH}COCl$ $\xrightarrow{AlCl_3}$ Ac, tetralin, Me $+$ CO

(w) O_2N, $\underset{\underset{\|}{C}}{O}$—⟨S⟩, COOH $\xrightarrow{H_2SO_4}$ ⟨—⟩, $\underset{\underset{\|}{C}}{O}$—⟨S⟩, COOH, O_2N

(x) ⟨—⟩—$NH-\underset{\underset{\|}{C}}{S}-Ph$, Br $\xrightarrow[NH_3]{KNH_2}$ benzothiazole $\underset{S}{\overset{N}{⟩}}$—Ph

7. Predict the chief products for the following reactions, justifying in each case:

(a) 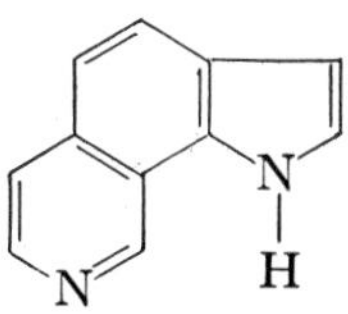 $+$ $1 CH_3I$ $\longrightarrow$

(b) 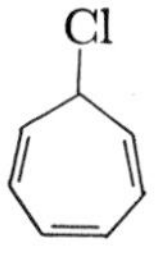 $+$ $AgBF_4$ $\xrightarrow{CH_3CN}$

(c) 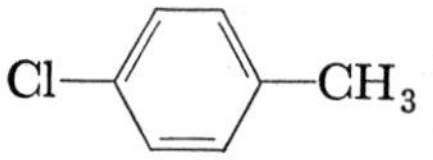 Cl——CH_3 $+$ conc HNO_3 $\xrightarrow{CH_3NO_2}$

(d) Ferrocene $+ 3CH_3COCl + 2AlBr_3 \longrightarrow$

(e) 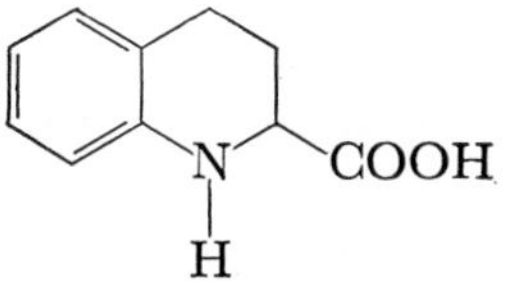 $+$ HNO_2 $\longrightarrow$ $\xrightarrow{Ac_2O}$

(f) $N_2O_5 +$ conc $H_2SO_4 \longrightarrow$

(g) $PhB(OH)_2 + H_2O_2 \xrightarrow{H^+}$

(h) 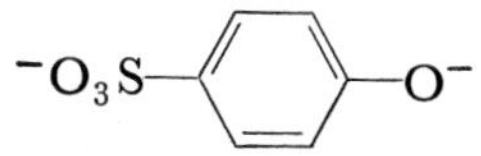 ^-O_3S——O^- $+$ $3 Br_2$ $\longrightarrow$

(i) m-Nitroacetophenone $+ HNO_3 \xrightarrow{H_2SO_4}$

(j) $PhHgCl + ICl \xrightarrow{benzene}$

(k) $Ph_2CHCH_2Cl + C_6H_6 \xrightarrow{AlCl_3}$

(l) n-BuBr $+ TiBr_4 +$ thiophene $\longrightarrow$

(m) 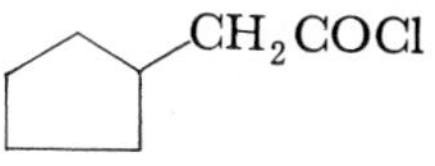 $+$ $AlCl_3$ $+$ C_6H_5F $\longrightarrow$

(n) 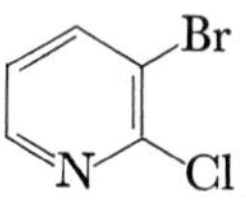 $+$ $C_6H_5NH_2$ $\longrightarrow$

(o) 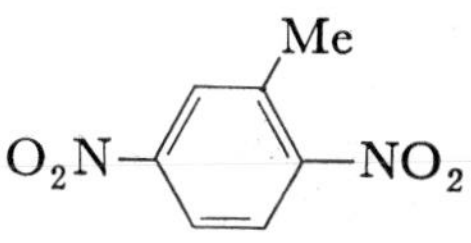 O_2N——NO_2 $+$ NH_3 $\longrightarrow$

(p) o-Chloroanisole $+ LiNEt_2 \xrightarrow{ether}$

8. Consider the sequence of steps in the amination of halobenzenes by the "benzyne" mechanism:

(a) What evidence is there that the rate-determining step does not occur *after* the formation of benzyne (that is, that the formation of benzyne from the halobenzenes is neither fast and irreversible nor fast and reversible)?

(b) What evidence is there that the first step is not fast and irreversible with the second step slow?

(c) From (a) and (b), it follows that the initial step must be either fast and reversible (with the second step slow) or slow (with the second step fast). Outline an experiment with an *o*-deuterohalobenzene to decide which possibility is correct.

(d) When *o*-deuterofluorobenzene is treated with KNH_2 in liquid ammonia it is converted to unlabeled fluorobenzene, but no appreciable amination occurs. Explain.

(e) When *o*-deuterochlorobenzene is treated with KNH_2 in liquid ammonia and the unreacted halide is reisolated before amination is complete, the deuterium content of the aryl halide is found to *decrease*. If the corresponding experiment is carried out with *o*-deuterobromobenzene, the deuterium content in the unreacted halide is found to *increase*. Explain.

(f) The rates of amination of aryl halides with KNH_2 in liquid ammonia lie in the order: PhBr > PhI > PhCl ≫ PhF. Explain.

(g) The aminations of both *o*-chloroanisole and *m*-chloroanisole yield only *m*-anisidine. Explain.

9. Explain each of the following:

(a) The rates of nitration of nitrobenzene in H_2SO_4—HNO_3 mixtures parallel the degree to which indicator LXVIII is converted to its acidic form but do not parallel indicator LXIX (anthraquinone) is converted to is acidic form.

LXVIII   LXIX

(b) Iodination of mesitylene in CCl_4 with ICl is third order with respect to ICl, but the same reaction in liquid CF_3COOH is first order with respect to ICl.

(c) Aromatic nitrations with N_2O_5 in CCl_4 may be accelerated by addition of pure HNO_3.

(d) The bromination of *m*-xylene in acetic acid is accelerated by the addition of water, but the sulfonation of xylene in concentrated H_2SO_4 is retarded by the addition of water.

(e) No isomerization of the alkyl group is observed in Friedel-Crafts alkylations with *t*-butyl chloride, but extensive isomerization is observed in alkylations with $C_2H_5C(CH_3)_2Cl$.

(f) Rearrangement of the side chain occurs in the cyclization of chloride LXX with $AlCl_3$ but not in the cyclization of LXXI.

$$CH_3\overset{\displaystyle}{\underset{\displaystyle O}{\overset{\|}{C}}}-\langle\rangle-(CH_2)_3Cl \qquad\qquad Ph(CH_2)_3Cl$$

LXX   LXXI

(g) The yield of *n*-propyl derivative from the reaction of *m*-xylene with *n*-PrBr in the presence of $GaBr_3$ is greater than that obtained from the corresponding reaction of *p*-xylene.

(h) The ring closure of acyl halide LXXII in the presence of $AlCl_3$ occurs without decarbonylation, but this is not true for acyl halide LXXIII.

$$Ph(CH_2)_2CMe.COCl \qquad\qquad Ph(CH_2)_3CMe_2COCl$$
$$\text{LXXII} \qquad\qquad\qquad \text{LXXIII}$$

(i) The reaction of 2,4-dinitrochlorobenzene with LiOMe in absolute methanol is accelerated greatly by addition of KOAc, accelerated slightly by addition of NaOAc, retarded slightly by the addition of LiOAc, and retarded greatly by addition of $LiClO_4$.

(j) The extent of decarbonylation occurring during the Friedel-Crafts reaction of trimethylacetyl chloride with toluene in CS_2 is increased when the reaction is carried out at high dilution.

(k) The decomposition of *o*-toluenediazonium chloride in water is much faster than that of *p*-toluenediazonium chloride under comparable conditions.

(l) The decomposition of the $D_3C-\langle\rangle-N_2^+$ ion is about 1 percent faster than that of the unlabeled *p*-toluenediazonium ion under identical conditions.

(m) *o*-Bromonitrobenzene does not undergo the von Richter reaction.

(n) The yield of *p*-toluidine from the amination of *m*-bromotoluene (with KNH_2 and liquid ammonia) is considerably larger than that from the amination of *m*-chlorotoluene.

Beta-elimination Reactions

THE INTRODUCTION OF UNSATURATION into a molecule generally involves the loss of two substituents from a pair of adjacent atoms in a chain or ring. Commonly, a proton is lost from one of two bound carbon atoms and a nucleophile, X:, is lost from the other.

$$X-\overset{\alpha}{\underset{|}{\overset{|}{C}}}-\overset{\beta}{\underset{|}{\overset{|}{C}}}-H \xrightarrow{-HX} \overset{\alpha}{\underset{/}{\searrow}}C=\overset{\beta}{\underset{\searrow}{\overset{/}{C}}}$$

$$(-X = -\text{halogen}, -NR_3^+, -OH_2^+, -SR_2^+, -O-\underset{\underset{O}{\|}}{C}-R, \text{ etc.})$$

This is a *beta elimination*, the carbon atom bearing substituent $-X$ being designated the α-carbon, and the carbon atom from which the proton is removed being the β-carbon. A number of additional types of beta elimination have been studied in some detail, among them

$$ArCH=N-Cl \xrightarrow{-HCl} ArC\equiv N^{1(a)}$$

$$R_2CH-O-NO_2 \xrightarrow{-HNO_2} R_2C=O^{1(b)}$$

and $\quad CH_3CCH_2CMe_2-OH \xrightarrow{OH^-} CH_3CCH_3 + Me_2C=O^{1(c)}$
$\qquad\quad \underset{O}{\|} \qquad\qquad\qquad\qquad \underset{O}{\|}$

However, in this chapter, we shall be concerned only with those beta eliminations in which olefins and acetylenes are formed.[2]

---

[1] (a) Hauser, LeMaistre, and Rainsford, *J. Am. Chem. Soc.*, **57**, 1056 (1935). (b) Baker and Easty, *J. Chem. Soc.*, **1952**, 1193, 1208. (c) LeMer and Miller, *J. Am. Chem. Soc.*, **57**, 2674 (1935).

[2] For reviews of olefin-forming eliminations see (a) Cram, "Olefin-forming Elimination Reactions" in Newman's *Steric Effects in Organic Chemistry*, John Wiley and Sons, Inc., New York, 1956, pp. 305–348; (b) Ingold, *Structure and Mechanism in Organic Chemistry*, Cornell University Press, Ithaca, 1953, pp. 420–472; and (c) Dhar, *et al.*, *J. Chem. Soc.*, **1948**, 2093.

Unimolecular Eliminations. The $E1$ Mechanism

In discussing substitution reactions, we noted that S_N1 reactions are often accompanied by olefin formation, which does not, however, alter their kinetic character (p. 263). In such cases, the carbonium ion formed in the initial slow step may be attacked in more than one way by nucleophilic species present in solution. Consider, for example, the ethanolysis of t-butyl bromide, which, according to our present picture, proceeds through the t-butyl cation (I):

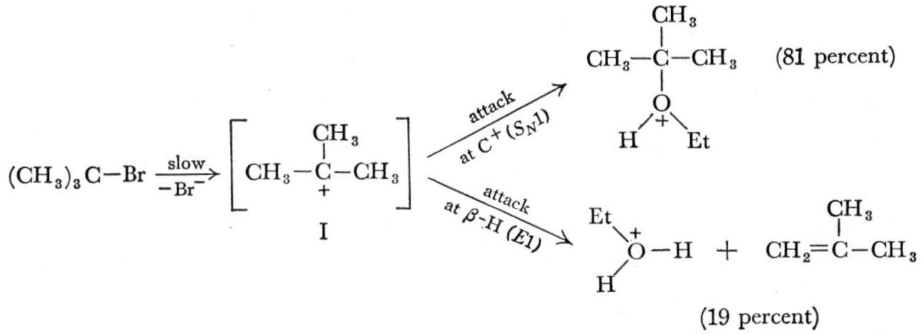

As indicated, a molecule of ethanol may attach itself to the positively charged carbon, completing the substitution process, or it may extract a β-hydrogen from the carbonium ion, forming isobutene. With t-butyl bromide, in which all β-hydrogens are equivalent, only one olefin is formed, but with more complicated substrates such as t-amyl bromide, $EtCMe_2Br$, elimination may take place in two (or even three) directions, forming two (or three) olefins.

The slow step in the elimination reaction is the ionization of the substrate. Since this step is unimolecular, this elimination and others like it are often designated unimolecular elimination $(E1)$ reactions, in obvious analogy to unimolecular nucleophilic-substitution (S_N1) reactions. The $E1$ mechanism is an important one for olefin-forming eliminations; it has been established for a number of alkyl halides and sulfonium salts,[3] and it is almost certainly the path by which acid-catalyzed "dehydrations" of many alcohols proceed. We would expect to encounter this mechanism in cases where the substrate may yield a relatively stable carbonium ion—that is, when the α-carbon is secondary or tertiary, and, more particularly, when an α-phenyl or α-vinyl group is present. Needless to say, the substrate must also have one or more β-hydrogen atoms.

Assuming that the initial slow heterolysis (rate constant k_{het}) is irreversible, the competition between unimolecular substitution and elimination reactions leads to the rate expression for elimination:

$$(\text{rate})_{\text{elim}} = k_{\text{het}}(\text{R}X)\,\frac{k_E}{k_S + k_E} \qquad (1)$$

[3] Hughes, Ingold, *et al.*, *J. Chem. Soc.*, **1937**, 1271–1285; **1940**, 2038–2093.

where k_S and k_E are the rate constants for the substitution and elimination reactions which consume the carbonium ion. This expression emphasizes the close relationship between the rates of elimination and heterolysis and tells us that any environmental factor that affects the rate of heterolysis must also affect the rate of elimination to about the same extent. Thus, the $E1$ reactions of alkyl halides will be faster in polar than in nonpolar solvents and should be accelerated by addition of noncommon-ion salts.

The proposed mechanism for unimolecular elimination requires that the elimination to substitution ratio associated with a given alkyl group in a substrate be independent of the leaving group; although RBr, RI, and RSMe$_2^+$ react at different rates in a given medium, the ratio of substitution product to olefin should be the same for each. As we have already seen (p. 263), this is true only to a first approximation, for changing the leaving group sometimes introduces minor but unmistakable variations in the $S_N1/E1$ ratio.[4] It therefore appears that in some cases the leaving group remains close enough to the carbonium-ion intermediate to influence slightly (in a manner not yet clear) the mode of subsequent reaction.

Broadly speaking, unimolecular elimination, even more than unimolecular substitution, is favored by branching at the β-carbon atoms. Table 12-1 lists the percent olefin produced in the unimolecular solvolysis of a number of alkyl chlorides ("80 percent" alcohol at 25°).[5] Note that at one end of the scale,

Table 12-1. Percent Olefin Formed in the Solvolyses of Some Alkyl Chlorides

Alkyl Chlorides	Percent Olefin	Alkyl Chlorides	Percent Olefin
		H	
		$\|$	
$(CH_3)_3CCl$	16	$(CH_3)_2C\!-\!C(CH_3)_2Cl$	62
$CH_3CH_2C(CH_3)_2Cl$	34	$(CH_3)_3C\!-\!C(CH_3)_2Cl$	61
$(CH_3CH_2)_2C(CH_3)Cl$	41	$(i\text{-}Pr)_2C(CH_3)Cl$	78
$(CH_3CH_2)_3CCl$	40	$(CH_3)_3C\!-\!C(C_2H_5)_2Cl$	90
$CH_3CH_2CH_2C(CH_3)_2Cl$	33		

t-butyl chloride (in which none of the β-carbons bear alkyl substituents) is solvolyzed with only 16 percent elimination, whereas t-BuC(Et)$_2$Cl (in which there are five methyl groups bound to β-carbons) is solvolyzed with 90 percent elimination. The yields of olefins from the remaining chlorides (which have one

[4] For example, in 80 percent EtOH, the $S_N1/E1$ ratio for t-BuCl at 65° is the same as that for t-BuSMe$_2^+$, but the ratios for the corresponding t-amyl derivatives (at 50°) differ by about 30 percent. Likewise, the $S_N1/E1$ ratios for t-AmBr and t-AmI (at 25°) are the same, but are about 35 percent greater than the ratio for t-AmCl.

[5] (a) Brown and Fletcher, *J. Am. Chem. Soc.*, **72**, 1223 (1950). (b) Brown and Berneis, *ibid.*, **75**, 10 (1953).

to four alkyl groups bound to β-carbons) lie between these extremes. Without looking too closely at the intermediate values, we might suspect that this trend in olefin yield is steric in origin. We have already seen that S_N1 reactions of crowded substrates are subject to steric assistance (p. 279) since strain 's released when the leaving group departs in the rate-determining step, allowing the bond angles about the α-carbon to increase from about 109° (in the substrate) to 120° (in the carbonium-ion intermediate). Extending this reasoning, it might be supposed that the fate of the carbonium ion, once formed, is also subject to steric influences; for if the carbonium ion loses a β-hydrogen (elimination), the bond angles about the β-carbon also decrease, and the molecule becomes even less crowded, whereas if the carbonium ion becomes bound to another nucleophile (substitution), crowding is again increased. It has thus been argued that steric crowding should not only favor S_N1 reactions over S_N2, but should also favor $E1$ reactions over S_N1.[5]

Yet, this cannot be the entire story, for there are a number of cases where an increase in crowding results in a slight decrease in the $E1/S_N1$ ratio. We see, for example, that Et_3CCl gives slightly less olefin than Et_2CMeCl, that n-$PrCMe_2Cl$ gives less olefin than $EtCMe_2Cl$, and that t-$BuCMe_2Cl$ gives a little less than i-$PrCMe_2Cl$; whereas considering only preferential steric assistance to elimination, we would predict the opposite in all three cases. Quite obviously, the elimination to substitution ratio associated with a carbonium ion is being influenced by another factor, which may best be understood by briefly digressing to the related problem of *orientation* in $E1$ reactions.

Although only a limited number of cases have been studied, it now seems clear that when two different olefins may result from an $E1$ reaction, the olefin bearing the *larger number of alkyl substituents* will predominate. (To this statement must be added the familiar and conveniently vague reservation, "In the absence of complicating effects.") Typically, when t-amyl bromide, $EtCMe_2Br$, is solvolyzed in 80 percent ethanol, roughly four fifths of the resulting olefin is compound II (with three alkyl groups) and the remaining fifth is compound III (with but two alkyl groups).[6]

$$CH_3-CH_2-\underset{\underset{CH_3}{|}}{\overset{\overset{CH_3}{|}}{C}}-Br \xrightarrow{\text{80 percent EtOH}}$$

$$CH_3-CH=C\overset{\diagup CH_3}{\diagdown CH_3} \quad + \quad CH_3-CH_2-\underset{\underset{CH_3}{|}}{C}=CH_2 \quad + \quad \begin{cases} t\text{-AmOH} \\ t\text{-AmOEt} \end{cases}$$

II	III	
(32 percent)	(8 percent)	(60 percent)

[6] Dhar, Hughes, and Ingold, *J. Chem. Soc.*, **1948**, 2065.

This preference for the "more substituted" olefin brings to mind the evidence that from heats of combustion and hydrogenation the stability of a double bond may be significantly increased by alkyl substitution on the double-bonded atoms (p. 49)—a stabilization which we attributed to hyperconjugation. Moreover, since C—H hyperconjugation (IV) is presumably more important than C—C hyperconjugation (V), a methyl group, with three hydrogen atoms available for hyperconjugation, is a more effective "stabilizer" than other alkyl

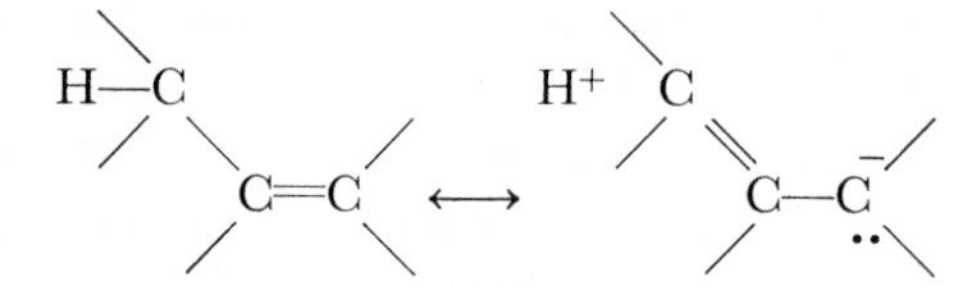

IV

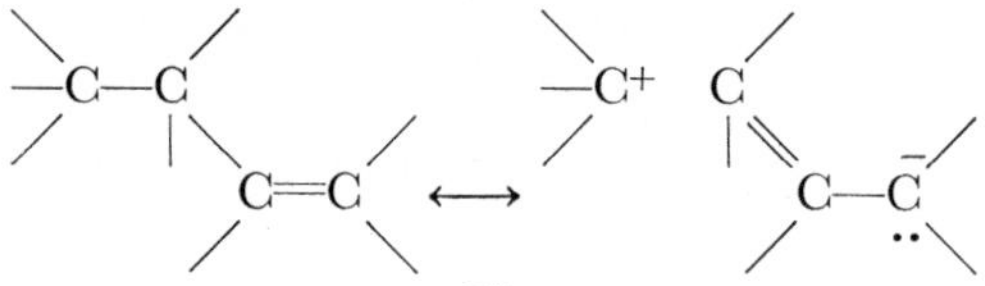

V

groups with fewer available hydrogens.

On this basis, we can understand why Et_2CMeCl, which yields principally olefin VI, having two methyl groups in hyperconjugation with the double bond, exhibits a somewhat higher $E1/S_N1$ ratio than Et_3CCl, which yields olefin VII with only a single methyl group in hyperconjugation. Similarly $EtCMe_2Cl$,

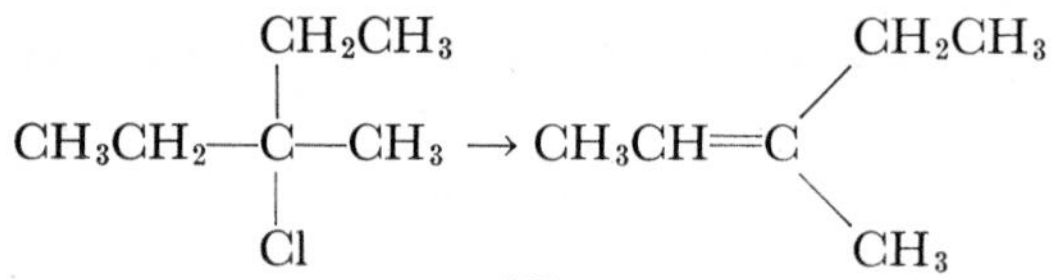

VI

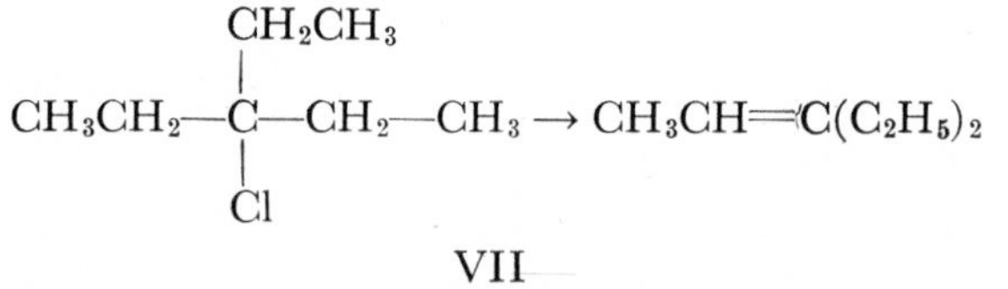

VII

which forms a triple-methylated olefin, exhibits a slightly larger $E1/S_N1$ ratio than n-$PrCMe_2Cl$, which forms a double-methylated olefin. It is thus reasonably clear that the degree to which a carbonium ion may undergo elimination rather than substitution depends both on steric and hyperconjugative effects, although there is some disagreement concerning the relative importance of the two types of effects.[7]

[7] For differing outlooks on this question, see (a) Brown and co-workers, (Ref. 5), who emphasize the importance of steric effects; and (b) Hughes, Ingold, and Shiner, *J. Chem. Soc.*,

Although orientation in elimination by the $E1$ mechanism is generally determined by hyperconjugation, here again there are cases where steric effects are evident. For example, in the mixture of olefins resulting from the solvolysis of brosylate VIII in acetic acid, olefin IX (an "expected" product) predominates, olefin X is a minor product, and olefin XI (the *cis* isomer of IX) is present in only trace amounts.[8(a)] The very low yield of olefin XI is almost certainly due

$$t\text{-Bu—CH}_2\text{—CHMe} \xrightarrow[70°]{\text{HOAc}}$$

$$\underset{\displaystyle\text{OBs}}{|}$$

VIII

t-Bu   H   t-Bu—CH$_2$ t-Bu   Me
   \\   /   \\   \\   /
    C=C   +   C=CH$_2$ +   C=C
   /   \\   /   /   \\
  H   Me   H   H   H
  IX, 75 percent   X, 24 percent   XI, 1 percent

to the operation of a steric effect, for a scale model of this isomer shows that there is significant steric interference between the *t*-butyl and methyl groups situated *cis* to each other, and it is very likely that the transition state leading to olefin XI is, despite hyperconjugation, somewhat less stable than that leading to olefin X.[9] Moreover, with the very crowded chloride XII, loss of HCl in the direction dictated by maximum hyperconjugation must yield olefin XIII, in which one of the methyl groups lies *cis* to the *t*-butyl group. It is therefore not surprising that this elimination leads predominantly to the 1-olefin, XIV, yielding only minor amounts of the more crowded olefin, XIII.[5(b),8(b)]

$$t\text{-Bu—CH}_2\text{—C(CH}_3)_2\text{—Cl} \xrightarrow{-\text{HCl}}$$

XII

t-Bu   Me   t-BuCH$_2$ H
   \\   /   \\   /
    C=C   +   C=C
   /   \\   /   \\
  H   Me   Me   H
  XIII (minor)   XIV (predominant)

---

who emphasize the importance of hyperconjugation. In support of the latter view, it is to be noted that there is no kinetic evidence for significant steric assistance in the *substitution* reactions of any of the chlorides in Table 12-1 save the last two. It is the opinion of the present author that if steric crowding is not important in a particular alkyl halide, it is not likely to be important in the carbonium ion derived from that halide since the carbonium ion is generally less crowded than the halide from which it is derived.

[8] (a) Brown and Okamoto, *J. Chem. Soc.*, **77**, 3619 (1955). (b) Brown and Moritani, *ibid.*, **77**, 3607 (1955).

[9] We are, in effect, assuming that the stabilities of the olefins derived from a single substrate through a common carbonium-ion intermediate lie in the same order as the respective transition states leading to these olefins. Later we shall see that the geometry of the transition state in the $E1$ reaction is rather similar to that of the resulting olefin and that such an assumption is, in the large majority of cases, justified (p. 494).

Bimolecular Elimination. The $E2$ Mechanism[10]

An important diagnostic feature of eliminations by the $E1$ mechanism is that, aside from salt effects, their rates are not affected by the addition of bases. On the other hand, as the reader is probably aware, there are a large number of olefin-forming eliminations that are accelerated by base, many of these being exceedingly slow in the absence of base. Most eliminations of this type which have been investigated kinetically exhibit second-order rate laws—first order each in substrate and in base, $B:$.

$$\text{rate} = k_2(\text{substrate})(B:) \tag{2}$$

Two simple mechanisms are consistent with this rate law. In the first, a one-step or "concerted" mechanism, the base removes the β-hydrogen *while* the leaving group departs from the α-carbon.

$$B: \quad + \quad H{-}\overset{|}{\underset{|}{C}}{-}\overset{|}{\underset{|}{C}}{-}X \quad \longrightarrow \quad BH^+ \quad + \quad \overset{\diagdown}{\diagup}C{=}C\overset{\diagup}{\diagdown} \quad + \quad :X \tag{3}$$

In the second, the base removes the β-hydrogen to form a carbanion which, after a significant length of time, loses the leaving group to form the olefin.

$$B: + H{-}\overset{|}{\underset{|}{C}}{-}\overset{|}{\underset{|}{C}}{-}X \underset{k_{-1}}{\overset{-B:H^+,\ k_1}{\rightleftharpoons}} {-}:\overset{|}{C}{-}\overset{|}{\underset{|}{C}}{-}X \overset{k_2}{\to} \overset{\diagdown}{\diagup}C{=}C\overset{\diagup}{\diagdown} + :X \tag{4}$$

$$\text{carbanion}$$

There is no evidence that *measurable* amounts of carbanion form during the usual elimination reactions. It may therefore be presumed that if the second ("two-stage") mechanism operates, the carbanion must be either rapidly reconverted to the substrate (making the initial step reversible) or else rapidly converted to the olefin.

One of the substrates most likely to undergo elimination by preliminary reversible carbanion formation is β-phenylethyl bromide, $PhCH_2CH_2Br$; for as we have already emphasized (p. 370), the ionization of a C—H bond to form a carbanion is very much facilitated by a benzene ring bound to the carbon atom. If the first step in the base-catalyzed conversion of this halide to styrene were the reversible formation of the anion $^-:CHPh{-}CH_2Br$, this conversion,

[10] (a) For studies establishing the $E2$ mechanism for alkyl halides, see Hughes, Ingold, and co-workers, *J. Chem. Soc.*, **1935**, 244; **1936**, 225; **1937**, 1177, 1192; **1940**, 899; **1948**, 2043–2068. (b) For evidence of this mechanism in the elimination reactions of tetra-alkylammonium salts, see von Braun, *et al.*, *Ann.*, **472**, 121 (1929); *Ber.*, **64**, 2610 (1931); **65**, 1580 (1932); and Ingold *et al.*, *J. Chem. Soc.*, **1927**, 997; **1928**, 3125; **1933**, 68, 523, 526. (c) Base-catalyzed elimination reactions of trialkylsulfonium salts have been studied quantitatively by Hughes, Ingold, and co-workers, *J. Chem. Soc.*, **1933**, 533, 991, 1571; **1935**, 236; **1948**, 2043, 2072, 2090.

when carried out in D_2O or in a deuterium-labeled alcohol, should be accompanied by the incorporation of deuterium into the unconverted alkyl halide, and thence into the styrene formed.

$$PhCH_2CH_2Br \rightleftharpoons :\bar{C}HPhCH_2Br \rightleftharpoons PhCHDCH_2Br \rightleftharpoons$$

$$:\bar{C}DPhCH_2Br \xrightarrow{-Br^-} PhCD{=}CH_2$$

However, it has been found that when this conversion is brought about by the action of NaOEt in EtOD, both the unreacted bromide and the styrene formed are free of deuterium.[11(a)] We may then rule out elimination via reversible carbanion formation for this alkyl halide; and similar studies with $Et_2CD{-}CH_2Br$[11(b)] and with the tetra-alkylammonium iodide XV[11(c)] allow

$$O_2N{-}\langle\ \rangle{-}CHT{-}CH_2{-}N(CH_3)_3^+\ I^-$$

XV

the same conclusion to be drawn for these substrates also. On the other hand, it is quite likely that the base-catalyzed elimination reactions of trialkylsulfonium salts or of substrates having —CN, —NO₂, or —C— groups bound to the

$$\overset{\|}{O}$$

β-carbon atom do proceed through reversible carbanion formation, for such substances are known to be very readily converted to carbanions in basic media (p. 367).[12]

The possibility of an initial slow formation of a carbanion, followed by a rapid conversion of the carbanion to an olefin, is not easily dismissed. Such a mechanism would be very similar in character to the one-step concerted elimination process (2); a reliable distinction between the two mechanisms may be drawn only by making available to the carbanion intermediate (if such exists) some fate other than immediate conversion to the olefin—that is, by "diverting" the carbanion. The fact that such a "diversion" has not yet been accomplished leads us to believe that in most cases a carbanion as such is *not* formed; and, as we shall presently see, the stereochemistry of base-promoted

---

[11] (a) Skell and Hauser, *J. Am. Chem. Soc.*, **67**, 1661 (1945). (b) Hill *et al.*, *ibid.*, **76**, 5129 (1954). (c) Hodnett and Flynn, *ibid.*, **79**, 2300 (1957). (d) For a single instance in which base-promoted elimination is accompanied by a small amount of hydrogen-exchange, see Cristol and Fix, *ibid.*, **75**, 2647 (1953).

[12] It has recently been found (Saunders and Asperger, *J. Am. Chem. Soc.*, **79**, 1612 (1957)), that substitution of S^{34} for S^{32} in the base-catalyzed elimination reaction of $PhCH_2CH_2SMe_2^+Br^-$ results in a *negligible kinetic-isotope effect*, indicating that the activation process in the rate-determining step involves practically no stretching of the C—S bond in the substrate. This result suggests, although it does not demand (p. 194), the intervention of a carbanion intermediate that is rapidly converted to olefin.

elimination reactions likewise suggests that, *except for a few special substrates, a concerted, rather than a stepwise, process operates.*

Whether or not a carbanion intermediate intercedes, eliminations that require the participation of an ion (or molecule) of base are *bimolecular* and their mechanism is designated *E2*. This path is the most usual one for olefin-forming eliminations, embracing not only many of the dehydrohalogenations of primary, secondary, and tertiary alkyl halides,[10(a)] but also the important "Hofmann elimination" of tetra-alkylammonium hydroxides,[10(b)]

$$HO^- \ + \ H-\overset{|}{\underset{|}{C}}-\overset{|}{\underset{|}{C}}-NMe_3 \ \longrightarrow \ HOH \ + \ \underset{/}{\overset{\backslash}{C}}=\underset{\backslash}{\overset{/}{C}} \ + \ NMe_3$$

and in addition, the base-promoted elimination reactions of less familiar substrates such as tetra-alkylphosphonium salts, $R_4P^+X^-$,[13(a)] and alkyl sulfones,

$$RCH_2-CHR'-\overset{\displaystyle O}{\underset{\displaystyle O}{\overset{|}{\underset{|}{S}}}}-R.$$

[13(b)] The *E2* mechanism is favored by strongly electron-attracting groups in the substrate (for example, $-NR_3^+$ and $-SO_2R$), for these ease the removal of the β-hydrogen. It is also favored by attachment of a benzene ring to the β-carbon, for this not only increases the acidity of the β-hydrogen, but also stabilizes the resulting olefin.[14] However, the manner in which *alkyl* substitution and branching in the substrate affect bimolecular elimination is not completely straightforward, for the direction of such effects depends upon the nature of the leaving group and, to some extent, on the identity of the attacking base. This question is best considered along with the orientation problem in such reactions.

Orientation in $E2$ Reactions. Hofmann- and Saytzeff-like Eliminations

It has been recognized for many years that two distinct empirical rules are needed to summarize orientation in base-promoted eliminations. When more than one olefin may form from a *tetra-alkylammonium* or *trialkylsulfonium salt*, the olefin bearing the *smaller* number of alkyl groups will predominate, whereas in situations where a pair of olefins may result from the dehydrohalogenation of an *alkyl halide*, the olefin bearing the *larger* number of alkyl groups will often (but not always) predominate. Bimolecular eliminations of 'onium salts are said to proceed according to the *Hofmann rule*,[15(a)] whereas those eliminations

[13] (a) Fenton and Ingold, *J. Chem. Soc.*, **1929**, 2343; Hey and Ingold, *ibid.*, **1933**, 531. (b) Fenton and Ingold, *ibid.*, **1928**, 3127; **1929**, 2338; **1930**, 705.

[14] Ingold, *et al.*, *J. Chem. Soc.*, **1927**, 997; **1948**, 2072.

[15] (a) Hofmann, *Ann.*, **79**, 11 (1851). (b) Saytzeff, *ibid.*, **179**, 296 (1875).

that lead preferentially to the "more substituted" olefin are said to be governed by the *Saytzeff rule*.[15(b)] Typical Hofmann- and Saytzeff-type eliminations are illustrated below, together with an "atypical" dehydrohalogenation in which the "less-substituted" olefin predominates over the "more-substituted" olefin in the product:

$$\text{Et—CH—}\overset{+}{\text{S}}\text{Me}_2 \xrightarrow{\text{OEt}^-} \text{EtCH=CH}_2 + \text{MeCH=CHMe} \quad \text{(Hofmann)}^{16(a)}$$
$$\underset{\text{Me}}{|} \qquad\qquad\qquad (74 \text{ percent}) \qquad (26 \text{ percent})$$

$$\text{Et—CH—Br} \xrightarrow{\text{OEt}^-} \text{EtCH=CH}_2 + \text{MeCH=CHMe} \quad \text{(Saytzeff)}^{16(b)}$$
$$\underset{\text{Me}}{|} \qquad\qquad (29 \text{ percent}) \qquad (71 \text{ percent})$$

$$\text{Et—CH—Br} \xrightarrow{\text{t-BuO}^-} \text{EtCH=CH}_2 + \text{MeCH=CHMe} \quad \text{(Hofmann)}^{16(c)}$$
$$\underset{\text{Me}}{|} \qquad\qquad (73 \text{ percent}) \qquad (27 \text{ percent})$$

We have already encountered Saytzeff-type elimination (although we did not refer to it as such) in considering unimolecular eliminations; for it was emphasized that $E1$ reactions, regardless of the nature of the substrate, will yield mainly the olefin having the larger number of alkyl groups. It seems likely that the reasoning used at that point to account for preferential formation of the more highly substituted olefin also applies here. Once more it might be argued that since the olefin having the larger number of alkyl groups (attached to the double-bonded carbons) is—because of hyperconjugation—the more stable, the activated complex leading to that olefin should also be the more stable. We are here assuming, in effect, that all factors aside from the stability of the double bond being formed are of secondary importance.

Such an assumption is obviously not valid where Hofmann-type elimination is observed, for here the less stable olefin predominates. There is some disagreement as to the reason for this. Until recently, it was generally felt that an elimination reaction would proceed according to the Hofmann rule if *its direction were determined by the acidity of the proton being removed*.[17] Thus, it was argued, of the five β-hydrogens in a substrate such as XVI, the two on the methylene group are

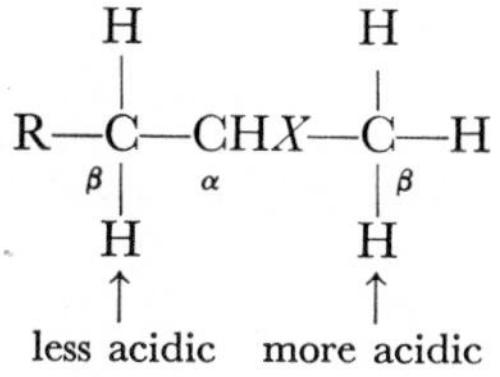

$$\overset{\displaystyle \text{H} \qquad\qquad \text{H}}{\underset{\displaystyle \text{H} \qquad\qquad \text{H}}{\text{R—C—CHX—C—H}}} \qquad (\text{XVI: R = alkyl;} \; -X = -\overset{+}{\text{N}}\text{Me}_3, \; -\overset{+}{\text{S}}\text{Me}_2)$$
$$\quad\;\; \beta \quad \alpha \qquad\quad \beta$$

less acidic   more acidic

---

[16] (a) Hughes, Ingold, Maw, and Woolf, *J. Chem. Soc.*, **1948**, 2077. (b) Dhar, Hughes and Ingold, *ibid.*, **1948**, 2058. (c) Brown, Moritani, and Okamoto, *J. Am. Chem. Soc.*, **78**, 2193 (1956).

[17] See, for example, Ingold, Ref. 2(b), pp. 429–434, and Dhar, *et al.*, *J. Chem. Soc.*, **1948**, 2093.

significantly less acidic than the three on the methyl group, due to the acid-weakening *inductive effect* of the alkyl group, R— (p. 205). This being the case, the removal of a methyl hydrogen by the attacking base is more likely than the removal of a methylene hydrogen, and Hofmann-type orientation results. Extending this reasoning, we may make the more general statement: Alkyl substitution at the β-carbon of an 'onium salt reduces the acidity of the remaining β-hydrogens and retards bimolecular elimination at this site. This statement should apply not only to different sites in the same substrate (in which case it becomes a principle governing orientation), but also to different substrates being treated under equivalent conditions.[18,19]

The suggestion that Hofmann-type elimination stems, at least in part, from inductive effects is not unreasonable, for we have independent evidence that the rates of $E2$ reactions are subject to inductive influences. It has been found, for example, that the specific rates of the $E2$ reactions of ring-substituted 2-phenylethyl bromides ($ArCH_2CH_2Br$) may be correlated with Hammett's σ values for the ring substituents, which, as we have seen, are measures of the electron-attracting or electron-donating power of these substituents.[20] The specific rates of the $E2$ reactions of the corresponding dimethylsulfonium bromides ($ArCH_2CH_2SMe_2^+Br^-$) may be similarly correlated, and as may be expected, the reactions of the sulfonium salts (for which ρ is found to be 2.7) are more susceptible to polar influences than are those of the alkyl bromides ($\rho = 2.1$). However, the difference is a small one. From it we would certainly not predict that when steric and hyperconjugative effects are brought back into the picture by alkyl substitution at the β-carbon, inductive effects continue to dominate for the sulfonium salts but not for the alkyl bromides. Yet, this, in effect, is the view that we must defend when we assume the Hofmann rule to arise principally from inductive effects, for Hofmann-like eliminations are observed for sulfonium salts but not (except under special circumstances) for alkyl halides.

Reexamining the question, it is to be noted that the leaving groups from

substrates that undergo Hofmann-type elimination $\left(\begin{array}{c} \quad\quad O \\ \quad\quad \| \\ -SMe_2^+, \quad -S-Me, \\ \quad\quad \| \\ \quad\quad O \end{array} \right.$

---

[18] It has been found, for example, that the specific rates of ethoxide-promoted eliminations of $CH_3CH_2SMe_2^+$, $CH_3CH_2CH_2SMe_2^+$, and $(CH_3)_2CHCH_2SMe_2^+$ lie in the ratio 4:2:1. See Hughes, Ingold, and Maw, *J. Chem. Soc.*, **1948**, 2072.

[19] On the other hand, alkyl substitution at the α-carbon of an 'onium salt *accelerates* bimolecular elimination. Thus, the ethoxide-promoted eliminations of $CH_3CH_2SMe_2^+$, $(CH_3)_2CHSMe_2^+$, and $(CH_3)_3CSMe_2^+$ exhibit rate constants in the ratio of 1:20:600. Here, it may be argued that the acid-weakening inductive effect exerted by a β-methyl on a β-hydrogen is very slight and that the observed trend therefore reflects the increase in hyperconjugative effects (which tend to accelerate elimination) as branching at the α-position is increased. See Hughes, Ingold, and Woolf, *J. Chem. Soc.*, **1948**, 2084.

[20] (a) Saunders and Williams, *J. Am. Chem. Soc.*, **79**, 3712 (1957). (b) DePuy and Froemsdorf, *ibid.*, **79**, 3710 (1957).

—NMe$_3^+$) are *decidedly bulkier* than halide ions, which depart during the course of Saytzeff-like eliminations. It has, in fact, been found that the fraction of "Hofmann product" in the mixtures of olefins resulting from the *E*2 reactions of 2-pentyl derivatives progressively increases as the bulk of the leaving group increases.[21]

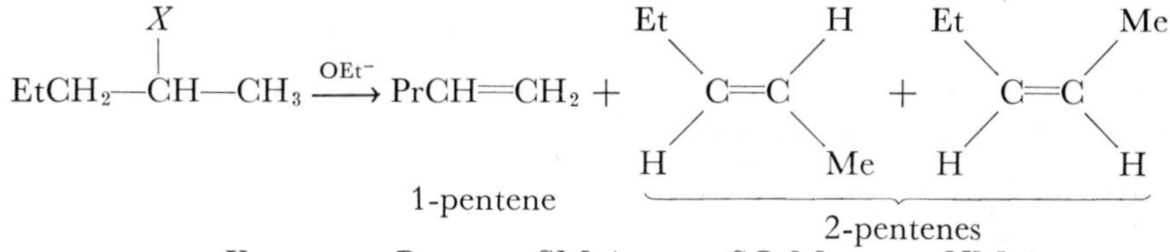

$$\underset{\substack{|\\ X}}{\text{EtCH}_2\text{—CH—CH}_3} \xrightarrow{\text{OEt}^-} \underset{\text{1-pentene}}{\text{PrCH}=\text{CH}_2} + \underset{H}{\overset{Et}{\diagdown}}C=C\underset{Me}{\overset{H}{\diagup}} + \underset{H}{\overset{Et}{\diagdown}}C=C\underset{H}{\overset{Me}{\diagup}}$$

2-pentenes

—*X*	—Br	—SMe$_2^+$	—SO$_2$Me	—NMe$_3^+$
$\dfrac{\text{1-pentene}}{\text{2-pentenes}}$	0.45	6.7	7.7	ca. 50

Furthermore, we now know that the *E*2 reactions of alkyl halides can be made to exhibit Hofmann-like, rather than Saytzeff-like, orientation by sufficiently increasing either the degree of branching in the substrate or the steric requirements of the attacking base.[16(c),21,22] Thus, when the tertiary bromides listed below are dehydrohalogenated under conditions that insure bimolecular elimination (concentrated KOEt in dry alcohol at 70°), the ratio of 1-olefin ("Hofmann product") to 2-olefins ("Saytzeff product") increases with branching as shown below:[22]

	EtCMe$_2$Br	(*n*-Pr)CMe$_2$Br	(*i*-Bu)CMe$_2$Br	(*neo*-C$_5$H$_{11}$)CMe$_2$Br
$\dfrac{\text{1-olefin}}{\text{2-olefins}}$	0.43	1.00	1.17	6.1

The effect of increasing the bulk of the attacking base may be even more striking. In the mixture of olefins resulting from the action of alkoxide bases on the bromide Me$_2$CHCMe$_2$Br, the ratio of 1-olefin to 2-olefins has been found to range from 0.25 (when OEt$^-$ is used) to 11.4 (when Et$_3$CO$^-$ is used).[17(c)]

---

[21] Brown and Wheeler, *J. Am. Chem. Soc.*, **78**, 2199 (1956). In the absence of quantitative data as to the steric requirements of the various leaving groups, it may be assumed that the bulkiness of these groups increases as branching is increased at the atom that links the leaving group to the remainder of the substrate. Thus —Br is "nonbranched," —SMe$_2^+$ is "double branched," and —SO$_2$Me and —NMe$_3^+$ are "triple branched." The —NMe$_3^+$ group may be considered to be bulkier than —SO$_2$Me since the covalent radius of formally positive sulfur is very small and the van der Waal's radius of the methyl group is considerably greater than that of an oxygen atom. The —OSO$_2$C$_6$H$_4$CH$_3$ (tosylate) group is, in the present sense, "single branched," and the ratio of 1-pentene to 2-pentenes resulting from the *E*2 reaction of 2-pentyl tosylate with ethoxide is 0.97. While it is true that the tosylate group has considerable bulk, most of its bulk is in the benzene ring and the *p*-CH$_3$ group which molecular models show to be far removed from the remainder of the substrate.

[22] Brown, Moritani, and Nakagawa, *J. Am. Chem. Soc.*, **78**, 2190, 2197, 2203 (1956).

	EtO^-	$t\text{-}BuO^-$	$EtCMe_2O^-$	Et_3CO^-
$\dfrac{\text{1-olefin}}{\text{2-olofins}}$	0.25	2.7	4.3	11.4

Similarly, the ratio of 1-olefin to 2-olefins in the mixture obtained from the $E2$ reaction of t-amyl bromide is 0.43 when the attacking base is OEt^- but 7.7 when the attacking base is Et_3CO^-.[16(c)]

To account for these trends, each of which indicates a shift from Saytzeff-like to Hofmann-like elimination as steric crowding is increased, let us compare the transition states for the two modes of reaction. According to our present picture of the activated complex in the usual $E2$ reaction, the five most important atoms involved in the elimination lie in or near a common plane. These are the "attacking atom" of the base, the β-hydrogen, the α- and β-carbons, and the departing halogen (or oxygen, sulfur, or nitrogen) atom. Moreover, the attacking base and the leaving group are situated *trans* (or "*anti*") to each other. (We shall shortly review the evidence for this picture.) Such an activated complex may be represented as shown in Figure 12-1, or, more conveniently,

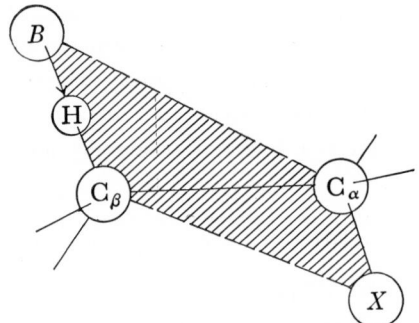

Fig. 12-1. Activated Complex in an E2 Reaction

using the Newman convention (p. 73), as XVII. In the latter, it will be recalled, the bond between the α- and β-carbon atoms is placed perpendicular to the plane of the page.[23] Suppose now that the substrate is $RCH_2\!\!-\!\!C(CH_3)_2$.
$$\underset{X}{|}$$

[23] The view of the activated complex is an $E2$ reaction shown in Figure 12-1 is commonly abbreviated in two ways:

$$B:$$

In the present text, the first of these, rather than the second, will be used, since it indicates the

The activated complex for Saytzeff-type elimination (in which a methylene hydrogen is removed) is represented as **XVIII**, whereas that for Hofmann-type elimination (in which a methyl hydrogen is removed) is **XIX**. From the "Newman pictures" of these (**XVIII′** and **XIX′**, respectively), it is evident that steric interference might arise between groups R— and X— if either or

$$
\begin{array}{ccc}
\textbf{XVII} & \textbf{XVIII} & \textbf{XIX}
\end{array}
$$

XVII: B: → H ; X↓

XVIII: B: → H, Me / R—C⟍—C—Me / H, X

XIX: B: → H, CH$_2$R / H—C⟍—C—Me / H, X

XVIII′: B: ↓ H ; Me, Me / R, H ; X↓

XIX′: B: ↓ H ; Me, CH$_2$R / H, H ; X↓

both become bulky. Under these conditions, transition state **XIX** (in which R— is free to move out of the way of X—) will be favored, and Hofmann-type elimination will be observed. Similarly, if the attacking base, B:, is excessively bulky, it will interfere more with group R— in **XVIII** than in **XIX**, and again Hofmann-type elimination will be favored.

In summary then, there can be scarcely any question that steric effects markedly influence orientation in $E2$ reactions. It is possible that inductive effects also play a part; but except for a few special cases (see, for example, Ex. 6d), this role seems not to have been unequivocally demonstrated.

Competition between Elimination and Substitution

The yield of olefin in a given preparation will depend largely upon how effectively the desired elimination reaction competes with the S_N reaction(s) that generally accompany it. This question is most easily considered when both elimination and substitution are unimolecular; for under these conditions, the E/S_N ratio is very nearly independent of the identity of the nucleophilic leaving

---

direction of reaction, since the perspective is a little clearer to the untrained eye, and since there is no possibility of confusing the dashed lines (representing bonds back of the page) with dotted lines (representing bonds in the process of formation and breakage).

group (p. 474), and, in practice, very nearly independent of the concentration and identity of bases present in solution.[24] The variations in the $E1/S_N1$ ratio with structural changes in the substrate may, as we have seen, be easily interpreted, largely in terms of hyperconjugative effects. The problem becomes more complex when unimolecularity is no longer guaranteed (that is, in the presence of moderate or high concentrations of base); for now E/S_N ratio may depend upon the identity of the attacking base, the alkyl group (R—) of the substrate (RX), and the leaving group (—X). Moreover the possibility exists that a change in substrate or a variation in reaction conditions may bring about a change in the predominating mechanism for elimination, for substitution, or for both.

Let us begin with the alkyl group, R—. It has been emphasized (p. 275) that, due to the operation of steric and ponderal effects, branching at either the α- or the β-carbon generally retards S_N2 reactions. At the same time, however, branching at the α-carbon accelerates $E2$ reactions; for an alkyl group on an α-carbon is in a position to stabilize the double bond of the resulting olefin (and presumably the double bond being formed in the activated complex) through hyperconjugation.[25]

It follows then that the $E2/S_N2$ ratio must increase with branching at the α-carbon atom—that is, this ratio tends to be greatest for tertiary halides and 'onium salts and least for primary halides and 'onium salts. It is less safe to generalize concerning the effect of branching at the β-carbon, for although hyperconjugative effects arising from such branching tend to accelerate elimination, steric (and perhaps inductive) effects tend to retard it. Data are not plentiful, but it appears that in those cases where β branching retards $E2$ reactions, it retards S_N2 reactions even more effectively. *Thus, β substitution, like α substitution, generally favors bimolecular elimination at the expense of substitution.*

When a substrate is undergoing bimolecular substitution and bimolecular elimination at the same time, the $E2/S_N2$ ratio should be independent of the

[24] It is, of course, conceivable that the addition of a weakly basic but strongly nucleophilic species (such as N_3^-) would lower the E/S_N ratio by diverting some of the carbonium-ion intermediate (in this case to an aliphatic azide). However, such species, except by accident, are not generally present when elimination reactions are carried out.

[25] The effect of α substitution on the rates of $E2$ reactions of sulfonium salts has already been noted (Ref. 20). Similarly, the specific rates of the $E2$ reactions of CH_3CH_2Br, $(CH_3)_2CHBr$, and $(CH_3)_3CBr$ (with NaOEt at 25°) lie in the ratio $1:5:40$ (see, for example Refs. 6 and 16b).

concentration of the added base, $B:$, for the rates of both reactions are proportional to the product $(RX)(B:)$. When both the elimination and the substitution reactions are unimolecular, the $E1/S_N1$ ratio is also independent of $(B:)$, indicating that the carbonium ion intermediate suffers attack by solvent rather than by $B:$. However the $E2/S_N2$ ratio is not (except by extraordinary coincidence) equal to the $E1/S_N1$ ratio for the same substrate, and it may then be asked whether the transition from uni- to bimolecularity as the concentration of base is increased favors elimination or substitution.

Again, considerably more data would be desirable, but it appears at present that the E/S_N ratio may be either raised or lowered, depending upon the nature of the base involved. If the base is weak but is strongly nucleophilic toward carbon (for example, PhS⁻), it will be very effective in bringing about bimolecular substitution (where attack on carbon is required) but far less effective in bringing about bimolecular elimination (where extraction of a proton is required). Hence, when such a base is gradually added to a solution of the substrate, it will soon become involved in bimolecular substitution, lowering the E/S_N ratio. At much larger concentrations of base, bimolecular elimination may occur at an appreciable rate, but the substitution will benefit more from the change in molecularity than will the elimination. Quite obviously, it would be foolish to use such bases as PhS⁻, N_3^-, and CN⁻ as "catalysts" in the preparation of olefins.

With very strong bases, the reverse is true. As hydroxide or alkoxide is added to a solution of a secondary or tertiary halide undergoing unimolecular elimination and substitution, it is the elimination reaction that first changes its molecularity. Substitution becomes predominantly bimolecular only at higher concentrations of base and benefits less from the change in mechanism than does elimination. Typically, for i-PrBr at 55°, the elimination to substitution ratio has been found to be 0.03 in dry alcohol but 3.8 in 2.0 N NaOEt; the corresponding ratios for t-BuBr are 0.37 in alcohol and 13 in 2.0 N NaOEt.[26] It is thus apparent why synthetically useful conversions of alkyl halides to olefins in solution generally employ *strong bases at high concentrations.*

For each secondary or tertiary halide, there should be a range of base concentration within which elimination with strong base is bimolecular but substitution is unimolecular, and within which the E/S_N ratio will depend on the concentration of base. This range of concentration depends upon the base employed, the polarity of the medium, and the nature of the substrate. In particular, since tertiary halides undergo ionization more readily than secondary, a higher concentration of base will be required to bring about the $E1$ to $E2$ transition for tertiary than for secondary halides. We can thus understand why, for example, i-PrBr gives a higher yield of olefin than does t-BuBr when both

[26] Hughes, Ingold, Masterman, and MacNulty, *J. Chem. Soc.*, **1940**, 899.

are treated with dilute (about 0.05 N) NaOEt, although the tertiary halide gives more olefin both in the absence of base and in concentrated NaOEt.[26] In 0.05 N NaOEt, i-PrBr has apparently adopted the $E2$ mechanism (resulting in a higher olefin yield) while t-BuBr continues to undergo elimination by the $E1$ mechanism.

The elimination to substitution ratio associated with a given substrate may also be influenced by the polarity of the solvent. There are two distinct ways in which this might come about. Let us compare, for example, the transition states for the S_N2 and $E2$ reactions of an alkyl halide, brought about by a negatively charged base (such as hydroxide or alkoxide):

$$
\begin{array}{ccc}
& \left[\begin{array}{ccc}
\overset{\delta-}{RO} \text{---} \overset{|}{\underset{/}{C}} \text{---} \overset{\delta-}{Hal} \\
H \text{---} C \diagdown \\
\qquad |
\end{array}\right] & (S_N2)
\end{array}
$$

$$
\begin{array}{ccc}
H\text{---}\underset{|}{\overset{|}{C}}\text{---}\underset{|}{\overset{|}{C}}\text{---}Hal \;+\; RO^- & &
\end{array}
$$

$$
\left[\overset{\delta-}{RO}\text{---}H\text{---}\overset{|}{C}\!=\!=\!\overset{|}{C}\,\overset{\delta-}{Hal}\right] \quad (E2)
$$

For both reactions, a negative charge originally concentrated on one atom becomes dispersed over several atoms in the transition state. Both reactions should therefore be favored by a decrease in solvent polarity; but, since the charge in the $E2$ reaction is dispersed over the greater area, low solvent polarity will favor elimination even more than substitution. Suppose further that the reaction is carried out in or near the region of mechanistic change. A decrease in solvent polarity will tend to favor the S_N2 and $E2$ reactions in relation to the S_N1 and $E1$ reactions (which require separation of unlike charges in the transition state). This factor will also tend to increase the E/S_N ratio, for we have seen that when the base is strong, the shift to bimolecularity favors elimination over substitution. Regardless of which of these two effects predominates, we would expect the *E/S_N ratio resulting from the reaction of an alkyl halide with hydroxide or alkoxide to increase as the solvent is made less polar.* Typically, the reaction of i-PrBr with NaOH (at 55°) results in an E/S_N ratio of 1.17 when carried out in 60 percent ethanol, 1.44 in 80 percent ethanol, and 2.45 in dry ethanol.[27]

It is to be noted that the activation process for an $E2$ reaction requires

[27] Cooper, et al., *J. Chem. Soc.*, **1948**, 2045. Using very similar reasoning, we would predict that the E/S_N ratio resulting from the action of hydroxide or alkoxide on an 'onium salt should *decrease* as the solvent is made less polar. Data on this point are sparse, but Gleave, et al., (*J. Chem. Soc.*, **1935**, 236) report quantitative yields of ethylene from the action of base on Et_3S^+ (at 100°) in 60 to 80 percent EtOH, but only an 86 percent yield of olefin in water. This difference may be due in part to the fact that the only attacking base in water is OH^-, whereas in aqueous alcohol the more strongly basic OEt^- is also available for attack on the sulfonium ion.

the stretching of a rather strong C—H bond, whereas the activation process for an S_N2 reaction does not. Although this extra expenditure of energy for elimination is eventually refunded, at least in part, by the conversion of a C—C single bond to a double bond, we should nevertheless expect the energy of activation for elimination to be somewhat greater than that for substitution. This means that both elimination and substitution are accelerated by an increase in temperature, but elimination is accelerated more; that is, the $E2/S_N2$ ratio associated with a given substrate (regardless of type) should increase with an increase in temperature. This is what is observed.[28] Typically, the $E2/S_N2$ ratio for i-PrBr in 60 percent ethanol is 1.14 at 45° but 2.42 at 100°. A similar differential temperature effect should be observed for unimolecular reactions, for the $E1/S_N1$ ratio depends upon an analogous competition. Here the carbonium ion may be converted either to an olefin (requiring the stretching and breaking of a C—H bond) or to a substitution product (requiring no such stretching or breaking). Typically, the $E1/S_N1$ ratio for t-BuCl in 80 percent ethanol rises from 0.20 to 0.57 when the reaction temperature is raised from 25° to 65°.

In summary then, bimolecular elimination is facilitated (at the expense of substitution) by: (a) branching at either the α- or β-carbon atom, (b) the action of strong bases at high concentrations, (c) nonpolar solvents, and (d) high temperatures.

Stereochemistry of Eliminations in Noncyclic Systems. "Eclipsing" Effects

We have already noted (without, however, citing supporting evidence) that $E2$ reactions are, except in special cases, *trans* eliminations; that, is the activated complexes in these reactions adopt conformations in which the *departing nucleophile is as far removed as possible from the proton being extracted by the attacking base*, (Fig. 12-1).[29] Many examples of *trans* eliminations, some leading to olefins, others leading to acetylenes, have been reported;[30] of these, we need consider only a few. The dehydrobrominations of the two diastereomeric stilbene dibromides XX and XXII give two different α-bromostilbenes, XXI and XXIII. Dibromide XX, the *meso* form, gives a *cis* olefin (XXI), whereas the d,l-di-

---

[28] Cooper, *et al.*, *J. Chem. Soc.*, **1948**, 2049. The explanation for this effect suggested by these authors is very much different from that presented in the present text. See also Ingold, Ref. 2(b), pp. 460–463.

[29] A number of workers prefer the term "*anti* elimination" to "*trans* elimination," feeling that the conformation adopted by substituents during a reaction and the configuration of reactants or products should not be designated by the same term. This dual usage is likely to lead to confusion only in the discussions of certain cyclic compounds (particularly cyclohexane derivatives) in which *trans* 1,2 substituents need not lie in the positions necessary for facile elimination.

[30] For a summary of *trans* eliminations in the early literature, see Frankland, *J. Chem. Soc.*, **1912**, 654.

bromide (**XXII**) gives the *trans* olefin (**XXIII**).[31] Both conversions, shown below using two conventions, are stereospecific:

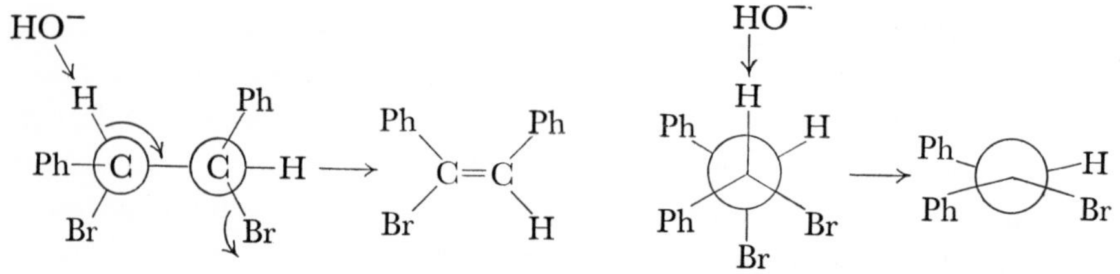

XX, *meso*   XXI, *cis*   XX'   XXI'

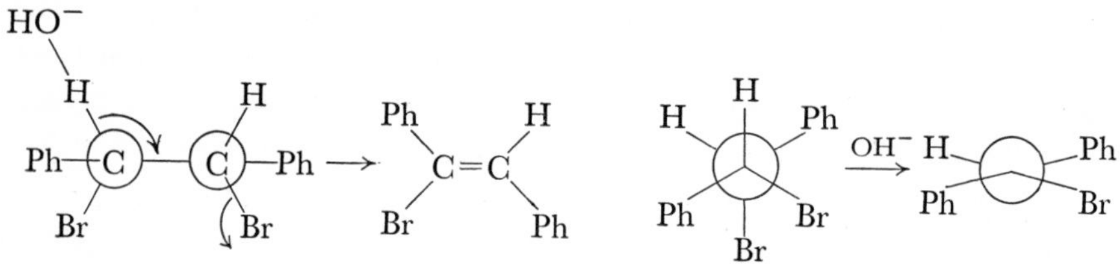

XXII, *d, l*   XXIII, *trans*   XXII'   XXIII'

Similar stereospecificity has been observed in the base-promoted elimination reactions of compounds **XXIV**, **XXV**, and **XXVI**. Each of these has two

$$PhCHMe—CHPh—NMe_3^+I^-$$
XXIV

$$PhCHMe—CHMe—OTos$$
XXV

$$Ph—\underset{\underset{O}{\|}}{C}—CHBr—CHPhBr$$

XXVI

adjacent asymmetric carbons and therefore exists in *threo* and *erythro* modifications (which are closely analogous to *d,l* and *meso* forms, respectively, except that the two asymmetric carbons have two, rather than three, substituents in common). In each case, the *erythro* ("*meso*-like") form has been found to give the *cis* olefin, whereas the *threo* ("*d,l*-like") form gives the *trans* olefin. The reaction of one member of each of these pairs is shown as follows:[32,33]

---

[31] Pfeiffer, *Z. physik. Chem.*, **48**, 40 (1904).

[32] (a) Cram, Greene, and DePuy, *J. Am. Chem. Soc.*, **78**, 790 (1956). (b) Cram, *ibid.*, **74**, 2149 (1952). (c) Lutz, Hinkley, and Jordan, *ibid.*, **73**, 4647 (1951).

[33] It may be asked how we may be certain that the configurations of the reactants and products in these conversions are as represented. With the olefinic products, there is generally little difficulty, for enough *cis-trans* pairs of olefins have been prepared and characterized so that we may say with confidence that of such pairs, the *trans* compound almost always has the higher melting point, the lower boiling point, the lower solubility in a given solvent, and the lower dipole moment. In addition, spectral evidence is occasionally of use here.

For the reactants, the problem becomes more complex. Sometimes a *meso* form may be

(XXIV', threo) $\xrightarrow{\text{OEt}^-}$ (trans) [32(a)]

(XXV', erythro) $\xrightarrow{\text{OEt}^-}$ (cis) [32(b)]

(XXVI', threo) $\xrightarrow{\text{Et}_3\text{N}}$ (trans) [32(c)]

Moreover, it has long been recognized that haloalkenes and related compounds in which a hydrogen and halogen are *trans* to each other (for example,

are much more rapidly converted by base to acetylene derivatives than are the corresponding *cis* compounds.

The overwhelming predominance of *trans* elimination in most *E*2 reactions has not yet been explained in a fully satisfactory manner. It cannot be ascribed to electrostatic repulsion between the attacking base (which is often negatively charged) and the departing nucleophile (which frequently bears a partial negative charge), for 'onium salts such as **XXIV** also undergo *trans* elimination although the leaving group in the activated complex bears a partial positive charge. Some workers prefer to regard the change at the α-carbon during the elimination process as sort of a Walden inversion in which the attacking species

distinguished from a *d,l* form by resolution of the latter into enantiomorphs; and, in isolated instances, the complete structure determination by x-ray diffraction of one or both of a pair of diastereomers may allow an unequivocal assignment of relative configurations about the asymmetric carbons. However, since 1950, almost all configurational assignments for *threo-erythro* pairs have been based upon their methods of synthesis, generally via addition reactions on unsaturated compounds of known configuration. Such assignments require that we know the mechanisms, or at least the stereochemical rules, for such addition reactions (a topic to be treated in the following chapter).

is the pair of electrons derived from the β-carbon atom when a β-hydrogen is extracted. On this basis, it might be argued that, as in the S_N2 reaction, the attacking species must approach the reaction center (that is, the α-carbon) from one side while the leaving group departs from the opposite side. However, the geometry of the activated complex in an S_N2 reaction is considerably different from that in an E2 reaction; and, according to our present picture, the electrons from the β-carbon do not "attack" the α-carbon in the same way as does an external nucleophile but may be said, more accurately, to "drift into place." It therefore seems that the analogy between the stereochemistries of the E2 and S_N2 reactions is, at best, a very broad one and is in no sense an "explanation."

Quite naturally, when the members of a *erythro-threo* pair (or a *meso-d,l* pair) of diastereomers undergo elimination reactions to give different products, their reaction rates will be different. The *threo* form of methiodide XXIV, for example, reacts with NaOEt over 50 times as rapidly as the *erythro* form[32(a)], corresponding to a difference in $\Delta F^{\ddagger}$ of 2.3 kcal per mole. Since it is extremely improbable that the difference can be due to a large difference in stabilities of the reactants,[34] it may be inferred that the activated complex leading to the *trans* olefin considerably more stable than that leading to the *cis* olefin. Comparing the two activated complexes (XXVII and XXVIII), we see that the

| XXVII | | XXVIII | | XXIX |
| (less crowded) | | (more crowded) | | |

large phenyl groups interfere with each other in XXVIII but not in XXVII. Thus, the elimination proceeding through transition state XXVII takes place more readily than that proceeding through XXVIII. The relatively slow reaction leading to the *cis* olefin is sometimes said to be due to the "*cis* effect" or an "*eclipsing effect*" (for as the reaction proceeds from the transition state to the olefinic product, one phenyl group appears to "pass in front of" the other). Exactly the same argument may be used to explain why dibromide XXVI', the *threo* form of benzalacetophenone dibromide (XXVI), undergoes dehydro-

---

[34] Abd Elhafez and Cram, *J. Am. Chem. Soc.*, **75**, 339 (1953), have studied the equilibrium between the *thtreo* and *erythro* forms of the formates related to XXIV (in which the —NMe$_3^+$ group has been replaced by an —OCHO group), and have found ΔF for the *erythro-threo* conversion to be only −0.14 kcal per mole. It seems very unlikely that the difference in stabilities of the corresponding trimethylammonium iodides is very much greater than this.

bromination with Et_3N about 100 times as rapidly as does the corresponding *erythro* form;[32(c)] the reaction of the latter must proceed through activated complex XXIX, in which the large phenyl and benzoyl groups are becoming "eclipsed."

Eclipsing effects may also determine the predominant product resulting from elimination from a single substrate when more than one β-hydrogen is present. Thus, when 2-bromopentane is treated with KOEt, almost three times as much *trans*-2-pentene is formed as is *cis*-2-pentene,[8(b)] for in the transition state, XXX, leading to the *cis* olefin, the methyl and ethyl groups have begun to "eclipse each other."

The same effect is even more marked when the leaving group is very bulky. Ester XXXI, for example, undergoes an $E2$ reaction (with breakage of the alkyl-oxygen bond) when treated with t-BuOK. The olefinic product is almost exclusively *trans*-stilbene.[35] The predominance of *trans* olefins in the products

resulting from $E1$ reactions (p. 477) may be explained on much the same basis. Here, however, we must consider the activated complexes lying between the carbonium-ion intermediate and the various olefinic products.

[35] Curtin and Kellom, *J. Am. Chem. Soc.*, **75**, 6011 (1953).

$$t\text{-BuCH}_2\overset{\text{OBs}}{\underset{}{\text{CHCH}_3}} \xrightarrow[\text{HOAc}]{-\text{OBs}^-} t\text{-BuCH}_2\overset{+}{\text{CHCH}_3}$$

As shown, the methyl and *t*-butyl groups are becoming eclipsed in the transition state leading to the *cis* olefin but not in that leading to the *trans* olefin.

Aside from eclipsing effects of this type, we would perhaps expect unimolecular eliminations to be nonstereospecific, for there is a time lag between the departure of the leaving group and the extraction of the β-hydrogen. However, there is evidence that some E1 reactions are complicated by *neighboring group effects* that lead not only to stereospecificity but also to the possibility of rearrangement (see Chap. 14).

Trans elimination has been observed for other reactions which do not, however, involve loss of a proton. Vicinal (α, β) dibromides are known to react with iodide ion, yielding I_2, Br^-, and the corresponding olefin. The reaction is second order,[36]

$$-\overset{|}{\underset{\underset{\text{Br}}{|}}{C}}-\overset{|}{\underset{\underset{\text{Br}}{|}}{C}}- + 2I^- \rightarrow \overset{\backslash}{\underset{/}{C}}=\overset{/}{\underset{\backslash}{C}} + I_2 + 2Br^-; \quad \text{rate} = k_2(I^-)(\text{dibromide}) \quad (5)$$

and appears to be stereospecific,[36(a),37] for *meso*-2,3-dibromobutane and *meso*-stilbene dibromide yield *trans* olefins, whereas the corresponding *d,l*-dibromides yield *cis* olefins. The stereochemistry, at first glance, seems opposite to that observed for dehydrohalogenation reactions (where *meso* dihalides yield *cis* olefins), but the apparent contrast is due to the nature of the reactions rather than to differing stereochemistries; for a dehydrohalogenation involves removal of one, rather than two, halogen atoms.

[36] (a) Winstein, Pressman, and Young, *J. Am. Chem. Soc.*, **61**, 1645 (1939); (b) Dillon, *ibid.*, **54**, 952 (1932); (c) Weinstock, Lewis, and Bordwell, *ibid.*, **78**, 6042 (1957).
[37] Young, et al., *J. Am. Chem. Soc.*, **61**, 1640 (1939); **65**, 2099 (1943).

As with dehydrohalogenations, the reactions leading to the *cis* olefins are considerably slower than those leading to *trans* olefins.

The following mechanism is consistent with both the rate law and the stereochemistry:

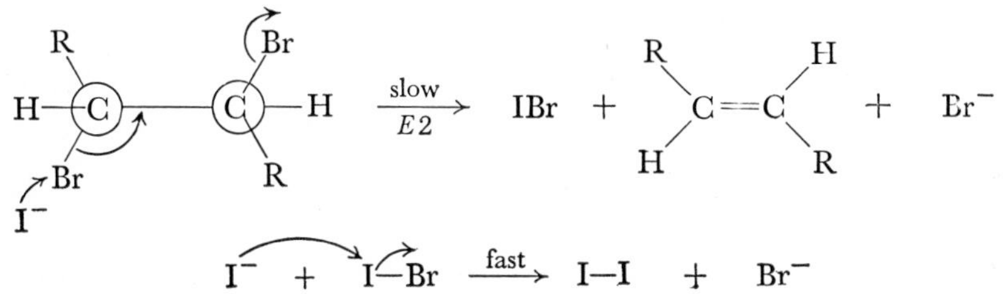

If this mechanism is correct, an iodide ion extracts Br^+ in the rate-determining step in much the same way as a base extracts a proton in an $E2$ reaction of the more usual type. This sequence, however, does not explain satisfactorily why debrominations leading to terminal olefins ($RCH\!\!=\!\!CH_2$) are considerably faster than those leading to olefins of the type $RCH\!\!=\!\!CHR$,[36(b)] and it has been suggested that dibromides such as $MeCHBr\!-\!CH_2Br$ are first converted to bromoiodides, which are then attacked by iodide in the manner shown for dibromides in sequence (6).[38] Dibromide **XXXII** would be more readily con-

$$RCHBr\!-\!CH_2Br \xrightarrow[S_N2]{I^-} RCHBr\!-\!CH_2I \xrightarrow[E2]{I^-} Br^- + RCH\!\!=\!\!CH_2 + I_2 \quad (6)$$
$$\quad\text{XXXII}\qquad\qquad\quad\text{XXXIII}$$

verted to a bromoiodide than would, say, 2,3-dibromobutane, since one of the bromine atoms in **XXXII** is bound to a primary carbon at which S_N2 reactions readily occur. Furthermore, the iodine atom in bromoiodide **XXXIII** is more susceptible to nucleophilic attack than is a bromine atom, for iodine readily "expands its valence shell" (activated complex **XXXIV**), allowing formation of a new $I\!-\!I$ bond *before* the $I\!-\!C$ bond breaks. The initial step in

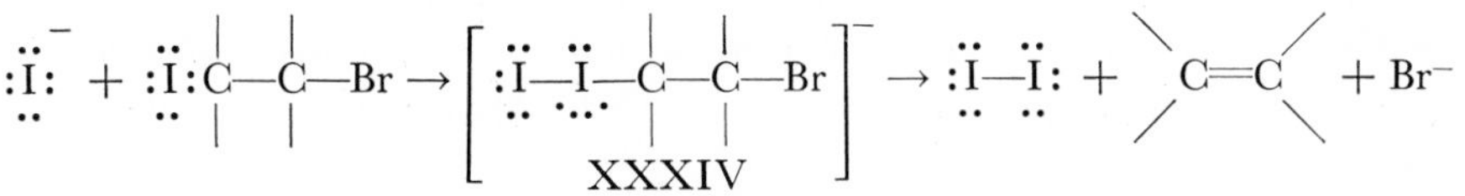

sequence (6) would result in an inversion of configuration about the terminal carbon, but this could not be detected unless the reaction were carried out using the deuterium-labeled dibromide, $RCHBr\!-\!CHDBr$ (Ex. 7).

Still another example of a reaction involving *trans* elimination is the "decarboxylative debromination" of β-halo acids.[39]

   [38] Hine and Brader, *Am. J. Chem. Soc.*, **77**, 361 (1955).
   [39] (*a*) Cristol and Norris, *J. Am. Chem. Soc.*, **75**, 632, 2645 (1953). (*b*) Grovenstein and Lee, *ibid.*, **75**, 2639 (1953). (*c*) Curtin and Luberoff, *Record Chem. Progress*, **15**, 116 (1954). (*d*) For an exceptional case, see Vaughan and Scheonthaler, *J. Am. Chem. Soc.*, **80**, 1956 (1958).

$$RCHBr\text{---}CHR\text{---}COOH \xrightarrow{\text{weak base}} RCH\text{=}CHR + Br^- + CO_2$$

This elimination, if carried out in ethanol or in a less polar solvent, is stereospecific; anions XXXV and XXXVI yield *trans* olefins, whereas the diastereomeric forms, XXXVII and XXXVIII, respectively, react more slowly to give *cis* olefins.[40]

We may then represent this reaction, which is first order in carboxylate anion,[39(a)] simply as

When carried out in water, this reaction tends to lose its stereospecificity. In aqueous solution, anion XXXVI continues to yield a *trans* olefin, but anion XXXVIII yields a mixture of *cis* and *trans* olefins with the *trans* isomer constituting about three fourths of the product. It seems likely that in the more polar medium the reaction proceeds, at least in part, by preliminary ionization of the C—Br bond to give a "zwitterion" (XXXIX), which then undergoes

XXXIX

[40] The fact that anions XXXV and XXXVI both yield *trans* olefins even though XXXV is an *erythro* form while XXXVI is a *threo* form has no fundamental significance since it is due only to the circumstance that one of the substituents in XXXVI that is not involved in the elimination (—Br) is the same as one that is involved. The same description applies to substrates XXIV, XXV, and XXVI, for with each of these, a *threo* compound yields a *trans* olefin.

decarboxylation. In this sequence, the asymmetry about the β-carbon is lost in the initial step, and the intermediate is converted principally to the *trans* olefin, very probably because the formation of the *cis* olefin must pass through a transition state in which the bulky bromo and phenyl groups are being eclipsed (p. 494).

Cyclic Systems. Possibility of Elimination by a Carbanion Mechanism

Thus far, we have considered only noncyclic systems, in which rotation about the C_α—C_β single bond is permitted (although the molecule may prefer some conformations to others). When this bond is incorporated into a ring (having fewer than about nine members), rotation becomes restricted. In a cyclohexane ring, for example, two equatorial substituents on adjacent carbons (which lie *trans*, but in an unfavorable position for bimolecular elimination) may be moved into the axial positions (*trans*, but in a favorable position for elimination) simply by "turning the ring inside out"—a process which is permitted, except in special cases (p. 241). However, *cis* substituents on adjacent atoms (one substituent axial, the other equatorial) may *not* be moved into positions favorable for an E2 reaction without introducing considerable strain in the ring, and such substituents do not participate in the usual type of bimolecular elimination reactions. We may thus appreciate why menthyl chloride, XL (which has only one β-hydrogen *trans* to the chlorine) yields only one olefin upon treatment with NaOEt. In contrast, neomenthyl chloride, XLI (with two β-hydrogen atoms *trans* to the chlorine) yields a mixture of two olefins with olefin XLIII predominating (as would be predicted by considering hyperconjugative effects).[41]

XL →(OEt⁻) XLII (slow)

XLI →(OEt⁻) XLII (23 percent) + XLIII (77 percent)

Furthermore, the formation of 2-menthene (XLII) from chloride XLI is over 40 times as fast as its formation from chloride XL. Both reactions must pass through transition states in which the chlorine is axial, but the methyl and isopropyl groups in XLI are equatorial, whereas in XL they are axial. Since

[41] (a) Hughes, Ingold, and Rose, *J. Chem. Soc.*, **1953**, 3839. (b) Huckel, Tappe, and Legutke, *Ann.*, **543**, 191 (1940).

bulky groups prefer to occupy equatorial positions (p. 241), chloride **XLII** yields a transition state of lower energy than does chloride **XL** and therefore reacts more rapidly.

The flexibility of the cyclohexane ring may be very much diminished by incorporating it into a bicyclic system such as that appearing in compound **XLIV** or that in **XLV**. Both of these chlorides undergo bimolecular eliminations

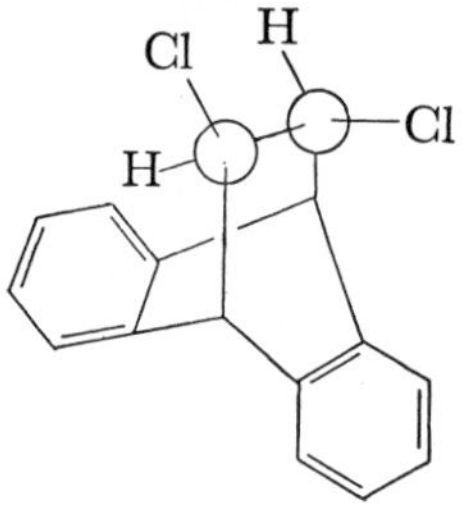

XLIV

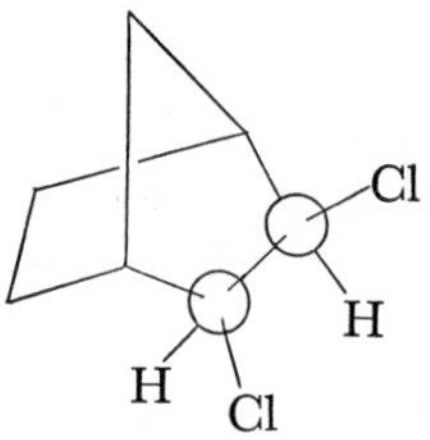

XLV

at very low rates,[42] even though both have hydrogen and chlorine atoms in *trans* positions on adjacent carbons; for the rings in both compounds are rigid and cannot be twisted so that the four atoms involved in the elimination (two carbons, an α-chlorine, and a β-hydrogen) lie near a common plane. Moreover, the *trans* isomers of **XLIV** and **XLV**, in which the hydrogen and chlorine atoms lie *cis* to each other, react somewhat more rapidly than **XLIV** and **XLV** themselves, although the differences are not sufficiently large to be attributed with confidence to any single factor. Since the usual structural requirements for an *E*2 reaction cannot be met in these cases, it may be asked how the slow, but observable, elimination reactions of these compounds proceed. A number of workers feel that the alternative mechanism for bimolecular elimination, the "carbanion mechanism" (sequence 3, p. 478), comes into play here. If this is so, the rate-determining step is the conversion of the substrate to its carbanion, followed by the rapid loss of Cl$^-$ from the carbanion,

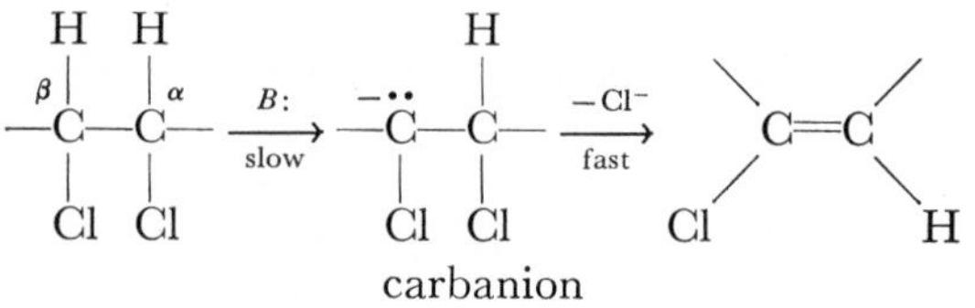

carbanion

and we would therefore anticipate any structural modification that boosts the acidity of the β-hydrogen (without introducing other complicating effects) to accelerate the elimination. Thus, it is not surprising that substitution of the

[42] (a) Cristol and Hause, *J. Am. Chem. Soc.*, **74,** 2193 (1952). (b) Cristol and Hoegger, *ibid.*, **79,** 3438 (1957).

strongly acid-strengthening $Me-\!\!\!\bigcirc\!\!\!-\overset{\overset{O}{|}}{\underset{\underset{O}{|}}{S}}-$ group for one of the chlorine

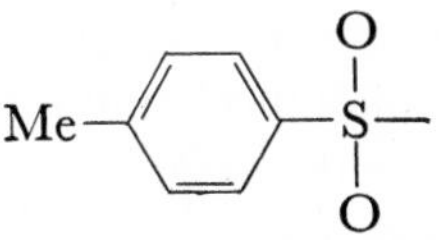

atoms in **XLIV** (converting it to β-chlorosulfone **XLVI**) increases the rate of dehydrochlorination—the magnitude of the effect (about 10^{10}) being remarkably large.[43]

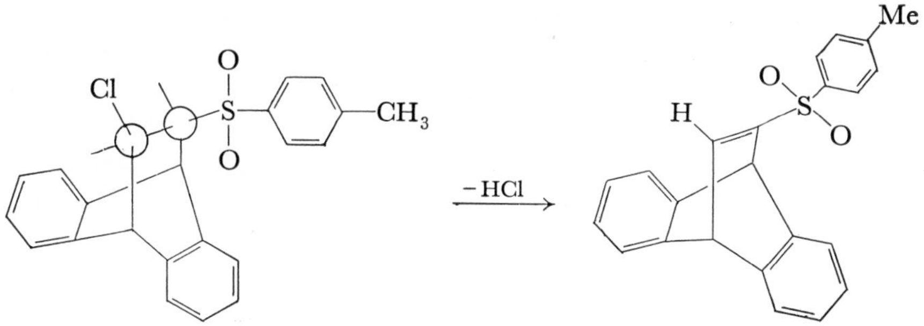

XLVI

So powerful, in fact, is the action of the sulfone linkage in facilitating elimination reactions, that it can bring about *cis* elimination, even when *trans* elimination is structurally possible. It has been found, for example, that treatment of sulfone **XLVII** with base yields olefin **XLVIII** with the double bond adjacent to the sulfone group rather than to olefin **XLIX**, the product which would result from *trans* elimination.[44] The "detosylation" of the cyclopentyl sulfone **L** proceeds in the same manner.[45]

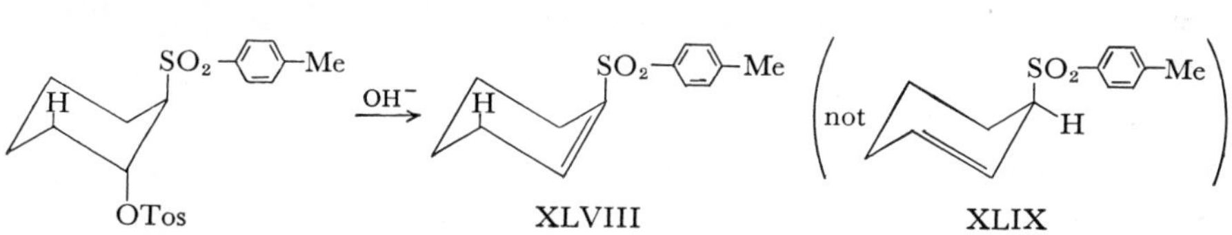

XLVII   **XLVIII**   **XLIX**

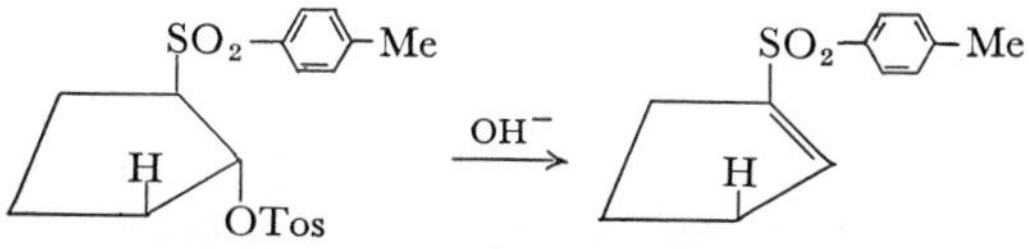

L

[43] Cristol and Arganbright, *J. Am. Chem. Soc.*, **79**, 3442 (1957). This ratio of rate constants is approximate since, obviously, the two rates cannot be accurately measured at the same temperature. The specific rates for dehydrochlorination of **XXXV** were determined at temperatures near 150°, then extrapolated to 12°, a temperature at which the dehydrochlorination of the toluenesulfonyl-substituted compound proceeds at a convenient rate.

[44] Bordwell, *et al.*, *J. Am. Chem. Soc.*, **77**, 1141, 1145, 6706 (1955).

[45] Weinstock, Pearson, and Bordwell, *J. Am. Chem. Soc.*, **78**, 3468 (1956).

Although the action of the sulfone group in accelerating eliminations is consistent with a two-step carbanion mechanism, it does not demand it; for an elimination reaction proceeding by the usual one-step mechanism should also be facilitated by groups that greatly increase the acidity of the β-hydrogen(s). Indeed, the two types of mechanism merge into each other as the lifetime of the carbanion intermediate becomes progressively shorter. For the usual E2 reactions, that lifetime is experimentally indistinguishable from zero; and even when eliminations are facilitated by a sulfone group, there is strong evidence that a carbanion intermediate, if it forms at all, is extremely short lived. It is now known that the elimination reactions of substrates such as XLVII and L are catalyzed by amines (as they should be) but not retarded by the conjugate acids of these amines.[46] However, if the initial formation of the carbanion were reversible, then the concentration of carbanion LI (hence the rate of the overall

$$-\overset{\overset{\displaystyle O}{\|}}{\underset{\underset{\displaystyle O}{\|}}{S}}-CH-\overset{|}{\underset{|}{C}}-X + R_3N: \;\rightleftharpoons\; -\overset{\overset{\displaystyle O}{\|}}{\underset{\underset{\displaystyle O}{\|}}{S}}-\overset{|}{\underset{|}{\overset{..}{C}}}-\overset{|}{\underset{|}{C}}-X^- + R_3NH^+$$

LI

reaction) should be inversely proportional to (R_3NH^+). Since this inverse dependence is not observed, we may conclude that if carbanion LI is formed, its conversion to an olefin is much faster than its return to the substrate, a reaction which itself would be expected to be very rapid. In the opinion of the present author, the question of a carbanion intermediate in E2 reactions (except perhaps in eliminations facilitated by nitro, cyano, or keto groups) remains open.[47]

Intramolecular (cis) Eliminations

Of the many compounds that undergo pyrolytic eliminations, at least three types almost certainly react unimolecularly through cyclic transition states. These are carboxylic esters:

$$-\overset{|}{\underset{|}{C}}-\overset{|}{\underset{\underset{\displaystyle H}{|}}{C}}-O-\overset{\overset{\displaystyle}{}}{\underset{\underset{\displaystyle O}{\|}}{C}}-R \overset{\Delta}{\rightarrow} \underset{/}{\overset{\backslash}{C}}=\underset{\backslash}{\overset{/}{C}} + HO-\overset{}{\underset{\underset{\displaystyle O}{\|}}{C}}-R$$

[46] Weinstock, Pearson, and Bordwell, *J. Am. Chem. Soc.*, **78**, 3473 (1956); Pearson and Vogelsong, *ibid.*, **80**, 1048 (1958).

[47] For further arguments in favor of the intercession of a carbanion intermediate in E2 reactions promoted by a sulfone group, see Goering, Relyea, and Howe, *J. Am. Chem. Soc.*, **79**, 2502 (1957). For arguments to the contrary, see Bordwell and Landis, *ibid.*, **79**, 1579 (1957); and Skell and McNamara, *ibid.*, **79**, 85 (1957).

xanthates, (the "Chugaev reaction"):

$$-\overset{\displaystyle |}{\underset{\displaystyle H}{C}}-\overset{\displaystyle |}{\underset{\displaystyle |}{C}}-O-\overset{\displaystyle |}{\underset{\displaystyle S}{C}}-SMe \xrightarrow{\Delta} \overset{\backslash}{\underset{/}{C}}=\overset{/}{\underset{\backslash}{C}} + O{=}C{=}S + HSMe$$

and trialkylamine oxides, (the "Cope reaction"):

$$-\overset{\displaystyle |}{\underset{\displaystyle H}{C}}-\overset{\displaystyle |}{\underset{\displaystyle |}{C}}-\overset{R}{\underset{O\ \ R}{N}} \xrightarrow{\Delta} \overset{\backslash}{\underset{/}{C}}=\overset{/}{\underset{\backslash}{C}} + R_2N{-}OH \text{ (an N,N-dialkylhydroxylamine)}$$

The decompositions of carboxylic esters and alkyl methyl xanthates at high temperatures in the absence of solvent obey first-order rate laws and exhibit negative entropies of activation.[48] Thus, motion is more restricted in the transition state than in the reactants, and we may suspect that a ring forms during the activation process (p. 182). However, the strongest evidence in support of a cyclic transition state is stereochemical in character; for unlike the eliminations taking place in polar solvents, the elimination reactions of esters and xanthates are *cis* eliminations. Typically, the predominant product obtained from xanthate LII is olefin LIII, showing that the hydrogen lost in the reaction lies *cis* to the xanthate group; whereas pyrolysis of xanthate LV yields chiefly the isomeric olefin, LIV.[49] As shown, there are two β-hydrogens *cis* to the xanthate group

LII   LIII 93 percent   LIV 7 percent

LV   LIII 14 percent   +   LIV 86 percent

in LV, but the predominant olefin is LIV, in which the double bond is conjugated with the benzene ring. Moreover, *cis* elimination may also be observed

---

[48] (*a*) O'Connor and Nace, *J. Am. Chem. Soc.*, **74**, 5454 (1952); **75**, 2118 (1953). (*b*) Barton, Head, and Williams, *J. Chem. Soc.*, **1953**, 1715.

[49] Alexander and Mudrak, *J. Am. Chem. Soc.*, **72**, 1810, 3194 (1950). For similar experiments in the menthyl and neomenthyl series, see Ref. 41(b). An important exceptional case is described by Bordwell and Landis, *J. Am. Chem. Soc.*, **80**, 2450 (1958).

in noncyclic systems by comparing the olefins formed from diastereomeric xanthates.[50]

$$(Xan = -O-\underset{\underset{S}{\parallel}}{C}-SMe)$$

Similar experiments point to *cis* elimination in the pyrolysis of carboxylic esters. In the pyrolyses of the diastereomeric forms of the labeled acetate PhCDH—CHPh—OAc,[35] for example, the *erythro*-acetate, LVI, retains almost all of its deuterium, whereas the *threo*-acetate (not shown) loses most of its deuterium. Although both forms may conceivably lose either the β-hydrogen or the β-deuterium, one reaction path involves eclipsing of the two phenyl groups and is therefore less favored.[51]

It seems likely that the mechanism for the pyrolytic conversion of esters to olefins is similar to that for the Chugaev reaction. It is often assumed that the breakage of the C_α—O bond is synchronous with that of the C_β—H bond; that is, the transition states for these two reactions may be represented respectively as LVII and LVIII. While these activated complexes account for the

[50] Cram, *J. Am. Chem. Soc.*, **71**, 3883 (1949); Cram and Abd Elhafez, *ibid.*, **74**, 5828 (1952).

[51] A more detailed analysis of this situation must also consider the fact that a C—D bond is more difficult to break than a C—H bond in the corresponding location. This complication does not, however, alter the qualitative conclusion derived from these experiments—that *cis* elimination is very much more likely than *trans* elimination. For further evidence that the conversion of esters to olefins involves *cis* elimination (based largely on reactions in the steroid and triterpenoid series) see Barton, *et al.*, *J. Chem. Soc.*, **1949**, 2174, 2459; **1952**, 453. See also Marvel and Williams, *J. Am. Chem. Soc.*, **70**, 3842 (1948).

LVII

LVIII

predominance of *cis* elimination, they do not explain the small, but detectable, degree of *trans* elimination. Assuming that the latter does not arise from isomerization of the substrate before the elimination or isomerization of the olefin after the elimination, we must consider the possibility that, in some cases at least, the breakage of the C—O bond occurs *before* that of the C—H bond. If this is true, the reacting system exists, for a significant time interval, as an intimate ion pair or (less likely)[52] as a pair of radicals. During this interval, molecular rotation may allow a β-hydrogen to approach the xanthate or carboxylate ion (or radical) which originally lay *trans* to it, and to undergo extraction. This reaction path would almost certainly require a higher energy of activation than an elimination passing through a cyclic intermediate such as LVII or LVIII, and *cis* elimination would therefore predominate, although *trans* elimination would become increasingly important at higher temperatures.

Conversely, *trans* elimination would be expected virtually to disappear at sufficiently low temperatures. For example, at about 120° (a temperature at which most ester and xanthate pyrolyses are far too slow to follow conveniently), a number of amine oxides (R₃N—O) undergo almost exclusive *cis* elimination,[53(a)] very probably through a transition state such as LX. Thus, the *threo*

---

[52] These reactions do not display the usual characteristics of free-radical reactions; they have no induction period and are insensitive to surface area and to the more usual free-radical inhibitors. (See Blades, *Can. J. Chem.*, **32**, 366 (1954); and Barton, *et al.*, Ref. 48b.) However, the time interval between the breakage of the C—O and C—H bonds is assuredly very short, and "diversion" of the radical (if such is formed) by an outside reagent would be expected to be difficult.

[53] (a) Cram and McCarty, *J. Am. Chem. Soc.*, **74**, 2137 (1952); **76**, 5740 (1954). (b) For further discussion of the conversion of amine oxides to olefins, see Cope, *et al.*, *ibid.*, **71**, 3929 (1949); **75**, 3213 (1953); **79**, 4720, 4729 (1957). Kinetic studies of this reaction have not yet been made, but its stereochemistry strongly indicates that it is similar in character to the pyrolyses of carboxylic esters and xanthates.

amine oxide, LIX, decomposes to yield a mixture of olefins, 93 percent of which is the *cis* olefin, LXI, and 7 percent of which is the "terminal" olefin, LXII.

Only traces of the *trans* isomer of LXI could be detected. Thus, stereospecificity is more extreme here than in the pyrolysis of the corresponding *threo*-xanthate,[50] for the latter yields a mixture of olefins in which the *cis* to *trans* ratio is only 3.3. Similarly, the *trans* to *cis* ratio resulting from the *erythro* amine oxide (diastereomeric to LIX) is 30, whereas the same ratio from the corresponding xanthate is only 9.[53(b)]

The Possibility of Ionic Reactions in the Vapor Phase

In proposing a mechanism for the *trans* elimination that almost invariably accompanies the more favored *cis* elimination in the pyrolyses of carboxylic esters and xanthates, it was suggested that the initial bond breaking in the substrate was *heterolytic* rather than *homolytic; that is,* the reaction proceeded through an ion pair rather than a radical pair. It should be noted, however, that before the 1950's it was generally felt that ionic organic reactions could *not* proceed in the vapor phase. Consider, for example, isopropyl bromide, a substrate that undergoes heterolysis rather easily in polar solvents. It has been estimated[54(a)] that dissociation of this compound into Me_2CH^+ and Br^- in the vapor state requires an energy input of about 150 kcal per mole, whereas dissociation into $Me_2CH\cdot$ and $Br\cdot$ requires an input of only 60 kcal per mole.[54(b)] Comparing these values, it might be argued that in this case, heterolysis may not compete effectively with homolysis in the vapor phase, except perhaps at exceedingly high

[54] (a) Stevenson, in Streitwieser's "Solvolytic Displacement Reactions," *Chem. Revs.*, **1956**, 614. (b) Farmer and Loosing, *Can. J. Chem.*, **33**, 861 (1955). The 90 kcal difference between these two values represents the difference between the ionization potential of the isopropyl group and the electron affinity of the bromine atom.

temperatures. The situation should be even more extreme for substrates that undergo heterolysis less readily. However, an argument of this sort overlooks the fact that much of the energy input presumably necessary for heterolysis is used in separating the ions *after* their formation in a medium having a dielectric constant of very nearly unity (for example, increasing the separation between two univalent ions of opposite charge from 4 Å to 100 Å requires an energy input of about 80 kcal per mole). It may thus be seen that *gas-phase reactions proceeding through ion pairs are not energetically prohibited.*

Indeed, there is evidence which suggests (although it does not prove) that the dehydrohalogenations of alkyl chlorides and bromides in the vapor state may proceed through a rate-determining conversion to an ion pair—that is, that they are, in effect, $E1$ reactions in the vapor state.

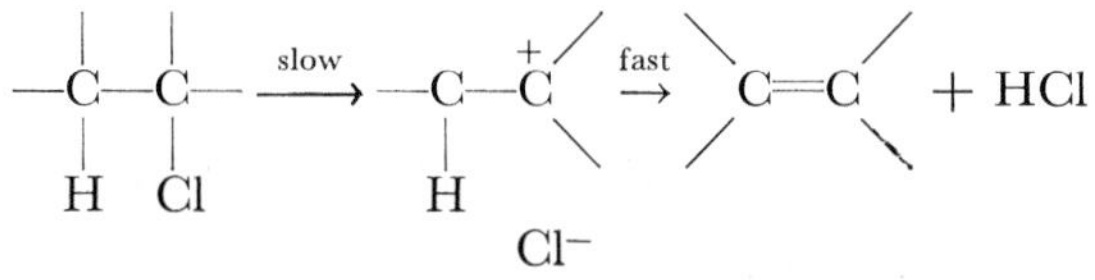

The study of such reactions is often complicated by free-radical side reactions that may be accelerated not only by elemental oxygen or halogen, but also by contact with glass surface. However, when precautions are taken to minimize these complications, it is found that these dehydrohalogenations are frequently first-order reactions, many of them giving good yields of olefins.[55] The kinetics are obviously consistent with a one-step mechanism proceeding through a cyclic transition state, LXIII (analogous to that proposed for the pyrolyses of car-

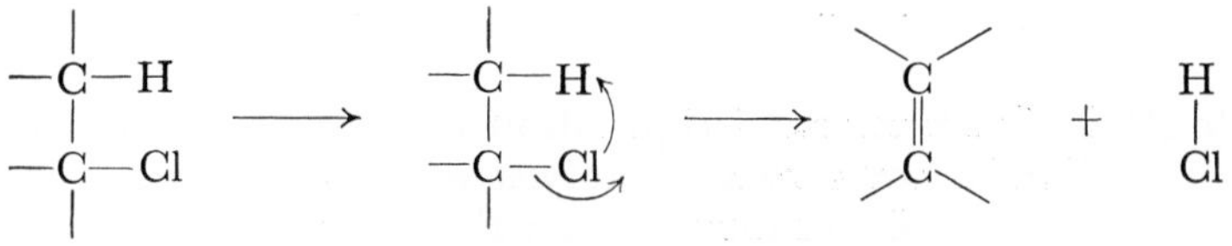

LXIII

boxylic esters, xanthates, and amine oxides); but the relationships between structure and reactivity in these dehydrohalogenations are strikingly similar to those observed for conventional S_N1 and $E1$ reactions.[56] The following relative rate constants (380°) show that branching of the α-carbon greatly accelerates the reaction, whereas branching at the β-carbon is very much less effective:

[55] Barton, *et al.*, *Trans. Faraday Soc.*, **45**, 725 (1949); **46**, 114 (1950); *J. Chem. Soc.*, **1949**, 155, 165; **1951**, 2039. Howlett, *ibid.*, **1952**, 3695.

[56] Maccoll, *et al.*, *J. Chem. Soc.*, **1955**, 979, 2445, 2454; *Nature*, **176**, 391 (1955). For a short summary of this and more recent work, see Ingold, *Proc. Chem. Soc.*, **1957**, 285.

	EtBr	n-PrBr	Me₂CHCH₂Br	i-PrBr	t-BuBr	EtCMe₂Br
$\dfrac{k}{k_{EtBr}}$	1	3.5	6.3	170	32,000	46,000

These figures indicate that the activation process in the rate-determining step involves partial bond breaking at the α-carbon, but probably not at the β-carbon, and that the bond breaking is greatly facilitated by hyperconjugative effects arising from α branching. Furthermore, it has been found that bromides LXIV and LXV undergo dehydrobromination at almost the same rate, even though the reaction of the latter involves the removal of an allylic hydrogen to form a conjugated diene.

$$\text{Me—CH—CH—Me} \xrightarrow{-\text{HBr}} \text{MeCH}=\text{CHMe};$$
$$\underset{\text{H} \quad \text{Br}}{\qquad \qquad \ \ |\quad \ \ |\qquad}$$

LXIV

$$\text{CH}_2=\text{CH—CH—CH—Me} \xrightarrow{-\text{HBr}} \text{CH}_2=\text{CH—CH}=\text{CHMe}$$
$$\underset{\text{H} \quad \text{Br}}{\qquad \qquad \qquad \ \ |\quad \ \ |\qquad}$$

LXV

This again suggests that the β-hydrogen has not been appreciably loosened, nor has the new double bond begun to form, during the activation process of the rate-determining step, for both hydrogen loosening and double-bond formation should be greatly facilitated by the γ,δ double bond in LXV.

Finally, let us compare (Table 12-2) the energies of activation, E_A, for a number of these gas-phase eliminations to two sets of bond-dissociation energies: first, to the energies needed to split the various substrates into free radicals;[57] and, second, to the energies needed to break them into ions.[54(a)] We see that

Table 12-2. Comparison of Activation Energies for Vapor-phase Eliminations with Homolytic and Heterolytic Bond-dissociation Energies

	EtBr	i-PrBr	t-BuBr	EtCl	i-PrCl	t-BuCl
E_A (elim) (kcal)	53.9	47.8	42.2	60.2	50.5	41.4
ΔE (for $RX \rightarrow R\cdot + X\cdot$)	67.2	67.6	63.8	80.9	82.2	78.3
ΔE (for $RX \rightarrow R^+ + X^-$)	183	156	132	192	168	158

[57] These *bond-dissociation energies* are similar in nature to the more usual *bond energies* (Chap. 2) but refer to the breakage of individual bonds in specified compounds. The determination of these values, which is generally more difficult than the determination of bond energies, has been discussed by Szwarc, *Chem. Revs.*, **47**, 75 (1950); and by Walling, *Free Radicals in Solution*, John Wiley and Sons Inc., New York, 1957, pp. 40–53.

the trend in activation energies for elimination is similar to that for heterolytic bond-dissociation energies; that is, both sets of energies decrease as branching at the α-carbon is increased. On the other hand, the energies of activation bear no obvious relationship to the homolytic dissociation energies that are greater for the isopropyl halides than for the ethyl and t-butyl halides. From these figures, we would strongly suspect that the activation process in these gas-phase dehydrohalogenations is heterolytic (ionic) rather than homolytic (free radical) in character.

EXERCISES FOR CHAPTER 12

1. (a) It has been noted that the replacement of Me— by Et— as group R— in the tertiary halide
$$R—\overset{\overset{\displaystyle R'}{|}}{\underset{\underset{\displaystyle R''}{|}}{C}}—Cl$$
raises the rate at which the double bond enters group R— in an $E1$ reaction but lowers the rate at which the double bond enters groups R'— and R''— if the latter two are not altered. Explain.

   (b) Assume, more specifically, that the replacement of Me— by Et— as group R— raises the rate at which the double bond enters R— by a constant factor, a; lowers the rate at which it enters R'— and R''— by a constant factor, b; but does not affect the rate at which the carbonium-ion intermediate, RR'R''C^{+}, reacts with the solvent to give a substitution product. From the following yields of olefin (80 percent EtOH, 25°, Ref. 5a), calculate the factors a and b:

   Me$_3$CCl   15 percent   EtCMe$_2$Cl   34 percent   Et$_2$MeCl   40 percent

   (c) Calculate the percent yield of olefin from Et$_3$CCl. (Observed 39 percent)
   (d) Calculate the ratio of olefins obtained from EtCMe$_2$Cl and Et$_2$CMeCl.

2. Predict which reactions in each of the following pairs results in the higher ratio of elimination to substitution:
   (a) i-PrCMe$_2$Br or n-PrCMe$_2$Br; heat in aqueous alcohol.

   (b) Et$_2$CMeCl or
$$EtCH_2—\overset{\overset{\displaystyle Et}{|}}{\underset{\underset{\displaystyle Me}{|}}{C}}—Br;$$
heat in aqueous dioxane.

   (c) n-PrSMe$_2^+$I$^-$ or n-Pr$_3$S$^+$I$^-$; treat with alcoholic NaOEt.
   (d) PhCH$_2$CMe$_2$SMe$_2^+$I$^-$ or PhCH$_2$CH$_2$CMe$_2$Br; heat in aqueous alcohol.

   (e)
$$Et—\overset{\overset{\displaystyle O}{|}}{\underset{\underset{\displaystyle O}{|}}{S}}—Ph \quad or \quad Me_2CH—\overset{\overset{\displaystyle O}{|}}{\underset{\underset{\displaystyle O}{|}}{S}}—Me;$$
treat with alcoholic KOH.

   (f) PhCH$_2$CH$_2$Br or i-PrBr; treat with alcoholic NaOEt.
   (g) t-BuCH$_2$CMe$_2$Br; treat with NaOEt in EtOH or with t-BuOK in t-BuOH.
   (h) EtCHBrMe; treat with 1 N NaOAc or 1 N NaOH in aqueous alcohol.
   (i) i-Pr$_2$CClEt; heat in t-BuOH or in EtOH.

(j) *t*-BuCH₂—C(Et)(Me)—Cl or *t*-BuCHMe—CMe₂Cl; heat in aqueous alcohol.

(k) *sec*-BuBr or *sec*-BuSMe₂⁺I⁻; treat with NaOEt in alcohol.

(l) Cyclohexyl chloride; treat with 1 N NaOH in 50 percent EtOH or with 1 N NaOH in dry EtOH.

(m) *trans*-4-Phenylcyclohexyl bromide; treat with NaOMe in refluxing MeOH or with NaOEt in refluxing EtOH.

(n) ; treat with 0.01 N NaCN or with 2.0 N NaCN in aqueous alcohol.

(o) ; heat in aqueous ethanol or treat with NaOEt in EtOH?

(p) EtCHBrMe or *i*-PrCHBrMe; treat with NaOEt in EtOH.

(q) or ; treat with NaOEt in EtOH.

(r) *meso*- or *d,l*-2,3-Dichlorobutane; treat with NaOEt in EtOH.

(s) *threo*- or *erythro*-MeCHPh—CHPh—OTos; treat with NaOH in EtOH.

(t) or ; treat with NaCN in EtOH.

(u) *cis*- or *trans*-4-*t*-Butylcyclohexyl bromide; treat with NaOEt in EtOH.

(v) or ; treat with AgNO₃ in EtOH.

3. Suggest mechanisms for the following conversions:

(a) $\xrightarrow[\text{heat}]{\text{HCOOH}}$

(b) $\xrightarrow[\text{NaNH}_2]{\text{NH}_3}$

(c) 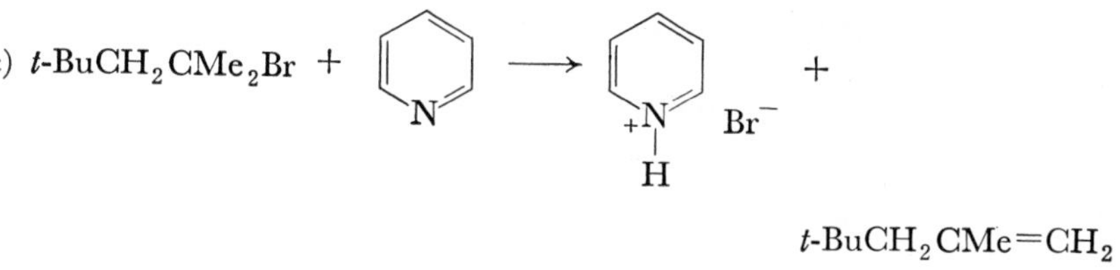 $t\text{-BuCH}_2\text{CMe}_2\text{Br}$ + ⟶ +

$t\text{-BuCH}_2\text{CMe}{=}\text{CH}_2$

(d) 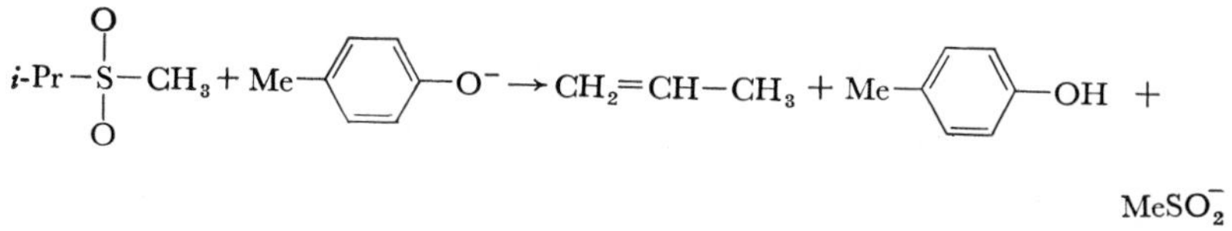 $\text{CH}_2{=}\text{CH}{-}\text{CH}_3$ + +

MeSO_2^-

(e) $\text{PhCHMe}{-}\text{O}{-}\text{O}{-}\text{CMe}_3 + \text{OEt}^- \rightarrow \text{PhCCH}_3 + t\text{-BuO}^-$
$$\overset{\displaystyle\|}{}\text{O}$$

(f) $2\text{Me}_3\text{SiCH}_2\text{CH}_2\text{Cl} + \text{OH}^- \rightarrow \text{Me}_3\text{Si}{-}\text{O}{-}\text{SiMe}_3 + 2\text{C}_2\text{H}_4 + 2\text{Cl}^-$

(g) $+ \text{OEt}^- \rightarrow$ $+ \text{Cl}^-$

(h) 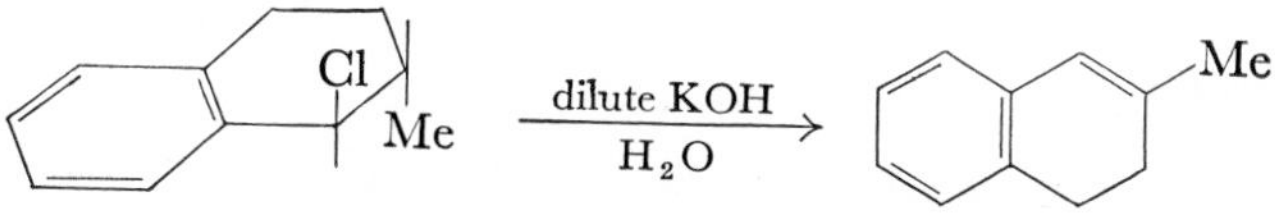 $\xrightarrow[\text{H}_2\text{O}]{\text{dilute KOH}}$

(i) $\text{CH}_3\text{CHCl}{-}\text{O}{-}\text{CH}_3 \xrightarrow[\text{vapor phase}]{200°} \text{CH}_2{=}\text{CHOCH}_3 + \text{HCl}$

(j) 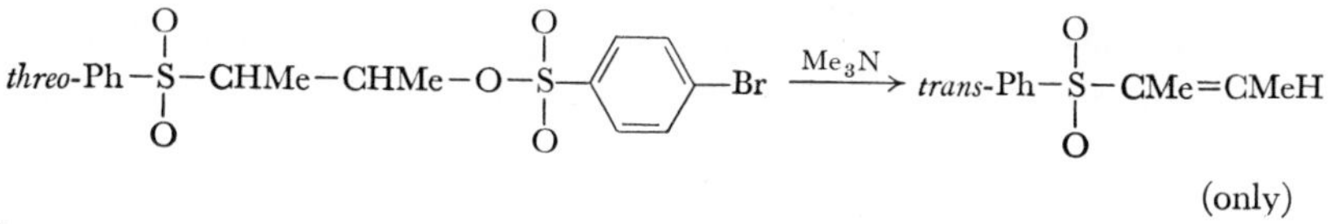 $\xrightarrow{\text{Me}_3\text{N}}$

(only)

(k) 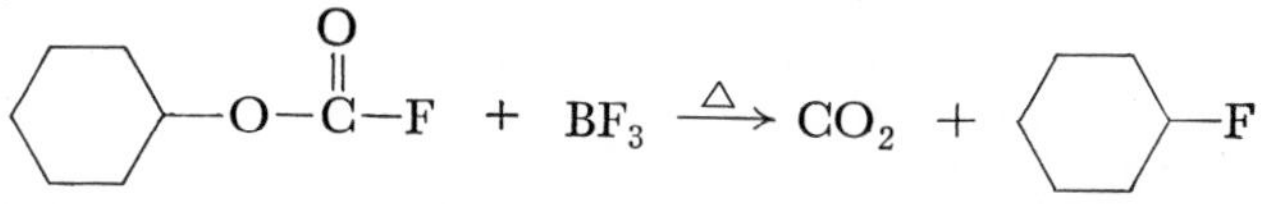 $+ \text{BF}_3 \xrightarrow{\Delta} \text{CO}_2 +$

(l) $\text{Ph}_2\text{C}{-}\text{CH}_2{-}\text{CHPh}{-}\text{NHPh} \xrightarrow[\Delta]{\text{Ac}_2\text{O}} \text{Ph}_2\text{C}{=}\text{CH}_2 + \text{PhCH}{=}\text{NPh}$
$\phantom{\text{Ph}_2\text{C}{-}\text{CH}}\big|$
$\phantom{\text{Ph}_2\text{C}}\text{OH}$

(m) $\text{PhCH}_2{-}\text{CHMe}{-}\text{O}{-}\text{S}{-}\text{OEt} \xrightarrow{\text{heat}} \text{SO}_2 + \text{EtOH} + \text{PhCH}{=}\text{CHMe}$
$$\overset{}{\underset{\displaystyle\text{O}}{}}$$

(n) 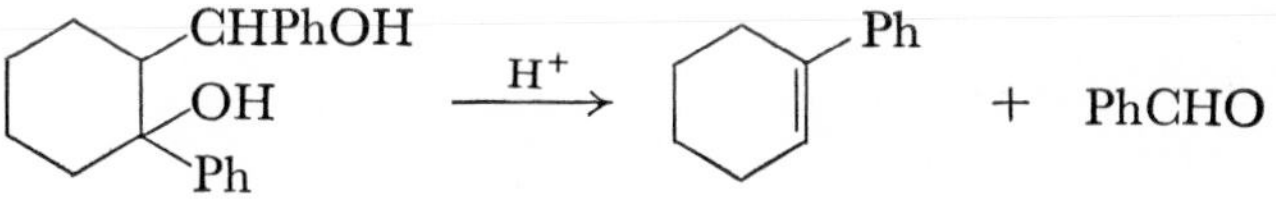 $\xrightarrow{\text{H}^+}$ $+ \text{PhCHO}$

(o) 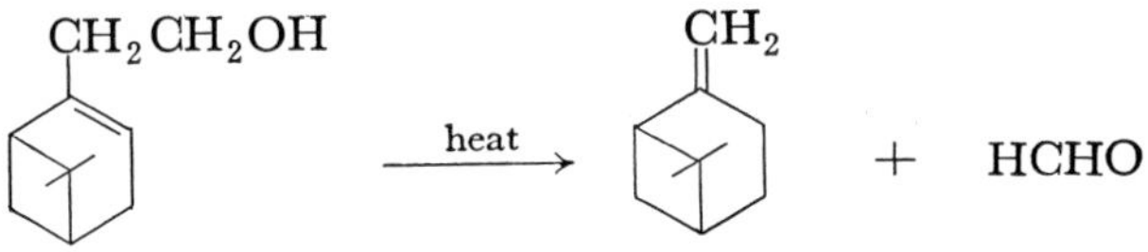 [structure: CH₂CH₂OH substituted bicyclic] $\xrightarrow{\text{heat}}$ [structure: CH₂ bicyclic] + HCHO

(p) 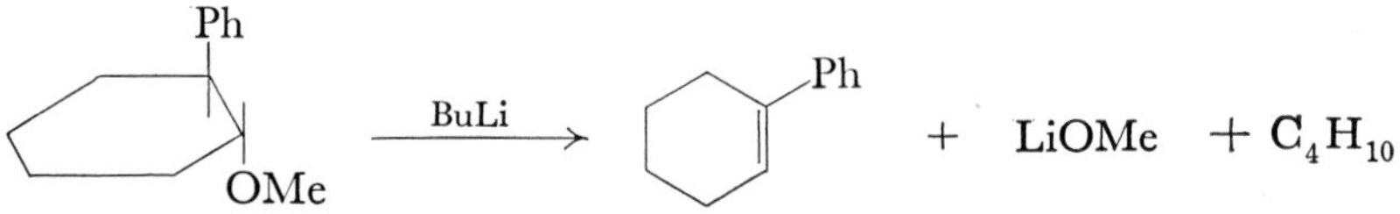 [structure: cyclohexane with Ph and OMe] $\xrightarrow{\text{BuLi}}$ [structure: cyclohexene with Ph] + LiOMe + C_4H_{10}

(q) 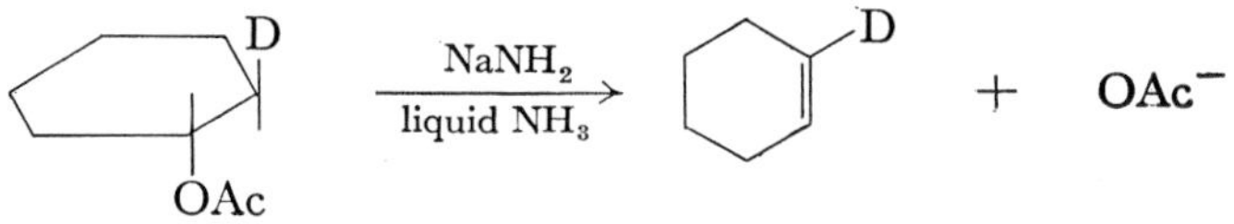 [structure: cyclohexane with D and OAc] $\xrightarrow[\text{liquid NH}_3]{\text{NaNH}_2}$ [structure: cyclohexene with D] + OAc⁻

(r) 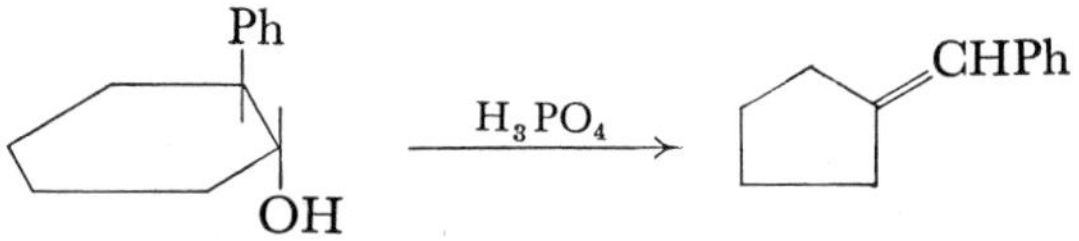 [structure: cyclopentane with Ph and OH] $\xrightarrow{\text{H}_3\text{PO}_4}$ [structure: cyclopentane =CHPh]

(s) $Ph_2C\!=\!CHBr$ 　[below: CH_2Br]　$\xrightarrow{\text{NaNH}_2}$ PhC≡CPh

(t) Me_2C [branches to CH_2OH below] + OH⁻ → CH₂=CMe₂ + HCHO

4. (a) Excluding optical isomerism, there are eight possible benzene hexachlorides (1,2,3,4,5,6-hexachlorocyclohexanes). Sketch these.

(b) Of these, five have been prepared, with the following structures assigned:

Isomer	α	β	γ	δ	ϵ
Structure (cis Cl's)	1:2:4	1:3:5	1:4	1:3	1:2:3

Each of these, on treatment with base, loses 3 moles of HCl to give one or more trichlorobenzenes. However one of the five isomers above reacts about 1000 times as slowly as the remaining four. Which one is this? Explain.

(c) Two of the remaining four prepared isomers lose their second molecule of HCl much more rapidly than they lose the first. Which are these?

(d) Of the remaining two isomers, one isomer loses the second molecule of HCl about one half as rapidly as the first HCl, whereas the other isomer loses the second HCl about one twelfth as rapidly as the first HCl. For which of these two isomers is the ratio k_2/k_1 the smaller? Explain.

5. Predict the predominant products in each of the following cases, specifying, where possible, whether an olefin formed is the cis or trans isomer:

(a) n-Pr—C—Br [with Me above and Et below] $\xrightarrow{\text{(heat, HOAc)}}$

(b)

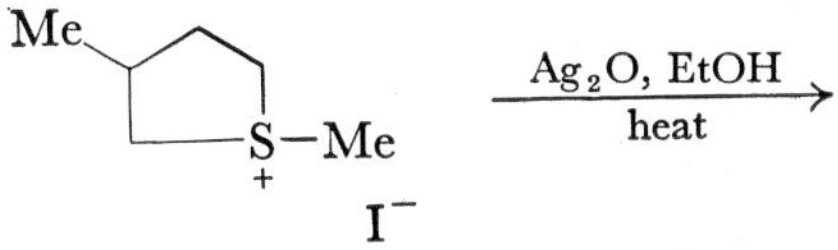

$$\xrightarrow[\text{heat}]{\text{Ag}_2\text{O, EtOH}}$$

(c) 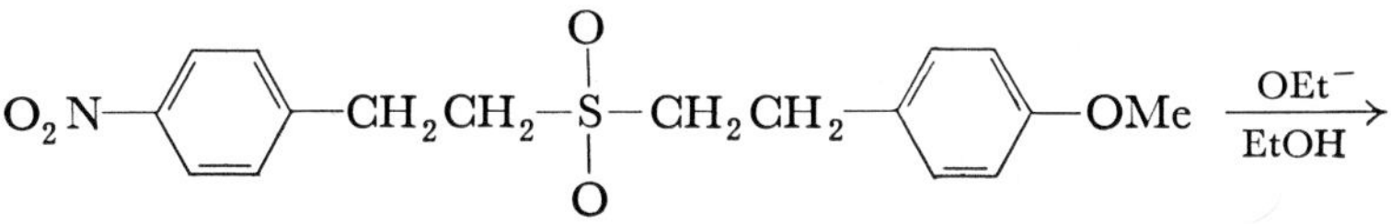 O_2N—⟨⟩—CH_2CH_2—$\overset{\overset{O}{\|}}{\underset{\underset{O}{\|}}{S}}$—$CH_2CH_2$—⟨⟩—$OMe$ $\xrightarrow[\text{EtOH}]{\text{OEt}^-}$

(d)

$\xrightarrow{\text{$i$-PrO}^-}$

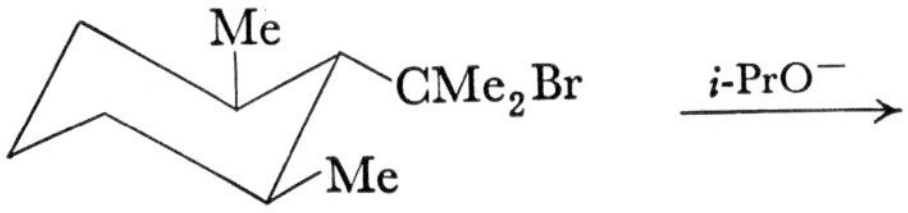

(e) $EtSMe_2^+I^- \xrightarrow[\text{heat}]{\text{MeOH}}$

(f) $EtCMe_2Br + i\text{-Pr}_3N \xrightarrow{\text{heat}}$

(g)

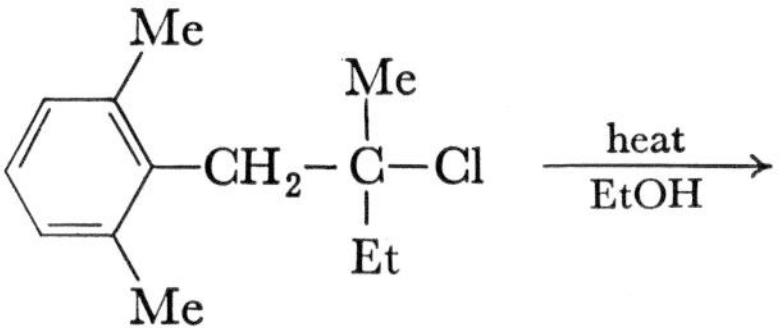

$\xrightarrow[\text{EtOH}]{\text{heat}}$

(h) *erythro*-PhCHMe—CPhBrMe $\xrightarrow{\text{OEt}^-}$

(i) n-Bu—CHMe—PMe$_3^+$I$^-$ + HgO $\xrightarrow{\text{EtOH}}$

(j) n-Bu—CHICH$_3$ + OEt$^-$ →

(k) *meso*-HOOC—CHBr—CHBr—COOH $\xrightarrow{\text{OH}^-}$

(l) *threo*-Ph—$\overset{\overset{}{\underset{\underset{O}{\|}}{C}}}{}$—CHBr—CHPhBr + NH$_4$I $\xrightarrow{\text{EtOH}}$

(m)

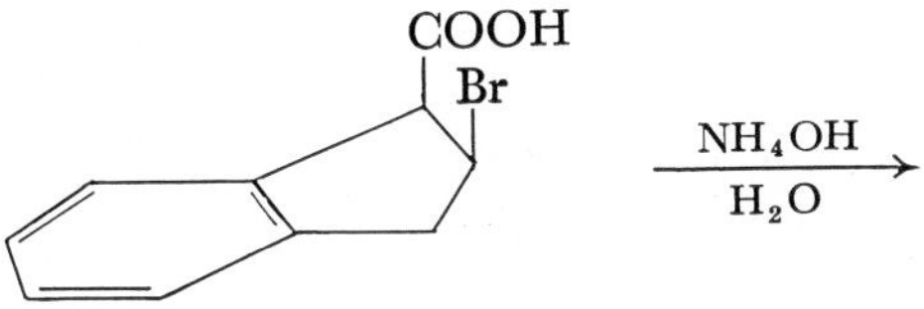

$\xrightarrow[\text{H}_2\text{O}]{\text{NH}_4\text{OH}}$

(n)

$\xrightarrow[\text{H}_2\text{O}]{\text{NH}_4\text{OH}}$

(o)

$\xrightarrow[\text{OEt}^-]{-1 \text{ HBr}}$

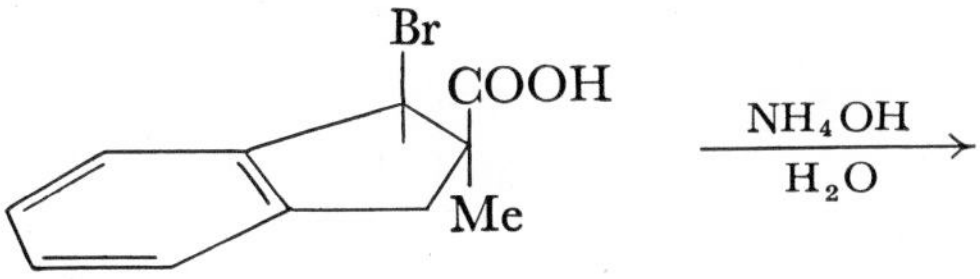

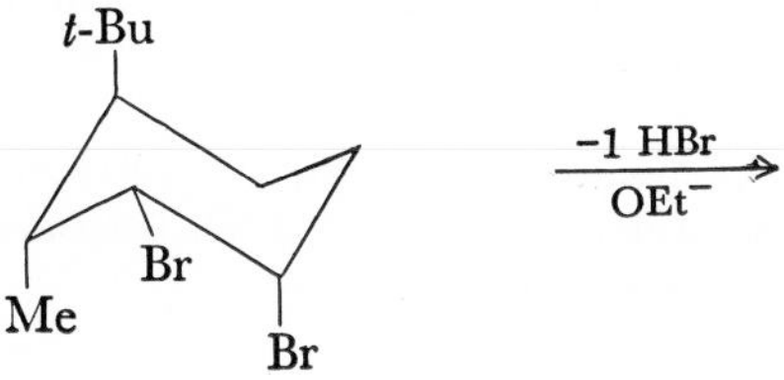

(p) 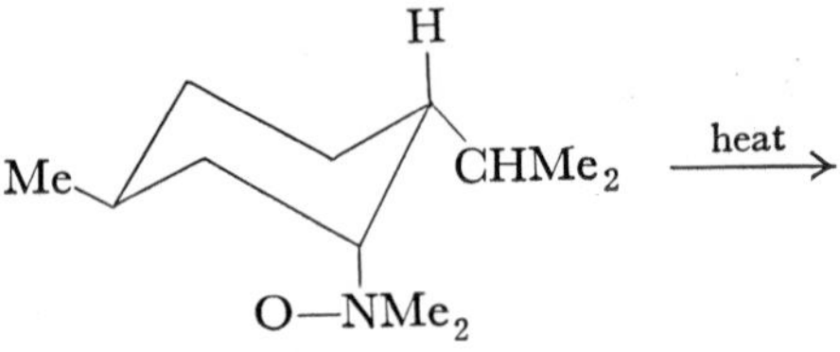 $\xrightarrow{\text{heat}}$

(q) 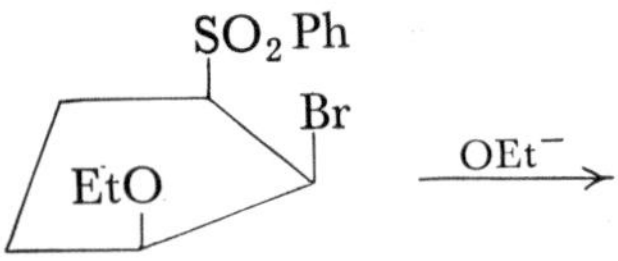 $\xrightarrow{\text{OEt}^-}$

(r) 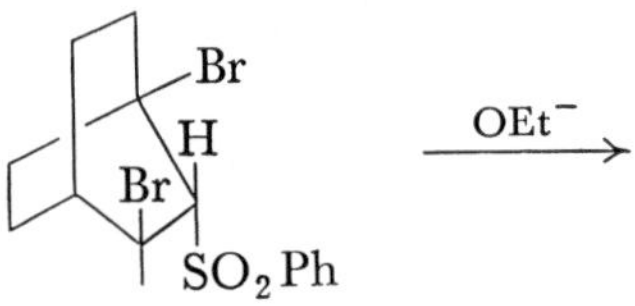 $\xrightarrow{\text{OEt}^-}$

6. Explain each of the following observations:

(a) The ratio of *cis*-2-olefin to *trans*-2-olefin obtained from the unimolecular elimination reaction of EtCHMe—OBs is about twice that obtained from *i*-BuCHMe—OBs under comparable conditions.

(b) Although the —SR$_2^+$ and the —SO$_2$—R groups are easily removed in elimination reactions, the —SR group is not.

(c) The ratio of 2-olefin to 1-olefin obtained from the action of NaOEt on *n*-PrCHBrMe is less than that obtained from EtCHBrMe.

(d) In the bimolecular dehydrochlorination of CHCl$_2$CH$_2$Cl, the chlorine lost is the "single" one (that is, the product is CCl$_2$=CH$_2$); but in the bimolecular dehydrobromination of MeCBr$_2$CHBrMe, the bromine lost is one of a pair (that is, the product is MeCBr=CBrMe).

(e) The mass law effect (p. 256) is much more commonly observed in S_N1 reactions than in $E1$ reactions.

(f) There are two very different concentrations (c and c') of NaOEt (in dry ethanol at a given temperature) at which the elimination to substitution ratio for *i*-PrBr is the same as that for *t*-BuBr. Between c and c', the E/S_N ratio is greater for *i*-PrBr, but at concentrations less than c or greater than c', the E/S_N ratio is greater for *t*-BuBr.

(g) When the *threo* form of ester LXVI is treated with base, practically no deuterium is lost. When the *erythro* form of this ester is so treated, almost all of the deuterium is lost.

(h) When the ammonium ion LXVII is treated with base, the major products are an olefin and Me$_3$N; but when ion LXVIII is so treated, the major products are amine LXIX and MeOH.

(i) When the *threo* isomer of acid LXX is treated with pyridine, it undergoes "decarboxylative debromination," but when the *erythro* form of LXX is treated in the same way, it undergoes simple dehydrobromination.

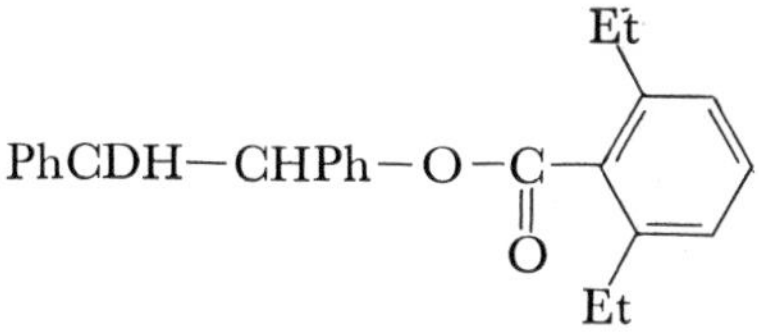

PhCDH—CHPh—O—C

Et ... Et (ring structure)

LXVI

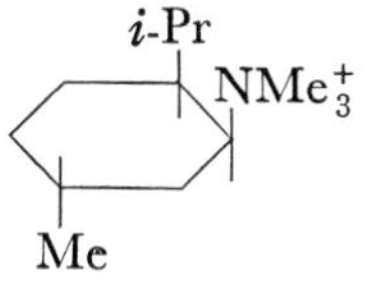

i-Pr, NMe$_3^+$, Me

LXVII

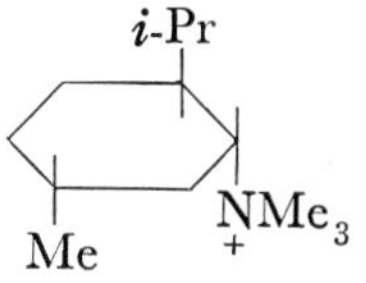

i-Pr, NMe$_3^+$, Me

LXVIII

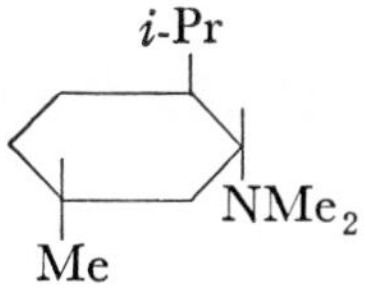

i-Pr, NMe$_2$, Me

LXIX

PhC—CHBr—CHPh—COOH
‖
O

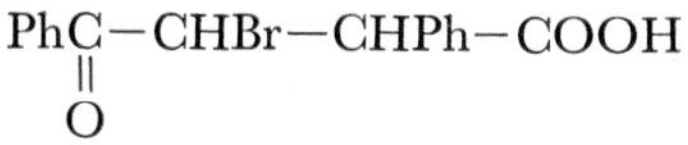

LXX

(j) The dehydrochlorination of CH_3CHCl—O—CH_3 in the vapor phase at 200° is almost one million times as rapid as that of i-PrCl at the same temperature.

(k) The rate of bimolecular elimination which chloride LXXI undergoes is almost the same as that which tosylate LXXII undergoes, although —OTos is a much more effective leaving group than —Cl.

(l) The debrominative decarboxylation of anion LXXIII is stereospecific in aqueous alcoholic solutions in which the corresponding reaction of

PhCHBr—CHBr—COO⁻

is not.

(m) Treatment of the *erythro* form of bromide LXXIV with base gives mainly a *trans* olefin, but similar treatment of the *erythro* form of bromide LXXV gives mainly a *cis* olefin.

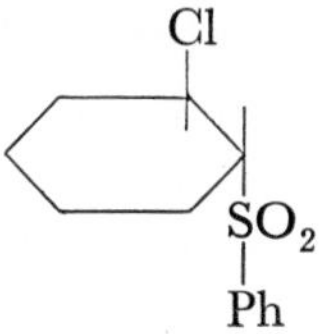

Cl, SO$_2$, Ph

LXXI

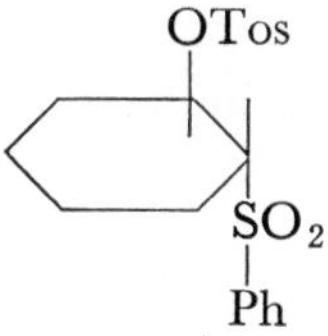

OTos, SO$_2$, Ph

LXXII

O_2N— —CHBr—CHBr—COO⁻

LXXIII

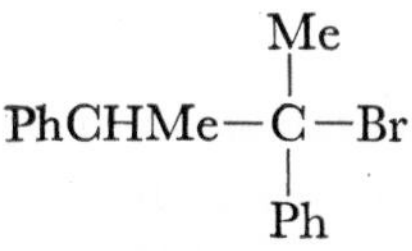

Me
|
PhCHMe—C—Br
|
Ph

LXXIV

Me
|
Ph—C—CHMe—Br
|
Br

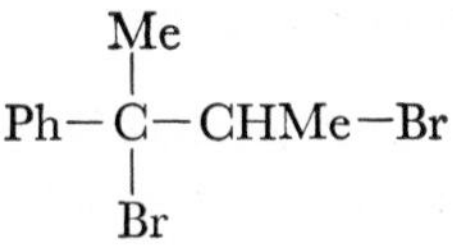

LXXV

7. Treatment of PhC≡CD with H_2 on Pt gives *cis*-PhCH=CDH, the infrared spectrum of which is easily distinguishable from that of the *trans* isomer. Suggest a series of experiments, starting with readily available materials, to determine whether the debromination of PhCHBr—CH_2Br with iodide proceeds by sequence (5) or sequence (6) (p. 494).

Addition Reactions

AMONG THE HUNDRED-ODD chemical elements, only carbon, nitrogen, oxygen, and sulfur form double bonds in the usual sense;[1] and of these only carbon and nitrogen form true triple bonds. Although nine different types of multiple bond may be formed from the various combinations of these elements, our knowledge of addition reactions is based largely on studies of the transformations of C=C and C=O bonds.

The reader is reminded that addition reactions of the C=O group are often initiated by nucleophilic attack on the carbon atom, although in strongly acid solutions the oxygen atom may be protonated first. On the other hand, the addition reactions of olefins are generally initiated by electrophilic attack, although initial nucleophilic attack is possible if strongly electron-attracting groups lie near the C=C bond. Moreover, additions to the C=C bond may also be initiated by free radicals, but such reactions are not to be considered until Chapter 16.

The Hydration of Olefins

The dehydration of alcohols to olefins, generally carried out in solutions of strong acids, is reversible; treatment of the olefin with dilute acid may regenerate an alcohol.

[1] In addition, a few compounds with B=N bonds are known, and there is some (inconclusive) evidence that a number of bonds in inorganic compounds (for example, the P—O bonds in phosphates, and the metal-carbon bond in some cyano complexes) have "double-bond character." Although such bonds resemble the more usual double bonds in certain respects (being especially strong and unusually short), they do not undergo addition reactions in the same manner as do C=C, C=O, and C≡C bonds, and are thus not "unsaturated" from the organic chemist's point of view.

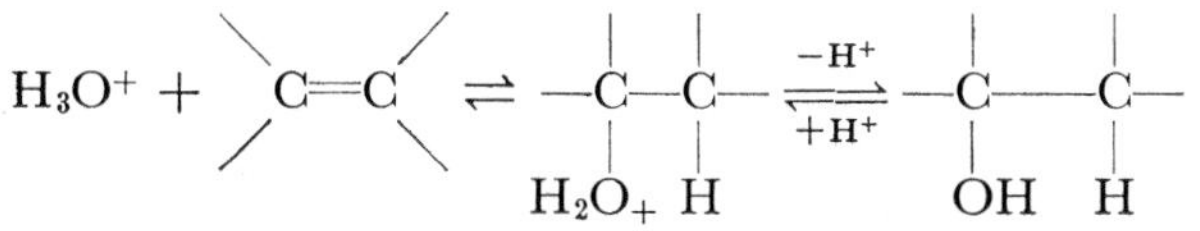

$$H_3O^+ + \quad \diagdown C{=}C \diagup \quad \rightleftharpoons \quad -\overset{|}{\underset{|}{C}}-\overset{|}{\underset{|}{C}}- \quad \underset{+H^+}{\overset{-H^+}{\rightleftharpoons}} \quad -\overset{|}{\underset{|}{C}}-\overset{|}{\underset{|}{C}}-$$

$$\underset{H_2O_+ \ H}{} \qquad \qquad \underset{OH \ H}{}$$

If we assume that the dehydration is a simple unimolecular elimination reaction, the principle of microscopic reversibility (p. 319) requires us to assume that the hydration proceeds by a similarly simple two-step sequence. The con-

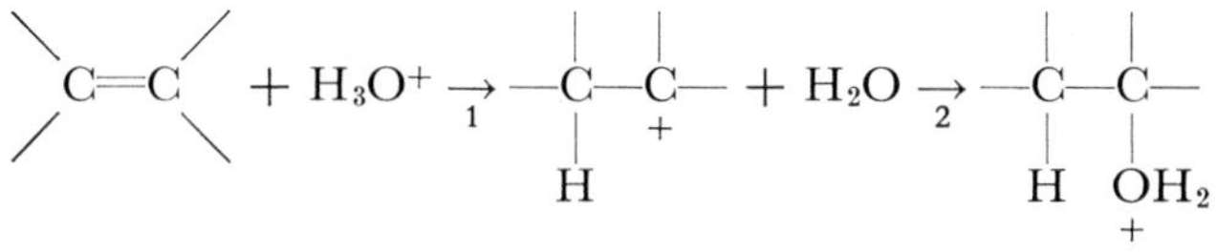

$$\diagup_{\diagdown} C{=}C \diagdown_{\diagup} + H_3O^+ \overset{1}{\rightarrow} -\overset{|}{\underset{|}{C}}-\overset{|}{\underset{+}{C}}- + H_2O \overset{2}{\rightarrow} -\overset{|}{\underset{|}{C}}-\overset{|}{\underset{|}{C}}- \tag{1}$$

$$\underset{H}{} \qquad \qquad \underset{H \ \underset{+}{OH_2}}{}$$

$$\mathbf{I}$$

centration of carbonium ion I must remain low in an aqueous medium, so we may infer either that this ion is consumed (in step 2) essentially as rapidly as it is formed (in step 1), or that its formation is reversible (in which case, step 2 would be rate determining). The second of these possibilities is excluded by a number of observations, of which we need consider only two. It has been found that if the hydration of an olefin is initiated in acidified D_2O but stopped in its early stages, the unreacted olefin has acquired *no* deuterium and has undergone no isomerization,[2] whereas, as shown below with methylenecyclobutane, both deuteration and isomerization should be expected if the reversible formation of a carbonium ion were involved.

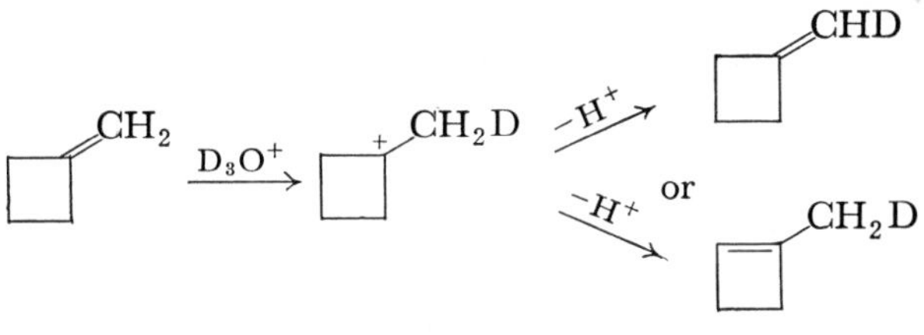

We are then left with the alternate possibility, the slow formation of carbonium ion I, but this appears to be excluded by the observed rate law. For it has been found that the rate of hydration is proportional, not to (H_3O^+), but to Hammett's h_0 function,[3]

$$\text{rate} = h_0 \ (\text{olefin}) \tag{2}$$

[2] (a) Purlee and Taft, *J. Am. Chem. Soc.*, **78**, 5807 (1956). (b) Reisz, Taft, and Boyd, *ibid.*, **79**, 3724 (1957). In the experiments described here, the reaction times were much too short to allow equilibrium between the olefin and carbinol to be established.

[3] (a) Taft, *J. Am. Chem. Soc.*, **74**, 5372 (1952); (b) Levy, et al., *ibid.*, **73**, 7392 (1951). (c) Agreement is not complete that the observed rate law rules out a rate-determining proton transfer from H_3O^+ to the olefin; see, for example, Long and Paul, *Chem. Revs.*, **57**, 943 (1957).

indicating that the rate-determining step involves a molecule of olefin and a proton *but no other species.* It has thus been proposed [5(a)] that sequence (1) must be expanded by addition of another step in which the solvent does not take part. Now, it is probable that when the proton first attaches itself to the olefin, it is attracted to the π electrons of the double bond rather than specifically to one of the two unsaturated carbons—that is, that it first forms a π complex (p. 119). However, the added proton is obviously associated with just one of the carbon atoms in the resulting carbinol and in the carbonium ion, I, leading to it (that is, the carbonium ion is a "σ complex"). The observed rate law then suggests the following mechanism for the hydration of olefins, with the rate-determining step being the conversion of the π complex (II) to the carbonium ion, I:

$$\begin{matrix} & & & \pi \text{ complex} & & \text{carbonium} & & & \\ & & & \text{II} & & \text{I} & & & (3) \\ & & & & & \text{ion} & & & \end{matrix}$$

If this mechanism is correct, we must infer that the π complex II is also an intermediate in the reverse reaction, the acid-catalyzed dehydration of the carbinol. However, this complex would not be detected in kinetic studies of the latter, for, as is indicated above, it is formed and destroyed *after* the rate-determining step in the dehydration.

In contrast to the hydration of simple olefins, the rates of acid-catalyzed hydrations of the double bonds in α,β-unsaturated aldehydes and ketones have been found to be proportional to (H_3O^+), rather than to h_0.[4] This, along with other evidence, suggests that these additions proceed by a mechanism other than that represented in sequence (3) (see Ex. 1).

Additions of Hydrogen Halides. Markownikoff's Rule

The addition of hydrogen halides to double bonds is not conveniently studied in hydroxylic solvents; for hydrogen halides are largely dissociated in such media, and acid-catalyzed hydration (or "alcoholation") of the olefin will compete with, and may overshadow, the desired addition. When such reactions are transferred to nonionizing solvents, it is found that the kinetic picture becomes considerably more complex than that which we have considered for hydra-

[4] Lucas, *et al.*, *J. Am. Chem. Soc.*, **59**, 1461 (1937); **66**, 1818 (1944).

tion. Specifically, the addition of HCl to $Me_2C{=}CH_2$ and that of HBr to $CH_3CH{=}CH_2$ (both in pentane and both at 0°) have been observed to be first order in olefin and of an indefinite order (near three, but not equal to it) in hydrogen halide.[5] Such a rate law is similar in nature to that for the alcoholysis of acyl chlorides in CCl_4 (p. 334) and that for the iodination of mesitylene with ICl (p. 443). It indicates that besides the molecule of HX actually involved in the addition, the activated complex for the slow step is associated with about two "extra" molecules of hydrogen halide. It is probable that the function of these two (or more) "extra" molecules is to increase the polarity of the medium in the immediate vicinity of the reaction site, thus facilitating the ionic cleavage of the attacking molecule. They may even serve to "pull" the halide ion away from the hydrogen-halide molecule, as indicated in the mechanism proposed below:

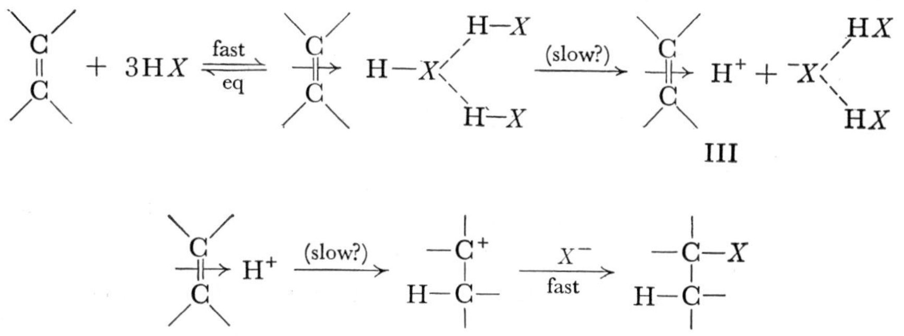

Of the stepwise nature of these additions there can be no doubt, for rearrangements may accompany the reaction, even though neither the adduct itself nor the olefin itself rearranges under the reaction conditions employed. Thus, the addition of HCl to $i\text{-}PrCH{=}CH_2$ yields some rearranged product, IV,[6(a)] whereas addition of HI to $t\text{-}BuCH{=}CH_2$ yields a large amount of iodide V, likewise a rearranged product.[6(b)] These rearrangements, as shown, almost certainly proceed through carbonium-ion intermediates.

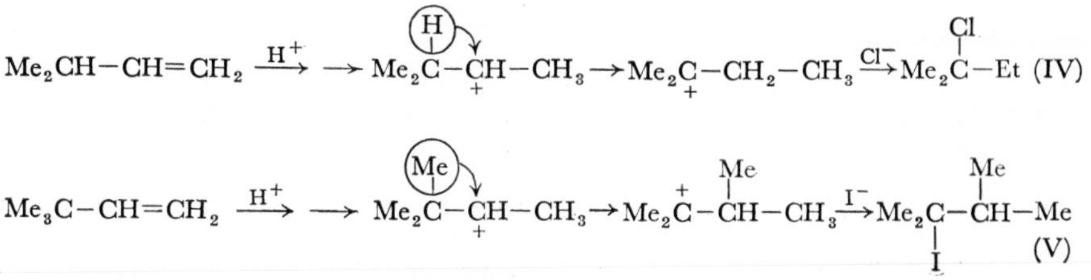

---

[5] Mayo, et al., J. Am. Chem. Soc., **69**, 1339, 1348 (1947).

[6] (a) Whitmore and Johnston, J. Am. Chem. Soc., **55**, 5020 (1933). (b) Ecke, Cook, and Whitmore, ibid., **72**, 1511 (1950).

From the evidence available at present, we cannot tell whether the formation or the destruction of the π complex (III) is rate determining.

When the original olefin is unsymmetric, two (unrearranged) addition products are possible, for the hydrogen ion may attach itself to either the α- or the β-carbon. In such instances, the predominant direction of addition will depend upon which of the two possible carbonium-ion intermediates is the more stable. Specifically, since tertiary carbonium ions are more stable than secondary, which are, in turn, more stable than primary, an addition reaction proceeding through a secondary or tertiary carbonium ion should be favored over one proceeding through a primary carbonium ion. This is the basis of the familiar *Markownikoff rule*, which stipulates that in the addition of HX to an olefin, *group —X becomes bound to the more highly substituted* of the unsaturated carbon atoms. Typically, the addition of HI to 1-butene[7(a)] and the heterolytic addition of HBr to 2-methylpropene[7(b)] yield secondary and tertiary halides VI and VIII, respectively, rather than primary halides VII and IX. Similarly, the

$$
\begin{array}{l}
\overset{H}{\underset{\underset{H}{\overset{|}{EtC}}}{|}} {\overset{+}{=}} CH_2
\end{array}
\quad
\begin{array}{l}
\nearrow \; Et\overset{+}{C}H{-}CH_3 \text{ (more stable)} \xrightarrow{I^-} EtCHICH_3 \text{ (observed)} \\
\qquad\qquad\qquad\qquad\qquad\qquad\qquad VI \\
\searrow \; EtCH_2{-}CH_2^+ \text{ (less stable)} \xrightarrow{I^-} EtCH_2CH_2I \text{ (not observed)} \\
\qquad\qquad\qquad\qquad\qquad\qquad\qquad VII
\end{array}
$$

$$
\begin{array}{l}
Me_2C{\overset{+}{=}}CH_2 \\
\qquad\quad \overset{\downarrow}{H}
\end{array}
\quad
\begin{array}{l}
\nearrow \; Me_2\overset{+}{C}{-}CH_3 \text{ (more stable)} \xrightarrow{Br^-} Me_2CBrCH_3 \text{ (observed)} \\
\qquad\qquad\qquad\qquad\qquad\qquad\qquad VIII \\
\searrow \; Me_2CH{-}CH_2^+ \text{ (less stable)} \xrightarrow{Br^-} Me_2CHCH_2Br \text{ (not observed)} \\
\qquad\qquad\qquad\qquad\qquad\qquad\qquad IX
\end{array}
$$

addition of HCl to $CH_2{=}CHBr$ proceeds through the carbonium ion, $CH_3\text{-}CHBr^+$ (with three β-hydrogens), to give $CH_3CHBrCl$, rather than through $^+CH_2CH_2Br$ (with only two β-hydrogens), which would give $ClCH_2CH_2Br$.[8] Apparent exceptions to Markownikoff's rule may be encountered where factors other than hyperconjugation influence the relative stabilities of the two carbonium ions derived from a single olefin. Thus, both neurine (X)[9(a)] and trifluoromethylethylene (XIII)[9(b)] undergo "anti-Markownikoff addition"; for, in both cases, the carbonium ion intermediates for Markownikoff addition (XI and XIV) are energetically less favorable than the respective alternative carbonium ions (XII and XV). Carbonium ion XI would be expected to be

[7] (a) Kharasch and Hannum, *J. Am. Chem. Soc.*, **56,** 1782 (1934). (b) Kharasch and Hinckley, *ibid.*, **56,** 1212 (1934).

[8] Reboul, *Ann.*, **155,** 29 (1870).

[9] (a) Schmidt, *Ann.*, **267,** 300 (1891). (b) Henne and Kaye, *J. Am. Chem. Soc.*, **72,** 3369 (1950).

$$\overset{+}{Me_3N}-CH=CH_2 \xrightarrow{H^+} \overset{+}{Me_3N}-CH \overset{H}{\underset{+}{=\!\!=}} CH_2$$

X

$$\overset{+}{Me_3N}-\overset{+}{CH}-CH_3 \xrightarrow{I^-} \overset{+}{Me_3N}-CHI-CH_3$$

XII (Mark'ff product, not observed)

$$\overset{+}{Me_3N}-CH_2-CH_2^+ \xrightarrow{I^-} \overset{+}{Me_3N}-CH_2-CH_2I$$

XII (anti-Mark'ff product, observed)

$$F_3C-CH-CH_2 \xrightarrow{H^+} F_3C-CH \overset{H}{\underset{+}{=\!\!=}} CH_2$$

XIII

$$F_3C-\overset{+}{CH}-CH_3 \xrightarrow{Cl^-} F_3C-CHCl-CH_3$$

XIV (Mark'ff product, not observed)

$$F_3C-CH_2-CH_2^+ \xrightarrow{Cl^-} F_3C-CH_2-CH_2Cl$$

XV (anti-Mark'ff product, observed)

rather unstable since there are positive charges on adjacent atoms. Similarly, despite hyperconjugation, ion XV appears to be somewhat more stable than ion XIV; for in the latter, the positively charged carbon is adjacent to the carbon atom of the F_3C- group which, because of the strong electron-attracting action of three fluorine atoms, also bears a partial positive charge.

Anti-Markownikoff addition of HBr to olefins is often observed when no effort is taken to exclude peroxides or elemental oxygen from the reaction mixture. This, the familiar "*peroxide effect*," is due to a fundamental change in the nature of the addition that, under such conditions, proceeds by a free-radical mechanism, with Br·, rather than H^+, attacking the double bond.

$$\underset{/}{\overset{\backslash}{C}}=\underset{\backslash}{\overset{/}{C}} \xrightarrow{Br\cdot} -\underset{Br}{\overset{|}{C}}-\underset{\cdot}{\overset{|}{C}}- \xrightarrow{HBr} -\underset{Br}{\overset{|}{C}}-\underset{H}{\overset{|}{C}}- + Br\cdot \xrightarrow{\overset{\backslash}{C}=\underset{/}{C}} \text{etc. (see Chap. 16)}$$

There are indications that occasionally the addition of a hydrogen halide may bypass the carbonium ion; that is, the halide ion may attack the π complex directly. For example, the additions of HI to the *cis-trans* pair of acids—tiglic acid and angelic acid—in chloroform have been found to be stereospecific; tiglic acid gives an *erythro* β-iodo acid, whereas angelic acid gives a *threo* β-iodo acid.[10]

Me－C(COOH)＝C(Me)(H) $\xrightarrow{HI}$ (Newman projection: I, Me, COOH, Me, H)

tiglic acid
cis
erythro

Me－C(COOH)＝C(H)(Me) $\xrightarrow{HI}$ (Newman projection: I, Me, COOH, H, Me)

angelic acid
trans
threo

[10] Young, Dillon, and Lucas, *J. Am. Chem. Soc.*, **51**, 2528 (1929).

Such stereospecificity would not be expected if the addition proceeded through a carbonium ion analogous to I; for free rotation about the C_α—C_β single bond in such an ion is presumably permitted (XVI $\rightleftharpoons$ XVII), and, contrary to what

is observed, a mixture of *erythro* and *threo* β-iodo acids would result from both unsaturated acids. Since the additions are *trans*, they cannot be one-step processes in which the hydrogen attacks one unsaturated carbon while, at the same time, the iodide attacks the other. Instead, it is likely that the halide ion attacks the π complex (XVIII) on the side opposite to that where the proton lies.

Hydrogen halides may add to *triple* bonds in much the same way, for with these reactions also (in aqueous media) *trans* addition is observed. It has long been known, for example, that both acetylenedicarboxylic acid (XIX) and propiolic acid (XX) undergo *trans* addition with hydrogen halides.

Additions of Halogens[12] and Hypohalous Acids

A worker wishing to study the addition of halogens to unsaturated linkages, if he chooses to carry out his experiments in nonpolar solvents, will soon become

[11] (a) Michael and Brown, *Ber.*, **20**, 550 (1887). (b) Friedrich, *Ann.*, **219**, 320 (1883).
[12] For reviews of halogen additions, see (a) Williams, *Trans. Faraday Soc.*, **37**, 749 (1941); and (b) de la Mare, *Quart. Revs.*, **3**, 126 (1949).

convinced that he is dealing with a very complex subject. If he purifies his solvents carefully and works in the dark, the addition reactions will be very slow; however, they are accelerated by light and are strikingly catalyzed by small quantities of such polar substances as hydrogen halides and water, although generally there is no simple algebraic relationship between the concentrations of such catalysts and the rates of catalyzed addition. Moreover the addition rate may easily be increased by adding glass beads to the reaction mixture, showing that the reaction is sensitive to glass surfaces and suggesting the possibility that additions in the dark in the absence of polar catalysts take place largely (or perhaps exclusively) on the glass walls of the container.

On the other hand, these complications virtually disappear when such additions are transferred to polar solvents, and most of what is known at present concerning the mechanisms of halogen-addition reactions in solution is based upon studies of reactions in hydroxylic solvents, particularly water and the alcohols.[13]

The additions of halogens, like those of hydrogen halides, are stepwise reactions; that is, they proceed through intermediates in which *only one of the two halogen atoms has become attached to the olefin*. The intervention of such an intermediate in the bromination of ethylene has been clearly demonstrated by carrying out the addition in the presence of NaCl or $NaNO_3$, for under these conditions a bromochloride (XXII) or a bromonitrate (XXIII) is formed along with the expected dibromoethane.[14] We would then expect the "half-brominated" intermediate to be carbonium ion XXI which, when formed, may react either with one of the anions present in solution or with the solvent.

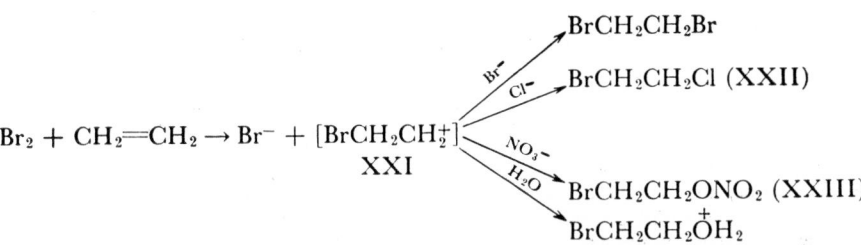

$$Br_2 + CH_2 = CH_2 \rightarrow Br^- + [BrCH_2CH_2^+]$$
$$XXI$$

$BrCH_2CH_2Br$

$BrCH_2CH_2Cl$ (XXII)

$BrCH_2CH_2ONO_2$ (XXIII)

$BrCH_2CH_2\overset{+}{O}H_2$

In interpreting these results as diversions of a common cationic intermediate, we are assuming that the monobromo compounds XXII and XXIII are not formed in substitution reactions on ethylene dibromide; this assumption is certainly justified, for it may be shown that although $BrCH_2CH_2Br$ does react both with Cl^- and NO_3^-, these reactions are far slower than the formation of the

[13] The reactions of elemental fluorine with olefins are almost invariably homolytic in character. They must be studied in the vapor phase or in a nonpolar halogenated solvent, since F_2 reacts readily with the available polar solvents. See, for example, Bigelow, *Chem. Revs.*, **40**, 51 (1947).

[14] Francis, *J. Am. Chem. Soc.*, **47**, 2340 (1925).

bromochloride or bromonitrate by the action of bromine on ethylene. We are further assuming that the monobromo compounds are not formed by the direct addition of BrCl and $BrONO_2$ to the C=C double bond; this assumption is likewise justified since BrCl is too strong an oxidizing agent to be formed under these conditions and the species $BrONO_2$ is, to date, unknown.

Moreover, addition of bromine to stilbene (PhCH=CHPh) in methanol yields, along with stilbene dibromide, a β-bromo ether, XXV.[15(a)] It can

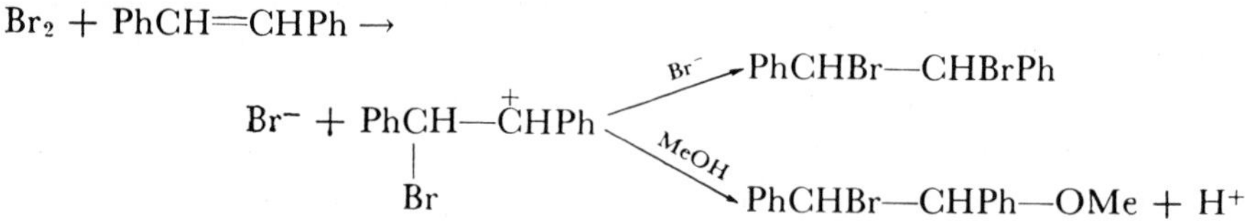

$$Br_2 + PhCH=CHPh \rightarrow$$

$$Br^- + \underset{\underset{XXIV}{\overset{|}{Br}}}{PhCH}-\overset{+}{C}HPh \begin{cases} \overset{Br^-}{\longrightarrow} PhCHBr-CHBrPh \\ \underset{MeOH}{\searrow} PhCHBr-CHPh-OMe + H^+ \\ \qquad\qquad\qquad XXV \end{cases}$$

be shown that ether XXV does not result from the (very slow) reaction of methanol with stilbene dibromide, nor does it arise from the addition of methyl hypobromite, CH_3—O—Br, to the double bond.[16] Similarly, when the sodium salt of dimethylmaleic acid is treated with aqueous bromine or aqueous chlorine, a β-lactone (XXVII) is formed.[17] In this case, the addition reaction is completed when the single-halogenated intermediate (which we may represent for the time being as XXVI) reacts "with its own tail." The salt of dimethylfumaric

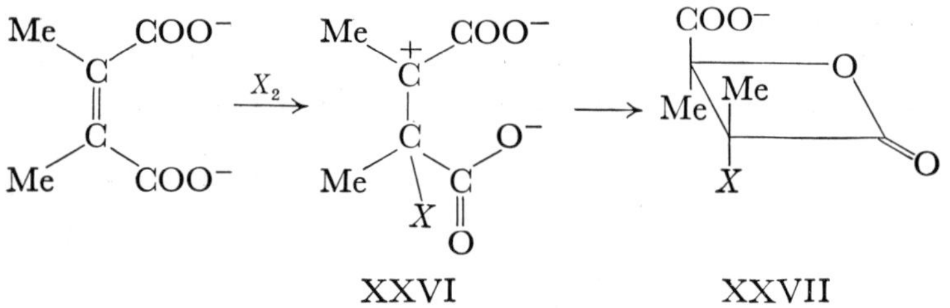

XXVI   XXVII

---

[15] (a) Bartlett and Tarbell, *J. Am. Chem. Soc.*, **58**, 466 (1936). (b) For additional experiments in which the "half-halogenated intermediate" is diverted by reaction with solvent, see Read, *et al.*, *J. Chem. Soc.*, **1920**, 359, 1214; **1921**, 1774; **1922**, 989, 2550; **1928**, 745 (additions in water); and Bockemuller and Hoffmann, *Ann.*, **519**, 165 (1935) (additions in acetic acid).

[16] The unimportance of the addition of methyl hypobromite, MeOBr, to the double bond may be established by the following argument: The formation of this hypobromite from methanol and bromine cannot be rate determining, for the formation of ether XXV is found to be first order in stilbene; that is, stilbene is involved in the rate-determining step. Since large quantities of hypobromite are not detected during the course of the addition, it must then be reversibly in the following reaction:

$$Br_2 + MeOH \rightleftharpoons MeOBr + H^+ + Br^-$$

This being the case, the concentration of MeOBr, hence the rate of reaction, should be inversely proportional to (H^+). Since, however, the rate of addition is found to be independent of acidity, we may conclude that methyl hypobromite, if it is formed at all, is not an important intermediate in the production of ether XXV.

[17] Bartlett and Tarbell, *J. Am. Chem. Soc.*, **59**, 407 (1937).

acid reacts in the same way, and for both of these reactions it may be shown that the lactone does *not* form from the anion of the α,β-dihalo acid.

In representing the intermediate in halogen additions as a halogenated carbonium ion, we have ignored one important feature—these reactions are, in a number of cases, *stereospecific*. For example, it has already been noted that the addition of bromine to maleic acid yields *d,l*-dibromosuccinic acid, whereas the addition to fumaric acid yields *meso*-dibromosuccinic acid (p. 150). This stereochemical situation is inconsistent with intermediate carbonium ion **XXVIII** (if free rotation about the C—C bond in this carbonium ion is assumed), but consistent with the *cyclic bromonium ion* **XXIX**.[18] Using Newman-

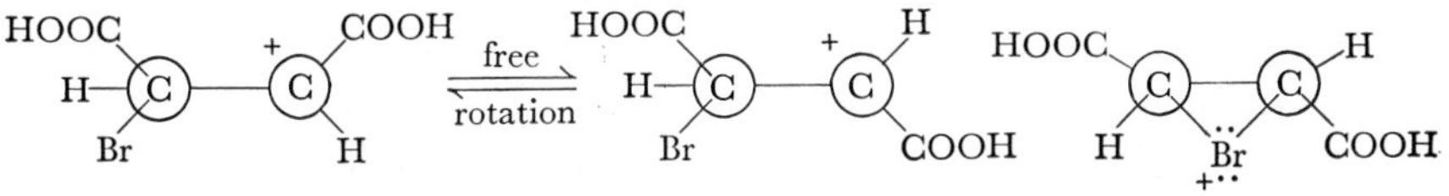

XXVIII   XXVIII   XXIX

type projections, we may depict the addition of bromine to fumaric acid as follows:

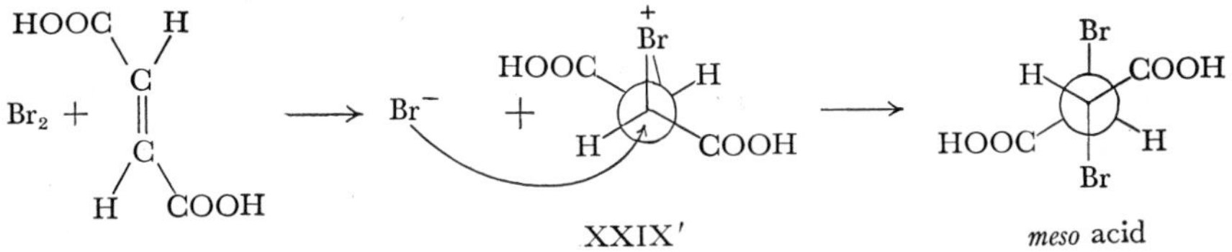

XXIX'   *meso* acid

Note that the second step, the attack on the bromonium ion, is in essence a Walden inversion. The net result, like the reactions of hydrogen halides with unsaturated acids (p. 519), is *trans* addition. Assuming that other halogen additions follow a similar path, we may provisionally rewrite proposed intermediates **XXI**, **XXIV**, and **XXVI** as cyclic bromonium ions **XXX**, **XXXI**, and **XXXII**, respectively.

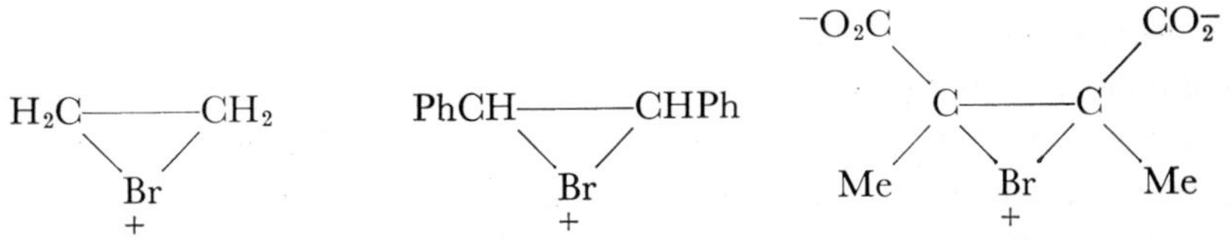

XXX   XXXI   XXXII

[18] The assumption that intramolecular rotation in a carbonium ion is much more rapid than attack by an external nucleophile on such an ion is, at present, open to serious doubt (see for example, Benjamin, Schaeffer, and Collins, *J. Am. Chem. Soc.*, **79**, 6160 (1957)). This being the case, the "halogenonium-ion" mechanism for halogen addition, despite its widespread acceptance, must be considered tentative. Although in the present chapter a number of additions are discussed in terms of this mechanism, the reader should bear in mind that few organic reaction mechanisms have been accepted so widely while supported with such limited data.

The question as to whether the formation of the initial cation (from the olefin and Br_2) or its destruction (by attack of Br^-) is rate determining is not an easy one to answer. In either case, the transition state would be composed of a molecule of substrate and (disregarding electron distribution) two bromine atoms. Hence, kinetic studies which indicate that, in polar solvents, the additions are first order each in olefin and halogen[15(a)],[19] are of little direct help here. A tentative answer has been obtained for the addition of bromine to stilbene in methanol[15(a)] which, we have noted, gives a mixture of stilbene dibromide and β-bromo ether XXV. From a careful examination of the relationship between the ratio of products and the concentration of added bromide ion (see Ex. 2 for details), it is concluded that, for this reaction at least, *the formation of the initial cation is rate determining* and its destruction is rapid.

For additions of bromine, iodine, and the interhalogens, BrCl, IBr, and ICl, in poorly ionizing solvents (such as acetic acid and nitrobenzene) another term must be included in the rate law. This term is second order in halogen and becomes predominant at moderate halogen concentrations:[20]

$$\text{rate} = k_2 \left(\overset{\diagdown}{\underset{\diagup}{C}} = \overset{\diagup}{\underset{\diagdown}{C}} \right) (X_2) + k_3 \left(\overset{\diagdown}{\underset{\diagup}{C}} = \overset{\diagup}{\underset{\diagdown}{C}} \right) (X_2)^2 \qquad (4)$$

The second term suggests a picture similar to that proposed for the additions of hydrogen halide in nonpolar solvents (p. 517). In poorly ionizing media, the formation of the presumed halogenonium-ion intermediate (a reaction requiring charge separation) is difficult, but is aided by a second molecule of halogen which helps disperse the negative charge by formation of the large trihalide ion, X_3^-.

$$\underset{\diagup\diagdown}{\overset{\diagdown\diagup}{\underset{C}{\overset{C}{\|}}}} + X_2 \underset{eq}{\overset{fast}{\rightleftarrows}} \underset{\diagup\diagdown}{\overset{\diagdown\diagup}{\underset{C}{\overset{C}{|}}}} X-X \overset{X_2}{\underset{slow}{\longrightarrow}} \underset{-\overset{|}{\underset{|}{C}}}{\overset{-\overset{|}{C}\diagdown}{}} X^+ + X_3^- \overset{fast}{\longrightarrow} \underset{-\overset{|}{\underset{|}{C}}-X}{\overset{X-\overset{|}{C}-}{}} + X_2 \qquad (5)$$

In keeping with this suggestion, no third-order term has been found for the additions of chlorine, which forms the Cl_3^- ion only with extreme difficulty.[21]

The additions of bromine to allyl halides, vinyl halides, and vinylaceto-nitrile in glacial acetic acid have been found to be catalyzed by added bromide and, more effectively, by added chloride.[22] This is not merely a salt effect, for the additions of acetates, nitrates, or bisulfates to the reaction mixtures cause

[19] (a) Robertson, *et al.*, *J. Chem. Soc.*, **1937**, 335; **1950**, 1624. (b) Berthoud and Mosset, *J. chim. phys.*, **33**, 272 (1936).

[20] Robertson, *et al.*, *J. Chem. Soc.*, **1938**, 179; **1945**, 129; **1947**, 628; **1950**, 812, 2191.

[21] Chattaway and Hoyle, *J. Chem. Soc.*, **123**, 654 (1923); Sherrill and Izard, *J. Am. Chem. Soc.*, **53**, 1667 (1931).

[22] Nozaki and Ogg, *J. Am. Chem. Soc.*, **64**, 697–716 (1942).

only small increases in rate. Assuming that, in the absence of added halide, the addition would proceed according to sequence (5), we must suppose that the halide ion intervenes before the rate-determining step. Probably it competes with a halogen molecule in destroying the intermediate π complex, XXXIII.

$$
\begin{array}{c}
\diagdown \diagup \\
C \\
\| \\
C \\
\diagup \diagdown
\end{array}
+ Br_2
\underset{eq}{\overset{fast}{\rightleftharpoons}}
\begin{array}{c}
\diagdown \diagup \\
C \\
\| \cdots \\
C \\
\diagup \diagdown
\end{array}
\rightarrow Br—Br
\overset{X^-}{\underset{slow}{\longrightarrow}}
\begin{array}{c}
X—\overset{|}{C}— \\
| \\
—\underset{|}{C}—Br
\end{array}
+ Br^-
\qquad (6)
$$

XXXIII

We then may ask why Br⁻, which is almost always more nucleophilic toward carbon than is Cl⁻, is less potent in catalyzing the addition. The answer is probably that although Br⁻ is more efficient than Cl⁻ in attacking the intermediate complex XXXIII, the addition of Br⁻ converts a significant fraction of Br_2 in solution to Br_3^-. This lowers the equilibrium concentration of this intermediate, thus tending to nullify the catalytic action.

Although it is quite possible that the addition reactions of chlorine and

HOCl pass through cyclic chloronium ions $\left(\begin{array}{c} \diagdown \diagup \\ C———C \\ \diagup \diagdown \diagup \diagdown \\ Cl \\ + \end{array} \right)$ analogous to

bromonium ions XXX, XXXI, and XXXII, evidence is accumulating which

indicates that "classical" chlorinated carbonium ions $\left(\begin{array}{c} | \quad | \\ —C—C—Cl \\ + \quad | \end{array} \right)$ are also

involved. Consider, for example, addition of HOCl to isobutene, $Me_2C{=}CH_2$, which is known to yield as the predominant product the α-chlorohydrin Me_2CCH_2Cl.[23] If the product were formed by attack of water on the chloronium

OH

ion XXXIV, we would expect the alternate chlorohydrin XXXV to predominate, since "S_N2" attack at the primary carbon would be favored (as is the case with substituted ethylene oxides, p. 292). We may, however, account for the predominance of chlorohydrin XXXVII by assuming that the chloronium

$$
Me_2C{=}CH_2 \xrightarrow{ClOH_2^+} MeC\underset{\underset{\text{XXXIV}}{+Cl}}{\overset{}{—\!\!—}}CH_2
$$

$$
\xrightarrow{+H_2O\,(S_N2)}
\begin{array}{c}
Cl \\
| \\
Me_2C—CH_2OH \quad \text{(minor product)} \\
\text{XXXV}
\end{array}
$$

$$
\xrightarrow{(S_N1)}
\underset{\text{XXXVI}}{Me_2\overset{+}{C}—CH_2Cl}
\xrightarrow{H_2O}
\underset{\substack{\text{XXXVII} \\ \text{(main product)}}}{\overset{OH}{\overset{|}{Me_2C—CH_2Cl}}}
$$

[23] Michael and Leighton, *Ber.*, **39**, 2157 (1906).

ring opens to give a tertiary carbonium ion **XXXVI** *before* H_2O or OH^- attacks. If carbonium ion **XXXVI** is indeed an intermediate, we must consider the possibility that, instead of reacting with a molecule of water to form chlorohydrin **XXXVII**, it may lose a proton, forming an olefin. Moreover, since this carbonium ion is the same as that which would result from ionization of isobutene dichloride (Me_2CCl—CH_2Cl) in water, the ratio of olefin to chlorohydrin resulting from the treatment of isobutene with HOCl should be very nearly the same as that resulting from the hydrolysis of the dichloride under the same conditions. The two reactions have, in fact, been compared (at 45°), and in both cases the mixture of products contains about 85 percent chlorohydrin **XXXVII** and 10 percent of the olefin CH_2=CMe—CH_2Cl.[24]

Although the cyclic chloronium ion (for example, **XXXIV**) is assumed to intervene largely on the basis of analogy with stereospecific bromine additions, there is independent evidence of its existence (the necessary reasoning is a little involved, and the reader may have to go over the following section more than once before he feels completely at ease with the subject). The addition of HOCl to CH_2=$CMeCH_2Cl$ gives principally chlorohydrin **XXXVIII**, with minor amounts (about 6 percent) of the isomeric chlorohydrin **XXXIX**, which, for our present purpose, is the more interesting product. If the addition is carried out on a substrate "labeled" with Cl^{36}, it may be shown that about one third of the chlorine in the 2 position in chlorohydrin **XXXIX** was originally at the end position in the substrate.[25]

$$\overset{\text{Me}}{\underset{|}{CH_2=C-CH_2Cl*}} \xrightarrow{ClOH_2^+}$$

$$\begin{cases} \overset{\text{OH}}{\underset{|}{ClCH_2-CMe-CH_2Cl*}} \text{ (XXXVIII) major product} \\ HOCH_2-CMeCl-CH_2Cl* \text{ (XXXIX) minor product} \\ HOCH_2-CMeCl*-CH_2Cl \text{ (XXXIX') minor product} \end{cases}$$

Now, if the observed reaction passes through a "classical" carbonium ion, that ion is almost certainly the symmetrical species, $ClCH_2$—$\overset{+}{C}Me$—CH_2Cl* (**XLI**); for there seems no way in which the rearranged chlorohydrin **XXXIX'** could form from the alternate carbonium ion, $^+CH_2$—$CMeCl$—CH_2Cl* (except perhaps by preliminary rearrangement of the latter to **XLI**). The rearranged chlorohydrin could easily form from **XLI**, simply by a shift of the labeled chlorine through the cyclic structure, **XL'**. Yet *all* **XXXIX** and

[24] De la Mare and Salama, *J. Chem. Soc.*, **1956**, 3337. The mixtures of products need not be identical, for both isobutene and its dichloride may react to a small extent through alternate paths.

[25] Ballinger and de la Mare, *J. Chem. Soc.*, **1957**, 1481.

$$\underset{CH_2=CCH_2Cl^*}{\overset{Me}{|}} \xrightarrow{ClOH_2^+}$$

unrearranged chlorohydrins
(XXXVIII and XXXIX)

XXXIX′ cannot be formed through carbonium ion XLI, since a symmetrical carbonium ion should yield (except for a negligible isotope effect) equal quantities of XXXIX and XXXIX′, whereas the unrearranged chlorohydrin XXXIX is found to predominate. Hence a fraction of chlorohydrin XXXIX must arise in a different way—very probably, as indicated above, by direct attack by water on chloronium ion XL. The fact that ion XL (which, aside from labeling, is identical to XL′) may undergo two different reactions indicates that XL (hence XL′) is an *intermediate* rather than a mere *transition state*, since we would not expect to find two different reactions proceeding through the same activated complex.

Nucleophilic Additions to C=C Bonds

From the mechanism proposed to explain the catalysis of halogen addition by halide ions in acetic acid (sequence 6), it would be supposed that HBr or HCl would be no more effective catalysts than the corresponding lithium halides. This is the case when the substrate contains no oxygen (for example, in additions to vinyl and allyl halides); but for additions to α,β-unsaturated ketones, aldehydes, acids, and esters, the hydrogen halides are found to be much more potent catalytically than are the alkali halides.[22] Since the substrates that undergo additions preferentially catalyzed by hydrogen halides are compounds that may be converted (at least in part) to their conjugate acids under the conditions employed, it appears likely that these conjugate acids have become involved in the catalyzed additions. Moreover, such additions, unlike "ordinary" additions, are retarded, rather than accelerated, by alkyl substitution on the olefinic carbons,[26] suggesting that the attack on the C=C bond is *nucleophilic* rather than electrophilic. The following mechanism then seems consistent with what is known about additions of this type:

[26] Morton and Robertson, *J. Chem. Soc.*, **1945**, 129.

$$-\overset{|}{\underset{|}{C}}=\overset{|}{\underset{\underset{O}{\overset{\shortparallel}{|}}}{C}}-\overset{|}{\underset{}{C}}-\overset{H^+}{\underset{}{\rightleftharpoons}} -\overset{|}{\underset{}{C}}\overset{+}{-}\overset{|}{\underset{OH}{C}}=\overset{|}{\underset{}{C}}- \overset{Br^-}{\longrightarrow} -\overset{|}{\underset{Br}{C}}-\overset{|}{\underset{OH}{C}}=\overset{|}{\underset{}{C}}- \overset{Br_2}{\longrightarrow} -\overset{Br}{\underset{Br}{\overset{|}{C}}}-\overset{OH}{\underset{Br}{\overset{|}{C}}}-\overset{}{\underset{+Br^-}{\overset{|}{C}\!\!\pm}} \overset{-H^+}{\rightleftharpoons} -\overset{Br}{\underset{Br}{\overset{|}{C}}}-\overset{|}{\underset{}{C}}-\overset{O}{\overset{\shortparallel}{C}}-$$

These additions are catalyzed, although much less effectively, by strong acids in the apparent absence of added halide ion (for example, by $HClO_4$, H_2SO_4, and HNO_3).[27] Here a similar mechanism may be written, except that the conjugate acid is attacked by a molecule of solvent (or by HSO_4^- or NO_3^-) rather than by a halide ion during the initial stages of the reaction, thus diverting a portion of the substrate to a single-halogenated product. As the reaction proceeds and more halide ion is generated, more and more dihalide is formed.

In these reactions, initial attack on the olefinic carbon is nucleophilic rather than (as is more usually the case) electrophilic, even though the attacking species present in solution are not strongly nucleophilic. This is because the normally strong electron-withdrawing action of the $C{=}O$ group has been augmented by the acquisition of a proton. If more powerful nucleophiles are available in solution, nucleophilic attack at a $C{=}C$ (or a $C{\equiv}C$) bond in conjugation with a $C{=}O$ or $C{\equiv}N$ linkage may occur without prior protonation. Of the many and varied "1,4 additions" that take place in basic media, most conform to this description. In addition to the Michael condensation (p. 392) and the 1,4 additions of Grignard reagents to α,β-unsaturated ketones, in which the attack is by a strongly nucleophilic carbanion, the following may be considered typical:

$$PhCH{=}C\!\!\begin{array}{l}\diagup C{\equiv}N\\[4pt]\diagdown COO^-\end{array} + CN^- \rightarrow PhCH\overset{-}{\underset{\underset{CN}{|}}{-}}C\!\!\begin{array}{l}\diagup C{\equiv}N\\[4pt]\diagdown COO^-\end{array} \overset{H_2O}{\longrightarrow}$$

$$PhCH\underset{\underset{CN}{|}}{-}CH\!\!\begin{array}{l}\diagup CN\\[4pt]\diagdown COO^-\end{array}\quad {}^{28}$$

$$CH_2{=}CH{-}CN + PhNH\underset{\underset{S_-}{|}}{-}C{=}NPh \xrightarrow{H_2O} CH_2\underset{\underset{S-C{=}NPh}{|}}{-}CH_2{-}CN^{29}$$

$$\underset{\qquad\qquad NHPh}{}$$

[27] Robertson, et al., J. Chem. Soc., **1945**, 888; **1948**, 980.

[28] For kinetic studies of this addition, see Jones, J. Chem. Soc., **105**, 1547 (1914).

[29] The 1,4 addition reactions of acrylonitrile (cyanoethylations) have been summarized by Bruson in Organic Reactions, Vol. V (edited by Adams), John Wiley and Sons, Inc., New York, 1949, p. 79.

$$HC\equiv C-\underset{\underset{O}{\parallel}}{C}-Ph \ + \ Me-\hexagon-SH \ \xrightarrow{OEt^-} \ Me-\hexagon-S \underset{H}{\overset{\diagdown}{\underset{}{C}}}=\underset{H}{\overset{COPh}{\underset{}{C}}} \quad 30$$

For much the same reason, the olefinic carbons in polyfluoro-olefins may suffer nucleophilic attack, for the electron density at these carbons has been considerably depleted due to electron withdrawal by the strongly electronegative fluorine atoms, for example,

$$RSH \ + \ CF_2{=}CF_2 \ \xrightarrow{OH^-} \ RS{-}CF_2{-}CF_2H^{31}$$

Somewhat unexpectedly, the conversion of the 2-bromocyclopropane-carboxylic ester XLII to the corresponding t-butoxy compound, XLIV, appears to involve a nucleophilic addition also, in this case an addition to the *cyclopropene* derivative, XLIII. It is not surprising that the bromo ester XLII is

very nearly inert both to KI in acetone and to alcoholic $AgNO_3$; for, as we have pointed out, cyclopropyl derivatives undergo nucleophilic substitutions (by both the S_N1 and S_N2 mechanisms) with great difficulty (p. 240). On the other hand, the conversion of this bromo ester to the butoxy ester, XLIV, using t-BuOK in t-BuOH takes place with ease. Moreover, if this reaction is carried out in a deuterated solvent (t-BuOD), deuterium is found in the cyclopropane ring of the resulting ester *at both the α- and β positions*,[32] although both the butoxy ester itself and the bromo ester undergo deuterium exchange much too slowly to account for the observed deuteration. By assuming that the reaction passes through cyclopropenecarboxylic ester, XLIII, we may easily account for the rapid loss of bromide and for deuteration at the α position. However, β deuteration is less expected and indicates that the β-hydrogen in cyclopropenecarboxylic ester is significantly acidic—that is, similar in character to the hydrogen atoms in acetylene.[33]

[30] Truce and Heine, *J. Am. Chem. Soc.*, **79**, 5311 (1957); Truce and Kassinger, *ibid.*, **80**, 1916 (1958).

[31] Pruett, *et al.*, *J. Am. Chem. Soc.*, **72**, 3642 (1950). For a summary of the nucleophilic additions of fluoro-olefins, see Musgrave, *Quart. Revs.*, **VIII**, 335 (1954).

[32] Wiberg, Barnes, and Albin, *J. Am. Chem. Soc.*, **79**, 4994 (1957).

[33] The similarity between the cyclopropane ring and the carbon-carbon double bond is well recognized and has been considered in detail by several workers (see, for example, Coulsen and Moffitt, *J. Chem. Phys.*, **15** 151 (1947); and Robertson, *et al.*, *J. Am. Chem. Soc.*, **72**, 5260 (1950)). While it is perhaps reasonable to assume that cyclopropene resembles acetylene to

Additions to Conjugated Polyolefins

In the absence of extensive information concerning the kinetics and stereochemistry of additions to polyolefinic systems, it is convenient (and it may even be correct) to assume that such additions proceed by the same types of mechanisms as do additions to mono-olefins under corresponding conditions. Recently, it has been demonstrated that the 1,4 addition of chlorine to butadiene is a *trans* addition—that is, that the chloromethyl groups in the *product* lie *trans* to each other.[34]

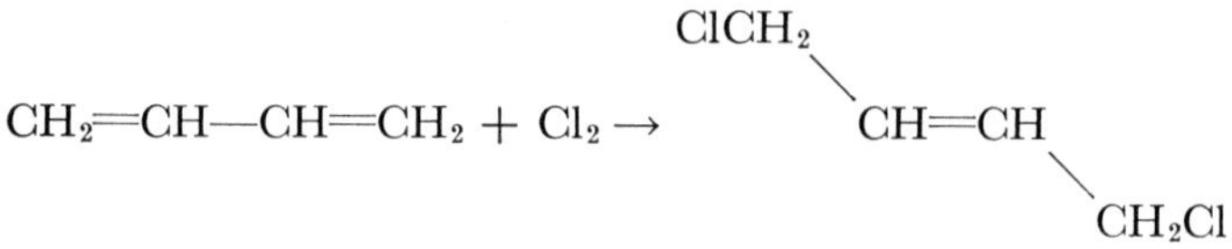

$$CH_2{=}CH{-}CH{=}CH_2 + Cl_2 \rightarrow$$
$$\begin{array}{c} ClCH_2 \\ \diagdown \\ CH{=}CH \\ \diagdown \\ CH_2Cl \end{array}$$

This shows the addition to be a stepwise process (that is, it excludes a transition state such as XLV) and indicates also that the addition does not proceed through chloronium ion XLVI (in which the chlorine is incorporated into a five-membered ring), for both such routes would lead to a *cis* dichloride. Instead, as with mono-olefins, it appears that addition occurs through the chloronium ion XLVII, the chlorinated carbonium ion XLVIII, or through both.

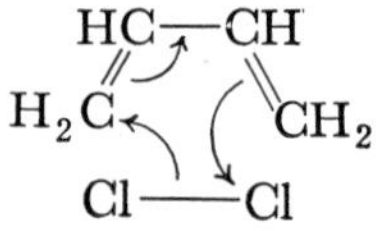

XLV 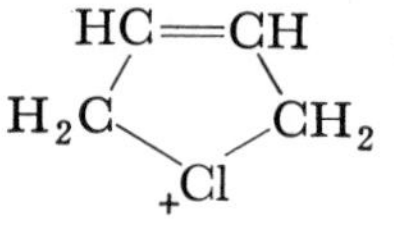   XLVI 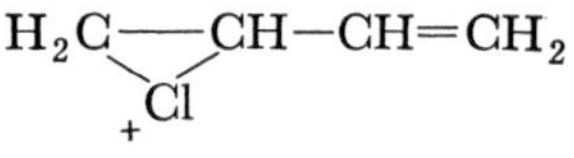   XLVII

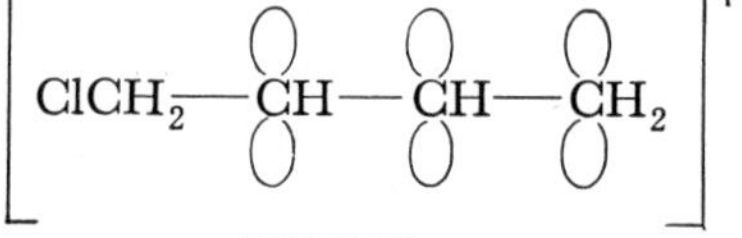

XLVIII

The 1,2 addition of chlorine to butadiene (giving $ClCH_2CHClCH{=}CH_2$) accompanies the 1,4 addition considered in the preceding paragraph and, at room temperature predominates.[35(a)] As the reaction temperature is raised, 1,4 addition becomes increasingly important, since the activation energy for 1,4 addition is greater than that for 1,2 addition. Nevertheless, the 1,4 dichloride

---

about the extent that cyclopropane resembles ethylene, more data concerning cyclopropene and its derivatives must be obtained before we can be at all confident that such an analogy is well taken.

[34] Mislow and Hellman, *J. Am. Chem. Soc.*, **73**, 244 (1951).

[35] (a) Muskat and Northrup, *J. Am. Chem. Soc.*, **52**, 4042 (1930). (b) Pudovik, *J. Gen. Chem. (U.S.S.R.)*, **19**, 1179 (1949); *Chem. Abstr.*, **44**, 1005 (1950).

is actually the more stable isomer; for if the mixture of isomers obtained at room temperature is heated to 200° or merely treated with $ZnCl_2$ to bring about equilibration by loss and return of Cl^-, the resulting mixture contains about 70 percent of the 1,4-dichloride.[35(b)] Thus, we have here a situation in which the less stable product is formed more rapidly than the more stable—that is, where the addition at moderate temperatures is *kinetically*, rather than *thermodynamically*, controlled. This is also the case for the additions of bromine to cyclopentadiene,[36(a)] 1,3-cyclohexadiene,[36(a)] and butadiene (in nonpolar solvents),[36(b)] the addition of HCl to isoprene,[36(c)] and the addition of HCl and HBr to butadiene.[36(d)] In each of these instances the mixture of products resulting from addition at room temperature or below contains significantly more 1,2 adduct and significantly less 1,4 adduct than corresponds to a mixture of the two at equilibrium. We may now ask: (a) why the 1,4 adducts in these reactions are more stable than the 1,2 adducts; and (b) why the 1,2 adducts tend to form more readily than the 1,4 adducts. Neither of these questions is easy to answer, and any attempted explanation based on structural considerations must be regarded with skepticism since we are probably dealing with energy differences of well less than 1 kcal per mole. In the noncyclic series, it may be that the increased possibilities for hyperconjugation stabilize 1,4 adducts such as XLIX with respect to 1,2 adducts such as L,

$$CH_2\!\!=\!\!C\!-\!CH\!\!=\!\!CH_2 \xrightarrow[\text{(or } HX)]{X_2} CH_2\!-\!\underset{H(X)}{C}\!\!=\!\!CH\!-\!CH_2X + CH_2\!-\!\underset{H(X)}{CX}\!-\!CH\!\!=\!\!CH_2$$

XLIX   L

whereas in the addition of halogens to cyclic dienes, it may be that the 1,4 adducts (for example, LI) are slightly more stable than the 1,2 adducts (for example, LII), because in the former, dipole-dipole repulsion resulting from the two C—X linkages is somewhat less than in the latter. As for the *kinetic*

LI   LII

advantage in 1,2 addition, let us suppose that the course of the addition of a halogen X_2 to a diene is determined by the position at which X^- attacks the halogenonium-ion intermediate LIII, whereas the course of a hydrogen-halide addition is determined by the position of attack by X^- on carbonium ion LIV.

[36] (a) Farmer and Scott, *J. Chem. Soc.*, **1929**, 172. (b) Farmer, Lawrence, and Thorpe, *J. Chem. Soc.*, **1928**, 729. (c) Ultree, *ibid.*, **1948**, 530. (d) Kharasch, Kritchevsky, and Mayo, *J. Org. Chem.*, **2**, 489 (1938).

It is reasonable that attack at the 2 position of LIII (leading to 1,2 addition)

$$-\underset{\underset{X}{\diagdown\;\diagup}}{\overset{|}{C}}\underset{2}{\overset{|}{C}}-\overset{|}{C}=\underset{4}{\overset{|}{C}}- \qquad -\overset{|}{C}-\overset{\overset{2}{|}}{\underset{\underset{H}{|}}{C}}-CH=\overset{4}{C}H_2 \leftrightarrow -\overset{|}{C}-\underset{\underset{H}{|}}{\overset{|}{C}}=CH-\overset{+}{C}H_2$$

$$\underset{+}{}$$

| LIII | LIV | LIV' |

will be slightly favored over attack at the 4 position (leading to 1,4 addition); for the former involves only the breakage of the three-membered ring, whereas the latter requires, in addition, a rather extensive redistribution of π-electron density. Turning now to the attack on the hybrid ion LIV $\leftrightarrow$ LIV', we may assume that nucleophilic attack will occur preferentially at the carbon having the highest density of positive charge. Recalling that a secondary or tertiary carbon will, in general, tolerate positive charge more easily than will a primary carbon, it seems probable that the positive charge in LIV, although spread over three carbons, will be most concentrated at the 2 carbon and that, once again, 1,2 addition will be kinetically favored over 1,4 addition.

If we consider the additions that we have just described as typical, we are apt to suppose, as have a number of workers,[37] that additions to dienoid systems at moderate temperatures result in a predominance of a less stable adduct. If we adopt this view, then we must infer that those additions that are observed to result predominantly or exclusively in the more stable adduct (for example, reactions 7 through 10) first yield the less stable adduct, which then isomerizes before the product can be identified. The alternate (unobserved) adducts are shown in square brackets in these sequences; each has at least one very labile allylic bromine and would be expected to undergo allylic-rearrangement or internal-return reactions (or both) (p. 286) with ease. Note that the addition of HCl to

less stable adduct
(not observed)

$$CH_2\!=\!CMeCH\!=\!CH_2 \xrightarrow[\text{(or HBr)}]{Br_2} \left[\underset{\underset{Br}{|}}{CH_2}\!-\!CMe\!-\!CH\!=\!CH_2 \right] \rightarrow$$

more stable adduct
(observed)

$$\underset{\overset{|}{CH_2}\!-\!CMe\!=\!CH\!-\!CH_2Br^{38(a,b)}}{\overset{Br(H)}{|}} \qquad (7)$$

$$CH_2\!=\!CMeCMe\!=\!CH_2 \xrightarrow[\text{(or HBr)}]{Br_2} \left[\underset{\underset{Br}{|}}{CH_2}\!-\!CMe\!-\!CMe\!=\!CH_2 \right] \rightarrow$$

$$\underset{\overset{|}{CH_2}\!-\!CMe\!=\!CMe\!-\!CH_2Br}{\overset{Br(H)}{|}} \;{}^{(b,c)} \qquad (8)$$

[37] See, for example, Hughes, Ingold, de la Mare, and Catchpole, *J. Chem. Soc.*, **1948**, 8,17.

$$\underset{\text{LV}}{PhCH=CHCH=CH_2} \xrightarrow[\text{(or HBr)}]{Br_2} \left[\underset{\overset{|}{Br}}{PhCH-CH=CH-CH_2} \underset{\overset{|}{Br(H)}}{} \right] \rightarrow$$

$$\underset{\overset{|}{Br(H)}}{PhCH=CH-CHBr-CH_2} \text{ 38(d,e)} \qquad (9)$$

$$\underset{\text{LVI}}{PhCH=CHCH=CHPh} \xrightarrow{Br_2} [PhCHBr-CH=CH-CHBrPh] \rightarrow$$

$$PhCHBr-CHBr-CH=CHPh \text{38(d)} \qquad (10)$$

isoprene results largely in the kinetically favored 1,2 adduct, whereas the addition of HBr results in the thermodynamically favored 1,4 adduct, presumably because Br^- is much more easily detached and more easily refastened to the carbon chain than is Cl^-.

In the author's opinion, however, there is considerable doubt that the less stable adduct invariably forms first, then isomerizes (either slowly or rapidly) to the more stable adduct. Especially in cases where the 1,2 adduct is the more stable, it seems quite possible that the thermodynamically favored product is also favored kinetically. It would be interesting to carry out the addition of bromine to dienes LV and LVI in methanol and examine the methoxy bromides formed during the early stages of the reaction. If 1,2 addition predominates here also, it could be assumed that the 1,4 adduct had not intervened, for a rapid allylic rearrangement involving a methoxide group is extremely unlikely.

One further point: when addition to an *extended* conjugated system is thermodynamically controlled (and this is generally the case), orientation will be such as to preserve conjugation to the greatest extent possible. Thus, addition to 1,4-diphenylbutadiene (LVI) yields a 1,2-dibromide rather than a 1,4-dibromide, since in the 1,2 adduct (but not in the 1,4 adduct) the remaining C=C bond lies in conjugation with one of the benzene rings. Similarly, the addition of 1 mole of bromine to hexatriene LVII yields a mixture of 1,2 and 1,6 adducts (both of which have two double bonds in conjugation), but no 1,4 adduct:[39]

$$\underset{\text{LVII}}{CH_2=CHCH=CHCH=CH_2} \xrightarrow{1Br_2} \begin{cases} BrCH_2CHBrCH=CHCH=CH_2 + \\ BrCH_2CH=CHCH=CHCH_2Br \\ (no\ BrCH_2CH=CHCHBrCH=CH_2) \end{cases}$$

Cis Additions to the C=C Bond. The Diels-Alder Reaction

We have referred to addition of bromine via the bromonium-ion mechanism as a *trans* addition (p. 523), but this description is appropriate only because the second step, in which the bromonium-ion ring is destroyed, involves an inversion

---

[38] (a) Staudinger, et al., Helv. Chim. Acta., **5,** 756 (1922). (b) Farmer and Marshall, J. Chem. Soc., **1931,** 129. (c) Farmer, Lawrence, and Scott, ibid., **1930,** 510. (d) Strauss, Ber., **42,** 2866 (1909). (e) Riiber, ibid., **44,** 2974 (1911).

[39] Farmer, et al., J. Chem. Soc., **1927,** 2937.

of configuration. The initial step—the formation of the ring—is itself a *cis* addition, for substituents lying *cis* to each other in the parent olefin also lie *cis* to each other in the cyclic intermediate. Of the other types of *cis* addition known, most involve cyclization; two, in particular, result in three-membered rings which, unlike that in the bromonium ion, can be readily isolated. Olefins may be converted to substituted ethylene oxides ("epoxidation") with peroxy acids.

This addition is facilitated by electron-releasing alkyl groups on the olefin, suggesting that the attack on the double bond is electrophilic. In polar media, particularly in solutions of formic or acetic acid, the attacking reagent may be the hydroxonium ion, OH^+, formed in the equilibrium.

$$R-C-OOH + AcOH \rightleftharpoons OH^+ + R-C-OH + OAc^-$$
$$\quad\;\; \| \qquad\qquad\qquad\qquad\qquad\quad \|$$
$$\quad\;\; O \qquad\qquad\qquad\qquad\qquad\quad O$$

However, epoxidation occurs readily in nonpolar solvents also. Here, the most satisfactory mechanism (which may apply as well to polar solvents) is[40]

The addition of carbon dibromide, CBr_2, to olefins also appears to be stereospecific. From *cis*-2-butene, a derivative of *cis*-dimethylcyclopropane, LVIII, is obtained, whereas *trans*-2-butene yields a *trans*-dimethyl derivative, LIX.[41] At present we do not know whether CBr_2 has zero or two unpaired electrons—that is, whether it is a "diradical" or merely an electron-deficient fragment. The principle that electrons associated with a given energy level remain unpaired if possible, which applies straightforwardly to free atoms (p. 9), does not help us here; for there is undoubtedly some drift of electron density from the filled p orbitals of the bromine atoms to the electron-deficient carbon, and it is difficult to predict how this will affect the energies of the two possible forms. It has been found, however, that the relationships between the structures

[40] Bartlett, *Rec. Chem. Prog.*, **11**, 47 (1950).
[41] Skell and Garner, *J. Am. Chem. Soc.*, **78**, 3409, 5430 (1956).

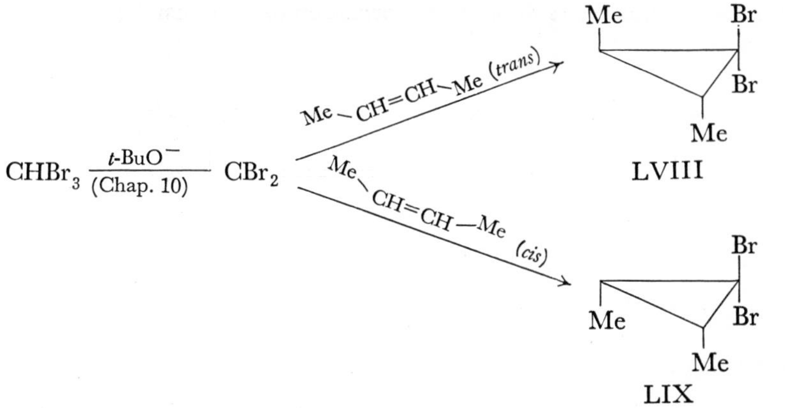

$$CHBr_3 \xrightarrow[\text{(Chap. 10)}]{t\text{-BuO}^-} CBr_2$$

Me–CH=CH–Me (trans) → LVIII

Me, CH=CH–Me (cis) → LIX

of olefins and their reactivities toward CBr_2 parallel the structure-reactivity relationships observed for heterolytic bromine addition[42(a)] and those for olefin epoxidation.[42(b)] The following reactivity sequence applies to all three types of addition reaction:[41]

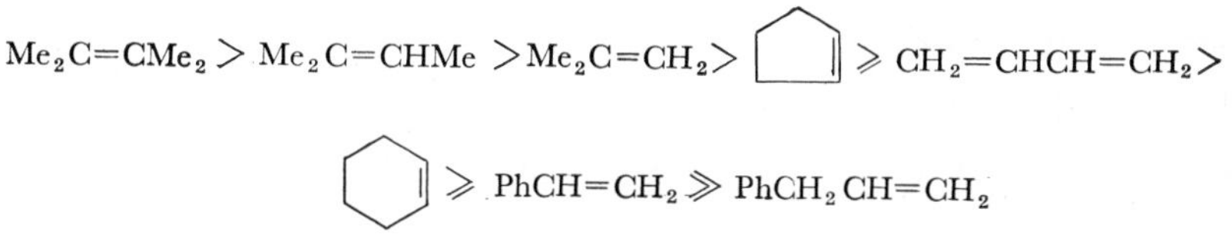

$$Me_2C=CMe_2 > Me_2C=CHMe > Me_2C=CH_2 > \text{[cyclopentene]} \geqslant CH_2=CHCH=CH_2 >$$

$$\text{[cyclohexene]} \geqslant PhCH=CH_2 \gg PhCH_2CH=CH_2$$

On the other hand, these olefins follow a very different sequence with respect to their reactivity toward addition of CCl_3Br in the presence of peroxides,[42(c)] a reaction in which the C=C bond is attacked by a $Cl_3C\cdot$ radical (Chap. 16). Here the following order is observed:

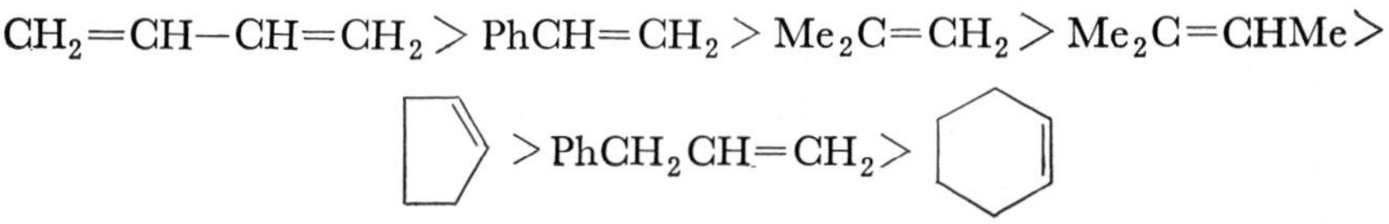

$$CH_2=CH-CH=CH_2 > PhCH=CH_2 > Me_2C=CH_2 > Me_2C=CHMe >$$

$$\text{[cyclopentene]} > PhCH_2CH=CH_2 > \text{[cyclohexene]}$$

Thus, until more definitive evidence is available, we may infer that CBr_2 attacks as an electrophile rather than as a radical—that is, that it has zero unpaired electrons rather than two.

A somewhat similar question is associated with the familiar Diels-Alder reaction, which, the reader will recall, consists of the addition of a diene to a second unsaturated molecule—generally designated as a *dienophile* (which often, but not invariably, has one or more electron-attracting groups in conjugation

[42] (a) Ingold, et al., J. Chem. Soc., **1931**, 2354; **1935**, 984, 1396. (b) Swern, J. Am. Chem. Soc., **69**, 1692 (1947). (c) Kharasch, et al., J. Org. Chem., **14**, 239, 537 (1949); **18**, 328 (1953).

with a C=C bond)—resulting in the formation of a six-membered ring:[43]

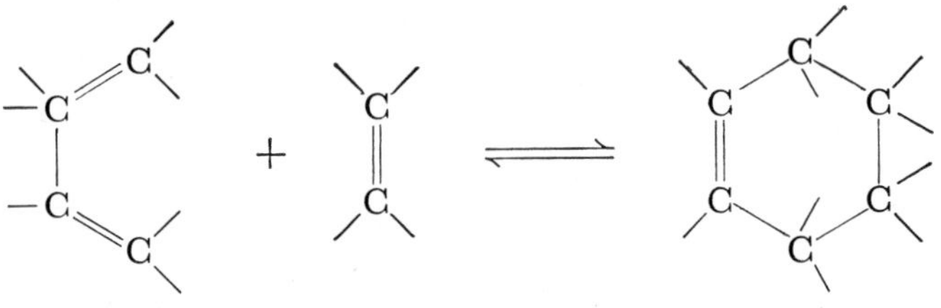

diene   dienophile   adduct

The Diels-Alder reaction is, in essence, a reorganization of electron density, during which two single bonds are created, two double bonds are converted to single bonds, and one single bond is converted to a double bond. At present we cannot say whether the electrons shift one by one or in pairs—that is, whether the reaction is homolytic (involving a *diradical* such as LX) or heterolytic.[44]

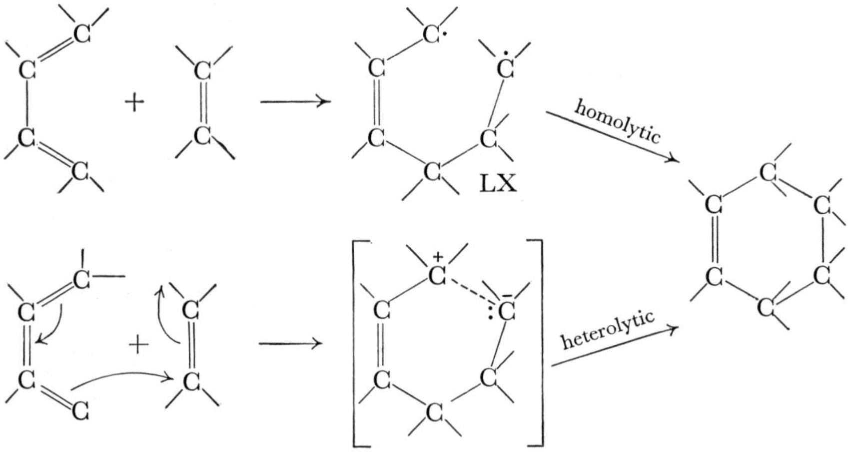

LXI

---

[43] The role of the diene in the Diels-Alder reaction may be assumed not only by the more usual acyclic and cyclic dienes, but also by such compounds as anthracene (which is attacked at the center ring) and furan. Typical dienophiles are maleic anhydride, acrolein, acetylenedicarboxylic acid, and *p*-benzoquinone. For reviews of the Diels-Alder reaction, see the following articles in *Organic Reactions* (edited by Adams), John Wiley and Sons, Inc., New York: Kloetzel, **4**, 1 (1948); Holmes, **4**, 160 (1948); Butz and Rytina, **5**, 136 (1949).

[44] Because Diels-Alder reactions exhibit characteristics in common with both free-radical and ionic reactions, it is sometimes said that such reactions are "partially homolytic" or, alternately, "partially heterolytic" (see for example, Ingold, *Structure and Mechanism in Organic Chemistry*, Cornell University Press, Ithaca, 1953, p. 718). The significance of such a description is not clear, for quantum mechanics assures us that bound electrons in a chemical system are either paired or unpaired; there can be no middle ground. It is, of course, possible that some Diels-Alder reactions are homolytic and others heterolytic or (less probably) that a given adduct may be formed by simultaneous operation of homolytic and heterolytic additions.

The rate law, which stipulates that the additions are first order each in diene and dienophile,[45(a)] is noncommittal on this question, and the highly negative entropies of activation which are observed (from −20 to −25 cal per deg mole) could conceivably be due either to loss in freedom of motion when noncyclic reactants form a cyclic transition state (p. 182) or to the necessity for an electron-unpairing process of low probability. The fact that the Diels-Alder reaction is not accelerated by such radical-producing agents as peroxides does not exclude homolytic addition; for these so-called "initiators" are effective only in the formation of monoradicals that almost certainly would become involved in side reactions before being converted to diradicals. Moreover, the rates of Diels-Alder reactions appear to be more sensitive to the polarity of the solvent used than are those of many typical free-radical reactions, but less sensitive than are the rates of the large majority of heterolytic reactions.[45(b)]

The Diels-Alder reaction is a *cis* addition, both with respect to the diene (otherwise a stable six-membered ring could not form) and with respect to the dienophile;[45(c)] that is, groups lying *cis* to each other in the dienophile also lie *cis* to each other in the adduct. This suggests that if the reaction passes through LX, this diradical must undergo ring closure before rotation about the C—C bond derived from the dienophile can occur. If the reaction is heterolytic, the interval between the formation of the first and second of the new C—C bonds must be similarly short; indeed, a number of workers feel that these bonds form simultaneously[46(a)]—that is, that "zwitterion" LXI does not intervene at all. However, the observed relationships between structure and reactivity suggest that, in some cases at least, there is an interval early in the progress of the reaction, during which considerable electron density has been transferred from diene to dienophile but little, if any, is transferred from dienophile to diene. Electron-donating groups (alkyl and alkoxyl) on the diene generally facilitate the addition, and electron-attracting groups on the dienophile almost invariably have the same effect. This is consistent with the formation of intermediate LXI, but it may merely reflect the preliminary formation of a complex between the two reactants[46(b)] before the series of bond breakings commences. In either case, the general acid catalysis of the Diels-Alder reaction which is sometimes (but not always) observed may be attributed to coordination of the acid with the dienophile, drawing electron density away from the reaction site and thus making the dienophile more electrophilic.[45(b)]

[45] (a) Wassermann, *Trans. Faraday Soc.*, **34**, 128 (1938). (b) Wassermann, *et al., J. Chem. Soc.*, **1939**, 870; **1942**, 618, 623; **1949**, 3046. (c) Alder and Stein, *Angew. Chem.*, **47**, 837 (1934); **50**, 510 (1937).

[46] (a) See, for example, Rubin and Wassermann, *J. Chem. Soc.*, **1950**, 2205; Evans and Warhurst, *Trans. Faraday Soc.*, **34**, 614 (1938); **35**, 824 (1939). (b) For evidence of preliminary complex formation between diene and dienophile in the Diels-Alder reaction, see Andrews and Keefer, *J. Am. Chem, Soc.*, **77**, 6284 (1955); and Berson, Reynolds, and Jones, *ibid.*, **78**, 6049 (1956).

Hydroxylation of Olefins with Permanganate

The oxidation of olefins with permanganate at high pH values may be easily controlled so that the predominant product is a 1,2 diol. This is another *cis*-addition reaction, for cyclic olefins are invariably oxidized to *cis* glycols.[47(a)] Moreover, it has been shown, using MnO_4^- labeled with O^{18}, that *both* oxygen atoms in the glycol are derived from the permanganate, rather than from the solvent.[47(b)]

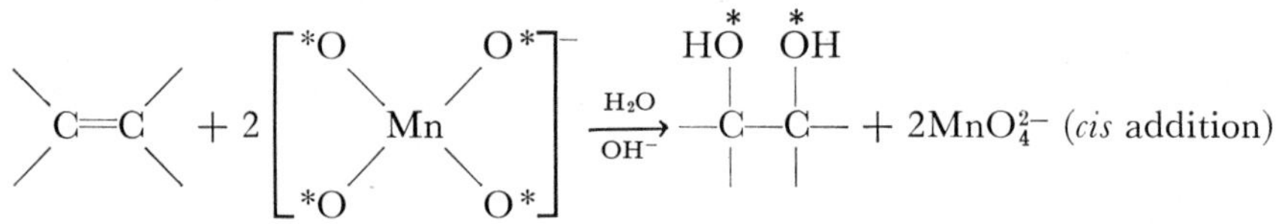

The occurrence of *cis* addition suggests the intervention of the cyclic complex LXII in a mechanism such as:

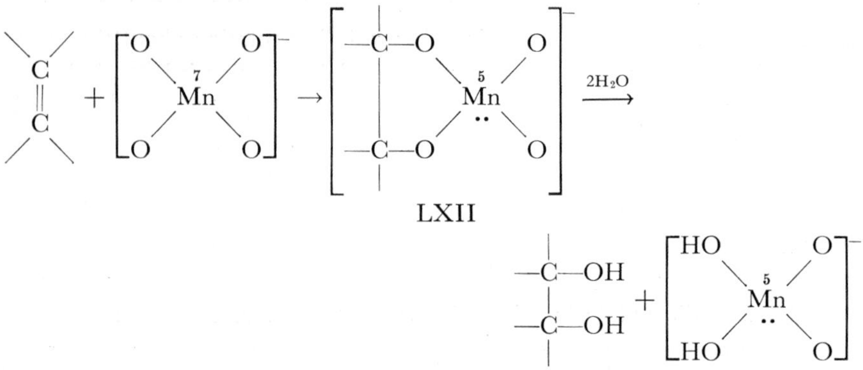

LXII

then,

$$H_2MnO_4^- + MnO_4^- + 2OH^- \xrightarrow{fast} 2MnO_4^{2-} + 2H_2O$$

As indicated, the formation of complex LXII involves the transfer of a pair of electrons from the olefin to the manganese atom through an oxygen. The $+5$ oxidation state of manganese (such as exists in $H_2MnO_4^-$) is relatively unfamiliar, but it has been shown to be stable in cold 8 to 10 N alkali.[47(c)] At lower basicities, it would be expected to react with MnO_4^- to form the (green) MnO_4^{2-} ion. The latter oxidizes olefins to glycols also,[47(c)] but much more slowly than does MnO_4^-; this is likewise a *cis* addition, and for it a sequence very similar to that above may be written.

No salt containing an anion such as LXII has as yet been isolated, nor has

---

[47] (a) Boeseken, *Rec. trav. chim.*; **40**, 553 (1921); **47**, 683 (1928). (b) Wiberg and Saegebarth, *J. Am. Chem. Soc.*, **79**, 2822 (1957). (c) Pode and Waters, *J. Chem. Soc.*, **1956**, 717.

substantial spectral evidence for the intervention of this intermediate been obtained. However, osmium-containing esters having the ring structure

have been isolated from reaction mixtures in which olefins are undergoing hydroxylation with osmium tetroxide, OsO_4.[48] This hydroxylation, like that with permanganate, is a *cis* addition, and is often assumed to proceed by an analogous path.[49]

Additions to the C=O Double Bond

Unlike the usual C=C bonds, the C=O bonds are strongly polarized and may be attacked either at the electron-rich oxygen atom by electrophiles or at the electron-deficient carbon atom by nucleophiles. Of the familiar carbonyl-addition reactions, most involve weak acids in which the hydrogen is bound to carbon, nitrogen, or oxygen.

When the acidic hydrogen is bound to a saturated carbon atom, the attacking nucleophile is necessarily the conjugate base, $B:^-$, and the addition is subject to base catalysis (either general or specific); we have seen this to be the case, for example, in the aldol condensation (p. 389) and the benzoin condensation, (p. 394). When the acidic hydrogen is bound to oxygen or nitrogen (that is, when the addendum is water, an alcohol, an amine, or a substituted hydrazine), initial nucleophilic attack by the addendum itself is also possible, for such compounds are Lewis bases. Addition of a stronger acid, HA, to the reaction mixture

will partially convert the carbonyl compound to its conjugate acid, $\overset{+}{C}$—OH,

---

[48] Criegee, Marchand, and Wannowius, *Ann.*, **522**, 75 (1936); **550**, 99 (1938).

[49] Oxidations of organic compounds by permanganate constitute a complex topic, for there is evidence for the occurrence of a number of different mechanisms. The mechanism operating in a particular case may depend not only on the nature of the organic substrate but also on the acidity of the solution and its temperature. For a brief review of this topic, see Ladbury and Cullis, *Chem. Revs.*, **58**, 403 (1958). For a more detailed view, see Drummond and Waters, *J. Chem. Soc.*, **1953**, 435, 440, 2836, 3119; **1954**, 2456; **1955**, 497.

or perhaps to a hydrogen bonded complex, $\overset{\diagdown}{\underset{\diagup}{C}}{=}O \cdots H{-}A$. In either case, electron density is drawn away from the carbon atom, and attack by a basic oxygen or nitrogen atom is facilitated. Thus, carbonyl additions in which the addendum itself, rather than its conjugate base, attacks the carbon atom should be catalyzed by acid, provided, of course, the attacking nucleophile is not completely converted to its own conjugate acid.

The hydration of acetaldehyde and its reversal

$$CH_3CHO + H_2O \rightleftharpoons CH_3C\overset{\diagup OH}{\underset{\diagdown OH}{}}$$

have been studied in some detail.[50] Hydration is extensive (about 60 percent at 20°)[51] in distilled water, but much less complete in aqueous acetone, and both the forward and backward reactions are subject to general acid and general base catalysis. We should have little difficulty in suggesting a mechanism for the acid-catalyzed reaction, for here, the hydrogen-bonded complex $CH_3CH{=}O \cdots HA$ is evidently involved. The formation and dissociation

$$\left.\begin{array}{l} \text{MeCHO} \\ \text{+ } HA \end{array}\right\} \overset{\text{fast}}{\underset{\text{fast}}{\rightleftharpoons}} \; \overset{\text{H}}{\underset{\text{LXIII}}{\text{MeC}{=}O}} \cdots HA \; \underset{-H_2O,\ \text{slow}}{\overset{+H_2O,\ \text{slow}}{\rightleftharpoons}} \; \overset{\text{H}}{\underset{\overset{|}{\underset{H \diagdown \ \diagup H}{\overset{+}{O}}}}{\text{MeC}{-}\overset{-}{O}}} \cdots HA \; \overset{\text{fast}}{\underset{\text{fast}}{\rightleftharpoons}}$$

$$\overset{\text{H H}}{\underset{\overset{|}{\underset{H \diagup}{O}}}{\text{MeC}{-}O}} \cdots HA \; \overset{\text{fast}}{\underset{\text{fast}}{\rightleftharpoons}} \left\{\begin{array}{l} \text{MeCH(OH)}_2 \\ \text{+ } HA \end{array}\right.$$

LXIV

of the hydrogen-bonded complexes LXIII and LXIV and the transfer of a proton from one oxygen atom to another are assumed to be rapid, whereas the

---

[50] Bell, et al., Proc. Roy. Soc., 197A, 141 (1949); Trans. Faraday Soc., 46, 34 (1950). The reaction may be conveniently followed dilatometrically—that is, by measuring the changes in volume of the reaction mixture as the hydration proceeds. For a further discussion of this reaction, see Swain, J. Am. Chem. Soc., 72, 4578 (1950).

[51] Bell and Clunie, Trans. Faraday Soc., 48, 439 (1952). A number of aldehydes undergo hydration when dissolved in water, but the isolation of the pure hydrates is generally difficult. However, stable and readily isolable hydrates are formed from aldehydes having strongly electron-attracting groups lying near the —CHO group (for example, $Cl_3CH(OH)_2$ and $O{=}CH{-}CH(OH)_2$).

formation of a new C—O bond (in the hydration) and its breakage (in the dehydration) are assumed to be rate determining.

For hydration in the presence of OH⁻, the slow step is almost certainly the attack by the OH⁻ ion at the C=O group of the aldehyde. However, when a weak base (which we may designate B:) is also present, a second mode of attack may occur, for this base also accelerates the hydration, even though (OH⁻) is kept constant by simultaneous addition of conjugate acid B:H⁺. Here it is likely that the attacking reagent is a water molecule that has been made more nucleophilic by coordination with the base, forming the hydrogen-bonded complex, B: · · H—O—H,

$$B\colon \cdots H-O\diagdown_{H} \quad + \quad \diagup^{\diagdown}C=O \underset{slow}{\overset{slow}{\rightleftharpoons}} BH^{+} + HO-\overset{|}{\underset{|}{C}}-O^{-} \underset{fast}{\overset{fast}{\rightleftharpoons}}$$

$$B\colon + HO-\overset{|}{\underset{|}{C}}-OH$$

As might be expected, complex B: · H—O⟋H is a much less powerful nucleophile than is OH⁻, and weak bases are considerably less effective catalysts than is hydroxide ion. Indeed, for the hydration of acetone, complexes such as B: · · HOH are ineffective as catalysts, and this hydration appears to be subject to specific hydroxide ion catalysis.[52(a)] However, acid-catalyzed hydration of this ketone appears to follow the same course as the hydration of acetaldehyde, for like the latter reaction, it is subject to general acid catalysis. Furthermore, a very similar mechanism may be written for the reaction of methanol with acetaldehyde to form hemiacetal, LXV, for general acid catalysis operates here also.[52(a)]

$$CH_3CHO + MeOH \overset{HA}{\rightleftharpoons} CH_3CH\diagup^{OH}_{\diagdown OMe}$$

LXV

The reverse reaction—the splitting of a hemiacetal into its parent alcohol and aldehyde—is conveniently studied when the hemiacetal is optically active due (partially or solely) to an asymmetric α-carbon atom, for the incorporation

[52] (a) Cohn and Urey, *J. Am. Chem. Soc.*, **60**, 679 (1938). Since the concentration of acetone hydrate at equilibrium is much too small to be measured by conventional methods, the hydration rate was determined by carrying out the reaction in H_2O^{18} and measuring the rate at which O^{18} replaced O^{16} in the acetone. (b) Meadows and Darwent, *Can. J. Chem.*, **30**, 501 (1952); *Trans. Faraday Soc.*, **48**, 1015 (1952).

of that carbon atom into a C=O group destroys its asymmetry. The sugars in their cyclic forms are hemiacetals of this sort, as they may be considered derived from a —CHO group at one end of the molecule and an —OH group near the other end. The scission of the hemiacetal linkage in sugar solutions results in the familiar phenomenon of *mutarotation*—that is, a drift in the optical rotation of the solution to a constant value (complete loss of optical activity does not occur since a number of additional asymmetric carbon atoms in the sugar molecule are not affected). The mutarotation of glucose (LXVI) in aqueous solutions[53(a)] and that of 2,3,4,6-tetramethyl glucose (LXVII) in organic sol-

LXVI   LXVII   LXVIII

vents[53(b)] have been studied carefully. In an earlier chapter (p. 139) it was seen that mutarotation of the tetramethyl compound required catalysis by *both* an acid and a base, and that 2-hydroxypyridine (LXVIII), in which the acidic and basic centers are held rigidly in positions favorable for attack, is a particularly effective catalyst. The mutarotation of glucose itself in aqueous solution is subject to general acid and general base catalysis. Assuming that a similar mechanism operates here, we may assign to the solvent the role of a base if the reaction is carried out in the presence of added acid (reaction 11), and the role of an acid if the reaction is carried out in the presence of added base (reaction 12).

[53] (a) Brønsted and Guggenheim, *J. Am. Chem. Soc.*, **49**, 2554 (1929). (b) Lowry, *et al.*, *J. Chem. Soc.*, **1925**, 1385, 2883; **1927**, 2554; Swain and Brown, *J. Am. Chem. Soc.*, **74**, 2534, 2538 (1952).

As yet there is no evidence for catalysis of glucose mutarotation by an acid-base pair that does not include at least one molecule of water.

Next let us consider the conversions of carbonyl compounds to semicarbazones (LXX),[54(a)] oximes (LXXI),[54(b)] and phenylhydrazones (LXXII).[54(c)]

$$
\begin{array}{l}
\diagdown \\
C=O \\
\diagup
\end{array}
\quad
\begin{array}{l}
\xrightarrow{NH_2NHCONH_2} \quad -C(OH)-NHNHCONH_2 \xrightarrow{-H_2O} -C=N-NHCONH_2 \quad (LXX)\\[2ex]
\xrightarrow{NH_2OH} \quad -C(OH)-NHOH \xrightarrow{-H_2O} -C=N-OH \quad (LXXI)\\[2ex]
\xrightarrow{NH_2NHPh} \quad -C(OH)-NHNHPh \xrightarrow{-H_2O} -C=N-NHPh \quad (LXXII)
\end{array}
$$

These reactions probably proceed in much the same manner as does the formation of hemiacetals. Again, general acid catalysis suggests that the nucleophile (which we may designate RNH_2) may attack either the conjugate acid of the carbonyl compound or a hydrogen-bonded complex, LXXIII (analogous to LXII).

$$
\begin{array}{c}
\diagdown \\
C=O \cdots HA + NH_2R \xrightarrow{slow} -\overset{|}{\underset{|}{C}}-\overset{-}{O} \cdots HA \xrightarrow{fast} \\
\diagup \\
\text{LXXIII} \qquad\qquad\qquad NH_2R \\
\overset{+}{}
\end{array}
$$

$$
\begin{array}{c}
H \\
| \\
-\overset{|}{\underset{|}{C}}-O \cdots HA \xrightarrow[-H_2O]{fast} \overset{\diagdown}{\underset{\diagup}{C}}=NR + HA \\
| \\
NHR
\end{array}
$$

$$(RNH_2 = NH_2NHCONH_2, NH_2OH, \text{ or } NH_2NH_2)$$

The relationships between reaction rate and acidity are complicated here by an additional factor: addition of appreciable quantities of acid protonates the basic nitrogen atom of the addendum, converting it to an inactive species. Suppose, for example, that there is just one catalytically active weak acid, HA, present in solution. Then the rate of the reaction is

$$
\text{rate} = (RNH_2) \left(\overset{\diagdown}{\underset{\diagup}{C}}=O \right) [k_{H^+}(H^+) + k_{HA}(HA)] \qquad (13)
$$

where k_{H^+} and k_{HA} are the catalytic constants for the hydronium ion and weak acid, HA, respectively. However, the concentration of nucleophile RNH_2 is *not* the concentration added to the solution (which may be designated $(RNH_2)_{added}$), for this base has been partially converted to RNH_3^+. It may be shown (Ex. 4)

[54] (a) Conant and Bartlett, *J. Am. Chem. Soc.*, **54**, 2881 (1932); Westheimer, *ibid.*, **56**, 1962 (1934); Cross and Fugasi, *ibid.*, **71**, 223 (1949). (b) Barrett and Lapworth, *J. Chem. Soc.*, **93**, 85 (1908). (c) Stempel and Schaffel, *J. Am. Chem. Soc.*, **66**, 1158 (1944).

that the rate expression may be rewritten

$$\text{rate} = \left[\begin{array}{c} \diagdown \\ C=O \\ \diagup \end{array} \right] (RNH_2)_{\text{added}} \left[\frac{k_{H^+}(H^+)}{1 + (H^+)/K_{RNH_3^+}} + \frac{k_{HA}(HA)}{1 + (H^+)/K_{RNH_3^+}} \right] \quad (14)$$

where $K_{RNH_3^+}$ is the acidity constant of the conjugate acid RNH_3^+. As in equation (13), the first term in parenthesis refers to catalysis by H_3O^+ and the second term to catalysis by HA. If we attempt to accelerate the reaction by gradually adding a strong acid, the first of these terms will increase rapidly at first; but as (H^+) approaches, then exceeds, $K_{RNH_3^+}$ (which is 4×10^{-5} for $NH_2NHCONH_2$ and 1.5×10^{-6} for NH_2OH), the first term will tend to approach the constant value, $k_{H^+}K_{RNH_3^+}$. At the same time, the second term will be decreasing. On the other hand, if we gradually add acid HA, the first term will be only slightly affected, but the second term will increase steadily, since (HA) in its numerator will be increasing more rapidly than (H^+) in its denominator. Moreover, the second term may be made to increase still more markedly by adding, along with acid HA, its salt, Na^+A^-, for now (HA) will increase while (H^+) may be kept constant. It should thus be clear why the addition reactions under consideration proceed most rapidly in the presence of a high concentration of slightly ionized acid, together with a correspondingly high concentration of its salt. It may further be shown (Ex. 4) that the most effective acidic catalyst for such reactions is one having an acidity constant equal to $K_{RNH_3^+}$.

The formation of oximes is catalyzed not only by acids but also by strong base,[54(b)] the base-catalyzed reaction almost certainly involving the attack of the conjugate base $NH_2\text{-}O^-$ (or its tautomer $HO\text{—}NH^-$) on the carbonyl group. The additions of semicarbazide and phenylhydrazine should, in principle, also be subject to base catalysis, but such catalysis seems not to have been reported. It may be noted, however, that semicarbazide and phenylhydrazine, having no O—H bonds, are much weaker acids than hydroxylamine. At concentrations of base necessary to convert appreciable quantities of these addenda to their conjugate bases, side reactions such as the aldol condensation, the Cannizzaro reaction, and destruction of the addendum itself may compete significantly with the desired addition.

Hydride-transfer Reactions

In a number of reductions of aldehydes and ketones to carbinols, the key step is the transfer of a hydrogen, *together with its pair of electrons*, from the reducing agent to the carbon atom of the C=O group, thereby converting the carbonyl compound to an alkoxide. We have already seen that the reduction of ketones with the β-hydrogen of a Grignard reagent or a dialkylmagnesium compound is a hydride-transfer reaction, for which we proposed the cyclic transition state, LXXIV (p. 403). A very similar transition state, LXXVI, may be written for the familiar reduction of carbonyl compounds with aluminum isopropoxide (the so-called *Meerwein-Pondorff reduction*), but in this case, an α-hydrogen is transferred. Thus, when the reduction is carried out with deuterium-labeled isopropoxide, LXXV, the deuterium becomes attached to the α position of the resulting carbinol.[55] The same reaction may be used to oxidize secondary

LXXIV   LXXV   LXXVI

alcohols to ketones. When the alcohol is added to $(t\text{-BuO})_3\text{Al}$, it forms an aluminum salt, liberating t-BuOH, a weaker acid than the secondary alcohol. When the aluminum salt reacts with acetone, it transfers an α-hydrogen (as hydride) to the latter, converting it to a salt of isopropyl alcohol, and is itself oxidized to a carbonyl compound (the Oppenauer oxidation).

Reductions with optically active Grignard reagents (in which the β-carbon is asymmetric) are stereospecific.[56] For example, when the Grignard reagent derived from the optically active chloride, $(+)\text{-EtCHMeCH}_2\text{Cl}$, reduces the

$$\overset{\text{O}}{\overset{\|}{\text{ketone MeCCMe}_3},}$$

the resulting mixture of D- and L-MeCH(OH)CMe$_3$ contains an excess (of about 14 percent) of the dextrorotatory carbinol. This stereospecificity is consistent with the cyclic transition state LXXIV; for it may be argued that conformation LXXVII, in which the ethyl and t-butyl groups lie *trans* to each other, is somewhat favored over the alternate activated complex, LXXVIII, in which these groups lie *cis*. Similar stereospecificity in reductions

[55] Williams, Krieger, and Day, *J. Am. Chem. Soc.*, **75**, 2404 (1953). For further evidence that this reaction involves a hydride transfer, see Doering and Aschner, *ibid.*, **75**, 393 (1953). Transition state LXXVI was suggested by Woodward, Wendler, and Brutschy, *ibid.*, **67**, 1425 (1945).

[56] Mosher, *et al.*, *J. Am. Chem. Soc.*, **72**, 3994 (1950); **78**, 4374, 4959 (1956).

LXXVII   LXXVIII

with optically active aluminum alkoxides (in this case, with the α-carbon asymmetric)[57] is likewise consistent with the cyclic transition state, LXXVI. In either reaction, however, stereospecificity does not, in itself, demand a cyclic activated complex; for it is quite possible that one conformation of a noncyclic transition state be energetically favored over others.[58] In the opinion of the present author, the strongest evidence for the cyclic transition state in Grignard reductions is the inhibition of reduction by added anhydrous magnesium halides (p. 404). If the attacking hydride were to come from a Grignard molecule other than that already coordinated to the C=O group, magnesium halides (being more effective Lewis acids than Grignard reagents) should facilitate the reduction, as they do the Grignard addition reaction which competes with the reduction. Similarly, it would be of some interest to determine the effect of added anhydrous aluminum halides on the rate of reductions by aluminum isopropoxide (in, let us say, toluene or xylene).

The *Cannizzaro reaction*—the reaction of two aldehyde molecules in strongly basic solutions to give a carboxylate anion and a molecule of carbinol—is doubtless a hydride-transfer reaction.[59] The hydrogen that converts one of the aldehyde molecules to an alcohol must arise directly from the second aldehyde molecule, rather than from the solvent, for if the reaction is carried out in

[57] Doering and Young, *J. Am. Chem. Soc.*, **72**, 631 (1950).

[58] Stereospecificity has been observed—for example, in the conversion of carbonyl compounds to cyanohydrins—when the reaction is catalyzed by the conjugate acids of optically active amines (Prelog and Wilhelm, *Helv. Chim. Acta*, **37**, 1634 (1934)). This conversion very probably proceeds through the noncyclic transition state LXXIX.

LXXIX

[59] There is evidence that, in some instances, the Cannizzaro reaction may proceed homolytically (see, for example, Kharasch and Foy, *J. Am. Chem. Soc.*, **57**, 1510 (1935)), or that it may be catalyzed, in a manner which is not yet clear, by finely divided metals, metallic oxides, or metallic hydroxides (see, for example, Pearl, *ibid.*, **68**, 429, 1100 (1946); *J. Org. Chem.*, **12**, 79, 85 (1947)). However, we shall be concerned here only with Cannizzaro reactions carried out under the more usual conditions—that is, homogeneously, and in the absence of radical initiators.

D_2O, the alcohol formed has no C—D bonds.[60] The reaction in some cases exhibits third-order kinetics (rate law 15),[61(a)] in some cases fourth-order kinetics (rate law 16),[61(b)] and in still other instances kinetics of mixed order.[61(c)]

$$2RCHO + OH^- \rightarrow RC\!\!\underset{\substack{\| \\ O}}{}\!\!-O^- + RCH_2OH \qquad \text{rate} = (RCHO)^2(OH^-) \qquad (15)$$

$$\text{or} \qquad \text{rate} = (RCHO)^2(OH^-)^2 \qquad (16)$$

In the third-order reaction (which, the kinetics suggests, passes through an activated complex consisting of two aldehyde molecules and a hydroxide ion) the rate-determining step is very probably a hydride transfer from the aldehyde-hydroxide adduct, $R\!\!\underset{\substack{| \\ O_-}}{\overset{\substack{OH \\ |}}{—C—}}\!\!H$, formed in an initial rapidly established equilibrium, to a second molecule of aldehyde.

$$(17)$$

Here, the hydride is, in a sense, "pushed off" by the negative charge on the carbonyl-hydroxide adduct. The fourth-order rate law (reaction 16), which applies to the Cannizzaro reaction of furfural and formaldehyde at high concentrations of base, is consistent with two mechanisms. In the first of these (reaction 18), a hydride is transferred from one carbonyl-hydroxide anion to another; in the second, the hydride is transferred from the doubly charged anion LXXX to an aldehyde molecule (reaction 19).

$$(18)$$

$$(19)$$

LXXX

[60] Fredenhagen and Bonhoeffer, Z. physik. Chem., 181A, 379 (1938).
[61] (a) Eitel and Lock, Monatsh., 72, 392 (1939). (b) Euler and Lovgren, Z. anorg. Chem., 127, 123 (1925). (c) Eitel, Monatsh., 74, 136 (1942); Paul, J. Gen. Chem. (U.S.S.R.), 11, 1121 (1941).

Path (18) seems extremely unlikely, for when an aldehyde molecule accepts a hydroxide ion, it loses almost all of its electrophilic character and becomes very much less subject to further attack by hydride. Moreover, no instances are known where a hydride attacks a saturated carbon atom, displacing OH^-.[62] On the other hand, path (19) is quite reasonable; for anion LXXX, although present only in low concentration, would be expected to be an extremely potent hydride donor. Where mixed third- and fourth-order kinetics are observed, the reaction presumably proceeds by simultaneous operation of sequences (17) and (19).

A reaction similar in nature to the Cannizzaro reaction, but occurring in acid solution, is the "disproportionation" of the diaryl carbinol LXXXII into a ketone and the parent diarylmethane:[63]

$$2(MeO-\langle\rangle-)_2CHOH \xrightarrow{Cl_3CCOOD} (MeO-\langle\rangle-)_2C=O + (MeO-\langle\rangle-)_2CH_2$$

LXXXII   (not deuterated)

This reaction almost certainly proceeds through hydride transfer to the carbonium ion LXXXIII, derived from the diaryl carbinol,

$$(MeO-\langle\rangle-)_2C(\!-\!H) + \overset{+}{C}H(-\langle\rangle-OMe)_2 \longrightarrow (MeO-\langle\rangle-)_2\overset{+}{C} +$$

with OH groups

LXXXIII

$$CH_2(-\langle\rangle-OMe)_2$$

In contrast to the Cannizzaro reaction, in which the hydride is "pushed off" by a high concentration of negative charge on the hydride source, the hydride in the reaction above is "pulled off" by the positive carbon of the carbonium ion. In the Meerwein-Pondorff reduction, the hydride involved in the transfer is subject both to push and pull; for, as shown in structure LXXXIV, the carbon atom to which the hydride becomes attached bears a partial positive charge,

---

[62] A path sometimes proposed for the (third-order) Cannizzaro reaction (see, for example, Geissman in *Organic Reactions*, Vol. 2, John Wiley and Sons, Inc., New York, 1944, p. 94),

$$:\overset{..}{\underset{..}{O}}{}^{-}\!\!-\!\!C \cdots C-OH \longrightarrow O=C-O-CH_2R \xrightarrow{saponification} RCOO^- + RCH_2OH$$

with R, O, R groups; R group

LXXXI

involving transition state LXXXI, is open to similar objection. In this case also, attack on a saturated carbon by hydride, displacing hydroxide, is assumed. Further evidence against this mechanism has been summarized by Ingold, *Structure and Mechanism in Organic Chemistry*, Cornell University Press, Ithaca, 1953, p. 708.

[63] Bartlett and McCullom, *J. Am. Chem. Soc.*, **78**, 466 (1956).

whereas the hydride departs from a region bearing a partial negative charge.

LXXXIV

Among the additional hydride-transfer reactions which have been studied recently are the following:[64]

$$Ph_2C=S + \quad \text{(structure)} \longrightarrow Ph_2CDS^- + \text{(structure)} \quad \text{[64(a)]} \quad (20)$$

$$\text{(structure)} \xrightarrow{H^+} \text{(structure)} \quad \text{[64(b)]} \quad (21)$$

$$R_2C=O + H_4B^- \longrightarrow R_2CH-O-BH_3^- \quad \text{[64(c)]} \quad (22)$$

Reaction (20), which requires neither strong acid nor strong base, is thought to be similar to certain enzyme-catalyzed reductions in which the reducing agent (the so-called "co-enzyme") has a reduced pyridine ring system. Reaction (21) is a *trans*-annular (across-the-ring) hydride shift, somewhat analogous to the pinacol rearrangement (Chap. 14). Finally, reaction (22) is the first step in the reduction of ketones by the very useful hydride-transfer reagent, sodium borohydride; this reaction has been found to be first order in each reactant,[64(c)] but further information is needed before a reliable guess as to its mechanism may be made.

Stereochemistry of C=O Additions. Cram's Rule

At present we cannot meaningfully speak of *trans* or *cis* addition to a C=O double bond, since, thanks to free rotation about the C—O single bond in the product, the initial conformation of this product persists for only an instant after its formation. There is, however, a different type of stereochemical prob-

[64] (a) Abeles, Hutton, and Westheimer, *J. Am. Chem. Soc.*, **79**, 712 (1957). (b) Prelog and Kung, *Helv. Chim. Acta*, **39**, 1395 (1956). (c) Brown, Wheeler, and Ichikawa, *Tetrahedron*, **1**, 214 (1957).

lem associated with C=O additions. Unless the substrate is formaldehyde or a symmetric ketone (such as acetone or benzophenone), such additions may convert the carbon of the carbonyl group to an asymmetric center. If the reaction occurs under "symmetric conditions," equal numbers of D and L molecules should form; that is, the product will be racemic. On the other hand, if the substrate is optically active, particularly if the α-carbon is asymmetric, the addition reaction may be said to take place in an asymmetric environment. Since there will be two asymmetric carbons in the addition product, two diastereomeric forms (*threo* and *erythro*) will be possible and one of these will generally predominate. In short, the presence of one asymmetric center in the substrate influences the ratio of isomers formed when a second asymmetric center is created. Generally, the predominant product is that resulting from an activated complex in which steric interference is minimal. Consider, for example, the conversion of the ketone PhCHMe—C—Me to a carbinol, using a

$$\overset{\|}{\underset{O}{}}$$

Grignard reagent or a hydride donor (such as LiAlH$_4$, NaBH$_4$, or Al(i-PrO)$_3$). Regardless of the detailed mechanism of the reaction, we may suppose that the oxygen of the carbonyl group becomes involved in complex formation (with a magnesium, aluminum, or boron atom) before the carbon of the carbonyl group is attacked. We would, on this basis, expect the carbonyl group, with whatever Lewis acid is complexed with it, to take a position as far as possible from the bulky phenyl group (LXXXV); and we would further expect the incoming nucleophile (which we may designate as X:) to attack preferentially on the side near the α-hydrogen, leading to diastereomer LXXXVI, rather than on the side adjacent to the more bulky α-methyl group, which would result in the formation of diastereomer LXXXVII. This type of argument may

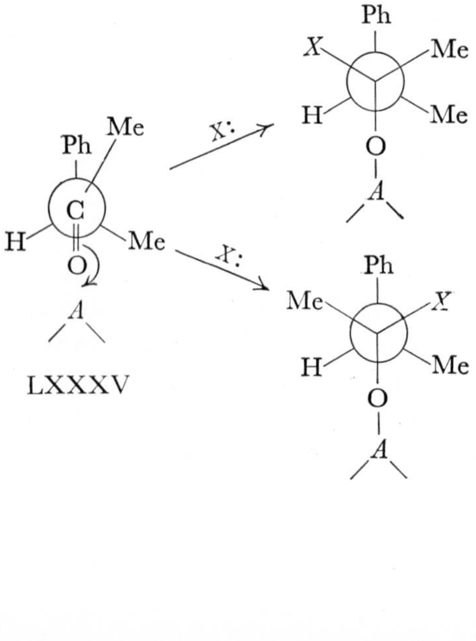

(LXXXVI, major product)

(LXXXVII, minor product)

LXXXV

be applied in many similar situations and has been summarized by Cram's rule of "steric control of asymmetric induction," which may be stated as follows: When an addition reaction generates an asymmetric center adjacent to one already in existence, the double bond in the preferred transition state will be "flanked" by the two least bulky *alpha* substituents, and the attacking nucleophile will approach from the least hindered side of the double bond.[65] Schematically, if we designate the substituents on the α-carbon as L (large), M (medium sized), and S (small), we may represent an addition proceeding according to Cram's rule as follows:

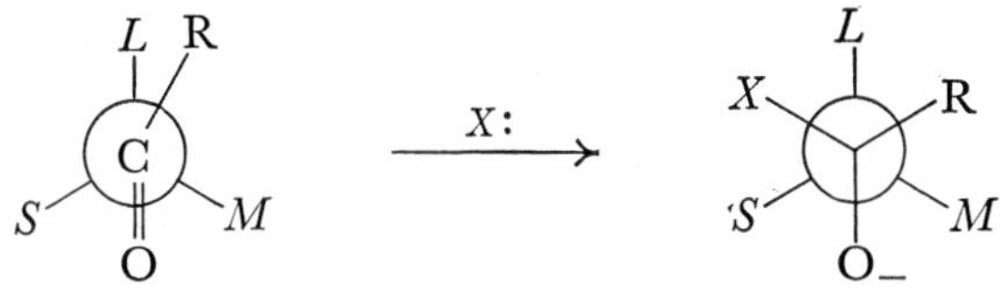

This rule would not be expected to apply to heterogeneously catalyzed additions, (for example, to catalytic hydrogenations), for the stereochemistry of these reactions is often determined by the orientation of the substrate as it lies on the surface of the catalyst. Moreover, the rule may be applied to the addition reactions of substituted cyclic ketones only with reserve; for here the relative stabilities of the possible transition states will be determined not only by the interactions between the α substituents and the addendum, but also by the conformations (axial or equatorial) of the various ring substituents.[66]

An asymmetric center may influence the stereochemistry of an addition reaction, even if it is several atoms removed from the reaction site. If, for example, the phenylglyoxylic ester of an optically active alcohol (LXXXVIII) is treated with a Grignard reagent, the α-hydroxy ester formed (LXXXIX) has a new asymmetric center and yields, upon hydrolysis, an optically active α-hydroxy acid.[67] The situation may be analyzed in much the same way as

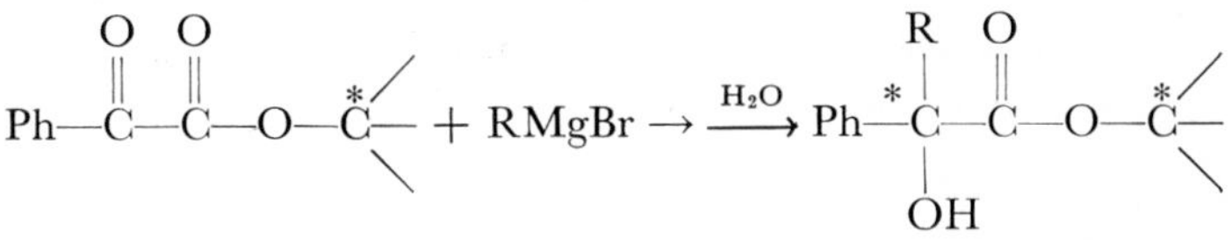

LXXXVIII   LXXXIX

[65] Cram and Abd Elhafez, *J. Am. Chem. Soc.*, **74**, 5828 (1952). These authors list over fifty additions which appear to proceed in accordance with this rule. For additional examples, see Cram, *et al.*, *ibid.*, **74**, 5835 (1952); and Curtin, *et al.*, *ibid.*, **74**, 2901 (1952).

[66] For a discussion of the rather more complex question of the stereochemistry of the additions to substituted cyclohexanones, see Dauben, Fonken, and Noyce, *J. Am. Chem. Soc.*, **78**, 2579 (1956).

[67] Prelog, *et al.*, *Helv. Chim. Acta*, **36**, 308, 320, 325 (1953).

may those additions falling within the scope of Cram's rule, again designating the three substituents on the asymmetric carbon in ester LXXXVIII as S, M, and L. Because of repulsion between the C=O dipoles, the most stable conformation of the phenylglyoxylic ester may be assumed to be LXXXVIII′, in which the C=O groups lie at an angle of 180°. Again, we may suppose that the alkyl group of the Grignard reagent will attack the keto group preferentially from the *least hindered side*, that the predominant form of the α-hydroxy ester formed will be LXXXIX, and that this ester will give, upon hydrolysis, acid

LXXXVIII′   LXXXIX   XC   XCI

XC. This conversion is of interest, for it allows us to relate the configuration about the asymmetric carbon in acid XC with that about the asymmetric carbon in carbinol XCI, and further allows us to compare the configurations of two optically active alcohols having asymmetric α-carbon atoms. Let us suppose that dextrorotatory *sec*-butyl alcohol (the configuration of which is thought to be XCII),[68] and an alcohol of an unknown configuration are converted to their respective phenylglyoxylic esters. Suppose further that both esters are treated with CH_3MgBr, that the α-hydroxy esters which result are then hydrolyzed, and that the directions of optical rotation of the acids formed in the hydrolyses are compared. If rotation of the two hydroxy acids is of the same sign, showing that the direction of stereospecificity is the same in both cases, we may assume that the unknown alcohol, like (+)-*sec*-butyl alcohol, has a configuration which may be represented as XCIII. Conversely, if the direction of stereospecificity is different for the two series of conversions, the configuration of the unknown alcohol would, in all probability, be XCIV.

XCII   XCIII   XCIV

[68] Kirkwood, *J. Chem. Phys.*, **5**, 479 (1937); Kuhn, *Z. physik. Chem.*, **B31**, 23 (1936).

EXERCISES FOR CHAPTER 13

1. Propose a mechanism for the acid-catalyzed hydration of acrolein,

$$CH_2\!\!=\!\!CH\!\!-\!\!CHO + H_2O \xrightarrow{H^+} HO\!\!-\!\!CH_2\!\!-\!\!CH_2CHO$$

consistent with the following observations:
(a) The rate is much greater than the rates for hydration of 2-butene or crotyl alcohol under similar conditions.
(b) The rate is proportional to (H_3O^+), rather than to h_0.
(c) The entropy of activation is much more negative than that for the acid-catalyzed hydration of 2-butene or crotyl alcohol.

2. The rate of addition of Br_2 to stilbene in methanol is decreased by adding Br^- to the reaction mixture, due to the formation of the less electrophilic Br_3^- anion. The apparent specific rate for this addition may be defined

$$k_{app} = \frac{-d(S)/dt}{(S)(Br_2)_{added}}$$

where (S) is the concentration of stilbene and $(Br_2)_{added}$ is the stoichiometric concentration of added bromine (present both as Br_2 and Br_3^-). It is found[17] that k_{app} varies with (Br^-) as follows:

$$k_{app} = \frac{a(Br^-) + bK}{K + (Br^-)} \tag{23}$$

where a and b are constants and K is the dissociation constant of Br_3^- into Br_2 and Br^-.
(a) Show that this relationship is consistent with the following mechanism:

and that $k_1 = a$ and $k_2 = b$.
(b) Show that the fraction of product diverted to the α-bromoether is

$$f_{MeO-Br} = \frac{1}{1 + \dfrac{k_3}{k_4}(Br^-)}$$

(c) When $(Br^-) = 0.1$, the fraction of α-bromoether is 0.90. When (Br^-) is raised to 0.2, this fraction falls to 0.82. Calculate two values for the ratio k_3/k_4.
(d) The value of K under the reaction conditions employed is 0.0024. Values of k_{app} in

the presence of 0.1 and 0.01 F LiBr are, respectively, 40.5 and 6.7. Calculate k_1 and k_2.

(e) Show that expression (23) is consistent also with the following mechanism:

and that $K'k_5 = a$ and $K'k_6 = b$. Show also that in this case

$$f_{\mathrm{MeO-Br}} = \frac{1}{1 + \dfrac{k_5}{k_6}(\mathrm{Br}^-)}$$

(f) From the values of a and b, calculate the ratio k_5/k_6, and estimate values for $f_{\mathrm{MeO-Br}}$ when the concentration of Br^- is 0.1 and 0.2 F. Which of the two mechanisms above is the more satisfactory?

3. Predict which addition reaction in each of the following pairs has the higher specific rate, and justify your guess:

(a) HBr or HI to propylene in dioxane?

(b) HOCl to $CF_3CH{=}CHCH_3$ or to 2-butene in water?

(c) ICl or IBr to ethylene in methanol?

(d) HCN to acetaldehyde or to acetone in water?

(e) p-Nitrophenylhydrazine or 2,4-dinitrophenylhydrazine to acetone in acetic acid?

(f) Br_2 to 1,1-diphenylethylene or to isobutene in nitromethane.

(g) H_2O to $CH_2{=}CMe_2$ with 1 N HNO_3 in water or in 50-50 water-dioxane?

(h) H_2O to $CH_3CH{=}CHCHO$ or to $CH_3CH{=}CHCF_3$ with 1 N HNO_3 in water-dioxane?

(i) Br_2 to stilbene in methanol or in dioxane?

(j) HF or Cl_2 to cyclohexene in glacial acetic acid?

(k) Br_2 to cyclopentene in acetic acid with added NaCl or added $AlBr_3$?

(l) Br_2 to in acetic acid with added NaCl or added HBr?

(m) PhSH to $PhC{\equiv}CH$ or to , in EtOH with added NaOEt?

(n) EtOH to $CF_2{=}CCl_2$ or to $CF_2{=}CF_2$, catalyzed by NaOEt?

(o) Acetylenedicarboxylic acid to or to in xylene?

(p) Br_2 to ⟦cyclobutane with =CH₂ substituent⟧ or to ⟦cyclopentane with =CH₂ substituent⟧ in acetic acid?

(q) 1,3-Butadiene to ⟦quinone structure with Me⟧ or to ⟦quinone structure with Cl substituents⟧ in CCl_4?

(r) Br_2 to PhCH=CH—CH=CHPh or to PhCH₂—CH=CH—CH₂Ph in nitro-benzene?

(s) Semicarbazide to ⟦naphthalene with Ac and Me substituents⟧ or to ⟦naphthalene with Ac and Me substituents⟧ in dilute HOAc?

(t) Hydroxylamine to cyclohexanone in the presence of an equimolar mixture of HOAc and OAc^- or an equimolar mixture of $Cl_2CHCOOH$ and Cl_2CHCOO^- in water?

(u) Maleic anhydride to furan or to benzofuran in chlorobenzene?

4. (a) Consider the general-acid-catalyzed addition of nucleophile RNH_2 to an aldehyde or ketone $\left(\text{designated} \diagdown \text{C}=\text{O} \diagup\right)$. Show that under conditions where the added nucleophile exists both as RNH_2 and RNH_3^+, the rate of addition is given by equation (14), page 544.

(b) Assume that in this case, the first term in parenthesis in equation (14) (representing catalysis by H_3O^+) may be neglected in comparison with the second. Suppose now that this reaction is carried out in the presence of a fixed quantity of weak acid, HA, with enough base added to convert a portion of this acid to A^-. Show that under these conditions, the rate will be a maximum when enough base has been added so that

$$(H^+) = \sqrt{K_{HA}K_{RNH_3^+}}$$

(Hint: remember that $(HA) + (A^-)$ remains constant, and differentiate.)

(c) Assuming that a buffer system may work effectively when (HA) lies near (A^-), show that the most effective catalytic acid for this reaction is one for which K_{HA} lies very near $K_{RNH_3^+}$.

5. Suggest mechanisms for the following conversions:

(a) ⟦cyclopentene⟧ + HBr $\xrightarrow{PhNO_2}$ ⟦bromocyclopentane⟧

(b)

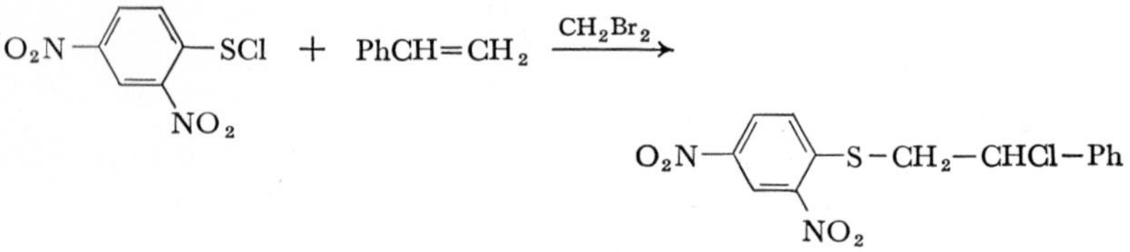

$O_2N-\langle\rangle-SCl + PhCH=CH_2 \xrightarrow{CH_2Br_2}$

$O_2N-\langle\rangle-S-CH_2-CHCl-Ph$
with NO_2

(c) $CH_2=CHBr + HI \xrightarrow[\text{air}]{\text{benzene}} CH_3CHBrI$

(d) $Me_2C=CH_2 + ICl \xrightarrow[\text{NaBr}]{\text{HOAc}} Me_2CBr-CH_2I + NaCl$

(e)

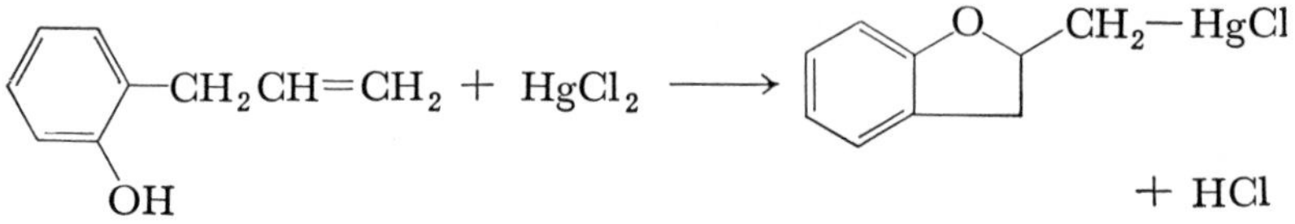

$\langle\rangle-CH_2CH=CH_2 + HgCl_2 \longrightarrow$ (benzofuran)$-CH_2-HgCl$
with OH
$+ HCl$

(f) $Ph-\underset{O}{\underset{\|}{C}}-CHO + OH^- \xrightarrow{H_2O} PhCHOH-COO^-$

(g) $Me_2C=CH-\underset{Me}{\underset{|}{C}}=O + Me_2NH \xrightarrow{H_2O} Me_2\underset{NMe_2}{\underset{|}{C}}-CH_2-\underset{CH_3}{\underset{|}{C}}=O$

(h) $MeCH=CHCOOEt + Br_2 \xrightarrow[\text{HBr}]{\text{HOAc}} MeCHBr-CHBr-COOEt$

(i) 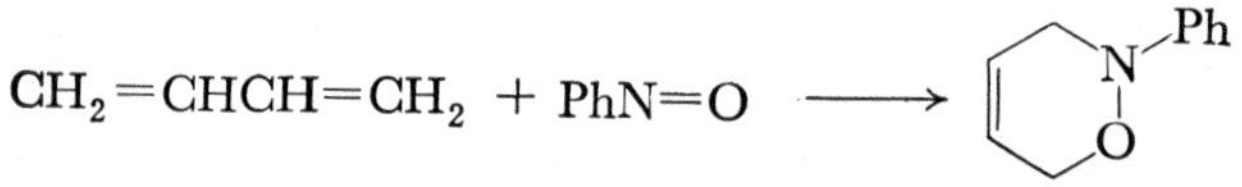 $CH_2=CHCH=CH_2 + PhN=O \longrightarrow$

(j) 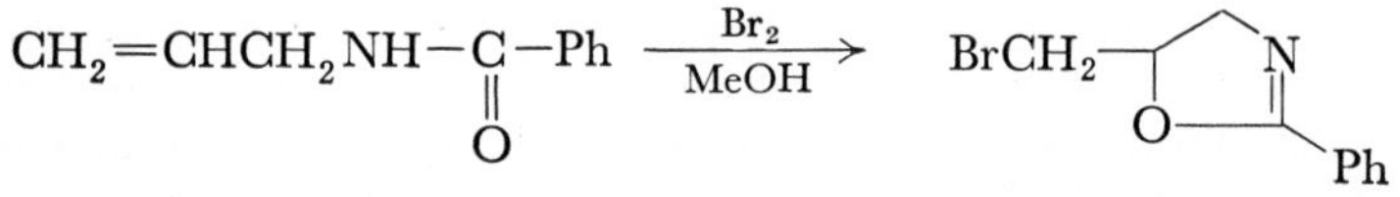 $CH_2=CHCH_2NH-\underset{O}{\underset{\|}{C}}-Ph \xrightarrow[\text{MeOH}]{Br_2}$ $BrCH_2-$

(k) 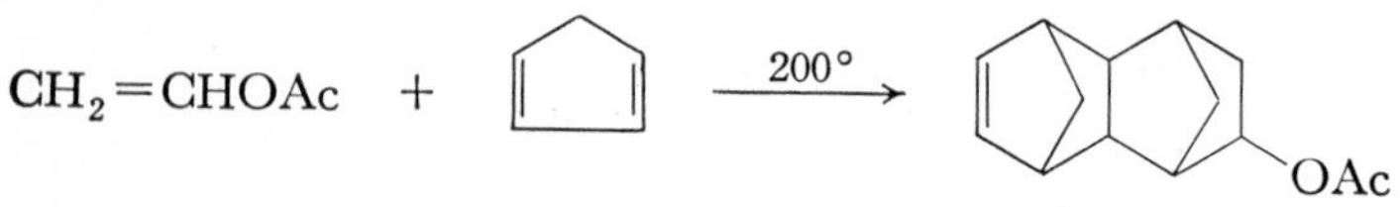 $CH_2=CHOAc +$

$\xrightarrow{200°}$

(l)

$\xrightarrow{OH^-}$

$+ Ph-\underset{O}{\underset{\|}{C}}-Me$

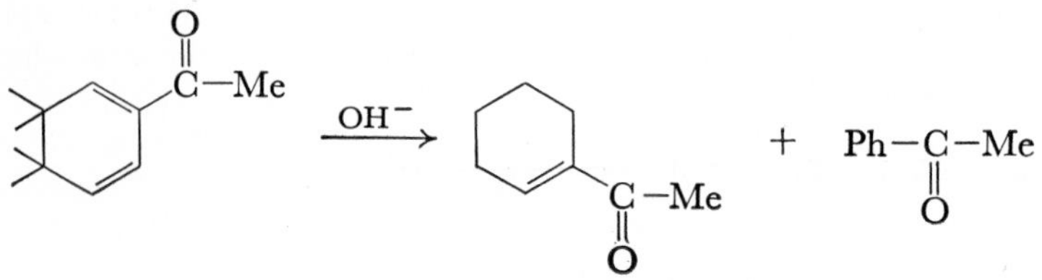

(m) 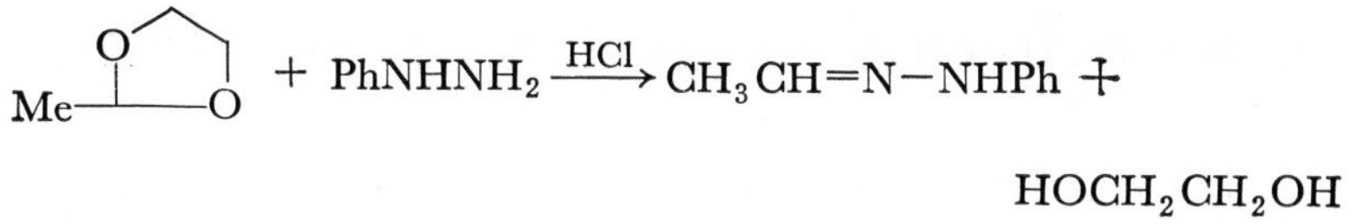 + PhNHNH₂ $\xrightarrow{\text{HCl}}$ CH₃CH=N—NHPh +

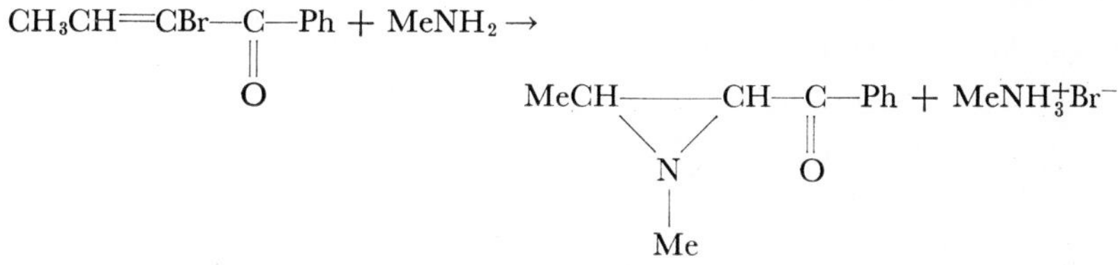

$$HOCH_2CH_2OH$$

(n) CH₃CH=CBr—C—Ph + MeNH₂ →
      $\underset{\text{O}}{||}$

MeCH————CH—C—Ph + MeNH₃⁺Br⁻
      $\underset{\underset{\text{Me}}{|}}{\diagdown N \diagup}$ $\underset{\text{O}}{||}$

(o) —CH₂MgCl + HCHO ⟶

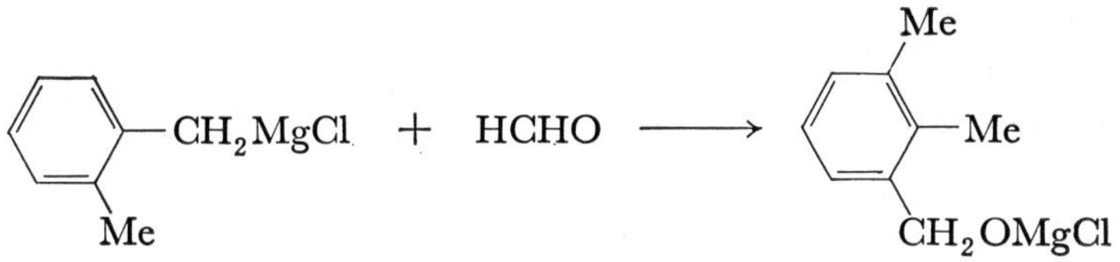

(p) 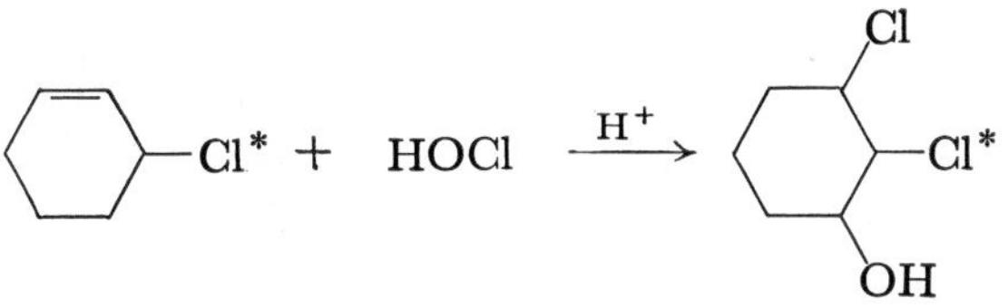 —Cl* + HOCl $\xrightarrow{\text{H}^+}$

(q) 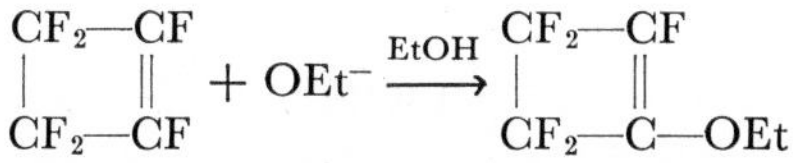 CF₂—CF
      $|$ $||$ + OEt⁻ $\xrightarrow{\text{EtOH}}$ CF₂—CF
    CF₂—CF $|$ $||$
                            CF₂—C—OEt

(r) cis-MeCH=CHMe + N₂O₅ → erythro-MeCH—CHMe—ONO₂
                                              $\underset{\text{NO}_2}{|}$

(s) 2PhCHO $\xrightarrow{\text{Al(OCH}_2\text{Ph)}_3}$ Ph—C—O—CH₂Ph
                                $\underset{\text{O}}{||}$

(t) 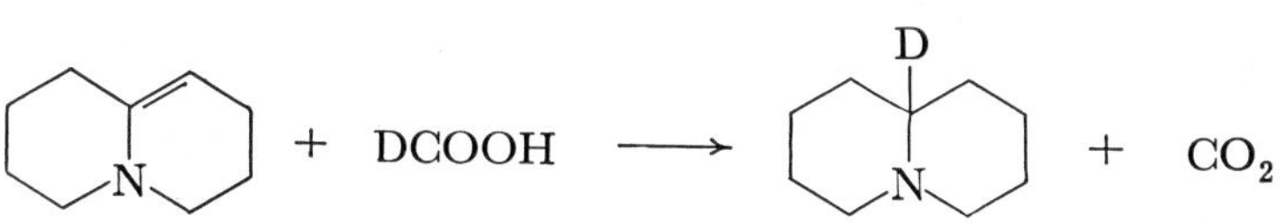 + DCOOH ⟶ + CO₂

(u) 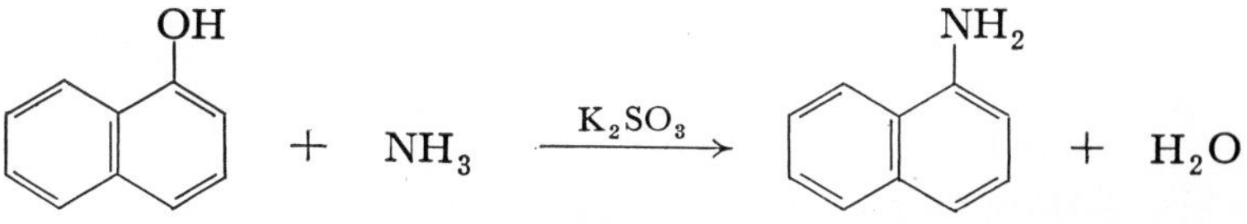 + NH₃ $\xrightarrow{\text{K}_2\text{SO}_3}$ + H₂O

(v) CH₂=CCl₂ + PhS⁻ $\xrightarrow{\text{OH}^-}$ cis-PhSCH=CHSPh

6. Predict the predominant products, indicating the direction of stereospecificity where appropriate. Justify your guess in each case.

(a) *trans*-EtCH=CHMe + O_2N—⟨benzene⟩—SCl $\xrightarrow{CH_2Br_2}$

(b) Ph_3C—CH=CH$_2$ + Br$_2$ $\xrightarrow{MeOH}$

(c) CH_2=CHCN + ICl $\xrightarrow{PhNO_2}$

(d) Me_2C=CHMe + OH$^-$ $\xrightarrow{HCCl_3}$

(e) *trans*-MeCH=CHCOOH + HBr $\xrightarrow{H_2O}$

(f) HCHO + NaNH$_2$ $\xrightarrow{liquid\ NH_3}$

(g) Me_2C=CH$_2$ + NOCl + ⟨pyridine⟩ $\longrightarrow$

(h) PhCH=CH—⟨benzene⟩—NO$_2$ + N$_2$O$_5$ $\xrightarrow{CCl_4}$

(i) CH_2=C(OMe)—CH=CH$_2$ + CH$_2$=CHCHO →

(j) Me_2C=CHCH=CHPh + 1 ⟨benzene-COOH, C–OOH⟩ $\xrightarrow{H^+}$

(k) ⟨glucose structure: CH$_2$OH, O, OH, HO, OH, OH⟩ + H_2N—⟨benzene⟩—COOH $\xrightarrow{EtOH}$

(l) ⟨bicyclic alkene⟩ + HBr $\xrightarrow{HOAc}$

(m) Me—⟨benzene⟩—CH=CH—CH=CH—⟨benzene⟩—Cl $\xrightarrow{1Br_2}$

(n) ⟨norbornene structure⟩ + Br$_2$ $\xrightarrow{EtOH}$

(o) ⟨structure: COO$^-$, H, CHMe–MgBr, C, Ph, Me⟩ + *i*-Pr—C(=O)—Et $\longrightarrow$

(p)

+ EtMgBr ⟶

(q)

+ Ph—C—CH₃ ⟶

7. Outline a series of experiments to show that the addition reaction

$$R-\underset{\underset{O}{\parallel}}{C}-\underset{\underset{O}{\parallel}}{C}-O-\overset{*}{\underset{\alpha}{C}}\Big\langle + R'MgBr \rightarrow R-\underset{\underset{OMgBr}{|}}{\overset{R'}{\underset{|}{C}}}-\underset{\underset{O}{\parallel}}{C}-O-\overset{*}{\underset{\alpha}{C}}\Big\langle$$

proceeds stereospecifically in the direction dictated by minimum steric interaction between R' and the groups on Cα while the keto ester lies in conformation LXXXVIII' (p. 552). Assume that the absolute configurations of the reactants and products are unknown.

8. Explain each of the following observations:

(a) The rate of formation of ethylene bromide from the reaction of bromine with ethylene in water is increased by the addition of NaBr, but the rate of disappearance of the olefin is decreased.

(b) The rate of addition of hydrogen halides to olefins in nitrobenzene is increased by the addition of $SnCl_4$.

(c) The rate of addition of Br_2 to cinnamic acid in water is decreased by the addition of small quantities of dilute HNO_3.

(d) ICl adds more rapidly to stilbene than does Br_2 under comparable conditions.

(e) Cyclopentadiene undergoes the Diels-Alder reaction more readily than does 1,3-butadiene.

(f) The low temperature addition of HCl to isoprene gives $CH_3CMeClCH=CH_2$ when equimolal quantities of reactants are used. However, with a slight excess of HCl, the chief product is $CH_3CMe=CHCH_2Cl$.

(g) The dimerization of cyclopentadiene is catalyzed by trichloroacetic acid more effectively in CCl_4 than in dioxane.

(h) The conversion of an aldehyde to a hemiacetal in water exhibits general acid catalysis, but the further conversion to an acetal is catalyzed only by H_3O^+.

(i) When benzaldehyde undergoes the Cannizzaro reaction, one of the products is benzyl benzoate, although benzyl alcohol and benzoic acid do not react to form this ester under the reaction conditions employed.

(j) The rate of hydration of methylenecyclobutane (in aqueous HNO_3) is nearly the same as that for methylenecyclopentane, although the equilibrium constant for the former hydration is about 10,000 times that for the latter.

(k) The yields of CH_2=CMe—CH_2Cl and $Me_2C(OH)$—CH_2Cl from the reaction of HOCl with Me_2C=CH_2 in dilute acid are nearly the same as the yields of these products from the hydrolysis of Me_2CClCH_2Cl at the same temperature and pH. However, the yield of Me_2C=$CHCl$ resulting from the latter reaction is considerably greater than that resulting from the former.

(l) The migration of Cl^* during the addition of HOCl to CH_2=$CMeCH_2Cl^*$ takes place to a much greater extent than during the addition of HOCl to CH_2=$CHCH_2Cl$.

(m) The addition of PhSH to HC≡C—$COOEt$ in base is a *trans* addition; the addition of PhSH to HC≡C—$COONa$ in base is a *cis* addition.

(n) When acid chloride XCV is converted to carbinol XCVI by treatment first with Me_2Cd, then with EtLi, the resulting product is diastereomeric with the carbinol formed by treatment of the same acid chloride, first with Et_2Cd, then with MeLi.

XCV   XCVI

Participation of Neighboring Groups in Nucleophilic Substitution Reactions and in Rearrangements[1]

IN CHAPTER 7 we considered the ways in which the reactions of an organic molecule could be accelerated or retarded by groups that lie near the reaction site but, nevertheless, do not participate directly in the reaction. We attributed the action of such groups to inductive, conjugative, and steric effects, or to combinations of these. In the present chapter, however, we shall be concerned with reactions where neighboring groups become more deeply involved—where, in fact, such groups become bonded (fully or partially) to the reaction center for an interval of time during the reaction's progress.

There are three principal types of evidence that point to neighboring group participation. First, if such participation occurs during the rate-determining step, the reaction is almost certain to be significantly more rapid than other reactions that are similar but do not involve such participation. Typically, the β-chloro sulfide, $ClCH_2CH_2SEt$, is hydrolyzed over 10,000 times as rapidly as is the corresponding ether, $ClCH_2CH_2OEt$ (in aqueous dioxane).[2] This rate difference is far too great to be attributed to differences in inductive, conjugative, or steric effects, but suggests rather that the hydrolysis of the sulfide (but not the ether) proceeds through a cyclic 'onium ion (in this case, sulfonium ion I). The intermediate, because of the strained three-membered ring, is readily hydrolyzed to the observed products.

---

[1] For reviews of this subject, see (a) Winstein, *Bull. soc. chim. France*, **18**, C55 (1951), and (b) Streitwieser, *Chem. Revs.*, **56**, 675 (1956).

[2] Bohme and Sell, *Ber.*, **81**, 123 (1948).

$$\underset{Et}{\overset{..}{S}}\overset{CH_2}{\underset{CH_2}{\diagdown}}Cl \xrightarrow{-Cl^-} \underset{Et}{\overset{+}{S}}\overset{CH_2}{\underset{CH_2}{\diagup}} \xrightarrow[very\ fast]{H_2O} EtSCH_2CH_2OH + H^+$$

I

Secondly, the *stereochemistry* of a reaction might suggest that neighboring groups become involved. In an earlier chapter, we saw that the hydrolysis of the α-bromopropionate ion in water or dilute base yields lactate with *retention of configuration* about the α-carbon (p. 270). Since nucleophilic substitutions at secondary carbon atoms almost invariably result in partial or complete inversion of configuration, it was assumed that *two* displacements were actually involved:

$$\overset{O}{\underset{\|}{}}$$

the first a displacement of bromide by the neighboring $-C-O^-$ to form the nonisolable α-lactone (II), and the second a very rapid cleavage of the lactone by water. Inversion presumably occurred in both displacements, the second inversion "nullifying" the first.

II

Finally, neighboring group participation may lead to molecular rearrangement when the neighboring group remains bonded to the reaction center but breaks away from the atom to which it was originally attached in the substrate. Thus, the chlorinated amine III yields, upon basic hydrolysis, the rearranged aminohydrin, V, presumably because the intermediate imonium ion, IV, is attacked preferentially at the primary α-carbon atom rather than at the secondary β-carbon atom.[3]

$$\overset{..}{Et_2N}\overset{CHEt}{\underset{CH_2}{\diagdown}}Cl \xrightarrow{-Cl^-} \overset{+}{Et_2N}\overset{CHEt}{\underset{CH_2}{\diagup}} \xrightarrow{OH^-} Et_2N\overset{CHEt}{\underset{CH_2OH}{\diagdown}}$$

III   IV   V

A reaction that is accelerated by neighboring group participation is sometimes said to be *anchimerically assisted*,[4] for such a reaction proceeds through what is, in effect, an "internally attached form" of the substrate (for example, structures I and IV).

[3] Ross, *J. Am. Chem. Soc.*, **69**, 2982 (1947).

[4] Winstein, Lindegren, Marshall, and Ingraham, *J. Am. Chem. Soc.*, **75**, 147 (1953).

Intramolecular Displacement by Oxygen

The nature of neighboring-group reactions was first elucidated through experiments involving participation of the carboxylate group $\left(\begin{array}{c} -C-O^- \\ \parallel \\ O \end{array}\right)$, particularly through studies of the hydrolysis and alcoholysis of the anions derived from α-halocarboxylic acids. In discussing a typical reaction of this sort, the hydrolysis of α-bromopropionate (p. 270), it was suggested that the carboxylate group does not displace the α-bromine directly, but rather that the formation of the α-lactone (II) *follows* the ionization of the C—Br bond. This conclusion arises from the observed catalysis of the reaction by Ag^+,[5(a)] its acceleration when the degree of branching at the α-carbon is increased,[5(b)] and the observed positive kinetic salt effect[5(c)] (each of these features being characteristic of S_N1-like, rather than S_N2-like solvolyses). However, although direct displacement may be difficult, due to the strain involved in forming a three-membered ring, the departure of Br^- is doubtless facilitated by a combination of the inductive and field effects of the —COO$^-$ group. As soon as the bromide ion has receded a bit from the α-carbon, the energy needed to form the three-membered lactone ring becomes available from the neutralization of charge upon formation of the C_α—O bond.[6]

As the distance between the halogen atom and the carboxylate group is increased, the cyclic structure involved in direct intramolecular displacement becomes much less strained. Reaction by displacement becomes favored, and solvolysis is no longer facilitated by branching at the halogen-bearing carbon or by the addition of Ag^+. Thus the conversion of γ-bromovalerate in water to the five-membered ring lactone, VII, proceeds by direct displacement,[7(a)] and the same is probably true for the formation of β-butyrolactone (VI).[7(b)] But, as is the case with other types of cyclization, formation of rings of seven or more members entails some difficulty, due to the low probability for collision between the opposite ends of a long chainlike molecule. When ϵ-bromocaproic acid (VIII) is treated with Ag_2O in water, ordinary solvolysis to give the ϵ-hydroxy acid

---

[5] (a) Cowdrey, Hughes, and Ingold, *J. Chem. Soc.*, **1938**, 1243. (b) Lane and Heine, *J. Am. Chem. Soc.*, **73**, 1348 (1951). (c) Grunwald and Winstein, *ibid.*, **70**, 841 (1948).

[6] It has been found (Ref. 5c) that solvolysis of the α-bromopropionate ion is accelerated by a factor of only 2.4 when transferred from methanol to water, in contrast to rate increases by factors of several hundred when the solvolyses of ordinary secondary alkyl bromides are transferred from methanol to water; that is, the presence of the —COO$^-$ group lowers the sensitivity of the solvolysis to the dielectric constant of the medium. This indicates that the degree of charge separation in the transition state is much less for solvolysis of the bromopropionate ion than for solvolysis of, say, isopropyl chloride and confirms the picture of a transition state in which the positive charge developing at the α-carbon is partially neutralized by interaction with the neighboring —COO$^-$ group.

[7] (a) Levene and Mori, *J. Biol. Chem.*, **78**, 1 (1928). (b) Johansson and Hagman, *Ber.*, **55**, 647 (1922). (c) Marvel, et al., *J. Am. Chem. Soc.*, **46**, 2838 (1924). (d) von Braun, *Ber.*, **39**, 4364 (1906).

competes with neighboring-group participation (which gives the seven-membered ring lactone, IX).[7(c)] Anion X yields only a hydroxy acid (no eight-membered ring lactone).[7(d)]

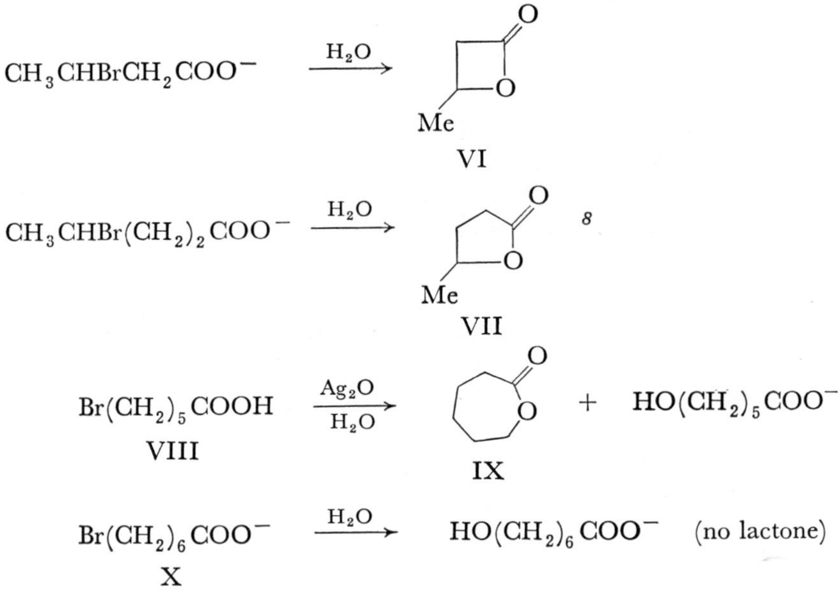

$$CH_3CHBrCH_2COO^- \xrightarrow{H_2O}$$

Me

VI

$$CH_3CHBr(CH_2)_2COO^- \xrightarrow{H_2O}$$

8

Me

VII

$$Br(CH_2)_5COOH \xrightarrow[H_2O]{Ag_2O}$$

VIII

$+$ $HO(CH_2)_5COO^-$

IX

$$Br(CH_2)_6COO^- \xrightarrow{H_2O} HO(CH_2)_6COO^- \quad \text{(no lactone)}$$

X

When the carboxylate group is converted by protonation to the carboxyl group, —COOH, it becomes very much less nucleophilic and loses a great deal of its effectiveness as a participant. The substitution of a carboxyl group for an α-methyl in $(CH_3)_2CHBr$ *lowers* the rate of solvolysis in water about a hundred-fold,[9(a)] whereas a similar substitution in PhCHMeBr *retards* solvolysis by a factor of about 10^5.[9(b)] If any anchimeric assistance effects are present, they are com-

---

[8] Although neighboring-group participation in the solvolysis of salts of simple δ-halocarboxylic acids has not yet been demonstrated, it almost certainly occurs in the hydrolysis of anion XI (which is analogous to the salt of a δ-halocarboxylic acid in that the chlorine atom is separated from the carboxylate group by a chain of four atoms). It is found that anion XI may be easily hydrolyzed in boiling water although its *para* isomer, XII, is inert under the same conditions (Bordwell and Cooper, *J. Am. Chem. Soc.*, **79**, 916 (1957).

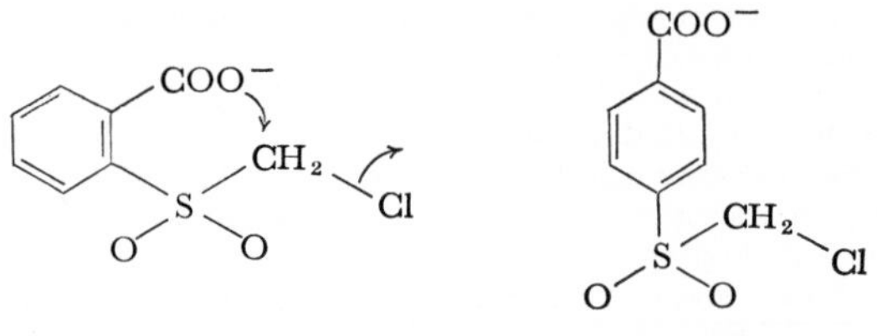

XI

XII

[9] (a) Winstein, Grunwald, and Jones, *J. Am. Chem. Soc.*, **73**, 2700 (1951). (b) Taylor, *J. Chem. Soc.*, **1937**, 343.

pletely overshadowed by the strongly negative inductive effect of the —COOH group. It has been found that the "deaminations" of α-amino acids proceed with retention of configuration,[10] but in this case it is not clear whether participation

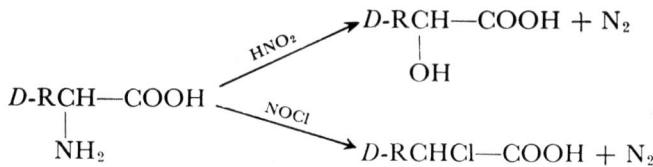

by the —COOH or the —COO⁻ group is involved, since the intermediate, D-RCH—COOH, is a strong acid.

$$\text{D-RCH—COOH} \quad (\text{+N} \equiv \text{N})$$

Whether or not an ester linkage functions as a neighboring group depends largely upon how it is situated with respect to the reaction center in the substrate. The solvolyses of $CH_3CHBrCOOEt^{5(a)}$ and the deamination of $CH_3CH(NH_2)$-$COOEt^{10}$ result in inversion of configuration about the α-carbon, suggesting that there is negligible participation by the —C—OEt group when the reaction ‖ O

center lies *alpha* to the C=O bond of the ester. This is what we might expect, for such participation would require the formation of a strained three-membered ring

$$\left(\begin{array}{c} | \\ —C———\overset{+}{C}—OR \\ \diagdown \diagup \\ O \end{array} \right)$$ without any compensating charge neutralization. On the

other hand, ester participation has been observed in a number of substitutions in which the reaction center is located in the alkyl, rather than the acyl, section of the ester molecule; in each of these, the anchimeric intermediate contains a five-membered ring. We have already considered the stereochemical evidence that the conversion of *trans*-2-acetoxycyclohexyl brosylate (XIII) to *trans*-diacetoxycyclohexane proceeds through the symmetric intermediate *acetoxonium ion*, XV (p. 271), and similar evidence points to the same intermediate in the reaction of *trans*-2-acetoxycyclohexyl bromide (XIV) with silver acetate.[11] As indicated, addition of small quantities of water to either reaction mixture diverts some of intermediate XV to the monoacetate of *cis*-1,2-cyclohexanediol (XVI), presumably through intermediate XVI.

The formation of XV from brosylate XIII or bromide XIV almost certainly involves direct displacement of the leaving group by the acetoxy lying *trans* to it, the neighboring group being in a position favorable for attack. In contrast, the

[10] Brewster, Hiron, Hughes, Ingold, and Rao, *Nature*, **166**, 178 (1950).
[11] Winstein and Buckles, *J. Am. Chem. Soc.*, **64**, 2780, 2787 (1942). See also Roberts, *et al.*, *ibid.*, **80**, 1247 (1958).

accounted for. At present, the most satisfactory explanation is that steric crowd-ing in the parent chlorohydrin is somewhat relieved as the epoxide is formed, for reduction of one of the bond angles about a carbon to 60° allows the other bond angles about that carbon to "open up" well beyond their "normal value" of 108°. There is thus less interference between groups bound to the same carbon in the epoxide than in the chlorohydrin, and the greatest relief of strain will presumably result from ring closure of the most crowded chlorohydrin.[15]

In intramolecular displacements, as in their intermolecular analogs, the entering nucleophile must approach the reaction center from one side while the leaving group departs from the other, resulting in an inversion of configuration. This means that at the instant before the closure of chloroalkoxide ion XIX, the oxygen atom must lie *trans* to the chlorine. Thus, *trans*-2-chlorocyclohexanol can be converted by base to cyclohexene oxide, but its *cis* isomer cannot.[16] Due to freedom of rotation about C—C single bonds in noncyclic molecules, both the *erythro* and *threo* diastereomers of an aliphatic 1,2-halohydrin may be converted to epoxides; but since both forms must, during reaction, adopt conformations in which the oxygen and halogen lie *trans* to each other, the conversions are stereo-specific. As shown below for the 3-bromo-2-butanols,[13(a)] the *erythro*-halohydrin yields a *trans*-oxide whereas a *threo*-halohydrin yields a *cis*-oxide:

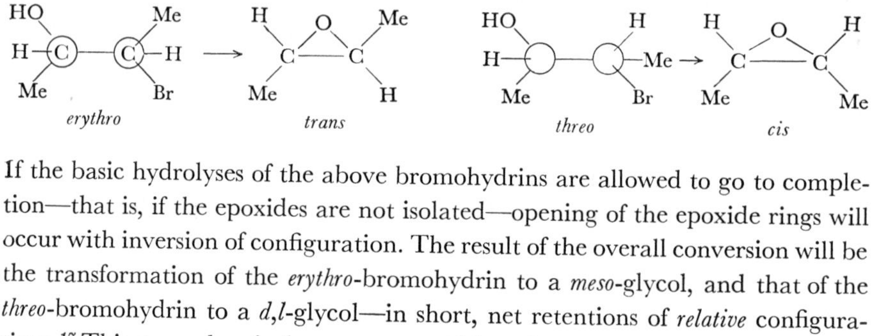

If the basic hydrolyses of the above bromohydrins are allowed to go to comple-tion—that is, if the epoxides are not isolated—opening of the epoxide rings will occur with inversion of configuration. The result of the overall conversion will be the transformation of the *erythro*-bromohydrin to a *meso*-glycol, and that of the *threo*-bromohydrin to a *d,l*-glycol—in short, net retentions of *relative* configura-tions.[17] This stereochemical outcome would have led us to suspect intervention of the epoxide, even if the latter were not isolable. As with the carboxylate group, protonation of the —O⁻ group to —OH greatly lowers its tendency to partici-

[15] In support of this explanation, apparently first suggested by Beesley, Ingold, and Thorpe (*J. Chem. Soc.*, **107**, 1080 (1915)), it has been found that the H—C—H angles in cyclopropane are 118°, rather than the "usual" 109° (see Donohue, Humphrey, and Schomaker, *J. Am. Chem. Soc.*, **67**, 332 (1945)).

[16] Bartlett, *J. Am. Chem. Soc.*, **57**, 224 (1935).

[17] The term "relative" is used here to distinguish the stereochemical result from retention of absolute configuration such as occurs, for example, in the hydrolysis of the salts of α-halo-carboxylic acids by dilute base. Although we may start with an optically active *threo*-bromo-hydrin, the resulting glycol must be racemic, for the intermediate *cis*-epoxide has a plane of symmetry. However, the configurations about the two asymmetric carbons in this glycol will be the same (both *D*- or both *L*-), in contrast to the *erythro*-bromohydrin and the *meso*-glycol derived from it, in which the two asymmetric carbon atoms in a molecule have opposite configurations.

pletely overshadowed by the strongly negative inductive effect of the —COOH group. It has been found that the "deaminations" of α-amino acids proceed with retention of configuration,[10] but in this case it is not clear whether participation

$$D\text{-RCH}\underset{\displaystyle \underset{|}{\text{OH}}}{\text{—COOH}} + N_2$$

$$D\text{-RCH}\underset{\displaystyle \underset{|}{\text{NH}_2}}{\text{—COOH}} \quad \xrightarrow{\text{HNO}_2} \quad$$

$$\xrightarrow{\text{NOCl}} \quad D\text{-RCHCl—COOH} + N_2$$

by the —COOH or the —COO⁻ group is involved, since the intermediate, D-RCH—COOH, is a strong acid.

$$\underset{\displaystyle \underset{+}{\text{N}\equiv\text{N}}}{|}$$

Whether or not an ester linkage functions as a neighboring group depends largely upon how it is situated with respect to the reaction center in the substrate. The solvolyses of $CH_3CHBrCOOEt$[5(a)] and the deamination of $CH_3CH(NH_2)$-$COOEt$[10] result in inversion of configuration about the α-carbon, suggesting that there is negligible participation by the —C—OEt group when the reaction

$$\underset{\displaystyle \underset{\|}{\text{O}}}{}$$

center lies *alpha* to the C=O bond of the ester. This is what we might expect, for such participation would require the formation of a strained three-membered ring

$$\left(\underset{\displaystyle \underset{\diagdown}{\text{C}}}{|}\underset{\displaystyle \underset{\diagup}{\text{O}}}{}\overset{+}{\text{C}}\text{—OR} \right)$$ without any compensating charge neutralization. On the

other hand, ester participation has been observed in a number of substitutions in which the reaction center is located in the alkyl, rather than the acyl, section of the ester molecule; in each of these, the anchimeric intermediate contains a five-membered ring. We have already considered the stereochemical evidence that the conversion of *trans*-2-acetoxycyclohexyl brosylate (XIII) to *trans*-diacetoxycyclohexane proceeds through the symmetric intermediate *acetoxonium ion*, XV (p. 271), and similar evidence points to the same intermediate in the reaction of *trans*-2-acetoxycyclohexyl bromide (XIV) with silver acetate.[11] As indicated, addition of small quantities of water to either reaction mixture diverts some of intermediate XV to the monoacetate of *cis*-1,2-cyclohexanediol (XVI), presumably through intermediate XVI.

The formation of XV from brosylate XIII or bromide XIV almost certainly involves direct displacement of the leaving group by the acetoxy lying *trans* to it, the neighboring group being in a position favorable for attack. In contrast, the

[10] Brewster, Hiron, Hughes, Ingold, and Rao, *Nature*, **166**, 178 (1950).
[11] Winstein and Buckles, *J. Am. Chem. Soc.*, **64**, 2780, 2787 (1942). See also Roberts, *et al.*, *ibid.*, **80**, 1247 (1958).

solvolyses of the *cis* isomers of XIII and XIV are governed by the rate at which these substrates lose brosylate or bromide ion, such ionizations being, in these cases, anchimerically unassisted. Hence, it should not surprise us that XIII and XIV are solvolyzed several hundred times more rapidly than their respective *cis* isomers under the same conditions.

There is evidence that the acetoxonium ion XV is also an intermediate in the conversion of the *cis*-monoacetate XVII to *trans*-2-acetoxycyclohexyl chloride (XVIII) with concentrated HCl, a reaction for which the following path has been proposed:[12]

The difficulty in carrying out a similar conversion with the *trans* isomer of XVII (which cannot form intermediates XVI and XV) and the difficulty in converting cyclohexanediols to chlorohydrins in the absence of acetic acid tend to support this mechanism.

The negative oxygen in alkoxides is one of the most familiar neighboring groups, its participation leading to alkene oxides, many of which are readily isolable. The basic hydrolysis of ethylene chlorohydrin, $HOCH_2-CH_2Cl$, yields ethylene oxide, and the hydrolyses of more complex, 1,2-chlorohydrins

[12] Boschan and Winstein, *J. Am. Chem. Soc.*, **78**, 4921 (1956).

often yield substituted ethylene oxides. These ring closures exhibit second-order rate laws:[13]

$$-\overset{|}{\underset{OH}{C}}-\overset{|}{\underset{Cl}{C}}- + OH^- \rightarrow -\overset{\diagdown}{C}\underset{O}{\diagup}\overset{\diagup}{C}- + Cl^- + H_2O$$

$$\text{rate} = k\left(-\overset{|}{\underset{OH}{C}}-\overset{|}{\underset{Cl}{C}}-\right)(OH^-) \quad (1)$$

which point to the following mechanism:

$$-\overset{|}{\underset{OH}{C}}-\overset{\overset{Cl}{|}}{\underset{|}{C}}- \underset{\text{fast, eq}}{\overset{OH^-}{\rightleftharpoons}} -\overset{|}{\underset{:O:^-}{C}}-\overset{\overset{Cl}{|}}{\underset{|}{C}}- \overset{\text{slow}}{\longrightarrow} \overset{\diagdown}{\underset{O}{C}}\overset{\diagup}{\underset{}{C}} + Cl^-$$

$$\text{XIX}$$

Intramolecular displacements forming epoxides should occur more readily than those forming α-lactones, for alkoxide oxygens are far more basic than carboxylate oxygens, and the epoxide ring is somewhat less strained.[14] Moreover, it has been found that intramolecular displacements leading to epoxides are, as a group, thousands of times faster (under comparable conditions) than their intermolecular counterparts, the attack of alkoxides on alkyl chlorides.[13(b,c)] Although the formation of an epoxide is (because of ring strain) somewhat less favored energetically than the formation of a noncyclic ether, far less restriction of motion is necessary in closing a small ring than in bringing together two free molecules into a single activated complex. The ease of formation of epoxides is then an entropy effect, and the same effect facilitates the formation of three-membered rings containing nitrogen or sulfur (for example, cations I and IV).

Somewhat surprisingly, epoxide formation is markedly facilitated by alkyl substitution, as shown by the following comparison of rate constants (water 18°):[13(c)]

	HOCH$_2$CH$_2$Cl	HOCHMeCH$_2$Cl	HOCMe$_2$CH$_2$Cl	HOCMe$_2$CMe$_2$Cl
$\dfrac{k}{k_{HOCH_2CH_2Cl}}$	1.0	21	250	1370

This trend is contrary to what would be expected from consideration of intermolecular substitution, and there is some question as to how it may best be

[13] (a) Winstein and Lucas, *J. Am. Chem. Soc.*, **61**, 1576 (1939). (b) Warner, *et al.*, *ibid.*, **70**, 2449, 4030 (1948). (c) Nilsson and Smith, *Z. physik. Chem.* **166A**, 136 (1933).

[14] The incorporation of a carbonyl carbon into an α-lactone ring requires squeezing of the bond angle at this carbon from 120° to about 60°. Incorporation of an alkoxide carbon into an epoxide ring requires a decrease in bond angle from 108° to about 60°.

accounted for. At present, the most satisfactory explanation is that steric crowding in the parent chlorohydrin is somewhat relieved as the epoxide is formed, for reduction of one of the bond angles about a carbon to 60° allows the other bond angles about that carbon to "open up" well beyond their "normal value" of 108°. There is thus less interference between groups bound to the same carbon in the epoxide than in the chlorohydrin, and the greatest relief of strain will presumably result from ring closure of the most crowded chlorohydrin.[15]

In intramolecular displacements, as in their intermolecular analogs, the entering nucleophile must approach the reaction center from one side while the leaving group departs from the other, resulting in an inversion of configuration. This means that at the instant before the closure of chloroalkoxide ion **XIX**, the oxygen atom must lie *trans* to the chlorine. Thus, *trans*-2-chlorocyclohexanol can be converted by base to cyclohexene oxide, but its *cis* isomer cannot.[16] Due to freedom of rotation about C—C single bonds in noncyclic molecules, both the *erythro* and *threo* diastereomers of an aliphatic 1,2-halohydrin may be converted to epoxides; but since both forms must, during reaction, adopt conformations in which the oxygen and halogen lie *trans* to each other, the conversions are stereospecific. As shown below for the 3-bromo-2-butanols,[13(a)] the *erythro*-halohydrin yields a *trans*-oxide whereas a *threo*-halohydrin yields a *cis*-oxide:

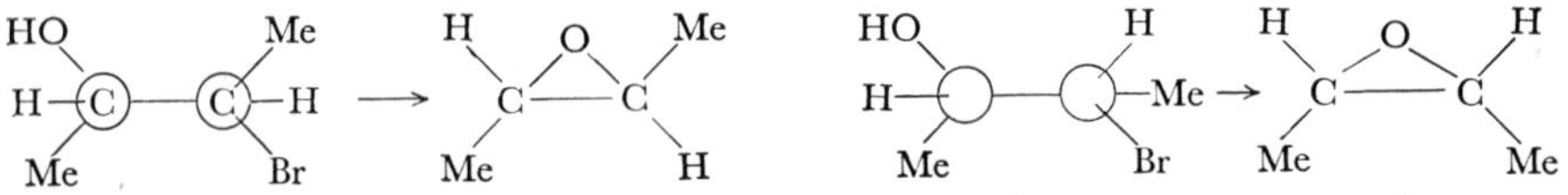

If the basic hydrolyses of the above bromohydrins are allowed to go to completion—that is, if the epoxides are not isolated—opening of the epoxide rings will occur with inversion of configuration. The result of the overall conversion will be the transformation of the *erythro*-bromohydrin to a *meso*-glycol, and that of the *threo*-bromohydrin to a *d,l*-glycol—in short, net retentions of *relative* configurations.[17] This stereochemical outcome would have led us to suspect intervention of the epoxide, even if the latter were not isolable. As with the carboxylate group, protonation of the —O⁻ group to —OH greatly lowers its tendency to partici-

---

[15] In support of this explanation, apparently first suggested by Beesley, Ingold, and Thorpe (*J. Chem. Soc.*, **107**, 1080 (1915)), it has been found that the H—C—H angles in cyclopropane are 118°, rather than the "usual" 109° (see Donohue, Humphrey, and Schomaker, *J. Am. Chem. Soc.*, **67**, 332 (1945)).

[16] Bartlett, *J. Am. Chem. Soc.*, **57**, 224 (1935).

[17] The term "relative" is used here to distinguish the stereochemical result from retention of absolute configuration such as occurs, for example, in the hydrolysis of the salts of α-halocarboxylic acids by dilute base. Although we may start with an optically active *threo*-bromohydrin, the resulting glycol must be racemic, for the intermediate *cis*-epoxide has a plane of symmetry. However, the configurations about the two asymmetric carbons in this glycol will be the same (both *D*- or both *L*-), in contrast to the *erythro*-bromohydrin and the *meso*-glycol derived from it, in which the two asymmetric carbon atoms in a molecule have opposite configurations.

pate. One of the very few unequivocal examples of hydroxyl participation is the ring closure of tetramethylene chlorohydrin in water to yield tetrahydrofuran (XX):[18]

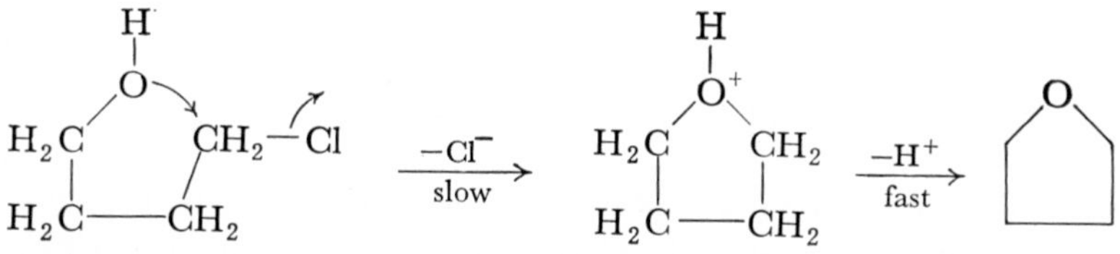

On the other hand, the hydrolyses of ethylene chlorohydrin, ethylene iodohydrin, and trimethylene chlorohydrin in the absence of base are much slower than the hydrolyses of the corresponding nonhydroxylated halides, there being no evidence for the intervention of an alkene oxide in these cases.

Alkoxy groups are only slightly more effective participators than the hydroxy group. Because of the $-I$ effect of $-OR$ groups, 2-alkoxyethyl halides undergo solvolysis much more slowly than ethyl halides[19(a)] and anchimeric assistance, if rendered at all, is not detectable. However, incorporation of a δ-methoxy group in n-butyl brosylate boosts its rate of destruction in acetic acid almost one thousandfold, whereas incorporation of an ε-methoxy group in n-amyl brosylate increases its rate of acetolysis by a factor of well over a hundred.[19(b)] In these cases, anchimeric assistance involves formation of five- and six-membered rings:

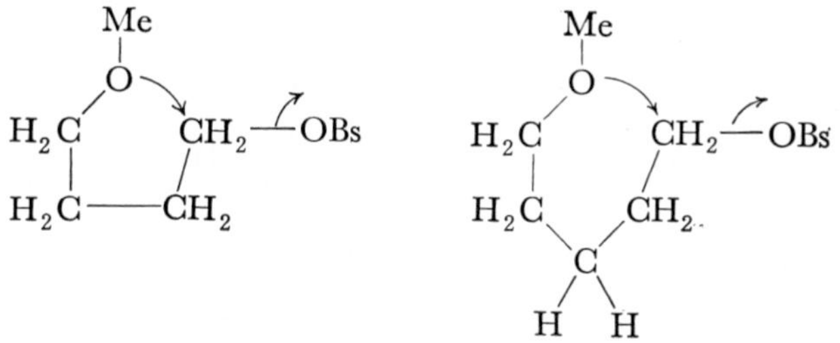

The stereochemistry of the acetolysis of β-bromoethers XXI and XXII in the presence of AgOAc suggests methoxide participation. Here, once again,

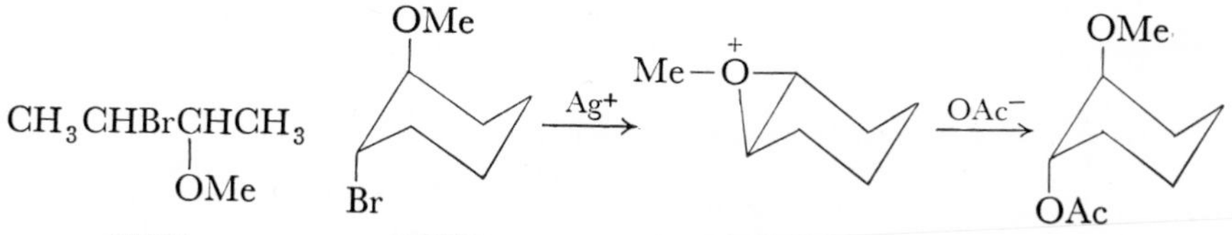

[18] Heine, Miller, Barton, and Greiner, J. Am. Chem. Soc., **75**, 4779 (1953).
[19] (a) Klemperer, McCabe, and Sindler, J. Am. Chem. Soc., **75**, 4779 (1953). (b) Winstein, Allred, Heck, and Glick, Tetrahedron, **3**, 1 (1958). (c) Winstein and Henderson, J. Am. Chem. Soc., **65**, 2196 (1943).

nucleophilic substitution results in retention of relative configuration about the reaction center.[19(c)] The anchimeric intermediate, as shown below for the acetolysis of *trans*-2-methoxycyclohexyl bromide (**XXII**) is a bridged methoxonium ion (**XXIII**).

Neighboring Nitrogen, Sulfur, and Halogen

Without considering the possibility of neighboring-group interaction, we might expect such halogenated amines as $Br(CH_2)_4NH_2$ and $Cl(CH_2)_2NMe_2$ to behave in substitution reactions in much the same way as do ordinary alkyl halides. Specifically, we might predict that these amines be hydrolyzed in aqueous base at about the same rates as are simple primary halides (for the inductive effects of the $-NH_2$ and $-NMe_2$ groups are slight), and that these hydrolyses be first order in hydroxide. It is found, however, that treatment of these amines with aqueous base releases halide ion thousands of times as rapidly as the hydrolyses of nonaminated alkyl chlorides, and that the formation of halide is zero order in (OH^-).[20,21] Yet, in spite of their kinetic character, these reactions are not ordinary S_N1 solvolyses, for they are not accelerated by the addition of Ag^+; moreover, there is no obvious reason why the presence of a nitrogen atom in the substrate should greatly facilitate the usual type of solvolytic ionization. Instead, the rapid release of halide ion in these cases is due to internal attack by the nitrogen atom at the halogenated carbon, forming a cyclic ammonium ion (such as **XXIV** or **XXV**). As indicated, the five-membered ring ammonium

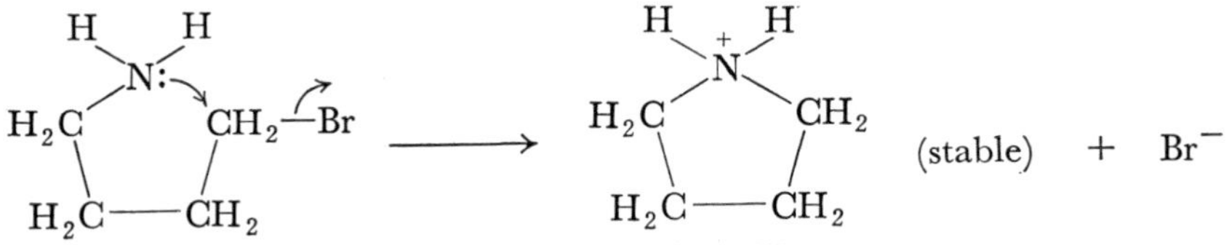

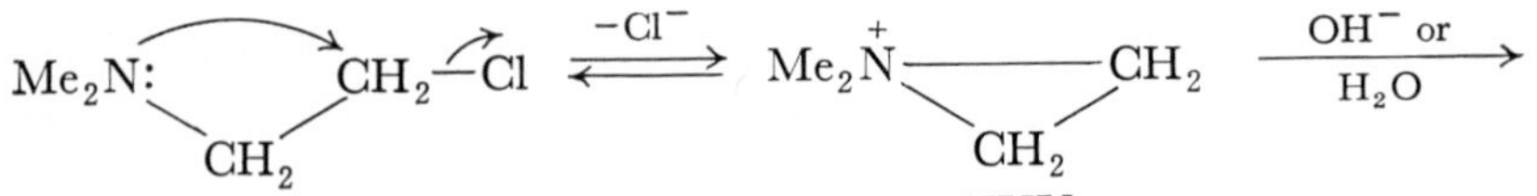

[20] For studies of the reactions of bromoalkylamines, see: (a) Freundlich, *et al.*, *Z. physik. Chem.*, **76**, 79 (1911); **79**, 681 (1912); **87**, 69 (1914); **101**, 177 (1922); **122**, 39 (1926); **166**, 161 (1933). (b) Salomon, *Helv. Chim. Acta.*, **16**, 1361 (1933); **17**, 851 (1934); **19**, 743 (1936).

[21] The substitution reactions of 2-dialkylaminoalkyl chlorides (the so-called "nitrogen mustards") have been investigated by a number of workers. See: (a) Bartlett, *et al.*, *J. Am. Chem. Soc.*, **69**, 2971, 2977 (1947); **71**, 1415 (1949); (b) Cohen, *et al.*, *ibid.*, **70**, 281 (1948); **74**, 1875, 1787 (1952); (c) Golumbic, *et al.*, *J. Org. Chem.*, **11**, 518, 536, 550 (1946); (d) Thompson, *et al.*, *Can. J. Research*, **26B**, 181, 193 (1948).

ion (the pyrrolidinium ion, **XXIV**) is stable. *Ethyleneimonium ions* (such as **XXV**) are, as a class, somewhat more reactive than ethylene oxides, although salts containing such ions can, with care, be isolated.

As might be expected, the rate at which the various cyclic ammonium ions are formed depends markedly on the number of atoms in the ring. Rings of five and six members are readily formed, not only because they are stable, but also because collision of a nitrogen on one end of a molecule with a halogenated carbon atom four or five atoms removed is a fairly frequent occurrence (thus the formations of such rings have high entropies of activation). On the other hand, since the bond angles in a four-membered ring lie near 90°, the formation of this ring will involve considerable strain (that is, a high energy of activation) and will therefore be slow. Formation of rings having seven or more members will likewise be slow, not because they are unstable, but rather because collisions between two groups separated by six or more atoms in a chain are rare. Finally, despite the instability of three-membered rings, ethyleneimonium ions, like ethylene oxides, will form with ease since the neighboring group engaged in the attack lies so conveniently close to the reaction center. Like ethylene oxides, ethyleneimonium ions are of particular interest, for they are formed readily and react readily, thus furnishing easy paths for reactions that would otherwise proceed much more slowly. Intervention of ethyleneimonium ion intermediates accounts not only for the great ease with which 2-haloalkylamines are hydrolyzed, but also for the readiness with which they react with a host of nucleophiles, among them amines, carboxylate ions, and such inorganic anions as $S_2O_3^{2-}$ and SO_4^{2-}.[22] These imonium ions undoubtedly also intercede in rearrangements, not only of such aliphatic haloalkylamines as **III** (p. 562), but also of such heterocyclic amines as N-ethyl-2-chloromethylpyrrolidine (**XXVI**):[23]

What has been said about neighboring-group participation by nitrogen may be applied, with but slight modification, to sulfur. The hydrolyses of β- and δ-chlorosulfides are thousands of times as rapid as those of the corresponding chloroethers and, when carried out in the presence of base, are zero order in

[22] Ross, *J. Chem. Soc.*, **1949**, 2589.
[23] Fuson and Zirkle, *J. Am. Chem. Soc.*, **70**, 2760 (1948).

base.[2,24] These reactions doubtless proceed through cyclic sulfonium ions of the type XXVII and XXVIII, analogous to the cyclic ammonium ions XXIV and XXV:

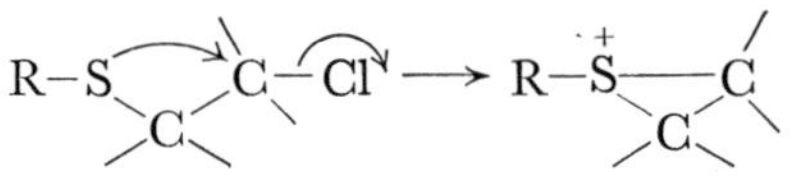

XXVII 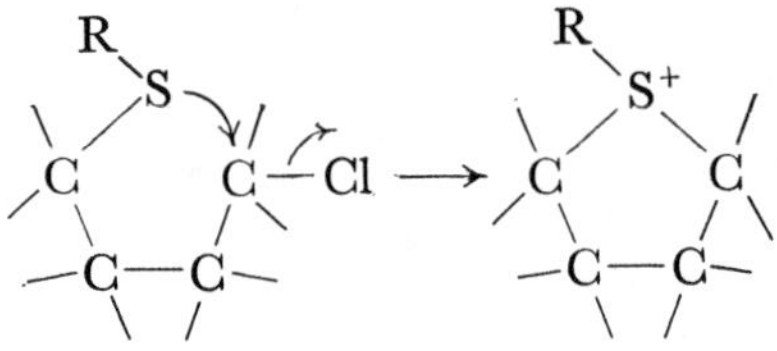   XXVIII

The most familiar (and the most extensively studied) chloroalkyl sulfide is "mustard gas" (β,β'-dichlorodiethyl sulfide), the hydrolysis of which involves the formation of the *ethylenesulfonium ion*, XXIX, followed by the much faster destruction of this ion by water. As befits a reaction sequence of this type, the first-order rate constant for the hydrolysis will "drift downward" as the reaction proceeds, due to the reversal of the cyclization when intermediate XXIX is attacked by Cl⁻ accumulating in solution (the *mass law effect*, see p. 256). Moreover, if the reaction is carried out in the presence of an additional nucleophile, even one as weakly nucleophilic as formate or chloroacetate, much of intermediate XXIX may be converted to a substitution product (for example, formate XXXI) rather than to the hydrolysis product, XXX:

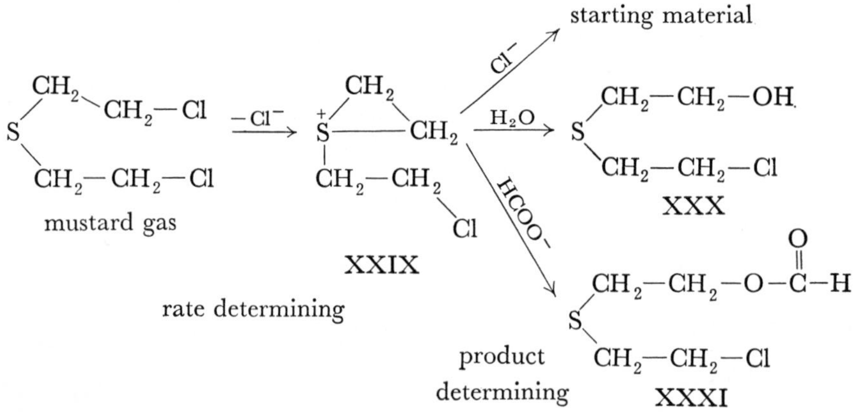

The fact that such relatively weak nucleophiles as chloride and formate may, even at low concentration, compete with the solvent water for the cationic intermediate is further evidence that this intermediate is indeed a sulfonium

[24] For mechanistic studies of the reactions of chlorosulfides, see: (a) Bartlett and Swain, J. Am. Chem. Soc., 71, 1406 (1949); (b) Ogston, et al., Trans. Faraday Soc., 44, 45 (1948); (c) Bennett, et al., J. Chem. Soc., 1927, 1676; 1929, 2567; 1938, 813; (d) Goering and Howe, J. Am. Chem. Soc., 79, 6542 (1957).

ion, rather than the very much more reactive primary carbonium ion, $ClCH_2$-$CH_2SCH_2CH_2^+$. While the latter is not excluded by the kinetics, its lifetime would be extremely short, and all but a very small fraction of such ions would be converted to the hydrolysis product, **XXX** (by action of a solvent molecule from their solvent "cages") before colliding with a nucleophilic species present in small concentration in solution.

As we have noted, anchimeric assistance by negatively charged oxygen or by an ester linkage requires that the assisting group and the leaving group lie *trans* to each other. The fact that the *trans* forms of 2-chlorocyclohexyl phenyl sulfide (**XXXII**) and the corresponding cyclopentyl derivative are hydrolyzed 10^5 to 10^6 times as rapidly as their respective *cis* isomers indicates that *trans* orientation is required for β-sulfur participation also.[24(d)] But *trans* orientation,

XXXII

XXXIII

XXXIV

$$(Ar = -\underset{}{\bigcirc}-Me)$$

although necessary, is apparently not sufficient; for it has been found that the *trans*-chlorosulfide **XXXIII** is solvolyzed (in 85 percent aqueous ethanol) at very nearly the same (very low) rate as is its *cis* isomer, and that the *trans*-chlorosulfide **XXXIV** is solvolyzed similarly slowly.[25] The reader will recognize the ring systems in compounds **XXXIII** and **XXXIV** as those present in certain dichlorides that were considered in Chap 12. It will be recalled that the rigidity of the ring systems in these compounds prohibited the formation of the transition states necessary for *trans* elimination, thus leading to very low rates of bimolecular dehydrochlorination, even when hydrogen and chlorine atoms on adjacent carbons lay *trans* to each other. Since the same rigidity of structure in compounds **XXXIII** and **XXXIV** will prevent a coplanar arrangement of the four atoms involved in formation of the sulfonium bridge (the sulfur atom, the chlorine atom, and the α- and β-carbons), it is reasonable to infer that the stereochemical requirements for anchimeric assistance by β-sulfur (and probably for assistance by β-nitrogen and β-halogen also) are similar in nature to those for facile bimolecular elimination. Although more data are clearly needed, it may be tentatively assumed that effective anchimeric assistance requires a transition

[25] Cristol and Arganbright, *J. Am. Chem. Soc.*, **79**, 3441 (1957).

state in which the α- and β-carbons, the leaving group, and the "assisting atom" lie in or near a common plane.

Neighboring-group participation by a β-bromo or β-iodo group results in the formation of a cyclic (three-membered ring) *bromonium* or *iodonium* ion of the type discussed in connection with the addition of halogens to olefins (p. 523). Although such halogenonium ions are too reactive to be isolated, the stereochemistry of conversions of the diastereomeric 3-bromo-2-butanols to dibromo-butanes,[26] and that of the acetolyses of these dibromides in the presence of Ag+,[11] point to the intervention of bromonium ion **XXXV** in the *erythro-meso* series, and to the intervention of the *cis* isomer of **XXXV** in the *threo-d,l* series.

As shown, the conversion of the bromohydrin to the dibromide and the conversion of the latter to the acetoxy bromide (**XXXVI**) involve retention of relative configuration. Retention of configuration is also observed for the corresponding reactions in the *threo-d,l* series.

Since chloride is considerably less nucleophilic than bromide, the β-chloro group would be expected to be a less effective "participator" than the β-bromo group. Although some reactions appear to proceed through a chloronium-ion bridge (see, for example, p. 525), there is no evidence that a chloro group renders appreciable anchimeric assistance. On the other hand, participation by the very

[26] Winstein and Lucas, *J. Am. Chem. Soc.*, **61**, 2845 (1939).

nucleophilic iodine atom may greatly accelerate a reaction. It has been found, for example, that the acetolysis of *trans*-2-iodocyclohexyl brosylate (**XXXVII**) is almost 3 million times as rapid as that of its *cis* isomer, quite obviously because the reaction of the *trans* (but not that of the *cis*) compound may proceed through iodonium ion **XXXVIII**.[27] With the corresponding bromobrosylates the *trans*

isomer is likewise solvolyzed more rapidly than the *cis*, but here the effect $(k_{trans}/k_{cis} = 800)$ is much less striking.

Aryl Participation. The Phenonium Ion

The neighboring groups considered thus far are nucleophilic in the classical sense, for each has unpaired electrons available for coordination or displacement. As we have emphasized on several occasions, the aromatic ring also has nucleophilic character, and we might therefore expect that, under favorable conditions, neighboring-group participation by aryl groups might be observed. Strong evidence for phenyl participation arises, for example, from the stereochemistry of the acetolyses of the stereoisomers of 3-phenyl-2-butyl tosylate, PhCHMe—CHMe—OTs.[28] Acetolysis of the *threo* tosylate (**XXXIX**) yields a *threo* acetate which is, however, racemic whether or not the original tosylate was optically active. On the other hand, acetolysis of the *erythro* tosylate (**XL**) proceeds with retention of configuration (both relative and absolute), the resulting *erythro* acetate having very nearly the same optical purity as the *erythro* tosylate. The stereochemical facts are consistent with the intervention of *phenonium-ion* intermediates **XLI** and **XLII** which may suffer attack either at C_α or C_β. Note that phenonium ion **XLI** has a plane of symmetry (if the plane of the six-membered ring is assumed to be perpendicular to that of the three-membered ring) and therefore may yield only racemic products, whereas ion **XLII** is asymmetric. Similar evidence points to phenonium-ion intermediates in the acetolysis of the tosylates and brosylates of PhCHMeCHEtOH and PhCHEtCHMeOH.[29] Here, however, the substituents at C_α in the intermediate

[27] (a) Winstein, Grunwald, and Ingraham, *J. Am. Chem. Soc.*, **70**, 821 (1948). (b) Grunwald, *ibid.*, **73**, 5458 (1951).

[28] Cram, *J. Am. Chem. Soc.*, **71**, 3863 (1949).

[29] Cram, *J. Am. Chem. Soc.*, **71**, 3875, 3883 (1949); **74**, 2159 (1952).

are not the same as those at C_β, and attack at C_β results in the formation of a rearranged acetate (for example, XLIV).

It may then be asked whether the third criterion for neighboring-group participation, the enhancement of reaction rate, is also applicable to cases involving benzonium-ion intervention. It is difficult to answer this for simple monophenylated substrates such as XXXIX, XL, and XLIII, since anchimeric assistance by a single phenyl is slight and is opposed by a rate-retarding inductive effect associated with the same phenyl.[30] However, it has been found that

[30] Using a modification of the Taft treatment (p. 227), Streitwieser estimates (Ref. 1(b), p. 718) that introduction of a 3-phenyl group in 2-butyl tosylate should lower the rate of acetolysis by a factor of about 8 (in the absence of participation). Since, however, tosylates XXXIX and XL are solvolyzed about half as rapidly as 2-butyl tosylate, we may assume a rate enhancement of a factor of 4 due to participation.

brosylate XLV undergoes acetolysis 36 times as rapidly as does brosylate XLVI, although the inductive and steric effects of the β-methyl and β-phenyl groups

$$(CH_3)_2CPh—CH—OBs$$
$$|$$
$$CH_3$$

XLV

$$CH_3CH_2—CH—OBs$$
$$|$$
$$CH_3$$

XLVI

could not account for the magnitude of this difference.[31] It is interesting that dialkylation of the β-carbon apparently facilitates the formation of the benzonium-ion bridge, just as it facilitates the formation of epoxy bridges (p. 567). Moreover, 3-p-anisyl-2-butyl brosylate (XLVII) suffers acetolysis, almost certainly through the "anisonium-ion" intermediate (XLVIII), almost 300 times as rapidly as tosylates XXXIX and XL; this suggests, as we might have anticipated, that the p-methoxy group on the benzene ring eases the formation of the phenonium bridge by helping to disperse the positive charge.[32] Finally, it has

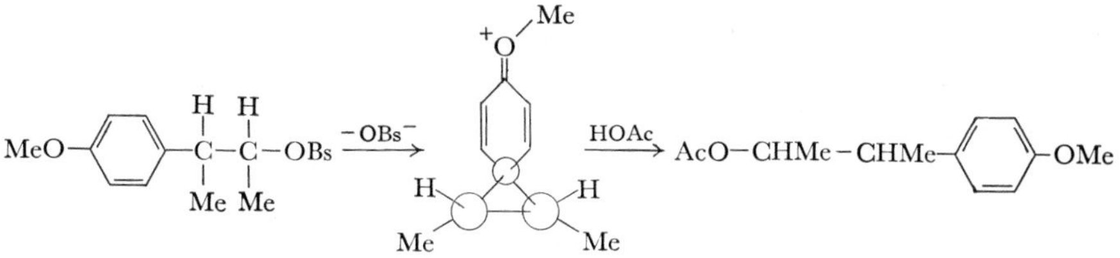

XLVII   XLVIII

been found that the cyclic tosylate L is solvolyzed in formic acid only one thousandth as rapidly as is its isomer, LI, for "formolysis" of the latter may proceed through the bridged cation, LII.[33]

[31] For studies of anchimeric assistance by aryl groups in the solvolyses of brosylates, see papers by Winstein and co-workers, J. Am. Chem. Soc., **74,** 1113, 1120, 1127, 1140, 1147, 1157 (1952).

[32] The fact that the methoxy group occupies the *para* position in the products as well as in the reactant excludes the bridged structure XLIX as an intermediate in the solvolysis of XLVII, for in XLIX a substituent lying *para* to C_β lies *meta* to C_α. Similarly the positions of

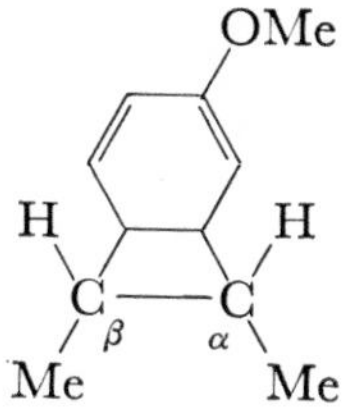

(XLIX)

ring substituents do not change in most other reactions involving migration of aryl groups; for these, intermediates or transition states analogous to XLIX may likewise be ruled out.

[33] Experiments by Huisgen, reported by Streitwieser, Ref. 1(b), p. 719.

L   LI   LII

It may *not* be assumed that phenonium-ion intermediates will invariably intervene in solvolyses of substrates having β-aryl groups. If the solvent is sufficiently nucleophilic, it will compete with the aryl group for a position at the rear of the α-carbon of the substrate. Instead of a phenonium-bridged ion, a solvated nonbridged ("classical") carbonium ion may form, or, quite possibly, solvolysis might occur by direct displacement. The net result, in either case, will be solvolysis with (partial or complete) inversion of configuration. Typically, ethanolysis of 1-phenyl-2-propyl tosylate (PhCH$_2$CHMe-OTos) proceeds with almost complete inversion,[34] ruling out appreciable phenyl participation. Acetolysis proceeds with 65 percent inversion, allowing (but not demanding) some degree of phenyl participation;[31] however, in the strongly ionizing but weakly nucleophilic solvent, formic acid, solvolysis results in 85 percent retention of configuration[31]—that is, reaction predominantly through a phenonium-ion intermediate.

Aryl participation also becomes less likely when a reaction may pass through a "classical" (nonbridged) carbonium ion having some stability, in particular when one or two aryl groups are bound to the α-carbon of the substrate. Thus, the acetolyses of the *threo* and *erythro* forms of tosylate LIII yield, in addition to the rearranged acetate LIV, a mixture of the *threo* and *erythro* forms of acetate LV.

(*threo*   Ph—CMe—CHPhOTos $\xrightarrow{\text{HOAc}}$ EtCMe—CHPh$_2$
or *erythro*) | |
                      Et   OAc

          LIII   LIV

                              + Ph—CMe—CHPhOAc
                                      |
                                      Et

                                      LV
                              (mixture of *threo* and
                                  erythro forms)

Moreover, the *erythro* to *threo* ratio in the acetate mixture derived from the *threo* tosylate indicates predominant inversion of relative configuration, whereas the

[34] Phillips, *J. Chem. Soc.*, **123**, 44 (1923).

corresponding ratio from the *erythro* tosylate indicates predominant retention.[35(a)] This suggests that some of the acts of substitution in these acetolyses proceed through a classical carbonium ion, whereas others proceed only through a phenonium-ion intermediate.

In special cases, participation by aryl groups lying three atoms removed from the reaction center (δ-aryl participation) may occur. It has recently been found that substitution of methoxy groups into 4-phenyl-1-butyl brosylate, $Ph(CH_2)_4OBs$, increases its ease of solvolysis. Incorporation of methoxy groups at the 2 and 4 positions of the benzene ring boosts the rate of formolysis by a factor of 10, whereas incorporation of methoxy groups at the 3 and 5 positions accelerates formolysis about sixfold. Somewhat smaller increases are observed for acetolysis rates.[36(a)] Since these methoxy groups are too far removed from the reaction center to exert appreciable inductive or steric effects, it may be inferred that they assist the solvolyses by facilitating aryl participation. The solvolysis of the 2,4-dimethoxy compound very probably proceeds through the tetramethylenephenonium ion, LVI, analogous to the ethylenephenonium ions that intervene in the course of β-aryl participation. It is considerably less likely, however, that the solvolysis of the 3,5-dimethoxy compound involves the corresponding tetramethylenephenonium ion, LVII; for in this ion the methoxy groups lie

[35] (a) Cram and Allinger, *J. Am. Chem. Soc.*, **79**, 2858 (1957). (b) For evidence against a phenonium-ion intermediate in the acetolysis of Ph₂CHCHPhOAc, see Collins and Bonner, *ibid.*, **77**, 92, 99 (1955).

[36] (a) Heck and Winstein, *J. Am. Chem. Soc.*, **79**, 3105, 3114 (1957). (b) Baird and Winstein, *ibid.*, **79**, 756, 4238 (1957).

meta to the reaction center, and due to the "alternate" character of atoms comprising a conjugated system (p. 214), the methoxy groups in LVII cannot aid in the dispersal of positive charge as can the methoxy groups in LVI. It is instead more probable that the intermediate in the solvolysis of the 3,5-dimethoxy compound is cation LVIII, in which the methoxy groups lie *ortho* and *para* to the reaction center. Indeed, the major product from the latter solvolysis is 5,7-dimethoxytetralin (LIX), which may be formed merely by the removal of a proton from cation LVIII. As indicated, tetralin LIX is also obtained from the solvolysis of the 2,4-dimethoxybrosylate,[36(b)] very probably via rearrangement of intermediate LVI (this rearrangement being similar in nature to the dienone-phenol rearrangement, p. 639). Apparently, aryl participation is unusually sensitive to the size of the ring formed, for no significant increase in solvolysis rate results when methoxide groups are incorporated into the benzene rings of $Ph(CH_2)_3OBs$ or $Ph(CH_2)_5OBs$.[37]

Intimate and Solvent-separated Ion Pairs

Let us return momentarily to the reaction we called upon to introduce the phenonium-ion intermediate (p. 575), the acetolysis of the diastereomers of PhCHMeCHMeOTos. In particular, we may reconsider the acetolysis of an optically active *threo* form of this tosylate to the racemic *threo* acetate LXII, bearing in mind that in the poorly ionizing solvent, acetic acid, the proposed phenon-

$$threo\text{-MeCH}-\text{CHMe} \longrightarrow \text{MeCH}\cdots\text{CHMe} \longrightarrow threo\text{-MeCH}-\text{CHMe (racemic)}$$

(active)	LXI	LXII

[37] Since five-membered rings are, in many cases, formed more readily than six-membered rings of the same type, it may be asked why aryl participation leading to an intermediate analogous to LVIII does not assist the solvolysis of $3,5\text{-}(MeO)_2C_6H_3(CH_2)_3OBs$. The answer is probably that the transition state, LX, leading to such an intermediate is rather strained. Assuming that the five-membered ring in LVII is nearly planar, that the bond angles at C_1

LX

and C_5 are near 90°, and that the angle at C_4 is near 120°, the angles at both C_2 and C_3 would have to approach 120°, considerably larger than their "preferred" value of 109.5°. The six-membered ring in the transition state leading to cation LVIII would be puckered and, almost certainly, less strained.

These rearrangements (and many similar conversions) proceed most readily under conditions that, for an ordinary alkyl derivative, would favor substitution via a carbonium-ion intermediate. The reactions of neopentyl halides, for example, are catalyzed by such electrophilic species as Ag^+ and $HgCl_2$ and take place at rates similar to those at which the corresponding ethyl halides undergo S_N1 reactions under ionizing conditions.[43(b)] It is very likely then that these rearrangements proceed through the neopentyl ion, $Me_3CCH_2^+$; but since nonrearranged products are apparently *not* formed, it is equally likely that this carbonium ion rearranges to the *t*-amyl ion, $Me_2\overset{+}{C}CH_2Me$, very soon after the initial heterolysis.

$$Me_2C\!-\!CH_2X \xrightarrow[\text{slow}]{-X^-} Me_2C\!-\!CH_2^+ \xrightarrow{\text{fast}} Me_2\overset{+}{C}\!-\!CH_2Me \xrightarrow[\text{fast}]{Y:} Me_2C\!-\!CH_2Me$$
$$\underset{Me}{|} \qquad\qquad \underset{Me}{|} \qquad\qquad\qquad\qquad\qquad \underset{Y}{|}$$

For an instant (or perhaps for an appreciable period of time) during the reaction, the migrating group lies equidistant from the β-carbon (the migration source) and the α-carbon (the migration terminus). At this point, the system has assumed the configuration LXIX which brings to mind the phenonium-ion inter-

$$Me$$
$$Me_2C\overset{\diagup\ \ \diagdown}{\underline{\quad + \quad}}CH_2$$

LXIX

mediate through which many aryl shifts proceed. Yet there is an important difference; since the carbon of the migrating methyl group is bound to three hydrogen atoms, it cannot be fully bound (in the usual sense of the word) to both the α- and β-carbons simultaneously. In this respect, a bridged carbonium ion such as LXIX is even less "classical" than a phenonium-bridged ion. This does not mean that alkyl-bridged carbonium ions are automatically excluded as intermediates in alkyl shifts; indeed, stable compounds having alkyl bridges of this sort are known.[44] We would expect, however, that much less anchimeric

---

[44] Perhaps the most familiar compound having alkyl bridges is the dimer of trimethylaluminum, LXX (Snow and Rundle, *Acta Cryst.*, **4**, 348 (1951)). For a brief discussion of the

LXX

electron structures of this and related species (including those with hydrogen bridges), see Longuet-Higgins, *Quart. Revs.*, **XI**, 121 (1957).

assistance be rendered by neighboring alkyl groups (which are essentially non-nucleophilic) than by neighboring aryl groups under similar circumstances. Typically, neopentyl chloride is hydrolyzed (with rearrangement) somewhat more slowly than ethyl chloride (without rearrangement), whereas Ph_3CCH_2Cl is hydrolyzed (with rearrangement) over 10,000 times as rapidly.[45] We may assume the hydrolysis of the neopentyl halide to be virtually unassisted anchimerically, but hydrolysis of the triphenylethyl halide is quite obviously assisted.[46]

In very few cases is there substantial reason for supposing that an alkyl shift in a noncyclic system proceeds through an alkyl-bridged *intermediate* (as distinguished from an alkyl-bridged *activated complex*). The strongest evidence to date for a methyl-bridged intermediate arises from the deamination (with HNO_2 in acetic acid) of *threo*-3-phenyl-2-butylamine, PhCHMe—CHMeNH_2.

$$
\begin{array}{c}
\text{Me} \\
| \\
\text{PhCHMe—CH—N}_2^+ \\
\textit{threo}
\end{array}
\xrightarrow[\text{HOAc}]{-N_2}
\left\{
\begin{array}{l}
44\% \text{ PhCHMeCHMeOAc (57\% threo, 49\% erythro)} \\
\quad \text{(from simple substitution and phenyl shift)} \\
24\% \text{ PhCMeCH}_2\text{Me (from hydride shift)} \\
\qquad\qquad | \\
\qquad\qquad \text{OAc} \\
32\% \text{ PhCHCHMe}_2, \textit{ about } \frac{1}{6} \textit{ optically active} \\
\qquad | \qquad\qquad \text{(from methyl shift)} \\
\qquad \text{OAc}
\end{array}
\right.
$$

LXXIII

Here we are concerned with the methyl shift that, as indicated, competes favorably with the phenyl shift, and which is stereospecific in the direction of *inversion of configuration* about C_β. If the methyl shift were to proceed wholly through the "open" carbonium ion LXXVI, the resulting acetate LXXIII should be racemic, whereas if none of the acts of methyl rearrangement were to proceed through ion LXXVI, complete inversion of configuration at C_β would be expected. The observed partial inversion of configuration then suggests the intervention of the methyl-bridged carbonium ion LXXV, which may be attacked at C_α to give unrearranged product, or attacked at C_β to give rearranged product

---

[45] Charlton, Dostrovsky, and Hughes, *Nature*, **167**, 986 (1951).

[46] The solvolyses, with rearrangement, of such very crowded substrates as LXXI and LXXII are also unusually rapid (Bartlett, *et al.*, *J. Am. Chem. Soc.*, **77**, 2801, 2804, 2806 (1955)). The high rates in such cases are frequently attributed to *steric acceleration* (release of steric strain

$$
\begin{array}{c}
\text{CHMe}_2 \\
| \\
\text{Me}_3\text{C—C—Cl} \qquad \text{(LXXI)} \\
| \\
\text{CHMe}_2
\end{array}
\qquad\qquad
(\text{Me}_3\text{C—})_3\text{C—O—}\overset{\displaystyle O}{\overset{\|}{\text{C}}}\text{—}\!\!\diamond\!\!\text{—NO}_2 \quad \text{(LXXII)}
$$

when the reactant is converted to the transition state) rather than to anchimeric assistance. There is, at present, no way of distinguishing between these two "effects" for reactions in which alkyl groups migrate.

(with inversion), or may open to "classical" ion LXXVI, resulting in rearrangement with racemization:[47]

$$
\underset{\underset{\text{Me Me}}{|}}{\overset{\overset{\beta \quad \alpha}{}}{\text{PhCH-CH-N}_2^+}} \xrightarrow{-N_2} \underset{\underset{\text{Me}}{|}}{\overset{+}{\text{PhCH-CHMe}}} \rightarrow \underset{\underset{\text{Me}}{\overset{+}{\text{LXXV}}}}{\overset{\overset{\beta \quad \alpha}{}}{\text{PhCH ---- CHMe}}}
$$

LXXIV   LXXV

$$\xrightarrow[\text{(at } C\alpha)]{\text{HOAc}} \text{PhCHMe-CHMe-OAc}$$

$$\xrightarrow[\text{(at } C_\beta)]{\text{HOAc}} \text{Ph-CH(OAc)-CHMe}_2 \quad \text{(active)}$$

$$\searrow \underset{\underset{\text{LXXVI}}{+}}{\text{PhCHCHMe}_2} \rightarrow \underset{\text{OAc}}{\underset{|}{\text{PhCHCHMe}_2}}$$

(racemic)

It may be noted in passing that there are marked differences between the acetolysis of the diazonium ion, PhCHMeCHMeN_2^+ (just described) and that of the corresponding tosylate, PhCHMeCHMeOTos (p. 575). When the leaving group is N_2, then a phenyl, a methyl, or a hydrogen may migrate; whereas with $OTos^-$ (or OBs^-) as the leaving group, only phenyl shifts. Moreover, solvolysis of the diazonium ion is considerably less stereospecific than that of the tosylate; acetolysis of the *threo* tosylate gives only *threo* acetate, but acetolysis of the *threo* diazonium ion gives (in addition to products derived from methyl and hydrogen shifts) a mixture of *threo* and *erythro* acetates.[47] All this suggests that $OTos^-$ must be "pushed" from the α position of the tosylate by the β-phenyl group but, because of the unusual stability of the nitrogen molecule, N_2 may depart from the diazonium ion without the benefit of anchimeric assistance, leaving behind a classical carbonium ion.[48] In the latter case, the group that migrates is very probably that closest to the empty p orbital of the α-carbon in the carbonium ion. The fate of a given carbonium ion will then depend upon its conformation the instant before migration; that is, adoptions of conformations LXXVIII, LXXIX, and LXXX by the unrearranged carbonium ion will

[47] Cram and McCarty, *J. Am. Chem. Soc.*, **79**, 3866 (1957). As these authors suggest, the stereospecificity of the methyl migration may be explained without invoking a methyl-bridged intermediate if it is assumed that the open carbonium LXXVI exists predominantly in conformation LXXVII and is attacked preferentially by HOAc in the direction indicated below by the dotted arrow (where crowding is minimal).

LXXVII

[48] For somewhat different views, see: Streitwieser and Schaeffer, *J. Am. Chem. Soc.*, **79**, 2888 (1957); and Bonner and Tanner, *ibid.*, **80**, 1447 (1958).

result, respectively, in phenyl, hydrogen, or methyl migration. It should also be

LXXVIII   LXXIX   LXXX

borne in mind that the bridged ions resulting from acetolyses of tosylates and brosylates are present in ion pairs, whereas the carbonium ions formed in deamination reactions are more nearly free, and therefore considerably more reactive.

When an ethyl or *n*-propyl group is substituted for one of the β-hydrogens of an alkyl halide or alkyl arenesulfonate, solvolysis rates suffer only minor changes, for anchimeric assistance by β-alkyl groups is negligible. If, however, the ethyl or propyl group is "tied back" onto the β-carbon, forming a *cyclopropyl* or *cyclobutyl* ring (which does not include the α-carbon), the specific rates for solvolysis (under ionizing conditions) rise markedly and may exceed those for noncyclic substrates by factors of several hundred or more.[49] Here it is probable that solvolysis is being facilitated by a combination of field and anchimeric effects. It is thought (although agreement is not complete on this point) that the field effect associated with the cyclopropyl group arises because the regions of maximum electron density lie well outside the ring instead of on the straight lines connecting the carbon nuclei. For maximum bonding interaction (that is, maximum overlap), the bonding orbitals of each carbon atom should be directed toward the attached atoms, necessitating that one of the angles between orbitals in cyclopropane (for each carbon) be 60°. However, quantum mechanics stipulates that the orbitals about any first-row element may not form an angle of less than 90°, and that, in particular, when a carbon atom forms four bonds, angles approaching 109° are favored. Now, substantial overlap may still occur when the angle between orbitals is 109°, but it has been calculated that the best compromise (energetically speaking) involves an interorbital angle of 104°[50]

[49] (a) Typically, benzenesulfonate LXXXI suffers ethanolysis over 500 times as rapidly as does ethyl benzenesulfonate (Bergstrom and Siegel, *J. Am. Chem. Soc.*, **74**, 145, 254 (1952));

LXXXI   LXXXII

(*b*) Brosylate LXXXII undergoes acetolysis over 500 times as rapidly as does isopropyl brosylate (Winstein and Marshall, *ibid.*, **74**, 1120 (1952)).
[50] Coulsen and Moffitt, *Phil. Mag.*, **40**, 1 (1949).

(although there is, at present, no direct way to verify this value experimentally). This, in effect, means that the bonds between carbons in cyclopropane are "bent," somewhat like bananas, as shown in Figure 14-1, and that three regions of high electron density lie outside the triangle of carbon nuclei. (The bonds between carbons in cyclobutane are thought to be bent also, but to a lesser degree.) When a cyclopropylcarbinyl derivative, in which —X is the leaving group, adopts the conformation shown, one of the electron-rich regions outside the ring approaches C_α from the side opposite —X, facilitating the departure of the latter.

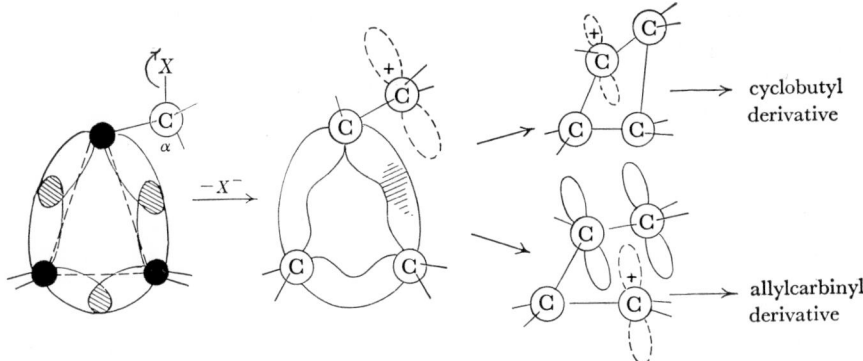

cyclobutyl derivative

allylcarbinyl derivative

Fig. 14-1. Formation and Rearrangement of a Cyclopropylcarbinyl Cation

As evidence for neighboring-group participation by the cyclopropyl ring, we may note the extensive rearrangement that occurs when cyclopropylcarbinyl derivatives are solvolyzed in weakly nucleophilic solvents. A cyclopropylcarbinyl cation in the conformation shown may rearrange to a cyclobutyl or allylcarbinyl cation merely by redistribution of the electrons comprising the "banana bond" nearest the positively charged carbon. Thus, it has been found that hydrolysis of cyclopropylcarbinyl benzenesulfonate (LXXXI) or of the corresponding chloride, or deamination of aminomethylcyclopropane LXXXIII (with HNO_2) yields mixtures of cyclopropylcarbinol, cyclobutanol, and allylcarbinol, (CH_2=$CHCH_2CH_2OH$).[51] Moreover, if the hydrolysis of the benzenesulfonate or chloride is halted in its early stages, rearranged benzenesulfonate or chloride is found in the mixture, suggesting ionization, rearrangement, and internal return. Rearrangement during solvolysis of the chloride is much less extensive in the more poorly ionizing solvent, ethanol.[49]

If conversion of a cyclopropylcarbinyl to a cyclobutyl derivative proceeds by the path suggested in Figure 14-1, the carbon atom (designated C_α) originally bearing the leaving group —X should become a β-carbon in the cyclobutyl compound. It has, however, been shown that if the aminomethylcyclopropane is

[51] Roberts and Mazur, *J. Am. Chem. Soc.*, **73**, 2509, 3542 (1952).

labeled at C_α with C^{14} (LXXXIII), very nearly one third of the labeled carbon in the resulting cyclobutanol lies in the γ position, virtually none in the α position, and two thirds in the β position.[51] This points to the intervention of an intermediate in which the two carbons which ultimately become β-carbons, and the single carbon which ultimately becomes a γ-carbon, in cyclobutanol are geometrically equivalent. No classical structure fulfilling this requirement comes readily to mind, but Roberts has proposed carbonium ion LXXXIV, which is very "nonclassical" indeed. Such an intermediate could conceivably be formed if the —CH_2^+ group of the cyclopropylcarbinyl cation moved back of the cyclopropane ring and became attracted to the electron-rich portion of the "banana bond" directly opposite it. Under such an electrostatic stress, the two electrons comprising this relatively weak bond could be redistributed in the regions between the three methylene groups, resulting in partial bonding (as represented in LXXXIV by the broken lines).[52] Conversion of this very strained intermediate to the cyclobutyl cation requires breakage of one of the "full" bonds (a, b, or c) and one of the "one-third" bonds (a', b', or c'). Disregarding isotope effects, the three modes of conversion are equally probable. In examining the

second major product from this deamination, cyclopropylcarbinol, it is found that much of the labeled carbon has entered the cyclopropane ring. If *all* of this product had been formed through intermediate LXXXIV, the ratio of labeled carbon in the side chain to that in the ring should be $\frac{1}{2}$, since there are *two* methylene groups in the ring. Since this ratio is found instead to be 0.83, we may assume that although some of the cyclopropylcarbinol forms through LXXXIV, some also forms from the classical cyclopropylcarbinyl cation without intervention of LXXXIV.

[52] Proposed intermediate LXXXIV is somewhat analogous to alkyl-bridged carbonium ions that have been suggested as intermediates in some reactions involving alkyl migrations (for example, cation LXXV). Both types are electron deficient; but in an alkyl-bridged cation, two electrons form two partial bonds, whereas in LXXXIV, two electrons (those comprising the original "banana bond") form three partial bonds. The bonds represented by broken lines in LXXXIV thus have a bond order of one third.

Anchimeric assistance to ionization by saturated rings of five or more members has not been shown to be significant for simple systems. However, *after* ionization has occurred, a ring carbon may migrate from a β to an α position, resulting in an expansion of the ring (if the positive charge lies outside the ring) or a contraction (if the positive charge lies on the ring). Two typical 1,2 shifts involving monocyclic systems are shown:

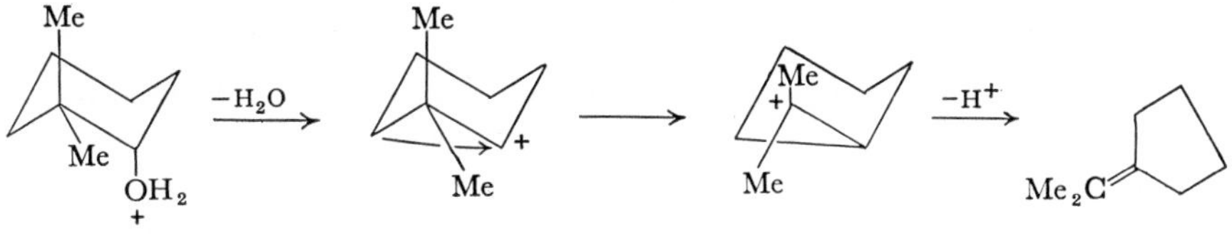

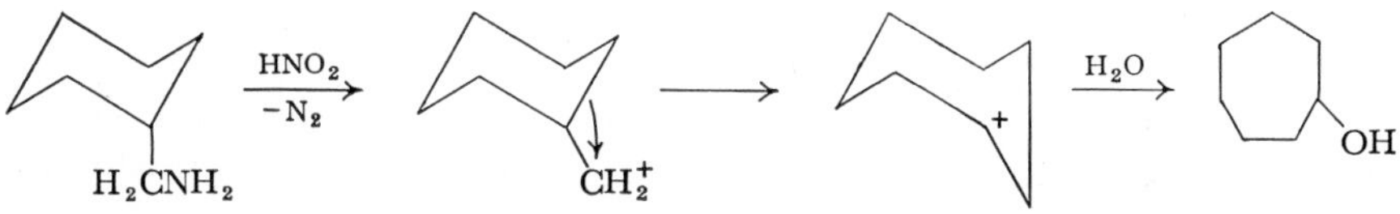

However, the most interesting examples of 1,2 rearrangements involving ring carbons occur in the chemistry of polycyclic systems. A number of these are discussed in a subsequent section.

Neighboring Hydrogen

Although hydride shifts in reactions involving carbonium-ion intermediates are well known, we should expect a β-hydrogen, like a β-alkyl group, to be quite ineffective in rendering anchimeric assistance toward ionization at the α position. As with neighboring-group participation by other species, hydride migration generally becomes more important as branching at the β-carbon is increased. Thus, reactions of isobutyl (Me_2CHCH_2-) compounds under ionizing conditions often yield predominantly products derived from the *t*-butyl cation, $Me_3\overset{+}{C}CH_3$, but practically no hydrogen migration occurs in reactions proceeding through the ethyl cation, $CH_3CH_2^+$ (as may be demonstrated by examining the reactions of β-deuteroethyl compounds[54]). Nevertheless, the reactions of isobutyl compounds are not significantly faster than those of ethyl compounds, showing that in the isobutyl-to-*t*-butyl transformation the migrating hydrogen does not exert appreciable pushing action on the leaving group. This is probably because

[53] (a) Meerwein, *Ann.*, **405**, 129 (1914); **417**, 255 (1918). (b) Ruzicka and Brugger, *Helv. Chim. Acta*, **9**, 318 (1926).

[54] It has been found for example, that the decomposition of the deuterated diazonium ion, $CH_2DCH_2N_2^+$ in water yields ethanol containing less than 2 per cent CH_3CHDOH, the product that would be expected from a deuterium shift (Roberts and Yancey, *J. Am. Chem. Soc.*, **74**, 5943 (1952)).

the bond to the leaving group is completely or nearly broken *before* the hydrogen migration gets under way. The hydrogen-bridged carbonium ion LXXXV

$$\underset{\text{H}}{\overset{\text{H}}{\underset{|}{Me_2C}}}-CH_2N_2^+ \xrightarrow{-N_2} \underset{\text{H}}{\overset{\text{H}}{\underset{|}{Me_2C}}}-CH_2^+ \longrightarrow \left[\underset{\text{LXXXV}}{\overset{\text{H}}{Me_2C\text{---}CH_2}} \right]^+ \longrightarrow Me_2\overset{+}{C}-CH_3 \xrightarrow{H_2O}$$

t-BuOH (3)

(which may be either an activated complex or an unstable intermediate) is structurally similar to a π complex formed by protonation of an olefin. Such a complex was proposed as an intermediate in the acid-catalyzed addition of water to olefins to account for the observed dependence of rate on h_0 (p. 516). Yet it may be shown if olefin-hydration proceeds through a π complex, the hydrogen shift (sequence 3) does not. It will be recalled that the equilibrium between an olefin and its protonated π complex is rapidly established, whereas the conversion of the complex to a classical carbonium ion was presumed to be slow. Therefore, if LXXXV were a π complex, it should exchange protons rapidly with the solvent water. Now, when the decomposition of the diazonium ion is run in D_2O, the resulting alcohol is essentially free of carbon-bound deuterium, proving that the hydrogen that migrates does not become equilibrated with protons of the solvent.[55] We may thus infer that the "hydrogen bridge" and the "protonated π complex" are different species although the positions of the atoms are very nearly the same in both. It seems likely that the proton in a π complex lies near the "edges" of the π-electron clouds and distorts them only slightly (LXXXVI), whereas the proton in a hydrogen bridge is deeply imbedded in a single cloud of electric charge that occupies space above both carbon atoms (LXXXVII).

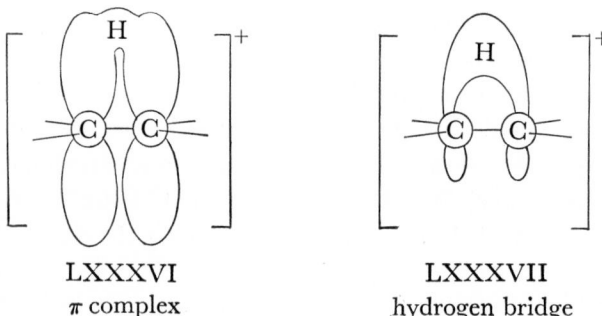

LXXXVI	LXXXVII
π complex	hydrogen bridge

To date the clearest evidence that participation by β-hydrogen may appreciably (although not spectacularly) affect reaction rates has been obtained from studies of cyclohexyl derivatives. Compare, for example, the *cis* and *trans* isomers of 2-methylcyclohexyl tosylate. For both, the bulky methyl group prefers

[55] Cannell and Taft, *J. Am. Chem. Soc.*, **78**, 5912 (1956).

to lie in an equatorial position, rather than a more crowded axial position (p. 241). As a result, the tosylate group assumes an axial position in the favored conformation of the *cis* isomer (LXXXVIII) and an equatorial position in the favored conformation of the *trans* isomer (LXXXIX). We should then expect the *cis* tosylate to undergo unimolecular solvolyses about two or three times as

LXXXVIII   LXXXIX.   XC   XCI

rapidly as the *trans* tosylate (Chap. 7, Ref. 54), since more crowding is relieved when an axial —OTs group departs. However, the acetolysis of the *cis* tosylate has been found to be over 70 times as fast as that of the *trans* tosylate.[56] It is likely then that the ionization of tosylate LXXXVIII is anchimerically assisted by the hydrogen at the 2 position, for this lies *trans* to the —OTs group and both substituents occupy axial positions in the favored conformation of the tosylate. In tosylate LXXXIX, the methyl lies *trans* to the —OTs group but does not significantly assist its departure; in the favored conformation of this tosylate, the bonds to the —Me and —OTs substituents are not coplanar with the bond linking C_1 and C_2, and the system may not, without considerable strain, assume the transition state necessary for anchimeric assistance (p. 573). Assistance by hydrogens at the 6 position may be ignored in both cases since these are bound to a secondary, rather than to a tertiary, carbon atom. In a similar way we may understand why neomenthyl tosylate (XC) is acetolyzed almost 80 times as rapidly as is menthyl tosylate (XCI),[31] and why the ratio of solvolysis rates for the corresponding chlorides in 80 percent ethanol is 41.[57]

The stereochemistry of the formolysis of neomenthyl tosylate, XC, points clearly to hydrogen participation. If only the "classical" carbonium ion, XCV, were involved, there should be formed, in addition to neomenthyl formate, two olefins, 2- and 3-menthene, and both should be optically active since the asymmetric center at C_1 would not be affected. It is found, however, that the only olefin formed is 3-menthene (XCIV), and that this olefin is racemic,[31] although optically active 3-menthene is not itself racemized under the solvolysis conditions. This suggests the intervention of the hydrogen-bridged carbonium ion, XCII, which is converted to the symmetric carbonium ion XCIII.

[56] Huckel and Sauerland, *Ann.*, **592**, 190 (1955). Presumably, the favored conformation for tosylate LXXXVIII is dictated by the steric requirements of the methyl group, rather than those of the —OTs group. Although the latter is the larger, most of its bulk is held far away from the cyclohexane ring and does not interfere with the hydrogen atoms bound to the ring.

[57] Hughes, Ingold, and Rose, *J. Chem. Soc.*, **1953**, 3839.

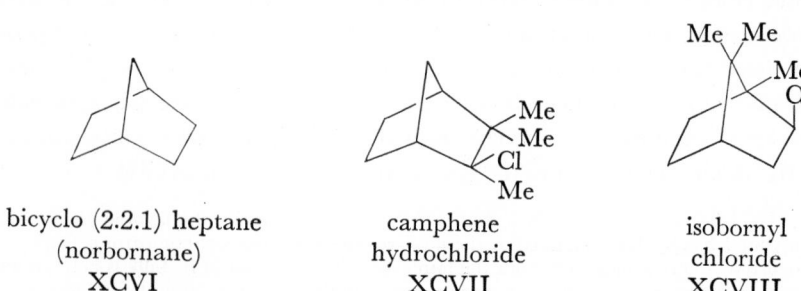

i-Pr $\quad$ $\overset{+}{\underset{H}{}}$ Me $\longrightarrow$ should give 2- and 3- menthenes
(both active)

XCV

Bicyclic Systems

In the reactions of bicyclic systems, 1,2 shifts are frequently encountered. Although these are similar in principle to the alkyl shifts that occur in noncyclic compounds, they often appear more complex; for migration of a ring carbon, together with three of the bonds attached to it, may result in the formation of a new ring system. The following are typical examples:

58(a)

58(b)

A number of rearrangements in the bicyclo(2.2.1)heptyl series (parent hydrocarbon XCVI) have been studied in some detail. The conversion, for

bicyclo (2.2.1) heptane
(norbornane)
XCVI

camphene
hydrochloride
XCVII

isobornyl
chloride
XCVIII

[58] (a) Doering and Farber, *J. Am. Chem. Soc.*, **71**, 1514 (1949). (b) Meerwein and van Emster, *Ber.*, **53**, 1815 (1920); **55**, 2500 (1922).

example, of camphene hydrochloride (XCVII) to isobornyl chloride (XCVIII) is a classic example of the Wagner-Meerwein rearrangement. The bicyclo-(2.2.1)heptyl system appears both in the reactant and the product but, as is shown below by numbering the carbon atoms, there is a "reshuffling" of four of the seven carbons in the rings (those designated as 1, 2, 3, and 7). This transformation proceeds most readily in polar solvents such as sulfur dioxide and nitromethane, which promote the ionization of tertiary halides without destroying them. Moreover, it is catalyzed by such Lewis acids as $HgCl_2$ and $SnCl_4$, and also by HCl, but not by ionic chlorides.[58(b),59] Since the function of these catalysts is evidently to remove chloride from the substrate rather than to supply chloride, we may suppose that the rearrangement involves ionization of XCVII. However, the ionization cannot be rate determining, for it has been found that the rate of exchange between HCl^{36} and camphene hydrochloride is much greater than that of the rearrangement.[60] Instead, it appears that the ionization of XCVII is rapid and reversible but the subsequent "collapse" of the ion

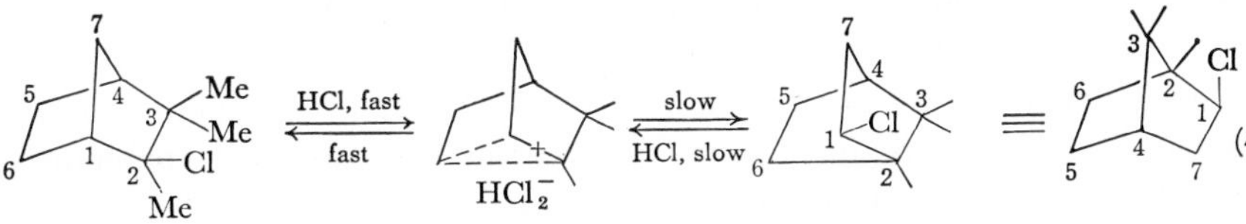

pair (XCIX) to give isobornyl chloride, XCVIII, is slow. (Similar paths may be written for this rearrangement, using $HgCl_2$, $SnCl_4$, or $FeCl_3$ as the electrophile that facilitates removal of the chloride.) As indicated, the isomerization is reversible, the reverse reaction passing through the same series of transition states and intermediates as does the forward reaction (as is required by the principle of microscopic reversibility). If, as we have suggested, the conversion of ion pair XCIX to camphene hydrochloride is rapid, then the slow step in the reverse reaction is the ionization of isobornyl chloride.

According to the sequence above, camphene hydrochloride is converted to the bridged carbonium ion (in ion pair XCIX) without intervention of a classical carbonium ion. Since the solvolyses of this chloride (under ionizing conditions) proceed from 300 to 8000 times as rapidly as those of ordinary tertiary chlorides,[61] it seems very likely that the carbon atom at the 6 position is rendering anchimeric assistance to ionization at the 2 position—that is, that the bond from C_6 to C_2 is forming at the same time the C_2—Cl bond is breaking. Likewise, no classical carbonium ion is inserted between isobornyl chloride and the bridged ion pair

[59] (a) Meerwein, *Ann.*, **453**, 16 (1927). (b) Bartlett and Pockel, *J. Am. Chem. Soc.*, **59**, 820 (1937).

[60] Nevell, de Salas, and Wilson, *J. Chem. Soc.*, **1939**, 1188.

[61] (a) Hughes, *J. Chem. Soc.*, **1935**, 255; (b) Brown, Hughes, Ingold, and Smith, *Nature*, **168**, 65 (1951).

XCIX in the reverse reaction, since solvolyses of this chloride are thousands of times as fast as those of ordinary secondary chlorides,[61,62] strongly suggesting a concerted ionization process here also. Furthermore, if carbonium ion C were to intervene in this reaction, we would expect the formation of appreciable quanti-

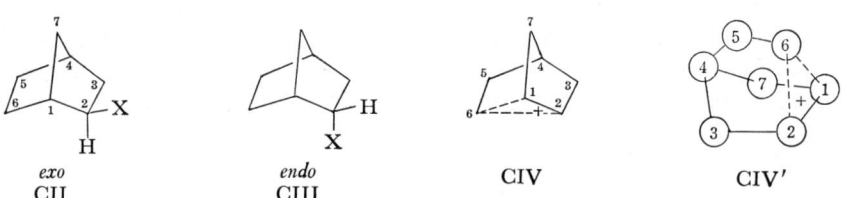

C   CI

ties of bornyl chloride (CI), for at room temperature this halide is very nearly as stable as the isobornyl isomer.[58(b)]

As we might predict, isobornyl chloride (XCVIII) is solvolyzed far more rapidly than bornyl chloride (CI), a 36,000-fold difference in rate having been noted in 80 percent ethanol.[62] In the isobornyl halide, the assisting ethylene bridge ($-C_5-C_6-$) is held *trans* to the departing chlorine—a position favorable for intramolecular attack—whereas in the bornyl halide, this bridge lies *cis* to the departing chlorine and ionization must proceed without assistance. Similar differences in reactivity have been observed among norbornyl compounds: *exo*-norbornyl chloride (CII), in which the assisting ethylene bridge lies *trans* to the departing chloride, is solvolyzed 70 times as rapidly in 80 percent ethanol as is *endo*-norbornyl chloride (CIII).[63] The ratio of acetolysis rates for the cor-

exo CII   *endo* CIII   CIV   CIV'

responding isomeric brosylates (at 25°) is 350.[31] The differences in the nor-bornyl series are considerably less striking than those in the bornyl-isobornyl series, suggesting that anchimeric assistance is more powerful in the latter. Comparing the bridged carbonium-ion intermediates for the two series (XCIX and CIV), we see that one of the carbon atoms sharing the positive charge in the bornyl cation (carbon 2) bears a methyl group. This, by reason of its hyper-conjugative effect, would be expected to make the bridged bornyl cation (and the activated complex leading to it) more stable than the bridged norbornyl cation, CIV (and the activated complex leading to it).

When *exo*-norbornyl brosylate (CII, X = OBs) undergoes solvolysis via the

[62] Roberts, Urbanek, and Armstrong, *J. Am. Chem. Soc.*, **71**, 3049 (1949).
[63] Roberts, Bennett, and Armstrong, *J. Am. Chem. Soc.*, **72**, 3329 (1950); **76**, 4623 (1954).

bridged cation CIV, the "rearrangement" product is also an *exo*-norbornyl derivative in which, however, the carbon atoms have become "shuffled." Now cation
CIV has a plane of symmetry, which, as may be more clearly seen from CIV',
passes through C_4, C_5, and C_6, midway between C_1 and C_2, and midway between C_3 and C_7. Therefore, the product of a reaction which passes through CIV
should be racemic, whether or not the starting material is optically active. The
rate of racemization may be taken as the rate of ionization of the brosylate, and
this has been found to be considerably greater than the rate of solvolysis (production of H+OBs⁻).[64] Thus, the ionization of the brosylate, while necessary for
solvolysis, is not a sufficient condition for it, and we may once more attribute
the lag between ionization and solvolysis to internal return (p. 581)—that is, to
collapse of the ion pair R+OBs⁻ to form ROBs once again.

$$\text{ROBs} \xrightarrow{\text{ionization}} \begin{array}{c} \text{R}^+ \text{ (racemic)} \\ \text{OBs}^- \\ (\text{R}^+ = \text{ion CIV}) \end{array} \underset{\xrightarrow{SOH \ (solvent)}}{\overset{\xrightarrow{\text{internal return}} \text{ROBs (racemic)}}{}} \text{ROS (racemic)} + \text{H}^+\text{OBs}^-$$

As in other such cases, internal return is less important for solvolyses in such
nucleophilic solvents as ethanol and aqueous acetone than in acetic acid; for the
more nucleophilic the solvent, the more likely it is to attack the ion pair before
the latter has a chance to collapse to starting material.[65]

An additional complication associated with the acetolysis of brosylate CII
(and very probably with the solvolyses of other bicyclic substrates as well) is the
occurrence of an intramolecular *1,3-hydride shift* (from C_6 to C_2), which may be
detected by acetolyzing a sample of this brosylate which has been labeled with
C^{14} in the 2 and 3 positions (CV).[66] If the sole ion-pair intermediate in this

[64] Winstein and Trifan, *J. Am. Chem. Soc.*, **74**, 1147, 1154 (1952).
[65] Winstein and Schreiber, *J. Am. Chem. Soc.*, **74**, 2165, 2171 (1952).
[66] Roberts, Lee, and Saunders, *J. Am. Chem. Soc.*, **76**, 4501 (1954).

solvolysis were CVI, we would expect half of the labeled carbon originally at C_2 and C_3 in brosylate CV to turn up at C_1 and C_7 in the resulting acetate, for acetic acid would be just as likely to attack CVI at C_1 as at C_2. Since, however, substantial amounts of labeled carbon are found also at C_5 and C_6 (CIX), it appears that a portion of the solvolysis proceeds through a hydrogen-bridged ion pair such as CVIII.

The 1,4-endoxocyclohexyl system, present in halides CIX and CXIII, is structurally similar to the norbornyl system. Again it is found that the *exo*-halides (CIX) are very much more reactive than the *endo*-halides (CXIII), the hydrolysis rates differing by factors of from 200 to 300.[67] Rearrangement, analogous to those occurring in the norbornyl and isobornyl series, is very nearly complete, but the product isolated is 3-formylcyclopentanol, rather than hemi-acetal CXII, which is unstable under hydrolysis conditions. The fact that non-

CIX   CX   CXI   CXII   CHO

CXIII   CXIV

rearranged products are not formed suggests that the bridged carbonium ion, CX is converted irreversibly and almost immediately after it is formed, to the rearranged oxonium ion, CXI. The hydrolyses of the *endo*-halides (CXIII) also yield 3-formylcyclopentanol, and it may well be that these too proceed through the bridged ion CX. Since, however, the ethylene bridge in CXIII lies *cis* to the halogen, it cannot assist the breakage of the carbon-halogen bond, and formation of the bridged ion may not occur until after the ionization. Here, then, the classical carbonium ion, CXIV, is probably a precursor of the bridged ion.

Very spectacular anchimeric assistance by the π electrons associated with a C=C double bond has been noted in the reactions of *anti*-7-norbornenyl derivatives (CXV).[68] The *anti*-7-tosylate (CXV, X = OTs) is solvolyzed over a billion times faster than its saturated analog (CXVII, X = OTs), and the ratio of rates for ethanolyses of the corresponding chlorides is about a million. As shown in CXVIII, the π-electron lobes in the *anti*-7-norbornenyl derivatives lie near C_7 on the side opposite the leaving group. Not only may these electrons

[67] Martin and Bartlett, *J. Am. Chem. Soc.*, **79**, 2533 (1957).

[68] (a) Winstein and Shatavsky, *J. Am. Chem. Soc.*, **78**, 592 (1956). (b) Woods, Carboni, and Roberts, *ibid.*, **78**, 5653 (1956).

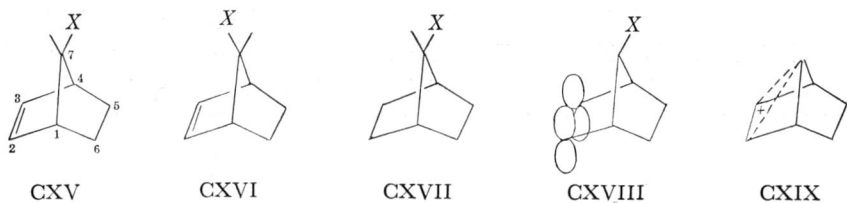

CXV   CXVI   CXVII   CXVIII   CXIX

help "push off" the leaving group, but after its departure, they may help accommodate the positive charge by drifting toward C_7 and allowing this charge to spread over three atoms (CXIX) rather than being confined to just one. Assistance by the π electrons requires that these lie opposite the leaving group; thus, the *syn* forms of 7-norbornenyl halides and sulfonates (CXVI) are solvolyzed more slowly than are the corresponding *anti* forms by factors of more than 10^5.

Finally, it should be noted that the π-electron lobes associated with the double bond between C_2 and C_3 in the norbornenyl system are "tipped" so that they lie much nearer to C_7 than to C_5 or C_6. We should therefore expect (and we find) that such a double bond renders much less assistance to ionization of substituents at C_5 or C_6 than to ionization at C_7. The *exo*-chloride CXX undergoes solvolysis in 80 percent ethanol about 150 times as rapidly as the *endo*-chloride, CXXI,[63] a difference in reactivity not much greater than that observed for the corresponding saturated chlorides.

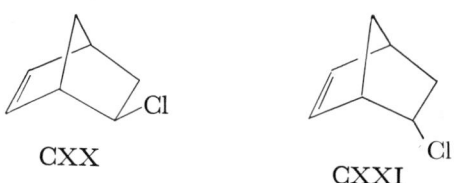

CXX

CXXI

Transannular Rearrangements

Group shifts in which the migration origin and the migration terminus are separated by one, two, or more atoms are rare, except in certain cyclic systems where the puckering of the ring allows the close approach of positions that are not bonded to each other.[69] The norbornyl system, in which a 1,3-hydride shift has been established, is one of these, and the cyclooctyl system is another. It has been found, for example, that formolysis of *trans*-cyclooctene oxide (CXXII) gives predominantly the *trans*-1,4-monoformate (CXXIV),[70(a)] suggesting that

[69] See, however, Mosher and Cox, *J. Am. Chem. Soc.*, **72**, 3701 (1950); Herz, *ibid.*, **76**, 3350 (1954).

[70] (a) Cope, Fournier, and Simmons, *J. Am. Chem. Soc.*, **79**, 3905 (1957). (b) Cope, Fenton, and Spencer, *ibid.*, **74**, 5884 (1952). (c) For similar studies in the cyclodecyl series, see Prelog, Schenker, and Kung, *Helv. Chim. Acta*, **35**, 2044 (1952); **36**, 471 (1953).

the reaction proceeds in part through the bridged cation CXXIII. Similarly, formolysis of the *cis*-oxide (CXXV) produces, in addition to the expected product, CXXVIII, substantial amounts of the *cis*-1,4-monoformate, CXXVII,[70(b)] which likewise suggests a 1,4-hydrogen shift (CXXVI). The fact that both of

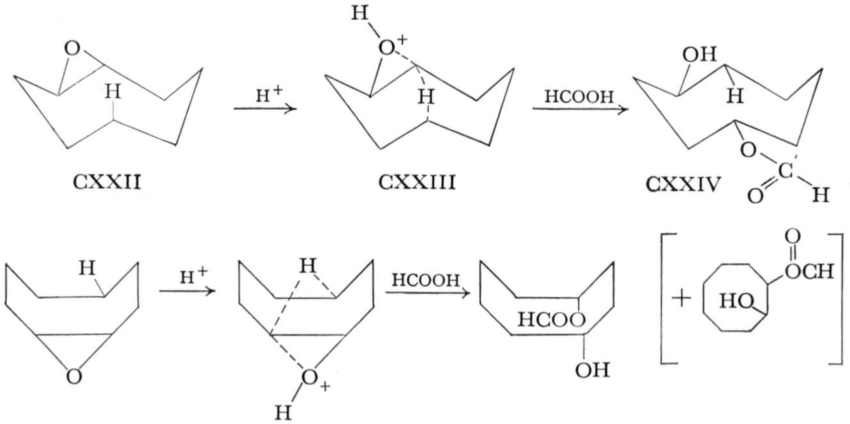

CXXII   CXXIII   CXXIV

CXXV   CXXVI   CXXVII   CXXVIII

these conversions are stereospecific indicates that no classical carbonium-ion intermediate intervenes in either. Hydrogen-bridged intermediates (CXXIII and CXXVI) are likely in both. An analogous path may be assumed for the conversion of *trans*-cyclooctene dibromide to *trans*-1,4-diacetoxycyclooctene (CXXXI) with AgOAc in acetic acid.[71] Note that the bridged bromonium ion,

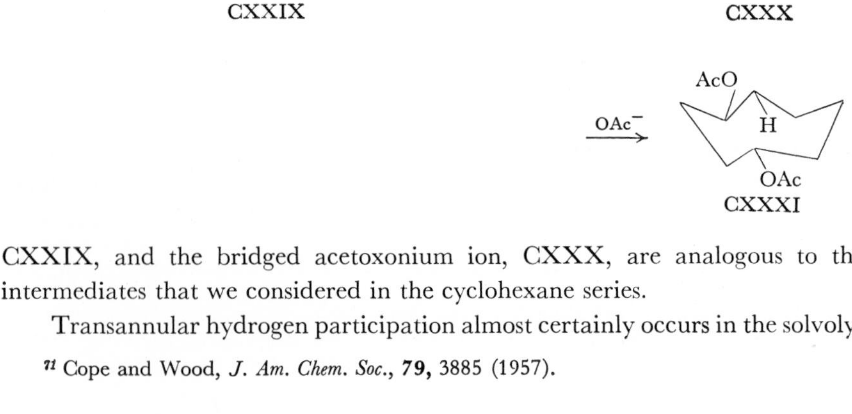

CXXIX   CXXX

CXXXI

CXXIX, and the bridged acetoxonium ion, CXXX, are analogous to the intermediates that we considered in the cyclohexane series.

    Transannular hydrogen participation almost certainly occurs in the solvoly-

[71] Cope and Wood, *J. Am. Chem. Soc.*, **79**, 3885 (1957).

ses of cyclooctyl, cyclononyl and cyclodecyl tosylates, for it has been observed that these undergo acetolysis 20 to 30 times as rapidly as cyclopentyl and 300 to 500 times as rapidly as cyclohexyl tosylate.[72(a)] Moreover, by the use of labeled carbon, it has been shown that transannular hydrogen migration occurs during the solvolyses of the cyclodecyl compound.[72(b)]

Transannular rearrangements need not involve hydrogen shifts. Two reactions in which other substituents migrate are shown below. In the first, the methoxy group (a nucleophile) migrates, whereas in the second, the acetyl group (an electrophile) migrates. Compounds CXXXIV and CXXXV, the

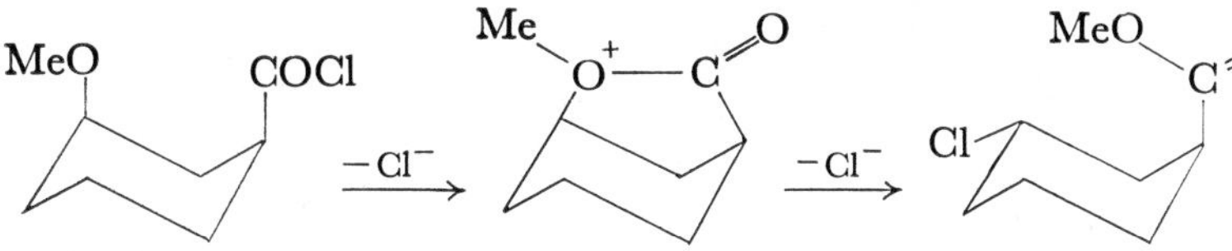

73(a)

CXXXII

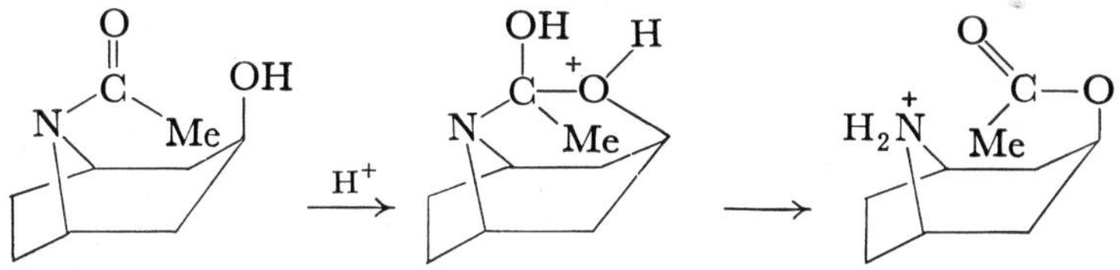

73(b)

CXXXIII

diastereomers of CXXXII and CXXXIII, respectively, do not undergo these rearrangements, for in both the migration origin is too far removed from the site that would otherwise be the migration terminus.[73]

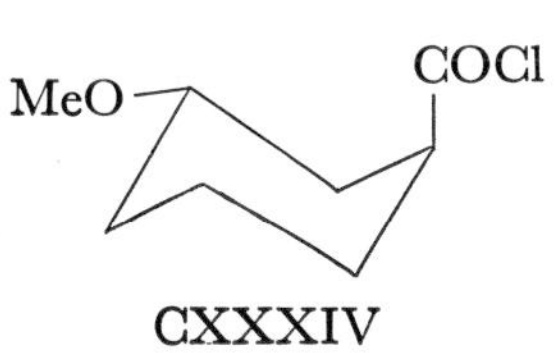

CXXXIV

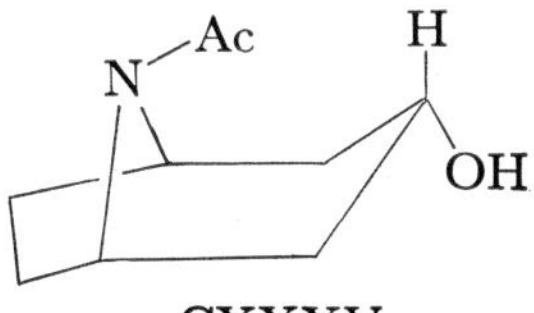

CXXXV

The Pinacol and Related Rearrangements

The pinacol rearrangement—the transformation of a 1,2-glycol to an aldehyde or ketone, via the migration of an alkyl or aryl group—is similar in principle to

[72] (*a*) Roberts and Chambers, *J. Am. Chem. Soc.*, **73**, 5034 (1951); Heck and Prelog, *Helv. Chim. Acta*, **38**, 1541 (1955). (*b*) Urech and Prelog, *ibid.*, **40**, 477 (1957).

[73] (*a*) Noyce and Weingarten, *J. Am. Chem. Soc.*, **79**, 3093, 3098 (1957). (*b*) Fodor, Nador, and Kovacs, *J. Chem. Soc.*, **1953**, 721, 724.

the 1,2 shifts that we have considered.[74] The conversion is generally carried out in the presence of strong acid and may be assumed to proceed through at least one carbonium-ion intermediate. Whether this is a "nonclassical" (bridged) or a "classical" (open) carbonium ion, and whether there are two, or perhaps three, such intermediates (that is, CXXXVI, CXXXVII, and CXXXVIII, or any two of these) interceding between reactant and product are matters that should be investigated for various individual cases. Along with the pinacol re-

$$
\begin{array}{l}
\underset{\substack{| \ | \\ HO\ OH_2 \\ +}}{-C-C-} \rightarrow
\left[
\underset{\substack{| \ | \\ HO \\ + \\ CXXXVI}}{-C-C-} (??) \rightarrow
\underset{\substack{| \\ HO \\ CXXXVII}}{-C \cdots\cdots C-} (??) \rightarrow
\underset{\substack{+\ | \\ HO \\ CXXXVIII}}{-C-C-} (??)
\right]
\xrightarrow{--H^+}
\end{array}
$$

$$
\underset{\substack{\| \ | \\ O}}{-\overset{R}{C}-C-}
$$

arrangement, we may consider the reactions of β-halo-hydrins with Ag^+ or Hg^{2+}:

$$
\underset{\substack{| \qquad | \\ OH \quad X}}{-\overset{R}{C}-\overset{}{C}-}
\xrightarrow[\text{(or } Hg^{2+})]{Ag^+}
\underset{\substack{\| \qquad | \\ O}}{-\overset{R}{C}-\overset{}{C}-}
+ H^+ + AgX \text{ (or } HgX^+)
$$

and the deaminations of β-aminohydrins:

$$
\underset{\substack{| \qquad | \\ OH \quad NH_2}}{-\overset{R}{C}-\overset{}{C}-}
\xrightarrow{HNO_2}
\underset{\substack{| \qquad | \\ OH \quad N_2^+}}{-\overset{R}{C}-\overset{}{C}-}
\rightarrow
\underset{\substack{\| \qquad | \\ O}}{-\overset{R}{C}-\overset{}{C}-}
+ H^+ + N_2
$$

The products resulting from these reactions are equivalent to those resulting

[74] Such conversions as that of $\underset{\substack{| \\ OH}}{PhCH}$—$CPh_2OH$ to $\underset{\substack{\| \\ O}}{PhCC}Ph_2H$ may proceed by a path analogous to that of the pinacol rearrangement, but with hydride, rather than an alkyl or aryl group, shifting. However, an alternate path, indicated below, apparently has not yet been ruled out for such reactions:

$$
PhCHOH-CPh_2OH \xrightarrow{H^+} PhCHOH-CPh_2^+ \xrightarrow{-H^+} \underset{\substack{| \\ OH}}{PhC}=CPh_2 \rightarrow \underset{\substack{\| \\ O}}{PhC}-CPh_2H
$$

In view of this ambiguity, only those pinacol rearrangements involving alkyl or aryl shifts are to be considered. For kinetic studies of the pinacol rearrangement see: Gebhardt and Adams, *J. Am. Chem. Soc.*, **76**, 3925 (1954); Duncan and Lynn, *J. Chem. Soc.*, **1956**, 3512, 3519, 3674.

from the pinacol rearrangement, and it is very likely that the mechanisms are very similar.

The stereochemical requirements for these rearrangements are most readily apparent from the study of substrates in which the C_α—C_β bond is incorporated into a ring, thus restricting freedom of rotation. From such systems we find that it is desirable, if not necessary, that the migrating group and the leaving group lie *trans* to each other during the early stages of bond breaking. Thus, the *cis* form of 1,2-dimethylcyclohexane-1,2-diol (CXXXIX) (in which the methyls lie *trans* to the hydroxyl groups) undergoes the pinacol rearrangement easily in dilute H_2SO_4 with migration of a methyl group; whereas the *trans* glycol, CXL (in which the methyls lie *cis* to the hydroxyl groups) undergoes rearrangement under similar conditions with contraction of the ring.[75(a)] Similarly, only the *cis*

CXXXIX   CXL

form of the isomeric 1,2-dimethylcyclopentane-1,2-diols undergoes rearrangement with methyl migration. Both the *cis* and *trans* forms (CXLI and CXLII) of 7,8-diphenylacenaphthene-7,8-diol undergo the pinacol rearrangement with phenyl migration; however, the *trans* isomer is converted to ketone CXLIII only one sixth as rapidly as is the *cis*. Moreover, since the *trans* diol is readily converted to the *cis* under the reaction conditions used, it is likely that the latter is an intermediate in the transformation of the *trans* diol to CXLIII.[75(b)]

CXLI   CXLIII   CXLII

The evidence that the migrating group approaches the migration terminus (C_α) from the side opposite the leaving group strongly suggests that an inversion of configuration occurs at this carbon. While this apparently has not yet been demonstrated directly for the pinacol rearrangement as such, it has been shown for the deamination of the optically active aminohydrin CXLIV, which yields predominantly ketone CXLV:[76]

[75] (a) Bartlett, Pockel, and Bavley, *J. Am. Chem. Soc.*, **59**, 820 (1937); **60**, 2416 (1938). (b) Bartlett and Brown, *ibid.*, **62**, 2927 (1940).
[76] Bernstein and Whitmore, *J. Am. Chem. Soc.*, **61**, 1324 (1939).

$$\text{H}_2\text{N}\underset{\beta}{-}\overset{\overset{\text{H}}{|}}{\underset{\text{CPh}_2\text{OH}}{\boxed{\alpha}}}\text{—Me} \xrightarrow{\text{HNO}_2} \text{Me}\underset{\underset{\text{O}}{\overset{\text{Ph—C}}{\underset{\beta}{\|}}}}{\overset{\overset{\text{H}}{|}}{\boxed{\alpha}}}\text{—Ph}$$

CXLIV   CXLV

(For proof that this conversion proceeds as shown, see Ex. 3.)

However, although inversion predominates, about 25 percent of the resulting ketone is racemic, showing that the rearrangement proceeds, at least in part, through the open carbonium ion, $\text{Me}\overset{+}{\text{C}}\text{H}—\text{CPh}_2\text{OH}$, which has no center of asymmetry. Recently, this reaction has been reexamined, using aminohydrin CXLVI stereospecifically labeled in only one of the benzene rings with C^{14},[77] and it has been found that virtually all migration of Ph* takes place with *inversion of configuration* about C_α, whereas very nearly all migration of *unlabeled phenyl* occurs with *retention of configuration* about C_α. This rather unexpected result indicates not only that the aminohydrin greatly prefers conformation CXLVI (in which the hydrogen bound to C_α lies between the two bulky phenyl groups on C_β), but also that the carbonium ion reacts preferentially in conformation CXLVIII, leading to the observed inversion at C_α and migration of Ph*. A small fraction (about 12 percent) of the carbonium-ion intermediate reacts in conformation CXLIX (leading to retention at C_α and migration of unlabeled Ph), but practically none of the intermediate reacts in conformations CL or CLI. It is reasonable that the carbonium-ion intermediate, when initially formed, should adopt conformation CXLVIII (which is similar to the preferred conformation of the substrate). Some conversion to CXLIX (requiring a 60° rotation around C_α—C_β) occurs, but conversion to CL (requiring a 120° rotation) or to CLI (requiring a 180° rotation) is negligible. If this interpretation is correct, *the time interval between formation of the carbonium ion and migration of the*

[77] Benjamin, Schaeffer, and Collins, *J. Am. Chem. Soc.*, **79**, 6160 (1957). Stereospecific labeling was accomplished by treating the SnCl₄ adduct of benzene-labeled 2-aminopropiophenone (CXLVII) with unlabeled PhMgBr. As stipulated by Cram's rule (p. 549), the incoming (unlabeled) phenyl group should attack preferentially on the less crowded side (that is, on the left side in the drawing shown). Here the degree of stereospecificity is much greater than that which would be observed in the corresponding attack on a nonchelated substrate; for chelation assures us that virtually all molecules of the aminoketone assume conformation CXLVII.

CXLVII $\xrightarrow{\text{PhMgBr}}$ $\xrightarrow{\text{H}_2\text{O}}$ CXLVI

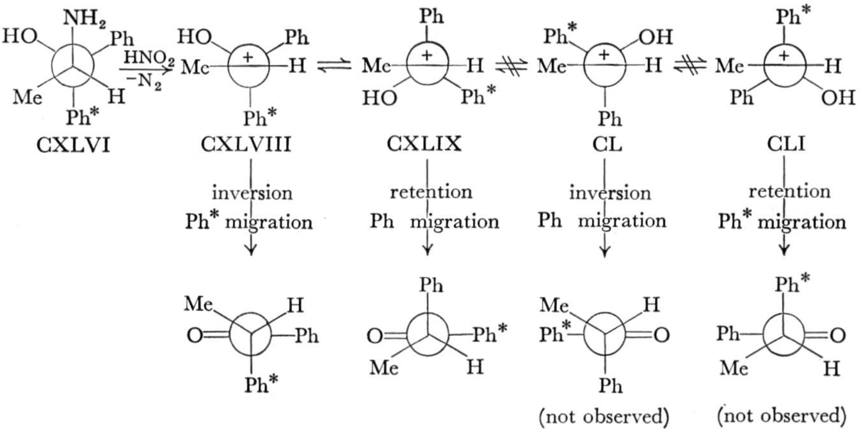

CXLVI   CXLVIII   CXLIX   CL   CLI

inversion
Ph* migration

retention
Ph migration

inversion
Ph migration

retention
Ph* migration

(not observed)   (not observed)

phenyl group must be very short—considerably shorter than the period necessary for a 120° rotation about C_α—C_β in the carbonium ion. Indeed, we cannot as yet rule out the possibility that migration with inversion at C_α occurs *in part* through a bridged carbonium ion—that is, that in some cases the departure of N_2 and the migration of the phenyl group are contemporaneous.

We may use similar reasoning to explain why the *erythro* form of amino-hydrin CLII undergoes deamination principally through conformation CLIII with phenyl migration, whereas the *threo* form undergoes deamination largely via conformation CLV with migration of the anisyl group.[78] Again, the favored

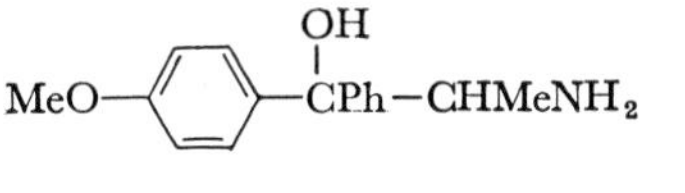

$$\text{MeO}-\underset{\overset{\displaystyle |}{\text{CPh}-\text{CHMeNH}_2}}{\bigcirc}-\text{OH} \quad \text{(CLII)}$$

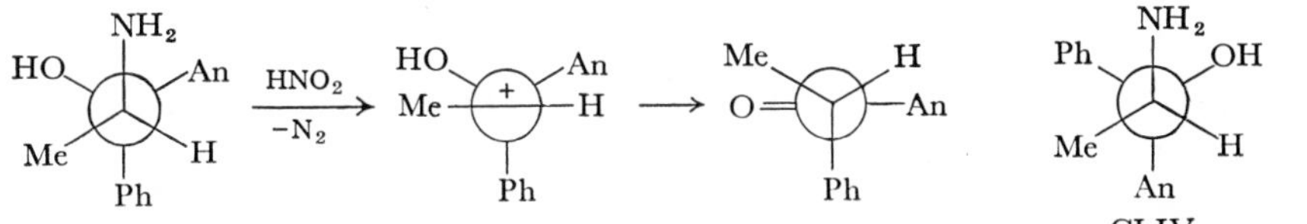

CLIII   CLIV

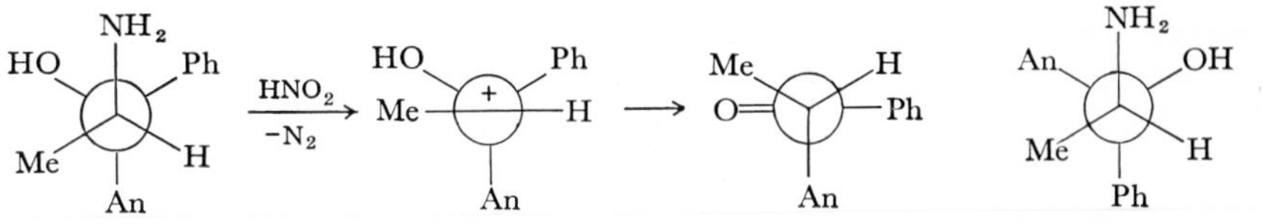

CLV   CLVI

[78] Curtin and Crew, *J. Am. Chem. Soc.*, **77**, 355 (1955). Since the asymmetric carbon atoms in these aminohydrins have no substituents in common, we may designate the substituents on

conformations for the *erythro* and *threo* forms of CLII are CLIII and CLV, respectively, for in both, the smallest substituent on C_α (—H) lies between the two large aryl substituents on C_β. This is in contrast to the alternate conformations CLIV and CLVI, in which the more bulky methyl group lies between the two aryl substituents. Suppose, as seems to be the case with aminohydrin CXLVI, that the carbonium-ion intermediate which is first formed resembles the more favored conformation of the substrate, and suppose also that the aryl migration is more rapid than rotation about C_α—C_β; phenyl migration should then predominate in deamination of the *erythro* aminohydrin (as is observed), whereas anisyl (An-) migration will predominate in deamination of the *threo* aminohydrin.

The migrational preferences in these deaminations may also be accounted for by assuming the intervention of aryl-bridged carbonium-ion intermediates. It may be argued that the favored bridged intermediates from CLIII and CLV are CLVII and CLVIII, respectively; for in the alternate structures, CLIX and CLX, there is aryl-methyl eclipsing. Opening the bridge at C_β in CLVII and

CLVIII leads the observed ketones. Since, however, deamination of aminohydrin CXLVI has been shown to proceed partly, if not wholly, through an open carbonium ion, it seems likely that the deaminations of CLIII and CLV likewise proceed, at least in part, through open carbonium ions. There is, at present, a similar ambiguity in interpretation of the rearrangements (in the presence of

---

each of the two carbons as *L* (largest), *S* (smallest), and *M* (medium-sized), then apply the *threo* and *erythro* prefixes in the usual way (p. 490).

Ag^+) of the diastereomers of Cl—⟨ ⟩—CPh—$CHPhBr$.[79] As with the deamina-
$\underset{OH}{|}$

$(Ar = Cl$—⟨ ⟩—$)$

tions just considered, the identity of the migrating aryl group is different for the
threo- and *erythro*-bromohydrins. Once again, we cannot say whether the observed
stereospecificity is due to conformational preferences in the reactant or to such
preferences in a bridged carbonium-ion intermediate (or perhaps to a combination of both).

Migratory Aptitude

During the 1930's, a number of workers felt that a "migratory aptitude" could
be assigned to each of the various alkyl and aryl groups, representing the ability
of that group to shift between adjacent bound carbon atoms in molecular rearrangements. It was hoped that, by applying these values to substrates having
two or more groups which might migrate, the ratio of possible products could be
estimated; implicit in this hope was the assumption that the ratio of migratory
aptitudes for two different groups was independent of the substrate at hand.
From the previous sections it should be clear that the migratory aptitude of a
substituent is linked to its effectiveness as a neighboring group and this is, in
turn, governed largely by its nucleophilicity. Typically, the extent of migration
of substituent R— in the deamination of RCH_2—$C^*H_2NH_2$ decreases progressively in the following series:[80]

$$R\text{—}CH_2\text{—}C^*H_2\text{—}NH_2 \xrightarrow[-N_2]{HNO_2} HO\text{—}CH_2\text{—}C^*H_2\text{—}R$$

$R-$ $=$ MeO—⟨ ⟩— ; 33 percent rearrangement

$=$ ⟨ ⟩— ; 24 percent rearrangement

$=$ O_2N—⟨ ⟩— ; 5 percent rearrangement

$=$ H_3C-; 1 percent rearrangement

[79] Curtin and Meislich, *J. Am. Chem. Soc.*, **74**, 5905 (1952).
[80] Roberts, *et al.*, *J. Am. Chem. Soc.*, **74**, 5943 (1952); **75**, 2069, 5759 (1953).

Now, the difficulty in evaluating migratory aptitudes by examining the rearrangement of unsymmetrically substituted pinacols should be evident. For example, a methyl rather than a phenyl group migrates in the rearrangement of glycol CLXI, not because methyl is a more effective migrator, but instead because the phenylated carbon can support a positive charge in the carbonium-ion intermediate, CLXII, more readily than can the methylated carbon. If the for-

$$\underset{\substack{\text{OH} \quad \text{OH} \\ \text{CLXI}}}{\text{Ph}_2\text{C} \text{---} \text{CMe}_2} \xrightarrow{\text{H}^+} \underset{\substack{\text{OH} \\ \text{CLXII}}}{\text{Ph}_2\overset{+}{\text{C}}\text{---}\text{CMe}_2} \rightarrow \underset{\substack{\text{Me} \quad \text{OH}}}{\text{Ph}_2\text{C}\text{---}\overset{+}{\text{C}}\text{Me}} \rightarrow \underset{\substack{\text{Me} \quad \text{O}}}{\text{Ph}_2\text{C}\text{---}\text{CMe}}$$

mation of the initial carbonium ion is essentially irreversible, the group migrating in the rearrangement of a pinacol $R_2C\overset{\substack{\text{HO} \quad \text{OH}}}{\text{---}}CR'_2$ w'll be determined merely by the relative stabilities of the two possible carbonium ions that may be obtained by removal of an —OH group.[81]

To avoid this difficulty, we may consider systems having only one possible migration terminus—that is, α-halohydrins (in their reaction with Ag^+) or α-aminohydrins (in their reaction with HNO_2). Here again, however, the picture may not be straightforward, for, as we have seen, the group migrating in the reaction of an *erythro* substrate may not be the same as that migrating in the reaction of its *threo* isomer. In such cases, the identity of the migrating group may depend on the conformation assumed by the reactant or the transition state (or both) in order to minimize crowding.

The most successful evaluation of migratory aptitudes has been accomplished with "symmetric" tetraaryl pinacols of the type

$$\underset{\substack{\text{Ar}' \quad \text{Ar}'}}{\text{Ar---C(OH)---C(OH)---Ar,}}[82]$$

in which the two possible reaction sites are chemically equivalent. The ratio of the two ketones formed by migration of groups Ar— and Ar'— may be taken as the ratio of the migratory aptitudes of Ar and Ar', and by studying the rearrangements of a series of such "symmetric" pinacols, a number of migratory aptitudes may be evaluated. The following are typical values (*MA* for Ph— is

[81] Bachmann and Steinberger, *J. Am. Chem. Soc.*, **56**, 170 (1934).
[82] Bachmann and Ferguson, *J. Am. Chem. Soc.*, **56**, 2081 (1934). In this work the glycols were not separated into the *meso* and *d,l* forms before being subjected to reaction. However, the steric requirements of the various aryl groups would be expected to be very nearly the same, so conformational effects should be of minor importance.

fixed at 1.0):

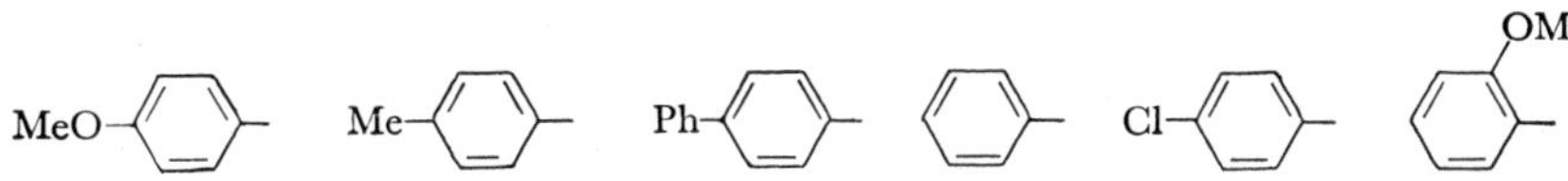

MeO⟨⟩	Me⟨⟩	Ph⟨⟩	⟨⟩	Cl⟨⟩	⟨OMe⟩
MA 500	16	12	1	0.7	0.3

These values are not only reasonable, they are, to a remarkable degree, internally consistent. For example, the migratory aptitudes of the *p*-tolyl group and the *p*-biphenylyl group have been found (from examination of the rearrangements of pinacols CLXIII and CLXIV to lie in the ratio 16/12 or 4/3). We should then

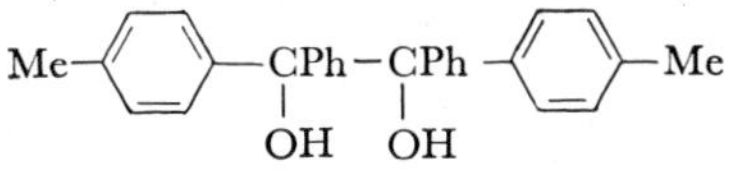

CLXIII

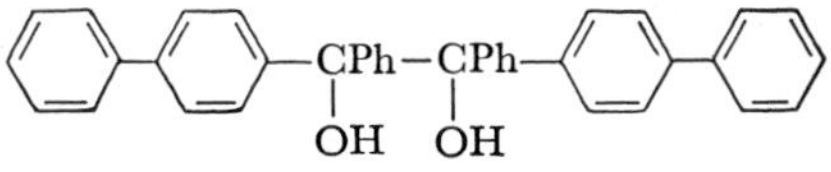

CLXIV

expect rearrangement of pinacol CLXV to result in a mixture of ketones CLXVI and CLXVII, in which the former (formed by migration of the *p*-tolyl group) predominates by a factor of 4/3. This is in excellent agreement with the observed ratio of ketones:

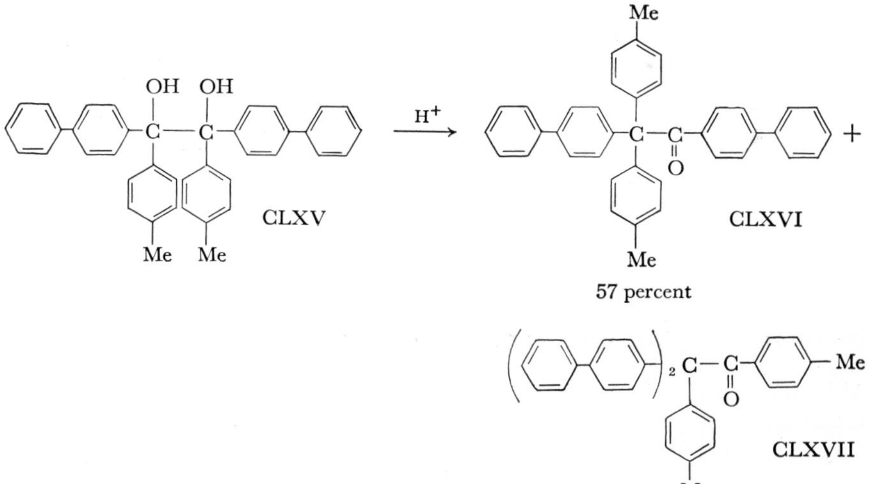

CLXV

CLXVI

57 percent

CLXVII

43 percent

The very low migratory aptitude of the *o*-anisyl group may be attributed to steric interference between the *o*-MeO group and the nonparticipating aryl groups in the transition state (CLXVIII):

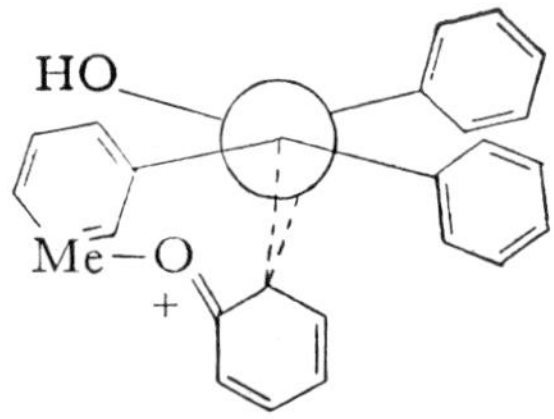

CLXVIII

It is emphasized that migratory aptitudes derived from studies of one type of rearrangement cannot be applied quantitatively to other rearrangements. More specifically, it appears that as the importance of "nucleophilic push" by the migrating group increases, the migration becomes electronically more selective. We have already noted that the identity of the migrating group in the rearrangements of aminohydrin CLII and bromohydrin CLXIX is determined largely by conformational effects, that is, the group migrating in rearrangement of the *threo* form is in both cases different from that migrating in rearrangement of the *erythro* form. In contrast, both the *threo* and *erythro* forms of brosylate

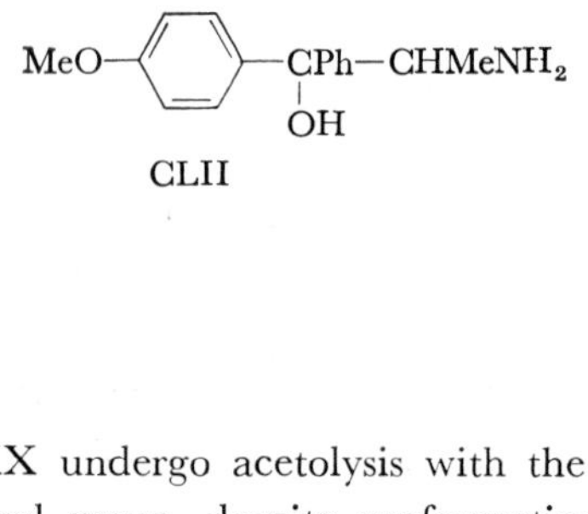

CLII

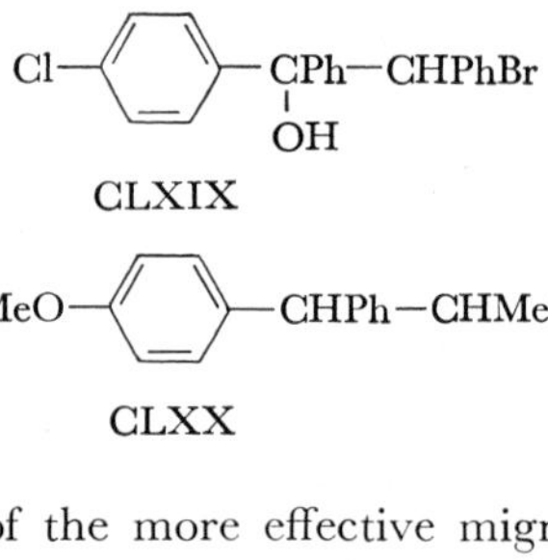

CLXIX

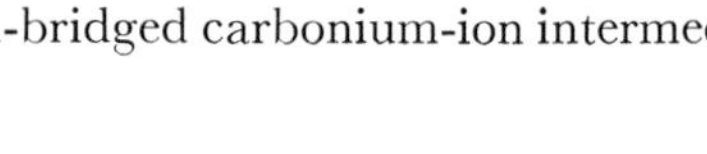

CLXX

CLXX undergo acetolysis with the shift of the more effective migrator, the *p*-anisyl group, despite conformational effects.[83] The latter reaction is of the type for which evidence pointing to an aryl-bridged carbonium-ion intermediate is more convincing.[84]

Neighboring-group Participation in Elimination and Addition

Although almost all of our discussion thus far has been concerned with the role of neighboring groups in substitution reactions (with or without rearrangement), it is reasonable to expect neighboring-group participation in other types of reactions that proceed through carbonium-ion or carboniumlike intermediates, in particular in $E1$-type elimination reactions and in electrophilic additions.

[83] Curtin and Bradley, *Rec. Chem. Prog.*, **15**, 121 (1954).
[84] For further work demonstrating the variations in relative migratory aptitudes with the nature of the reaction, see Raaen and Collins, *J. Am. Chem. Soc.*, **80**, 1409 (1958).

At present there is no convincing evidence that bridged carbonium-ion (anchimeric) intermediates may lose protons directly to form olefins. Instead, it appears that in $E1$ reactions, protons are lost from "classical" (open) carbonium ions. If this is so, elimination reactions involving neighboring-group participation are, except for the final step, analogous to reactions we have already considered. The following pair of examples are typical:

$$Ph_3C\!-\!CH_2Cl \xrightarrow[\text{HCOOH}]{H_2O} Ph_2\overset{\overset{\displaystyle Ph}{\overset{+}{\diagup\diagdown}}}{C}\cdots\cdots CH_2 \rightarrow Ph_2\overset{+}{C}\!-\!CH_2Ph \xrightarrow{-H^+} Ph_2C\!\!=\!\!CHPh^{45}$$

$$PhCHMe\!-\!CHMeOTs \xrightarrow[-OTs^-]{HOAc} PhCHMe\overset{+}{C}HMe \rightarrow Ph\underset{\underset{\displaystyle CH_3}{|}}{\overset{+}{C}}\!-\!CH_2Me \xrightarrow{-H^+} Ph\!-\!\underset{\underset{\displaystyle CH_2}{\|}}{C}\!-\!Et^{85}$$

Neighboring-group participation in electrophilic addition results in diversion of an 'onium intermediate to a cyclic derivative. Such reactions are not, in

$$86(a)$$

$$86(b)$$

$$86(c)$$

$$CLXXI$$

principle, different from the stepwise additions discussed in the previous chapter.

[85] Cram, J. Am. Chem. Soc., 74, 1037 (1952). In this reaction the cis and trans isomers of PhCMe=CHMe were also formed. These could arise either from the unrearranged or the rearranged carbonium-ion intermediate.

[86] (a) Tarbell and Bartlett, J. Am. Chem. Soc., 59, 407 (1937). (b) Winstein and Goodman, ibid., 76, 4368 (1954). (c) Kwart and Miller, ibid., 78, 5678 (1956).

EXERCISES FOR CHAPTER 14

1. For which member of each of the following pairs is anchimeric assistance during hydrolysis of greater importance? Justify your answer in each case:

(a) $MeSCH_2CH_2Br$ or $MeSeCH_2CH_2Br$?

(b) $Me_2NCHMeCH_2OTs$ or $Me_2NCH_2CHMeCH_2OTs$?

(c) $PhNMeCH_2CH_2Br$ or $PhCH_2NHCH_2CH_2Br$?

(d) $PhCHMeCH_2OBs$ or $PhCHMeCHPhOBs$?

(e) cis- or trans-2-benzoyloxycyclopentyl tosylate?

(f) $AcNHCH_2CHMeCl$ or $EtNHCH_2CHMeCl$?

(g) or ?

(h) or ?

(i) or ?

(j) or ?

(k) or ?

(l) $2\text{-MeO}-C_6H_4-CHMeCHMeOTs$ or $3\text{-MeO}-C_6H_4-CHMeCHMeOTs$?

(m) $PhCHMeCH_2OTs$ or $4\text{-MeO}-C_6H_4-CHMeCHMeCH_2OTs$?

(n) threo- or erythro-$MeSCHPhCHPhBr$?

(o) $MeO-$$-CHMeCHMeOBs$ or $MeO-$$-CHMeCHMeOBs$?

(p) or ?

(q) 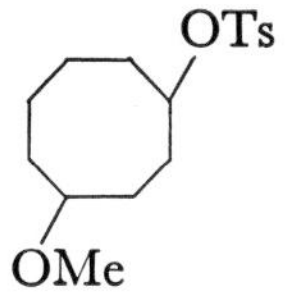 [structure: cyclooctane ring with OTs and OMe substituents] or [structure: cyclooctane ring with OTs and OMe substituents] ?

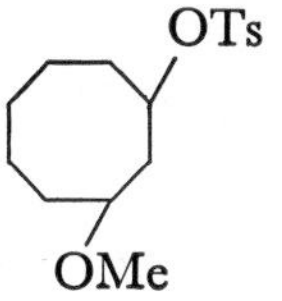

(r) 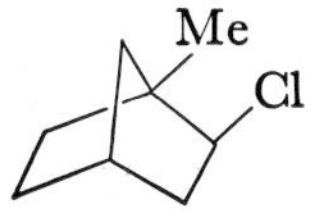 [bicyclic structure with Me and Cl] or [bicyclic structure with Cl and Me] ?

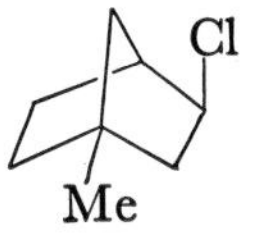

(s) 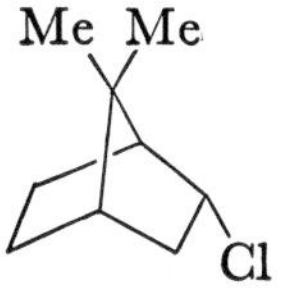 [bicyclic structure with Me Me and Cl] or [bicyclic structure with Me and Cl] ?

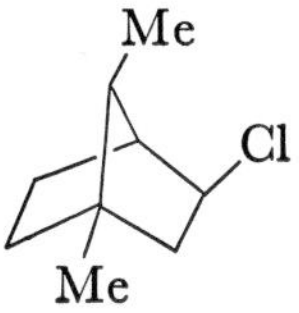

2. Assume that each of the following conversions proceeds through a bridged intermediate and that open carbonium ions do not intercede. Specify the configuration of the product(s) (*erythro, threo, meso,* or *d,l*) and indicate whether the product is optically active or racemic:

   (a) *D-erythro*-MeCH(OH)—CHMeBr $\xrightarrow{\text{OH}^-}$ oxide → MeCH(OH)—CHMe(OH)

   (b) *D-erythro*-MeCH(OMe)—CHMeBr $\xrightarrow{\text{Ag}^+,\ \text{HOAc}}$ MeCH(OMe)—CHMe(OAc)

   (c) *D-threo*-MeCH(OMe)—CHMeBr $\xrightarrow{\text{Ag}^+,\ \text{HOAc}}$ MeCH(OMe)—CHMe(OAc)

   (d) *D-erythro*-PhCH(OH)—CHMeBr $\xrightarrow{\text{OH}^-}$ oxide → PhCH(OH)CHMe(OH)

   (e) *D-erythro*-PhCHEt—CHMeOBs $\xrightarrow{\text{HOAc}}$

   PhCHEt—CHMeOAc + PhCHMe—CHEtOAc

3. Consider the deamination of $(-)$ MeCH(NH$_2$)—CPh$_2$OH to $(+)$ MeCH$\overset{\alpha}{—}$CPh.

   $\underset{\text{Ph}}{\overset{}{|}}$ $\underset{\text{O}}{\overset{}{||}}$

Both the aminohydrin and the ketone may be prepared from $(+)$ PhCHMe—COOH as shown:

$(+)$ PhCHMe—COOH $\xrightarrow[\text{Curtius}]{\text{SOCl}_2\ \text{Ph}_2\text{Zn}}$ $(+)$ MeCHPh—C—Ph $\overset{\text{O}}{\overset{||}{}}$

$(+)$ PhCHMe—COOH $\xrightarrow[\text{(ret)}]{\text{Curtius}}$ $(-)$ PhCHMeNH$_2$ $\xrightarrow{\text{BzCl [O]}}$ →

$(+)$ HOOC—CHMeNHBz

↓

$(+)$ EtOOC—CHMeNHBz

$(-)$ Ph$_2$C—CHMeNH$_2$ ← $(-)$ Ph$_2$C—CHMeNHBz $\overset{\text{PhMgBr}}{\longleftarrow}$

$\underset{\text{OH}}{\overset{}{|}}$ $\underset{\text{OH}}{\overset{}{|}}$

(Here the signs refer to the observed direction of optical rotation, rather than absolute configuration.) Bearing in mind that the Curtius reaction is known, from independent evidence, to proceed with retention of configuration, show that this series of conversions proves that the migration of the phenyl group in the deamination of the original aminohydrin brings about an *inversion of configuration* about C_α.

4. Predict the products, justifying your guess in each case:

(a) [structure: cyclohexane with S in ring, -CH₂Cl] $\xrightarrow{H_2O}$

(b) [bicyclic structure with NHBz and OTs] $\xrightarrow{EtOH}$

(c) D-*erythro*-MeCH(OAc)CHMeBr $\xrightarrow[AcOH]{Ag^+}$

(d) [structure: cyclobutane-cyclopentane with HO OH] $\xrightarrow{H_2SO_4}$

(e) $(MeO-\langle\rangle-)_2 \underset{OH}{\overset{|}{C}}-\underset{OH}{\overset{|}{C}}Ph_2$ $\xrightarrow{HCl}$

(f) *meso*-Me-⟨⟩-CMe(OH)−CMe(OH)-⟨⟩-Me $\xrightarrow{H_2SO_4}$

(g) [bicyclic structure with OH, -OMe, -Me, Me] $\xrightarrow{HCOOH}$ (brightly colored solution)

(h) [bicyclic structure with Me Me and OBs] $\xrightarrow{AcOH}$

(i) [tricyclic structure with Cl] $\xrightarrow{MeOH}$

(j) *erythro*-MeO-⟨⟩-CMe(OH)−CHPh(OH) $\xrightarrow{HCl}$

(k) [bicyclic structure with D, D, O] $\xrightarrow{HCOOH}$

(l) *threo*-Me-⟨⟩-CPh(OH)−CHMeNH₂ $\xrightarrow{HNO_2}$

(m) *trans*-1,2-Dibromocyclooctane + Me₄N⁺OAc⁻ →

(n) ClCHMeCH$_2$—N—CHMeCH$_2$Cl $\xrightarrow[\text{1HCO}_3^-]{\text{H}_2\text{O}}$
       |
       Me

(o) *erythro*-F—⟨benzene ring⟩—CPh—CHBr—CHMe$_2$ $\xrightarrow[\text{H}_2\text{O}]{\text{Ag}^+}$
                          |
                          OH

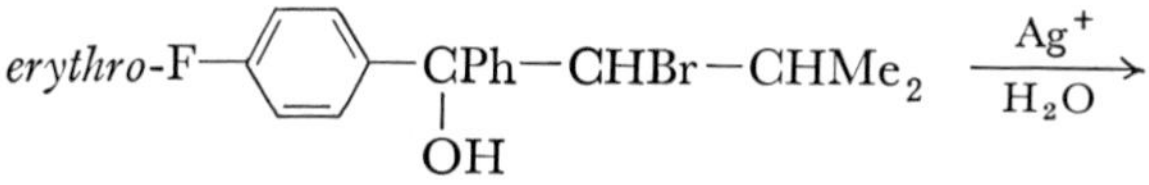

(p) *cis*-3-Methoxycyclohexanecarboxylic acid $\xrightarrow[\text{H}_2\text{SO}_4]{\text{Ac}_2\text{O}}$

(q)

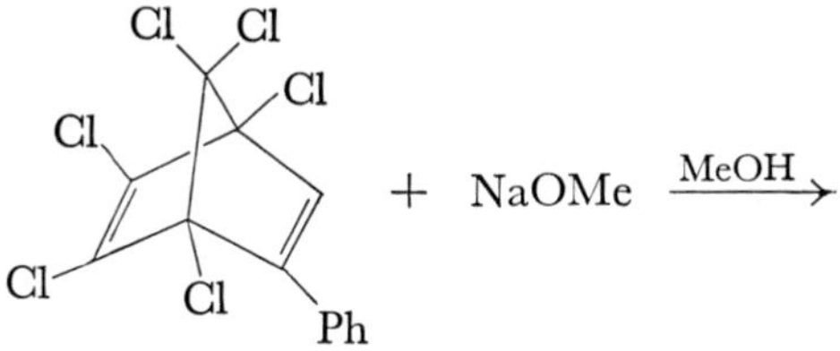

+ NaOMe $\xrightarrow{\text{MeOH}}$

(r)

$\xrightarrow{\text{HCOOH}}$

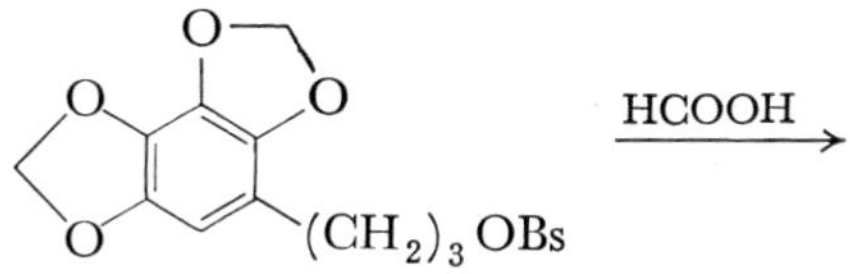

5. Suggest a mechanism for each of the following transformations:
   (a) EtSCHMeCH$_2$OH + HCl → EtSCH$_2$CHMeCl
   (b) PhCHMeCH$_2$ONO$_2$ $\xrightarrow{\text{HOAc}}$ PhCH$_2$CHMeOAc + NO$_3^-$
   (c)

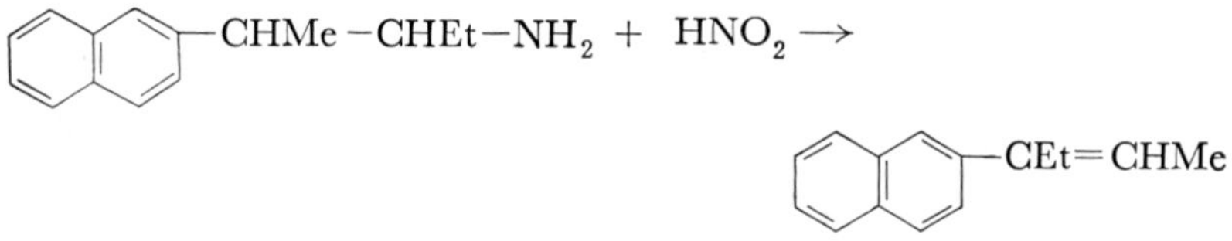

—CHMe—CHEt—NH$_2$ + HNO$_2$ →

—CEt=CHMe

(d)

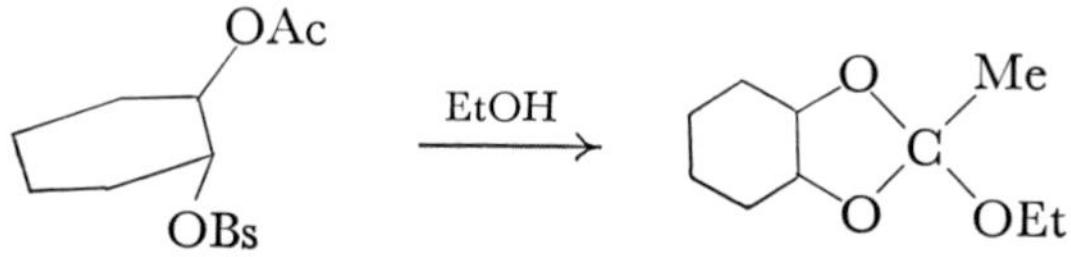

$\xrightarrow{\text{EtOH}}$

(e)

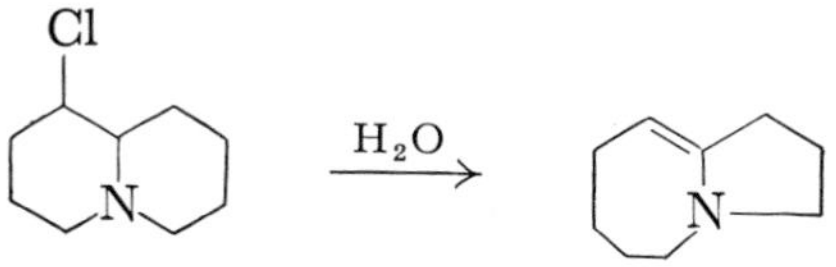

$\xrightarrow{\text{H}_2\text{O}}$

(f)

$\xrightarrow{\text{HCl}}$

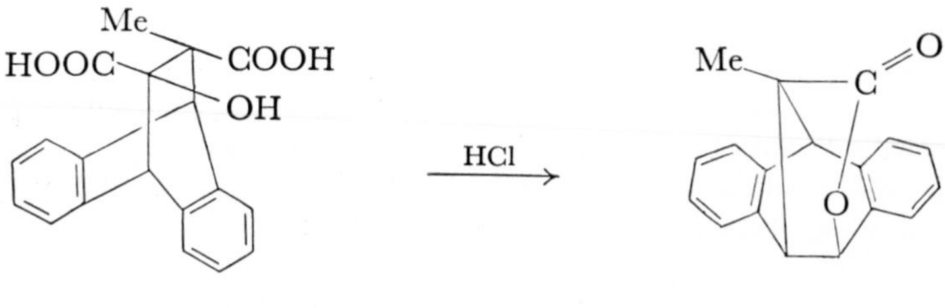

(g) $(+)$ [structure: Me-substituted cyclohexenyl ring]—CPh(OH)CH$_2$OH $\xrightarrow{H_2SO_4}$ $(+)$ [structure: Me-substituted cyclohexenyl ring]—CHPh—CHO

(h) 1,1-Dibromocyclohexane + AlBr$_3$ → cis-1,2-dibromocyclohexane

(i) Me$_3$C—C(=O)—CMe$_3$ + H$_2$SO$_4$ → Me—C(=O)—CMe$_2$CMe$_3$

(j) Me$_2$C(OMe)—CH$_2$OBs + H$_2$O → Me$_2$CHCHO + MeOH

(k) cis-2-Chlorocyclohexanol + OH$^-$ → cyclohexanone

(l) [structure with AcO and OH groups] $\xrightarrow{OH^-}$ [structure with AcO, OH, OH, O$_-$ groups]

(m) [bicyclic structure with OSO$_2$Me] $\xrightarrow{AcOH}$ [cycloheptatriene] + MeSO$_3$H

(n) Me$_2$C=CHCH$_2$CH$_2$Cl + H$_2$O $\xrightarrow{heat}$ Me$_2$C—[cyclopropyl] OH

(o) $(t\text{-Bu})_3$C—O—C(=O)—[benzene ring]—NO$_2$ $\xrightarrow[\text{dioxane}]{\text{aqueous}}$ O$_2$N—[benzene ring]—COOH +

$t\text{-Bu}—CMe_2—C(=CH_2)—C—CMe$
$\phantom{t\text{-Bu}—CMe_2—}\overset{\|}{CH_2}$

(p) [structure: cyclohexane with MeO and COOH] $\xrightarrow{Ac_2O}$ [structure with COOMe and AcO]

(q) [bicyclic epoxide structure] $\xrightarrow{HCOOH}$ [decalin structure with O—C—H and O]

6. Explain each of the following:

   (a) Hydrolysis of PhSCH$_2$CH$_2$Cl is considerably slower than that of EtSCH$_2$CH$_2$Cl.

   (b) Basic hydrolysis of (PhCH$_2$)$_2$NCH$_2$CHMeCl yields predominantly a primary alcohol, whereas neutral hydrolysis yields a secondary alcohol.

   (c) The rate of hydrolysis of chloride CLXXII is lowered by substitution of a p-NO$_2$ group in the benzene ring, but this is not the case for hydrolysis of chloride CLXXIII.

   (d) Treatment of (ClCH$_2$CH$_2$)$_2$O with Na$_2$Se in aqueous alcohol gives good yields

of selenoxane (CLXXIV), but the corresponding treatment of (ClCH$_2$CH$_2$)$_2$Se
with Na$_2$Se gives, instead of diselenane (CLXXV), only water-soluble products.

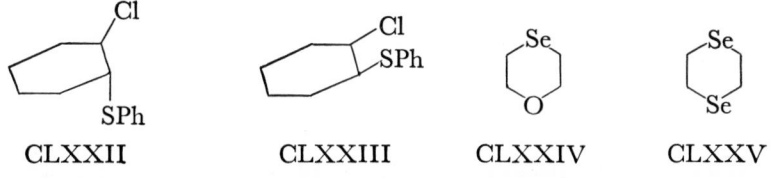

CLXXII   **CLXXIII**   **CLXXIV**   **CLXXV**

(e) Anchimeric assistance to solvolysis of β-phenyl alkyl brosylates is enhanced by
branching at C$_\beta$ but inhibited by branching at C$_\alpha$.

(f) Benzoyl migration (from N to O) is 70 times as fast for the *erythro* form of amide
CLXXVI as for the *threo* form.

BzNMe—CHMe—CHPhOH   Me$_2$CH—CH(OBs)—CHPh—CHMe$_2$
　　　　CLXXVI   CLXXVII

CLXXVIII   **CLXXIX**

(g) The rates of ionization in the series X—〈 〉—CMe$_2$CH$_2$OBs may be more

successfully correlated with Brown's σ^+ values (p. 435) than with Hammett's
σ values.

(h) Acetolysis of the *threo* form of brosylate CLXXVII is more rapid than that of the
erythro form.

(i) The conversion of BrCH$_2$CH$_2$Br (with methylamine in aqueous alcohol) to
MeNHCH$_2$CH$_2$NHMe proceeds in much poorer yield than the corresponding
conversion of Br(CH$_2$)$_3$Br to MeNH(CH$_2$)$_3$NHMe.

(j) Bromide CLXXVIII is much more slowly hydrolyzed than is CLXXIX.

(k) The downward drift in the apparent first-order rate constant for the hydrolysis
of Me$_2$NCH$_2$CH$_2$Cl is much more marked than that in the rate constant for the
hydrolysis of MeSCH$_2$CH$_2$Cl.

(l) The rates of racemization and solvolysis of *threo*-PhCHMeCHMeOTs are more
nearly equal in ethanol than in acetic acid.

(m) The hydrolysis of 7-chloronorbornane is much slower than the hydrolysis either
of cyclohexyl or cyclopentyl chloride.

(n) The apparent first-order rate constant for the solvolysis of cyclopropylcarbinyl
chloride in aqueous ethanol drifts downward as the reaction progresses, but this
is not the case for the solvolysis of this chloride in absolute ethanol.

(o) In the addition of p-Me—C$_6$H$_4$—SCl to norbornene, no product analogous to
CLXXI (p. 611) is formed.

(p) The "special salt effect" produced by dissolved LiClO$_4$ on the solvolysis of
p-MeO—C$_6$H$_4$—CHMeCHMeOBs in acetic acid is not observed when this
solvolysis is carried out in formic acid.

(q) The deuterium isotope effect in the formolysis of PhCD$_2$CH$_2$Cl is considerably
less than that in the formolysis of CD$_2$HCMe$_2$Cl.

CHAPTER 15

Further Molecular Rearrangements

THE PINACOL REARRANGEMENT, the semipinacolic deamination, and the Wagner-Meerwein rearrangement were considered in the preceding chapter. Each of these is, in essence, a 1,2 shift of a group (alkyl, aryl, or hydrogen), together with its pair of bonding electrons. In each, both the migration origin and the migration terminus are *carbons*. We now turn to a group of analogous 1,2 shifts in which, however, the migration terminus is a *nitrogen* atom, the more important of these being the familiar Beckmann, Hofmann, and Curtius rearrangements. Known, but less usual, are 1,2 shifts in which the migration terminus is an *oxygen* atom; these most often involve peroxy derivatives.

The Beckmann Rearrangement

The transformation of ketoximes to amides $\left(\begin{array}{c} R-C=N-OH \to R-C-NHR' \\ | \qquad\qquad\qquad \| \\ R' \qquad\qquad\qquad O \end{array}\right)$
is catalyzed by such acidic reagents as H_2SO_4, P_2O_5, SO_3, $SOCl_2$, PCl_5, and sulfonyl chlorides. In moderately concentrated sulfuric acid, rates of rearrangement are proportional to Hammett's h_0 function,[1] suggesting (p. 190) that the rate-determining step of the rearrangement involves the conjugate acid of the oxime, $R_2C=N-OH_2^+$. With other catalysts, the rearrangement very probably proceeds through an ester of the oxime (for example, $R_2C=N-OSO_2Ph$); for when such esters are prepared and purified, they are found to undergo rearrangement with ease in neutral solvents and in the absence of added catalysts.[2,3] The

[1] Hammett and Deyrup, *J. Am. Chem. Soc.*, **54**, 2721 (1932).

[2] (a) Chapman, *et al.*, *J. Chem. Soc.*, **1933**, 806; **1934**, 1550; **1935**, 1223; **1936**, 448. (b) Kuhara, *et al.*, *Chem. Abstr.*, **9**, 1613 (1915); **11**, 679 (1917). (c) Lampert and Bordwell, *J. Am. Chem. Soc.*, **73**, 2369 (1951). (d) For evidence that the Beckmann rearrangement may proceed

618

rearrangement of the benzenesulfonate of benzophenone oxime[2(c)] may be considered typical. The rate-determining step in such sequences is doubtless the

$$Ph_2C{=}N{-}OSO_2Ph \xrightarrow{CH_3CN} \underset{\underset{OSO_2Ph}{|}}{Ph{-}C{=}N{-}Ph} \xrightarrow{H_2O} \underset{\underset{O}{\|}}{Ph{-}C{-}NHPh} + PhSO_3H$$

heterolysis of the N—O bond, for the reactions have been found to be first order in substrate,[2(a,b)] and to proceed most readily in polar solvents. Rearrangement is facilitated by electron-attracting groups in the esterifying acid (which make the anion from this acid a more effective leaving group), but inhibited by the presence of such groups in the parent oxime (which would tend to strengthen the N—O bond).

At present we cannot say whether or not the breakage of the N—O bond in the Beckmann rearrangement and the shift of the alkyl (or aryl) group are concerted, but we may be certain that if these two acts are separated by an interval of time, this interval is very short. For it is now firmly established that the *migrating group in this rearrangement approaches the nitrogen atom from the side opposite to the departing oxygen atom.* This has been demonstrated in several cases,[4] of which we need consider only the one indicated below:[5]

As shown, ketoxime I may be converted to benzisoxazole III with base, thus

---

through the oxime anhydride, $R_2C{=}N{-}O{-}N{=}CR_2$, see Stephen and Staskun, *J. Chem. Soc.*, **1956**, 980.

[3] (a) Catalysis by HCl is complicated by the apparent necessity for small quantities of amide; it has been suggested (Ref. 2a) that in this case the rearrangement proceeds through oxime-amide adduct, $R_2C{=}N{-}O{-}CR{=}NR$. (b) Beckmann rearrangements in liquid SO_2 in the presence of Br_2 or I_2 have been described (Tokura, Asami, and Tada, *J. Am. Chem. Soc.*, **79**, 3135 (1957)). Although mechanisms have been proposed, further quantitative investigation of this modification is highly desirable.

[4] For summaries of this question, see: Blatt, *Chem. Revs.*, **12**, 20 (1933), and Wheland, *Advanced Organic Chemistry*, John Wiley and Sons, Inc., New York, 1949, p. 338.

[5] Meisenheimer, Zimmermann, and von Kummer, *Ann.*, **446**, 205 (1926).

indicating that the nitrated benzene ring lies on the same side of the C=N linkage as the —OH group. However, when ketoxime I undergoes the Beckmann rearrangement, the phenyl group, rather than the nitrated benzene ring, shifts. The necessity for backside attack by the migrating group in the Beckmann rearrangement suggests that migration occurs while the nitrogen atom is still shielded by (and perhaps partially bonded to) the leaving group.

A second stereochemical feature of this rearrangement deserves comment; when the migrating carbon atom is asymmetric, the configuration at that carbon is retained. Typically, ketoxime IV undergoes the Beckmann rearrangement (with H_2SO_4 in ether) with about 99 percent retention of configuration at the asymmetric carbon:[8]

The stereochemical evidence thus suggests structure VII as an activated complex (or perhaps a high-energy intermediate) for the Beckmann rearrangement in poorly ionizing solvents. As the solvent is made more polar, the complete departure of the OR— group (and its equilibration with other anions in solution) during the course of the reaction becomes more likely. Note that the migrating group does not become completely detached from the remainder of the molecule and that the *breakage of the C—C bond and the formation of the new C—N bond take place on the same side of the asymmetric carbon.* This accounts for the observed retention of configuration about the migrating carbon. Similar retention of configuration is very probably a feature of all 1,2-alkyl shifts in which the migrating

---

[8] Kenyon and Young, *J. Chem. Soc.*, **1941**, 263. To show that configuration was maintained in this rearrangement, acid V (R— = n-BuEtCH—) was converted to amide VI by two routes:

$$(+)\text{R—COOH} \rightarrow (+)\text{R—CONH}_2 \xrightarrow{\text{Hofmann, H}_2\text{O}} (+)\text{R—NH}_2 \xrightarrow{\text{Ac}_2\text{O}} (-)\text{R—NHAc, and}$$
V   VI

$$(+)\text{R—COOH} \rightarrow (+)\text{R—COBr} \xrightarrow{\text{Me}_2\text{Cd}} (+)\text{R—C—Me} \rightarrow (+)\text{R—C—Me} \xrightarrow{\text{Beckmann}}$$
V $\overset{\|}{O}$ $\underset{N-OH}{\overset{\|}{C}}$

$$(-)\text{R—NHAc}$$
VI

These sequences prove that *if* the Hofmann rearrangement proceeds with retention of configuration, then the Beckmann rearrangement does also. Retention of configuration in the Hofmann rearrangement has been independently demonstrated (p. 622).

VII

$$(R = HOSO_2-, ClCH_2\underset{\underset{O}{\|}}{C}-, \text{ etc.})$$

group retains its pair of electrons, although such retention has not yet been demonstrated in the pinacol and Wagner-Meerwein rearrangements.

The Hofmann Rearrangement

The rearrangement of N-chloro or N-bromoamides to isocyanates in basic solutions

$$R\underset{\underset{O}{\|}}{C}\!-\!NHX + OH^- \rightarrow R\!-\!N\!=\!C\!=\!O + H_2O + X^- \qquad (X = Cl, Br)$$

is most often used to convert amides to amines (having one less carbon); for N-haloamides are easily prepared from amides themselves, and amines are readily formed when isocyanates are treated with water. This rearrangement almost certainly proceeds through the conjugate base of the N-haloamide, $R\underset{\underset{O}{\|}}{C}\!-\!NX^-$; for with care, salts containing anions of this type may be prepared and are found to rearrange rapidly to isocyanates.[7] Moreover, halogenated N-alkylamides $\left(R\underset{\underset{O}{\|}}{C}\!-\!NR'X\right)$, which cannot form such an anion, do not undergo the rearrangement.

The rearrangement of N-bromobenzamide, $PhC\underset{\underset{O}{\|}}{}\!-\!NHBr$, is accelerated by incorporation of electron-donating groups in the benzene ring; for such groups not only ease the departure of the Br^- ion, but they facilitate the shift of the benzene ring (p. 607).[8] Thus, we may represent the Hofmann rearrangement as a simple 1,2 shift. Unlike the 1,2 shifts previously discussed, the migration termi-

[7] Mauguin, Ann. Chim., [8], **22**, 301 (1911).
[8] Hauser and Renfrow, J. Am. Chem. Soc., **59**, 121 (1937).

$$
\underset{\underset{O}{\overset{\displaystyle R}{\diagdown}}}{\overset{\displaystyle NHX}{\diagup}}\underset{OH^-}{\rightleftharpoons} \quad \underset{\underset{O}{\overset{\displaystyle R}{\diagdown}}}{\overset{\displaystyle \overset{..}{N}-X}{\diagup}} \quad \xrightarrow{slow} \left[\underset{\underset{O}{\overset{\displaystyle R}{\diagdown}}}{\overset{\displaystyle }{C{\text{-}}N{\text{-}}X}} \right]^- \quad \xrightarrow{-X^-} \quad O{=}C{=}N{-}R \quad \xrightarrow{H_2O} \begin{cases} RNH_2 \\ CO_2 \end{cases}
$$

$$IX$$

nus does not acquire a positive charge during the course of the rearrangement. However, the loss of a halide ion from anion IX would leave behind the species $R{-}\underset{\underset{O}{\|}}{C}{-}\overset{..}{N}{:}$, in which the nitrogen atom has only a *sextet of valence electrons* and is

thus electron deficient in much the same sense as is the boron atom in $B(CH_3)_3$. There is some doubt that this electron-deficient nitrogen species has an independent existence, for it may be argued that such a molecule would react rapidly with water to give a hydroxamic acid, $R{-}\underset{\underset{O}{\|}}{C}{-}NHOH$, whereas no hydroxamic

acids or products closely related to them have been found in the reaction mixtures.[9] For this reason, it is suggested that the departure of the halide ion and the shift of the migrating group in the Hofmann reaction are simultaneous or very nearly so.

As in the Beckmann rearrangement, we would expect retention of configuration at the migrating atom. This prediction has been confirmed most directly with amide X, derived from camphoric acid. When this amide, in which the —COOH and —CONH₂ groups lie *cis* to each other, is subject to the Hofmann rearrangement, amino acid XI results. In the latter, the —COOH and —NH₂ groups also lie *cis* to each other, for this amino acid readily forms lactam XII. (The *trans* amino acid (XIII), which would result from inversion of configuration at the migrating carbon, should not form such a lactam.[10]) More-

over, the bicyclic amide XIV readily undergoes the Hofmann rearrangement. In this case, the rigidity of the ring system prohibits inversion of configuration at C_α.[11]

[9] Hauser and Kantor, *J. Am. Chem. Soc.*, **72**, 4284 (1950).

[10] Noyes, *et al.*, *J. Am. Chem. Soc.*, **34**, 1067 (1912); **36**, 118 (1914); **37**, 189 (1915). Archer, *ibid.*, **62**, 1972 (1940). Amide X is known to be derived from a *cis*-dicarboxylic acid, for the parent acid forms a cyclic anhydride on heating.

[11] Bartlett and Knox, *J. Am. Chem. Soc.*, **61**, 3184 (1939).

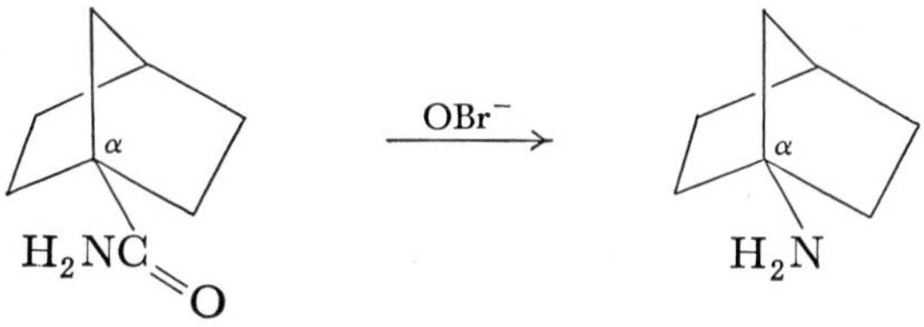

XIV

The *Lossen rearrangement*, which involves N-acyl derivatives of hydroxamic acids (XV), is obviously analogous to the Hofmann rearrangement, but here the leaving group is a carboxylate ion, rather than a halide. As expected, the reaction

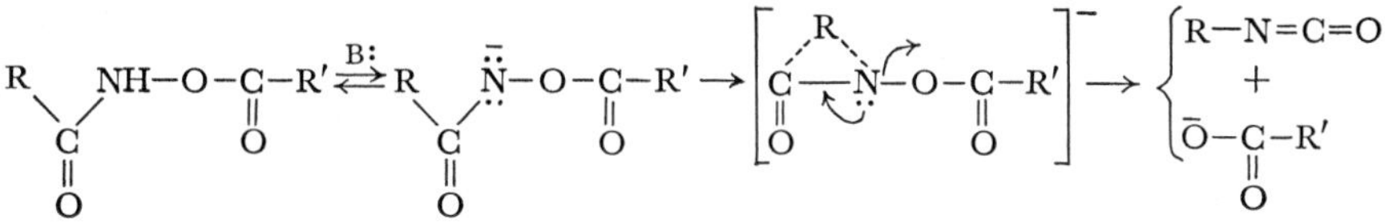

XV

is facilitated by electron-supplying substituents in R— but retarded by such substituents in R'—.[12] Again, virtually complete retention of configuration in R— is observed in its migration.[13]

Reactions of Azides. The Curtius and Schmidt Rearrangements[14]

Inorganic and organic azides, aside from a few ionic azides such as NaN_3, are relatively unstable substances. Often, in their decompositions, two of the three nitrogen atoms depart as N_2, leaving the third nitrogen atom and the remainder of the molecule to stabilize themselves as best they can. Acyl azides

$$\left(R\!-\!\underset{\underset{O}{\|}}{C}\!-\!N\!-\!N\!\equiv\!N \right),$$

which may be prepared either by the action of NaN_3 on acyl halides or by the action of nitrous acid on acid hydrazides ($RCONHNH_2$), decompose when heated, yielding nitrogen and isocyanates. The Curtius rearrangement may then be represented:

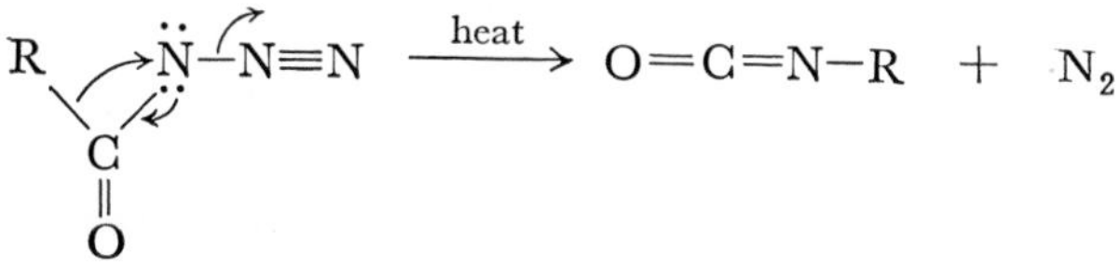

[12] Renfrow and Hauser, *J. Am. Chem. Soc.*, **59**, 2308 (1937).

[13] Wallis, Nagel, and Dripps, *J. Am. Chem. Soc.*, **53**, 2787 (1931); **55**, 1701 (1933). These workers show that a given optically active carboxylic acid (having an asymmetric α-carbon atom) yields the same optically active amine when its amide is subjected to the Hofmann reaction as when its acyloxyamide is subjected to the Lossen reaction.

[14] The Curtius reaction has been reviewed by Smith, and the Schmidt reaction by Wolff in Vol. III of *Organic Reactions* (edited by Adams), John Wiley and Sons, Inc., New York, 1946, pp. 337 and 307.

As shown, the mechanism is very similar to those for the Hofmann and Lossen rearrangements. Once again, retention of configuration is observed in the migrating group[15] and we have represented the departure of the leaving group and the shift of the migrating group as being synchronous.

The Curtius reaction is subject to acid catalysis.[16] This, at first glance, may seem surprising; for it might be argued that protonation of either the acyl group or the nondeparting nitrogen should pull electron density from the middle nitrogen in XVI toward the nitrogen on the left, thus making the heterolysis of this bond more difficult. However, from the π-electron diagram, XVII, we see that the N—N bond broken in the reaction has double-bond character. Protonation

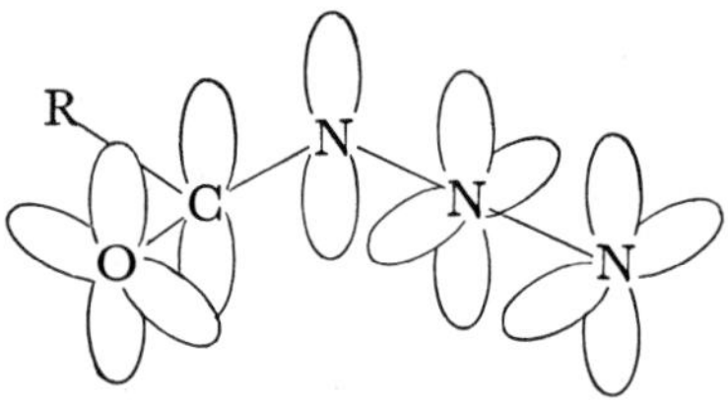

XVII

of the acyl group draws π-electron density from the nitrogen at the left even more effectively than it draws σ-electron density (for π electrons are the more polarizable). This reduces the double-bond character of the N—N bond at the left and facilitates its breakage.

The Schmidt rearrangement is actually a group of reactions, each employing as a reagent hydrazoic acid (HN_3) in sulfuric acid. We shall be concerned here only with the action of this reagent on carboxylic acids and carbonyl compounds. Carboxylic acids are converted to amines (having one less carbon atom), doubtless through an isocyanate, which is, however, generally not isolable from the reaction mixture. This reaction is thus closely related to the Curtius rearrangement and may be assigned the following mechanism:

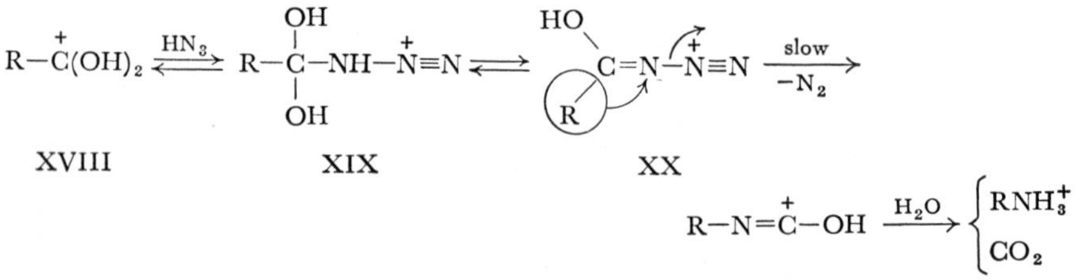

[15] Jones and Wallis, *J. Am. Chem. Soc.*, **48**, 169 (1926). These workers show that a given optically active carboxylic acid (having an asymmetric α-carbon) yields the same optically active amine when its azide is subjected to the Curtius reaction and the resulting isocyanate hydrolyzed, as when its amide is subjected to the Hofmann reaction (Ref. 13).
[16] Newman and Gildenhorn, *J. Am. Chem. Soc.*, **70**, 317 (1948).

Cation XVIII is the conjugate acid of the carboxylic acid that is taken as the substrate, whereas cation XXI is the conjugate acid of the isocyanate from which the resulting amine is presumably derived. The third step in the sequence is assumed to be rate determining, both by analogy, and in accord with the observation that electron-donating groups in R— increase the rate of rearrangement.[17] Cation XX, rather than XIX, has been designated as the active intermediate in the rearrangement; for if XIX could undergo rearrangement directly, there seems no reason why N-alkylated cations of the same type (for example, XXIV) could not also undergo rearrangement, and if this were the case, alkyl azides (for example, CH_3N_3) should enter into the Schmidt reaction, converting carboxylic acids to secondary amines. Such a modification of the Schmidt reaction is generally unsuccessful. As with the other rearrangements considered thus

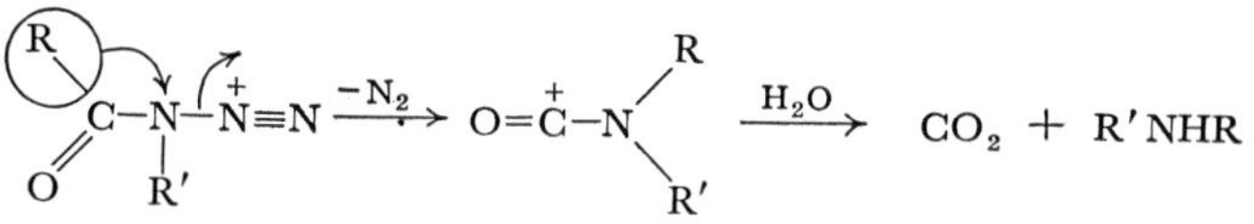

XXIV   (not observed)

far in the present chapter, the migrating group in the Schmidt reaction shifts with *retention of configuration*.[18]

[17] Briggs and Lyttleton, *J. Chem. Soc.*, **1943**, 421. The ease with which mesitoic acid undergoes the Schmidt rearrangement has aroused some interest. Since mesitoic acid is known from cryoscopic measurements (p. 99) to be very nearly completely converted to the mesitylium ion XXII, in concentrated sulfuric acid, it is often suggested that the reaction proceeds through this cation:

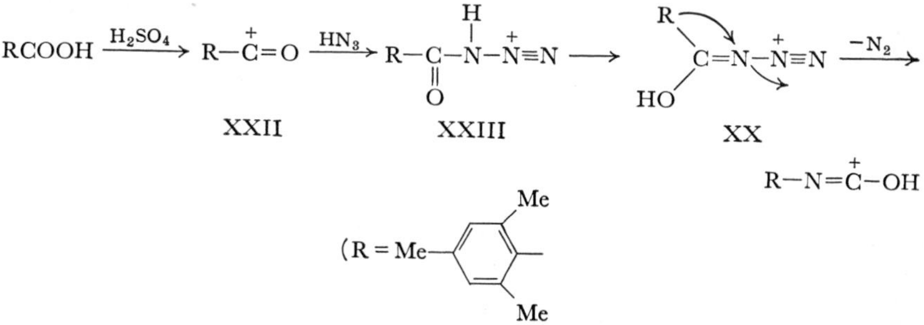

XXII   XXIII   XX

$$R-N=\overset{+}{C}-OH$$

$$(R = Me-\text{mesityl})$$

However, this view is inadmissible if it is assumed that the rate of rearrangement is determined by the rate of decomposition of cation XX; for if XX were in equilibrium with both XXII and XXIII, any steric and electronic factors that would favor the conversion of mesitoic acid to the mesitylium ion should likewise favor the return of cation XXIII to the mesitylium ion. On the other hand, the observed reactivity of mesitoic acid is consistent with a path in which the rate-determining step is the attack by the mesitylium ion, XXII, on HN_3 displacing N_2 (the alternate sequence shown above). If the latter mechanism is correct, mesitoic acid, unlike most unhindered carboxylic acids, should undergo the Schmidt rearrangement with alkyl azides, as well as with HN_3.

[18] Campbell and Kenyon, *J. Chem. Soc.*, **1946**, 26.

When a symmetric ketone ($R_2C{=}O$) is treated with hydrazoic acid in sulfuric acid, an amide results. With an unsymmetric ketone ($RR'C{=}O$), a mixture of two amides is obtained, whereas an aldehyde generally yields a mixture of an N-alkylated formamide and a nitrile. Although little quantitative study has been devoted to this phase of the Schmidt reaction, the following mechanism, based largely on analogy, may be considered a likely one:

$$
\begin{array}{ccccc}
\underset{R'}{\overset{R}{\diagup}}\kern-6pt\text{C-OH} & \underset{}{\overset{HN_3}{\rightleftharpoons}} & R'-\underset{\underset{OH}{|}}{\overset{\overset{R}{|}}{C}}-\overset{\overset{H}{|}}{N}-\overset{+}{N}{\equiv}N & \rightleftharpoons & \underset{R'}{\overset{R}{\diagup}}\kern-6pt\text{C=N}\underset{\overset{+}{N{\equiv}N}}{\diagdown} & \overset{-N_2}{\longrightarrow} & R'-\overset{+}{C}{=}N{-}R & \overset{H_2O}{\longrightarrow} & R'-\underset{\overset{\|}{O}}{C}-NHR \\
XXV & & XXVI & & XXVII & & XXVIII
\end{array}
$$

Here, cation **XXV** is the conjugate acid of the aldehyde or ketone used. Once again we have suggested that N_2 is lost from cation **XXVII** rather than its hydrated form, **XXVI**, because of the presumed reluctance of alkyl and aryl azides to undergo an analogous reaction.[19] When an aldehyde is used, the intermediate corresponding to **XXVIII**, formed from hydride migration, is $R{-}\overset{+}{C}{=}N{-}H$. This cation may be assumed to form the observed nitrile directly (by loss of a proton), rather than being first converted to the amide, for under the conditions of the Schmidt reaction, amides cannot generally be dehydrated to nitriles.

With unsymmetric ketones the question arises as to which of the two possible amides will predominate. The intermediate from which nitrogen is presumably lost (cation **XXVII**) has a structure very much like that of an oxime. In analogy with the Beckmann rearrangement, we should then expect the migrating group to approach the migration terminus (the left-hand nitrogen in **XXVII**) from one side while N_2 leaves from the opposite side. When group R— lies *trans* (*anti*) to the azido group, then R— will migrate; when group R' lies *trans* to the azido group, then R'— will migrate. Cation **XXVII** will probably exist in both possible forms, but that form will predominate in which the larger of the two groups lies *trans* to the azido group (for in this form, steric interference will be less). We would thus expect the bulkier of the two groups in the parent ketone to

---

[19] However, it has been found (Boyer and Hamer, *J. Am. Chem. Soc.*, **77**, 951 (1955)) that β-azido alcohols (**XXIX**) react with aromatic aldehydes in concentrated sulfuric acid to give 2-aryloxazolines (**XXX**). It is possible that this reaction proceeds by a path analogous to that proposed for the Schmidt reaction.

$$
\begin{array}{ccccccc}
\underset{\overset{|}{OH}}{\overset{+}{ArCH}} + HOCH_2CHR{-}N_3 & \rightleftharpoons & Ar\underset{\underset{\overset{|}{OH}}{CH}}{\overset{\overset{H}{|}}{\underset{HO}{C}}}\kern-4pt{-}\overset{}{N}{-}\overset{+}{N}{\equiv}N\diagdown_{CHR} & \overset{-N_2}{\longrightarrow} & \underset{\underset{HO-CH_2}{\uparrow}}{\overset{\overset{OH}{|}}{Ar\overset{+}{C}}}\kern-4pt{-}NH\diagdown_{CHR} & \overset{-H^+}{\underset{-H_2O}{\longrightarrow}} & \underset{\overset{|}{O-CH_2}}{Ar C}{=}N\diagdown_{CHR} \\
& & XXIX & & & & XXX
\end{array}
$$

migrate preferentially in the Schmidt reaction, and this, generally speaking, is what is observed.[20] The ethyl group migrates preferentially in methyl ethyl ketone, the phenyl group in acetophenone, but very nearly equal quantities of the two possible amides are obtained from isobutyrophenone. Moreover, unsymmetrically *para*-substituted benzophenones generally give nearly equal quantities of both amides, for *para* substituents are held well out of the way of the departing nitrogen molecule and their steric effects in this reaction are negligible.

When an excess of HN_3 is used in the Schmidt reaction, a substituted *tetrazole* (**XXXI**) may be formed.[21] Since amides themselves do not react with HN_3 to form tetrazoles, we may assume that this product is formed by the action of a second molecule of hydrazoic acid on intermediate **XXVIII**.

$$R-N=\overset{+}{C}-R' + H-N-N\equiv N \longrightarrow R-N=C-R' \xrightarrow{-H^+} R-N \underline{\hspace{2cm}} C-R'$$

XXVIII

XXXI

(a tetrazole)

Both the Curtius and Schmidt rearrangements have analogs in which the leaving group is a N_2 molecule and the migration terminus is an electron-deficient but uncharged *carbon* atom. The *Wolff rearrangement* of diazoketones[22] is formally similar to the Curtius rearrangement, and may be assigned the mechanism:

a diazomethyl ketone   **XXXII**   a ketene

---

[20] Sanford, Blair, Arroya, and Sherk, *J. Am. Chem. Soc.*, **67,** 1942 (1945). See also Alexander, *Principles of Ionic Organic Reactions*, John Wiley and Sons, Inc., New York, 1950, p. 71. For recent evidence that electronic effects play little part in determining migratory aptitudes in the Schmidt reaction, see Saunders and Ware, *J. Am. Chem. Soc.*, **80,** 3328 (1958).

[21] Spielman and Austin, *J. Am. Chem. Soc.*, **59,** 2658 (1937).

[22] Diazoketones, $R-\overset{O}{\overset{\|}{C}}-CH-N_2$, are generally prepared from acyl halides and diazomethane, CH_2N_2. The Wolff rearrangement is the characteristic step in the *Arndt-Eistert synthesis* by which a carboxylic acid R—COOH is converted to its homolog, R—CH₂COOH. For a review of this method, see Bachmann and Struve in *Organic Reactions* (edited by Adams), John Wiley and Sons, Inc., New York, 1942, Vol. I, p. 38.

The following evidence supports this mechanism: (a) the carbonyl carbon in the diazomethyl ketone becomes the carboxyl carbon in the resulting acid (as has been shown in studies with C^{13});[23(a)] (b) group R— migrates with *retention* of configuration;[23(b)] and (c) in favorable cases and in the absence of water or alcohols, the intermediate ketene may be isolated.[23(c)] We have suggested here that the loss of nitrogen occurs before, rather than concurrently with the migration of R—, for one of the products sometimes resulting from the decomposition of the diazo ketone in water is the hydroxy ketone, R—C—CH₂OH. While it is

$$\underset{O}{\overset{\|}{R-C-CH_2OH}}$$

possible that this could result directly from the diazo ketone itself, it seems more likely that it is formed by hydrolysis of the electron-deficient species **XXXII** during the short time interval between the departure of N_2 and the rearrangement to the ketene.

$$\underset{\textbf{XXXII}}{\overset{O}{\overset{\|}{R-C-CH:}}} + H_2O \rightarrow \underset{-}{\overset{O}{\overset{\|}{R-C-\overset{..}{C}H-\overset{+}{O}}}} \overset{H}{\underset{H}{\diagup}} \rightarrow \underset{O}{\overset{\|}{R-C-CH_2OH}}$$

There is, however, one important feature of the Wolff rearrangement which the proposed heterolytic mechanism does not explain; it is often effectively catalyzed by silver compounds (for example, Ag_2O, $Ag(NMe_3)_2^+OBz^-$) under basic conditions. Since univalent silver may act as a single-electron acceptor, we cannot dismiss the possibility that this rearrangement, at least in some cases, may proceed by a free-radical mechanism such as the following:[24]

$$\underset{O}{\overset{\|}{R-C-CHN_2}} \overset{B:}{\rightleftarrows} \underset{O}{\overset{\|}{R-C-\overset{..}{C}-N\equiv N}} \overset{Ag^+}{\longrightarrow} \overset{O}{\overset{\|}{R\diagdown C}} \underset{}{C-N=N} \overset{-N_2}{\longrightarrow} O=C=\underset{.}{C}-R$$

$$\text{then } R-\overset{.}{C}=C=O + \underset{O}{\overset{\|}{R-C-CHN_2}} \rightarrow \left\{ \begin{array}{l} R-\overset{\overset{H}{|}}{C}=C=O \overset{H_2O}{\longrightarrow} RCH_2COOH \\ R-\overset{+}{\underset{O}{\overset{\|}{C}}}-\overset{.}{C}-N\equiv N \overset{-N_2}{\longrightarrow} \text{etc.} \end{array} \right.$$

Such a sequence, in the absence of further investigation, must be regarded as tentative.

The reaction of ketones with diazomethane is similar to their reaction with

[23] (a) Huggett, Arnold, and Taylor, *J. Am. Chem. Soc.*, **64**, 3043 (1942). (b) Lane and Wallis, *ibid.*, **63**, 1674, (1941); Wiberg and Hutton, *ibid.*, **78**, 1640 (1956). (c) Staudinger and Hirzel, *Ber.*, **49**, 2523 (1916); Schroeter, *Ber.*, **42**, 2346 (1909); **49**, 2704 (1916).

[24] Newman and Beal, *J. Am. Chem. Soc.*, **72**, 2438 (1950).

hydrazoic acid (CH_2N_2 and HN_3 have like structures and have the same number of electrons). With diazomethane the chief product is generally a new ketone having an extra —CH_2— linkage adjacent to the carbonyl group, with a substituted ethylene oxide formed in minor amounts.[25] In the absence of quantitative data concerning this reaction, we may provisionally assign to it the following mechanism (in analogy with the Schmidt reaction):

$$R{-}\underset{\underset{O}{\|}}{C}{-}R' + :CH_2{-}N{\equiv}N \rightarrow R'{-}\underset{\underset{O}{\diagup}}{C}{-}\underset{\underset{H}{|}}{\overset{\overset{R}{\diagdown}\ \ \overset{H}{|}}{C}}{-}\overset{+}{N}{\equiv}N$$

XXXIII

$$\xrightarrow[\text{(R- shifts)}]{-N_2} R'{-}\underset{\underset{O}{\|}}{C}{-}CH_2R$$

$$\xrightarrow[\text{(attack by -O-)}]{-N_2} \underset{R'}{\overset{R}{\diagdown}}C{\diagdown\diagup}\overset{CH_2}{\underset{O}{}}$$

Here, it is suggested that loss of nitrogen from intermediate XXXIII may be accompanied either by shift of R (or R′), yielding a ketone, or by attack by the negatively charged oxygen atom, forming the epoxide ring.

Rearrangements of Peroxy Derivatives

Depending upon conditions, an O—O bond may break homolytically (—O—O— → 2·O—), or heterolytically (—O—O— → $^{-}:\ddot{O}— + {}^{+}\ddot{O}—$), and in some cases both modes of breakage may operate together. This duality complicates the study of the reactions of peroxides and peroxy derivatives, although there are a number of diagnostic tests which, when taken together, will tell with some reliability whether homolytic or heterolytic cleavage is occurring.

Peroxy acids $\left(R{-}\underset{\underset{O}{\|}}{\overset{\overset{O}{\|}}{C}}{-}O{-}O{-}H \right)$ attack ketones in a manner which is formally analogous to attack by diazomethane or by hydrazoic acid. Diazomethane, as we have seen, interposes a —CH_2— group between the —$\underset{\underset{O}{\|}}{C}$— group and an α-carbon, whereas hydrazoic acid interposes an —NH— group in this position. Peroxy acids insert an —O— linkage, thus converting the ketone

$R{-}\underset{\underset{O}{\|}}{C}{-}R'$ to the ester $R{-}\underset{\underset{O}{\|}}{C}{-}OR'$, to the ester $R'{-}\underset{\underset{O}{\|}}{\overset{\overset{O}{\|}}{C}}{-}OR$, or to a mixture of

[25] Adamson and Kenner, *J. Chem. Soc.*, **1939**, 181; Mosettig and Burger, *J. Am. Chem. Soc.*, **52**, 3456 (1930).

the two. It has been shown, using labeled oxygen, that the carbonyl oxygen in the ketone becomes the acyl oxygen in the resulting ester,[26(a)] and, in further analogy to the Schmidt reaction, the migrating alkyl group has been found to shift with *retention* of configuration.[26(b)] We thus may infer that, as with HN_3, the peroxy acid first adds to the C=O linkage, and that the adduct (XXXIV) then suffers heterolytic cleavage at the O—O bond while (or just before) a 1,2 shift

$$
\text{Ac-OOH} + R_2\overset{\overset{\displaystyle H}{\underset{|}{\text{O}^+}}}{\text{C}} \rightleftharpoons R_2\overset{\overset{\displaystyle HO}{|}}{\underset{\underset{\displaystyle H}{|}}{\text{C}}}\overset{+}{-\text{O}}-\text{OAc} \xrightarrow{-\text{H}^+} \underset{\underset{\displaystyle R}{|}\,\underset{\displaystyle OH}{}}{\overset{\overset{\displaystyle R}{}}{\text{C}}}-\text{O}-\text{OAc} \xrightarrow{-\text{OAc}^-}
$$

$$
\text{peroxyacetic acid}
$$

XXXIV

$$
\underset{+}{R-\overset{\overset{\displaystyle OH}{|}}{C}-OR} \xrightarrow{-\text{H}^+} R\overset{\overset{\displaystyle O}{||}}{C}OR
$$

occurs from carbon to oxygen. (As yet, we cannot say whether the formation of the adduct or its rearrangement is rate determining.)

We would anticipate that when an unsymmetric ketone is subjected to this reaction, the identity of the predominant migration group will depend on the "migratory aptitudes" of the two substituents, and, when these substituents differ significantly in bulk, on conformational effects as well. Migratory aptitudes alone should govern the direction of rearrangement of unsymmetrically *para*-substituted benzophenones; for, as in the Schmidt reaction, the steric effects of *para* substituents should be negligible. Accordingly, it is not surprising that when this reaction is carried out with peroxyacetic acid in glacial acetic acid, the *p*-anisyl group is found to be a "better" migrator than the phenyl group, which is, in turn, a better migrator than the *p*-nitrophenyl group.[27] As in the pinacol rearrangement, the more nucleophilic substituents appear to shift more easily, probably because of the ease with which they form "bridged" intermediates or transition states. Under the same conditions, benzoylcyclohexane gives very nearly equal (but small) yields of the two possible esters. Here, it may be supposed that although the benzene ring has a much greater "intrinsic" migratory aptitude than the cyclohexyl group, the peroxy intermediate prefers conformation XXXV, in which the bulky cyclohexyl group lies *trans* to the acetate, and therefore in a position favoring cyclohexyl migration.[28] On the other hand, when

[26] (a) Doering and Dorfman, *J. Am. Chem. Soc.*, **75**, 5595 (1953); Bunton, Lewis, and Llewellyn, *J. Chem. Soc.*, **1956**, 1226. (b) Mislow and Brenner, *J. Am. Chem. Soc.*, **75**, 2318 (1953).

[27] Doering and Speers, *J. Am. Chem. Soc.*, **72**, 5515 (1950).

[28] It should be noted that the populations of the various conformations of intermediate XXXV can affect the ratio of products only if rotation about the C—O bond is slow compared

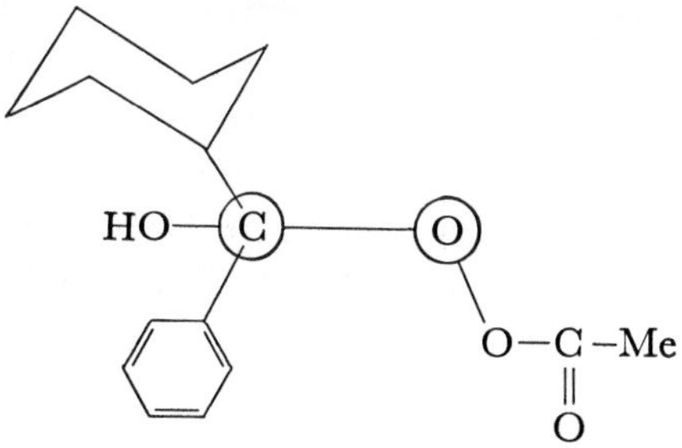

HO—C———O

O—C—Me
‖
O

XXXV

the same reaction is carried out in chloroform, cyclohexyl migration greatly predominates over phenyl migration,[29] although neither migratory aptitudes nor conformational effects should vary with the solvent used. It is probable then that a free-radical mechanism has become predominant in the less polar solvent, and it may well be that a significant, though smaller, fraction of the reaction proceeds by a radical path in the more polar solvents also. We may assume that adduct **XXXIV′** is common to both mechanisms, a possible path for its homolytic decomposition being as follows:

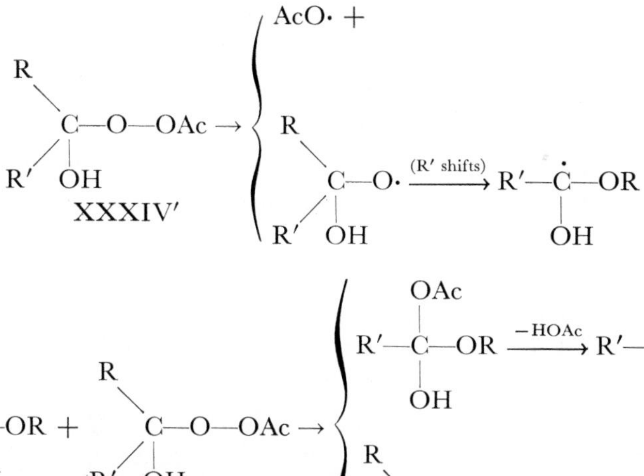

AcO· +

R
\
   C—O—OAc →
  / |
R′ OH
   XXXIV′

R
\
   C—O· $\xrightarrow{(R' \text{ shifts})}$ R′—C—OR
  / | |
R′ OH   OH

then,

R′—C—OR +
    |
    OH

R
\
   C—O—OAc →
  / |
R′ OH
   XXXIV

OAc
|
R′—C—OR $\xrightarrow{-\text{HOAc}}$ R′—C—OR
| ‖
OH   O

R
\
   C—O· $\xrightarrow{\text{etc.}}$
  / |
R′ OH

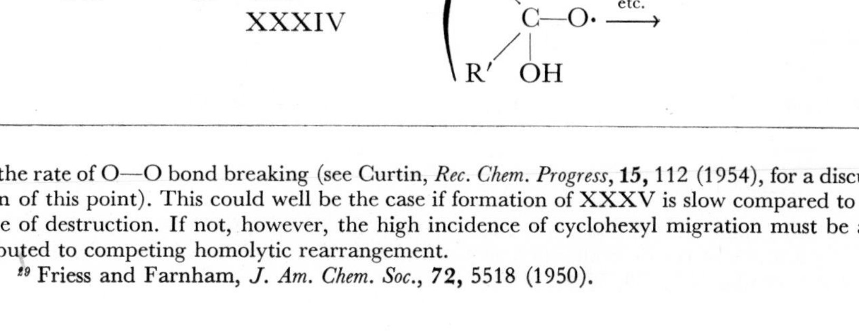

to the rate of O—O bond breaking (see Curtin, *Rec. Chem. Progress*, **15**, 112 (1954), for a discussion of this point). This could well be the case if formation of **XXXV** is slow compared to its rate of destruction. If not, however, the high incidence of cyclohexyl migration must be attributed to competing homolytic rearrangement.

[29] Friess and Farnham, *J. Am. Chem. Soc.*, **72**, 5518 (1950).

(Chain-reaction mechanisms, of which this is one, are to be considered in the following chapter.)

A similar duality in mechanism is associated with the decomposition of *p*-methoxy-*p*'-nitrobenzoylperoxide (XXXVI).[30] In nitrobenzene and in thionyl chloride, this unsymmetric diacyl peroxide rearranges predominately to carbonate XXXVIII. The preferential mode of heterolysis of the O—O bond is

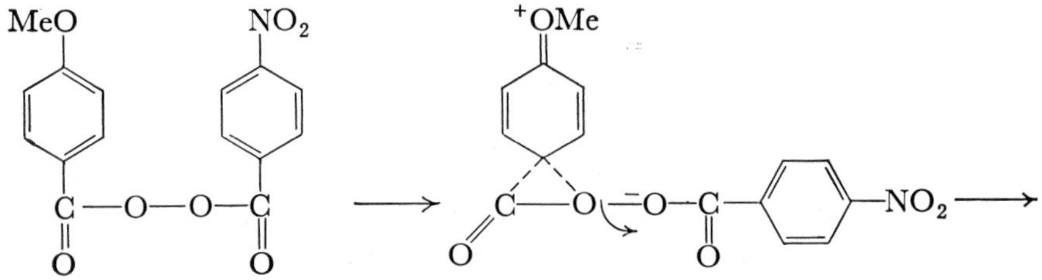

XXXVI → XXXVII

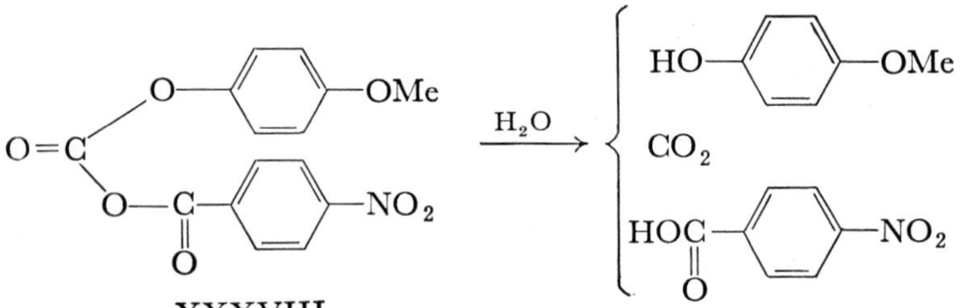

XXXVIII

in the direction shown (XXXVII), rather than in the opposite direction (which would result in formation of *p*-nitrophenol and *p*-methoxybenzoic acid), doubtless because the nitro group is a much stronger electron attractor than the methoxy group. Conversely, the *p*-anisyl group is far more effective in stabilizing the positively charged fragment. However, when the decomposition of peroxide XXXVI is carried out in benzene, very nearly equal quantities of *p*-nitrobenzoic and *p*-methoxybenzoic acids are formed, along with little, if any, phenolic

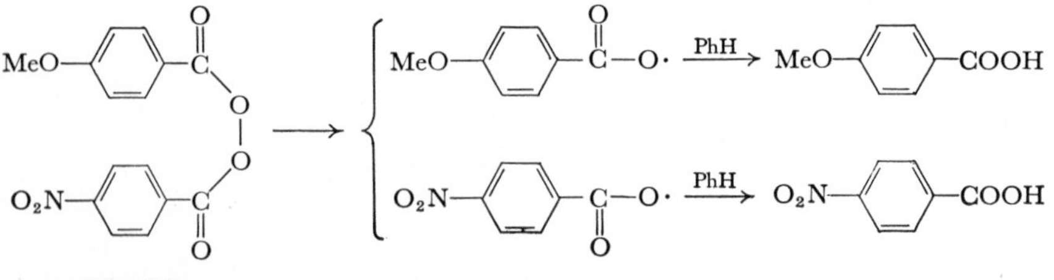

XXXVI

[30] (*a*) Leffler, *J. Am. Chem. Soc.*, **72**, 67 (1950). (*b*) Denney, *ibid.*, **78**, 590 (1956). (*c*) For a similar study of the decomposition of 4-methoxy-3′,5′-dinitrobenzoyl peroxide, see Leffler and Petropoulos, *ibid.*, **79**, 3068 (1957).

products.[30(a)] Under these poorly ionizing conditions, radical decomposition has evidently taken over.

The benzoate and substituted benzoates (XXXIX) of trans-9-decalyl hydroperoxide constitute an interesting series. These rearrange with migration of a bridgehead carbon, yielding derivatives of 1,6-epoxycyclodecane (XL).[31(a)]

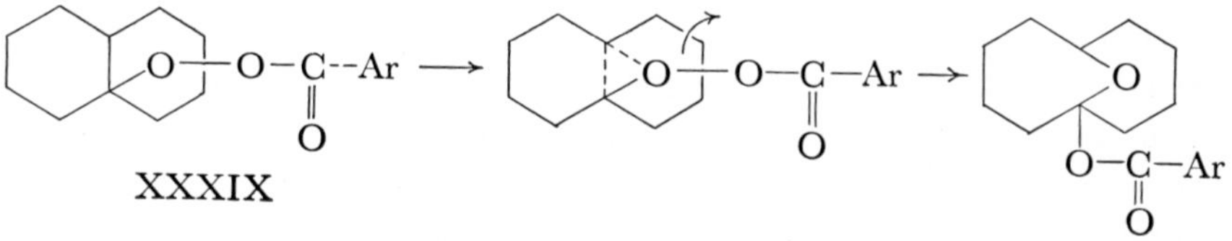

XXXIX

XL

This is obviously a heterolytic reaction, for the rates of rearrangement may be greatly increased by transferring the reaction from nonpolar to polar solvents. Electron-attracting substituents on the benzene ring (which improve the "departing effectiveness" of $Ar-\overset{\overset{O}{\|}}{C}-O^-$) accelerate the rearrangement, whereas electron-donating groups retard it.[31(b)] At present it appears that the movement of the benzoate ion (or substituted benzoate ion) is concurrent with the formation of the new C—O bond in the ring—that is, that the transition state may be represented as XLI. For if the rearrangement of the peroxybenzoate

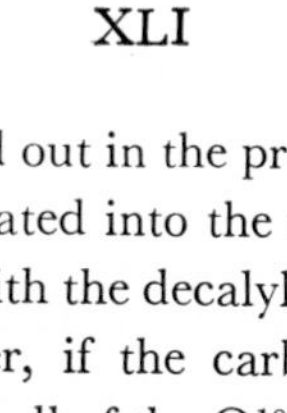

XLI

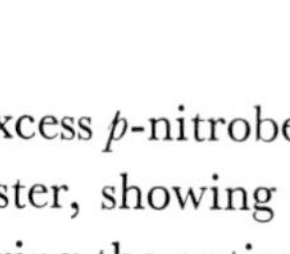

XLII

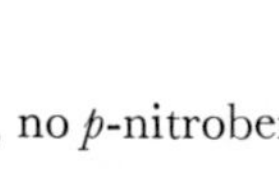

XLIII

is carried out in the presence of excess p-nitrobenzoate ion, no p-nitrobenzoate is incorporated into the resulting ester, showing that the benzoate ion stays associated with the decalyl system during the entire course of the rearrangement.[31(c)] Moreover, if the carbonyl oxygen of the peroxy ester is labeled with O^{18}, virtually all of the O^{18} in the resulting epoxy ester, XL, is found in the carbonyl group,[31(d)] whereas if the anion had strayed far enough from the decalyl system to allow the two benzoate oxygens to become equivalent, only half of the O^{18} should remain in the carbonyl group. In retrospect, it is not surprising that this

[31] (a) Criegee, Kaspar, and Dietrich, Ann., 560, 127, 135 (1948). (b) Bartlett and Kice, J. Am. Chem. Soc., 75, 5591 (1953). (c) Goering and Olson, ibid., 75, 5853 (1953). (d) Denney and Denney, ibid., 77, 1706 (1955); 79, 4806 (1957).

rearrangement does not pass through "classical" (nonbridged) cations. An "oxonium" ion such as XLII, having a positive charge solely on an oxygen atom, would be expected to be quite unstable, and a carbonium ion such as XLIII would have a positively charged carbon at the bridgehead of a bicyclic system—a very unfavorable location, since coplanarity of the bonds to that carbon would involve considerable strain (p. 280).

The geometric relationship between the positive and negative ions in the rearrangement of the unsymmetric diacyl peroxide XXXVI is more complex. When the carbonyl oxygen of the *p*-nitrobenzoyl group in the peroxide is labeled with O^{18}, only about 66 percent of the labeled oxygen is found in the *p*-nitrobenzoyl group, the other 34 percent being found at the position *between* the two carbonyl groups in the product. Thus, the rearrangement cannot proceed *solely* through ion pair XLIV nor *wholly* through XLV; for if the reaction chose the first of these paths, *none* of the labeled oxygen would move to the position between the carbonyl groups, whereas with the second path, *all* of the labeled oxygen would so move. Moreover, the reaction cannot proceed solely through an ion pair in which the carbonyl oxygens in the nitrobenzoate ion have

become equivalent, for in this case, just one half of the labeled oxygen would be found at the position between the two carbonyl groups. The observed degree of O^{18} rearrangement is, however, consistent with a combination of two or all three of these paths, or alternately, with an intermediate such as XLVI, in which the carboxyl oxygens of the *p*-nitrobenzoate group are not equidistant from the carbonyl carbon of the *p*-anisoyl group. In the latter case two modes of formation of the new C—O bond would be possible, but attachment by the unlabeled oxygen would predominate.

The Benzilic Acid and Related Rearrangements

The benzilic-acid rearrangement—the conversion in strong base of aromatic 1,2-diketones to salts of α-hydroxycarboxylic acids—is a 1,2 shift in which the migration terminus is a slightly electron-deficient carbon atom of a $C{=}O$ group.

| a benzil | XLVII | | anion of benzilic acid |

In our present picture for the mechanism of this rearrangement, the migration may be said to be due more to a "push" from the electron-rich migration origin than to a "pull" by the migration terminus. The second-order rate law for the reaction (first order each in diketone and hydroxide)[32(a)] does not tell us whether the formation of adduct XLVII is fast or is rate determining (or, indeed, whether this anion is actually an intermediate or merely an activated complex). However, the observation that the diketone undergoes O^{18} exchange in oxygen-labeled water in the presence of base, at a rate much greater than that of the rearrangement,[32(b)] indicates that XLVII is an intermediate and that its formation is rapid and reversible.[33] (The reasoning here is the same as that used to

demonstrate the existence of the intermediate $R'{-}\overset{\overset{\displaystyle OH}{|}}{\underset{\underset{\displaystyle OR}{|}}{C}}{-}O^-$ in ester saponifica-

tion, p. 317.)

[32] (a) Westheimer, *J. Am. Chem. Soc.*, **58**, 2209 (1936). (b) Roberts and Urey, *ibid.*, **60**, 880 (1938).

[33] It has been suggested (see, for example, Clark, Hendley, and Neville, *J. Am. Chem. Soc.*, **77**, 3280 (1955)) that the rate-determining step of the benzilic acid rearrangement involves simultaneous aryl migration and proton transfer. However, the rearrangement of benzil has

been found (Hine and Haworth, *J. Am. Chem. Soc.*, **80**, 2274 (1958)) to proceed almost *twice as rapidly* in D₂O-dioxane (in which OD⁻ becomes attached to the migration origin) as in H₂O-dioxane (in which OH⁻ becomes attached). This indicates strongly that proton transfer is *not* involved in the rate-determining step, for proton transfers are known almost invariably to be faster than deuteron transfers (see, for example, Wiberg, *Chem. Revs.*, **55**, 713 (1955)). The observed increase in reaction rate as D₂O is substituted for H₂O in this case is almost certainly due to the fact that OD⁻ is a considerably stronger base than OH⁻; (see, for example, Nelson and Butler, *J. Chem. Soc.*, **1938**, 957).

The *benzilic ester rearrangement* is a closely allied reaction, but here the initial attack is by alkoxide (for example, MeO^-, t-BuO^-) rather than by hydroxide. As may be expected, the product is an ester, $Ar_2C(OH)$—$COOR$, rather than the salt of a benzilic acid.[34] This variant does not proceed well with EtO^- or i-PrO^-,[35] for these anions readily reduce benzil to benzoin. The reaction also fails with phenoxides and substituted phenoxides,[32(a)] presumably because these anions are too weakly basic to carry out the initial attack.

In a similar manner, an aryl group is "pushed" from one carbon to another in the reaction of o-tolylmagnesium bromide with benzil. In this case, the product is the α-hydroxy-ketone XLIX, formed by phenyl migration:[36]

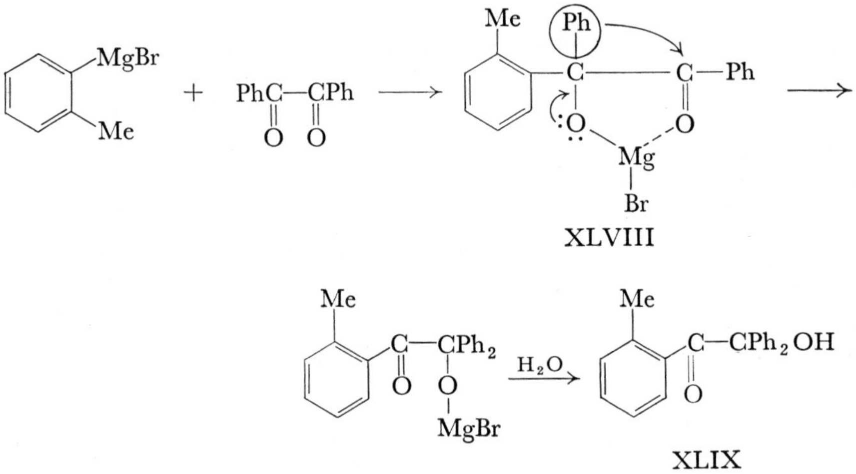

XLVIII

XLIX

It is likely that this rearrangement is facilitated by chelation with the magnesium atom (XLVIII), which increases the electrophilic character of the carbonyl group in the initial adduct. Note that the phenyl group migrates in preference to the somewhat more nucleophilic o-tolyl group, for, as is often the case, migration of an *ortho*-substituted aryl group involves an unduly crowded transition state.

Nucleophilic "push" and electrophilic "pull" probably operate together also in the rearrangement of the bromomagnesium derivative of the *cis*-chlorohydrin, L.[37] As shown in structure LI, the (partial) positive charge on the magnesium "pulls" at the chlorine while the (partial) negative charge on the oxygen facilitates the shift of the methyl group. In accord with this picture, the

[34] Doering and Urban, *J. Am. Chem. Soc.*, **78**, 5938 (1956).

[35] Lachmann, *J. Am. Chem. Soc.*, **45**, 1509 (1923).

[36] Roger and McGregor, *J. Chem. Soc.*, **1934**, 442. An analogous rearrangement has been observed with mesitylmagnesium bromide (Ref. 34).

[37] Geissman and Akawie, *J. Am. Chem. Soc.*, **73**, 1993 (1951).

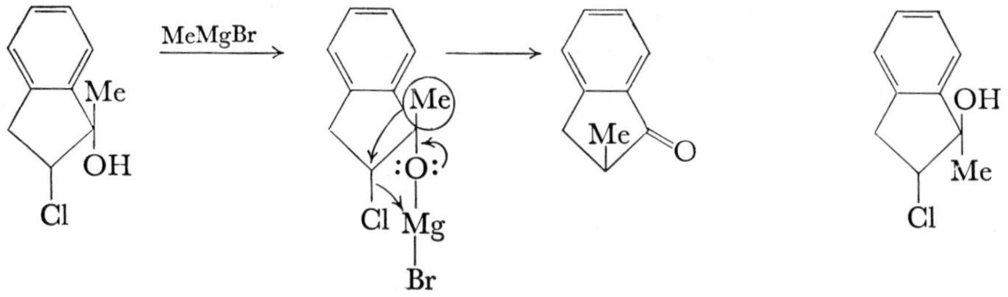

L LI LII LIII

trans isomer of L (chlorohydrin LIII) gives only traces of ketone LII when treated with MeMgBr.

Rearrangements of Aldehydes and Ketones in Acid

Protonation of a carbonyl group greatly increases its electrophilic character and may initiate rearrangement when nearby alkyl or aryl groups are in a position favorable for migration (and when a shift is energetically advantageous). Little quantitative study has been devoted to such rearrangements, but they are believed to proceed in much the same way as the pinacol rearrangement. The simplest occur with α-hydroxy-aldehydes and α-hydroxy-ketones. In the first of

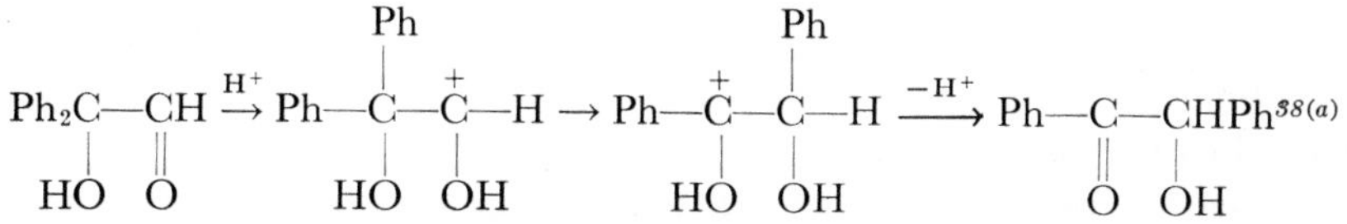

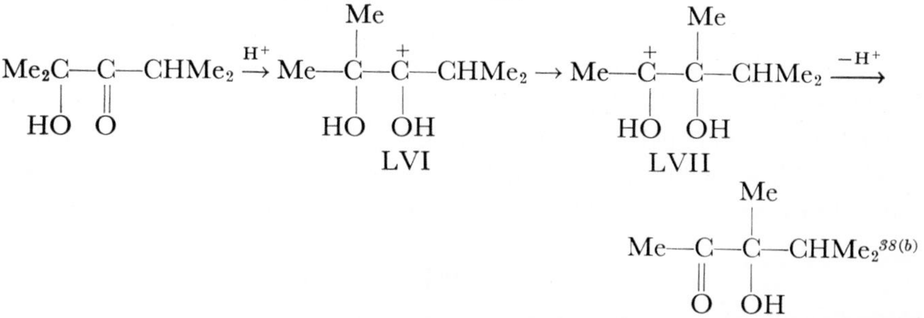

these, the system gains stability as a result of the conversion of LIV to LV, since in the latter the positive charge lies adjacent to a benzene ring and may distribute itself over the ring (p. 253). In the second rearrangement, the system gains hyperconjugative stability when LVI is transformed to LVII, for in the LVII

---

[38] (a) Danilov and Venus-Danilova, *Ber.*, **59**, 377, 1032 (1926); **60**, 2390 (1927). (b) Oumnov, *Bull. Soc. chim. France*, **43**, 568 (1928).

there are three hydrogens in the β positions, whereas in LVI there is only a single hydrogen. (A bridged carbonium-ion intermediate may intervene in the first rearrangement, but probably not in the second.)

The rearrangements of nonhydroxylated aldehydes and ketones in strong acid are more complex, for each of these reactions requires at least two shifts; for example,

These isomerizations are, in essence, exchanges of substituents between the carbonyl carbon and the carbon *alpha* to it. In the first of the rearrangements above, that of diphenylacetaldehyde, a phenyl group moves to the carbonyl carbon, after which a hydrogen shifts back to the α-carbon. In the second rearrangement, that of hexamethylacetone (LVIII), a shift of a methyl is followed by the "back shift" of a t-butyl group. A second path for conversions of the type LVIII → LX might be considered;[40] intermediate LIX could conceivably "close" to a protonated epoxide ring, LXI, which might then undergo ring opening with a methyl shift (rearrangements of this type have been observed with substituted ethylene oxides[40(b)]). However, this alternate path is ruled out

[39] (a) Barton and Porter, *J. Chem. Soc.*, **1956**, 2483; (b) Zook and Paviak, *J. Am. Chem. Soc.*, **77**, 2501 (1955).
[40] (a) Zook, Smith, and Greene, *J. Am. Chem. Soc.*, **79**, 4436 (1957). (b) See, for example, Lagrave, *Ann. chim.*, **8**, 363 (1927).

(at least in the example shown) by carrying out the rearrangement on a sample of ketone LVIII that has been labeled at the carbonyl carbon with C^{14}, for it has thus been demonstrated that the carbonyl carbon in ketone LVIII remains a carbonyl carbon in ketone LX.[39(a)] If the rearrangement proceeded through a protonated ethylene oxide as shown, the carbonyl carbon in LVIII would become an α-carbon in LX.

In the *dieneone-phenol rearrangement*, the migration terminus is not the carbon of a protonated carbonyl group, but rather a carbon in conjugation with it. As the name implies, this reaction results in the transformation of a quinoid structure to a benzenoid ring. Typically, treatment of ketone LXII with sulfuric acid and acetic anhydride yields acetate LXIII.[41(a)] In a like manner, ketone

LXIV, when treated with acid, yields naphthol LVX;[41(b)] as we might have predicted, the phenyl, rather than the methyl group, has shifted. Similarly, dienone LXVI yields 6-hydroxytetralin (LXVII).[42]

[41] (a) Arnold, Buckley, and Richter, *J. Am. Chem. Soc.*, **69**, 2322 (1947). (b) Arnold and Buckley, *ibid.*, **71**, 1781 (1949).
[42] Winstein, Heck, and Baird, *J. Am. Chem. Soc.*, **79**, 3109 (1957).

Rearrangements Proceeding through Carbanions or Related Species

One of the simplest rearrangements involving a carbanionlike intermediate is the *Stevens rearrangement*,[43] an early example of which is shown below:

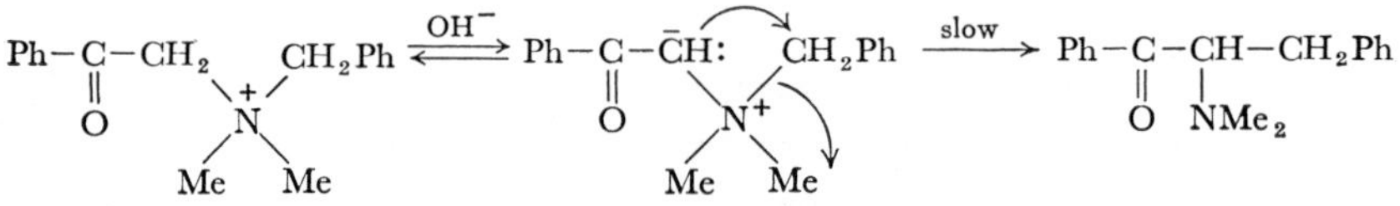

$$\text{Ph-C-CH}_2 \quad \text{CH}_2\text{Ph} \; \underset{\text{OH}^-}{\rightleftharpoons} \; \text{Ph-C-}\bar{\text{C}}\text{H:} \quad \text{CH}_2\text{Ph} \; \xrightarrow{\text{slow}} \; \text{Ph-C-CH-CH}_2\text{Ph}$$

LXVIII

(Note that the proposed intermediate, LXVIII, is not actually a carbanion, but instead a type of "zwitterion" in which the negative pole has carbanion character.) The evidence pointing to the mechanism above is relatively straightforward. First, the rearrangement does not proceed readily when the benzoyl group is replaced by a phenyl or alkyl group, these being relatively ineffective in "labilizing" the hydrogens on an adjacent methylene group.[44] Secondly, although the reaction is accelerated by base, a limit is reached when slightly more than one equivalent is added, at which point virtually all of the substrate has been converted to its conjugate base, LXVIII. Thirdly, when the rearrangement is carried out on the optically active ammonium ion, LXIX, the α-phenylethyl group migrates with retention of configuration,[45] indicating that the new C—C bond is formed and the old C—N bond breaks on the same side of C_α. Finally,

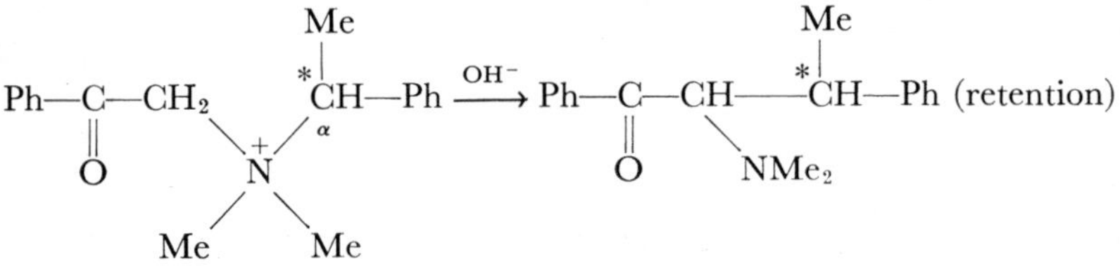

$$\text{Ph-C-CH}_2 \quad \overset{*}{\text{C}}\text{H-Ph} \; \xrightarrow{\text{OH}^-} \; \text{Ph-C-CH} \quad \overset{*}{\text{C}}\text{H-Ph} \; (\text{retention})$$

LXIX

the rearrangement is retarded by incorporation of electron-attracting substituents (—Cl, —NO$_2$, etc.) into the benzoyl group,[43] for these lower the electron density at the negatively charged attacking carbon.

---

[43] Stevens, *et al.*, *J. Chem. Soc.*, **1928**, 3193; **1930**, 2107, 2119; **1932**, 55, 1926; **1934**, 279.

[44] In the absence of a carbonyl, or similar acid-strengthening group, the α-hydrogen may be removed, and the Stevens rearrangement made to proceed, by use of an organolithium compound (Wittig, Mangold, and Felletschin, *Ann.*, **580**, 116 (1948)).

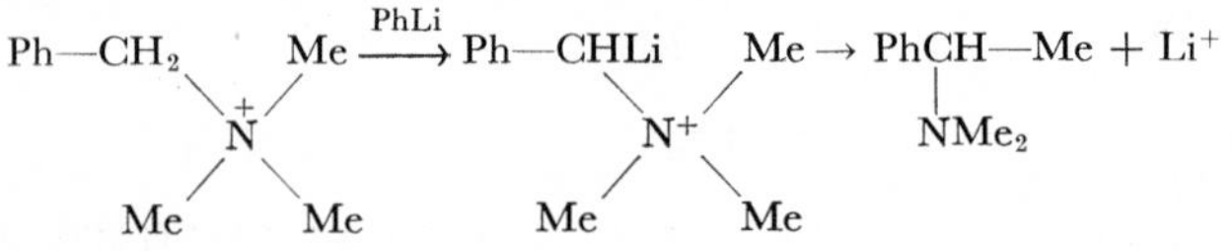

$$\text{Ph-CH}_2 \quad \text{Me} \; \xrightarrow{\text{PhLi}} \; \text{Ph-CHLi} \quad \text{Me} \to \text{PhCH-Me} + \text{Li}^+$$

[45] Campbell, Houston, and Kenyon, *J. Chem. Soc.*, **1947**, 93; Brewster and Kline, *J. Am. Chem. Soc.*, **74**, 5179 (1952).

Similar rearrangements have been observed with sulfonium salts, and, under sufficiently drastic conditions, with benzyl or allyl ethers.

$$Ph-\underset{\underset{O}{\|}}{C}-CH_2 \quad \underset{\underset{Me}{|}}{\underset{S_+}{}}CH_2Ph \xrightarrow{OH^-} Ph-\underset{\underset{O}{\|}}{C}-\bar{C}H: \quad \underset{\underset{Me}{|}}{\underset{S_+}{}}CH_2Ph \longrightarrow Ph-\underset{\underset{O}{\|}}{C}-CH-CH_2Ph \quad \underset{\underset{Me}{|}}{S} \quad 46$$

$$PhCH_2 \quad \underset{O}{} CH_3 \xrightarrow{KNH_2} K^+ \ Ph\bar{C}H: \quad \underset{O}{} CH_3 \longrightarrow PhCH-CH_3 \quad \underset{\underset{K^+}{}}{\underset{-O}{|}} \quad 47$$

(the Wittig rearrangement)

The Stevens and the Wittig rearrangements, which are thought to involve migration of a group *without* its pair of bonding electrons to an *electron-rich* carbon atom, are said by some workers to be *electrophilic rearrangements*, in contrast to the far more usual *nucleophilic rearrangements*, in which a group migrates *with* its pair of bonding electrons to an *electron-deficient* terminus. We shall, however, find it more convenient to regard carbanion rearrangements as internal nucleophilic substitutions (S_Ni reactions), with the negatively charged carbon atom the attacking nucleophile.

The *Sommelet-Hauser rearrangement*[48] is a S_Ni'-type analog (internal nucleophilic substitution with allylic rearrangement, p. 296) of the Stevens rearrangement. When benzyltrimethylammonium salts are treated with NaNH$_2$ in liquid ammonia, removal of the benzyl hydrogen, if it occurs at all, is reversible; whereas removal of a methyl hydrogen results in an attack on the benzene ring. The initial rearrangement product of ammonium ion LXX is the exomethylene derivative LXXI, which is readily isolable.[48(c)] However, when the benzene

LXX   LXXI

ring is not methylated, the corresponding rearrangement product, LXXII, is

---

[46] Thompson and Stevens, *J. Chem. Soc.*, **1932**, 69.

[47] Hauser and Kantor, *J. Am. Chem. Soc.*, **73**, 1437 (1951). See also Wittig, Lohman, and Happe, *Ann.*, **550**, 260 (1942); **557**, 205 (1947).

[48] (a) Hauser, Kantor, and Weinheimer, *J. Am. Chem. Soc.*, **73**, 4122 (1951); **76**, 1264 (1954). (b) Lednicer and Hauser, *ibid.*, **79**, 4449 (1957). (c) Hauser and Van Eenam, *ibid.*, **79**, 5512, 6274, 6277, 6280 (1957). (d) This rearrangement was discovered by Sommelet (*Compt. rend.*, **205**, 56 (1937)), but has been most intensively investigated by Hauser and co-workers.

not isolated; for it may be readily converted, merely by the loss and recovery of a proton, to an aromatic structure, LXXIII.[48(ad),49] An interesting variation of

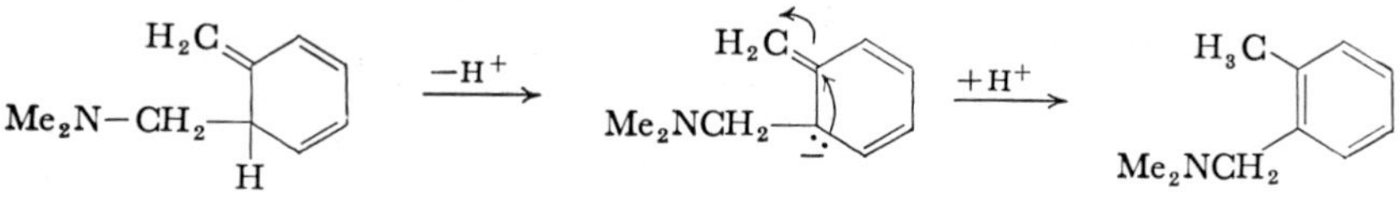

LXXII

LXXIII

this rearrangement has been achieved, using as a substrate the 1,1-dimethyl-2-phenylpiperidinium ion, LXXV.[48(b)] The resulting product has a nine-membered ring containing one nitrogen atom (LXXVI).

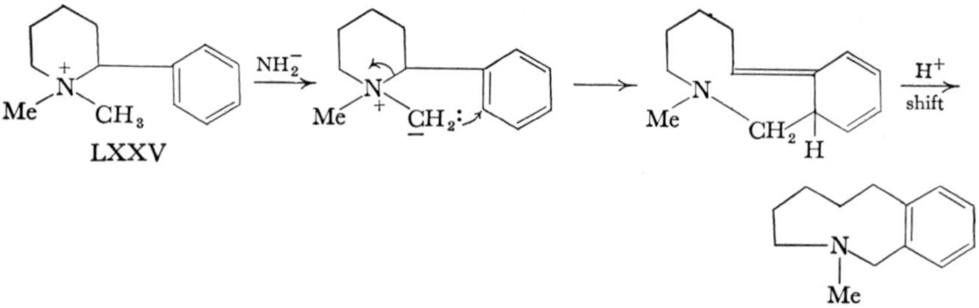

LXXV

LXXVI

In the *Favorskii rearrangement*, an α-halo ketone is transformed to an ester, using alkoxide, or to a carboxylate salt, using hydroxide. The mechanism which

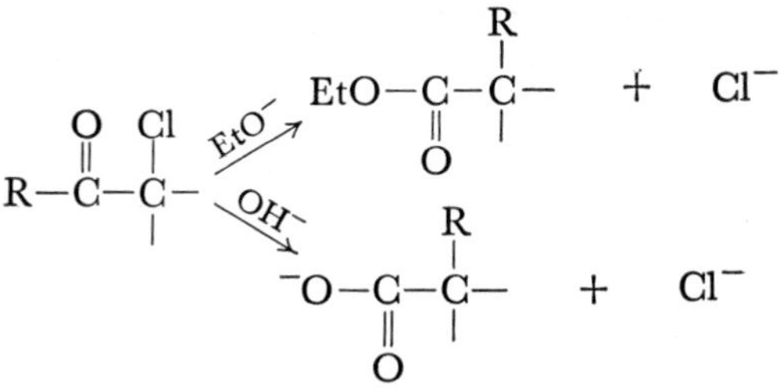

[49] So pronounced is the tendency toward aromatization in this type of rearrangement that even amine LXXI forms an aromatic system (LXXIV) on being heated to 150°.

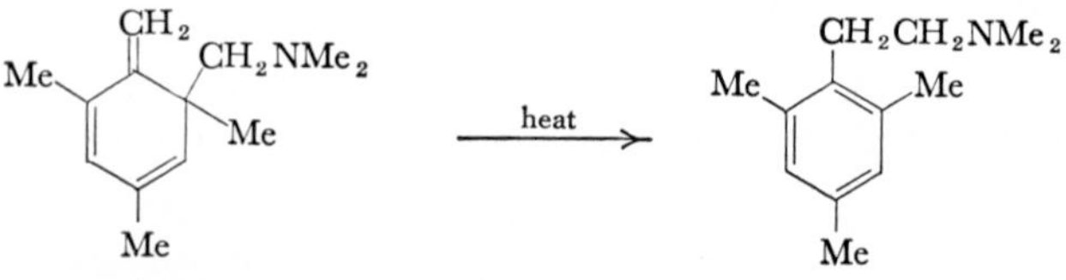

LXXI

LXXIV

The path by which this isomerization proceeds is, at present, unknown.

first comes to mind for such a rearrangement is very similar to that proposed for the benzilic acid and benzilic ester rearrangements; the basic anion attacks the carbonyl group, "pushing" substituent R— to the adjacent carbon where it, in turn, displaces halide. Yet this mechanism cannot be correct for the

rearrangement of 2-chlorocyclohexanone, as has been demonstrated by carrying out the reaction on a sample of this ketone labeled with C^{14} at the chlorinated carbon, LXXVII.[50] As shown, if the reaction proceeds by a path analogous to the benzilic-acid rearrangement, all of the labeled carbon should be present at the α position of the resulting ester, LXXVIII:

LXXVII   LXXVIII

Instead, just half of the labeled carbon is actually found at C_α in the ester, with the other half at C_β. This suggests the intervention of an intermediate in which C_α and C_β are equivalent, specifically the substituted cyclopropanone, LXXX, formed by internal substitution within carbanion LXXIX. The "cyclopro-

LXXIX   LXXX

panone mechanism" for the Favorskii rearrangement is obviously excluded for ketones such as 1-benzoylcyclohexyl chloride, in which the nonhalogenated α-carbon bears no hydrogen atom. Nevertheless, this ketone is found to re-arrange with ease to ester LXXXI.[51] It thus appears that there are at least two

[50] Loftfield, J. Am. Chem. Soc., 72, 632 (1950).
[51] Stevens and Farkas, J. Am. Chem. Soc., 74, 5352 (1952).

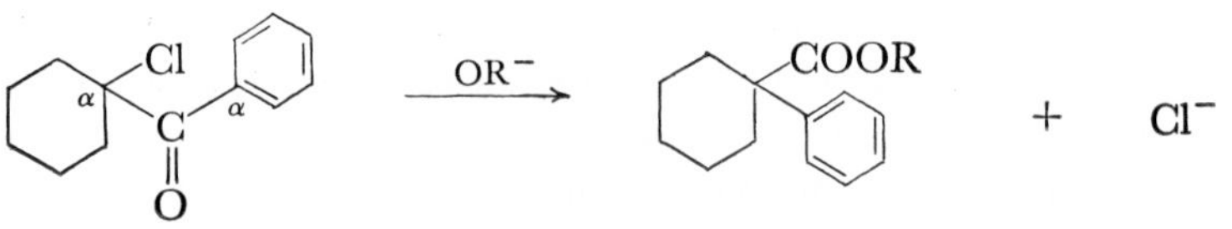

LXXXI

distinct paths by which the Favorskii rearrangement may proceed, and that a mechanism analogous to the benzilic-acid rearrangement (sequence 1), may operate when the "cyclopropanone" mechanism may not. We would also expect some ketones to rearrange by a combination of the two mechanisms, but this has not yet been confirmed.[52]

The Claisen Rearrangement and Related Reactions

In the Claisen rearrangement, the allyl or substituted-allyl group of an aryl allyl ether migrates to the *ortho* position of the benzene ring; if there are substituents at both *ortho* positions, the migration is to the *para* position. In an earlier chapter (p. 143) we noted that experiments with phenyl-allyl ether labeled at C_γ (LXXV) showed that the allyl group becomes attached to the *ortho* position in the ring at C_γ rather than C_α (that is, that the ends of the allyl system become interchanged during the migration).[53(a)] In a similar way, it has been shown, despite some early confusion on the question,[53(b)] that such an interchange does *not* occur in migration to the *para* position.[53(c)]

---

[52] Another carbanion rearrangement thought to proceed through a three-membered ring intermediate is the basic rearrangement of the tosylates of certain ketoximes to α-amino ketones (Neber, *et al.*, *Ann.*, **492**, 281 (1932); **515**, 283 (1935)). The proposed intermediate is an *azirine* (a three-membered cyclic imine, LXXXIII). In at least one case—the rearrangement of oxime LXXXII—this intermediate has been isolated and its structure verified by reduction to the substituted ethyleneimine, LXXXIV (Cram and Hatch, *J. Am. Chem. Soc.*, **75**, 33, 38 (1953)).

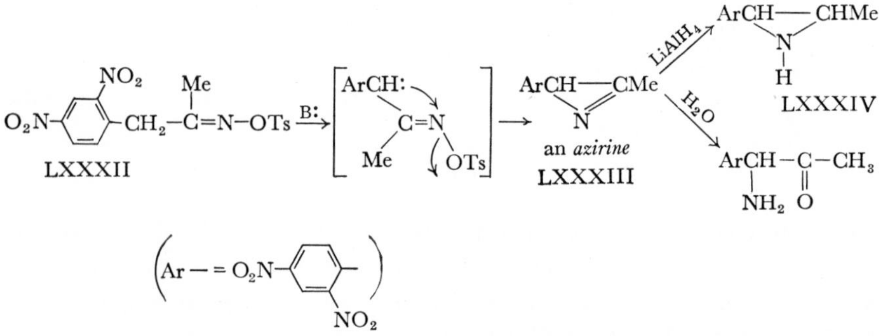

[53] (a) Schmid and Schmid, *Helv. Chim. Acta*, **35**, 1879 (1952); **36**, 489 (1953). (b) Munn, Hornhardt, and Diedrichsen, *Ber.*, **72**, 100 (1939). (c) Rhoades, Raulins, and Reynolds, *J. Am. Chem. Soc.*, **75**, 2531 (1953).

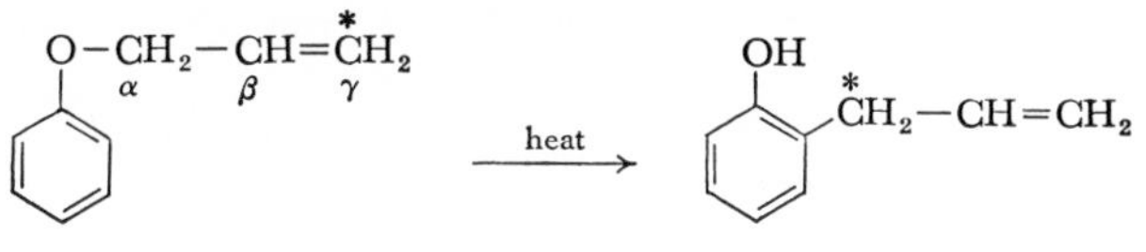

LXXXV

(reversal of the allyl group)

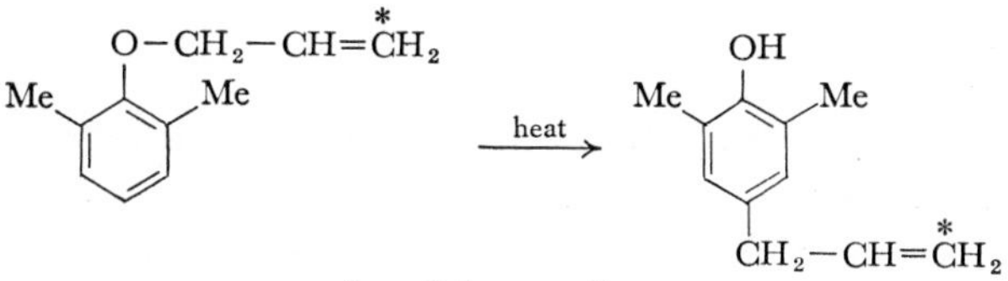

(no allyl reversal)

All attempts to detect fragments (ions or radicals) as intermediates in the Claisen rearrangement have failed. When the rearrangement is carried out in a nucleophilic solvent (for example, phenol or dimethylaniline), no product resulting from attack by the allyl ion on the solvent is formed. Nor is the reaction generally retarded by addition of free-radical reaction inhibitors. When two ethers having different aryl groups and differently substituted allyl groups are allowed to rearrange in the same solution, no "cross products" are obtained.[54] All this, together with the observed first-order rate law for the rearrangements and the negative entropies of activation (ranging from −2 to −16 kcal per degree, depending upon substituents),[55] suggests a cyclic mechanism in which

[54] Typically, rearrangement of a mixture of ethers LXXXVI and LXXXVII gives a mixture of phenols LXXXVIII and LXXXIX, but no detectable quantities of phenols XC or XCI (Hurd and Schmerling, *J. Am. Chem. Soc.*, **59**, 107 (1937)).

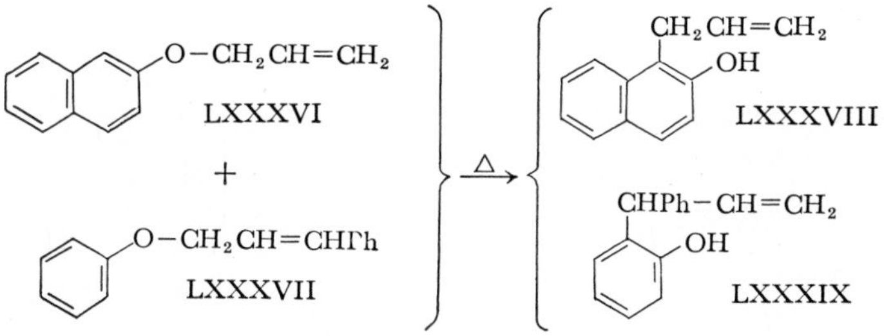

[55] (a) Kincaid and Tarbell, *J. Am. Chem. Soc.*, **61**, 3085 (1939); **62**, 1728 (1940). (b) Goering and Jacobson, *ibid.*, **80**, 3277 (1958).

the new C—C bond forms *while* the old C—O bond breaks; thus, for *ortho* migration,

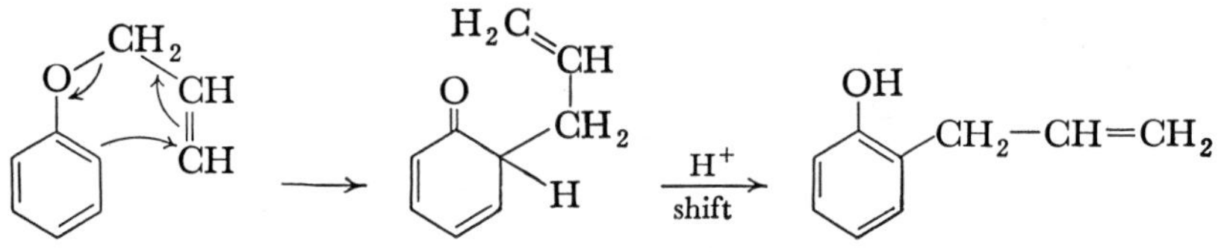

XCII

Here we have represented the electrons as moving in a "counterclockwise" direction (as they would move if the reaction were the attack of the allyl cation on the *ortho* position of the phenoxide anion). Yet, in a concerted cyclic mechanism of this sort it is often difficult to determine whether the direction of electron flow is that indicated, or the opposite, or, for that matter, whether the electrons move in pairs or become unpaired during the progress of the reaction.[56]

It is interesting that the Claisen rearrangement of optically active ether XCIII (in which C_α is asymmetric) leads to an optically active phenol, XCIV, in which a new carbon has become asymmetric.[57] This is a type of asymmetric

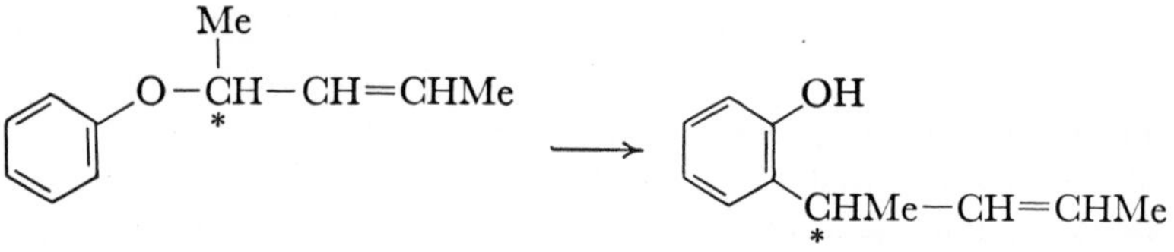

XCIII   XCIV

induction; it probably results because the transition state XCV, in which the methyl groups are *trans*, is sterically favored over transition state XCVI, in which they are *cis*.

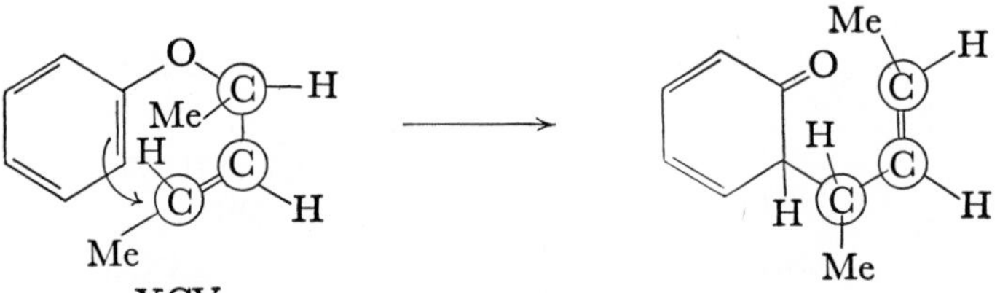

XCV

[56] For recent evidence that suggests that the direction of electron flow in the *ortho*-Claisen rearrangement is *opposite* to that shown in structure XCII, see White, Gwynn, Schlitt, Girard, and Fife, *J. Am. Chem. Soc.*, **80**, 3271 (1958). Reactions such as the Claisen rearrangement, the Diels-Alder reaction, and the Chugaev reaction—for which there is as yet no decisive experimental evidence for ions or radicals as intermediates—are classified by some workers as *four-center reactions*, indicating simply that there are four atoms undergoing covalency change at the same (or about the same) time; see, for example, Hine, *Physical Organic Chemistry*, McGraw-Hill Book Co., Inc., New York, 1956, p. 453.

[57] Alexander and Kluiber, *J. Am. Chem. Soc.*, **73**, 4305 (1951).

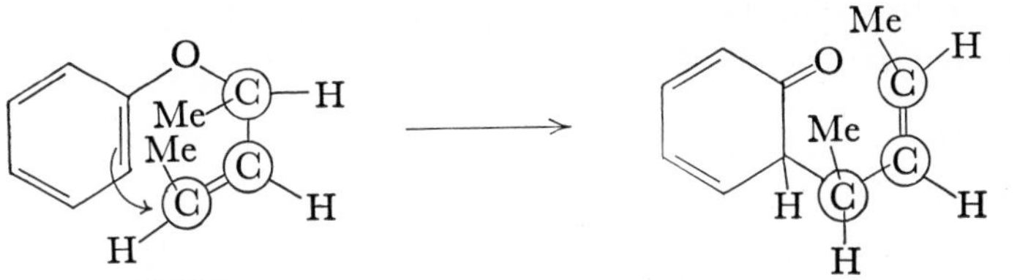

XCVI

It is now clear that the "*para* Claisen rearrangement," which occurs when both *ortho* positions are substituted, takes place in two stages—the allyl group being "reversed" in the first stage, then "unreversed" in the second. The initial stage is closely similar to that in the "*ortho* Claisen" rearrangement, but the intermediate dienone, XCVII, is considerably more stable, since it cannot undergo aromatization merely by tautomerization. This intermediate may be

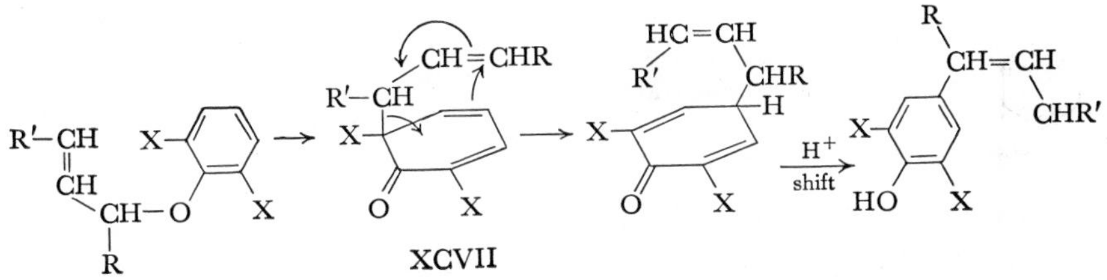

XCVII

trapped as a Diels-Alder adduct by carrying out the reaction in the presence of maleic anhydride.[58] Adduct C, when heated, gives the product (CI) resulting from "*para* rearrangement." Moreover, dienone XCIX has been prepared

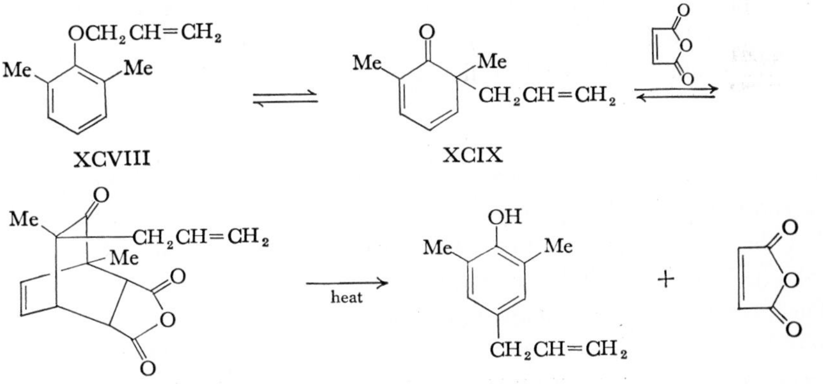

XCVIII   XCIX

C   CI

independently and has been found, on heating, to isomerize to a mixture of phenol CI and allyl ether XCVIII. Thus, the initial stage in the *para* Claisen rearrangement (XCVIII → XCIX) is, as indicated above, reversible.[59]

[58] Conroy and Firestone, *J. Am. Chem. Soc.*, **75**, 2530 (1953); **78**, 2290 (1956).

[59] Curtin and Crawford, *J. Am. Chem. Soc.*, **79**, 3156 (1957). For further evidence on this point, see Curtin and Johnson, *ibid.*, **76**, 2276 (1954).

The rearrangement of ethers such as CII and CIII is, at first glance, formally analogous to the Claisen rearrangement. Mechanistically, however,

there is little similarity, for there is strong evidence that the rearrangement of such nonallylic ethers involves the breakoff and migration of an alkyl cation.

Such rearrangements, although they sometimes occur merely on heating, are often catalyzed by protonic or Lewis acids, and may yield significant amounts of "fragments" derived from the alkyl group (thus the rearrangements of ethers CII and CIII yield styrene as a by-product). Moreover, when the rearrangement of the ether derived from one phenol is carried out in the presence of a second phenol, alkylation of the second phenol (formation of a "cross-product") may be observed.

We would accordingly be quite justified in assuming the simple mechanism given above for such rearrangements were it not for one difficulty; the rearrangement of an optically active ether (with an asymmetric α-carbon atom) often yields an isomeric phenol in which the configuration of the migrating carbon is *partially retained*,[60] although cross-products are racemic. It thus may be concluded that these rearrangements proceed, at least in part, through "intimate" ion pairs (p. 583), in which the environment of the carbonium ion is not symmetric. These ion pairs may "collapse," yielding an optically active product, or they may dissociate, yielding a symmetric carbonium ion in a symmetric environment which, in any subsequent reaction, forms an optically inactive product. Typically, the rearrangements of ethers CII and CIII are about 20 percent stereospecific.[60(b)]

On the other hand, a number of reactions are known which appear to be more authentic analogs of the Claisen rearrangement. Three of these are listed.

[60] (a) Sprung and Wallis, *J. Am. Chem. Soc.*, **56**, 1715 (1934). (b) Hart and Eleuterio, *ibid.*, **76**, 519 (1954).

61(a)

61(b) $(\triangle S^{\ddagger} = -12 \text{ cal}/°)$

61(c) $(\triangle S^{\ddagger} = -8 \text{ cal}/°)$

Note that the migrating allylic groups in CIV and CV are "reversed" in the rearrangements, this presumably also being the case with CVI (although we cannot be sure). The rearrangements of CV and CVI display, as they should, first-order rate laws and sizably negative entropies of activation consistent with the cyclic mechanisms indicated. A similar cyclic rearrangement has been proposed as a step in the oxidation of phenols with benzoyl peroxide.[62] This reaction, which generally yields *o*-benzoyloxy phenols, displays none of the characteristics of a free-radical reaction. The following path is suggested:

(Presumed intermediates CVII and CVIII are enclosed in parentheses since there is as yet no direct evidence for them.)

[61] (a) Mumm and Moller, *Ber.*, **70**, 2214 (1927). (b) Cope, *et al.*, *J. Am. Chem. Soc.*, **62**, 441 (1940); **63**, 1843, 1852 (1941); **69**, 1893 (1947). (c) Hurd and Pollack, *ibid.*, **60**, 1905 (1938); Schuler and Murphy, *ibid.*, **72**, 3155 (1950).
[62] Walling and Hodgdon, *J. Am. Chem. Soc.*, **80**, 228 (1958).

The Rearrangements of N-Haloanilides and Related Aromatic "Rearrangements"

When N-chloroacetanilide or a ring-substituted derivative of this chloroamide is treated with HCl in a hydroxylic solvent, the chlorine appears to "migrate" from the nitrogen atom to the *ortho* or the *para* positions (or both) in the ring.

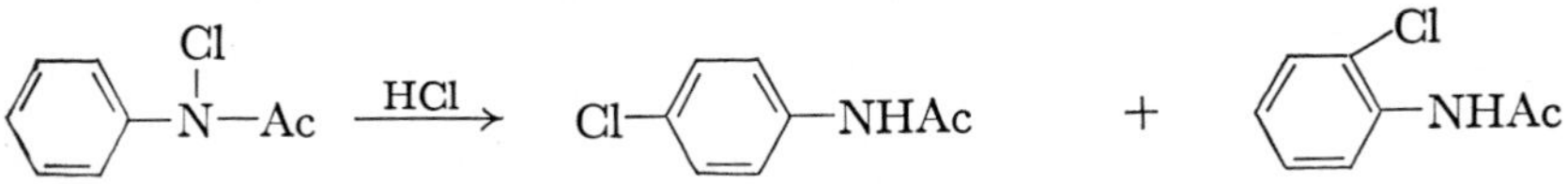

This reaction is sometimes called the *Orton rearrangement*.[63] The specific action of HCl in this reaction immediately suggests the possible intervention of chlorine; and indeed, if the reaction is carried out while air is bubbled rapidly through the solution, elemental chlorine is found to be carried away, leaving acetanilide behind. However, if no effort is made to remove chlorine from the solution, it chlorinates the benzene ring of acetanilide, a reaction that may independently be shown to be much faster than the rearrangement of the N-chloroanilide.[64] Moreover, the *ortho* to *para* ratio in the mixture of ring-chlorinated anilides resulting from direct chlorination is the same as that in the mixture obtained in the rearrangement (provided that the solvent is the same).[63] The Orton rearrangement may therefore be assumed to proceed by the following path:

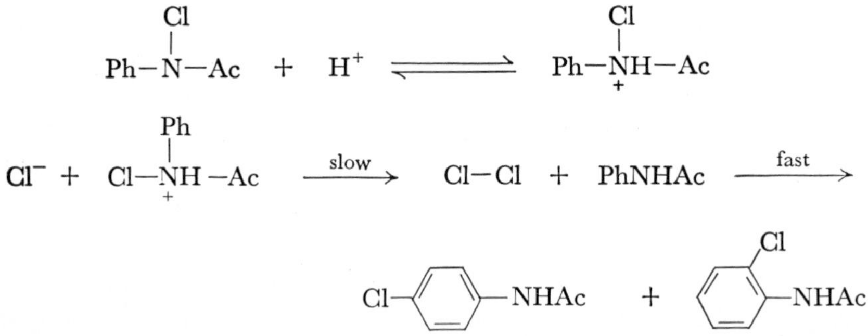

This rearrangement, then, unlike the rearrangements we have thus far considered (except perhaps the rearrangement of alkyl aryl ethers), is intermolecular. The "migrating group," the chlorine, becomes completely detached from the remainder of the molecule for a significant interval of time during the progress of the reaction, and there is no guarantee that the chlorine returning to a given molecule is that chlorine which has departed from it. In a sense, the Orton

[63] Orton, et al., J. Chem. Soc., **95**, 1456 (1909); **99**, 1185 (1911); **1927**, 986; **1928**, 782, 998.
[64] Soper, J. Phys. Chem., **31**, 1192 (1927).

rearrangement is not a rearrangement at all, but simply a heterolysis of the N—Cl bond, followed by a (completely independent) electrophilic attack on the benzene ring.

Other observations are consistent with the mechanism shown. If an N-chloroanilide with a "deactivated" ring, such as N-chloro-2,4-dichloroacetanilide, (CIX), is treated with HCl in the presence of acetanilide, the "labile" chlorine does not migrate to the ring of its parent molecule, but instead "crosses over" into the acetanilide ring, emphasizing the intermolecular character of the reac-

tion. Furthermore, if the rearrangement is carried out with chlorine-labeled N-chloroacetanilide, only a very small fraction of the radioactive chlorine is found bound to the benzene ring in the product.[65] Finally, the observed rate law also fits into the picture, for the reaction has been found to be of the third order.[66]

$$\text{rate} = k_3(\text{ArNAcCl})(\text{HCl})^2 \tag{2}$$

Assuming complete ionization of HCl, rate law (2) may be rewritten as follows:

$$\text{rate} = k_3(\text{ArNAcCl})(\text{H}^+)(\text{Cl}^-) = k'\left(\overset{\text{H}}{\underset{+}{\text{ArNAcCl}}}\right)(\text{Cl}^-) \tag{3}$$

This is obviously consistent with the proposed mechanism if the attack by chloride on the conjugate acid of the substrate is the rate-determining step.

Various modifications of the Orton rearrangement are known. The N—Cl bond in N-chloroanilides may be broken also by HBr and HI, but the resulting products are bromo and iodo compounds.[67] The intermediates in such cases are

---

[65] Olson, et al, J. Am. Chem. Soc., **58**, 2214, 2467 (1936); **59**, 1613 (1937); J. Org. Chem., **3**, 76 (1938). Since the two chlorine atoms in the intermediate (the Cl₂ molecule) are equivalent, we might expect just *half* of the labeled chlorine to be lost. However, exchange between Cl and Cl₂ in solution is known to be extremely rapid, due to the rapid formation and dissociation of Cl₃⁻.

$$*\text{Cl—Cl} + \text{Cl}^- \rightleftharpoons [*\text{Cl—Cl—Cl}]^- \rightleftharpoons *\text{Cl}^- + \text{Cl—Cl}$$

[66] (a) Harned and Seltz, J. Am. Chem. Soc., **44**, 1475 (1922). (b) Soper and Pryde, J. Chem. Soc., **1927**, 2761. (c) Dawson and Millet, ibid, **1932**, 1920.
[67] Richardson and Soper, J. Chem. Soc., **1929**, 1873.

$$Br^- + Cl-\overset{+}{\underset{Ac}{N}H}-Ar \longrightarrow BrCl + \underset{Ac}{NHAr} \longrightarrow \underset{Br}{\underset{(I^-)}{}}\overset{}{\bigcirc}-NHAc + HCl$$
$$(or\ I^-) \qquad\qquad\qquad (or\ ICl)$$

presumably BrCl and ICl (rather than Cl_2). As with direct halogenation (p. 443), the more electropositive halogen of the interhalogen intermediate attacks the benzene ring. The rearrangement may also occur, although at a much diminished rate, in aqueous solutions of strong "oxygen acids" (HNO_3, H_2SO_4, and $HClO_4$).[66(b),68] Here, it seems likely that the N—Cl bond is broken in attack by a water molecule, forming the H_2OCl^+ ion as an intermediate.

$$H_2O + Cl-\overset{Ac}{\underset{+}{N}H}-Ph \rightarrow \overset{H}{\underset{H}{\overset{+}{O}}}-Cl + \overset{Ac}{\underset{}{N}H}-Ph \rightarrow$$

$$o\text{- and } p\text{-AcNH}-C_6H_4-Cl + H_2O$$

It has even been found that the rearrangement of N-chloroanilides is promoted by light,[69] suggesting that the Orton rearrangement, like the Cannizzaro reaction, the Wolff rearrangement, and the decompositions of diacyl peroxides, may proceed by more than one class of mechanism.

There are a number of additional instances known in which a group attached to the nitrogen atom of an N-substituted aniline appears to migrate to the *ortho* or *para* position of the aromatic ring. Three of the more familiar of such reactions are shown:

$$O=N\overset{Me}{\underset{}{-}}N-Ph + H_3O^+ \longrightarrow O=N-\overset{H}{\underset{H}{\overset{+}{O}}} + MeNHPh \longrightarrow MeNH-\bigcirc-N=O \qquad 70(a)$$

$$Ph-N=N\overset{}{\underset{}{-}}NHPh + RCOOH \longrightarrow Ph-N\equiv N^+ \ ^-O-\overset{O}{\overset{\|}{C}}-R + NH_2Ph \longrightarrow$$
$$H_2N-\bigcirc-N=NPh + RCOOH \qquad 70(b)$$

$$n\text{-Bu}\overset{+}{\underset{}{-}}NH_2-Ph \ \ Cl^- \xrightarrow[300°]{heat} n\text{-BuCl} + NH_2Ph \longrightarrow \ \longrightarrow NH_2-\bigcirc-Bu + HCl \qquad 70(c)$$

[68] Similarly, N-haloacetanilides have been found to undergo rearrangement in chlorobenzene in the presence of strong carboxylic acids. Here, the intermediate is probably an acyl hypohalite, for example, CCl_3COOBr (see: Bell, *et al.*, *J. Chem. Soc.*, **1936**, 1154, 1520; **1939**, 1774; Israel, Tuck, and Soper, *ibid.*, **1945**, 547; Dewar and Scott, *ibid.*, **1955**, 1845; **1957**, 1445, 2676).

[69] Mathews and Williams, *J. Am. Chem. Soc.*, **45**, 2574 (1923).

[70] (a) Fischer and Hepp, *Ber.*, **20**, 2471 (1897); Neber and Rauscher, *Ann.*, **550**, 192

As indicated, each of these reactions is, like the *Orton* rearrangement, *intermolecular*. In each case, the migrating group may be intercepted by carrying out the reaction in the presence of an additional aromatic amine with a more "active" ring than that in substrate. In the third of these reactions (the so-called *Hofmann-Martius rearrangement*) the alkyl-halide intermediate is probably converted to a carbonium ion before it attacks the ring, since rearrangements in the migrating alkyl group are often observed.

The mechanisms here suggested for the rearrangement of N-substituted aniline derivatives are at variance with the views held by a number of workers[71] (principally in the late 1940's), who felt that some or all of these rearrangements proceeded through a π complex in which the migrating cation could move rather freely over the π-electron lobes associated with the aromatic ring before becoming bound to the ring at the *ortho* or *para* position. While it is possible that the system passes through such a complex before the departure of the migrating fragment or before the formation of the new bond (or before both), the unmistakably intermolecular character of these rearrangements would seem to rule out the possibility that such a complex is the *sole* intermediate between these steps. Moreover, now that the extreme lability of the π complex is recognized (p. 119), it seems very likely that any such complex, if formed, would be in mobile equilibrium with the fragments here proposed as intermediates.

When a phenyl ester is treated with anhydrous aluminum chloride, the acyl group migrates to the benzene ring, principally to the *ortho* position (when this position is available). This reaction, the useful *Fries rearrangement*, is likewise intermolecular, at least in part. If, for example, the rearrangement is carried out on a mixture of esters CX and CXI, four *o*-hydroxy ketones may be easily isolated from the reaction mixture.[72] The observed transfer of acyl groups from

one benzene ring to another suggests the following mechanism:

(1942); Glazer, *et al.*, *J. Chem. Soc.*, **1950**, 2657. (*b*) Goldschmidt, *et al.*, *Z. physik. Chem.*, **29**, 89, 1369 (1899); **110**, 251 (1924). (*c*) Hofmann and Martius, *Ber.*, **4**, 742 (1871); Hickinbottom, *et al.*, *J. Chem. Soc.*, **117**, 103 (1920); **1930**, 1566; **1931**, 1281; **1934**, 1700; **1935**, 1279; **1937**, 404.

[71] See, for example, Dewar, *The Electronic Theory of Organic Chemistry*, Oxford University Press, Oxford, 1949, p. 225.

[72] Rosenmund and Schnurr, *Ann.*, **460**, 96 (1927).

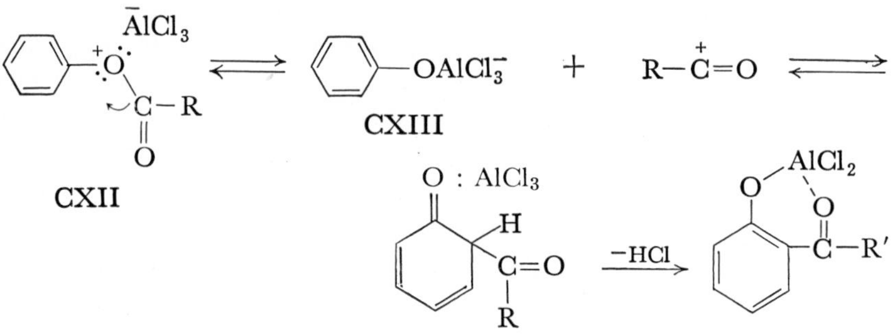

CXII   CXIII   CXIV

As indicated, the function of the aluminum chloride is the withdrawal of electron density from the acyl-oxygen bond by coordination (CXII), which facilitates the initial heterolysis. The acyl cation thus formed may attack the benzene ring of anion CXIII. We have assumed that, in the absence of water, the *ortho*-migration product is a chelated complex such as CXIV, from which the hydroxy ketone itself may be formed upon hydrolysis. Indeed, it is probable that chelation with tripositive aluminum significantly stabilizes the *ortho*-migration product; for the *para*-migration product (which obviously cannot form such a chelate) is known to be formed reversibly, whereas *ortho* migration is essentially irreversible. This effect accounts for the predominance of *ortho* migration often (but not always) observed in the Fries rearrangement.

But there is evidence that the mechanism above is somewhat oversimplified. Suppose *o*-cresyl acetate is rearranged in the presence of 2-hydroxybiphenyl. The predominant product is 3-methyl-4-hydroxyacetophenone (CXV), accompanied, as we might expect, by significant quantities of the acetylated biphenyl, CXVI. What is surprising, however, is that if the quantities of each of the

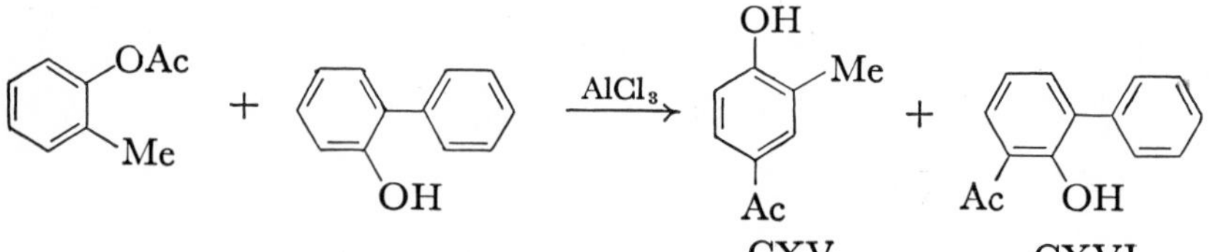

CXV   CXVI

reagents are kept constant but the volume of solvent used is allowed to increase, the ratio of ketone CXVI to ketone CXV steadily decreases.[73] This means that the reaction in which the "cross-product" (CXVI) is formed has a higher average kinetic order than that in which the "main product" (CXV) is formed, and

[73] Baltzley and Phillips, *J. Am. Chem. Soc.*, **70**, 1491 (1948). Typically, if 0.2 moles of each reagent are used, but the volume of solution raised from 500 to 2000 cc, the ratio CXVII:CXVI drops from 0.62 to 0.28.

suggests that the acyl ion is present in part as ion pairs, $R\overset{+}{C}\!\!=\!\!O\ ArOAlCl_3^-$. Such ion pairs may "collapse" with rearrangement to give CXV or its *ortho* isomer (first-order reactions), may react directly with hydroxybiphenyl to give CXVI (a second-order reaction), or may dissociate to a free acyl cation that may attack either of the two available ring systems.

A final rearrangement which, in a formal sense, is similar to those we have been considering, is that of N-nitroanilines (and related N-nitro amines) to *o*-nitroanilines in strong acid. On the basis of analogy to the rearrangements of

N-chloroanilides (p. 650) and N-nitroso-N-alkylanilines (p. 652), we might suppose that this reaction is intermolecular also—that is, that the —NO$_2$ group is removed from the substrate (for example, as $H_2ONO_2^+$ in water) and that, independently, nitration of the aromatic ring follows. However, a closer look at this reaction makes it apparent that such an analogy is poorly taken. Suppose that the nitrating species were to become completely independent of the remainder of the molecule (in this case an aromatic amine) before attacking the ring. We should then expect the same mixture of products from the rearrangement as is obtained when the amine is treated with an outside source of the nitrating agent under rearrangement conditions. Specifically, the same mixture of *o*-, *m*-, and *p*-nitroanilines should result from the rearrangement of N-nitroaniline (in, say, sulfuric acid) as is obtained from the nitration of aniline itself with HNO$_3$ (again in sulfuric acid). This comparison has been carried out in 85 percent H$_2$SO$_4$ at 10°,[74] under which conditions the rearrangement gives almost exclusively *o*-nitroaniline, but direct nitration gives a mixture of isomeric nitroanilines in which the $o:m:p$ ratio is $1:6:10$. Furthermore, it has been found that when the nitroamine CXVII undergoes rearrangement in the presence of dimethylaniline, the ring of the latter compound (which is much more susceptible to attack than the ring of *p*-nitroaniline) is not appreciably nitrated.[74(a)]

CXVII

$\left(\text{no } O_2N\!-\!\!\langle\ \rangle\!-\!NMe_2\right)$

[74] (a) Hughes and Jones, *J. Chem. Soc.*, **1950**, 2678. Here the nitrating agent may be assumed to be the NO$_2^+$ ion (p. 419). (b) For an older and less precise study, see Holleman, Hartogs, and van der Linden, *Ber.*, **44**, 704 (1911).

Finally, it has been found that if the rearrangement of N-nitroaniline is carried out in the presence of N-labeled nitrate, none of the labeled nitrogen is incorporated into the product.[75] We may thus rule out an intermolecular mechanism as playing a significant role in the nitroamine rearrangement.

It is not easy to visualize a simple mechanism in which the nitro group is transferred in a single step from the amino nitrogen to the *ortho* carbon, but the following tentative stepwise mechanism is not unreasonable:

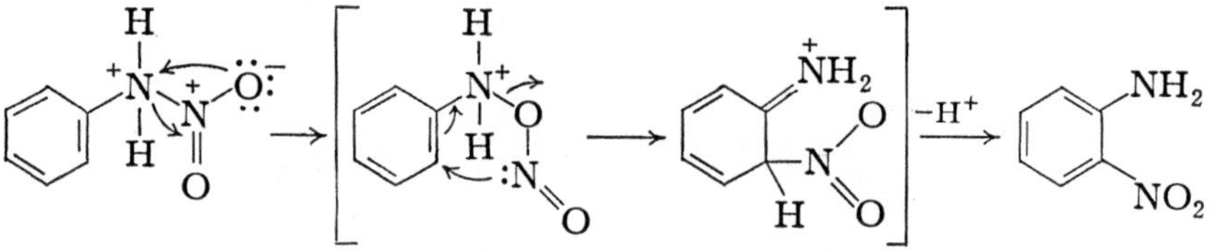

CXVIII

The rearrangement of the proposed "nitrito" intermediate, CXVIII, is a little like the Claisen rearrangement and, as with the latter, the indicated "direction of electron flow" is arbitrary. The presumed initial isomerization to CXIX brings to mind the Stevens rearrangement (p. 640).

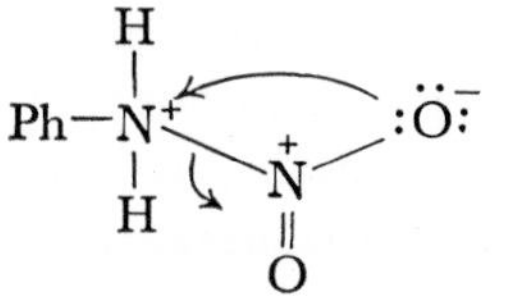

nitroamine
rearrangement

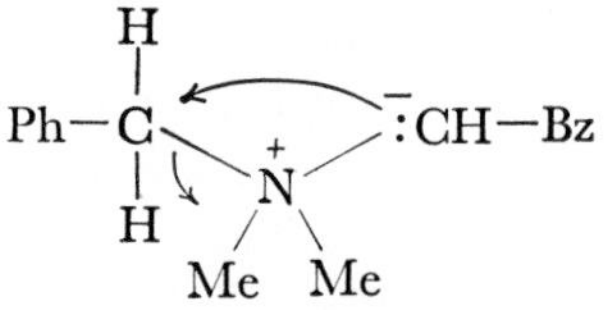

Stevens
rearrangement

The Benzidine Rearrangement

The most familiar of aromatic rearrangements, the benzidine rearrangement, is, in some respects, the most baffling. The most usual course of the reaction, the transformation of hydrazobenzenes to derivatives of p,p'-diaminobiphenyl, tends to predominate with *ortho*- and *meta*-substituted hydrazobenzenes and may also occur with certain *para*-substituted hydrazobenzenes if the *para* substituent is readily subject to electrophilic displacement. More generally, however, *para* substituents divert the rearrangement into one or more alternate courses. Hydrazobenzenes having *para* substituents on *both* rings are commonly trans-

---

[75] Brownstein, Bunton, and Hughes, *Chem. and Ind.*, **1956**, 981. Even the small amount of *p*-nitroaniline formed in the rearrangement is free of labeled nitrogen, suggesting that this product is formed by a stepwise, wholly intramolecular mechanism, analogous to that of the *para* Claisen rearrangement.

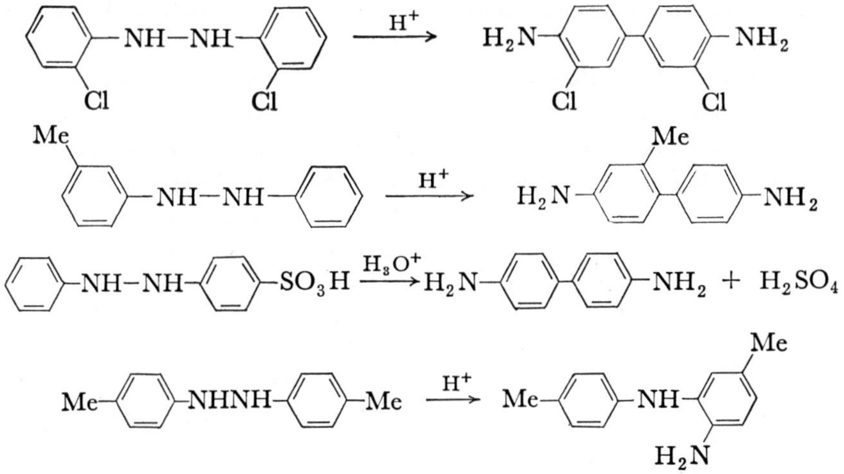

(an *ortho*-semidine)

formed to derivatives of 2-aminodiphenylamine (*ortho*-semidines); whereas hydrazobenzenes with single para substituents may be converted to derivatives of 2,4′-diaminobiphenyl (diphenylenes), to *para*-semidines, to *ortho*-semidines, or to mixtures of these products. Moreover, rearrangement of hydrazonaphthalenes

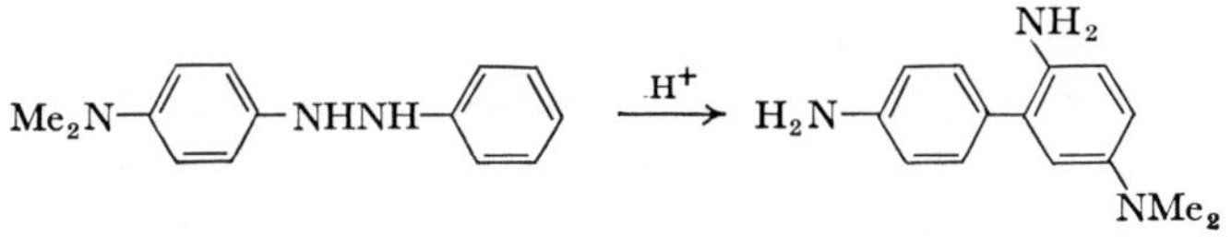

(a diphenylene)

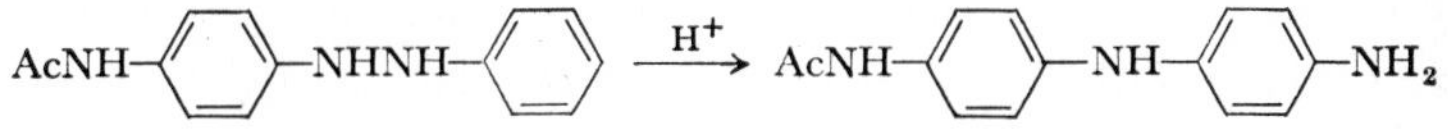

(a *para*-semidine)

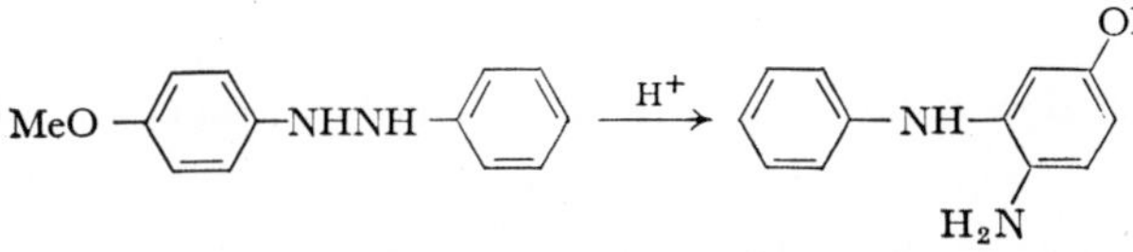

(an *ortho*-semidine)

(for example, CXIX) may result in a binaphthyl such as CXX, in which the ring systems are joined *ortho* to *both* amino groups. Any mechanism proposed for

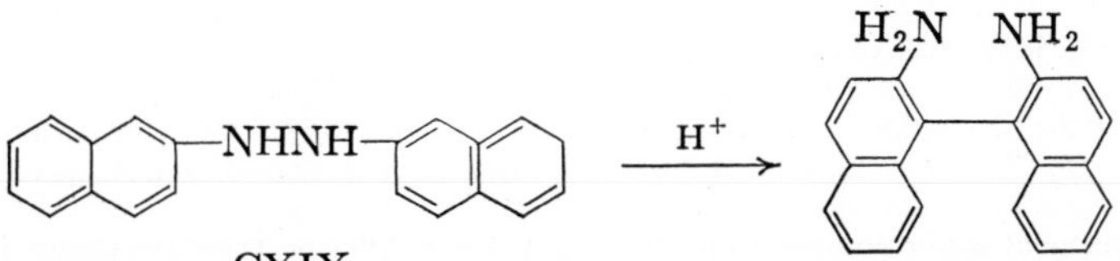

CXIX

CXX

the benzidine rearrangements must account for the formation of each of these products.

There is no doubt that the benzidine rearrangement is intramolecular. We have seen how this has been demonstrated by the nonformation of cross-over products when a mixture of 2,2′-dimethoxy- and 2,2′-diethoxy-hydrazobenzene is treated with acid (p. 141). It may just as convincingly be shown by the rearrangement of a mixture of methyl-labeled 2-methylhydrazobenzene (CXXI) and unlabeled 2,2′-dimethylhydrazobenzene (CXXII). In this case, the o-toli-

dine (CXXIII) formed is unlabeled.[76] We here assume also that the formations of semidines and diphenylenes are likewise intramolecular, although this apparently has not yet been rigorously demonstrated.

The rearrangements of hydrazobenzenes to benzidines,[77(a)] to diphenylenes,[77(b)] and to o-semidines[77(c)] are third-order reactions, first order in substrate and second order in hydrogen ion. The rearrangements are subject to specific hydronium ion, rather than general acid catalysis and proceed more *rapidly* in D_2O than in H_2O.[77(c)] It therefore appears likely that the rate-determining step involves only the "double conjugate acid" of the substrate—that is, the cation $Ar—\overset{+}{N}H_2—\overset{+}{N}H_2—Ar$.[78] It has also been found that *para*-deuterated hydrazobenzene (CXXIV) undergoes the benzidine rearrangement at very nearly the same rate as does nondeuterated hydrazobenzene,[79] suggesting that

CXXIV

[76] Smith, Schwartz, and Wheland, *J. Am. Chem. Soc.*, **74**, 2282 (1952).

[77] (a) Hammond and Shine, *J. Am. Chem. Soc.*, **72**, 220 (1950); Croce and Gettler, *ibid.*, **75**, 874 (1953); Blackadder and Hinshelwood, *J. Chem. Soc.*, **1957**, 2898. (b) Carlin, Nelb, and Odioso, *J. Am. Chem. Soc.*, **73**, 1002 (1951). (c) Bunton, Ingold, and Mhala, *J. Chem. Soc.*, **1957**, 1906.

[78] Agreement is not unanimous on this point. For a differing view, see Cohen and Hammond, *J. Am. Chem. Soc.*, **75**, 880 (1953).

[79] Hammond and Grundemeier, *J. Am. Chem. Soc.*, **77**, 2444 (1955).

the *para*-hydrogens become detached from the ring carbons *after*, rather than *during*, the rate-determining step (p. 193).

The available data on the benzidine rearrangement then point to the following cyclic mechanism:

CXXV   CXXVI

Here it may be assumed that the easy breakage of the N—N bond in CXV is due largely to electrostatic repulsion between the two positively charged nitrogen atoms. When there are substituents at the *para* positions of the substrate, intermediate CXXVII (corresponding to CXXVI in the "ordinary" benzidine rearrangement) cannot aromatize simply by loss of two protons. We would then expect CXXVII to survive long enough to undergo a second rearrangement, yielding the customarily observed *ortho*-semidine.

CXXVII.   *ortho*-semidine

The formations of *para*-semidines and diphenylenes probably also occur in two stages, the initial stage presumably being the rearrangement to cation CXXVIII, in which the rings are joined *ortho* to the amino groups.

There are two important questions in connection with the benzidine rearrangement to which satisfactory answers have not yet been obtained. First, it may be asked what holds the benzene rings so close to each other in the transition state of the slow step. We have already noted that, due to the π-electron lobes associated with the benzene ring, the normal "half thickness" of the ring is about 1.85 Å (p. 53). In the absence of special effects, considerable difficulty should therefore be encountered in moving two parallel (or nearly parallel)

benzene rings to within less than about 3.7 Å of each other. Indeed, the benzene rings in di-p-xylylene (CXXIX) have been found to be "buckled," due presumably to interference between the π-electron clouds of the two rings.[80] It has been

CXXIX

suggested that the transition state in the benzidine rearrangement (and in related arrangements) is subject to exceptional stabilization by resonance.[81] but the nature of this "extra resonance" is not clear. The transition states in these rearrangements are not even approximately planar, hence do not fulfill what is ordinarily a primary requirement for extensive delocalization of π-electron density over a conjugated system. The fact that a rather large number of hyperconjugated structures can be drawn for each of the various transition states is, in the opinion of the present author, not relevant.

The second question concerns the manner in which the substituent in singly $para$-substituted hydrazobenzenes directs the predominant course of the reaction. Why, for example, does a p-Cl substituent favor rearrangement to a

[80] Brown, *J. Chem. Soc.*, **1953**, 3265, 3278.
[81] Hughes and Ingold, *J. Chem. Soc.*, **1941**, 608; Hammick and Mason, *ibid.*, **1946**, 638.

diphenylene, a p-Me group favor rearrangement to an *ortho*-semidine, and a p-NH$_2$ group favor formation of a *para*-semidine?

Until more light is shed on these two (possibly related) questions, we cannot, in good conscience, claim that we understand the benzidine rearrangement.

EXERCISES FOR CHAPTER 15

1. (a) Outline an experiment, starting with available materials, to show that in the Wolff rearrangement (p. 627) the carbonyl carbon of the diazomethyl ketone becomes the carboxyl carbon of the resulting acid.
   (b) Outline a series of transformations to demonstrate that the migrating group in the Wolff rearrangement shifts with retention of configuration. (Assume that the relative configurations of reactants and products cannot be determined merely by comparing their directions of optical rotation.)

2. Which member in each of the following pairs will undergo the indicated rearrangement more readily? Justify your guess in each case:
   (a) Ph$_2$C=N—OAc or Ph$_2$C=N—OTs (Beckmann)?

   (b) MeO—⟨⟩—C(Ph)=N—OH   or   MeO—⟨⟩—C(Ph)=N—OH

   (Beckmann) ?

   (c) Ph$_2$C=N—OH + 2M H$_2$SO$_4$; in EtOH or in H$_2$O (Beckmann)?
   (d) AcNH$_2$ or AcNHMe (Hofmann)?
   (e) PhCONH$_2$ or PhCH$_2$CONH$_2$ (Hofmann)?

   (f) Me—⟨⟩—AcN—Cl   or   Me—⟨⟩(—Me)—AcN—Cl   (Orton) ?

   (g) p-Nitrobenzamide or p-chlorobenzamide (Hofmann)?

   (h) MeO—⟨⟩—CO—NH—O—C(=O)—⟨⟩—OMe   or

   MeO—⟨⟩—CO—NH—O—C(=O)—⟨⟩—OMe   (Lossen) ?

   (i) Cyclobutanone or cyclopentanone (Schmidt)?

(j) 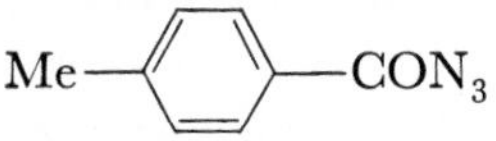 Me—⟨benzene⟩—CON$_3$ or   ⟨benzene⟩—CON$_3$ (Curtius) ?

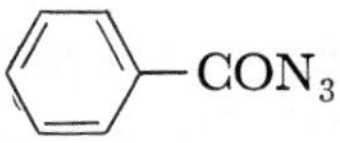

(k) 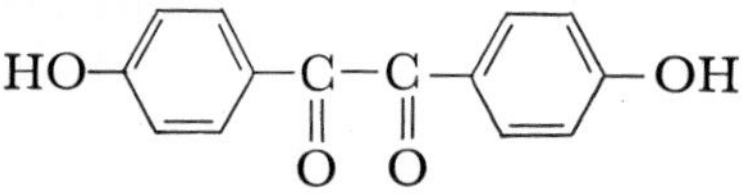 HO—⟨benzene⟩—$\overset{\text{C}}{\underset{\text{O}}{||}}$—$\overset{\text{C}}{\underset{\text{O}}{||}}$—⟨benzene⟩—OH or

MeO—⟨benzene⟩—$\overset{\text{C}}{\underset{\text{O}}{||}}$—$\overset{\text{C}}{\underset{\text{O}}{||}}$—⟨benzene⟩—OMe

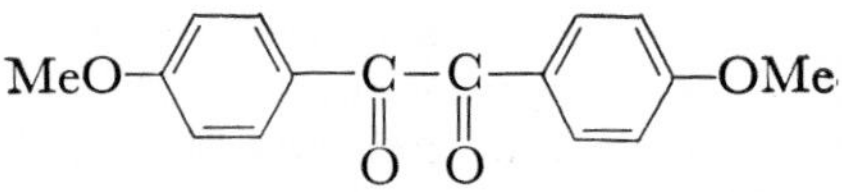

(benzilic acid rearrangement) ?

(l) PhCH$_2$NMe$_3^+$ or Ph$_2$CHNMe$_3^+$ (Stevens)?

(m) 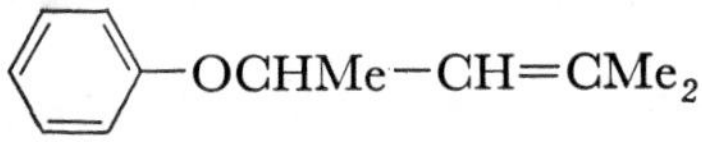 ⟨benzene⟩—OCHMe—CH=CMe$_2$ or

Me—⟨benzene, Me⟩—O—CHMe—CH=CH$_2$

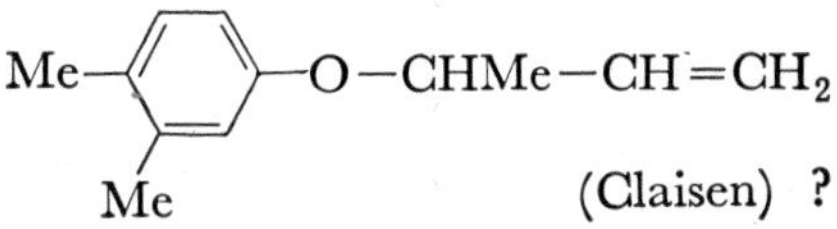

(Claisen) ?

(n) 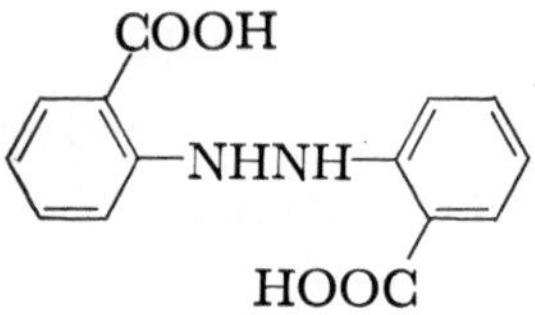 ⟨benzene with COOH⟩—NHNH—⟨benzene with HOOC⟩   or

⟨benzene with COOH⟩—NHNH—⟨benzene with COOH⟩   in dilute HCl

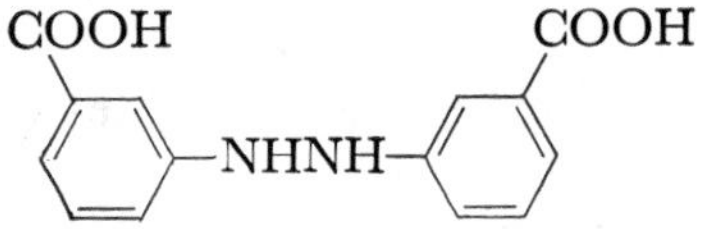

(benzidine rearrangement) ?

(o)

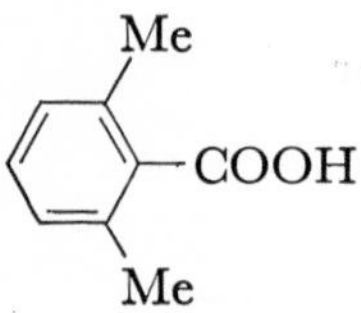

⟨benzene, Me, Me⟩—COOH   or   Me—⟨benzene, Me⟩—COOH   with HN$_3$ + conc H$_2$SO$_4$

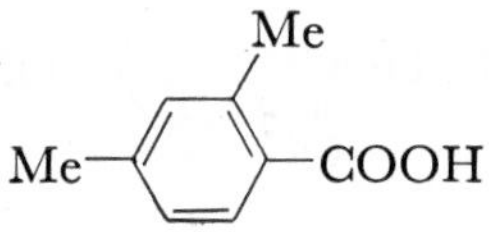

(Schmidt) ?

(p)

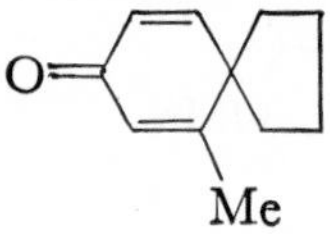

O=⟨spiro ring, Me⟩   or   O=⟨spiro ring, Me⟩   (dienone-phenol rearrangement) ?

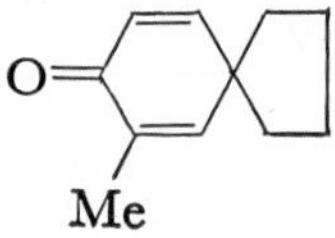

(q) $PhCOCH_2NMe_3^+$ or [structure: thiophene ring with $-COCH_2NMe_3^+$ substituent, S in ring]   (Stevens)   ?

(r) $CH_3CHCl\overset{O}{\overset{\|}{C}}CH_3$ or $CH_3CHCl\overset{O}{\overset{\|}{C}}CMe_3$ (Favorskii)?

3. Predict the products in each of the following reactions, justifying your guesses:

(a) 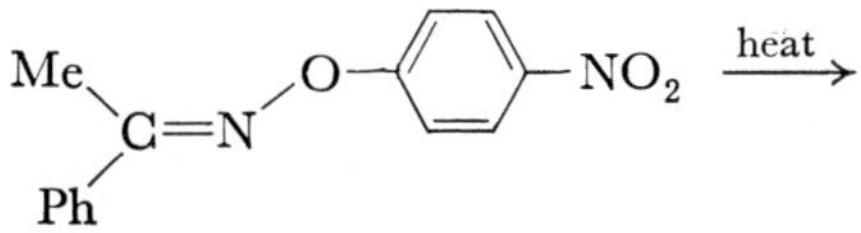 [structure: Me and Ph on C=N, then N—O—(benzene ring)—NO_2] $\xrightarrow{\text{heat}}$

(b) $NH_2\overset{O}{\overset{\|}{C}}NH_2 + OBr^- + OH^- \rightarrow$

(c) 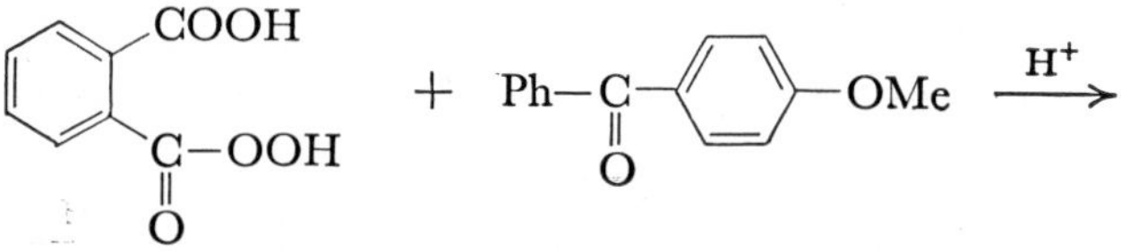 [benzene ring with COOH and $\overset{O}{\overset{\|}{C}}-OOH$] $+$ $Ph-\overset{O}{\overset{\|}{C}}-$(benzene ring)$-OMe$ $\xrightarrow{H^+}$

(d) 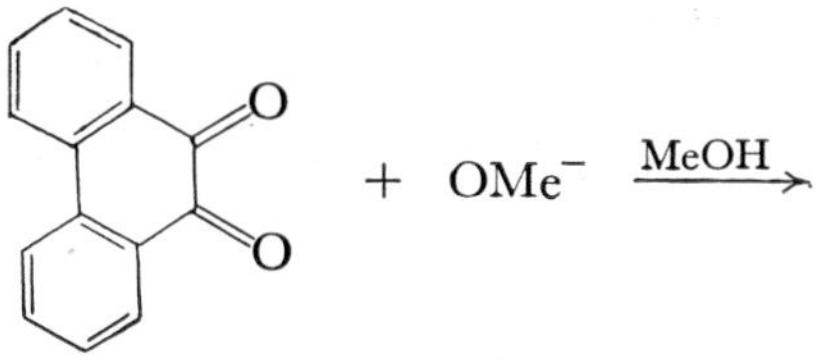 [phenanthrenequinone structure with two C=O] $+$ OMe^- $\xrightarrow{\text{MeOH}}$

(e) 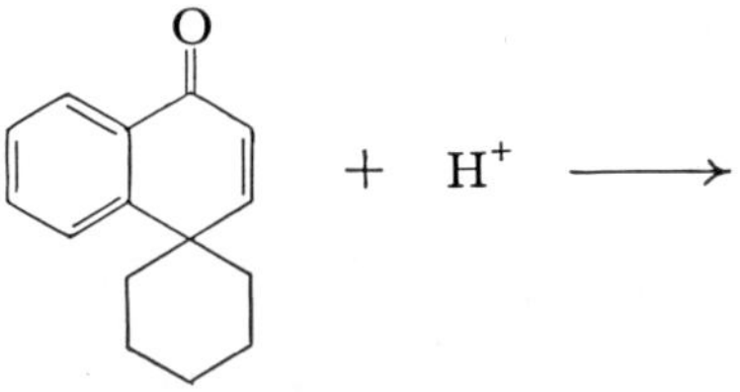 [spiro structure with naphthalenone and cyclohexane ring] $+$ H^+ $\longrightarrow$

(f) $Ph-NMe-NO + HCl + NH_2-\overset{O}{\overset{\|}{C}}-NH_2 \rightarrow$

(g) 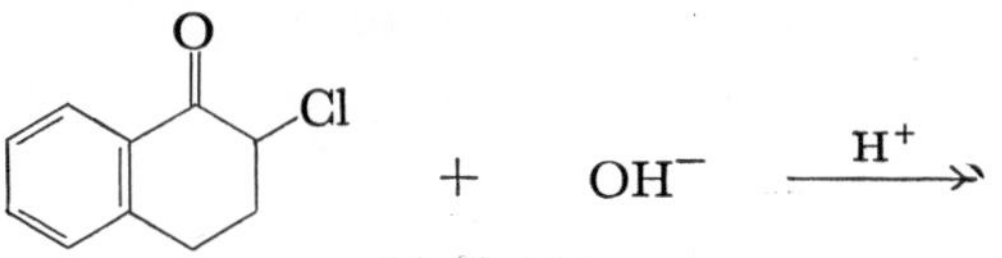 [tetralone structure with Cl] $+$ OH^- $\xrightarrow{H^+}$

(h) $Ph-S-O-CHPh-CH=CH_2 \xrightarrow{\text{heat}}$
    with O double bonded to S

(i) $Me_2C(OH)CH_2CH_2C{-}N_3$ $\xrightarrow{\text{heat}}$
$\quad\quad\quad\quad\quad\quad\quad\quad\overset{\|}{O}$

(j)  $NO_2\text{-}\langle\bigcirc\rangle\text{-}CPh_2{-}OOH$ $\quad + \quad H_2SO_4 \quad\longrightarrow$

(k) 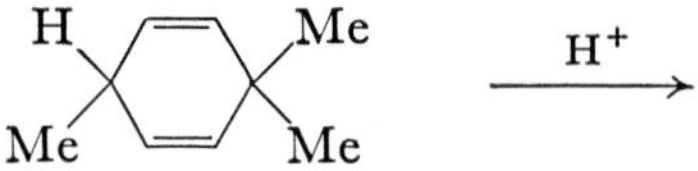 $\xrightarrow{H^+}$

(l) 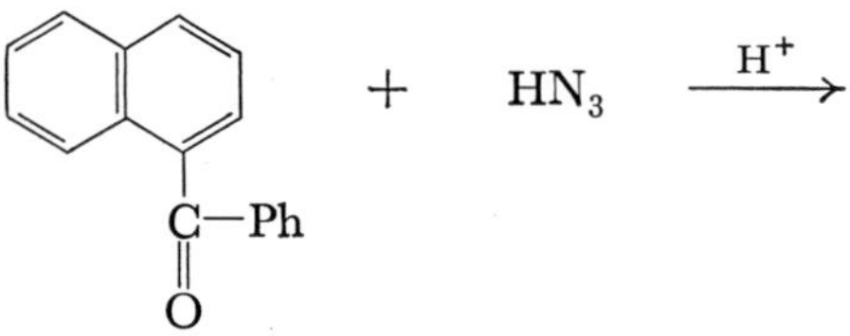 $\quad + \quad HN_3 \quad\xrightarrow{H^+}$

(m) $Ph{-}NAc{-}Br + HI \rightarrow$

(n) 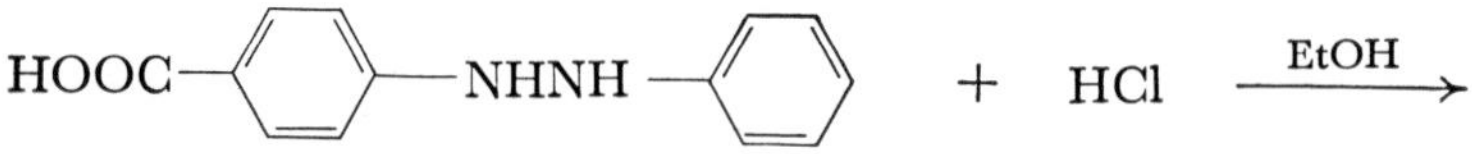 $HOOC\text{-}\langle\bigcirc\rangle\text{-}NHNH\text{-}\langle\bigcirc\rangle$ $\quad + \quad HCl \quad\xrightarrow{\text{EtOH}}$

(o) 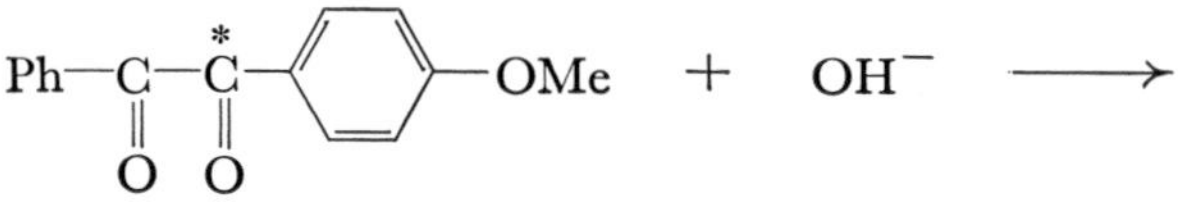 $Ph{-}\overset{\|}{\underset{O}{C}}{-}\overset{*\,\|}{\underset{O}{C}}\text{-}\langle\bigcirc\rangle\text{-}OMe$ $\quad + \quad OH^- \quad\longrightarrow$

(p) 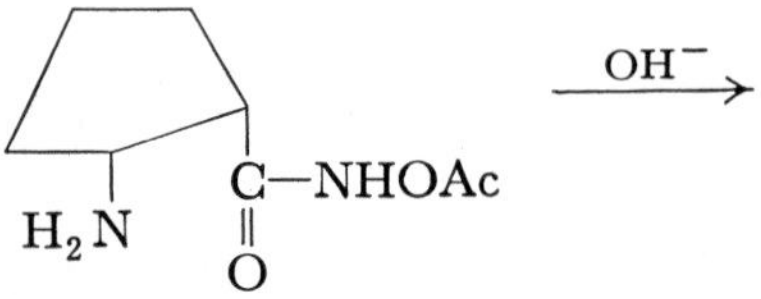 $\xrightarrow{OH^-}$

4. Predict the products in each of the following reactions, justifying your guesses (these are somewhat more difficult than the examples in the preceding exercise):

(a) 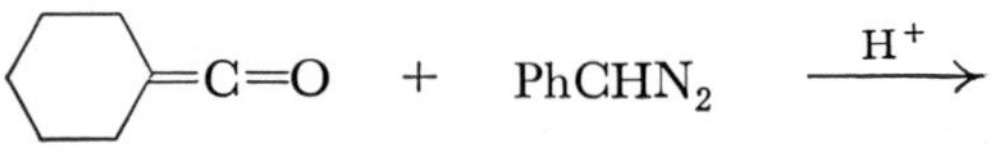 $=C=O$ $\quad + \quad PhCHN_2 \quad\xrightarrow{H^+}$

(b) $Me_2CH{-}\overset{\|}{\underset{O}{C}}{-}CMe_3 + \text{conc } H_2SO_4 \rightarrow$

(c) 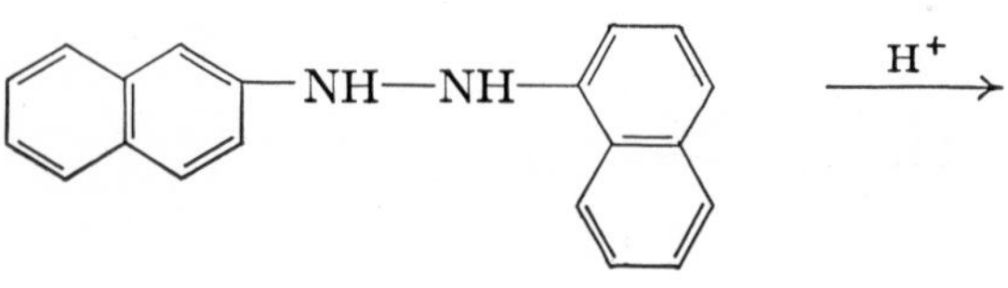 $\text{-}NH{-}NH\text{-}$ $\quad\xrightarrow{H^+}$

(d) $MeCH=CH-CH_2SCN \xrightarrow{heat}$

(e) $Ph_2C=N-NH_2 + HNO_2 \rightarrow$

(f) $Ph_2CH-CPh(OH)-\underset{\underset{O}{\|}}{C}-Ph \xrightarrow{conc\ OH^-}$

(g)
$\xrightarrow[(-2HBr)]{OEt^-}$

(h)
$+\quad NaNH_2 \longrightarrow$

(i) $C_5H_{12}-C\equiv C-CONH_2 \xrightarrow[OH^-]{OCl^-}$

(j) Cyclohexanone + excess $HN_3 \xrightarrow{H_2SO_4}$

(k)
$\xrightarrow{heat}$

(l)
$+\quad PhLi \longrightarrow$

(m)
$=N-OSO_3H \quad + \quad NaN_3 \xrightarrow{heat}$

(n) $O=C=C=C=O + CH_2N_2 \rightarrow$

(o) $PhCH_2-S-CH_2Ph + KNH_2 \xrightarrow{heat}$

(p)
$+\quad CH_2N_2 \longrightarrow$

(q)
$+\quad PhLi \longrightarrow$

5. Suggest mechanisms for each of the following conversions:

(a) $Me_3C-OCl + Ag^+ \xrightarrow{H_2O} (CH_3)_2C=O + MeOH$

(b) $Ph-N(Ac)_2 + ZnCl_2 \rightarrow Ac-$$-NHAc$

(c) $H-\overset{*}{O}-\overset{*}{O}-H + NO_2^- \rightarrow \left[O-N-O^* \right]^- + H_2O$

with $\overset{\|}{O_*}$ in the bracket

(d) 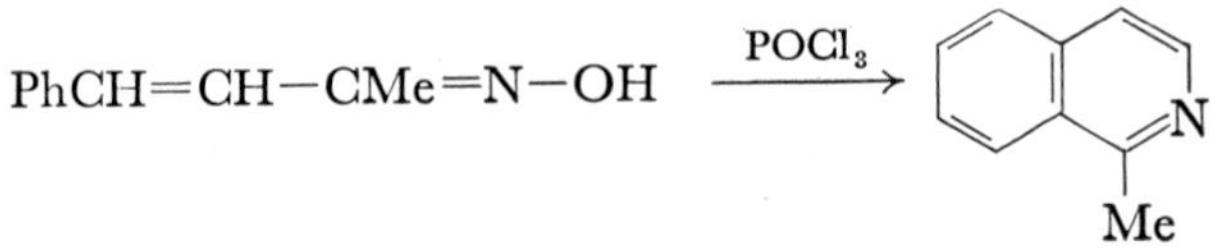 $PhCH=CH-CMe=N-OH \xrightarrow{POCl_3}$

Me

(e) 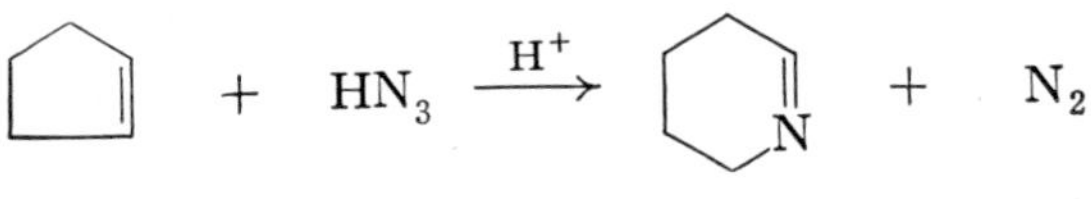 + $HN_3 \xrightarrow{H^+}$ + N_2

(f) 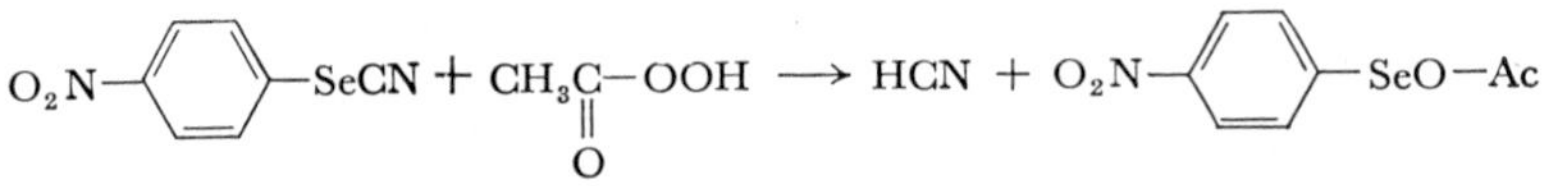 $O_2N-\!\!\!\!\bigcirc\!\!\!\!-SeCN + CH_3\overset{\|}{C}-OOH \rightarrow HCN + O_2N-\!\!\!\!\bigcirc\!\!\!\!-SeO-Ac$

(with O below the C)

(g) + $H_2O_2 \xrightarrow{OH^-}$ + $HCOO^-$

(h) + $H\overset{*}{C}HO \xrightarrow{OH^-}$

+ $HCOOH$

$^*CH_2OH$

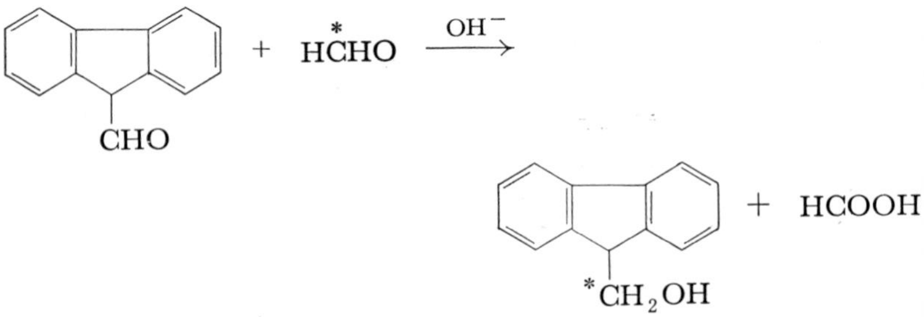

(i)  $(PhO)_2 C=S + CH_2N_2 \longrightarrow (PhO)_2C\underset{S}{\overset{\diagup\diagdown}{\quad}}CH_2$

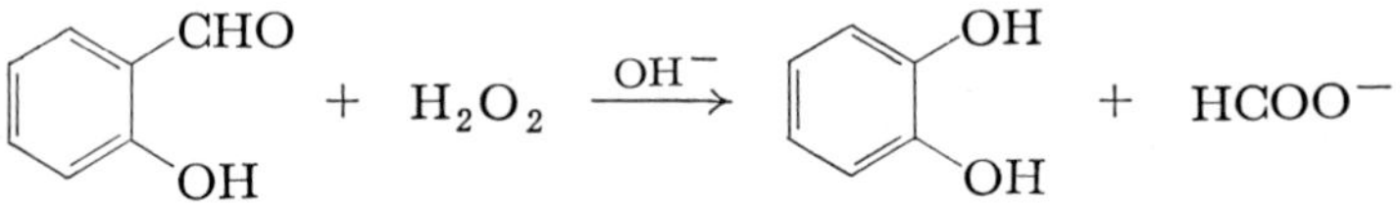

(j) 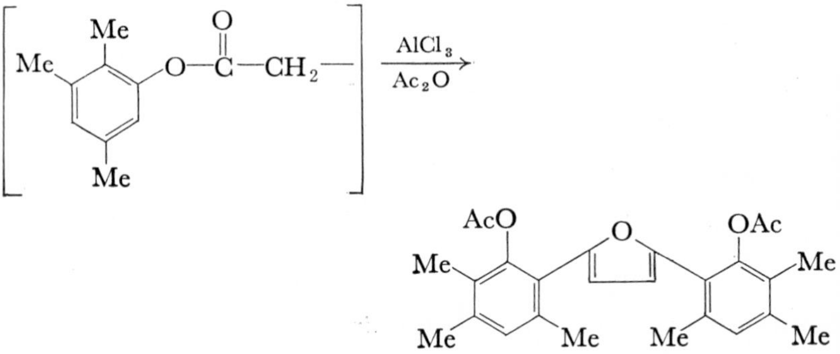 $\xrightarrow[Ac_2O]{AlCl_3}$

(k) 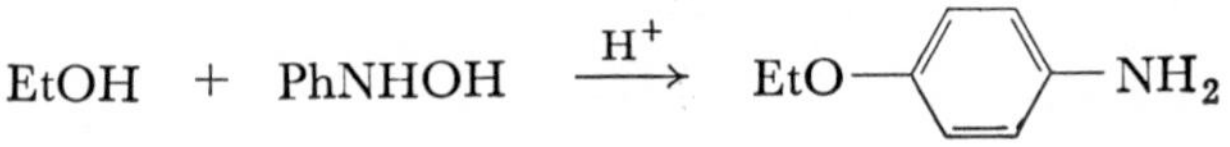 $EtOH + PhNHOH \xrightarrow{H^+} EtO-\!\!\!\!\bigcirc\!\!\!\!-NH_2$

(l)

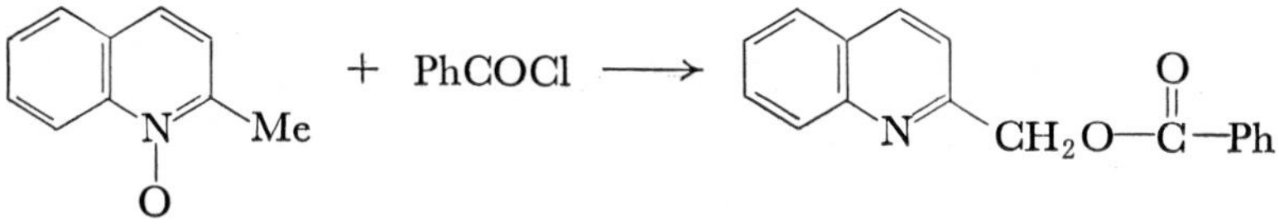

$+$ PhCOCl $\longrightarrow$

(m) $Ph_2C(OH)-\underset{\underset{O}{\|}}{C}-N_3 \; + \; PhNH_2 \; \longrightarrow Ph_2C{=}O \; + \; PhNH\underset{\underset{O}{\|}}{C}NH_2$

(n) 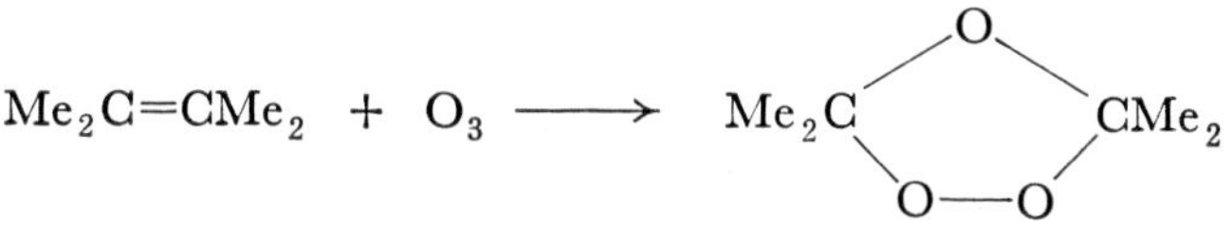 $Me_2C{=}CMe_2 \; + \; O_3 \; \longrightarrow$

(o)

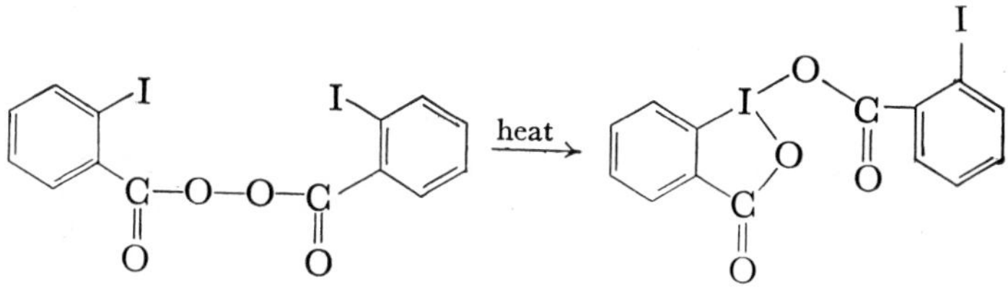

(p)

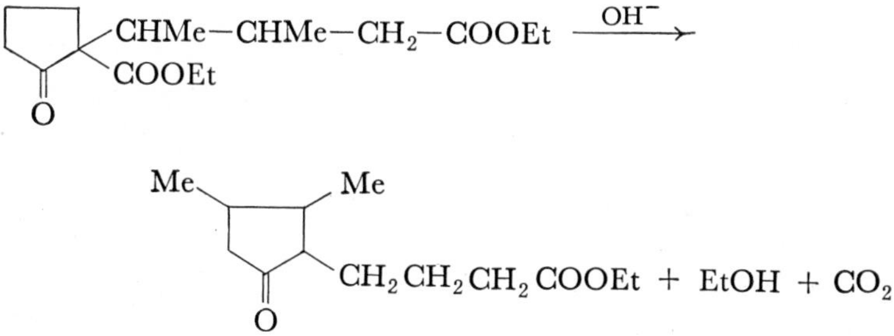

$\xrightarrow{\;OH^-\;}$

$CH_2CH_2CH_2COOEt \; + \; EtOH \; + \; CO_2$

(q)

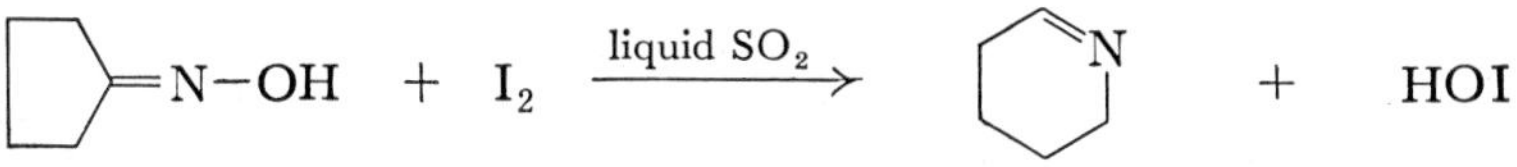

${=}N{-}OH \; + \; I_2 \; \xrightarrow{\text{liquid } SO_2}$

$+ \quad HOI$

(r)

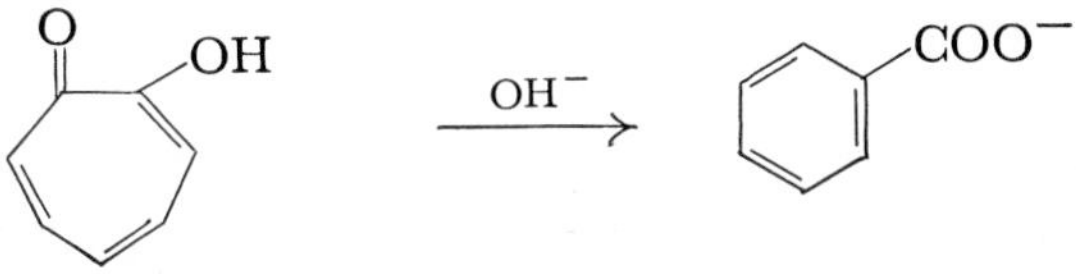

$\xrightarrow{\;OH^-\;}$

(s) 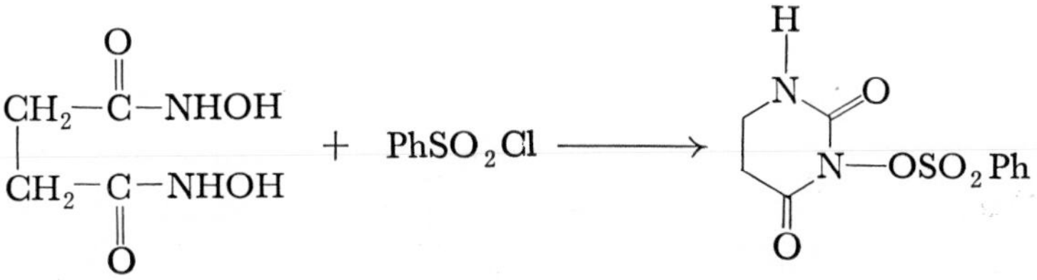 $\begin{array}{l} CH_2-\underset{\underset{}{\overset{\|}{O}}}{C}-NHOH \\ | \\ CH_2-\underset{\underset{O}{\|}}{C}-NHOH \end{array}$ $+ \; PhSO_2Cl \; \longrightarrow$

(t) 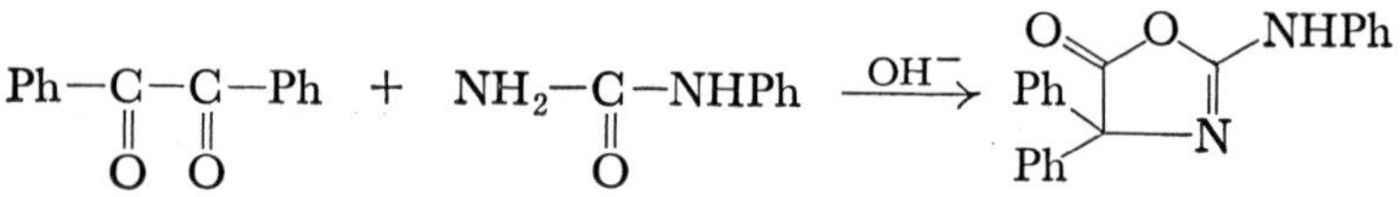 Ph—C—C—Ph + NH$_2$—C—NHPh $\xrightarrow{OH^-}$

(u) 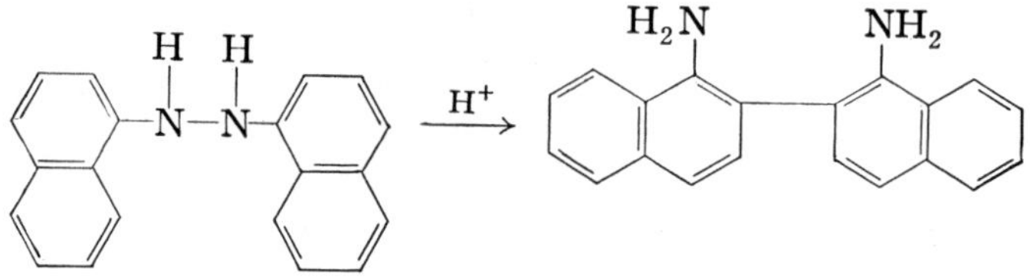 $\xrightarrow{H^+}$

6. Suggest mechanisms for the following conversions (these are more difficult than the examples in Ex. 5):

(a) 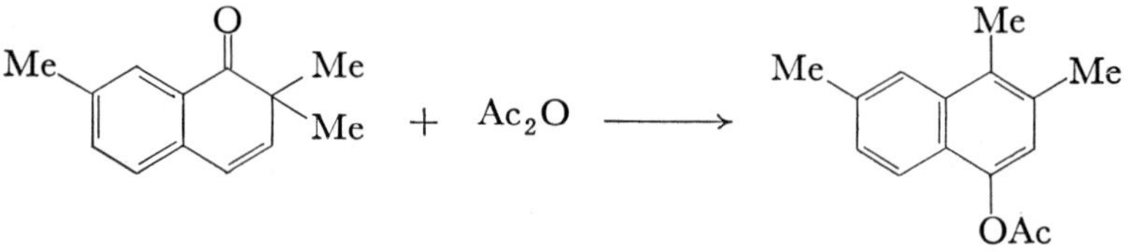 + Ac$_2$O $\longrightarrow$

(b) 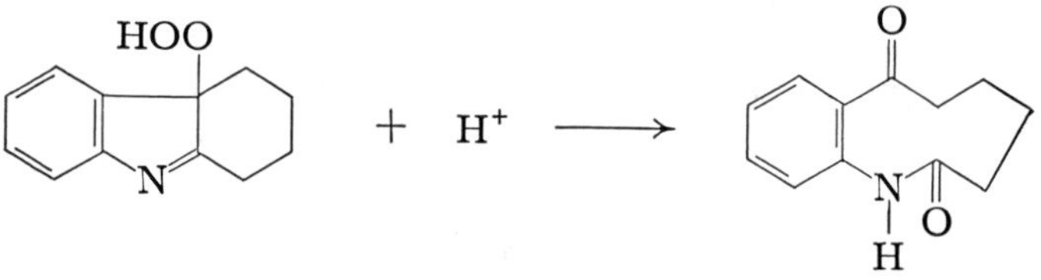 + H$^+$ $\longrightarrow$

(c) PhCN + H$_2$O$_2$ + OH$^-$ → O$_2$ + PhCONH$_2$ (This reaction is much faster than the normal hydrolysis of the nitrile.)

(d) 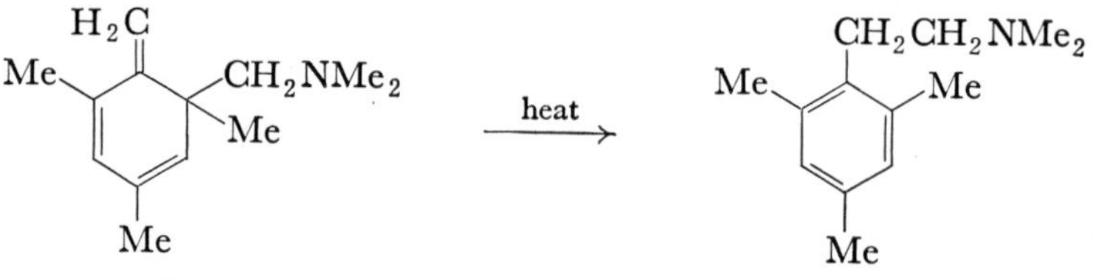 $\xrightarrow{heat}$

(e) 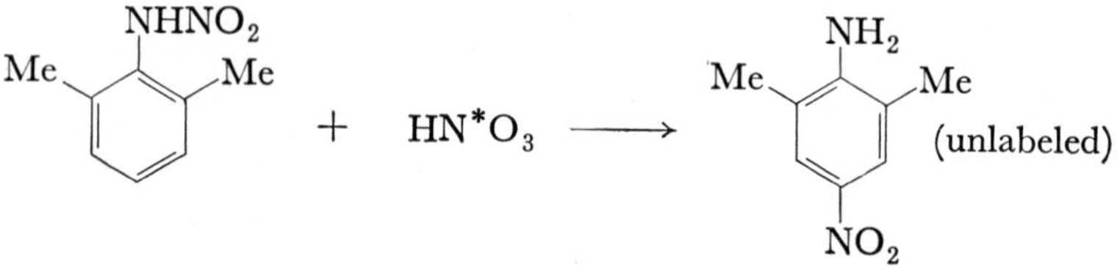 + HN*O$_3$ $\longrightarrow$ (unlabeled)

(f) 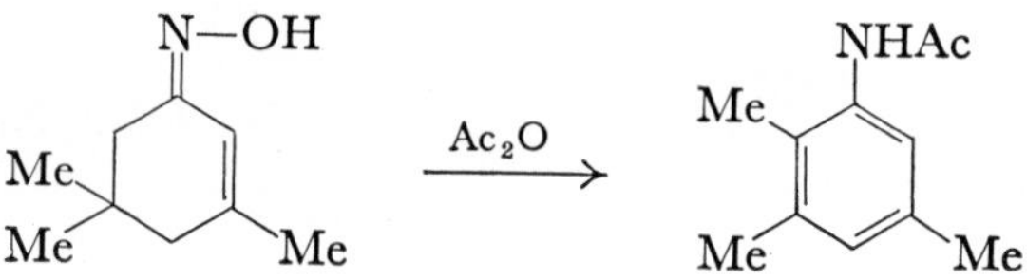 $\xrightarrow{Ac_2O}$

(g) 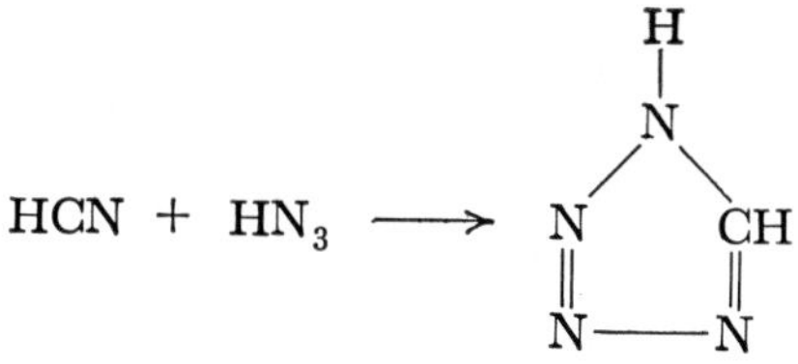 $HCN + HN_3 \longrightarrow$

(h) 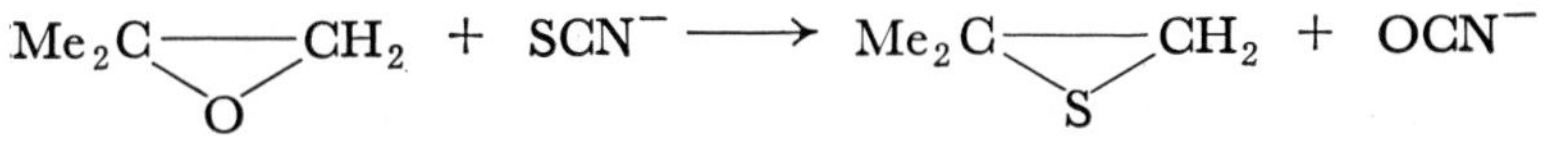 $Me_2C\underset{O}{\overset{}{\triangle}}CH_2 + SCN^- \longrightarrow Me_2C\underset{S}{\overset{}{\triangle}}CH_2 + OCN^-$

(i)

$+ H^+ \longrightarrow$

$+ NH_4^+$

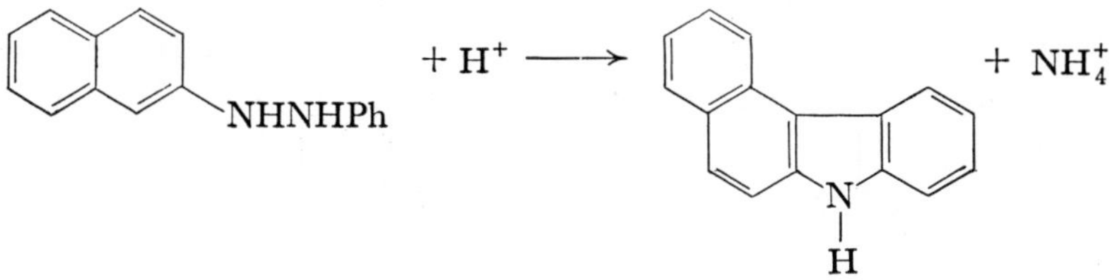

(j) $Ph\overset{*}{-}I{=}O + Ph-IO_2 \xrightarrow{Ag^+} (Ph_2\overset{*}{I})^+ + AgIO_3$

(k) $2Ph_3C-O-NO_2 \xrightarrow{heat} N_2O_4 + PhO-CPh_2-CPh_2-OPh$

(l)

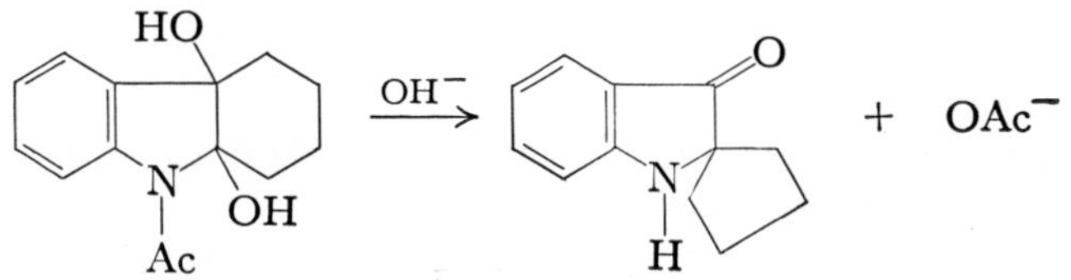

$\xrightarrow{OH^-}$

$+ OAc^-$

(m)

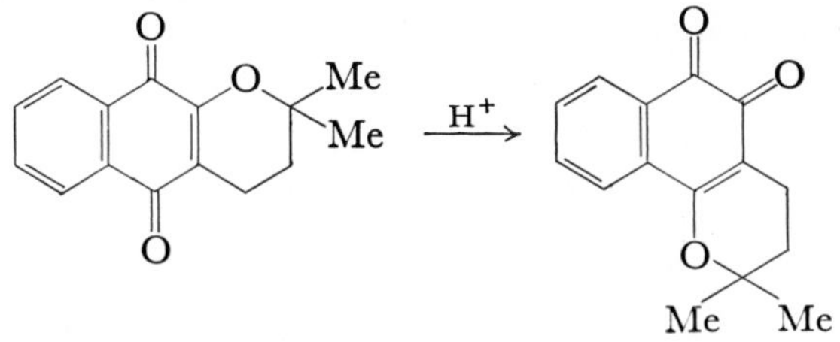

$\xrightarrow{H^+}$

(n)

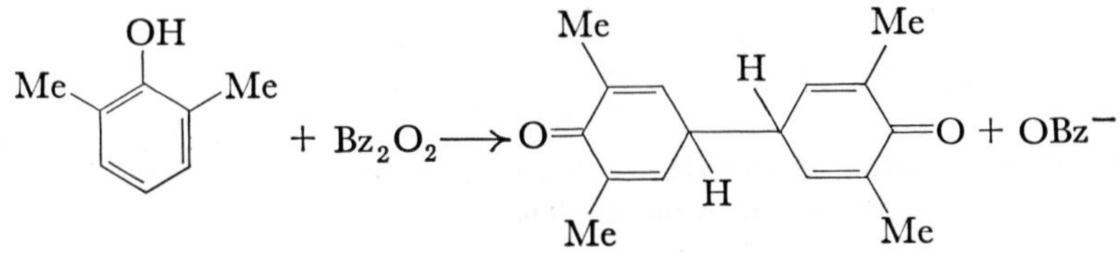

$+ Bz_2O_2 \longrightarrow$

$+ OBz^-$

(o)

$+ TsCl \longrightarrow$

$+ OTs^-$

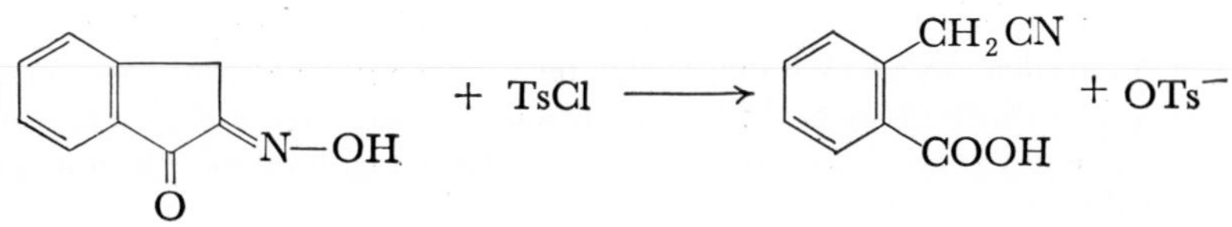

(p) 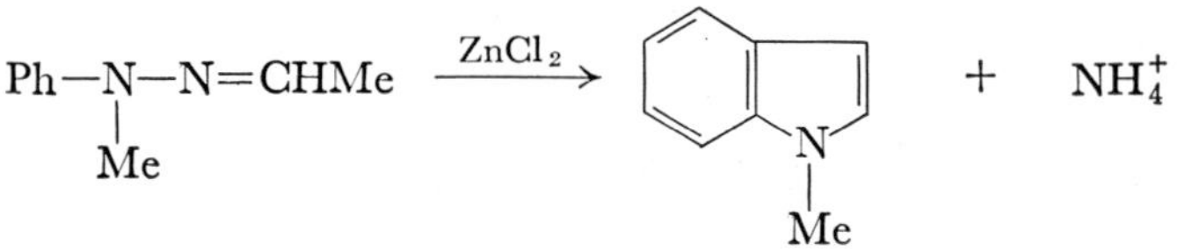 Ph—N—N=CHMe $\xrightarrow{\text{ZnCl}_2}$ + NH$_4^+$
    |
   Me

(q) 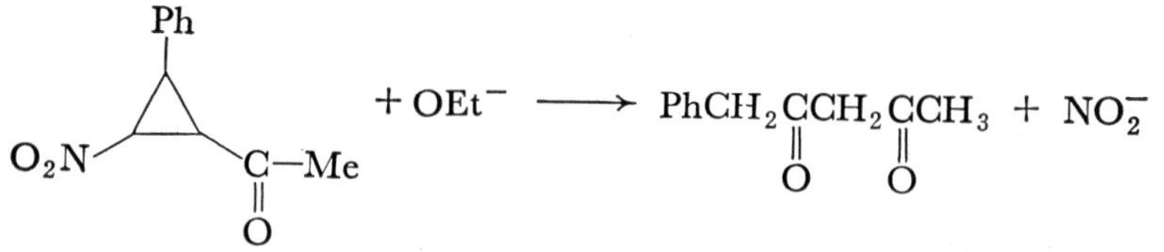 + OEt$^-$ ⟶ PhCH$_2$CCH$_2$CCH$_3$ + NO$_2^-$

(r) 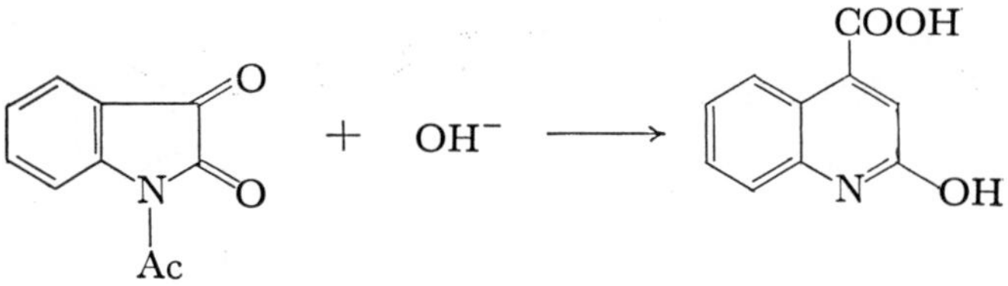 + OH$^-$ ⟶

(s) 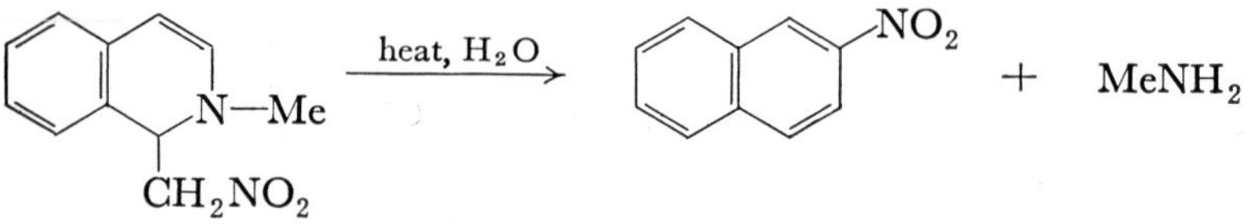 $\xrightarrow{\text{heat, H}_2\text{O}}$ + MeNH$_2$

7. Explain each of the following:

  (a) When benzophenone oxime is treated successively with PCl$_5$, then H$_2$O^{18}, O^{18} is found in the resulting benzanilide.

  (b) Of the two diastereomeric forms of oxime CXXX, that yielding amide CXXXI in the Beckmann rearrangement is resolvable into D and L forms, whereas that yielding amide CXXXII is not.

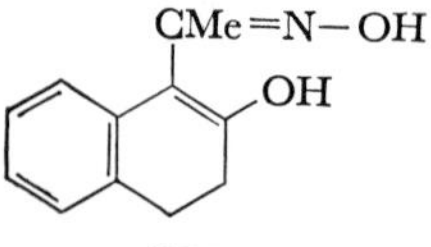

    CXXX 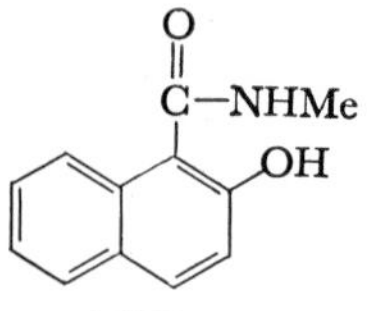   CXXXI 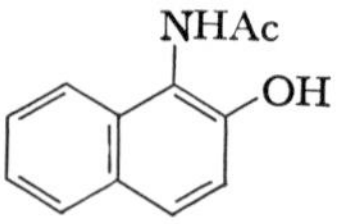   CXXXII

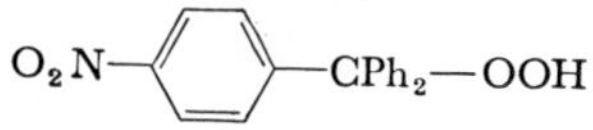

O$_2$N—⟨ ⟩—CPh$_2$—OOH

CXXXIII

  (c) When peroxide CXXXIII is heated in benzene, p-nitrophenol is produced in a greater yield than is phenol. The reverse is true for the decomposition of CXXXIII in ether-sulfuric acid.

  (d) The rearrangements of N-nitroamines are faster in D$_2$O than in H$_2$O.

  (e) When ether CXXXIV is subjected to the Claisen rearrangement, some migration of the *methallyl* group to the *para* position is observed. Moreover, if the reaction is halted in its early stages, the "unreacted ether" is found to be a mixture of allyl and methyllyl ethers.

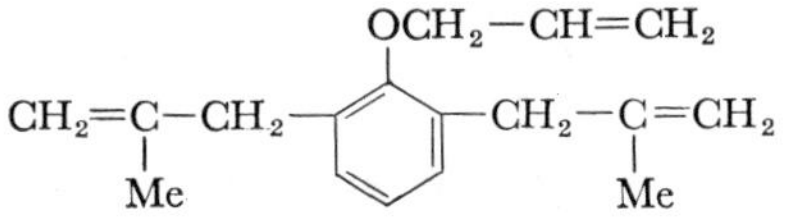

$$CH_2=C-CH_2-\overset{\overset{\displaystyle OCH_2-CH=CH_2}{|}}{\underset{}{\bigcirc}}-CH_2-C=CH_2$$
$$\underset{Me}{|} \qquad \underset{Me}{|}$$

CXXXIV

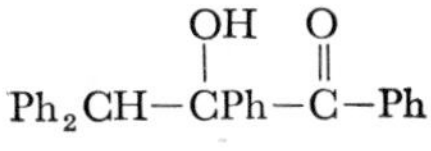

$$Ph_2CH-\overset{\overset{\displaystyle OH}{|}}{C}Ph-\overset{\overset{\displaystyle O}{||}}{C}-Ph$$

CXXXV

$$Ph_2CH-\overset{\overset{\displaystyle}{C}}{\underset{\underset{\displaystyle OH}{|}}{\overset{\displaystyle ||}{O}}}-CPh_2$$

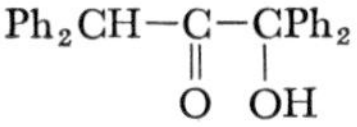

CXXXVI

(f) Hydrochloric and hydrobromic acids are much more effective catalysts for the rearrangement N-nitroso-N-methylaniline than are sulfuric and perchloric acids.

(g) The rate of the benzidine rearrangement in water-dioxane-HClO$_4$ mixtures is almost 30 times as rapid in 1.0 molar HClO$_4$ as in 0.5 molar HClO$_4$.

(h) The rearrangement of ketol CXXXV to ketol CXXXVI in base is much slower than typical benzilic acid rearrangements under comparable conditions, even though both reactions involve the 1,2 migration of a phenyl group to a carbonyl carbon.

(i) The decomposition of peroxide CXXXVII in chloroform is much faster than that of benzoyl peroxide under comparable conditions.

(j) The rearrangement of diazoaminobenzene (CXXXVIII) in aniline in the presence of added acid is found to be first order in acid when HCl or HNO$_3$ is used, but second order in acid when o-bromobenzoic acid is used.

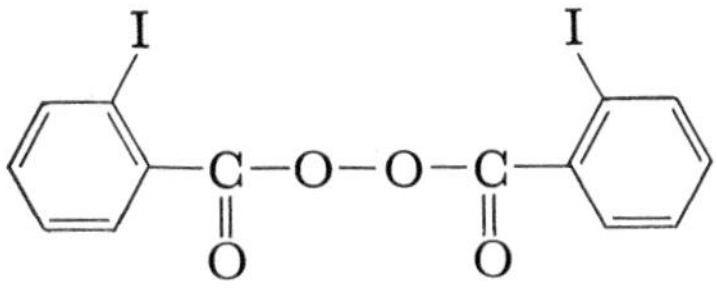

CXXXVII

$$Ph-N=N-NH-Ph$$

CXXXVIII

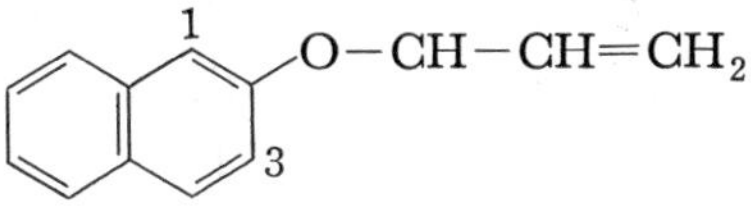

CXXXIX

(k) In the Claisen rearrangement of β-naphthyl allyl ether (CXXXIX), the allyl group migrates to the 1 position, rather than to the 3 position, although both positions are ortho to the 2 position.

CHAPTER 16

Free-radical Reactions[1]

FOR OUR PRESENT PURPOSES, we may define free radicals simply as *species having one or more unpaired electrons.*[2] Familiar examples are the methyl radical, $CH_3\cdot$, the triphenylmethyl radical, $Ph_3C\cdot$, the chlorine atom, $Cl\cdot$, and the nitric oxide molecule, $:N\!\cdot\!\cdot\!\cdot\!O:$, each of which has a single unpaired electron. *Homolytic reactions*—that is, reactions passing through free radical intermediates—have been mentioned at various points in the preceding chapters; but because such reactions are fundamentally different from the large body of heterolytic reactions, a detailed consideration of them has been postponed to this point.

Part I—LONG-LIVED AND SHORT-LIVED FREE RADICALS. FORMATION AND DETECTION OF FREE RADICALS

Triarylmethyl Radicals

The chemistry of organic free radicals may be said to date back to 1900, for it was in this year that Gomberg reported the synthesis and identification of the

---

[1] For more detailed treatments of this topic, see: (*a*) Steacie, *Atomic and Free Radical Reactions* (2d Ed.), Reinhold Publishing Corp., New York, 1954; (*b*) Walling, *Free Radicals in Solution*, John Wiley and Sons, Inc., New York, 1957; (*c*) Leffler, *The Reactive Intermediates of Organic Chemistry*, Interscience Publishers, Inc., New York, 1956, pp. 1–74, 234–251; (*d*) Waters, *The Chemistry of Free Radicals*, Oxford University Press, Oxford, 1946.

[2] We do not generally refer to ions of the transition metals or the rare earth metals (for example, Cr^{+3}, Yb^{+3}) or to complexes derived from these ions (for example, $Cr(NH_3)_6^{+3}$, $Yb(SO_4)_3^{-3}$) as free radicals, although such species may have one or more unpaired d or f electrons. These ions have some properties in common with free radicals (such as the ability to catalyze the conversion of *para*-hydrogen to normal hydrogen) but in general are very different chemically from the organic free radicals to be considered in this chapter.

672

first organic free radical, triphenylmethyl.[3] When triphenylmethyl chloride, Ph_3CCl, in benzene was treated with finely divided silver metal, there was obtained a *yellow solution*, which upon careful evaporation in the absence of air gave the expected product, hexaphenylethane, a white solid. To what then could the yellow color be attributed? This color disappeared slowly when the solution was exposed to air, but in this case, evaporation yielded triphenylmethyl peroxide, Ph_3C—O—O—CPh_3. Moreover, the color could be discharged by treatment with iodine or with nitric oxide, resulting in the formation, respectively, of triphenylmethyl iodide or triphenylmethylnitrosomethane (Ph_3-C—N=O). In short, the reactions of the yellow solution were those to be expected of the triphenylmethyl radical, although the molecular weight of the white solid indicated that it was largely, if not wholly, hexaphenylethane. The conclusion (much less obvious in 1900 than today) was that an equilibrium between hexaphenylethane and the triphenylmethyl radical existed in solution, and that this equilibrium was displaced when iodine, oxygen, or nitric acid destroyed the radical.

$$Ph_3C\text{—}Cl \xrightarrow{Ag} Ph_3C\text{—}CPh_3 \rightleftharpoons 2Ph_3C\cdot \begin{array}{l} \xrightarrow{O_2} Ph_3C\text{—}O\text{—}O\text{—}CPh_3 \\ \xrightarrow{I_2} Ph_3C\text{—}I \\ \xrightarrow{NO} Ph_3C\text{—}N\text{=}O \end{array}$$

Since 1900 a large number of hexaarylethanes have been prepared, and most have been found to be more dissociated (under similar conditions) than hexaphenylethane itself. The accurate determination of the various dissociation constants is, however, somewhat of a problem. In principle, the degree of dissociation of such hydrocarbons could be evaluated from cryoscopic measurements of their apparent molecular weights, but any worker who has carried out measurements of this type is well aware of the very approximate nature of the results. Somewhat more success is possible using colorimetric methods[4(a)] (for the radicals are colored whereas the hexaarylethanes are generally colorless), but care must be taken to prevent interference by colored decomposition products.[4(b)]

A third method, which is of considerable fundamental importance, makes use of the *magnetic properties* of free radicals. Ordinary organic compounds are *diamagnetic*; when they are placed in a magnetic field, tiny currents are set up in the filled orbitals, and these currents are associated with induced magnetic fields opposed in direction to the applied field. As a result, the sample of the

---

[3] (a) Gomberg, *Ber.*, **33**, 3150 (1900); *J. Am. Chem. Soc.*, **22**, 757 (1900). (b) For reviews on the triphenylmethyl and related radicals, see Wheland, *Advanced Organic Chemistry* (2d Ed.), John Wiley and Sons, Inc., New York, 1949, p. 680; and Bachmann in Gilman's *Organic Chemistry*, (2d Ed.), Vol. 1, John Wiley and Sons, Inc., New York, 1943, p. 593.

[4] (a) Ziegler and Ewald, *Ann.*, **473**, 163 (1929). (b) See, for example, Marvel, *et al.*, *J. Am. Chem. Soc.*, **61**, 2769, 2771 (1939); **66**, 415 (1944).

compound tends to be pushed *out* of the magnetic field. Ordinarily, the diamagnetism of a molecule may be estimated from its structure simply by adding together terms for each of the atoms, then making appropriate corrections for conjugation, in much the same way as we estimate molar refractivities.[5] However, if the compound has one or more unpaired electrons, these act as small electromagnets and tend to *pull the sample into* the applied magnetic field. In this case, the material is said to be *paramagnetic:* the paired electrons continue to exert their diamagnetic push, but for any individual radical this is overshadowed by the paramagnetic pull. Quite obviously, then, paramagnetism in an organic material is an excellent indication of the presence of relatively stable free radicals, and by measuring the paramagnetism of solutions of hexaarylethanes, it should be possible to estimate their degree of dissociation into triarylmethyl radicals. We need not be concerned here with the types of apparatus used to measure the susceptibility of materials to applied magnetic fields, nor with the details of magnetochemical calculations.[6] One difficulty should, however, be apparent. The usual methods measure a force that results from the combination of diamagnetic and paramagnetic effects; to obtain paramagnetic susceptibility, corrections must be made for diamagnetic susceptibilities—not only of the non-dissociated ethanes, but of the radicals themselves. When the degree of dissociation is small, the paramagnetic term is small, and any error made in estimating the diamagnetic contribution of the hexaarylethane will seriously affect the estimated paramagnetic term and, hence, the estimated radical concentration. When the degree of dissociation is large, it is the diamagnetic contribution of the radical that causes trouble, for there is good reason to suppose that the customary method of estimating diamagnetic susceptibilities cannot be applied to radicals of this type because of interaction (of as yet unknown magnitude) between the benzene rings.[7] Because of the uncertainties in interpreting magnetic measurements, the dissociation constants of substituted hexaphenylethanes, determined magnetically, are given in Table 16-1 only to one significant figure, and even this figure should be regarded as tentative.

In attempting to relate these dissociation constants to the structures of the various hydrocarbons and to the radicals derived from them, we must first decide why hexaarylethanes are dissociated at all at ordinary temperatures whereas ethane itself and hexa*alkyl*ethanes are not. Recalling the unusual stability of triaryl carbanions, we may be quite certain that one important factor

---

[5] See, for example, Bhatnagar and Mathur, *Physical Principles and Applications of Magnetochemistry*, Macmillan Co., London, 1935, Chap. 4; and Michaelis, *The Technique of Organic Chemistry* (edited by Weissberger), Vol. I, Interscience Publishers, Inc., New York, 1949, Chap. 29.

[6] For detailed discussions of these points, see Selwood, *Magnetochemistry* (2d Ed.), Interscience Publishers Inc., New York, 1956, pp. 1–35, 135–160.

[7] Selwood and Dobres, *J. Am. Chem. Soc.*, **72**, 3860 (1950). See also, Wheland (Ref. 3b), p. 695.

Table 16-1. Dissociation Constants of Some Substituted Hexaphenylethanes (benzene, 25°)[8]

	K_{diss}		K_{diss}
Ph_3C-CPh_3	0.0002	$(Ph-\bigcirc-)_3C-C(-\bigcirc-Ph)_3$	0.04
$MeO-\bigcirc-CPh_2-CPh_2-\bigcirc-OMe$	0.0008	$(\bigcirc-)_3C-C(-\bigcirc)_3$ OMe MeO	0.1
$(Me-\bigcirc-)_2C-C(\bigcirc-Me)_2$ Ph Ph	0.001	$(\bigcirc-)_2C-C(-\bigcirc)_2$ Me Ph Ph Me	2
$(Me-\bigcirc-)_3C-C(\bigcirc-Me)_3$	0.01	$(O_2N-\bigcirc-)_3C-C(-\bigcirc-NO_2)_3$	"large"

stabilizing triarylmethyl radicals is the capacity of the three benzene rings to delocalize the unpaired electron. This is a conjugation or resonance effect which, for the triphenylmethyl radical, may be represented pictorially by drawing contributing structures I′, I″, and many like them. Substituents at the *ortho*

and *para* positions may further delocalize the unpaired electron by electron donation (II ↔ II′), by electron withdrawal (III ↔ III′), or by hyperconjugation (IV ↔ IV′). The radical derived from hexa-*p*-biphenylylethane (radical V) is particularly stable, since the unpaired electron is "distributed over" *nineteen* positions (three positions on each of the six rings, in addition to the α-carbon).

[8] These values are taken mainly from the work of Marvel and coworkers, *J. Am. Chem. Soc.*, **61**, 77 (1939); **63**, 1892 (1941); **64**, 1824 (1942); **66**, 415 (1944). For some recent cryoscopic values, see Bowden, *J. Chem. Soc.*, **1957**, 4235.

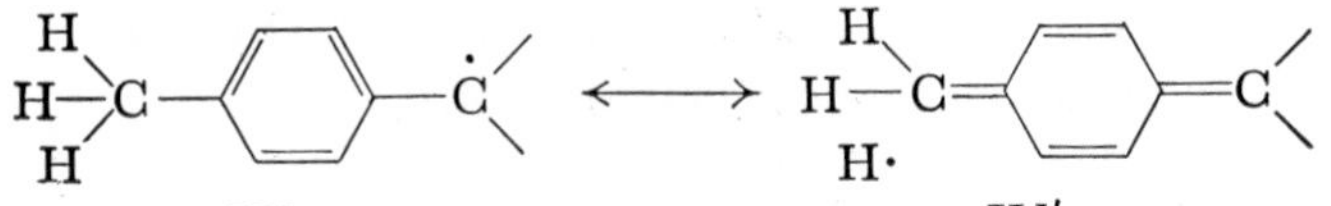

IV ⟷ IV'

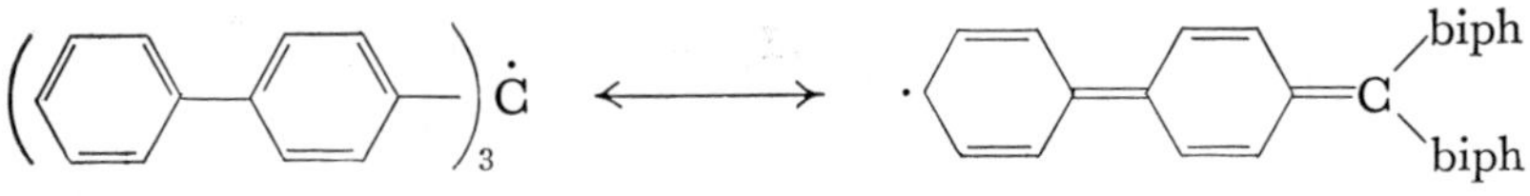

V ⟷ V'

The fact that *ortho* substituents are generally more effective than *para* substituents in promoting dissociation indicates that *steric assistance* is also coming into play. Using scale models, it may be shown that hexaphenylethane is a very "crowded" molecule, due largely to interference between the *ortho* hydrogens on the various benzene rings. When the molecule dissociates, the bond angles about the aliphatic carbon atoms increase from 108° to about 120°, allowing considerably greater freedom of motion.[9] When there are *ortho* substituents on the rings, the hexaarylethane becomes even more crowded. Hence, the release of steric strain accompanying dissociation into radicals becomes even more welcome (although it is probable that even in the triphenylmethyl radical, steric interaction among the *ortho*-hydrogen atoms is still sufficient to keep the phenyl groups from lying in the common plane,[10] as would be desirable for maximum resonance stabilization). It is interesting that hydrocarbon VI, in which two of the phenyl groups on each nonaromatic carbon are "tied back" in a fluorene ring, is not noticeably dissociated into free radicals except at high temperatures.[11] Since the

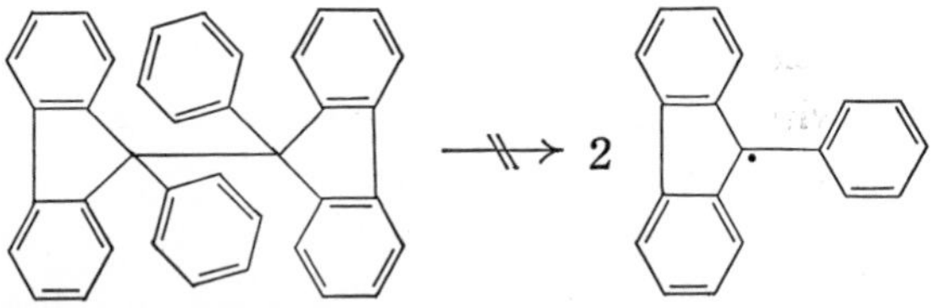

VI   ⟶̸ 2   (at room temperature)

[9] Further evidence that the breakage of the C—C bond in hexaphenylethane is sterically assisted comes from the comparison of the following heats of hydrogenolysis (Bent and Culbertson, *J. Am. Chem. Soc.*, **58**, 170 (1936)):

$Ph_3C—CPh_3 + H_2 \rightarrow 2Ph_3CH + 35$ kcal   (observed)
$H_3C—CH_3 + H_2 \rightarrow 2CH_4 + 13$ kcal   (calculated from heats of combustion)

Much more heat is released in the hydrogenolysis of hexaphenylethane than in the hydrogenolysis of ethane, indicating that the C—C bond in the latter is much more difficult to break. The relative ease in breaking the C—C bond in the hexaphenyl compound cannot be due to a resonance effect, since there is virtually no difference between the conjugated systems of the reactant and product in this case. It may be concluded therefore that the C—C bond in the hexaphenyl compound is weakened by excessive crowding.

[10] See, however, Karagounis, *Helv. Chim. Acta*, **34**, 994 (1951).
[11] Bent and Cline, *J. Am. Chem. Soc.*, **58**, 1624 (1936).

radical derived from this hydrocarbon should be no less "resonance stabilized" than a triphenylmethyl radical, we may conclude that dissociation does not occur in this case because of inadequate steric assistance.

Further Types of Stable Free Radicals

We have seen that the two features favoring the dissociation of a hydrocarbon into radicals are: (1) excessive crowding in the hydrocarbon itself, and (2) delocalization of the unpaired electron over a large area in the radical. The first of these features is mainly responsible for the observed dissociation of hydrocarbons VII[12(a)] and VIII,[12(b)] whereas the second factor accounts for the stabilities of radicals IX,[12(c)] X,[12(d)] and XI.[12(e)] With the help of pencil and paper (or per-

VII   VIII

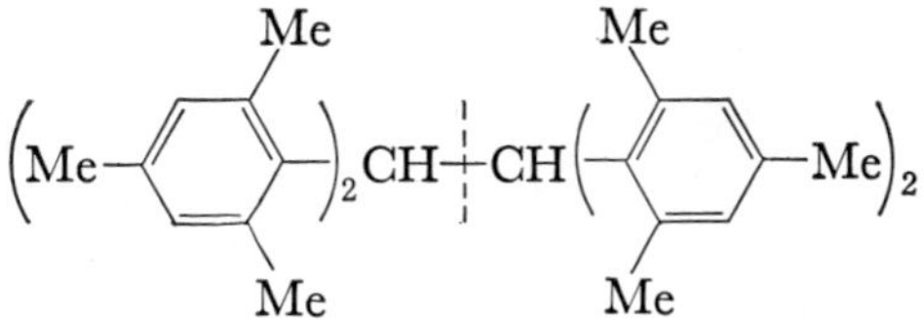

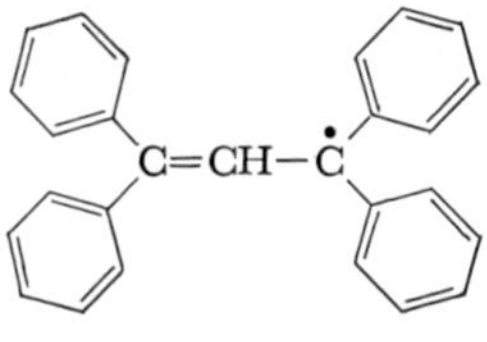

IX 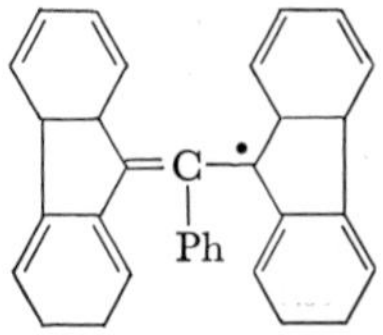   XI 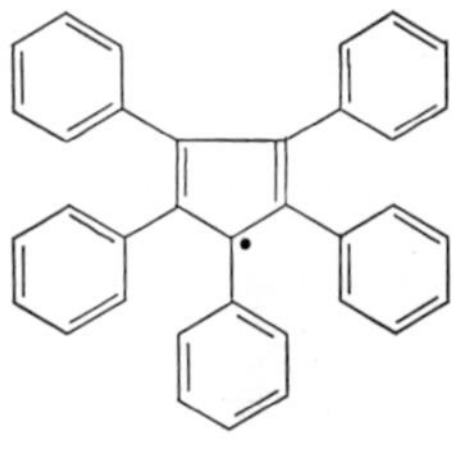   XI

haps merely by inspection), the reader may see that the unpaired electron may distribute itself over fourteen carbons in radicals IX and X, over no less than twenty carbons in radical XI, but over only seven carbons in the radicals formed by dissociation of VII and VIII.

Not all atoms comprising the conjugated system within a stable free radical need be carbons. Careful oxidations of triphenylamine, tetraphenylhydrazine (XII), and pentaphenylpyrrole (XIII) yield *aminium ion radicals* XIV,[13(a)] XV,[13(b)] and XVI,[13(c)] respectively:

[12] (a) Schlenk and Mark, *Ber.*, **55B**, 2285 (1922). (b) Jarrett and Sloan, *J. Chem. Phys.*, **22**, 1783 (1954). (c) Ziegler and Ochs, *Ber.*, **55**, 2257 (1922); *Ann.*, **434**, 34 (1923). (d) Koelsch, *J. Am. Chem. Soc.*, **79**, 4439 (1957). (e) Muller and Muller-Rodloff, *Ber.*, **69B**, 665 (1936).

[13] (a) Weitz and Schwechten, *Ber.*, **59**, 2307 (1926); **60**, 551 (1927). (b) Lewis, Lipkin, and Biegleisen, *J. Am. Chem. Soc.*, **64**, 2801, 2808 (1942). (c) Kuhn and Kainer, *Ber.*, **85**, 498 (1952).

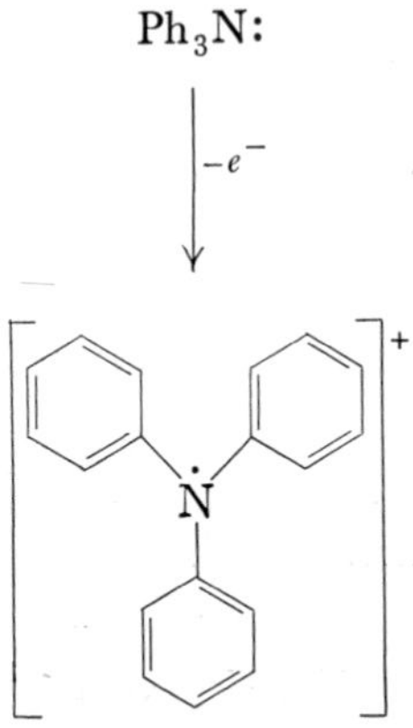

Ph$_3$N:

Ph$_2$Ṅ—ṄPh$_2$

XII

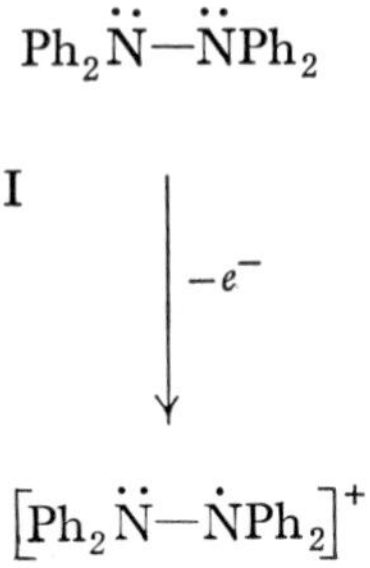

Ph, Ph, Ph, N, Ph, Ph (XIII)

$$\Big\downarrow -e^-$$

$$\Big\downarrow -e^-$$

$$\Big\downarrow -e^-$$

[structure XIV]

XIV

$$\left[Ph_2\ddot{N}—\dot{N}Ph_2 \right]^+$$

XV

[structure XVI]

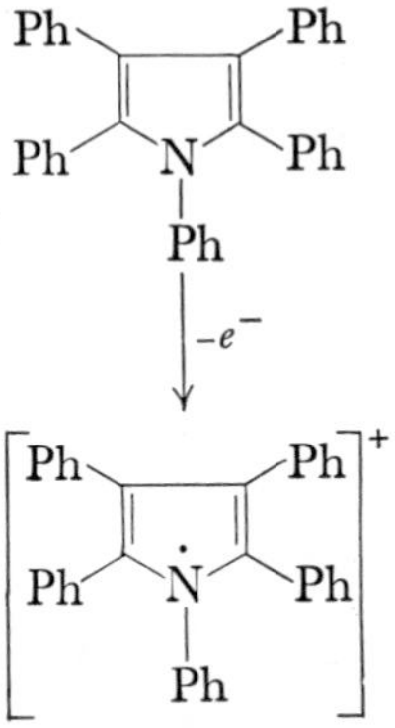

XVI

Radical ion XIV is obviously analogous to the triphenylmethyl radical in the carbon series, radical ion XV is not unlike the pentaphenylethyl radical (Ph$_3$C—CPh$_2$·), and radical ion XVI is closely allied to the pentaphenylcyclopentadienyl radical (XI). Radicals XIV, XV, and XVI, like the corresponding carbon radicals, are deeply colored and are paramagnetic. Each, however, bears a positive charge because of the "extra" proton in the nitrogen nucleus. The positive charges tend to prevent association of the radicals to their "dimeric" forms, for such dimers would be dipositive cations in which a normally weak N—N bond is further weakened by positive charges on adjacent nitrogen atoms (for example, Ph$_3$Ṅ—ṄPh$_3$).

Oxidation of p-phenylenediamine or an alkylated derivative of this amine in slightly acid solutions yields the so-called *Wurster salts*, in which the cations are radical ions of the type XVII.[14] Such cations, to which no simple carbon analogs appear to be known, are presumably stabilized by distribution of the unpaired electron over all six carbons in the ring as well as over both nitrogens. However,

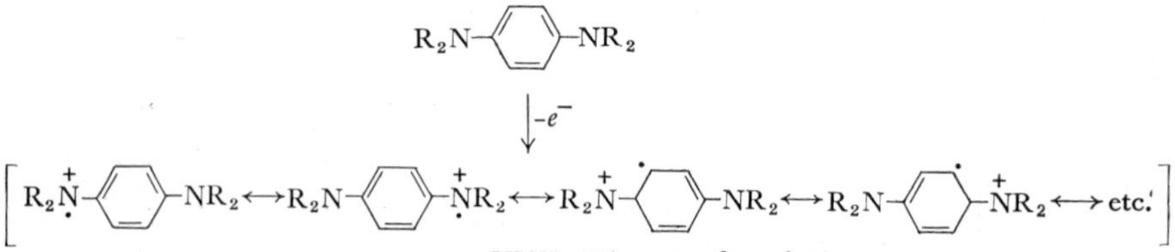

R$_2$N—⟨ ⟩—NR$_2$

$$\Big\downarrow -e^-$$

$$\left[R_2\overset{+}{N}—⟨\ ⟩—\overset{·}{N}R_2 \leftrightarrow R_2N—⟨\ ⟩—\overset{+}{\overset{·}{N}}R_2 \leftrightarrow R_2\overset{+}{\overset{·}{N}}—⟨\ ⟩—NR_2 \leftrightarrow R_2N—⟨\ ⟩—\overset{·}{\overset{+}{N}}R_2 \leftrightarrow \text{etc.} \right]$$

XVII (Wurster salt cation)

the fully methylated diamine, XVIII, does not form such a radical,[14(b)] almost

14 (a) Rumpf and Trombe, *J. chim. phys.*, **35**, 110 (1938); *Compt. rend.*, **206**, 671 (1938). (b) Michaelis, Schubert, and Granick, *J. Am. Chem. Soc.*, **61**, 1981 (1939).

$$\text{XVIII} \xrightarrow{\;/\!\!/\;}$$

certainly because the large departures from planarity resulting from interaction between the N-methyl and C-methyl groups prohibit the necessary resonance stabilization.

Closely related to the Wurster salt cations are the *semiquinones*,[15] the simplest of which is XIX. These, however, are anions, and unlike the Wurster salts, are most stable in basic solutions. Semiquinones represent the oxidation

state lying between hydroquinones and quinones, and, as indicated above, may be prepared by careful oxidation of the former (in basic media) or careful reduction of the latter (again in basic media). In neutral or acid solutions, semiquinones tend to disproportionate to mixtures of quinones and hydroquinones or to the familiar quinone-hydroquinone adducts (*quinhydrones*). In contrast to the semiquinones, themselves, to which the unpaired electron may be distributed over *six* ring carbons and two oxygens, resonance in the conjugate acids of semiquinones is somewhat restricted. The unpaired electron may again distribute itself over the nonprotonated oxygen and the positions *ortho* and *para* to it; but structures such as XX, in which the unpaired electron is "placed" on the protonated oxygen (or on positions *ortho* and *para* to it) should not be significant contributors, since these involve considerable separation of unlike charge. This

---

[15] For reviews of the chemistry of the semiquinones, see Michaelis, *Chem. Revs.*, **16**, 243 (1935), and Michaelis and Schubert, *ibid.*, **22**, 437 (1938).

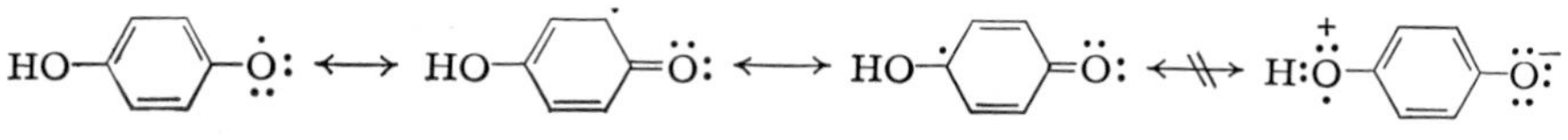

XX

accounts, at least in part, for the marked difference between the stabilities of the anionic and neutral forms of the semiquinones. On the other hand, radicals XXI[16(a)] and XXII,[16(b)] which are analogous to the neutral forms of semi-

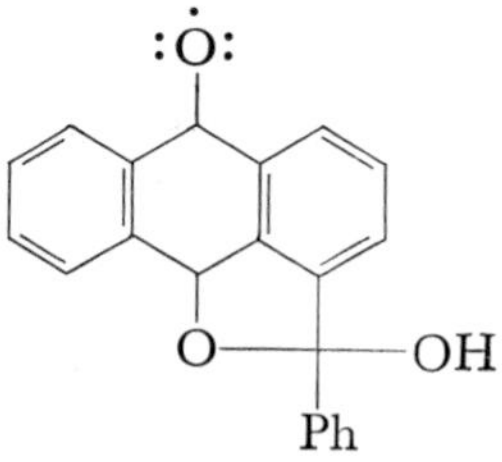

XXI 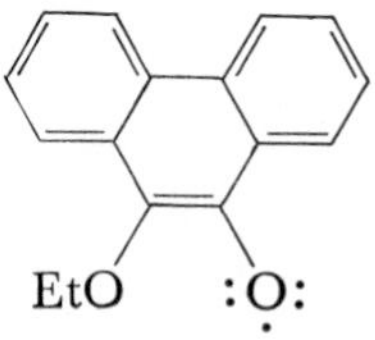   XXII

quinones, appear to be relatively long lived. Neither of these may undergo disproportionation to a quinone and hydroquinone without breakage of a C—O bond; moreover, both have more extended conjugated systems than are present in the simpler semiquinones.

Tetraphenylhydrazine, Ph$_2$N—NPh$_2$, and, more particularly, the tetra-p-methoxy and tetra-p-dimethylamino derivatives thereof, have been found to dissociate partially and reversibly into *diarylamino radicals* (Ar$_2$N·) in nonpolar solvents[17]

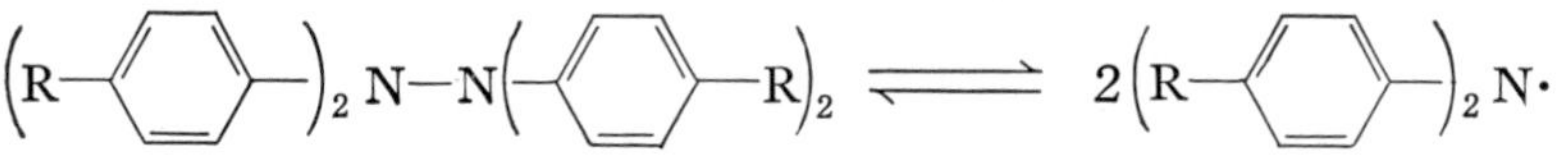

These homolyses bring to mind the dissociations of hexaarylethanes into triarylmethyl radicals, resonance stabilization of the radical being once again more important than that of the "dimer." With four, rather than six, aryl groups per molecule, steric assistance to dissociation is much less important than with the hexaarylethanes, but dissociation is favored by the low N—N bond energy (p. 37).

Some additional free radicals of long life are listed in Table 16-2, together with representative references. It is scarcely necessary to point out that in each of these radicals, the unpaired electron is incorporated into a conjugated system.

---

[16] (a) Fieser and Young, *J. Am. Chem. Soc.*, **54**, 4095 (1942). (b) Goldschmidt, Vogt, and Bredig, *Ann.*, **445**, 123 (1925); Cutforth and Selwood, *J. Am. Chem. Soc.*, **70**, 278 (1948).

[17] (a) Wieland, *Ann.*, **381**, 200 (1911); Holt and Hughes, *J. Chem. Soc.*, **1955**, 1320. (b) Recently the preparation of the free *dimethylamino radical*, Me$_2$N·, has been reported (Rice and Grelicki, *J. Am. Chem. Soc.*, **79**, 2679 (1957)). This is violet in color and much less stable than diarylamino radicals, for it decomposes above −160°.

Table 16-2. Some Types of Long-lived Free Radicals

References

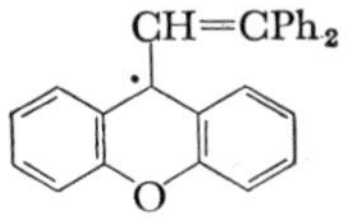

(XXIII)

Ziegler and Ochs, *Ber.*, **55**, 2257 (1922).

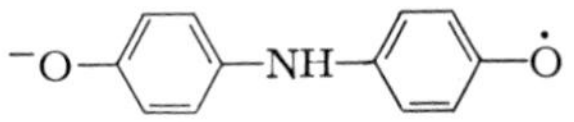

(XXIV)

Schwarzenbach and Michaelis, *J. Am. Chem. Soc.*, **60**, 1667 (1938).

$(Ph_2\overset{\cdot}{C}-\overset{\cdot\cdot}{\underset{\cdot\cdot}{O}}:)^-$, (a *ketyl*, XXV)

Bachmann, *J. Am. Chem. Soc.*, **55**, 1179 (1933); Wooster, *ibid.*, **56**, 2436 (1934); **59**, 377 (1937).

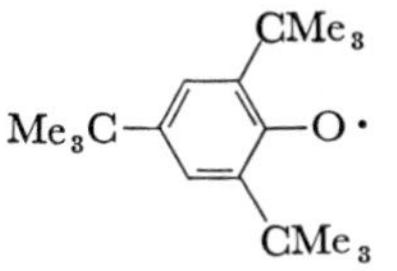

(XXVI)

Cook, *et al.*, *J. Am. Chem. Soc.*, **75**, 6242 (1953); **78**, 2002, 3797 (1956).

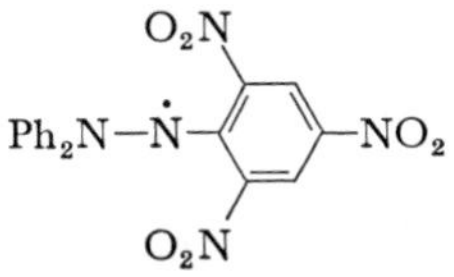

(diphenylpicryl-hydrazyl, XXVII)

Turkevich and Selwood, *J. Am. Chem. Soc.*, **63**, 1077 (1941).

$Ph_2N-\overset{\cdot}{N}-\overset{}{\underset{\underset{O}{\|}}{C}}-Ar$ (XXVIII)

Goldschmidt, *et al.*, *Ann.*, **477**, 194 (1924); **473**, 137 (1929).

$Ph_2\overset{\cdot}{N}-\overset{\cdot\cdot}{\underset{\cdot\cdot}{O}}:$ (XXIX)

Wieland and Offenbacher, *Ber.*, **47**, 2111 (1914).

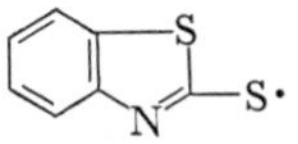

(XXX)

Cutforth and Selwood, *J. Am. Chem. Soc.*, **70**, 278 (1948).

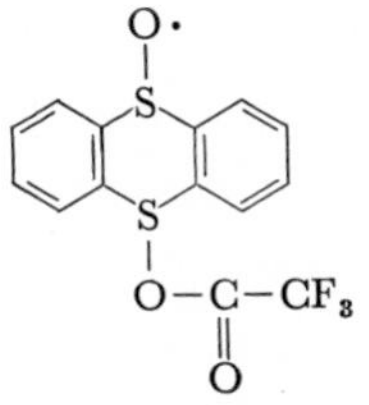

(XXXI)

Fava, Sogo and Calvin, *J. Am. Chem. Soc.*, **79**, 1078 (1957).

This becomes obvious even for **XXVIII** and **XXXI** when these are represented by one of their alternate structures. Resonance stabilization is least in the tri-*t*-

XXVIII ⟷ XXVIII′

XXXI ⟷ XXXI′

butylphenoxyl radical (**XXVI**), for which, however, dimerization is strongly sterically hindered.

Detection of Short-lived Free Radicals

We have emphasized the difficulties in estimating accurately the concentration of long-lived free radicals using cryoscopic, spectral, or conventional magnetic measurements; and it should be clear that such methods are likewise unsuited for the detection of very small quantities of *short-lived* free radicals that generally intervene as intermediates in the usual homolytic reactions.[18] For this purpose,

[18] A related technique for detecting and measuring the concentrations of free radicals— *para-ortho* hydrogen conversion—is interesting, but not significantly more sensitive than the usual magnetic measurements. In this case, the terms *ortho* and *para* have nothing to do with a benzene ring, but refer to the directions of nuclear spin in the H_2 molecule. Nuclei with odd numbers of protons or neutrons have, as do electrons, quantized spin. In *ortho*-hydrogen, the nuclear spins are unpaired, in *para*-hydrogen they are paired, and the two forms have slightly different physical properties. At low temperatures the *para* form is the more stable, but at room temperature a 3:1 *ortho-para* ratio prevails at equilibrium. However, the conversion of the *para* to the *ortho* form is very slow *except in the presence of species having unpaired electrons.* This conversion, which can be followed by very careful measurement of the thermal conductivity of H_2 gas in contact with the solution at hand, can be related to the concentration of free radicals in the solution (see Wigner, *Z. physik. Chem.*, **B23**, 38 (1933)). The sensitivity of the method is limited by the slow conversion of the *para* to the *ortho* form by the solvent itself in the absence of free radicals, and the technique is not suitable for measurement of radical concentrations of much less than 10^{-4} moles per liter. (For further information, see Farkas, *Ortho-hydrogen, Para-hydrogen, and Heavy Hydrogen*, Cambridge University Press, Cambridge, 1935; and *Ann. N.Y. Acad. Sci.*, **40**, 129 (1940).)

however, other means of investigation are available. The first compelling evidence for short-lived free radical intermediates in organic reactions arose from experiments in the vapor phase. During the period 1929–1935, Paneth and his coworkers[19] studied the thermal decompositions of certain volatile organometallics (for example, Me_4Pb and $(PhCH_2)_4Sn$) carried by an inert gas passing through a glass tube, a small portion of which had previously been coated with a "mirror" of zinc, antimony, or lead. No appreciable reaction occurred in the absence of heat, but if a small area of the tube were vigorously heated so that the molecules of substrate passed through the hot zone before reaching the mirror, a new metallic mirror (Pb or Sn) was deposited in the inside of the tube at the point of heating. More significantly, however, the gaseous decomposition products were found to *remove the original mirror as they passed over it*, although neither the carrier gas nor the stable final decomposition products could do this. Moreover, this mirror disappeared most rapidly when it was situated very close to the point of heating. It was thus inferred that the decomposition of the organometallic compound yielded the parent metal and free alkyl radicals (for example, $CH_3\cdot$ or $PhCH_2\cdot$), and that these free radicals reacted with the original metal mirror, converting this mirror to a volatile organometallic compound (which, indeed, could generally be isolated by condensing the emerging gases). However, if the mirror to be removed was too far from the site of heating, most of the radicals produced in the decomposition dimerized before reaching the mirror, and removal was slow.

The Paneth mirror-removal technique has been used to detect alkyl radicals, not only from the pyrolyses of organometallic compounds, but also from the decompositions of aliphatic azo compounds,[20(a)] from the pyrolyses of paraffin hydrocarbons,[20(b)] from the photolyses of aldehydes and ketones,[20(c)] and from the action of sodium vapor on alkyl and aryl halides.[20(d)] It is important that only a few of the simpler alkyl and aryl groups can exist as free radicals in the vapor state. (Although methyl, ethyl, phenyl, and benzyl radicals have been detected by Paneth's method, most of the higher straight-chained alkyl radicals have not. If formed at all, they rapidly undergo breakage into smaller fragments.)

The Paneth technique, as such, is not applicable to reactions in the liquid phase, but there are many substances that are known to react rapidly with short-lived free radicals in solution. Radical-consuming reagents whose disappearance may be measured quantitatively are particularly useful. Among these are diphenylpicrylhydrazyl (XXVII), whose consumption may be followed by the

[19] (a) Paneth and Hofeditz, *Ber.*, **62**, 1335 (1929). (b) Paneth and Lautsch, *Ber.*, **64B**, 2702 (1931); *J. Chem. Soc.*, **1935**, 380.

[20] (a) Leermakers, *J. Am. Chem. Soc.*, **55**, 3499 (1933). (b) Rice, *Trans. Faraday Soc.*, **30**, 152 (1934). (c) Pearson, *et al.*, *J. Chem. Soc.*, **1934**, 1718; **1935**, 1151; **1936**, 1777; **1939**, 589. (d) Horn, Polanyi, and Style, *Z. physik. Chem.*, **B23**, 291 (1933); **B25**, 151 (1934); *Trans. Faraday Soc.*, **30**, 189 (1934).

fading of its characteristic violet color,[21(a)] and $FeCl_3$, which often transfers chlorine atoms to active free radicals yielding the readily titratable $FeCl_2$.[21(b)] Occasionally the presence of radicals in solution is inferred from the ability of the solution to initiate polymerization of such unsaturated compounds as acrylonitrile and methyl methacrylate (even though species other than radicals are known to be capable of initiating such polymerizations). In any case, chemical detection of free radicals is possible only if the "test reaction" proceeds at a rate comparable to, or faster than, the reaction which the radicals would otherwise undergo (just as the Paneth technique is successful only when a large number of alkyl radicals react with the metal mirror rather than undergoing dimerization).

At present, the most promising method for studying small quantities of free radicals is *electron-spin resonance spectroscopy*.[22] As was pointed out in Chapter 1, the spin of an unpaired electron in the presence of an external magnetic field may become oriented in two ways, either "against" or "with" the field. These two orientations have slightly different energies and if radiation is supplied, a transition from one orientation to the other may occur. The energy difference between the two possible spin orientations is proportional to the strength of the applied magnetic field, but even in a very strong field, this difference is very small (for example, about 0.0026 kcal per "mole" of electrons at 10,000 gauss). To bring about this type of transition but with no high-energy processes, radiation in the microwave region (about 10^{10} cycles per second) must be used. Without attempting to describe the operational details,[23] we may note that in practice, the wavelength of the incident radiation is kept constant while the intensity of the magnetic field that surrounds the sample is continuously varied in an attempt to detect sudden small changes in the adsorption of microwave energy by the sample. No corrections for diamagnetism need be applied, and using this technique, radical concentrations as low as 10^{-7} molar have been detected. Moreover, by suitable refinements in the method, the *mean lifetimes* of the radicals may be estimated.

Furthermore the observed absorption bands are often found to have fine structure; that is, they are composed of two or more thin bands lying very close to each other. This splitting results from *interactions between the spin of the unpaired electron and the spins of one or more nuclei*. By analysis of the fine structure it is often possible to learn whether the unpaired electron is localized on a single atom or "spread over" a number of atoms. Thus, it has been found that, in accordance with the "resonance hybrid" representation of triphenylmethyl,

[21] (a) Henglein, *Makromol. Chem.*, **15**, 188 (1955). For a criticism of this procedure, see Hammond, Sen, and Boozer, *J. Am. Chem. Soc.*, **77**, 3244 (1955). (b) Bamford, Jenkins, and Johnson, *Nature*, **177**, 992 (1956).

[22] For a review of this topic, see Wertz, *Chem. Revs.*, **55**, 829 (1955).

[23] See, for example, Hirshon and Fraenkel, *Rev. Sci. Instruments*, **26**, 34 (1955).

the unpaired electron in this radical is spread over the benzene rings instead of being localized at the nonaromatic carbon atom.[24]

The Configurations of Free Radicals

Although steric interference among the *ortho*-hydrogen atoms in the triphenyl-methyl radical probably prohibits planarity of the entire radical, it is extremely likely that the three bonds to the methyl carbon in this and in related radicals lie in a common plane. Movement of one of these bonds out of the plane of the other two would lower resonance stabilization without relieving steric strain. For free radicals not stabilized by conjugation, we cannot at present say whether the configuration about the trivalent carbon is planar (**XXXII**) or pyramidal (**XXXIII**), or, indeed, whether all such radicals have similar configurations.

XXXII   **XXXIII**

It appears that the trivalent carbon in a carbon radical will generally not support asymmetry if the radical is truly "free." For example, the free-radical chlorination of (+)-1-chloro-2-methylbutane yields the racemic dichloro compound, **XXXIV**.[25(a)] Similarly, the free-radical decarbonylation of optically

$$D\text{-Et}\overset{*}{-}\text{CHMe}-\text{CH}_2\text{Cl} \overset{\text{Cl}\cdot}{\rightarrow} \text{Et}-\overset{\cdot}{\text{C}}\text{Me}-\text{CH}_2\text{Cl} \overset{\text{Cl}_2}{\rightarrow} \underset{\underset{\text{Me}}{|}}{\overset{\overset{\text{Cl}}{|}}{\text{Et}-\text{C}-\text{CH}_2\text{Cl}}} \quad \text{(racemic)}$$

XXXIV

active aldehyde **XXXV** in the presence of *t*-butyl peroxide yields racemic

$$i\text{-Bu}-\underset{\underset{\text{Et}}{|}}{\overset{\overset{\text{Me}}{|}}{\text{C}}}*-\text{CHO} \overset{t\text{-BuO}\cdot}{\longrightarrow} i\text{-Bu}-\underset{\underset{\text{Et}}{|}}{\overset{\overset{\text{Me}}{|}}{\text{C}}}*-\overset{\cdot}{\text{C}}=\text{O} \overset{-\text{CO}}{\longrightarrow}$$

XXXV

$$i\text{-Bu}-\underset{\underset{\text{Et}}{|}}{\overset{\overset{\text{Me}}{|}}{\text{C}}}\cdot \overset{\text{RCHO}}{\longrightarrow} i\text{-Bu}-\underset{\underset{\text{Et}}{|}}{\overset{\overset{\text{Me}}{|}}{\text{CH}}} \quad \text{(racemic)} \quad + \text{R}\overset{\cdot}{\text{C}}\text{O}$$

[24] Adam and Weissman, *J. Am. Chem. Soc.*, **80**, 2057 (1958). These authors point out, however, that the "unpaired-electron density" is highest at the methyl carbon—that "about two thirds of this electron" is concentrated at that carbon.

2,4-dimethylhexane.[25(b)] It is of interest, however, that a number of optically active diacyl peroxides of the type XXXVI, having asymmetric α-carbon atoms,

XXXVI   XXXVII   XXXVIII

decompose to esters in which the α-carbon atoms, both in the alkyl and acyl sections, retain their configurations.[26] Retention of configuration in the acyl group is to be expected, for in this group the asymmetric carbon is not affected. Retention of configuration in the alkyl group is more surprising. If the mechanism indicated above is correct, we may suppose that in many instances alkyl radical XXXVIII, formed in the decarboxylation of acyloxy radical XXXVII, reacts very rapidly, while still asymmetric, with a second acyloxy radical. (Since partial racemization of the alkyl group is always observed, a short time lag between decarboxylation and coupling may be inferred.) It seems probable that the alkyl and acyl groups of the resulting ester molecule stem from the *same* molecule of peroxide (although this has not yet been proven), and that the alkyl and acyloxy radicals recombine before they break out of the "solvent cage" that surrounded the initial peroxide molecule. However, we cannot neglect the possibility that a portion of the ester is formed in a cyclization without intervention of free radicals.

In any event, the stereochemical evidence now available does not distinguish between the planar and pyramidal configurations for free radicals if it is

---

[25] (a) Brown, Kharasch, and Chao, *J. Am. Chem. Soc.*, **62**, 3435 (1940). (b) Doering, Farber, Sprecher, and Wiberg, *ibid.*, **74**, 3000 (1952).

[26] (a) Kharasch, Kuderna, and Nudenburg, *J. Org. Chem.*, **19**, 1283 (1954). (b) Greene, *J. Am. Chem. Soc.*, **77**, 4809 (1955). (c) DeTar and Weis, *ibid.*, **79**, 3045 (1957).

assumed that a pyramidal free radical can "turn itself inside out" (XXXIX $\rightleftharpoons$ XL) many times per second, as molecules of ammonia and amines are known to do. Neither a planar radical nor a pyramidal radical that can undergo rapid

XXXIX   XL

inversion should support asymmetry when free, but either type could if suitably shielded.

Note, however, that a pyramidal configuration is virtually mandatory for free radicals in which the trivalent carbon is situated at the bridgehead of a rigid tricyclic ring system. A species of this sort is the apocamphyl radical, XLII, an intermediate, the decomposition of apocamphyl peroxide (XLI).[27]

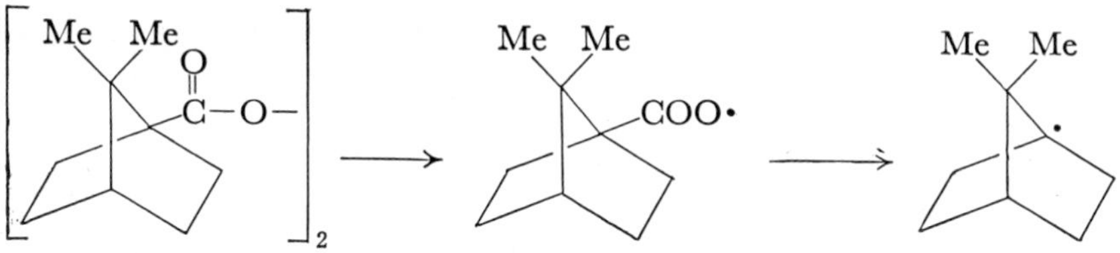

XLI   XLII

Formation of Free Radicals. Initiators

Most of the free-radical reactions with which we shall be concerned are *chain reactions;* they are initiated by small quantities of reactive free radicals that may produce relatively large amounts of final product. An *initiator* is, as its name implies, a substance that, under reaction conditions, furnishes a sufficient number of radicals to get the reaction "under way." Organic free radicals are most often produced in solution by heating (or in some cases, merely dissolving) compounds having weak covalent bonds. Organic peroxides, which generally suffer homolysis at the weak O—O bond (ROOR $\rightarrow$ 2 RO·), are obviously initiators. These vary greatly in their stability; α-phenylpropionyl peroxide (XLIII), for example, is so unstable that it cannot be isolated under ordinary circumstances,[26(b)] whereas *t*-butyl hydroperoxide (XLIV) is stable for weeks in the dark at room

---

[27] Bartlett and Greene, *J. Am. Chem. Soc.,* **76,** 1088 (1954); Kharasch, Engelmann, and Urry, *J. Am. Chem. Soc.,* **65,** 2428 (1943). This is presumably the same radical through which the "brominative decarboxylation" of the silver salt of apocamphenecarboxylic acid proceeds (p. 355).

$$Ph—CHMe—\underset{\underset{O}{\|}}{C}—O—O—\underset{\underset{O}{\|}}{C}—CHMe—Ph \qquad\qquad Me_3C—O—O—H$$

$$\text{XLIII} \qquad\qquad\qquad\qquad \text{XLIV}$$

temperature and decomposes only slowly even when heated to 100°.[28] Azo compounds may likewise act as radical sources, for when these are heated, or merely allowed to stand, radicals break off from both ends of the molecule, leaving behind elemental nitrogen.

$$Ph_3C—N{=}N—Ph \xrightarrow{50°} Ph_3C\cdot + N_2 + Ph\cdot^{29(a)}$$
$$Ph—N{=}N—OH \xrightarrow{25°} Ph\cdot + N_2\ (+ \cdot OH)^{29(b)}$$

Substituted *azoacetonitriles* (for example, XLV) are particularly useful radical initiators; here, fragmentation is favored not only by the stability of the N_2 molecule, but also by delocalization of the unpaired electron over the $—C—C{\equiv}N$ conjugated system.

$$N{\equiv}C—CMe_2—N{=}N—CMe_2—C{\equiv}N \rightarrow$$
$$\text{XLV}$$

$$N{\equiv}C—CMe_2\cdot + N_2 + \cdot CMe_2—C{\equiv}N^{30}$$

Among the other types of compounds which yield organic free radicals when heated are alkyl nitrates,[31(a)] the carboxylic acid salts of Pb(IV),[31(b)] and organocobalt compounds.[31(c)]

$$RO—NO_2 \xrightarrow{200°} RO\cdot + NO_2$$

$$Pb\left(O—\underset{\underset{O}{\|}}{C}—R\right)_4 \xrightarrow{150°} Pb\left(O—\underset{\underset{O}{\|}}{C}—R\right)_2 + 2\cdot O—\underset{\underset{O}{\|}}{C}—R$$

$$RMgX + CoCl_2 \rightarrow R_2Co \xrightarrow{35°} Co + 2\ R\cdot$$

Photochemical dissociation is an extremely important method for the production of radicals, for many molecules are split by the action of visible or ultraviolet light, generally of a wavelength corresponding to their respective values of λ_{max}. Many of these are the same substances that undergo homolysis on heating, but some are not. Chief among the latter group are aliphatic carbonyl compounds,

[28] Stannett and Mesrobian, *J. Am. Chem. Soc.*, **72**, 4125 (1950).

[29] (a) Cohen and Wang, *J. Am. Chem. Soc.*, **75**, 5504 (1953). (b) This is a step in the familiar Gomberg-Bachmann reaction (see p. 729).

[30] Lewis and Matheson, *J. Am. Chem. Soc.*, **71**, 747 (1949).

[31] (a) Levy, *J. Am. Chem. Soc.*, **76**, 3254, 3790 (1954). (b) Hey, Stirling, and Williams, *J. Chem. Soc.*, **1954**, 2747; **1955**, 3969. (c) Reactions of this kind have been investigated in detail by Kharasch and co-workers (*J. Am. Chem. Soc.*, **63**, 2316 (1941); **65**, 491, 504 (1943); *J. Org. Chem.*, **13**, 101 (1948); **19**, 1477 (1955)). It is, however, not clear at present whether the organocobalt intermediate is R_2Co, RCoCl, or both; for a discussion of this point, see Wilds and McCormack, *J. Org. Chem.*, **14**, 45 (1949).

which have been studied most extensively in the vapor state.[32] Four typical homolyses are shown below:

$$Me_2CH—\overset{\overset{\displaystyle O}{\|}}{C}—CHMe_2 \overset{h\nu}{\to} Me_2CH—\overset{\overset{\displaystyle O}{\|}}{C}\cdot + \cdot CHMe_2{}^{33(a)}$$

$$Me—\overset{\overset{\displaystyle O}{\|}}{C}—CH_2Cl \overset{h\nu}{\to} Me—\overset{\overset{\displaystyle O}{\|}}{C}—CH_2\cdot + Cl\cdot{}^{33(b)}$$

$$Me_2CH—CHO \overset{h\nu}{\to} Me_2CH\cdot + \cdot CHO{}^{33(c)}$$

$$CH_3—\overset{\overset{\displaystyle O}{\|}}{C}—\overset{\overset{\displaystyle O}{\|}}{C}—CH_3 \overset{h\nu}{\to} 2CH_3\overset{\cdot}{C}{=}O{}^{33(d)}$$

Organic compounds may also be converted to free radicals by high-energy radiation, for when an α, β, or γ particle, or an x-ray collides with a molecule, ionization (electron removal) may occur. The resulting energy-rich ions may then break up, generally with homolysis of one or more bonds. Such effects, which account in great part for the action of radiation on biological material, are obviously of great importance. However, this topic is not directly related to the present discussion and will not be pursued further here.[34]

In some instances, free radicals may be produced by *electrolysis*. Anodic oxidations of carboxylic acid salts in aqueous solution, for example, yield carboxylate radicals, $RCOO\cdot$. These undergo decarboxylation to alkyl radicals $(R\cdot)$, which, in turn, rapidly dimerize. This set of reactions constitutes the familiar *Kolbe electrolysis*.[35]

$$RCOO^- \xrightarrow{-e^-} RCOO\cdot \xrightarrow{-CO_2} R\cdot \xrightarrow{\text{dimerizes}} R—R$$

The carboxylate radicals may be diverted by addition of anisole to the reaction mixture, whereupon an *o*-acyloxyanisole is formed.[35(b)] Similarly, alkyl or aryl radicals may be produced by electrolyses of Grignard reagents in ether.

$$RMgBr \xrightarrow{-e^-} R\cdot + MgBr^+ \to R—R{}^{36}$$

[32] The photolyses of aliphatic carbonyl compounds has been reviewed by Noyes, Porter, and Jolley (*Chem. Revs.*, **56**, 49 (1956)), and, more briefly, by Pitts (*J. Chem. Ed.*, **34**, 112 (1957)).

[33] (a) Whiteway and Masson, *J. Am. Chem. Soc.*, **77**, 1508 (1955). (b) Strachan and Blacet, *ibid.*, **77**, 5252 (1955). (c) Blacet and Calvert, *ibid.*, **73**, 667 (1951). (d) Nicholson, *Trans. Faraday Soc.*, **50**, 1067 (1954).

[34] For detailed information on the production of radicals by high-energy radiation, see Collinson and Swallow, *Quart. Revs.*, **9**, 311 (1955), and Collinson, *Chem. Revs.*, **56**, 471 (1956).

[35] (a) Weedon, *Quart. Revs.*, **6**, 380 (1952). (b) For a further study of this reaction, see Wilson and Lippincott, *J. Am. Chem. Soc.*, **78**, 4290 (1956).

[36] See, for example, Evans, Pearson, and Braithwaite, *J. Am. Chem. Soc.*, **63**, 2574 (1941); **64**, 2865 (1942). This formulation obviously ignores the complex nature of solutions of Grignard reagents (p. 402).

Likewise, radicals are produced at the cathode in the electrolyses of ketones in aqueous acid.

$$R_2C{=}O \xrightarrow{+e^-} R_2\overset{\centerdot}{C}{-}O^- \xrightarrow[+2H^+]{\text{dimerizes}} R_2\overset{\overset{\displaystyle HO}{|}}{C}{-}\overset{\overset{\displaystyle OH}{|}}{C}R_2{}^{37}$$

The same type of dimeric product is formed when benzophenone is electrolyzed in pyridine to which sodium iodide has been added, using magnesium electrodes. Here, however, the pinacol is formed at the *anode*, the pole at which electrolytic *oxidation* occurs. The reducing agent is almost certainly *unipositive magnesium*, formed by oxidation of the magnesium anode, for the ketone is not reduced at the electrode in the absence of the electric current.[38]

$$Mg \xrightarrow[2I^-]{-e^-} MgI_2^- \xrightarrow{Ph_2C{=}O} MgI_2 + Ph_2\overset{\centerdot}{C}{-}O^- \xrightarrow{\text{dimerizes}} \begin{matrix} Ph_2C{-}O^- \\ | \\ Ph_2C{-}O^- \end{matrix}$$

The reduction of ketones to pinacols with a combination of magnesium and magnesium iodide very probably proceeds in the same way.

Another important method for the production of free radicals is the action of inorganic "one-electron" oxidizing or reducing agents.[39] The most familiar reagent of this type is the Fe^{2+}-H_2O_2 couple ("Fenton's reagent"), from which *free hydroxyl radicals* may be obtained.

$$Fe^{2+} + HO{:}OH \rightarrow FeOH^{2+} + {\cdot}OH$$

(Note that in this reaction, iron has been converted from the dipositive to the tripositive state.) The free hydroxyl radical is very reactive and ordinarily would react with another Fe^{2+} ion. However, its existence in solution may be inferred from the ability of such solutions to initiate vinyl polymerization.[40] Similarly, dipositive iron reacts both with the peroxydisulfate ion $(S_2O_8^{2-})$[41(a)] and with organic hydroperoxides (for example, cumene hydroperoxide)[41(b)] to give free radicals.

$$Fe^{2+} + O_3S{-}O{:}O{-}SO_3^{2-} \rightarrow FeSO_4^+ + {\cdot}O{-}SO_3^-$$
$$Fe^{2+} + PhCMe_2{-}O{:}OH \rightarrow FeOH^{2+} + {\cdot}OCMe_2Ph$$

[37] See, for example, Haggerty, *Trans. Am. Electrochem. Soc.*, **56**, 421 (1929).

[38] Rausch, McEwen, and Kleinberg, *J. Am. Chem. Soc.*, **76**, 3622 (1954). For a review of reductions by unipositive magnesium, together with a summary of the evidence that this valence state exists, see Rausch, McEwen, and Kleinberg, *Chem. Revs.*, **57**, 417 (1957).

[39] For more detailed treatments of this topic see Bacon, *Quart. Revs.*, **IX**, 287 (1955). See also Walling, Ref. 1(b), pp. 564–579.

[40] See, for example, Baxendale, Evans, and Park, *Trans. Faraday Soc.*, **42**, 155 (1946).

[41] (a) Kolthoff, Medalia, and Raaen, *J. Am. Chem. Soc.*, **73**, 1733 (1951). (b) Kharasch, Arimoto, and Nudenburg, *J. Org. Chem.*, **16**, 1556 (1951). For work on the reaction between Co^{2+} and cumene hydroperoxide, see Kharasch, *et al.*, *J. Org. Chem.*, **17**, 207 (1952); **18**, 322 (1953).

The reaction of tripositive titanium with hydroxylamine in acid solution appears to generate amide radicals, $NH_2\cdot$, for such a solution likewise acts as a polymerization initiator.[42]

$$Ti^{+3} + HO—NH_2 \rightarrow TiOH^{+3} + \cdot NH_2$$

Finally, there may be occasions when two or more molecules react *in the absence of initiators*, resulting in the formation of new bonds and in the "unpairing" of electron spins. The proposed "homolytic" mechanism for the Diels-Alder reaction (p. 536) is of this type, and analogous processes have been proposed to account for the "uncatalyzed" polymerizations of styrene and methyl methacrylate.[43]

The Types of Free-radical Reactions and Some Common Characteristics

The two types of radical reaction in which we shall be most interested are *radical displacements* and *radical additions*. Radical displacements seldom take place on carbon atoms.[44] Most often they occur on hydrogen or halogen atoms, for example,

$$Cl\cdot + H—CMe_3 \rightarrow Cl—H + \cdot CMe_3$$
$$CH_3\cdot + Br—CCl_3 \rightarrow CH_3—Br + \cdot CCl_3$$

We may, of course, refer to radical *substitutions* on carbon, but such substitutions are generally the result of two (or more) independent reactions, neither of which, under ordinary circumstances, is a radical displacement on carbon—for example, the chlorination of isobutane.

$Cl\cdot + H—CMe_3 \rightarrow Cl—H + \cdot CMe_3$ (displacement on hydrogen by $Cl\cdot$)
$Me_3C\cdot + Cl—Cl \rightarrow Me_3C—Cl + Cl\cdot$ (displacement on chlorine by $Me_3C\cdot$)

On the other hand, in most radical additions, it is a carbon atom (or, rather a π-electron system associated with two or more carbon atoms) that suffers attack by the radical.

There are two processes of importance that may result from the collision of free radicals. *Radical coupling* is simply the combination of two radicals, with the pairing of electrons, to form a new covalent bond,

$$R\cdot + \cdot R \rightarrow R—R$$

[42] Davis, Evans, and Higginson, *J. Chem. Soc.*, **1951**, 2563.
[43] Walling, Briggs, and Mayo, *J. Am. Chem. Soc.*, **68,** 1141, 1145 (1946). For a discussion of this type of radical formation, see Walling (Ref. 1(b)), pp. 180–189.
[44] For possible exceptions see: (*a*) Pitts, *et al., J. Am. Chem. Soc.*, **79,** 6370 (1957); **80,** 66 (1958); (*b*) Herrmann and Noyes, *ibid.*, **78,** 5764 (1956).

whereas *radical disproportionation* is the transfer of an atom from one radical to another, forming a saturated and an unsaturated molecule.

$$2CH_3CH_2\cdot \rightarrow CH_2\!\!=\!\!CH_2 + CH_3CH_3$$

(The latter type of reaction may occur with alkyl, but not aryl, radicals.) In virtually all reactions that proceed through active free-radical intermediates, the concentration of radicals at ordinary temperatures is much less than the concentrations of other reactants (except perhaps during the final stages of reaction). It might therefore be expected that the yields of products resulting from radical-radical reactions would be negligible in comparison to the yields of products resulting from the action of radicals on nonradicals. Although this is sometimes true, there are many examples of reactions in which the "coupling product" forms a substantial fraction of the isolated material, probably because collisions between organic radicals, although relatively rare, may be extraordinarily efficient chemically. Since no bonds are broken during a coupling reaction, little or no activation energy should be necessary unless steric hindrance is significant. It has been calculated, for example, that over half of the collisions between methyl radicals in the gas phase (at 165° and moderate pressures) result in coupling.[45] The formation of disproportionation products, in greater than trace amounts, is less frequently observed, although many cases have been recorded in which disproportionation competes favorably with radical coupling.[46]

Finally, we may note that in favorable instances, free radicals may undergo eliminations, decarboxylations, or rearrangements.

$$Br_2CH\!-\!\overset{\bullet}{C}HBr \;\rightarrow\; Br\cdot \;+\; BrCH\!\!=\!\!CHBr^{47(a)}$$
$$CH_3COO\cdot \;\rightarrow\; CH_3\cdot + CO_2{}^{47(b)}$$
$$Me_2CPh\!-\!CH_2\cdot \rightarrow Me_2\overset{\bullet}{C}\!-\!CH_2Ph^{47(c)}$$

By now it should be obvious to the reader that the free-radical reactions observed in the laboratory are generally not single reactions but are rather composed of a number of steps. The "chainlike" character of most of such "composite" reactions arises from a simple mathematical principle—the sum of an even plus an odd number is always an odd number. If a radical (having an odd number of electrons) attacks a nonradical (having an even number of electrons), one of the resulting species must have an odd number of electrons and must itself be a radical, possibly different from the initial radical, but likewise capable of

[45] Kistiakowski, Gomer, and Roberts, *J. Chem. Phys.*, **19**, 85 (1951); **21**, 1637 (1953).

[46] See, for example: Ivin and Steacie, *Proc. Roy. Soc.*, **208A**, 25 (1951); Bickel and Waters, *Rec. trav. chim.*, **69**, 312 (1950); Overberger and Lombardino, *J. Am. Chem. Soc.*, **80**, 2317 (1958).

[47] (a) Steinmetz and Noyes, *J. Am. Chem. Soc.*, **74**, 4141 (1952). (b) Kharasch, Rowe, and Urry, *J. Org. Chem.*, **16**, 905 (1951). (c) Seubold, *J. Am. Chem. Soc.*, **75**, 2532 (1953).

attacking a nonradical. Attack by the second radical should produce a third radical, which may or may not be the same as the first, but which, in any case, may participate in a third attack, producing a fourth radical, and so on. Such a sequence (a *chain reaction*) may continue until the radicals are destroyed or the reactants are fully consumed. Thus, a single radical may bring about the successive formation and destruction of thousands of radicals, and hence bring about changes in thousands of molecules.

On the other hand, radical chain reactions may be strikingly retarded, or even halted, by reagents which react with active radicals, forming less active radicals or nonradicals. Among such "chain breakers" (generally called *retarders* or *inhibitors*) are elemental iodine and aromatic sulfides.

$$\begin{array}{ccccc} \textit{active radical} & & & & \textit{less active radical} \\ \text{R·} & + & \text{I—I} \longrightarrow \text{RI} & + & \text{I·} \\ \text{R·} & + \text{ArS—SAr} \longrightarrow \text{RSAr} & + & \text{ArS·} \end{array}$$

Moreover, such stable free radicals as nitric oxide and diphenylpicrylhydrazyl (XXVII), which are presumed to couple with active radicals, are likewise retarders. Elemental oxygen constitutes a special case; as we shall presently emphasize, it is a type of *biradical* (that is, it has two unpaired electrons per molecule) and may act as an initiator when no better initiator is available. However, O_2 generally reacts with carbon radicals to yield peroxy radicals;

$$-\overset{|}{\underset{|}{C}}\text{·} + O_2 \rightarrow -\overset{|}{\underset{|}{C}}\text{—O—O·}$$

and radicals of the latter type tend to be relatively unreactive. Hence, in the presence of more effective initiators, oxygen may act as a retarder. As a result, we find that a number of free-radical reactions exhibit an *induction period* if oxygen is not rigorously excluded. More specifically, such reactions begin very sluggishly, but their rates suddenly increase when all of the oxygen has been consumed.

The induction period and inhibition by retarders are two features that distinguish homolytic from heterolytic reactions. There are others: heterolytic reactions are not accelerated by light, whereas, as we have seen, homolytic reactions frequently are. On the other hand, free-radical reactions are much less frequently subject to acid or base catalysis than are heterolytic reactions. Moreover, the rates of free-radical reactions (except, perhaps, those involving radical ions) tend to be much less sensitive to changes in solvent polarity and in ionic strength than are the rates of most heterolytic reactions. Finally, the relationships between structure and reactivity are (at least at present) somewhat more clear-cut for heterolytic than for homolytic reactions. A heterolytic reaction that is retarded by incorporation of an electron-attracting group into one of the reactants will generally (although not invariably) be accelerated by an electron-donating group similarly placed; however, it is not uncommon for a homolytic reaction to be accelerated by substituents of both types.

The kinetic treatment of free-radical reactions tends to be more complex than that of most heterolytic reactions; for in addition to the *initiation* step(s), there may be several *propagation* and several *termination* steps. Consider, for example, the addition of HBr to propylene, catalyzed by benzoyl peroxide (Bz_2O_2). Although this is not a particularly complicated reaction (compared to many other free-radical reactions), we may write two initiation steps, two propagation steps, and three termination steps.

(1) $Bz_2O_2 \xrightarrow{k_1} 2 \; BzO\cdot$

(2) $BzO\cdot + HBr \xrightarrow{k_2} BzOH + Br\cdot$ $\Big\}$ (initiation)

(3) $Br\cdot + MeCH{=}CH_2 \xrightarrow{k_3} Me\overset{\cdot}{C}H{-}CH_2Br$

(4) $Me\overset{\cdot}{C}H{-}CH_2Br + HBr \xrightarrow{k_4} MeCH_2{-}CH_2Br + Br\cdot$ $\Big\}$ (propagation)

(5) $2Br\cdot \xrightarrow{k_5} Br_2$

(6) $2Me\overset{\cdot}{C}H{-}CH_2Br \xrightarrow{k_6} \begin{array}{c} MeCH{-}CH_2Br \\ | \\ MeCH{-}CH_2Br \end{array}$

(7) $Me\overset{\cdot}{C}H{-}CH_2Br + Br\cdot \xrightarrow{k_7} MeCHBr{-}CH_2Br$

$\left.\begin{array}{c} \\ \\ \\ \\ \end{array}\right\}$ (termination)

(Even this sequence is a simplification, for we have ignored reversibility of individual steps and have assumed that all benzoate radicals react with HBr.) Now the net rate of reaction may be taken as the rate of formation of *n*-propyl bromide, reaction (4), that is, $k_4(Me\overset{\cdot}{C}H{-}CH_2Br)(HBr)$. The concentration of HBr is measurable; but the concentration of the $Me\overset{\cdot}{C}H{-}CH_2Br$ radical is not, and therefore must be expressed in terms of measurable concentrations and the various rate constants. This is a difficult task since this radical is being created (in reaction 3) and destroyed (in reaction 7) by action of the $Br\cdot$ radical, the concentration of which is likewise immeasurable. Here then, we have a problem that can best be handled by the steady-state approximation (p. 170); that is, it may be assumed that very soon after the reaction gets under way, the concentrations of each of the three free-radical intermediates ($BzO\cdot$, $Br\cdot$, and $Me\overset{\cdot}{C}H{-}CH_2Br$) remain constant. If only the steps in the above sequence are of importance, the three "steady-state equations" become

$$\frac{d(BzO\cdot)}{dt} = 0 = 2k_1(Bz_2O_2) - k_2(HBr)(BzO\cdot) \tag{8}$$

$$\frac{d(Br\cdot)}{dt} = 0 = k_2(HBr)(BzO\cdot) - k_3(Br\cdot)(MeCH{=}CH_2)$$

$$+ k_4(Me\overset{\cdot}{C}H{-}CH_2Br)(HBr) - k_5(Br\cdot)^2 - k_7(Br\cdot)(MeCH{-}CH_2) \tag{9}$$

$$\frac{d(Me\overset{\cdot}{C}H\!\!-\!\!CH_2Br)}{dt} = 0 = k_3(Br\cdot)(MeCH\!\!=\!\!CH_2)$$

$$- k_4(HBr)(Me\overset{\cdot}{C}H\!\!-\!\!CH_2Br) - k_6(Me\overset{\cdot}{C}H\!\!-\!\!CH_2Br)^2$$

$$- k_7(Br\cdot)(Me\overset{\cdot}{C}H\!\!-\!\!CH_2Br) \quad (10)$$

If the concentrations of the radicals are considered "unknowns" but the rate constants and the concentrations of added reagents "knowns," the radical concentrations may be obtained by solving three simultaneous equations (two of them quadratic) in three unknowns. Thus, a rate expression may be derived. However, unless the problem is further simplified by assuming that certain of these steps are of negligible importance compared to others (and this is frequently possible), the algebra is not simple. Moreover, the rate constants for the separate steps become "lumped together" and cannot, generally speaking, be individually evaluated. For photochemically induced reactions, however, special methods are available with which the separate rate constants may sometimes be determined.[48]

Part II—HOMOLYSES AND FREE-RADICAL DISPLACEMENTS

Free-radical Halogenations

The chlorination of aliphatic hydrocarbons is generally one of the first reactions with which the student of elementary organic chemistry becomes familiar. It is a typical free-radical reaction, for it may be initiated photochemically or by such initiators as benzoyl peroxide, tetramethyllead, and azomethane,[49(a)] and may be inhibited by traces of elemental oxygen.[49(bc)] The propagation sequence is doubtless as follows:

[48] In the most important method for determining individual rate constants (the so-called "rotating-sector" method), the mixture is subjected to successive short periods of illumination and darkness by rotating an opaque disc, from which a sector of predetermined size has been cut, between source of light and the mixture. The "light" period is made short enough so that the concentration of radicals does not attain the steady-state value that would prevail with uninterrupted illumination, and the "dark" period is made short enough so that the radical concentration does not drop to a negligible value. In favorable cases, it becomes possible to evaluate individual rate constants from the manner in which the overall reaction rate varies with the known duration of the "light" and "dark" periods. For the (rather complex) mathematical treatment of such data, see: Flory, *J. Am. Chem. Soc.*, **59**, 241 (1937); and Matheson, et al., *ibid.*, **71**, 497 (1949). For descriptions of applications of this method, see: Bartlett and Swain, *J. Am. Chem. Soc.*, **67**, 2273 (1945); **68**, 2381 (1946); and Kwart, Broadbent, and Bartlett, *ibid.*, **72**, 1060 (1950).

[49] (a) Vaughan and Rust, *J. Org. Chem.*, **5**, 449 (1940). (b) Pease and Walz, *J. Am. Chem. Soc.*, **53**, 3728 (1931). (c) Ritchie and Winning, *J. Chem. Soc.*, **1950**, 3583.

$$RH + Cl \cdot \rightarrow \begin{cases} R \cdot \xrightarrow{Cl_2} RCl + Cl \cdot \xrightarrow{etc.} \\ HCl \end{cases}$$

and, as we have seen (p. 685), if the carbon atom at the substitution site is asymmetric, complete racemization occurs. At least two modes of chain termination $(R \cdot + Cl \cdot \rightarrow RCl$; and $R \cdot + R \cdot \rightarrow R—R)$ are possible, even if the system is rigorously protected. In the presence of trace impurities, to which these reactions are extremely sensitive, other termination mechanisms may become important. This may affect the apparent rate law,[49(c)] but not the yields of the possible chlorination products, for these should be determined by the rates at which the various (nonequivalent) hydrogen atoms of a hydrocarbon molecule are removed in the initiation step.

It has long been recognized[50] that tertiary hydrogens are removed more readily in free-radical chlorinations than are secondary, and that these are, in turn, removed more readily than primary. Typically, chlorination of isopentane (in the vapor phase at 300°) gives the following mixture of monochlorides:[50]

Noting that there are six equivalent hydrogens at the 1 positions (primary), a single hydrogen at the 2 position (tertiary), two at the 3 position (secondary), and three hydrogens at the 4 position (primary), we may estimate that reactivities of primary, secondary, and tertiary carbons lie in the ratio of about 1:3:4 (Ex. 2). Using these (or similar) values, it is possible to predict rather satisfactorily the ratios of products formed in the monochlorination of other aliphatic hydrocarbons under the same conditions.[50] Similar treatments, with somewhat different reactivity ratios, should apply to different temperatures.

The observed sequence in reactivities (tertiary > secondary > primary) brings to mind a similar sequence governing the reactivities of aliphatic halides in S_N1 reactions (Chap. 8) and suggests that the formation of a carbon radical, like that of a carbonium ion, may be facilitated by hyperconjugation involving α-alkyl groups.

[50] See, for example, Hass, McBee, and Weber, *Ind. Eng. Chem.*, **27**, 1190 (1935); **28**, 333 (1936).

On this basis, we would likewise expect a chloro or cyano substituent to facilitate radical attack at the α-carbon atom, for "resonance-stabilized" radicals should be obtained by removal of an α-hydrogen in either case

$$-\overset{\displaystyle\cdot}{\underset{|}{C}}-\overset{\displaystyle\cdot\cdot}{\underset{\cdot\cdot}{Cl}}: \;\leftrightarrow\; -\overset{\displaystyle--}{\underset{|}{C}}-\overset{\displaystyle\cdot\cdot+}{\underset{\cdot\cdot}{Cl}}: \qquad\qquad -\overset{\displaystyle\cdot}{\underset{|}{C}}-C\equiv N: \;\leftrightarrow\; -\overset{}{\underset{|}{C}}=C=\overset{\displaystyle\cdot}{N}:$$

We might therefore predict that alkyl chlorides and nitriles would undergo free-radical chlorination preferentially at the α positions. This is precisely what is *not* observed; it is now known that homolytic chlorinations of alkyl halides[51(a)] and aliphatic nitriles[51(b)] generally yield only minor amounts of the products resulting from α chlorination but much larger amounts of the products resulting from β, and where possible, γ chlorination. The same is true for chlorinations of carboxylic acids, esters, and acyl chlorides.[51(b),52] Some factor (or factors) other than the stability of the radical intermediate must then account for activation by an α-methyl group but deactivation by an α-chloro, and α-cyano, or an α-carboxyl substituent. It seems very likely that a series of *polar effects* are being observed—that is, that the attacking chlorine atom, besides being a radical, is an electrophilic species that seeks out an electron-rich site in the substrate for preferential attack. Thus, "$+I$ groups" facilitate chlorination, whereas "$-I$ groups," as observed, retard it.[53] Similarly, the side-chain chlorination of toluene has been found to be retarded by electron-attracting substituents in the benzene ring.[54]

As with many other reactions yielding a mixture of isomeric products, free-radical chlorination generally becomes less selective as the reaction temperature is increased; that is, at a high temperature a chlorine radical becomes more likely to extract the first hydrogen atom with which it comes into contact. Accordingly, it is somewhat surprising to find that in the chlorination of alkyl chlorides, the yield of 1,2-dichloro compound falls very nearly to zero at temperatures above $375°$.[55] This is almost certainly due to the tendency of radical XLVI (the pre-

[51] (a) Kharasch and Brown, *J. Am. Chem. Soc.*, **61**, 2142 (1939); Brown and Ash, *ibid.*, **77**, 4019 (1955). (b) Bruylants, *et al.*, *Bull. soc. chim. Belg.*, **58**, 210 (1949); **61**, 266 (1952).

[52] Kharasch and Brown, *J. Am. Chem. Soc.*, **62**, 925 (1940).

[53] The effect of an α-phenyl group on free-radical chlorination is of interest. On one hand, the methyl hydrogens in toluene are somewhat less reactive than the hydrogens in cyclohexane; but, on the other hand, cumene (PhCHMe$_2$) is chlorinated preferentially *alpha* to the benzene ring, rather than *beta* to it (Brown and Russell, *J. Am. Chem. Soc.*, **74**, 3996 (1952); **77**, 4578 (1955)). It is likely that the radical stabilizing ability of the phenyl group (which is unusually large) and its inductive effect are very nearly balanced. To predict, in a given case, whether an α-phenyl group will facilitate or retard chlorination probably requires further refinements in our present picture.

[54] Van Helden and Kooyman, *Rec. trav. chim.*, **73**, 269 (1954). A satisfactory correlation has been found here between the logarithms of the chlorination rates and the σ values for the various ring substituents.

[55] Vaughan and Rust, *J. Org. Chem.*, **6**, 479 (1941).

sumed intermediate in the formation of the 1,2-dichloro compound) to decompose to an olefin, which, under the reaction conditions does not add chlorine.

$$R—CH—CH_2Cl \xrightarrow{Cl\cdot} R—\overset{\cdot}{C}—CH_2Cl \xrightarrow{375°} R—C{=}CH_2 + Cl\cdot$$

XLVI

Elemental fluorine reacts violently with most organic compounds under ordinary circumstances, but fluorinations may be studied in the gas phase by diluting the reactants with nitrogen, or in the liquid phase by dilution with such inert solvents as CCl_3CF_3.[56] Even under very mild conditions, however, C—C bonds, as well as C—H bonds, are often attacked. The ease with which fluorinations occur in the gas phase and the frequent isolation of coupling products (as well as fragmentation products) leave little doubt that these reactions are homolytic and that they involve fluorine radicals. Since, however fluorinations often occur in the dark, at low temperatures, and in the absence of initiators, we may ask how these radicals arise. It has been suggested[57] that fluorine radicals are formed, together with alkyl radicals, when an energetic fluorine molecule collides with a hydrogen atom of a hydrocarbon chain.

$$—\overset{|}{\underset{|}{C}}:H + F:F \rightarrow —\overset{|}{\underset{|}{C}}\cdot + H:F + \cdot F$$

Such a reaction is favored thermodynamically by the low F—F bond energy (37 kcal) and the very high H—F bond energy (135 kcal) and, although it is quite unlike any other initiation process presently known to occur at low temperatures, no better possibilities come readily to mind. In any event, elemental fluorine, in the presence of compounds having C—H bonds, appears to be an excellent radical source, for traces of fluorine have been found to catalyze the homolytic chlorination and oxidation of such compounds very strikingly.[57]

Let us turn briefly to aliphatic bromination; although this is similar in a number of ways to chlorination, there is one fundamental difference. Since H—C bonds are generally stronger than the H—Br bond but weaker than the H—Cl bond, the hydrogen-removal step in bromination,

$$\left(—\overset{|}{\underset{|}{C}}—H + Br\cdot \rightarrow —\overset{|}{\underset{|}{C}}\cdot + HBr \right)$$

is often endothermic whereas that in chlorination,

[56] (a) Bigelow, *Chem. Revs.*, **40**, 51 (1947). (b) The fluorinations of polychlorinated hydrocarbons (for example, CCl_3CHCl_2) are much less vigorous, and may be studied at or near room temperature; see, for example, Miller, *J. Am. Chem. Soc.*, **62**, 341 (1940).
[57] Miller, Koch, and McLafferty, *J. Am. Chem. Soc.*, **78**, 4992 (1956).

$$\left(-\overset{|}{\underset{|}{C}}-H + Cl\cdot \rightarrow -\overset{|}{\underset{|}{C}}\cdot + HCl \right)$$

is exothermic. This difference is reflected in the respective activation energies; that for attack by bromine is about 14 kcal per mole more than that for attack by chlorine.[58] Consequently, a sizable fraction of the Cl· radicals present in a hydrocarbon-chlorine mixture may attack the hydrocarbon successfully at a temperature at which only the most energetic Br· radicals in a hydrocarbon-bromine mixture may attack. A chain reaction initiated by a given bromine atom proceeds relatively slowly and is likely to terminate when only a few molecules have become brominated (it is sometimes said that kinetic chains in bromination are "short," whereas those in chlorination are much "longer"). Many more acts of initiation are therefore needed to produce a given yield of bromination product than to produce the same yield of chlorination product under similar conditions.[59]

We have noted at several points during the earlier chapters that as a reagent becomes less reactive, it generally becomes more selective. We should therefore expect the secondary and tertiary halogenation products to predominate over primary halogenation products to an even greater degree in bromination than in chlorination, and this is what is found. Bromination of isobutane and cumene[60(b)] results in almost exclusive attack at the tertiary carbons, whereas the bromination of n-pentane yields a mixture of 2- and 3-bromopentane (both secondary bromides), but little, if any, 1-bromopropane.[60(a)]

$$\underset{\underset{H}{|}}{\overset{\overset{Me}{|}}{Me-C-Me}} \underset{Br\cdot}{\overset{Br_2}{\rightarrow}} \underset{\underset{Br}{|}}{\overset{\overset{Me}{|}}{Me-C-Me}}; \qquad PhCHMe_2 \underset{Br\cdot}{\overset{Br_2}{\rightarrow}} PhCBrMe_2$$

$$n\text{-}C_5H_{12} \underset{Br\cdot}{\overset{Br_2}{\rightarrow}} \underset{\underset{Br}{|}}{Me-CH-Pr} + \underset{\underset{Br}{|}}{Et-CH-Et} \qquad (no\ Me(CH_2)_4Br)$$

Similarly, attack by Br· is, to a marked degree, isotopically more selective than

---

[58] Anderson, Van Artsdalen, and Kistiakowski, *J. Chem. Phys.*, **10**, 305 (1942); **11**, 6 (1943); **12**, 28 (1944).

[59] Moreover, hydrogen abstraction by Br· is reversible; that is, the reaction

$$R\cdot + HBr \rightarrow RH + Br\cdot$$

proceeds readily; whereas hydrogen abstraction by Cl· is essentially irreversible, a circumstance which further lowers rates of homolytic bromination in relation to those of homolytic chlorination. The attack of HBr by alkyl radicals is an important step in the homolytic addition of HBr to olefins (p. 735), and the inactivity of such radicals toward HCl accounts in part for the difficulty in bringing about homolytic additions of HCl.

[60] (a) Kharasch, *et al.*, *J. Org. Chem.*, **6**, 818 (1940); *J. Chem. Phys.*, **20**, 1659 (1952). (b) Russell and Brown, *J. Am. Chem. Soc.*, **77**, 4025 (1955).

attack by Cl·. Typically, the removal of either hydrogen atom from the side chain of PhCH$_2$D using Cl· is about twice as fast as removal of the deuterium atom (that is, $k_H/k_D = 2.0$).[61(a)] When Br· is the attacking radical, the ratio $k_H:k_D$ rises to 4.6.[61(b)]

Free-radical halogenations may be carried out using reagents other than the molecular halogens. The most familiar of these "halogen carriers" is N-bromosuccinimide, XLVII, the N—Br bond of which is easily broken.[62] Although this

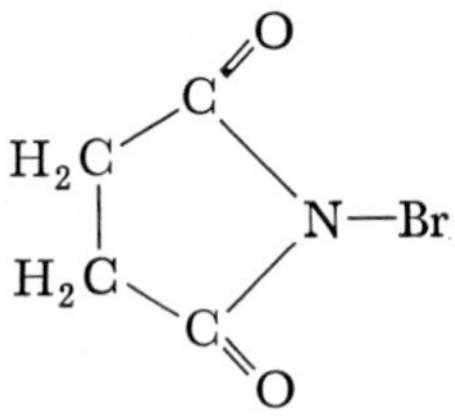

XLVII

is often considered a brominating agent specifically for allylic carbons (that is, for carbons *alpha* to C=C double bonds), it may, in the presence of efficient initiators, brominate saturated compounds as well.[63] In keeping with their homolytic character, brominations with N-bromosuccinimide (NBS) in non-hydroxylic solvents, may be accelerated photochemically or by addition of peroxides or azonitriles; moreover, they are subject to inhibition by hydroquinone, elemental iodine, or large quantities of oxygen.

Very probably, the initial attack on the substrate (RH) in these brominations is by the succinimido radical (XLVIII), after which the resulting carbon radical attacks a second molecule of NBS. If the carbon radical R· is allylic, it may react with the second molecule of NBS at one of two sites, leading to a mixture of bromides.

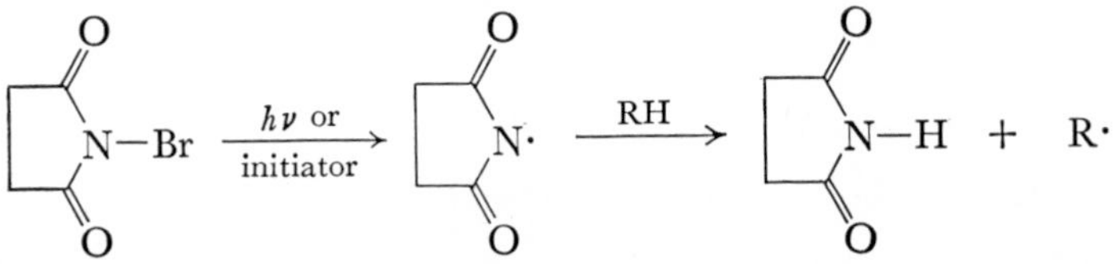

XLVIII

[61] (a) Brown and Russell, *J. Am. Chem. Soc.*, **74**, 3995 (1952). (b) Wiberg, *Chem. Revs.*, **55**, 731 (1955).

[62] Brominations with N-bromosuccinimide have been reviewed by Djerassi, *Chem. Revs.*, **43**, 271 (1948). Heterolytic brominations with this reagent are discussed by Ross, Finkelstein, and Peterson, *J. Am. Chem. Soc.*, **80**, 4327 (1958). Other N-haloimides and N-haloamides have been used as halogenating agents; see, for example, Wohl, *Ber.*, **52**, 51 (1919), and Hebbelynck and Martin, *Bull. soc. chim. Belges*, **59**, 193 (1950).

[63] Ford and Waters, *J. Chem. Soc.*, **1952**, 2240; Buu-Hoi and Demerseman, *J. Org. Chem.*, **18**, 649 (1953).

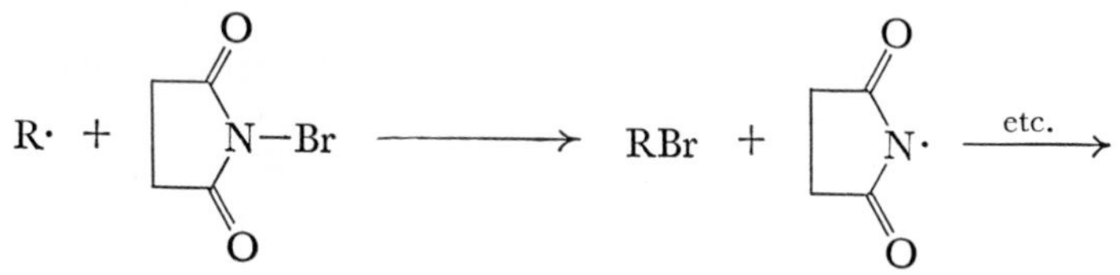

$$R\cdot \; + \; \underset{O}{\overset{O}{\left[\underset{}{\overset{}{N{-}Br}}\right]}} \longrightarrow RBr \; + \; \underset{O}{\overset{O}{\left[\underset{}{\overset{}{N\cdot}}\right]}} \xrightarrow{\text{etc.}}$$

$$AmCH_2CH{=}CH_2 \xrightarrow{-H\cdot} [Am\overset{\cdot}{C}HCH{=}CH_2 \leftrightarrow AmCH{=}CH{-}\overset{\cdot}{C}H_2] \xrightarrow{NBS}$$
$$(Am = n\text{-}C_5H_{12})$$

$$\begin{cases} \begin{array}{ll} \overset{\displaystyle Br}{\underset{\displaystyle |}{}} & \\ AmCH{-}CH{=}CH_2 & (17\%)^{64} \\ AmCH{=}CH{-}CH_2Br & (83\%) \\ \textit{cis and trans} & \end{array} \end{cases}$$

Moreover, if there are two nonequivalent allylic hydrogens in the substrate, as many as four different allylic bromides could conceivably be found in the resulting mixture (disregarding *cis-trans* isomerism). As yet, however, too few cases of this sort have been studied to allow us to say whether all possible bromides will be formed in significant amounts.[65]

Both the attack of the succinimido radical (XLVIII) on the substrate RH and the subsequent attack of the resulting carbon radical (R·) on a molecule of NBS may be stereospecific. When the *erythro* form (XLIX) of the deuterated bromide, PhCHD—CHBrPh, is treated with NBS, deuterium atoms are found to be removed from the substrate nearly twice as *rapidly* as are hydrogen atoms.[66]

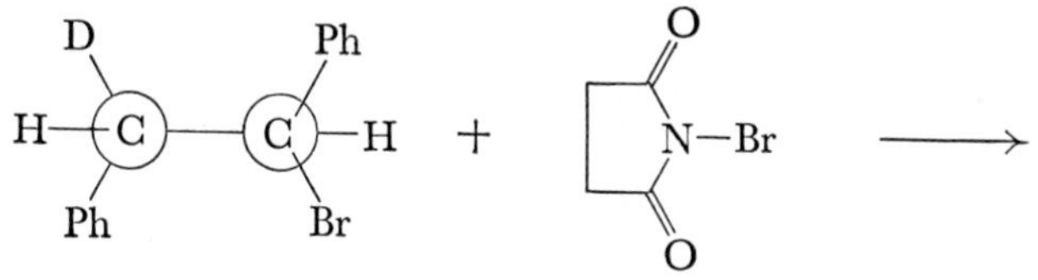

XLIX

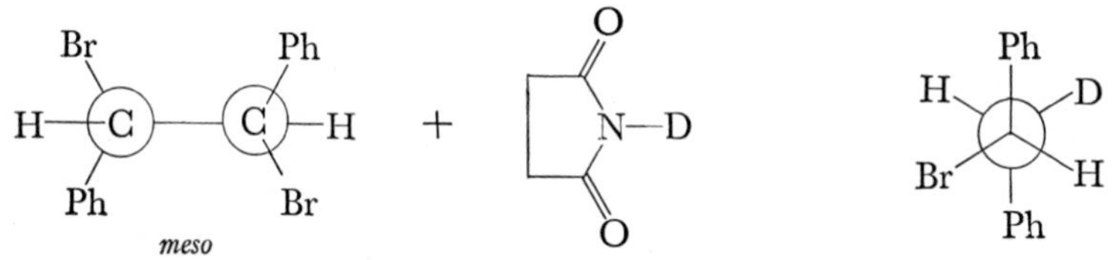

L
meso

LI

(predominant products)

This is a little surprising, since, under ordinary circumstances, C—H bonds are attacked about 2.5 times as often as are C—D bonds in brominations using

[64] Bateman and Cuneen, *J. Chem. Soc.*, **1950**, 941.
[65] See, for example, Greenwood and Kellert, *J. Am. Chem. Soc.*, **75**, 4842 (1953).
[66] Greene, Remers, and Wilson, *J. Am. Chem. Soc.*, **79**, 1416 (1957).

NBS.[61(b)] No doubt, this reversal of the "usual" isotope effect is partially a steric phenomenon; the preferred conformation of the substrate is presumably LI, in which the bulky phenyl groups are as far removed from each other as possible. We see that removal of a hydrogen atom from the carbon atom in back requires that the attacking radical approach on the more crowded side of LI (near the phenyl and bromo substituents), whereas to remove a deuterium atom, the radical approaches on the less crowded side (near the phenyl and hydrogen). Polar effects likewise favor removal of the deuterium atom, for it would be expected that the electronegative nitrogen atom in the attacking succinimido radical would keep as far as possible from the electronegative bromine atom in the substrate.

Nor is that all. As indicated above, the resulting dibromide, L, is largely (about 90 percent) in the *meso* form, indicating that the formation of the new C—Br is also stereospecific. This could be taken to mean that, in most instances, the trivalent carbon retains the same asymmetric configuration during the time interval between abstraction of the hydrogen (or deuterium) atom and formation of the new C—Br bond; however, we have already considered the evidence that such carbon atoms do not support asymmetry (p. 685). Instead, we may invoke reasoning similar to that used in Cram's rule concerning steric control of asymmetric induction (p. 549). The favored conformation of the radical intermediate is probably LII, in which, again, the phenyl groups lie as far apart as is possible,

and it may be supposed that the NBS molecule, from which radical LII extracts a bromine atom, approaches over the less crowded side (the left side in the drawing) of this radical.

The mode of action of a second familiar "halogen carrier," *sulfuryl chloride*, SO_2Cl_2, is not nearly so clear. A number of its peroxide-catalyzed reactions (such as the chlorinations of cyclohexane and the simpler carboxylic acids)[67] undoubtedly involve the Cl· radical as an intermediate, but because of the dissociation equilibria,

$$SO_2Cl_2 \rightleftharpoons Cl\cdot + SO_2Cl\cdot \rightleftharpoons 2Cl\cdot + SO_2$$

any mixture containing sulfuryl chloride at moderate temperatures must also contain the $SO_2Cl\cdot$ radical and molecular SO_2. Either, or both, of these species

[67] Kharasch and Brown, *J. Am. Chem. Soc.*, **61**, 2142 (1939); **62**, 925 (1940).

may enter the reaction chain, and is not surprising that chlorinations with SO_2Cl_2 are frequently accompanied by *sulfochlorinations* (that is, by conversions of the type $RH \rightarrow RSO_2Cl$).[68] Moreover, since hydrogen atoms may be removed from the substrate by $SO_2Cl\cdot$ radicals, as well as by $Cl\cdot$ radicals (and since the two types need not display the same selectivity), the mixtures of alkyl chlorides obtained in chlorinations with SO_2Cl_2 will not generally have the same compositions as the mixtures obtained in chlorinations with elemental chlorine alone.

Iodine Exchange Reactions

We should not expect homolytic iodinations of hydrocarbons with I_2 to occur. The hydrogen-removal step $\left(-\overset{|}{\underset{|}{C}}-H + I\cdot \rightarrow -\overset{|}{\underset{|}{C}}\cdot + HI \right)$ should be strongly endothermic, for the H—I bond is a weak one. *Organic iodine compounds* are, however, often attacked by elementary iodine (generally homolytically), with the main result being the substitution of iodine atoms from the elementary iodine for iodine atoms in the substrate—that is, *iodine exchange*.

$$R—I + I^*—I \rightarrow R—I^* + I—I$$

As indicated above, such a reaction is generally followed by using "tagged" iodine.

An important case of this sort is the reaction of optically active *sec*-butyl iodide with radioactive iodine.[69] If every act of iodine exchange involved a *sec*-butyl radical, $Et\overset{\cdot}{C}HMe$, racemization should occur at the same rate as exchange. However, it is found that racemization proceeds 1.5 times as rapidly as exchange. This calls to mind the reaction between optically active iodides and iodide ion, in which, as we emphasized (p. 266), every act of substitution is a Walden inversion, resulting in a rate of racemization twice that of iodide exchange. With elemental iodine, however, it appears that exchange takes place by a combination of at least two paths, the first a stepwise substitution.

$$R—I + {}^*I\cdot \rightarrow R\cdot + I—I^* \rightarrow R—I^* + I\cdot$$

This, if alone, should result in equal rates of exchange and racemization; and the second a direct displacement by iodine atoms,

$${}^*I\cdot + R—I \rightarrow {}^*I—R + I\cdot$$

which, if alone, should result in a 2:1 ratio between the rates of racemization

[68] See, for example: (a) Kharasch, Chao, and Brown, *J. Am. Chem. Soc.*, **62**, 2393 (1940); and (b) Asinger, *et al.*, *Ber.*, **75**, 35, 42, 344 (1942).

[69] Herrmann and Noyes, *J. Am. Chem. Soc.*, **78**, 5764 (1956).

and exchange. If this interpretation is correct, this reaction would constitute one of the few examples of a radical displacement on aliphatic carbon.[70]

Two mechanisms appear to operate also in the exchange of iodine between I_2 and iodobenzene.[71] The observed rate law is

$$\text{rate} = k_1(\text{PhI})(I_2)^{0.5} + k_2(\text{PhI})^2 \tag{11}$$

The first of these terms is not significantly affected by a change in solvent (suggesting that it is associated with a homolytic process). The second term, which does not involve (I_2), is very sensitive to solvent and may be made to disappear by transferring the reaction to nitrobenzene. Free phenyl radicals are not involved in either process, for the exchange is not retarded by oxygen. The first term is consistent with the following sequence:

the rate of the slow step being

$$\text{rate} = k(\text{PhI})(I\cdot) = kK(\text{PhI})(I_2)^{0.5} \tag{12}$$

Here, it is assumed that, as in electrophilic aromatic substitution, the new bond to the benzene ring forms before the old bond breaks.

The second term in equation (11) has been ascribed to a heterolytic process —the reaction of two iodobenzene molecules to form diphenyliodonium iodide (LIII). Presumably, this rapidly exchanges its ionic iodine with I_2, then decomposes, as diaryliodonium iodides are known to do,[72] to two molecules of iodobenzene. Although this sequence fits the observed kinetics, more convincing

---

[70] In the exchange of iodine with *sec*-butyl iodide, it is likely that the only important initiation step, except at high temperatures, is the homolysis of I_2. However, as the carbon-radical intermediate becomes more stable, a second mode of initiation may become significant. A kinetic analysis (which is too complex to be considered here) of the exchange of iodine with benzyl iodide (Gazith and Noyes, *J. Am. Chem. Soc.*, 77, 6091 (1955)) indicates that the initiation step,

$$\text{PhCH}_2\text{I} \rightarrow \text{PhCH}_2\cdot + I\cdot$$

has assumed importance in this reaction.

[71] Levine and Noyes, *J. Am. Chem. Soc.*, 80, 2401 (1958); these authors also discuss the kinetically more complex exchange of iodine between I_2 and *p*-nitroiodobenzene. For further work on the exchange between halogens and halobenzenes, see Voegtli, *et al.*, *Helv. Chim. Acta* 37, 1627 (1954).

[72] Beringer, *et al.*, *J. Phys. Chem.*, 60, 141 (1956).

evidence is needed to prove that the diaryliodonium iodide is formed under the conditions used. If indeed it is formed, we should be able to observe exchange of labeled iodine between one aryl iodide and another when the two are heated together in the absence of elemental iodine.

Finally, we may note that the exchange of iodine between I_2 and acyl iodides, R—C—I, takes place wholly heterolytically.[73] Such exchanges are not
$\quad\quad\quad\;\; \|$
$\quad\quad\quad\;\; O$

accelerated by illumination, but are catalyzed by traces of moisture and are very sensitive to the dielectric constant of the solvent. The observed rate law,

$$\text{rate} = k_2(\text{RCOI})(I_2) + k_3(\text{RCOI})(I_2)^2 \tag{13}$$

suggests two heterolytic processes. The first term corresponds to a rate-determining and reversible formation of an acyl tri-iodide (LIV),

$$\underset{\text{LIV}}{R{-}\overset{\displaystyle O}{\overset{\|}{C}}{-}I + I{-}I^* \xrightarrow{\;\text{slow}\;} [R{-}C{\equiv}O]^+[I{-}I{-}I^*]^- \to R{-}\overset{\displaystyle O}{\overset{\|}{C}}{-}I^* + I{-}I}$$

and the second term may well correspond to the similar formation of an acyl pentaiodide, $R{-}\overset{+}{C}{=}O\ I_5^-$.

Autoxidations

The reactions of organic compounds with elemental oxygen under mild conditions are generally referred to as *autoxidations*, for such oxidations often take place "by themselves" when the (slightly impure) substrate is exposed to the atmosphere. Compounds of many types, including alcohols,[74(a)] phenols,[74(b)] enols,[74(c)] ethers,[74(d)] amines,[74(e)] ketols,[74(f)] and Grignard reagents,[74(g)] may undergo autoxidation, but we shall confine our attention in this section to the autoxidations of hydrocarbons and aldehydes.

Under the mildest conditions in which a reaction can occur (temperatures below 100° in the presence of a free-radical initiator), oxygen often attacks hydrocarbons to form alkyl hydroperoxides (compounds containing the —OOH group). Some typical hydroperoxides formed in the autoxidation of hydrocarbons are shown as follows:

[73] Goldman and Noyes, *J. Am. Chem. Soc.*, **79**, 5370 (1957).
[74] (a) Brown, *et al.*, *J. Am. Chem. Soc.*, **77**, 1756 (1955). (b) James and Weissberger, *ibid.*, **60**, 98 (1938). (c) Fuson, Maynert, and Shenk, *ibid.*, **67**, 1939 (1945). (d) Rieche and Koch, *Ber.*, **76**, 1016 (1942). (e) Michaelis, *et al.*, *J. Am. Chem. Soc.*, **61**, 1981 (1939). (f) Weissberger, Lu-Valle and Thomas, *ibid.*, **65**, 1934 (1943). (g) Walling and Buckler, *ibid.*, **77**, 6032 (1955).

Of these, LV is obviously derived from decalin,[75(a)] LVI from cumene,[75(b)] LVII from tetralin,[75(c)] LVIII from cyclohexene,[75(d)] and LIX from the dimer of cyclopentadiene.[75(e)] Attack on such hydrocarbons may be initiated by a radical derived from an outside source (generally a peroxide), or, much less effectively, by molecular oxygen,[76] which is itself a "diradical."

$$R\cdot\ +\ -\overset{|}{\underset{|}{C}}-H \rightarrow R-H\ +\ -\overset{|}{\underset{|}{C}}\cdot$$

or

$$\cdot\ddot{O}-\ddot{O}\cdot\ +\ -\overset{|}{\underset{|}{C}}-H \rightarrow \cdot\ddot{O}-\ddot{O}:H\ +\ -\overset{|}{\underset{|}{C}}\cdot$$

The propagation sequence is simple.

$$-\overset{|}{\underset{|}{C}}\cdot\ +\ O_2 \rightarrow -\overset{|}{\underset{|}{C}}-O-O\cdot \xrightarrow{-\overset{|}{C}-H} -\overset{|}{C}-OOH\ +\ -\overset{|}{\underset{|}{C}}\cdot \xrightarrow{O_2} etc.$$

One of the termination reactions is undoubtedly the coupling of two alkyl radicals to form a alkane with twice the number of carbons, but the fate of the —C—OO· radicals, in the absence of added inhibitors, is a question that must be investigated for each individual instance.[77,78]

As is the case with hydrogen abstraction by other radicals, attack of a C—H

---

[75] (a) Criegee, *Ber.*, **77B**, (1944). (b) Armstrong, Hall, and Quinn, *J. Chem. Soc.*, **1950**, 666. (c) Farmer and Sundralingham, *ibid.*, **1942**, 121. (d) Criegee, Pilz and Flygare, *Ber.*, **B72**, 1799 (1939). (e) Hock and Depke, *Ber.*, **84**, 356 (1951).

[76] Kahn, *J. Chem. Phys.*, **22**, 2090 (1954). Agreement is, however, not complete that O_2 may react directly with C—H bonds to initiate radical chains at moderate temperatures. For an opposing view, see Bateman, Hughes, and Morris, *Discussions Faraday Soc.*, **14**, 190 (1953).

[77] Peroxy radical with α-hydrogens may, for example, disproportionate in the following manner:

$$2-\overset{|}{\underset{|}{C}}H-OO\cdot \rightarrow -\overset{|}{C}=O\ +\ -\overset{|}{\underset{|}{C}}HOH\ +\ O_2$$

(For evidence of such termination, see Russell, *J. Am. Chem. Soc.*, **77**, 4583 (1955)).

[78] A large number of kinetic studies of the autoxidation of hydrocarbons have been reported. See, for example: Bamford and Dewar, *Proc. Roy. Soc. London*, **A198**, 252 (1949); Bateman and Morris, *Trans. Faraday Soc.*, **48**, 1026 (1953); Mayo, Miller, and Russell, *J. Am. Chem. Soc.*, **80**, 2500 (1958); Bateman, *Quart. Revs.*, **8**, 147 (1954).

bond with ROO· radicals proceeds more readily if the carbon is tertiary or secondary than if it is primary, and removal of a hydrogen from an allylic or benzylic carbon is still easier. Indeed, it has been estimated[79] that incorporation of an additional alkyl group at the reaction site (converting a primary carbon to a secondary, or a secondary to a tertiary) facilitates the removal of a hydrogen from that site by a factor of about 3; whereas replacement of an α-hydrogen with a phenyl group or a vinyl group (converting the α-carbon to a benzylic or an allylic carbon) raises the reactivity of the C—H bonds 23-fold and 100-fold, respectively. Thus, it will be noted that in formation of hydroperoxides LV–LIX by autoxidation, attack has occurred at *alpha* to a double bond, *alpha* to a benzene ring, or at a tertiary carbon.

In the absence of added initiators, the autoxidations of many hydrocarbons are *autocatalytic*. Hydroperoxides, as might be expected, may act as free-radical initiators (although they are much less effective than dialkyl or diacyl peroxides). During the early stages of such reactions, the concentration of hydroperoxide is steadily increasing, and more and more kinetic chains are being initiated by the hydroperoxide formed. In fact, early in the reaction, the oxidation rate may be very nearly proportional to the quantity of oxygen that has already been absorbed.[80] Later, however, the reaction rate diminishes (as in an ordinary reaction) as the supply of hydrocarbon becomes depleted.

The preparation of hydroperoxides in high yield from hydrocarbons offers serious difficulties. If the temperature is too low, the chain reaction becomes inconveniently slow, but at higher temperatures homolytic decomposition of the hydroperoxide may greatly reduce the yield. Moreover, with unsaturated hydrocarbons, the hydroperoxides, when formed, can attack the double bonds of the remaining hydrocarbon molecules or those of olefinic hydroperoxides. Thus, although over 50 hydroperoxides have, to date, been prepared by autoxidation, only a few (including hydroperoxides LVI, LVII, and LIX) have been obtained in yields of over 30 percent.

The autoxidations of hexaarylethanes occur readily in the absence of outside initiators. These hydrocarbons, which, as we have seen, dissociate into triarylmethyl radicals, yield dialkyl peroxides,[81] almost certainly by the following path:

$$Ar_3C—CAr_3 \xrightarrow{\text{slow}} Ar_3C· \xrightarrow{O_2} Ar_3C—O_2· \xrightarrow{Ar_3C—CAr_3}$$
LV

$$Ar_3C—O_2—CAr_3 + Ar_3C· \xrightarrow{\text{etc.}}$$

[79] Bolland, *Trans. Faraday Soc.*, **46**, 358 (1950).

[80] For kinetic treatment of autocatalytic autoxidations, see, for example: (a) Bolland, *Proc. Roy. Soc. London*, **A186**, 218 (1946); (b) George, Rideal and Robertson, *ibid.*, **A185**, 288, 309 (1946); (c) Batten, Gardner, and Bridge, *J. Chem. Soc.*, **1955**, 3029.

[81] Ziegler, *Ann.*, **551**, 127 (1942).

In the presence of inhibitors such as catechol, radical LV is diverted, and the hydroperoxide, rather than the peroxide, is formed.

$$\text{Ar}_3\text{C}{-}\text{O}{-}\text{O}\cdot \;+\; \text{HO}{-}\underset{\text{HO}}{\bigcirc} \longrightarrow \text{Ar}_3\text{C}{-}\text{OOH} \;+\; \cdot\text{O}{-}\underset{\text{HO}}{\bigcirc}\; 82$$

LV

The autoxidation of aldehydes proceeds with ease, even at room temperature. This is likewise a chain reaction with steps analogous to those in the autoxidation of hydrocarbons.

$$R{-}\underset{\underset{O}{\|}}{C}{-}H \xrightarrow{\text{In}\cdot} \begin{cases} R{-}\underset{\underset{O}{\|}}{C}\cdot \xrightarrow{O_2} R{-}\underset{\underset{O}{\|}}{C}{-}O{-}O\cdot \xrightarrow{RCHO} R{-}\underset{\underset{O}{\|}}{C}{-}OOH + R{-}\underset{\underset{O}{\|}}{C}\cdot \xrightarrow[\text{etc.}]{O_2} \\ \text{InH} \end{cases}$$

Here, the product, a *peroxy acid* $\left(R{-}\underset{\underset{O}{\|}}{C}{-}OOH\right)$, is generally not isolated as such, but may be converted, by adding acetic anhydride, to a diacyl peroxide (LVI).

$$R{-}\underset{\underset{O}{\|}}{C}{-}OOH + Ac_2O \rightarrow R{-}\underset{\underset{O}{\|}}{C}{-}O{-}O{-}Ac + AcOH$$

LVI

Here, once again, the chain reaction may be initiated by a radical derived from an outside source (designated In·), or, less effectively, by O_2 itself;[83] and, once again, removal of a hydrogen atom from the substrate is facilitated by the presence of electron-donating groups.[84,85]

At present, the substances that are known to be most effective in inhibiting autoxidations are phenols and aromatic amines. In spite of the great importance of these *antioxidants*, their mode of action is not yet completely clear. There is little doubt, however, that they react with the *peroxy radicals* in the kinetic chain, rather than with the alkyl or acyl radicals; for such inhibitors differ considerably

[82] For a criticism of this interpretation, see Boozer, Hammond, Hamilton, and Sen, *J. Am. Chem. Soc.*, **76**, 386 (1954); **77**, 3233 (1955).

[83] Mulcahy and Watt, *Proc. Roy. Soc.*, **A216**, 10, 30 (1953). These authors, however, present kinetic evidence that the intermediates in the oxidation that is initiated by O_2 are somehow different from those in the reaction initiated by an added radical source. This very interesting question merits further investigation.

[84] Walling and McElhill, *J. Am. Chem. Soc.*, **73**, 2927 (1951).

[85] For kinetic studies of the autoxidation of aldehydes, see, for example: Cooper and Melville, *J. Chem. Soc.*, **1951**, 1984; Mulcahy and Watt, *ibid.*, **1954**, 2971; Fillet, Niclause, and Letort, *J. Chim. phys.*, **53**, 8 (1956). As with the autoxidation of many hydrocarbons, the nature of the termination steps is not yet clear.

from the species that are known to inhibit reactions involving only alkyl radicals (for example, polynitrobenzenes, disulfides, and iodine).[86] The simplest mecha-

$$R-O_2^\cdot + HO-\text{\textcircled{}}-OH \longrightarrow ROOH + \cdot O-\text{\textcircled{}}-OH \longrightarrow \begin{cases} HO-\text{\textcircled{}}-OH + \\ O=\text{\textcircled{}}=O \end{cases}$$

nism for inhibition is simply a hydrogen-atom transfer and this probably operates in some cases.[86(a)] On the other hand, it has been found that the deuterated amines PhNDMe and Ph$_2$ND inhibit the autoxidation of cumene just as effectively as do their respective nondeuterated analogs,[82] whereas if the inhibition process were to begin with a reaction involving the breakage of a N—H (or N—D) bond, the deuterated compounds should be less effective. Moreover, autoxidation is similarly inhibited by tetramethyl-p-phenylenediamine (p-Me$_2$N—C$_6$H$_4$—NMe$_2$), in which there are no N—H bonds. It therefore has been suggested[82] that the antioxidant action of aromatic amines (and possibly that of some phenols as well) is due not to hydrogen-atom transfer but rather to the formation of complexes with the peroxy radical; for example,

$$ROO\cdot + Me_2N-\text{\textcircled{}}-NMe_2 \longrightarrow \begin{bmatrix} \overset{NMe_2}{\underset{NMe_2}{\text{\textcircled{}}}} \rightarrow \cdot OOR \longleftrightarrow \overset{^+\overset{\cdot}{N}Me_2}{\underset{NMe_2}{\text{\textcircled{}}}}{}^-OOR \end{bmatrix}$$

LVII   LVII′

Note that the cation in the ionic structure of the complex is the cation present in Wurster's salts (p. 678). Indeed, the characteristic blue color of this cation is observed when solutions of cumene and the parent diamine are treated with oxygen.

Autoxidations are catalyzed by traces of metal salts. To be effective, the salt should be derived from a metal having at least two readily accessible oxidation states *differing by one unit* (for example, Fe, Co, Cu, V, Mn). Peroxides react with both the upper and lower oxidation states of these metals, for example,

$$Fe^{2+} \quad + ROOH \rightarrow Fe(OH)^{2+} + OR\cdot$$
$$Fe(OH)^{2+} + ROOH \rightarrow Fe^{2+} \quad + HOH + ROO\cdot$$

Hence, if a salt having the metal in the lower valence state is added to a solution containing peroxide, the metal ion will be oxidized, then reduced, then oxidized

---

[86] (a) The reaction of inhibitors with peroxy radicals, rather than with alkyl or acyl radicals, has been demonstrated by kinetic methods; see Bolland and ten Have, *Trans. Faraday Soc.*, **43**, 201 (1947). (b) For what appears to be an exceptional case, see Moore and Waters, *J. Chem. Soc.*, **1952**, 2432.

again, etc. Each of these changes will generate a radical capable of removing a hydrogen atom from a molecule of hydrocarbon (or aldehyde). As a result, these heavy-metal salts may greatly enhance the effectiveness of peroxy compounds as initiators.[87] On the other hand, since such salts, in effect, catalyze the decompositions of peroxides, the yields of peroxides obtained from such accelerated autoxidations are generally reduced.

Thermal Decompositions of Hydroperoxides and Dialkyl Peroxides

As we have noted, the autoxidations of hydrocarbons may become quite complex at temperatures above 100°, for the decompositions of the hydroperoxides (which are generally the initial products) become increasingly competitive as the temperature is raised. The nature of these complications may be more clearly understood by examining the decompositions of hydroperoxides in the absence of their parent hydrocarbons. Decomposition studies of a number of hydroperoxides, both alone and in solvent, have been carried out, with the greatest attention to date directed toward the two tertiary hydroperoxides, t-butyl hydroperoxide (t-BuO_2H) and cumene hydroperoxide ($PhCMe_2O_2H$).

t-Butyl hydroperoxide, either in the pure state at $100°$[88(a)] or in an inert solvent at below $140°$[28,88(b)] decomposes cleanly to t-butyl alcohol and elemental oxygen. The decomposition is evidently a chain process, for which the following mechanism[88(b)] seems likely:

$$Me_3C-OOH \rightarrow Me_3C-O\cdot + \cdot OH \qquad (14)$$

$$Me_3C-O\cdot + HOO-CMe_3 \rightarrow Me_3C-OH + \cdot OO-CMe_3 \qquad (15)$$

$$2Me_3C-OO\cdot \rightarrow O_2 + 2Me_3CO\cdot \xrightarrow{HOO-CMe_3} etc. \qquad (16)$$

The first two of these steps, the homolysis of the O—O bond and the transfer of a hydrogen atom, are of familiar types. The third is more interesting, for here, two radicals collide, yielding two new radicals and a diradical (the O_2 molecule).

In the decomposition of cumene hydroperoxide under similar conditions[28,89] two additional reactions of the alkoxyl radical ($PhCMe_2-O\cdot$) may assume importance. Coupling of these radicals gives appreciable yields of peroxide LVIII, whereas at somewhat higher temperatures, a radical elimination reaction occurs, yielding acetophenone. Broadly speaking, the dimerization

[87] For studies of autoxidations catalyzed by heavy-metal salts see, for example: Robertson, et al., Trans. Faraday Soc., **42,** 201, 217 (1946); Bawn, Discussions Faraday Soc., **14,** 181 (1953); Mesrobian, et al., J. Am. Chem. Soc., **72,** 1942 (1950); **75,** 6189 (1953).

[88] (a) Milas and Surgenor, J. Am. Chem. Soc., **68,** 206 (1946). (b) Bell, et al., Discussions Faraday Soc., **10,** 242 (1951).

[89] Kharasch, Fono, and Nudenburg, J. Org. Chem., **16,** 113 (1951); Fordham and Williams, Can. J. Research, **B27,** 943 (1949).

$$2\text{PhCMe}_2\text{O} \cdot \rightarrow \text{PhCMe}_2 \!-\! \text{O} \!-\! \text{O} \!-\! \text{CMe}_2\text{Ph} \quad \text{(in HOAc at } 100°\text{)}$$
$$\text{LVIII}$$

$$\text{PhCMe}_2\text{O} \cdot \ \rightarrow \ \text{Ph} \!-\! \overset{\overset{\text{O}}{\|}}{\text{C}} \!-\! \text{Me} + \text{Me} \cdot \qquad \text{(in decane at } 120°\text{)}$$

of alkoxy radicals to dialkyl peroxides at temperatures above 100° is rather rare, but the breakdown of alkoxy radicals to ketones (or aldehydes) and alkyl radicals is often observed. An analogous homolysis is of importance, for example, in the decomposition of hydroperoxide (LIX).[90]

LIX

Although the decompositions of a number of secondary hydroperoxides have been investigated,[91] these reactions do not, as yet, form a coherent picture. The decompositions of primary hydroperoxides are of considerable interest; for in addition to the "expected" homolytic decomposition, a second type of decomposition, probably proceeding by a cyclic mechanism, has been found to occur, and this yields *elemental hydrogen* as a major product.[92] The decomposition of n-butyl hydroperoxide at 85°, for example, has been studied with some care.[92(b)] The products with which we shall here be concerned are hydrogen, butyraldehyde, butyric acid, propane, n-butanol, and n-butyl formate.

$$n\text{-Bu} \!-\! \text{OOH} \rightarrow \begin{cases} \text{H}_2 \\ \text{C}_3\text{H}_7\text{CHO} \\ \text{C}_3\text{H}_7\text{COOH} \end{cases} + \begin{cases} \text{C}_3\text{H}_8 \\ n\text{-BuOH} \\ \text{H} \!-\! \overset{\overset{}{}}{\underset{\underset{\text{O}}{\|}}{\text{C}}} \!-\! \text{OBu} \end{cases}$$

yields increased by irradiation

When the decomposition is carried out with the aid of ultraviolet light at 25° (conditions known to favor homolytic cleavage of the O—O bond), the yields of the first three products drop sharply, whereas, as indicated, the yields of propane, n-butyl alcohol, and n-butyl formate rise. This suggests that the latter three

[90] Schmidt and Fisher, *J. Am. Chem. Soc.*, **76**, 5426 (1954).

[91] See, for example, Farkas and Passaglia, *J. Am. Chem. Soc.*, **72**, 333 (1950); Robertson and Waters, *J. Chem. Soc.*, **1948**, 1574; Bateman and Hughes, *ibid.*, **1952**, 4592.

[92] (a) Reiche and Hitz, *Ber.*, **62**, 2458 (1929); **63**, 2642 (1930). (b) Mosher, Wurster, and Durham, *J. Am. Chem. Soc.*, **77**, 5451 (1955); **80**, 327, 332 (1958).

products arise from a homolytic sequence, the first step of which is the breakage of the O—O bond in the hydroperoxide; but the details of this sequence have not yet been worked out.[93] The reaction in which hydrogen is formed exhibits an induction period, which may, however be eliminated by adding traces of aldehydes to the reaction mixture. The hydrogen formed is derived from C—H bonds rather than from the O—H bond; for if the reaction is carried out with n-Bu—OOD, H_2 rather than HD or D_2 is evolved. Moreover, since the reaction mixture exhibits none of the tests characteristic of atomic hydrogen, it may be assumed that the hydrogen *molecules* are formed as such, rather than by combinations of free atoms. The bulk of evidence points to the intervention of compound LX, a sort of "hemiacetal" derived from a mole each of aldehyde and hydroperoxide, which may decompose via the cyclic transition state LXI to hydrogen, butyraldehyde, and butyric acid. Indeed, α-hydroxyperoxides similar

$$PrCH_2OOH + PrCHO \longrightarrow PrCH_2\underset{HO}{\overset{O-O}{\diagup}}CH-Pr \longrightarrow \left[Pr-CH\overset{O-O}{\diagdown}\underset{H\ H\ OH}{C-Pr}\right] \rightarrow \begin{cases}PrCHO\\PrCOOH\\H_2\end{cases}$$

$$\text{LX} \qquad\qquad\qquad \text{LXI}$$

to LX have been prepared and have been found to decompose readily, evolving hydrogen and leaving behind a mixture of aldehyde and carboxylic acid. In the absence of added aldehyde, it is likely that n-butyl hydroperoxide is converted slowly to butyraldehyde, thence to intermediate LX, by the following sequence:

$$PrCH_2OOH \rightarrow Pr\overset{\cdot}{C}H—OOH \xrightarrow{-OH\cdot} PrCHO \xrightarrow{PrCH_2OOH} PrCH_2—OO—\overset{\overset{\displaystyle OH}{|}}{C}HPr$$
$$\text{LX}$$

The slow build-up of the concentrations of butyraldehyde and intermediate LX to their respective steady-state values accounts for the observed induction period.

The decompositions of *dialkyl peroxides* appear to be considerably less complex than those of hydroperoxides. One of the most stable of these is di-t-butyl peroxide ($Me_3C—OO—CMe_3$), the breakdown of which has been studied by a

---

[93] The following sequence of steps accounts for the observed products:

$$BuOOH \xrightarrow{-OH\cdot} BuO\cdot \overset{\displaystyle Pr\cdot + HCHO \rightarrow PrH + H—\overset{\cdot}{C}=O \xrightarrow{BuO\cdot} H—\overset{\overset{\displaystyle O}{\|}}{C}—OBu}{\underset{\overset{BuOOH}{\longrightarrow} BuOH + BuOO\cdot \rightarrow ????}{\diagup\diagdown}}$$

As indicated, the fate of the BuOO· radicals is in doubt. Interaction between two such radicals to form $2BuO\cdot + O_2$ (a reaction analogous to reaction (16)) appears unlikely, for only traces of O_2 have been isolated from the reaction mixture.

number of workers.[94] This decomposition is *not* a chain process, either in the vapor state or in hydrocarbon solvents, for it displays clean first-order kinetics and is not inhibited by addition of O_2 or NO. The decomposition of the vapor gives mainly acetone and ethane, and there is little doubt that the reaction sequence occurring here is

$$Me_3C-O-O-CMe_3 \xrightarrow{slow} 2Me_3C-O\cdot \rightarrow \begin{cases} 2Me_2C=O \\ 2Me\cdot \rightarrow C_2H_6 \end{cases}$$

Minor amounts of methyl ethyl ketone and methane may be attributed to attack of methyl radicals on the acetone formed.

$$CH_3\cdot + H_3C-\underset{\underset{O}{\|}}{C}-CH_3 \rightarrow CH_4 + \cdot H_2C-\underset{\underset{O}{\|}}{C}-CH_3 \xrightarrow{CH_3\cdot}$$

$$H_3C-CH_2-\underset{\underset{O}{\|}}{C}-CH_3$$

In a hydrocarbon solvent, the $Me_3CO\cdot$ radical may, instead of decomposing to acetone and $Me\cdot$, simply extract a hydrogen atom, forming *t*-butyl alcohol.

$$Me_3CO\cdot + HR \rightarrow Me_3C-OH + R\cdot$$

Generally, the ratio of acetone to *t*-butyl alcohol obtained from the reaction in such a solvent increases with temperature, indicating that the activation energy for the breakdown of the $Me_3CO\cdot$ radical is greater than that for hydrogen extraction. As may be expected, the acetone to *t*-butyl alcohol ratio depends also on the nature of the solvent, in particular on whether the hydrogen atoms available are bound to primary, secondary, or tertiary carbons. Thus, when the decomposition of di-*t*-butyl peroxide is carried out in cumene ($PhCHMe_2$), in which tertiary C—H linkages are available, the ratio of *t*-butyl alcohol to acetone in the product is about 4; whereas if the decomposition is carried out under similar conditions in *t*-butylbenzene (which has only primary and aromatic C—H linkages), this ratio drops to 0.6.

It appears that the decomposition of di-*t*-butyl peroxide as a pure liquid proceeds, at least in part, by a chain mechanism,[95] since the specific rates for decomposition of the pure peroxide are several times those for the peroxide in hydrocarbon solvents. Moreover, in addition to *t*-butyl alcohol, acetone, and methane, there may be isolated from the reaction mixture large quantities of

---

[94] See, for example; Raley, Rust, and Vaughan, *J. Am. Chem. Soc.*, **70**, 88 (1948); Lossing and Tickner, *J. Chem. phys.*, **20**, 907 (1952); Jaquiss, Roberts, and Szwarc, *J. Am. Chem. Soc.*, **74**, 6005 (1952); Williams, Oberright, and Brooks, *ibid.*, **78**, 1190 (1956). This reaction has been reviewed by Frost and Pearson, *Kinetics and Mechanism*, John Wiley and Sons, Inc., New York, 1953, p. 310–317.

[95] Bell, Rust, and Vaughan, *J. Am. Chem. Soc.*, **72**, 337 (1950).

isobutylene oxide, LXX, suggesting the sequence

$$Me_3C—OO—CMe_3 + Me_3CO\cdot \rightarrow$$

$$\left\{ \begin{array}{l} \cdot CH_2CMe_2—OO—CMe_3 \rightarrow CH_2\underset{\underset{O}{\diagdown\diagup}}{}CMe_2 + \cdot OCMe_3 \xrightarrow{\text{etc.}} \\[3mm] \qquad\qquad\qquad\qquad\qquad\qquad\qquad\quad LXII \\[3mm] t\text{-BuOH} \end{array} \right.$$

in addition to the "usual" decomposition yielding acetone and the methyl radical (which may also remove hydrogen from the peroxide). The intramolecular radical displacement on oxygen leading to epoxide LXII is unusual; this step may be regarded somewhat skeptically until further examples of such displacements are found.

The decompositions of a number of additional dialkyl peroxides have been studied,[96] but these appear to be more complex than that of di-t-butyl peroxide and need not be discussed here.

Decompositions of Diacyl Peroxides

The decompositions of *diacyl peroxides* are of considerable importance, for such peroxides are extensively used as chain initiators. The most familiar of these is benzoyl peroxide $\left(\begin{array}{c} Ph—C—OO—C—Ph \\ \parallel \parallel \\ O O \end{array} \right)$, the decomposition of which in most organic solvents proceeds by at least two distinct paths.[97] The first of these begins with a "spontaneous" *unimolecular* breakage of the O—O bond,

$$\underset{\underset{O}{\parallel}}{PhC}—O—O—\underset{\underset{O}{\parallel}}{CPh} \rightarrow 2Ph—\underset{\underset{O}{\parallel}}{C}—O\cdot$$

whereas the second path (induced decomposition) presumably involves attack on the O—O bond by a radical present in solution.

$$R\cdot + \underset{\underset{O}{\parallel}}{PhC}—O—O—\underset{\underset{O}{\parallel}}{CPh} \rightarrow R—O—\underset{\underset{O}{\parallel}}{CPh} + \cdot O—\underset{\underset{O}{\parallel}}{C}—Ph$$

[96] See, for example: (a) Takezaki and Takeuchi, *J. Chem. Phys.*, **22**, 1527 (1954) (on dimethyl peroxide); (b) Rebbert and Laidler, *ibid.*, **20**, 574 (1952) (on diethyl peroxide); (c) Rust, Seubold, and Vaughan, *J. Am. Chem. Soc.*, **72**, 338 (1950) (on t-butyl alkyl peroxides); (d) Kharasch, *et al.*, *J. Org. Chem.*, **16**, 1548 (1951) (on triarylmethyl t-butyl peroxides).

[97] For kinetic studies of the decomposition of benzoyl peroxide, see: (a) Nozaki and Bartlett, *J. Am. Chem. Soc.*, **68**, 1686 (1946); **69**, 2299 (1947); (b) Cass, *ibid.*, **68**, 1976 (1946); **69**, 500 (1947); (c) Swain, Stockmayer, and Clarke, *ibid.*, **72**, 5426 (1950); (d) Hammond and Soffer, *ibid.*, **72**, 3737, 4711 (1950); (e) Walling and Pellon, *ibid.*, **79**, 4786 (1957); (f) Batten, *J. Chem. Soc.*, **1956**, 4687; (g) Swain, Schaad, and Kresge, *J. Am. Chem. Soc.*, **80**, 5313 (1958). For a review of early work, see (h) Hey and Waters, *Chem. Revs.*, **21**, 202 (1937).

The fate of the benzoyloxy radicals depends largely upon the solvent used. If secondary or tertiary hydrogen atoms are available, they may be "extracted" from the solvent molecules by PhCOO· radicals, forming benzoic acid and radicals derived from the solvent (which may, in turn, induce the homolysis of additional peroxide molecules). With less active solvents, decarboxylation of the benzoyloxy radicals is likely to occur,

$$\text{Ph—}\overset{\displaystyle O}{\overset{\|}{\text{C}}}\text{—O·} \rightarrow \text{Ph·} + CO_2$$

and the resulting phenyl radicals may dimerize or may attack the solvent or peroxide. If the solvent is aromatic, free-radical arylation by the phenyl radical may occur. If the solvent is an olefin, polymerization may be observed. When the decomposition of benzoyl peroxide is carried out in damp CCl_4 in the presence of elemental iodine, the iodine reacts with the benzoyloxy radicals very soon after they are formed, suppressing the induced decomposition. The resulting product, benzoyl hypoiodite, PhC—OI, may be hydrolyzed to benzoic acid, which may $\overset{\|}{\underset{O}{}}$
then be recovered in almost quantitative yield,[97(d)] thus indicating that virtually all acts of "spontaneous" decomposition proceed through PhCOO· radicals.

$$\left(\overset{\displaystyle O}{\overset{\|}{\text{PhCO—}}}\right)_2 \xrightarrow{\text{slow}} 2\text{Ph—}\overset{\displaystyle O}{\overset{\|}{\text{C}}}\text{—O·} \xrightarrow[\text{fast}]{I_2} 2\text{Ph—}\overset{\displaystyle O}{\overset{\|}{\text{C}}}\text{—OI} \xrightarrow{H_2O} 2\text{PhCOOH} + 2\text{HOI}$$

In relatively inactive solvents, such as aromatic hydrocarbons and CCl_4, the induced decomposition very probably proceeds largely by the following path:

$$\text{PhCOO·} \xrightarrow{-CO_2} \text{Ph·} \xrightarrow{Bz_2O_2} \text{PhOBz} + \text{BzO·} \xrightarrow{-CO_2} \text{etc.}$$

which can be shown (Ex. 3d) to lead to a rate law for the overall decomposition:

$$\frac{-d(Bz_2O_2)}{dt} = k(Bz_2O_2) + k'(Bz_2O_2)^{3/2} \tag{17}$$

The rate constant for the "induced contribution," k', is nearly the same in a number of these solvents (for example, benzene, nitrobenzene, cyclohexene, and CCl_4),[97(a)] a further indication that radicals derived from the solvent are not involved in these cases. However, when the decomposition reaction is transferred from benzene to acetic acid, the rate of induced decomposition increases about twelvefold, suggesting that radicals from the solvent have begun to enter the picture. In aliphatic ethers and in alcohols having α-hydrogen atoms, decomposition is much faster still, indicating that the induced decomposition has overshadowed the "spontaneous." Here, the chain reaction is probably propagated by such solvent-derived radicals as R—$\overset{\cdot}{C}$HOH and R$\overset{\cdot}{C}$H—OR'. Once again, the rate-law is determined by the nature of the termination step(s); decompositions of benzoyl peroxide in alcohols or ethers follow, to a good approximation, first-order kinetics, which may be shown (Ex. 3c) to be consistent with termination by the following reaction:

$$R—\overset{\cdot}{C}H—OR + BzO\cdot \rightarrow RCH(OBz)—OR$$

Moreover, such benzoyloxy ethers may be isolated from the decompositions of benzoyl peroxide in aliphatic ethers.[97(b),98] In cyclohexane also, induced composition of benzoyl peroxide is caused by radicals derived from the solvent.[97(a)]

The effect of high *pressures* on the decomposition of benzoyl peroxide (in acetophenone) has recently been studied.[97(e)] Just as activation energies, $\Delta H^{\ddagger}$, may be obtained from the observed variation of reaction rates with temperature, so may "activation volumes," $\Delta V^{\ddagger}$ (volume changes in going from reactants to transition state), be obtained from the observed variation of reaction rates with applied pressure.[99] Unimolecular homolyses are generally retarded by application of high pressures, whereas bimolecular processes (for example, radical additions and displacements) in which the transition state is more compact than the reactants, are generally accelerated.[100] The decomposition of benzoyl peroxide in acetophenone is (as would be expected) gradually retarded as applied pressure is increased, but at very high pressures decomposition becomes sharply accelerated. The latter effect is almost certainly due to the *induced* decomposition that presumably requires a number of bimolecular processes in each kinetic chain.

Bearing in mind that the breaking point in the benzoyl peroxide molecule is the bond between two very electronegative oxygen atoms, we might expect the decomposition of the peroxide to be accelerated by substituents that supply further electron density to this reaction site and to be retarded by substituents which withdraw electron density. This effect is indeed observed;[97,101] moreover the rates of "spontaneous" decomposition of *meta*- and *para*-substituted benzoyl peroxides have been correlated satisfactorily using the Hammett equation (p.

---

[98] The analogous product resulting from the decompositions of Bz_2O_2 in a primary alcohol would be RCH(OH)OBz, which decomposes spontaneously to a carbonyl compound (in this case, an aldehyde) and benzoic acid (see, for example, Gelissen and Hermans, *Ber.*, **58B**, 765 (1925)). For the reaction of diacyl peroxides with phenols, which is almost certainly heterolytic at ordinary temperatures, see p. 649.

[99] Evans and Polanyi, *Trans. Faraday Soc.*, **31**, 875 (1935). Reactions in solution which are most affected by applied pressure are those involving creation or destruction of ionic charge. Thus, reactions resulting in separation of unlike charge are strongly accelerated by pressure, since pressure aids the "gathering together" of solvent molecules about the separating charges (see, for example, Burries and Laidler, *Trans. Faraday Soc.*, **51**, 1497 (1955), and Brower, *J. Am. Chem. Soc.*, **80**, 2105 (1958)).

[100] See, for example, Walling and Pellon, *J. Am. Chem. Soc.*, **79**, 4776, 4782 (1957).

[101] Blomquist and Buselli, *J. Am. Chem. Soc.*, **73**, 3883 (1951).

220), suggesting that polarity is the dominant factor leading to rate difference in this series. On the other hand, it appears that electron-withdrawing substituents accelerate the *induced* decomposition of these peroxides in dioxane,[97(c)] probably because such substituents increase the electrophilic character of the derived benzoyloxy radicals, hence the ease with which they withdraw hydrogen atoms from the solvent.[102]

The decomposition of acetyl peroxide, CH_3—C—O—O—C—CH_3, at
$\quad\quad\quad\quad\quad\quad\quad\quad\quad\quad\quad\quad\quad\quad\quad\quad\quad$ ‖ $\quad\quad$ ‖
$\quad\quad\quad\quad\quad\quad\quad\quad\quad\quad\quad\quad\quad\quad\quad\quad\quad$ O $\quad\quad$ O

moderate temperatures is similar in a number of respects to that of benzoyl peroxide; again, both a "spontaneous" and an induced decomposition occur.[103] The chief difference between decompositions of the two peroxides is the very short lifetime of the acetoxy radical, which, unlike the benzoyloxy radical, is not stabilized by conjugation between the carboxy group and the benzene ring. Even in very reactive solvents, acetyl peroxide decomposes to give virtually quantitative yields of CO_2, and acetoxy radicals cannot, at ordinary temperatures, be trapped by I_2.[104] Acetyl peroxide may thus be considered an excellent source of free methyl radicals in solution.

Methyl radicals attack most organic solvents, readily extracting hydrogen atoms bound to aliphatic, allylic, or benzylic carbon atoms; if no such hydrogens are available, attack on carbon-halogen bonds may occur.[105]

$$CH_3\cdot + PhCH_3 \quad\quad \rightarrow CH_4 \quad + PhCH_2\cdot$$
$$CH_3\cdot + CH_3COOMe \rightarrow CH_4 \quad + CH_2COOMe$$
$$CH_3\cdot + CCl_4 \quad\quad\quad \rightarrow CH_3Cl + CCl_3\cdot$$

Such reactions are rapid, but their relative rates may be compared by allowing acetyl peroxide to decompose in a known mixture of CCl_4 and a second solvent that may furnish hydrogen atoms, then comparing the quantities of methane and methyl chloride which are formed.

$$CH_3-\overset{O}{\overset{\|}{C}}-O-O-\overset{O}{\overset{\|}{C}}-CH_3 \rightarrow 2CH_3-\overset{O}{\overset{\|}{C}}-O\cdot \xrightarrow{-2CO_2} 2CH_3\cdot \underset{RH}{\overset{CCl_4}{\diagdown}} \begin{array}{l} CH_3Cl \\ \\ CH_4 \end{array}$$

---

[102] It might also be argued that in instances when the decarboxylation of the substituted benzoyloxy radical is a step in the induced decomposition, electron-withdrawing groups facilitate this step.

[103] Reliable specific rates for "spontaneous," but not induced, decompositions of dilute solutions of acetyl peroxide in a number of solvents in the temperature range 60 to 85° have been evaluated. See, for example: Levy, Steinberg, and Szwarc, *J. Am. Chem. Soc.*, **76**, 5978 (1954); Thomas and O'Shaughnessy, *J. Polymer Sci.*, **11**, 455 (1953).

[104] Rembaum and Szwarc, *J. Am. Chem. Soc.*, **77**, 3486 (1955).

[105] For a summary of the reactions of methyl radicals, see Trotman-Dickenson, *Quart. Revs.* **VII**, 198 (1953).

In this way, it may be shown, for example, that methyl acetate reacts with methyl radicals over 20 times as rapidly as does CCl$_4$, which, in turn, reacts 16 times as rapidly as does methyl benzoate.[106]

Moreover, it is found that chloroform, acetaldehyde, and methyl acetate are attacked by CH$_3$· radicals much more readily than are the ordinary aliphatic hydrocarbons. More generally, when the attacking radical is CH$_3$·, extraction of a hydrogen bound to an aliphatic carbon is facilitated both by an α-halogen atom and an α-carbonyl group, although, as we have seen, both such substituents tend to *retard* hydrogen extraction by a chlorine atom. The essential difference between the two types of attack is that the chlorine atom, besides being a free radical, has electrophilic character, whereas the methyl radical has not. The ease with which a substrate is attacked by a methyl radical is probably closely related to the stability of the resulting radical intermediate, and, as has been shown (p. 697) both an α-carbonyl and an α-halogen substituent tend to stabilize such a radical.

Methyl radicals also attack aromatic rings, but the nature of the reaction is not yet clear; it is generally assumed to be some sort of an addition reaction that does *not* yield methane. Thus, if acetyl peroxide is allowed to decompose in a mixture of an aliphatic hydrocarbon (which yields methane) and an aromatic substance (which does not), the yield of methane should drop as the reactivity of the aromatic increases, for more methyl radicals undergo addition rather than displacement. In this way it may be shown, for example, that anthracene is much more readily attacked by methyl radicals than is phenanthrene, which is, in turn, more readily attacked than biphenyl.[107]

The decompositions of a number of additional diacyl peroxides have been studied,[108] including peroxides XXXVI and XLI, which we have considered in relation to the stereochemistry of free radicals (p. 686). Certain of these studies emphasize that just as a distinction between ionization and dissociation must sometimes be drawn in polar reactions, so also must a distinction between homolysis and dissociation be made in free-radical reactions. More specifically, when a molecule within a "solvent cage" undergoes homolysis, the resulting radicals remain within this cage for a significant time interval, during which they

[106] Edwards and Mayo, *J. Am. Chem. Soc.*, **72**, 1265 (1950). Reactivity ratios obtained in this way are in only fair agreement with corresponding ratios for gas-phase reactions. See, for example, Trotman-Dickenson and Steacie, *J. Chem. Phys.*, **18**, 1097 (1950); **19**, 169 (1951). See also Ref. 101, p. 210.

[107] Levy and Szwarc, *J. Am. Chem. Soc.*, **77**, 1949 (1955). These authors use experiments of the type described to obtain quantities that they term "methyl affinities" for the various aromatics. However, such parameters can have little significance until the nature of the reaction between the methyl group and the aromatic ring is elucidated. For a similar treatment, in which the decompositions of propionyl peroxide are used to evaluate *ethyl affinities*, see Smid and Szwarc, *J. Am. Chem. Soc.*, **78**, 3322 (1956).

[108] See, for example; (*a*) Bartlett and Leffler, *J. Am. Chem. Soc.*, **72**, 3030 (1950); (*b*) Smid, Rembaum, and Szwarc, *ibid.*, **78**, 3315 (1956); (*c*) DeTar and Weis, *ibid.*, **79**, 3041 (1957).

$$(Et-CHMe-\overset{\overset{\displaystyle O}{\|}}{C}-O)_2$$

XXXVI

$$\left[\begin{array}{c} \text{Me} \underset{\text{Me}}{\overset{\text{Me}}{\diagdown}} \overset{\overset{\displaystyle O}{\|}}{C}-O- \end{array} \right]_2$$

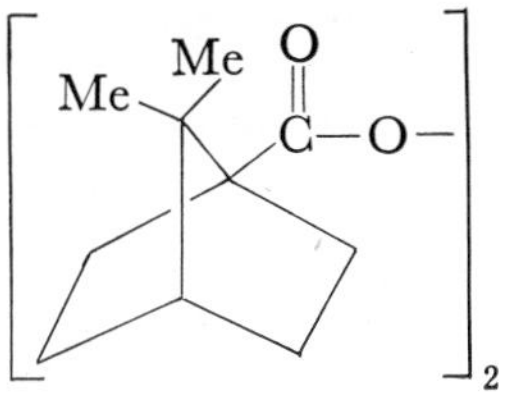

XLI

may be quite likely to recombine.[109] The dissociation-recombination sequence may sometimes be detected if one or both of the radicals are altered in some manner during this time interval. With acyloxy radicals, this "alteration" may be a decarboxylation that, in some cases, takes place very soon after the initial homolysis. When, for example, propionyl peroxide (XLIII) is allowed to decompose in hydrocarbon solvents, the propionoxy radicals first formed rapidly decarboxylate to ethyl radicals, and one of the products is, as expected, n-butane, formed by combination of ethyl radicals.[108(b)] Now, the fraction of ethyl radicals

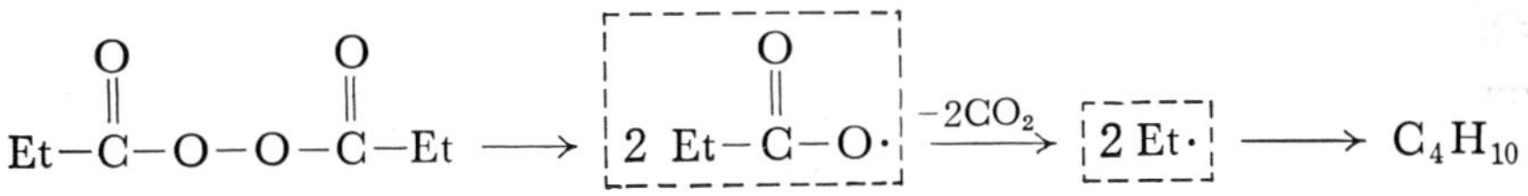

$$Et-\overset{\overset{\displaystyle O}{\|}}{C}-O-O-\overset{\overset{\displaystyle O}{\|}}{C}-Et \longrightarrow \boxed{2\ Et-\overset{\overset{\displaystyle O}{\|}}{C}-O\cdot} \xrightarrow{-2CO_2} \boxed{2\ Et\cdot} \longrightarrow C_4H_{10}$$

XLIII

that form butane has been found to be *very nearly independent of the initial peroxide concentration*, whereas if the ethyl radicals were to become independent of each other before combining, the extent of recombination should rise with peroxide concentration. We may then conclude that the two ethyl radicals that combine to form a given butane molecule are, in almost all cases, derived from the same peroxide molecule; that is, the entire sequence shown above occurs in the same solvent cage (represented by the dotted rectangle). Moreover, the addition of quinone, an excellent "scavenger" for free alkyl radicals, does not affect the yield of butane from this decomposition, again indicating that the ethyl radicals giving butane do not become free of their solvent cage.

In the decompositions of a number of diacyl peroxides (but not that of benzoyl peroxide) the decarboxylation follows the initial homolysis so closely that it may be asked whether these two steps are not concerted. While this question cannot be answered definitively for diacyl peroxides, evidence for a "concerted" mechanism has been obtained for the decompositions of the *t*-butyl esters of a number of peroxy acids.[110] The relative rate constants for a few of such decom-

[109] Franck and Rabinowitch, *Trans. Faraday Soc.*, **30**, 120 (1934).
[110] Bartlett and Hiatt, *J. Am. Chem. Soc.*, **80**, 1398 (1958).

positions (in chlorobenzene at 60°) are given below:

$$t\text{-BuO}\text{—O}\text{—}\underset{\underset{\text{O}}{\|}}{\text{C}}\text{—R} \rightarrow t\text{-BuO·} + CO_2 + R·$$

R—	—CH_3	—CH_2Ph	—CMe_2Ph	—CPh_2Me
k/k_{BuO_2Ac}	1	300	40,000	80,000

Quite obviously, the rate of decomposition rises sharply as the stability of radical R· increases. It is difficult to see why this should be so if the rate-determining step were merely the breakage of the O—O bond in the peroxy ester. It is, however, quite consistent with a mechanism in which the breakage of the O—O bond and the C—R bond in the ester are simultaneous; for if this were the case, factors which stabilize radical R· should also stabilize the transition state leading to it.[111]

Arylation of Aromatic Rings[112]

The decomposition of benzoyl peroxide (and substituted benzoyl peroxides) in aromatic solvents results mainly in *arylation* of the solvent—that is, the formation of substituted biphenyls. In analogy with the free-radical substitution reactions thus far considered, we might anticipate that arylations proceed by a sequence of steps such as

$$Bz_2O_2 \rightarrow BzO· \xrightarrow[\;]{-CO_2} Ph· \xrightarrow{ArH} Ar· \xrightarrow[\text{or Ph·}]{\left(\underset{}{PhC—O—}\right)_2} Ar—Ph$$

---

[111] It is probable that the decompositions of peroxy acids proceed by a different path. Rate data are available at present for the decomposition only of peroxylauric acid, $C_{11}H_{23}$-CO_3H (Parker, Witnauer and Swern, *J. Am. Chem. Soc.*, **80**, 323 (1958)). The decomposition of this acid in benzene, mainly to elemental oxygen and lauric acid, exhibits first-order kinetics; moreover, such solutions are very poor free radical initiators. It is doubtful then that this decomposition is homolytic. A cyclic mechanism, proceeding through transition state LXIV, is likely and is consistent with the greatly negative entropy of activation for this reaction.

$$R-C\overset{\displaystyle O}{\underset{\displaystyle O-O:}{\underset{}{\longrightarrow}}}H \longrightarrow R-C\overset{\displaystyle O-H}{\underset{\displaystyle O}{}} + \ddot{O}:$$

LXIV

The five-membered ring (chelated) monomer is known to be the predominant form of peroxy acids in nonhydroxylic solvents (Rittenhouse, Lobunez, Swern, and Miller, *J. Am. Chem. Soc.*, **80**, 4850 (1958)).

[112] For a review of homolytic aromatic arylation reactions, see Augood and Williams, *Chem. Revs.*, **57**, 123 (1957).

There are two lines of evidence *against* a mechanism of this sort. First, an arylation proceeding through an Ar· radical derived from the solvent ArH should
yield, as one of the by-products, compounds of the type Ar_2, which in fact have
not as yet been isolated. (More specifically, arylations carried out in chlorobenzene give no appreciable amounts of dichlorobiphenyls, and arylations in
nitrobenzene appear to give no dinitrobiphenyl.)

Secondly, it has been found that such arylations are *not* subject to a hydrogen-isotope effect. Thus, when 2,4-dinitrotritiobenzene (LXV) is arylated with
benzoyl peroxide, equal quantities of the labeled and unlabeled 2,4-dinitro-
biphenyl are formed, whereas if attack had begun with the breakage of a C—H
(or C—T) bond, removal of a hydrogen atom should be favored.[113] The absence

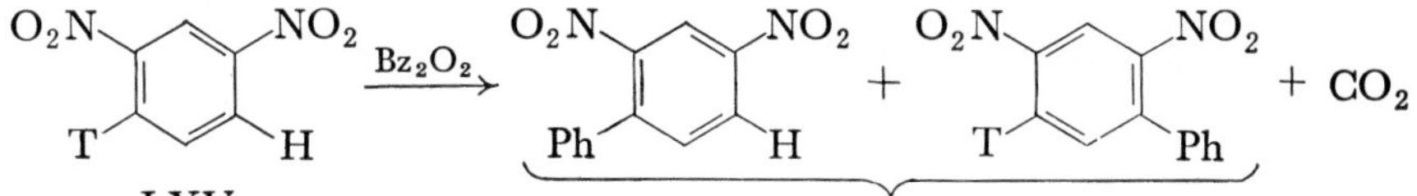

LXV

equal amounts

of a hydrogen-isotope effect also excludes a direct displacement mechanism for
arylation;

$$Ph\cdot + Ar—H \rightarrow Ph—Ar + H\cdot$$

for with this mechanism also, attack on the ring involves breakage of a C—H
bond. Moreover, since such a displacement sacrifices a C—H bond to form a
(somewhat weaker) C—C bond, it is energetically unfavorable.

The most likely mechanism for arylation then appears to involve preliminary addition of a phenyl radical to a solvent molecule, after which a hydrogen
atom is removed from the resulting radical LXVI by another radical or by a
second molecule of peroxide. If this scheme is, in the main, correct, we should

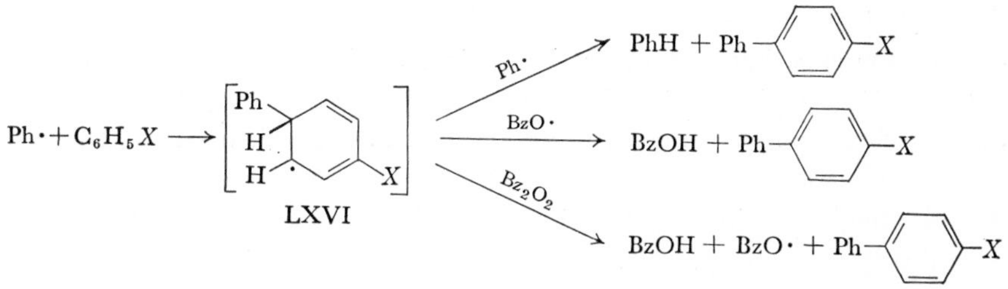

LXVI

expect to find species formed from the dimerization of radical LXVI among the
products. While dimers of this sort have not yet been isolated in large quantity

[113] Price and Convery, *J. Am. Chem. Soc.*, **79**, 2941 (1957); **80**, 4101 (1958). It is probable
(although it has not yet been demonstrated) that other homolytic arylations are likewise not
subject to hydrogen-isotope effects; however, for an example of such an isotope effect in homolytic acylation, see Denney and Klemchuk, *ibid.*, **80**, 3289 (1958).

from such reactions, they may well comprise a portion of the "high molecular weight, tarry material" which is always formed in considerable amount, along with the substituted biphenyls, in such decompositions.[114]

The reader will recognize that although the incoming phenyl group is shown entering the position *para* to substituent —*X* in the sequence above, *ortho* and *meta* arylation is also possible. Indeed, it is now recognized that the arylation of almost every monosubstituted benzene gives sizable amounts of all three isomeric products. Typical isomer distributions resulting from a number of phenylations with benzoyl peroxide are listed in Table 16-3. Quite obviously,

Table 16-3. Isomer Distributions Resulting from Phenylations with Benzoyl Peroxide[115]

Substrate	Percent *ortho*	Percent *meta*	Percent *para*
Toluene	71	17	12
t-Butylbenzene	24	50	27
Anisole	67	18	15
Chlorobenzene	62	24	14
Biphenyl	49	23	29
Nitrobenzene	60	9	32

the effects governing orientation in these arylations are very different from those governing orientation in aromatic nitration, halogenation, and other electrophilic substitutions. All substituents, regardless of their electronic character, appear to direct the incoming phenyl group preferably to the *ortho* and *para* positions. (In many cases, the yield of *meta* compound is somewhat greater than that of *para* compound, but the *meta* to *para* ratio never is as great as 2, the value that would result from random substitution.) Moreover, it may be shown by competition experiments that nearly all ring substituents, irrespective of their nature, facilitate phenylation.[115,116] Such rate increases are small, however, the largest being the fourfold acceleration produced by the nitro group. This is in marked contrast to electrophilic nitration and halogenation, where incorporation of a single substituent may raise or lower the rate of attack on the ring by several powers of ten (p. 428). In the same way, the orienting effects of substituents in phenylations are seen to be much less pronounced than in electrophilic

---

[114] See, however, DeTar and Long, *J. Am. Chem. Soc.*, **80**, 2742 (1958).

[115] These values were determined mainly by Hey and co-workers, *J. Chem. Soc.*, **1953**, 3412; **1954**, 3352; *Disc. Faraday Soc.*, **14**, 216 (1953); *J. Chem. Phys.*, **23**, 757 (1955). For a more extensive compilation, see Walling, Ref. 1(b), p. 484.

[116] (a) Hey, *et al.*, *J. Chem. Soc.*, **1952**, 2095; **1953**, 44; **1954**, 794; **1955**, 6. Possible exceptions are the *t*-butyl and trifluoromethyl groups. (b) It has recently been found that nitrobenzene is much less readily attacked by the triphenylmethyl radical than is benzene itself (see

substitutions where, in many cases, only a few percent of the "less favored" product is formed.

From the small increases in phenylation rates brought about by ring substituents, and from the relatively slight orienting effects of such substituents, we may infer that differences in activation energy due to the incorporation of substituents into the substrate are small, considerably less than 1 kcal per mole. It would therefore seem that any proposed correlation between structure and reactivity in this series should be taken with reserve. Nevertheless, it is often suggested that substituents lying *ortho* or *para* to the incoming phenyl group in the radical intermediate stabilize this intermediate (and the activated complex leading to it), whereas no such stabilization is possible for *meta* substitution.[117] (The

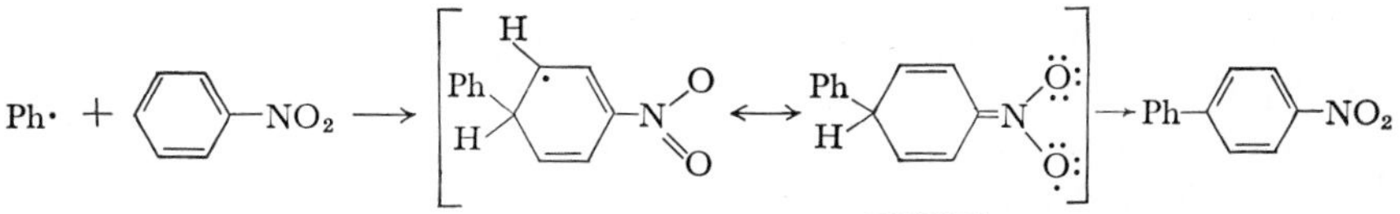

LXVII   LXVII'

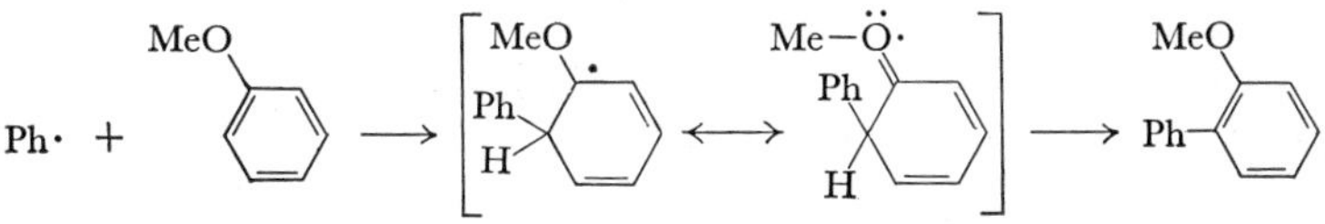

LXVIII   LXVIII'

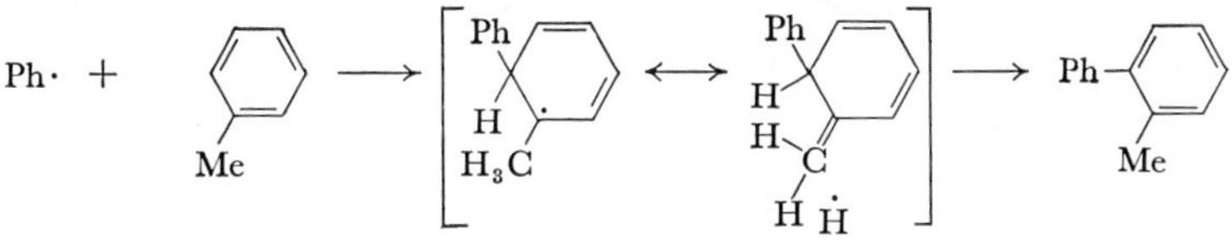

LXIX   LXIX'

reader will note the similarity between structures LXVII', LXVIII', and LXIX'

Benkeser and Schroeder, *J. Am. Chem. Soc.*, **80**, 3314 (1958)). It is suggested that there is electron withdrawal from the "trivalent carbon" by the benzene rings (p. 206) in the radical, and that this carbon, which is thus electron deficient, tends to coordinate with the electron-rich oxygen atoms in the nitro group rather than attacking the benzene ring

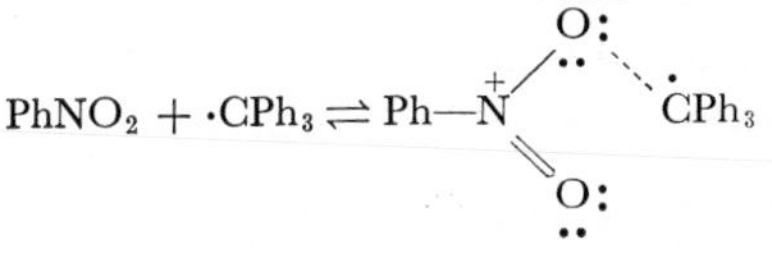

[117] A number of attempts to treat this problem theoretically have been carried out. See, for example, Brown, *Quart. Revs.*, **6**, 63 (1952).

on one hand, and the structures II′, III′, and IV′ on page 675 on the other. The latter three were employed in discussing the influence of substituents on the dissociation constants of hexaarylethanes, a situation in which the effect of the various substituents likewise did not depend directly upon their electron-attracting or electron-donating properties.) The relatively high yield in many cases of *meta*-substituted products seems a little puzzling. However, it should be remembered that the observed isomer distributions among the substituted biphenyls need not reflect accurately the relative rates of attack at the various positions, for the intermediate radical, formed by addition of Ph· to the substrate, need not be converted to a biphenyl. It may dimerize, may disproportionate, or otherwise be led astray; and the radical intermediate in *ortho* or *para* substitution may (for a reason which is not yet clear) be somewhat more likely to become involved in side reactions than the intermediate in *meta* substitution. Further investigation of this problem is obviously desirable.

Naphthalene is much more readily attacked by radicals than is benzene, and substituted naphthalenes are more active still.[118(a)] In fact, when benzoyl peroxide is decomposed in the presence of naphthalene or substituted naphthalenes, the benzoyloxy radicals attack before significant decarboxylation can occur, and benzoyloxynaphthalenes, rather than phenylnaphthalenes, are the major products. Benzoxylation, rather than phenylation, occurs also with a number of polynuclear aromatics (for example, anthracene and 1:2-benzanthracene).[118(b)]

Decomposition of Azo and Diazo Compounds

Aliphatic azo compounds, R—N=N—R′, may be prepared by oxidation of dialkylated hydrazines. The simplest azo compound, azomethane, decomposes unimolecularly in the vapor phase at temperatures above 300°, yielding methyl radicals and molecular nitrogen[119(a)]

$$H_3C:N=N:CH_3 \rightarrow H_3C· + N\equiv N + ·CH_3; \quad \text{rate} = k_1(\text{MeN}=\text{NMe})$$

In the absence of other substances, the methyl radicals dimerize, yielding ethane. As expected, the substitution of alkyl groups for methyl hydrogens in azomethane stabilizes the resulting alkyl radicals, hence facilitates the decomposition. The same effect is even more pronounced when aryl groups are so substituted. Typically, then, the energy of activation for the decomposition of azomethane is found to be 50 kcal per mole,[119(a)] that for the decomposition of $Me_2CH—N=N—CHMe_2$ is 41 kcal per mole,[119(b)] whereas that for the decom-

[118] (a) Dannley and Gippin, *J. Am. Chem. Soc.*, **74**, 332 (1952). (b) Roitt and Waters, *J. Chem. Soc.*, **1952**, 2695.

[119] (a) Rice and Sickman, *J. Chem. Phys.*, **4**, 608 (1936). (b) Ramsperger, *J. Am. Chem. Soc.*, **50**, 714 (1928). (c) Cohen and Wang, *ibid.*, **77**, 2475 (1955).

position of $Ph_2CH—N=N—CHPh_2$ (which decomposes readily in inert solvents at 65°) is only 27 kcal per mole.[119(c),120]

In the same way, α-cyano groups may act as radical stabilizers, thus greatly easing the decomposition of aliphatic azo compounds. Indeed, substituted *azoacetonitriles* (for example, LXX), which, in many cases, may be readily prepared from ketones, HCN, and hydrazine, have become very important as radical sources.

$$R_2C—N=N—CR_2 \rightarrow 2[R_2\overset{\cdot}{C}—C\equiv N: \leftrightarrow R_2C=C=N\cdot] + N_2$$
$$\underset{N\equiv C}{|} \qquad \underset{C\equiv N}{|}$$

LXX

The decompositions in solution of over thirty of such azonitriles have been studied kinetically;[121] almost all exhibit clean first-order kinetics with no significant induced decomposition. As may be expected, the specific rate for the decomposition of a given azonitrile is quite insensitive to solvent. A number of decomposition rates (in toluene at 80°) are compared below:

$$Me_2C—N=N—CMe_2 \qquad Et_2C—N=N—CEt_2 \qquad (n\text{-}Pr)_2C—N=N—C(n\text{-}Pr)_2$$
$$\underset{N\equiv C}{|} \qquad \underset{C\equiv N}{|} \qquad \underset{N\equiv C}{|} \qquad \underset{C\equiv N}{|} \qquad \underset{N\equiv C}{|} \qquad \underset{C\equiv N}{|}$$

$k\times10^4$ 1.53   0.84   1.15
sec^{-1}

$$PhCMe—N=N—CMePh$$
$$\underset{N\equiv C}{|} \qquad \underset{C\equiv N}{|}$$

$k \times 10^4$ "very fast"   0.002   0.73

Note that the nature of the alkyl groups bound to the α-carbon has little effect on the rate of decomposition, but that incorporation of α-phenyl groups, which

---

[120] The observation that the diisopropyl compound, $Me_2CH—N=N—CHMe_2$, decomposes much more rapidly than the monoisopropyl compound, $Me_2CH—N=N—Me$ (Ramsperger, *J. Am. Chem. Soc.*, **51**, 2134 (1929)), tends to rule out the stepwise mechanism:

$$R—N=N—R \xrightarrow{slow} R\cdot + \cdot N=N—R \xrightarrow{fast} 2R\cdot + N_2$$

for the decompositions of aliphatic azo compounds. For it may be argued that if the initial rate-determining step involved breakage of only *one* C—N bond, the overall rate should be determined chiefly by the identity of the more stable of the two alkyl radicals (that is, the alkyl radical lost first). Since, on the contrary, the reaction rate is strongly influenced by both alkyl radicals, it may be supposed that the rate-determining step involves breakage of *two* C—N bonds, resulting in the concerted formation of two alkyl radicals. However, the stepwise mechanism cannot be ruled out for the decompositions of such azo compounds as $PhCO—N=N—CPh_3$ (see Davies, Hey, and Williams, *J. Chem. Soc.*, **1956**, 4397).

[121] See, for example, (a) Overberger, *et al.*, *J. Am. Chem. Soc.*, **71**, 2661 (1949); **73**, 4880 (1951); **75**, 2078 (1953); **76**, 2722, 6186 (1954); (b) Lewis and Matheson, *ibid.*, **71**, 747 (1949).

further stabilize the cyanoalkyl radical, greatly facilitates homolysis. The decomposition of the cyclobutyl compound is unusually slow, presumably because angular strain in the four-membered ring of the α-cyanocyclobutyl radical pushes the bond angles about the trivalent carbon far from the preferred value of 120°.

The alkyl radicals formed in the decomposition of aliphatic azo compounds and the α-cyanoalkyl radicals formed in the decomposition of azonitriles will, in an inactive solvent, react further by a combination of dimerization and disproportionation, with disproportionation appearing to increase in importance as the substrate becomes more complex.[122] Once again, it may be asked whether the two alkyl radicals that couple or enter into a disproportionation reaction are necessarily derived from the same molecule of azo compound—that is, whether or not the entire reaction occurs within a single solvent cage. For azonitriles, the answer appears to be "no"; for if two azonitriles, LXXI and LXXIV, are decomposed in the same reaction mixture, the "crossover product," LXXV, is

formed, in addition to symmetric products.[123] However, when an azo compound in which the N=N linkage is incorporated into a cyclic system (for example, LXXVI[122(b)] and LXXVII[124]) is decomposed, the recombination step appears to involve two trivalent carbons from the same molecule; for the predominant products are cyclic hydrocarbons.

[122] See, for example: (a) Overberger and Berenbaum, *J. Am. Chem. Soc.*, **74**, 3293 (1952); (b) Overberger and Lombardino, *ibid.*, **80**, 2317 (1958). (c) There is evidence that a portion of the coupling product, LXXIII, isolated from the decomposition of azonitrile LXXI in toluene is formed in part through rearrangement of intermediate LXXII (see Talat-Erben and Bywater, *ibid.*, **77**, 3710 (1955))

The decompositions of other azonitriles in inactive solvents may well proceed, in part, through similar intermediates.

[123] Overberger and Berenbaum, *J. Am. Chem. Soc.*, **73**, 4883 (1951).

[124] Overberger and Lapkin, *J. Am. Chem. Soc.*, **77**, 4651 (1955).

LXXVI

LXXVII

The decomposition of unsymmetric phenylazo compounds such as Ph—N=N—CPh$_3$ yields phenyl radicals,[125] and if such decompositions are carried out in aromatic solvents, the phenyl radicals may attack the solvent in the same manner as do phenyl radicals derived from benzoyl peroxide (p. 720). *Aryldiazonium hydroxides*, Ar—N=N—OH, decompose into aryl radicals, and probably to OH· radicals as well.

$$Ar—N=N—OH \rightarrow Ar· + N_2 + OH·$$

Since these diazonium hydroxides are prepared with great ease merely by treating solutions of aryldiazonium salts with base, they are extremely useful sources of aryl radicals and are often used to convert benzene derivatives to substituted biphenyls (the Gomberg-Bachmann reaction).[126] Quantitative study of this reaction is difficult, for it is generally carried out in a two-phase system. Moreover, it is not a clean reaction; yields of the substituted biphenyls often drop below 30 percent and large amounts of tars are produced. The fate of the OH· radical (if indeed it is formed) has not yet been determined.

Arylations may be carried out much more cleanly using substituted *N-nitrosoacetanilides* $\left(\text{Ar—N—Ac} \atop \text{N=O} \right)$, which generally yield nitrogen quantitatively when allowed to decompose in aromatic solvents. Phenylations of toluene, nitrobenzene, cumene, pyridine, and *t*-butylbenzene using this reaction give, to within experimental error, the same ratios of isomeric biphenyls as are obtained in the corresponding phenylations using benzoyl peroxide.[127] Here again, then, aryl radicals are intervening. The rates of decomposition of substituted N-nitrosoacetanilides have been found to be very nearly independent of the solvent undergoing arylation, indicating that the latter does not participate directly in the

[125] See, for example, Cohen and Wang, *J. Am. Chem. Soc.*, **75**, 5504 (1953); **77**, 3628 (1955).

[126] For a review of this reaction, see Bachmann and Hoffmann in *Organic Reactions*, Vol. 2, John Wiley and Sons, Inc., New York, 1944, p. 224.

[127] See Dermer and Edmison, *Chem. Revs.*, **57**, 92 (1957), for a summary of isomer ratios resulting from various types of free-radical arylations.

rate-determining step.[128] Moreover if β-naphthol is added to a solution in which the N-nitrosoanilide is decomposing, a portion of the latter reagent is converted to dye LXXIX (almost surely a heterolytic reaction), but the rate of disappearance of the nitroso compound is virtually unchanged. It is thus extremely likely that the nitroso compound is, in the rate-determining step, being converted to a diazo acetate, LXXVIII, which may react rapidly, either homolytically or (under appropriate circumstances) heterolytically. The exact manner in which

(rate determining)   (product determining)

homolytic arylations occur in such cases is not yet clear. The first path that comes to mind involves the decomposition of diazo acetate LXXVIII to molecular nitrogen and to acetoxy and aryl radicals,

$$Ar-N{=}N-OAc \rightarrow N_2 + OAc\cdot + Ar\cdot$$
LXXVIII

followed by the attack by Ar· on the substrate. However, very little CO_2 is evolved in such arylations, whereas, as we have pointed out (p. 717), acetoxy radicals are thought to undergo decarboxylation readily. To account for this apparent inconsistency, it may be supposed that for a significant time interval after the above homolysis has occurred, the resulting radicals occupy a single "cage" of solvent molecules. One of these molecules is presumably attacked by the aryl radical, whereupon the acetoxy radical, before breaking out of its "solvent cage," attacks the composite radical, forming acetic acid (which is found to be a major product).

[128] Huisgen, Horeld, and Nakaten, Ann., **562**, 137 (1949); **573**, 163 (1951).

The Sandmeyer Reaction

The conversion of aromatic diazo compounds to aryl halides by use of cuprous halides (the *Sandmeyer reaction*) also appears to proceed through aryl radicals. Such radicals may be diverted from solutions in which this reaction is occurring by use of nitrobenzene[129(a)] or iodine.[129(b)] Moreover, with care, such solutions may be used to initiate the polymerization of acrylonitrile.[129(c)] The reaction is first order both in diazonium ion and in "cuprous chloride" (actually $CuCl_2^-$),[130] indicating a rate-determining reduction of the aryldiazonium ion with unipositive copper.

$$ArN_2^+ + CuCl_2^- \rightarrow Ar\cdot + N_2 + CuCl_2$$

However, the reaction is retarded by a large excess of added HCl, suggesting that the "higher" complex, $CuCl_4^{-3}$ is less effective (or ineffective) in converting the diazonium ion to an aryl radical. Essentially no univalent copper is consumed in the overall reaction;[130(b)] thus, the copper oxidized in the proposed rate-determining step must be reduced in a subsequent step. The following sequence then is consistent with what is known about the Sandmeyer reaction (involving chloride):

$$\text{Ar}\text{---}\text{N}\equiv\text{N}^+ + \text{Cl}\text{---}\text{Cu}\text{---}\text{Cl}^- \xrightarrow{\text{slow}} \text{Ar}\cdot + \text{Cl}\text{---}\text{Cu}\text{---}\text{Cl} \xrightarrow{\text{fast}} \text{Ar}\text{---}\text{Cl} + \text{CuCl}$$
$$+N_2 \qquad\qquad +N_2$$

The transfer of an electron from the $CuCl_2^-$ ion to the ArN_2^+ ion in the initial step probably occurs through a "chloride bridge" in an activated complex of the type Ar—N≡N · · Cl—Cu—Cl. Electron transfers of this sort are well recognized in inorganic chemistry.[131] The second step in the indicated sequence is merely a radical displacement by Ar· on the chlorine.

If an attempt is made to carry out the Sandmeyer reaction in a solution containing styrene, acrylonitrile, or a similar unsaturated compound, attack by the aryl-radical intermediate on the double bond may occur, with the more stable of the two possible radical adducts (for example, radical LXXX) being formed. This aralkyl radical then reacts with cupric chloride (or a chloro complex thereof), resulting in the formation of a "chloroarylation" product (for example, LXXXI).

$$CH_2\!\!=\!\!CH\text{---}CN \xrightarrow{Ar\cdot} ArCH_2\text{---}\overset{\displaystyle\cdot}{C}H\text{---}CN \xrightarrow{CuCl_2} ArCH_2\text{---}CHCl\text{---}CN + CuCl.^{132}$$
$$\qquad\qquad\qquad\quad \text{LXXX} \qquad\qquad\qquad \text{LXXXI}$$

[129] (a) Dickerman, Weiss, and Ingberman, *J. Org. Chem.*, **21**, 3801 (1956); **22**, 1070 (1957). (b) Kochi, *J. Am. Soc.*, **79**, 2942 (1957). (c) Cooper, *Chemistry and Industry*, **1953**, 407.

[130] (a) Cowdrey and Davis, *J. Chem. Soc.*, **1949**, S48; *Quart. Revs.*, **6**, 358 (1952). (b) Kochi, *J. Am. Chem. Soc.*, **78**, 1228 (1956). (c) Dickerman, Weiss, and Ingberman, *ibid.*, **80**, 1904 (1958).

[131] See, for example, Taube, *J. Am. Chem. Soc.*, **77**, 4481 (1955).

[132] This is often called the Meerwein reaction (see, for example; Meerwein, Buchner, and

PART III—Additions and Rearrangements
of Free Radicals

Homolytic Additions, Energetic Requirements

The type of free-radical addition reaction that has been most intensively studied is *addition polymerization*—that is, the build-up of long molecular chains from small unsaturated molecules, often with the aid of a radical initiator. In addition to the tremendous industrial importance of such polymerizations, much of our present knowledge concerning the nature of chain reactions in the liquid state is derived from investigation of such processes.[133(a)] Related to such reactions are the additions of elementary oxygen to olefins, forming polymeric peroxides.[133(b)]

$$R_2C{=}CH_2 + O_2 \rightarrow [{-}CH_2{-}CR_2{-}O{-}O{-}CH_2{-}CR_2{-}O{-}O{-}]_x$$

We shall make no attempt to consider either of these important topics, even briefly, but shall instead confine our attention here to addition reactions that yield relatively small molecules.

Suppose we are dealing with a chain process, initiated by species $In\cdot$, in which groups X and Y (derived from molecule $X{-}Y$) are adding to a $C{=}C$ double bond.

$$X{-}Y \xrightarrow{In\cdot} Y\cdot \xrightarrow{\overset{\diagdown}{\diagup}C{=}C\overset{\diagup}{\diagdown}} Y{-}\overset{|}{\underset{|}{C}}{-}\overset{|}{\underset{|}{C}}\cdot \xrightarrow{XY} Y{-}\overset{|}{\underset{|}{C}}{-}\overset{|}{\underset{|}{C}}{-}X + Y\cdot \xrightarrow{\overset{\diagdown}{\diagup}C{=}C\overset{\diagup}{\diagdown}}$$

$$Y{-}\overset{|}{\underset{|}{C}}{-}\overset{|}{\underset{|}{C}}\cdot \rightarrow \text{etc.}$$

In order that a significant kinetic chain length be maintained, it is necessary that both the attack by $Y\cdot$ on the double bond (the addition step) and the attack by

---

Van Emster, *J. prakt. Chem.*, **152**, 237 (1939); and Rondesvedt and Vogl, *J. Am. Chem. Soc.*, **77**, 3067 (1955)). A side reaction sometimes observed is the removal of a hydrogen atom from the radical intermediate resulting in the formation of an arylated olefin (for example, olefin ArCH=CH—CN from radical LXXX). For a suggestion as to how this occurs, see Dickerman, *et al.*, Ref. 130(c).

[133] (a) A number of works devoted nearly exclusively to consideration of polymerization and polymers are available. Among these are: Flory, *Principles of Polymer Chemistry*, Cornell University Press, Ithaca, 1953; Alfrey, Bohrer, and Mark, *Copolymerization*, Interscience Publishers, Inc., New York, 1952; D'Aleio, *Fundamental Principles of Polymerization*, John Wiley and Sons, Inc., New York, 1952; Schildknecht, *Vinyl and Related Polymers*, John Wiley and Sons, Inc., 1952. See also: Mayo and Walling, *Chem. Revs.*, **46**, 191 (1950); Bacon, *Quart. Revs.*, **IX**, 287 (1955); Dainton and Ivin, *ibid.*, **XII**, 61 (1958); and Walling (Ref. 1b), pp. 55–238. (b) The conversions of olefins to polymeric peroxides are discussed in some detail by Mayo, Miller, and Russell, *J. Am. Chem. Soc.*, **80**, 2465–2507 (1958).

radical Y—$\overset{|}{\underset{|}{C}}$—$\overset{|}{\underset{|}{C}}$• on molecule XY (the displacement step) be rapid in compari-

son to all chain-termination steps. Indeed, it may be assumed that if either of these two propagation steps is significantly endothermic, addition via a chain mechanism is difficult or impossible, no matter how effective an initiator is used. If both propagation steps are exothermic, addition via a chain process is possible; but it is not guaranteed, for even strongly exothermic reactions may have high energies of activation or highly negative entropies of activation. With this in mind, let us compare the energies of the propagation steps for some conceivable homolytic additions. In Table 16-4, for which propylene is chosen as a common substrate, the usual thermodynamic convention (negative ΔH values for exothermic reactions) is observed. These values tend to rule out long-chain

Table 16-4. Approximate Energies of Propagation Steps in Radical Additions to Propylene[134]

X—Y	Y• + MeCH=CH$_2$ → MeĊH—CH$_2$Y ΔH	MeĊH—CH$_2$Y + XY → MeCHX—CH$_2$Y + X• ΔH
H—OH	−36 kcal	26 kcal
H—Cl	−30	9
H—Br	−9	−7
H—I	3	−23
Cl—Cl	−30	−15
Br—Br	−9	−13
I—I	3	−10
H—CMe ‖ O	−20	−7
Cl—CCl$_3$	−18	−4

processes in which water or hydrogen chloride adds homolytically to propylene, for these are reactions in which the displacement step is endothermic, due largely to the difficulty in breaking the H—OH bond or the H—Cl bond. Similarly excluded are additions of iodine or hydrogen iodide to propylene, for here the addition step is endothermic, due largely to the weakness of the C—I bond.

[134] These values were estimated from the bond-dissociation energies tabulated by Walling (Ref. 1b, pp. 49, 50), assuming that the resonance energy of the isopropyl radical is not appreciably affected by a β substituent. Very nearly the same conclusions may be drawn if these ΔH values are estimated from Pauling's bond energies (p. 37), although this appears to be largely fortuitous.

However, the additions, via chain mechanisms, of hydrogen bromide, chlorine, bromine, acetaldehyde $\left(\text{as } H\!\!-\!\!\underset{\underset{O}{\|}}{C}Me\right)$, and carbon tetrachloride, are seen to be energetically feasible, since in these five cases, both the addition and the displacement step are exothermic. Each of these five additions has, in fact, been observed.

For the homolytic additions of these same reagents to styrene, $PhCH\!=\!CH_2$, the ΔH values for the various *addition steps are lower* (that is, the additions are more exothermic) than those for propylene, probably by about 20 kcal each. This difference reflects the added stability of radicals of the type $Ph\!-\!\overset{\cdot}{C}H\!-\!CH_2Y$, due to conjugation with the benzene ring. On the other hand, the ΔH values for the various *displacement steps* are undoubtedly *higher*, probably by about 20 kcal, than those for the propylene series, since the resonance-stabilized $Ph\!-\!\overset{\cdot}{C}H\!-\!CH_2Y$ radical necessarily attacks with less vigor than a radical of the type $Me\overset{\cdot}{C}H\!-\!CH_2Y$. With styrene, each of the addition steps, including those involving I·, becomes highly exothermic, but the displacement steps (except those involving Cl_2 and HI) *have become endothermic.* We thus see why a number of homolytic additions that occur readily by chain processes with ethylene and propylene must proceed by nonchain processes (if they proceed at all) with styrene. A radical such as $Ar\overset{\cdot}{C}H\!-\!CH_2Y$, although it may be formed with great ease, is a relatively ineffective displacing agent.

Addition of Hydrogen Halides

In the previous discussion of the addition of hydrogen halides to olefins (p. 519), the reader was reminded that the structure of the product resulting from the addition of HBr often depended upon the reaction conditions employed. More specifically, in polar solvents or in the presence of such inhibitors as thiophenol and hydroquinone, HBr adds to olefins in the same way as do HCl and HI, obviously by a heterolytic process. In nonpolar solvents in the presence of oxygen or peroxides, or with the aid of illumination, the direction of addition is frequently reversed, and the addition becomes just as obviously homolytic.

$$CH_2\!=\!CHR \begin{cases} \xrightarrow{H^+} CH_3\!-\!\overset{+}{C}HR \xrightarrow[\text{(heterolytic addition)}]{Br^-} CH_3\!-\!\overset{\overset{\displaystyle Br}{|}}{C}H\!-\!R \\ \\ \xrightarrow{Br\cdot} CH_2Br\!-\!\overset{\cdot}{C}HR \xrightarrow[\text{(homolytic addition)}]{HBr} BrCH_2\!-\!CH_2R + Br\cdot \xrightarrow{\text{etc.}} \end{cases}$$

The homolytic addition is the basis of the familiar *peroxide effect*, which, at a relatively early date, strikingly pointed out the necessity for distinguishing ionic from free-radical mechanisms.[135] The attacking bromine atom is probably generated from peroxides present by a sequence such as

$$RO—OR \rightarrow 2RO\cdot \xrightarrow{2HBr} 2ROH + 2Br\cdot$$

To account for orientation observed in the radical additions of HBr, we may invoke reasoning similar to that used in explaining orientation in heterolytic additions. Just as the secondary carbonium ion, CH_3—$\overset{+}{C}HR$, is more stable than the primary carbonium ion, $\overset{+}{C}H_2$—CH_2R, so also is the "secondary radical," CH_2Br—$\overset{\cdot}{C}HR$, assumed to be more stable than the "primary radical," $\overset{\cdot}{C}H_2$—CHR—Br; for, as we have seen, hyperconjugation appears to stabilize radicals in much the same way as it stabilizes carbonium ions (p. 696). Thus, the difference in orientations is not due basically to the fact that one process is heterolytic and the other homolytic, but rather to the circumstance that in one case addition begins with the formation of a new C—H bond, whereas in the other, it is the C—Br bond that is formed first. Markownikoff-type addition would presumably be observed for free-radical additions also if the reaction conditions could somehow be altered so that the initial attack on the double bond were carried out by a H· radical.

A glance at Table 16-4 indicates why the peroxide effect is observed for the addition of HBr but not, generally speaking, for additions of HCl or HI. By the argument already presented, the addition of HBr (in which *both* propagation steps are exothermic) may proceed readily by a chain mechanism, whereas the additions of HCl or HI (in which only *one* propagation step is exothermic) may not. At ordinary temperatures, even in the presence of radical initiators, additions of HCl and HI, if occurring at all, will tend to proceed preferentially by a heterolytic path.[136(a)] In rare instances, radical additions of HCl to olefins have been observed, but, except at high temperatures, kinetic chains are short.[136(b)]

It is interesting that the homolytic additions of HBr to substituted cyclohexenes are stereospecific *trans* additions. Addition to 1-methylcyclohexene gives *cis*-1-bromo-2-methylcyclohexane (LXXXII, R=Me)[137(a)] in which the incoming hydrogen and bromine atoms lie *trans* to each other, and similar *trans* additions have been observed with 1-bromo- and 1-chlorocyclohexene.[137(b)] Stereochemically these additions seem similar to the heterolytic additions of halogens

[135] For a summary of work leading to the elucidation of the peroxide effect, see Mayo and Walling, *Chem. Revs.*, **27**, 351 (1940).

[136] (a) See, for example, Kharasch and Hannum, *J. Am. Chem. Soc.*, **56**, 1782 (1954). (b) Raley, Rust and Vaughan, *ibid.*, **70**, 2767 (1948); Ecke, Cook, and Whitmore, *ibid.*, **72**, 1511 (1950); Mayo, *ibid.*, **76**, 5392 (1954).

[137] (a) Goering, Abell, and Aycock, *J. Am. Chem. Soc.*, **74**, 3588 (1952). (b) Goering and Sims, *ibid.*, **77**, 3465 (1955).

(R = Me, Cl, Br)

LXXXII **LXXXIII**

to double bonds (Chap. 13), and one is perhaps tempted to suppose that a bridged intermediate (in this case radical LXXXIII) intervenes here also. However, the bromine atom in this radical has nine valence electrons, a feature which makes this intermediate unlikely.[138] An alternative explanation of the stereospecificity[137(b),139(a)] is that the Br· radical attacks the double bond via the least hindered route. From LXXXIV, we see that this approach, somewhat paradoxically, corresponds quite closely to an *axial* direction in the cyclohexyl radical that results[139(b)] and we may suppose that the incoming bromine initially occupies an axial position in this radical. If it is assumed that the bonds about the trivalent

LXXXIV   **LXXXV**   **LXXXVI**   *trans* adduct
              (preferred)

carbon in the cyclohexyl radical are pyramidal rather than planar (as may often be the case in strained systems), then substituent R may occupy either an equatorial position (LXXXV) or an axial position (LXXXVI). Sterically, conformation LXXXV is preferred, leaving an axial position open to attack by HBr. Thus, the *trans* adduct should be formed preferentially. One proviso must be made however; the stereochemical argument implies that the attack by HBr on the cyclohexyl radical intermediate must occur *before* the ring has a chance to "turn itself inside out" (p. 241), for such a ring inversion would throw the bromine into the (thermodynamically preferred) equatorial position.

The homolytic addition of HBr to noncyclic olefins at room temperature and above is nonstereospecific, for attack by Br· converts a C=C double bond to a single bond, about which rotation may occur. Moreover, addition of Br· to

---

[138] Species in which bromine has an "expanded valence shell" (for example, BrF_3 and Br_3^-) are known, but in these, the bromine is bound only to halogen atoms not to carbons.

[139] (a) Brand and Stevens, *J. Chem. Soc.*, **1958**, 629. (b) Agreement that the attacking radical approaches in the direction perpendicular to the axis of the double bond is not unanimous. For an opposing view, see Bader, Buckley, Leavitt, and Szwarc, *J. Am. Chem. Soc.*, **79**, 5621 (1957).

simple olefins is often reversible and has been found, in a number of cases, to promote olefin isomerization.[140]

At very low temperatures, however, rotation about the C=C bond in the radical intermediate becomes much less free, and if a large excess of HBr is taken, stereospecificity may be restored. Thus, the homolytic addition of HBr to the stereoisomeric 2-bromo-2-butenes at $-80°$, using liquid HBr as a solvent, has been found to be very nearly completely stereospecific.[141] As indicated, the *cis* olefin

gives the *meso*-dibromide, LXXXVIII, in over 90 percent yield, whereas the *trans* olefin (not shown) gives the corresponding *d,l*-dibromide. We suspect then that the attacking HBr molecule approaches the intermediate radical, LXXXVII (or its counterpart in the *trans-d,l* series), keeping as far removed as is possible from the newly acquired bromine atom, this path presumably being the least hindered. This is, however, not the only possible explanation; it may be that the bromine radical, instead of attacking an olefin molecule, attacks a π complex

derived from the olefin and HBr, a path likewise resulting in stereospecific addition.

[140] (a) Derbyshire and Waters, *Trans. Faraday Soc.*, **45**, 749 (1949). (b) Steinmetz and Noyes, *J. Am. Chem. Soc.*, **74**, 4141 (1952).

[141] Goering and Larsen, *J. Am. Chem. Soc.*, **79**, 2653 (1957).

Homolytic Halogen Additions

There are several difficulties associated with the study of homolytic halogen additions. We have already noted (p. 521) that such additions in polar solvents tend to be overshadowed by *heterolytic* additions, and this may be the case also in nonpolar solvents if pains are not taken to exclude traces of water or hydrogen halides. Even if the reactants are mixed in the vapor phase, the addition may still proceed heterolytically on the glass walls of the container unless they are coated with a nonpolar and (presumably) inert material such as paraffin. Some judgment must be exercised in the choice of a reaction temperature, for at high temperatures homolytic *substitution* may compete effectively with addition. A final complication is the possibility that the addition of a halogen atom to the double bond may be significantly reversible.

The energy values in Table 16-4 suggest that the additions of chlorine and bromine, via a radical chain mechanism, to ordinary olefins should proceed with ease, whereas additions of iodine should not. Successful kinetic studies of additions of fluorine are exceedingly difficult, for such additions are generally violent, often resulting in the formation of a number of products.[56]

The usual chain mechanism for halogen addition

$$\frac{1}{2}X_2 \xrightarrow{h\nu} X\cdot \xrightleftharpoons{\overset{\diagup C=C\diagdown}{}} -\overset{\displaystyle|}{\underset{\displaystyle|}{C}}-\overset{\displaystyle\cdot}{C}- \xrightleftharpoons{X_2} -\overset{\displaystyle\overset{X}{|}}{\underset{\displaystyle|}{C}}-\overset{\displaystyle\overset{X}{|}}{\underset{\displaystyle|}{C}}- + X\cdot \xrightarrow{\text{etc.}} \quad 18$$

may lead to one of several rate laws, depending upon whether the addition or the displacement step (or both) are reversible, and depending also upon the nature of the termination step. For example, it may be shown (Ex. 6a) that a termination step involving the reaction between two $-\overset{\displaystyle\cdot}{C}-\overset{}{C}X-$ radicals results in a rate

proportional to $(X_2)^{3/2}$ (whether or not the addition step is reversible); the rate laws for the chlorination of $CH_2{=}CHCl$, $CHCl{=}CHCl$, $CHCl{=}CCl_2$, and $CCl_2{=}CCl_2$ in the vapor phase have been found to be of this type. On the other hand, a termination step involving the reaction between two unlike radicals leads to a rate law of the type

$$\text{rate} = kI^{1/2}\left(\overset{\diagup}{\diagdown}C{=}C\overset{\diagdown}{\diagup}\right)^{1/2}(X_2) \tag{19}$$

where I is the intensity of the radiation bringing about the dissociation of X_2. The rate law for the chlorination of ethylene itself is of this type.[143] Each of these re-

[148] Schumacher, *et al.*, *Z. physik. Chem.*, **B35**, 285, 455 (1937); **B49**, 107 (1941); **B52**, 72 (1942).

[143] Schmitz, Schumacher, and Jager, *Z. Physik. Chem.*, **B51281** (1942).

actions is inhibited by oxygen, as are the halogenations of aliphatic hydrocarbons (p. 695), and for the same reason, that is, the diversion of the chloroalkyl radical to the very much less reactive peroxy radical, XC,

$$-\overset{\displaystyle |}{\underset{\displaystyle |}{\overset{\displaystyle \cdot}{C}}}-\overset{\displaystyle |}{\underset{\displaystyle Cl}{C}}- + O_2 \rightarrow \quad -\overset{\displaystyle |}{\underset{\displaystyle \cdot O-O}{C}}-\overset{\displaystyle |}{\underset{\displaystyle |}{C}}-Cl$$

$$XC$$

Addition of Cl· to ordinary C=C double bonds appears substantially irreversible at temperatures below 200°, but reversibility becomes increasingly important as the temperature is raised. The rate of hydrogen abstraction likewise increases, and at temperatures above about 450° we may expect substitution at the allylic position to overshadow halogen addition. Typically, isobutylene is converted to methallyl chloride, CH_2=CHMe—CH_2Cl, in good yield by treatment with chlorine at 600°.[144]

In contrast to addition of Cl·, addition of Br· is often reversible at room temperature. This reversibility is most strikingly demonstrated by the ability of sources of bromine radicals to bring about *cis-trans* isomerization of olefins, a transformation that we have discussed in reference to homolytic additions of HBr. This process is of considerable interest since it is related to the rotation of a group about a single bond within the bromoalkyl radical. By using radioactive bromine it is possible to compare the rate of such a rotation to the rates of gain and loss of Br· by an olefin.[140(b)] Such comparisons have been carried out, using as a substrate *cis*-1,2-dibromoethylene, and it has been found that the proverbially "free" rotation in radical LXXXIX is not extremely fast, but actually about half as rapid as the loss of Br· from such a radical.

(at 40°, $k_e = 2k_r$)

Elemental iodine, when heated or irradiated in solution, likewise catalyzes the *cis-trans* isomerization of olefins,[145] indicating that, as expected, addition of iodine atoms to ordinary C=C double bonds is also reversible. As with bro-

[144] Groll and Hearne, *Ind. Eng. Chem.*, **31**, 1530 (1939).
[145] (a) Noyes, Dickinson, and Schomaker, *J. Am. Chem. Soc.*, **67**, 1319 (1945). (b) Dickinson, *et al.*, *ibid.*, **61**, 3259 (1939); **65**, 1427 (1943); **71**, 1238 (1949).

mine, the rate of iodine-catalyzed isomerization of *cis*-diiodoethylene has been compared to the rate of iodine exchange, using labeled iodine.[145(a)] Due probably to steric interaction between the large iodine atoms, rotation about the C—C bond in the CHI_2—$\overset{\cdot}{C}HI$ radical is quite slow; for the isomerization is found to proceed only about one hundreth as rapidly as iodine exchange. With iodine addition, the *displacement step* in sequence (18) is also reversible, making the overall addition reaction reversible. In fact, although additions of I_2 to olefins may be carried out at low temperatures,[146(a)] it is the reverse reaction which is more readily studied.[146(b)]

$$\underset{\underset{\text{I}}{|}}{\text{RCH}}-\underset{\underset{\text{I}}{|}}{\text{CHR}} \overset{\text{I·}}{\rightarrow} \text{RCH}=\text{CHR} + I_2$$

This homolytic elimination may be initiated by attack of I· on the bound iodine atom,

$$\text{RCHI}-\text{CHIR} + \text{I·} \rightleftharpoons \text{RCHI}-\overset{\cdot}{C}HR + I_2$$

or simply by photochemical breakage of the C—I bond by ultraviolet irradiation.[146(c)]

With allylic halides, the reversibility of halogen atom addition may lead to allylic rearrangement. Thus the conversion of 3-bromo-1-butene (XCI) to 1-bromo-2-butene (XCII) with HBr at −12° is catalyzed by peroxides, almost certainly through the intervention of Br· radicals.[147]

$$\underset{\text{XCI}}{\text{CH}_2=\text{CH}-\text{CHBr}-\text{CH}_3} \overset{\text{Br·}}{\rightleftharpoons} [\text{BrCH}_2-\overset{\cdot}{C}H-\text{CHBr}-\text{CH}_3] \overset{-\text{Br·}}{\rightleftharpoons}$$

$$\underset{\text{XCII}}{\text{BrCH}_2-\text{CH}=\text{CH}-\text{CH}_3}$$

No discussion of homolytic halogen additions should omit mention of the addition of chlorine to benzene, for this is one of the few cases in which a non-activated benzene ring undergoes addition rather than substitution under relatively mild conditions.[148] The resulting mixture of 1,2,3,4,5,6-hexachlorocyclohexanes contains five of the eight possible stereoisomers of that compound; the identification of these isomers has already been considered (Chap. 12, Ex. 4). There can be no doubt that the initial attack is homolytic, for it is initiated by

[145] (a) Forbes and Nelson, *J. Am. Chem. Soc.*, **59**, 693 (1937). (b) Schumacher, *et al.*, *Z. physik. Chem.*, **B11**, 45 (1931); **B12**, 349 (1951). (c) De Right and Wiig, *J. Am. Chem. Soc.*, **57**, 2411 (1935).

[147] Young and Nuzak, *J. Am. Chem. Soc.*, **62**, 311 (1940).

[148] (a) For quantitative studies of this reaction, see: Noyes, *et al.*, *J. Am. Chem. Soc.*, **54**, 161 (1932); **55**, 4444 (1933); and Schwabe and Rammelt, *Z. physik. Chem.*, **204**, 310 (1955). (b) Bromine may also be made to add to benzene; see, for example, Rabinowitch, *Z. physik. Chem.*, **B19**, 190 (1932).

light and by the addition of peroxides. The sequence represented below is purely schematic, for we know little about the intervening steps. Dichloride XCIV,

which should be extremely reactive, has not yet been isolated from the reaction mixture, but a mixture of four stereoisomers of tetrachloride XCV may, with care, be obtained.[149] These are readily chlorinated photochemically to mixtures of benzene hexachlorides, but react very slowly with chlorine in the dark. As indicated, radical intermediate XCIII may be "trapped" if the chlorination is carried out in the presence of maleic anhydride.[150] The "trapped" radical is isolated ultimately as phenylchlorosuccinic anhydride, XCVI.

Additions of Dinitrogen Tetroxide

The additions of N_2O_4 to olefins in nonpolar solvents are similar in a number of respects to homolytic halogen additions and may be considered briefly at this point. The N—N bond in N_2O_4 is extremely weak (13 kcal), and the tetroxide is measurably dissociated into NO_2 radicals, even at 0° C. The initial attack on the double bond is by NO_2, but it is not known whether the resulting nitroalkyl radical then reacts with NO_2, with N_2O_4, or with both.[151]

As shown, the second nitro group may become bonded to the carbon by its nitrogen atom, yielding a dinitro compound, or, alternatively, by an oxygen

[149] Calingaert, Griffing, Kerr, Kolka, and Orloff, *J. Am. Chem. Soc.*, **73**, 5224 (1951); **75**, 4243 (1953).
[150] Ecke, Buzbee, and Kolka, *J. Am. Chem. Soc.*, **78**, 79 (1956).
[151] This question is discussed by Brand and Stevens, Ref. 139(a).

atom, yielding the nitrite ester of an α-nitro alcohol.[152] The initial attack is represented as being reversible, for it has been found that NO_2, like iodine and bromine, catalyzes the *cis-trans* isomerization of olefins.[153] Until recently, a number of workers felt that this reaction was ionic—that is, that the NO_2^+ and NO_2^- ions were involved. However, the observed "diversion" of the nitroalkyl radical with iodine[154] and with $BrCCl_3$[139(a)] leaves little doubt that, in nonhydroxylic solvents at least, the reaction is homolytic.

$$CH_2{=}CH{-}Et \xrightarrow{\ N_2O_4 + I_2\ } O_2N{-}CH_2{-}CHI{-}Et$$

It is of interest that the addition of N_2O_4 to 1-methylcyclohexene, like the homolytic addition of HBr (p. 734), gives a nearly pure *trans* adduct, whereas the addition to cyclohexene itself yields a mixture of *cis* and *trans* adducts with the *trans* predominating slightly.[139(a)] If the additions are presumed to proceed by a path analogous to that for additions of HBr, the nitro groups in the nitrocyclohexyl radical intermediates should, at first, occupy *axial* positions. Assuming once again that the configuration of bonds about the trivalent carbon is pyramidal, it may be supposed that both the methyl group in XCVII and the hydrogen

shown in XCVIII prefer the less crowded equatorial position, but that this preference is much stronger for the bulkier methyl group. A significant fraction

[152] Levy, *et al.*, *J. Chem. Soc.*, **1946**, 1093, 1096, 1100; **1948**, 52; **1949**, 2627. Somewhat puzzlingly, glycol dinitrites, in which *both* nitro groups are attached through oxygen atoms, have not been isolated in significant yields from such reaction mixtures.

[153] Khan, *J. Chem. Phys.*, **23**, 2447 (1955).

[154] Stevens and Emmons, *J. Am. Chem. Soc.*, **80**, 338 (1958).

of the radical intermediate from cyclohexene may well assume conformation XCIX, resulting ultimately in *cis*, as well as *trans*, addition.[155]

Additions of Thiols

Although heterolytic additions of mercaptans and thiophenols are known[156] homolytic additions are considerably more important. Like the corresponding additions of HBr, these are initiated by peroxides, may be photochemically induced, and may be retarded by such inhibitors as hydroquinone. Moreover, the direction of addition is generally opposed to that predicted by Markownikoff's rule; for example,

$$RS \cdot + CH_2{=}CHR' \rightleftharpoons RS{-}CH_2{-}\overset{\cdot}{C}HR' \xrightarrow{\text{RSH}} RS{-}CH_2{-}CH_2R' + RS \cdot^{157}$$

For ordinary olefins, both propagation steps in the sequence above are exothermic. The addition step is about 10 kcal more exothermic than the corresponding addition of Br·, whereas the energy for the displacement step is very nearly that for attack of a $Br{-}CH_2{-}\overset{\cdot}{C}HR$ radical on HBr. Once again then, reaction via a chain mechanism is possible and, indeed, is observed.[157] The addition step is, at least in some cases, reversible, for *cis-trans* isomerization of olefins sometimes occurs during thiol addition reactions.[158]

Thiyl radicals (RS·), should, like chlorine and bromine radicals (p. 697), be *electrophilic*, and accordingly, we may expect electron-donating groups in the olefin to facilitate homolytic thiol additions. It has indeed been found that incorporation of a *p*-MeO group into α-methylstyrene increases its reactivity toward $HOOC{-}CH_2{-}S \cdot$ radicals by a factor of about 100, whereas incorporation of a *p*-F group decreases reactivity by a factor of two.[159(a)] By an extension of the same argument, electron-attracting groups in the thiol should increase the reactivity of the derived thiyl radical, and this too has been observed.[159(b)]

[155] (a) Additions of N_2O_4 to alkynes appear to be nonstereospecific. See Campbell, Shavel, and Campbell, *J. Am. Chem. Soc.*, **75**, 2400 (1953); and Freeman and Emmons, *ibid.*, **79**, 1712 (1957). (b) Homolytic mechanisms have been suggested also for the addition of N_2O_3 and NO_2Cl to olefins. See Schechter, *et al.*, *J. Am. Chem. Soc.*, **74**, 3052 (1952); *Chem. and Ind.*, **1955**, 535.

[156] Base-catalyzed additions of thiols to C=C or C≡C bonds lying near strongly electron-attracting groups are undoubtedly initiated by attack of RS⁻ on the double or triple bond (see for example, p. 529). On the other hand, acid-catalyzed additions of thiols to olefins (see, for example, Ipatieff, Pines, and Friedman, *J. Am. Chem. Soc.*, **60**, 2731 (1938)), involve preliminary protonation of the double bond.

[157] See, for example, Sivertz, *et al.*, *Can. J. Chem.*, **32**, 1078 (1954); **33**, 1034 (1955); *J. Polymer Sci.*, **19**, 587 (1956).

[158] Helmreich and Walling, Ref. 1(b), p. 323.

[159] (a) Walling, Seymour, and Wolfstirn, *J. Am. Chem. Soc.*, **70**, 2559 (1948). (b) Cunneen, *J. Chem. Soc.*, **1947**, 36, 134; other comparisons of thiol reactivities (see for example, Gregg, Alderman, and Mayo, *J. Am. Chem. Soc.*, **70**, 3740 (1948)) do not indicate clear trends in this direction.

The stereochemistry of thiol additions, like those of a number of homolytic additions, depends upon the substrate and, to a lesser extent, upon reaction conditions. Like the additions of N_2O_4 to alkynes, the addition of thio-*p*-cresol to phenylacetylene is nonstereospecific.[160] On the other hand, as we might predict, addition of thiols to 1-chlorocyclohexene gives predominantly *trans* addition; some *cis* addition is observed, but it becomes less important as the ratio of thiol to olefin is increased.[161] Here, it is likely that conformational effects analogous to those proposed for the homolytic additions of HBr (p. 734) come into play, with, however, the operation of one additional factor. Because thiols are considerably less reactive than HBr as hydrogen-transfer reagents, the radical intermediate C may exist for a significant time interval before attack by a second thiol molecule; indeed, it appears that during this interval, a fraction of these radicals may assume the alternate conformation, CI. If it is assumed that the chloro group in both C and CI prefers an equatorial position, conformation C leads to *trans* addition, whereas CI leads to *cis* addition. Moreover, as the concentration of

thiol is increased, radical C will be more and more likely to suffer attack by thiol before isomerization to CI can take place.

Still another stereochemical situation is encountered in the addition of thiols to the rigid bicyclic norbornene system (CII).[162] By the use of scale models, it may be shown that attack by a large radical on the "underside" of CII (*endo* attack) is considerably more hindered than attack on CII on the "flank" (*exo* attack). As a result, attack on CII by the *p*-thiocresoxy radical gives almost exclusively the *exo* radical CIII, which, in turn, leads almost exclusively to the *exo* adduct CIV. But this transformation does not tell us whether the overall

[160] Kohler and Potter, *J. Am. Chem. Soc.*, **57**, 1316 (1935).
[161] Goering, Relyea, and Larsen, *J. Am. Chem. Soc.*, **78**, 348 (1956); Bordwell and Hewett, *ibid.*, **79**, 3493 (1957).
[162] Cristol and Brindell, *J. Am. Chem. Soc.*, **76**, 5699 (1954).

additon is *cis* or *trans*. However, the homolytic addition of the same thiol to chloride CV has been found to be very nearly wholly *cis*, and addition of this thiol to chloride CVI is predominantly *cis*.[163] It thus appears that in homolytic

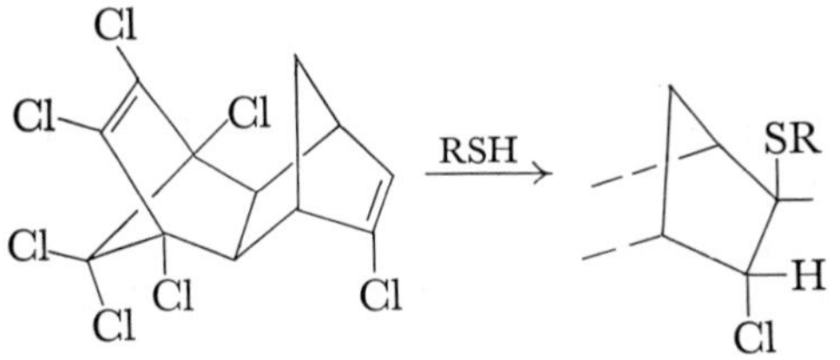

CV

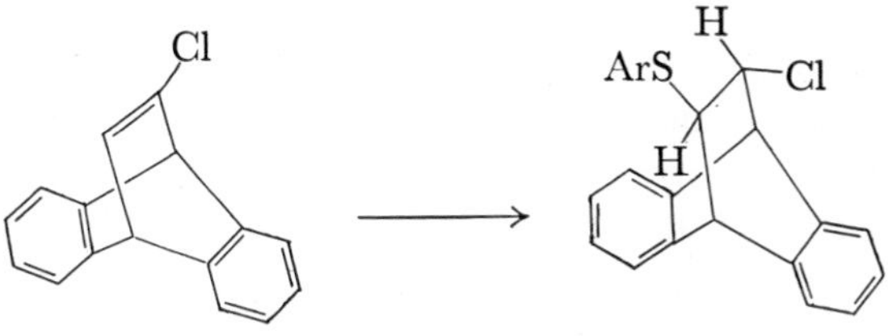

CVI

addition to CV (and almost certainly to CII also), both the attack on the double bond by ArS· and the subsequent attack upon the radical intermediate by ArSH are *exo* attacks. With chloride CVI, the two possible directions of attack are geometrically equivalent, and the predominance of *cis* addition is probably a reflection of the tendency of the bulky —Cl and —SR groups to keep as far from each other as possible.

Additions of Polyhalomethanes and Aldehydes

The addition of polyhalogenated methanes to olefins is a comparatively new reaction, being, in fact, one of the few organic reactions discovered since 1940

[163] Cristol and Arganbright, *J. Am. Chem. Soc.*, **79**, 6039 (1957). The predominant addition products in these cases were identical to the chloro sulfides resulting from the (heterolytic) addition to *p*-toluenesulfenyl chloride to compounds CVII and CVIII. The latter type of addition, which presumably passes through the bridged sulfonium ion, CIX, is known to be a *trans* addition; that is, the ArS— and Cl— groups in the product lie *trans* to each other. Hence the ArS— and H— substituents on adjacent carbons must lie *cis*.

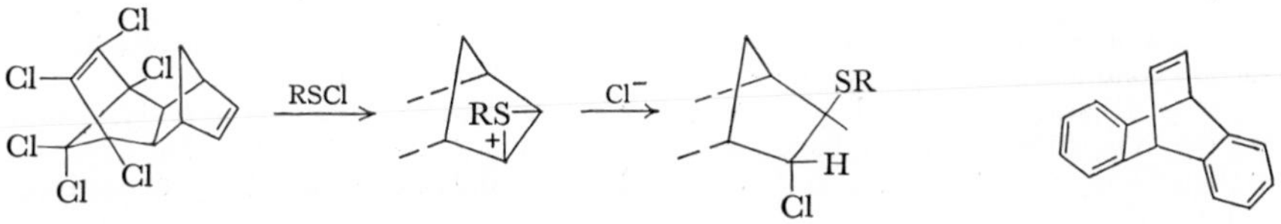

CVII   CIX   CVIII

that has achieved wide industrial importance. Glancing once more at Table 16-4, we see that both the addition and the displacement step in the sequence,

$$-CH=CH_2 + \cdot CCl_3 \rightarrow -\overset{\cdot}{C}H-CH_2CCl_3 \xrightarrow{CCl_4}$$

$$-CHCl-CH_2-CCl_3 + \cdot CCl_3$$

are ordinarily exothermic; thus, unless activation energies are prohibitive, addition of CCl_4 to olefins, via a chain mechanism, should be possible in the presence of a suitable initiator. Actually, this addition has, to date, been carried out successfully using about 30 different olefins, the yields of adduct being, in some cases, excellent.[164] Generally, the initiator is acetyl or benzoyl peroxide. Additions of $BrCCl_3$ occur even more readily, for the displacement step

$$R\cdot + Br-CCl_3 \rightarrow R-Br + \cdot CCl_3$$

is more exothermic than that with CCl_4. Bromotrichloromethane has been added to about 50 olefins and alkynes, and in most cases the addition may be initiated photochemically. Homolytic additions of about 20 additional polyhalides, among them CF_3I, CF_2Br_2, $CF_2=CFI$, CBr_4, and the haloforms, have been described. Five typical conversions are shown below:

$$CCl_3Br + CH_2=CHOAc \xrightarrow{Ac_2O_2}$$
$$Cl_3C-CH_2-CHBr-OAc \quad (90\%)^{165(a)}$$

$$CF_3I + CF_2=CHMe \xrightarrow{h\nu} F_3C-CHMe-CF_2-I \quad (75\%)^{165(b)}$$

$$CF_2=CFI + CH_2=CH_2 \xrightarrow{h\nu} CF_2=CF-CH_2CH_2I \quad (67\%)^{165(c)}$$

$$CHI_3 + CH_2=CH-CH_2OBz \xrightarrow{Ac_2O_2} I_2CH-CH_2-CHI-CH_2OBz^{165(d)}$$

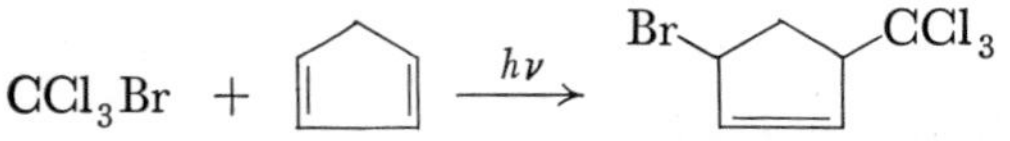

$$CCl_3Br + \text{[cyclopentene]} \xrightarrow{h\nu} \text{[product]} \quad (1,4 \text{ addition}) \quad 165(e)$$

In each of the polyhalides on the left, it is the bond from the carbon to the heavier halogen atom which is broken. Chloroform, adds as $H-\vert-CCl_3$, rather than as

$Cl-\vert-CHCl_2$, suggesting that the $\cdot CCl_3$ radical (in which the odd electron can distribute itself over three chlorines) is "stabilized by resonance" to a greater extent that is the $\cdot CHCl_2$ radical (in which the odd electron can distribute itself

---

[164] For a tabular summary of the additions of polyhaloalkanes to olefins (including yields, reaction conditions, and appropriate references) see Walling, Ref. 1(b), pp. 248–252.

[165] (a) Kharasch, Reinmuth, and Urry, *J. Am. Chem. Soc.*, **65**, 1105 (1947). (b) Haszeldine, *J. Chem. Soc.*, **1953**, 3565. (c) Park, Seffe, and Lacher, *J. Am. Chem. Soc.*, **78**, 59 (1956). (d) Weizmann, *et al.*, *ibid.*, **69**, 2569 (1947). (e) Kharasch and Friedlander, *J. Org. Chem.*, **14**, 239 (1949).

over only two chlorines). Such an inference is in accord with known bond-dissociation energies.[166]

A complicating factor which, in principle, is associated with all homolytic additions, may become particularly pronounced in additions of halomethanes. The radical intermediate $-\overset{.}{\underset{|}{C}}-\overset{|}{\underset{|}{C}}-CX_3$ may, instead of attacking a second molecule of halomethane, attack the double bond in a second molecule of olefin and the resulting radical may then attack a third molecule of olefin, and so on.

$$-\overset{.}{\underset{|}{C}}-\overset{|}{\underset{|}{C}}-CX_3 + \overset{\diagdown}{\diagup}C{=}C\overset{\diagup}{\diagdown} \rightarrow -\overset{.}{\underset{|}{C}}-\overset{|}{\underset{|}{C}}-\overset{|}{\underset{|}{C}}-\overset{|}{\underset{|}{C}}-CX_3$$

Such polymerization cannot, in the presence of excess halomethane, go far, for soon the growing carbon chain must attack a halomethane molecule. Thus, there

$$-\overset{.}{\underset{|}{C}}-\overset{|}{\underset{|}{C}}-\overset{|}{\underset{|}{C}}-\overset{|}{\underset{|}{C}}-CX_3 + CX_4 \rightarrow X-\overset{|}{\underset{|}{C}}-\overset{|}{\underset{|}{C}}-\overset{|}{\underset{|}{C}}-\overset{|}{\underset{|}{C}}-CX_3 + \cdot CX_3$$

("chain transfer")

may be formed a series of molecules in which a $X-$ and a X_3C- group are separated by two, four, six, or more carbon atoms. Such "short-chain polymers" are often called *telomers*. Telomerization, as may be expected, becomes important when the halomethane employed is relatively unreactive (or when its concentration is low). Thus, considerable quantities of telomeric materials are formed in the reaction of CCl_4, $HCCl_3$, or CF_2Br_2 with ethylene, but practically no telomer results from the addition of the more reactive halides, CCl_3Br and CBr_4, to the same olefin.[164] Similarly, allyl chloride gives much telomer in its reaction with CCl_4, but very little in its reaction with CCl_3Br under similar conditions. Telomerization is likewise favored by increasing the stability, hence the selectivity, of the $-\overset{.}{\underset{|}{C}}-\overset{|}{\underset{|}{C}}-CX_3$ radical intermediate; a more stable radical is more likely to survive in solution long enough to add to another olefin molecule, whereas a very reactive radical is more likely to react with the excess halomethane. It is found, for example, that the photochemically induced addition of CF_3I to acrylonitrile (which proceeds through the resonance-stabilized $F_3C-\overset{|}{\underset{|}{C}}-\overset{.}{\underset{|}{C}}-CN$ radical) yields a mixture of telomeric products, whereas addition of the same halide to $CH_2{=}CHF$ yields the expected monomeric addition product.[165(b)] Similarly,

---

[166] It has been found, for example, that the bond dissociation energy for the C—Br bond in CCl_3Br is 50 kcal, whereas that for the C—Br bond in $CHCl_2Br$ is 54 kcal (see Szwarc and Sehon, *J. Chem. Phys.*, **19**, 656 (1951)).

addition of bromoform to styrene (but not to 1-octene) results largely in telomer formation.[165(a)]

The reactivity increase within the sequence, $Cl-CCl_3 < Br-CCl_3 < I-CCl_3$, is undoubtedly related to the corresponding decrease in activation energies for displacements of the following type:

$$\diagdown\!\!\!-C\cdot + X-CCl_3 \rightarrow \diagdown\!\!\!-C-X + \cdot CCl_3$$

This, in turn, is related to the energies of the bonds being broken (p. 37). The reactivity increase within the sequence, $X-CH_3 < X-CH_2X < X-CHX_2 < X-CX_3$, is almost certainly related to the corresponding increase in resonance energies associated with the radicals being produced. Indeed, halomethanes having less than three halogen atoms undergo addition only with difficulty; however, additions of such compounds as $BrCH_2CN$ and $Cl_2CHCOOMe$ (which yield radical intermediates significantly stabilized by conjugation) have been reported.[167]

A further complication may enter the picture if the olefin has one or more allylic hydrogens, since the radicals produced in the initiation step may remove an allylic hydrogen rather than adding to the double bond. The allylic radical thus formed may dimerize or may react with another alkyl polyhalide molecule.[168] Finally, if the addition is carried out on an allylic halide, a halogen

atom may be lost from the radical intermediate, resulting in an "allylic rearrangement."

$$CH_2=CH-CH_2X \xrightarrow{\cdot CX_3} X_3C-CH_2-\overset{\centerdot}{C}H-CH_2X \xrightarrow{-X\cdot}$$
$$X_3C-CH_2-CH=CH_2 \text{[169]}$$

---

[167] See, for example, Kharasch, Skell, and Fisher, *J. Am. Chem. Soc.*, **70**, 1055 (1948).

[168] See, for example, Kooyman, *Disc. Faraday Soc.*, **10**, 163 (1951). In view of complications arising from telomerization and allylic termination, adequate kinetic treatments of polyhalide additions may offer considerable difficulty. For an attempt in this direction, see Melville, Robb, and Tutton, *ibid.*, **14**, 150 (1953).

[169] Kharasch and Sage, *J. Org. Chem.*, **14**, 573 (1949).

Another recently developed addition reaction is that of *aldehydes* to olefins.[170] This process, which is generally initiated by acetyl or benzoyl peroxide, proceeds, in all likelihood, via the following path:

$$RCHO \xrightarrow{In\cdot} R\dot{C}=O \xrightarrow{CH_2=CHR'} R-C-CH_2-\dot{C}HR' \xrightarrow{RCHO}$$
$$\underset{O}{\|}$$

$$R-C-CH_2-CH_2R' + R\dot{C}=O \xrightarrow[etc.]{CH_2=CHR'}$$
$$\underset{O}{\|}$$

This addition appears to proceed most cleanly with "terminal" olefins (having $=CH_2$ or $=CF_2$ groups) and with compounds in which the $C=C$ bond is in conjugation with a cyano, keto, or similar group. With substrates of the latter sort, the $R\dot{C}=O$ radical tends to attack the β-carbon, yielding a resonance-stabilized radical adduct; for example,

$$R\dot{C}=O + -\overset{|}{C}=\overset{|}{C}-\overset{|}{C}=O \rightarrow$$

$$\left[R-\overset{|}{\underset{\|}{C}}-\overset{|}{C}-\overset{\cdot}{C}-\overset{|}{C}=O \leftrightarrow R-\overset{|}{\underset{\|}{C}}-\overset{|}{C}-\overset{|}{C}=\overset{|}{C}-\ddot{\underset{\cdot\cdot}{O}}: \right]$$

However, if the β-carbon is sterically hindered, attack at the α-carbon may occur also. Thus, the addition of butyraldehyde to the acid, $Me_2C=CH-COOH$ yields a mixture of both possible addition products, with β attack predominating over α attack by a margin of 3 to 1.[170(c)]

$$PrCHO + Me_2C=CH-COOH \xrightarrow{Bz_2O_2}$$

$$\underset{\underset{\text{75 per cent}}{\underset{O}{\|}}}{PrC-CMe_2-CH_2-COOH} + \underset{\underset{\underset{\text{25 per cent}}{\underset{O}{\|}}}{C-Pr}}{Me_2CH-CH-COOH}$$

A similar ratio of products results from addition of the same aldehyde to the ester $Me_2C=CH-COOEt$, but if, however, mesityl oxide, $Me_2C=CH-\overset{O}{\overset{\|}{C}}-Me$, is taken as a substrate, β attack predominates over α attack by a margin of 10 to 1.[170(b)] Moreover, with nitrile $Me_2C=CH-CN$, attack is exclusively at the β position. This trend suggests that an α-cyano group is more effective in stabilizing

[170] (a) Kharasch, Urry, and Kuderna, *J. Org. Chem.*, **14**, 248 (1949). (b) Patrick, *ibid.*, **17**, 1009, 1269 (1952). (c) Huang, *J. Chem. Soc.*, **1957**, 1342. (d) For a tabular summary of the homolytic additions of aldehydes to olefins, see Walling, Ref. 1(b), pp. 274–275.

an adjacent radical center than is an α-keto group, which is, in turn, more effective than an α-carboxyl group.

As with homolytic additions of halomethanes, telomerization may accompany additions of aldehydes. Moreover, there is the possibility of *decarbonylation* (loss of CO) of the acyl radical intermediate.

$$R\!-\!\overset{\centerdot}{C}\!\!=\!\!O \rightarrow R\!\cdot + C\!\!\equiv\!\!O$$

This is an important step in the homolytic decompositions of aldehydes, and may occur also in the presence of added olefin, especially if the aldehyde is branched at the α position. In an extreme case, the addition of trimethylacetaldehyde, $Me_3C\!-\!CHO$, to 1-octene gives, as the chief product, hydrocarbon CX, together with an almost quantitative yield of carbon monoxide.

$$Me_3C\!-\!\overset{\centerdot}{C}O \xrightarrow{-CO} Me_3C\!\cdot \xrightarrow{H_2C=CHHx} Me_3C\!-\!CH_2\!-\!\overset{\centerdot}{C}HHx \xrightarrow{Me_3CCHO}$$

$$Me_3CCH_2CHHx + Me_3C\!-\!\overset{\centerdot}{C}O$$

$$(Hx\!-\! = n\text{-}C_6H_{13}\text{-})$$

CX

The fact that acyl radicals attack $F_2C\!\!=\!\!C\diagup^{\diagdown}$ groups more readily than $H_2C\!\!=\!\!C\diagup^{\diagdown}$ groups, and $H_2C\!\!=\!\!C\diagup^{\diagdown}$ groups more readily than $MeCH\!\!=\!\!C\diagup^{\diagdown}$ groups, suggests that these radicals (unlike the Cl·, Br·, RS·, and Ph₃C· radicals) have little, if any, electrophilic character. Indeed the carbon atom in an acyl radical may be appreciably nucleophilic, for electron density may drift from the oxygen to the "trivalent" carbon (CXI').

$$R\!-\!\overset{\centerdot\,\centerdot\centerdot}{C}\!::\!\overset{\centerdot\centerdot}{O}\!: \leftrightarrow R\!-\!\overset{\centerdot\centerdot}{\overline{C}}\!::\!\overset{\centerdot\centerdot}{O}\!:^+$$

CXI   CXI'

Homolytic Cyclizations. Diradicals

The oxygen molecule is paramagnetic and is known to have *two* unpaired electrons.[171] It is thus a *diradical*, although as we have seen, it is a relatively ineffective reagent for carrying out homolytic displacements or additions under ordi-

[171] Wheland, *Trans. Faraday Soc.*, **33**, 1499 (1937); Mulliken, *Phys. Rev.*, **32**, 880 (1928). Structure CXII, having two *three-electron bonds* (Pauling, *J. Am. Chem. Soc.*, **53**, 3225 (1931)), is preferable to structure CXIII; for the latter suggests that the bond in O_2 should have very nearly the same length and bond energy as the O—O single bond in, say, H_2O_2, whereas, in fact, the bond in O_2 is much shorter and considerably stronger. A satisfactory understanding

$$:\!\overset{\centerdot\centerdot}{O}\!\vdots\!\vdots\!\overset{\centerdot\centerdot}{O}\!: \qquad :\!\overset{\centerdot\centerdot}{O}\!-\!\overset{\centerdot}{\overset{\centerdot\centerdot}{O}}\!: \qquad :\!\overset{\centerdot\centerdot}{O}\!::\!\overset{\centerdot\centerdot}{O}\!:$$

CXII   CXIII   CXIV

nary conditions. It does, however, react with a number of cyclic dieneoid systems in the light to give six-membered ring ("transannular") peroxides such as CXV, CXVI, and CXVII. Sometimes, as is the case with the formation of ascaridole,

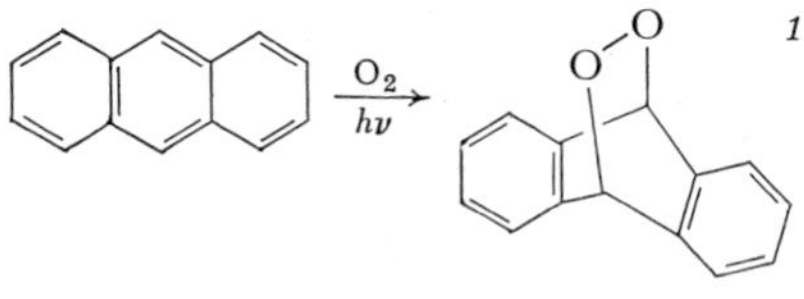

CXV

172(a)

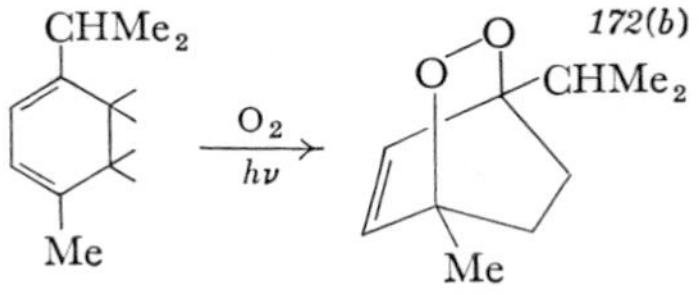

172(b)

CXVI
ascaridole

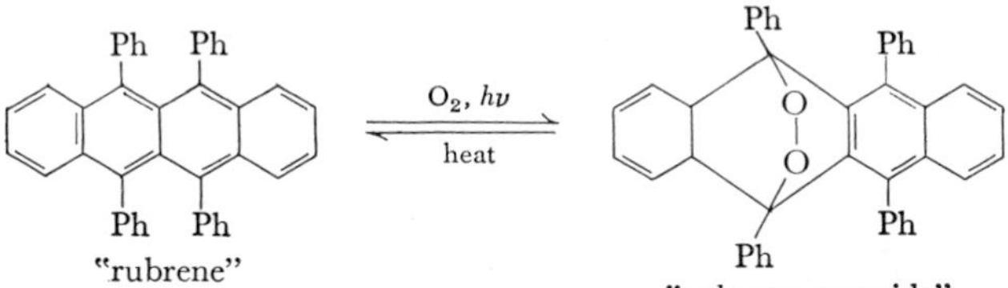

"rubrene"

172(c)

CXVII

"rubrene peroxide"

CXVI, the addition does not take place readily unless a *photosensitizer* is added; the latter is a colored substance (for example, eosin or methylene blue) that absorbs radiant energy, then transfers it to the substrate molecule during a collision. Although we cannot be sure, it appears that the light absorbed excites the dienoid structure to a diradical state, CXVIII, which, in turn, reacts rapidly

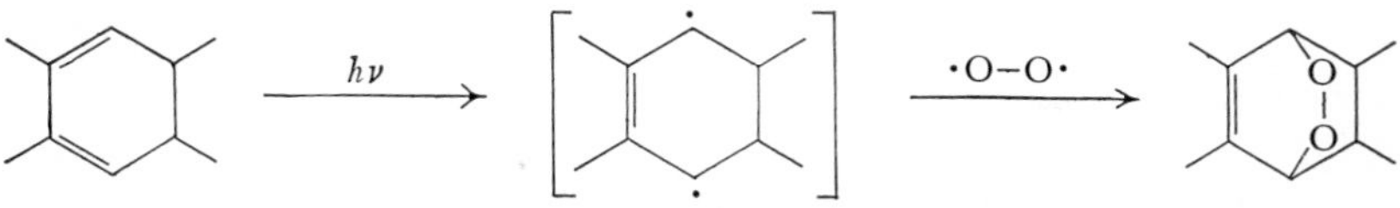

CXVIII

with the oxygen diradical. Since the overall process involves consumption of diradicals with no regeneration, these are not chain reactions. These additions bring to mind the Diels-Alder reaction (p. 536), which is not, however, photochemically induced and may therefore be assumed not to require preliminary conversion of the substrates to their diradical forms.

A number of additional photochemical cyclizations are known which are

of why molecular oxygen assumes a diradical structure rather than structure CXIV, which in the past was often assigned to it, requires some acquaintance with the molecular orbital treatment of diatomic molecules. For a qualitative summary, see Huckel, *Structural Chemistry of Inorganic Compounds*, Elsevier Publishing Co., Inc., New York, 1950, pp. 403—411. There is some objection among workers in photochemistry to applying the term "diradical" to species in which there is significant interaction between two unpaired electrons; see, for example, Simons, *Quart. Revs., XIII*, 10 (1959).

[172] (a) Dufraisse and Gerard, *Compt. rend.*, **202**, 1859 (1936). (b) Schenck and Ziegler, *Naturwissenschaften*, **32**, 157 (1944). (c) Moureau, Dufraisse, and Dean, *Compt. rend.*, **182**, 1440, 1584 (1926); note that the formation of peroxide CXVII (but not CXV and CXVI) is reversible.

likewise presumed to proceed through preliminary excitation of one or both reactants to a diradical. Four of these are listed below:

(20) 173(a)

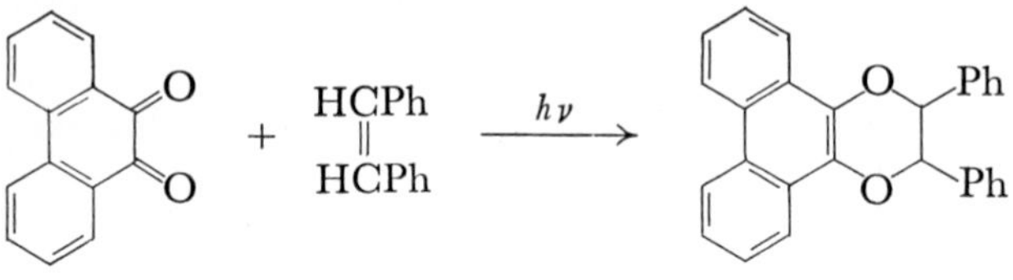

(21) 173(b)

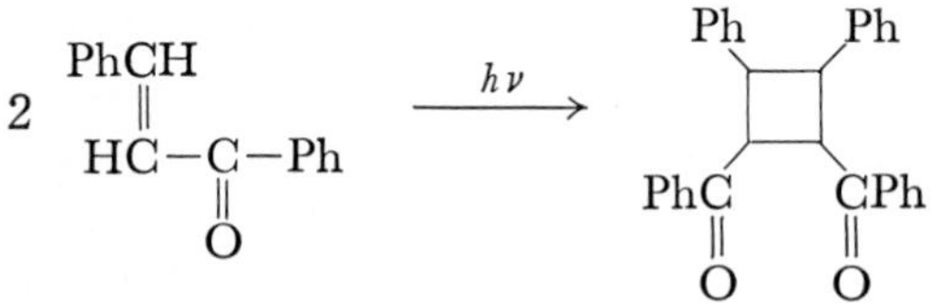

(22) 173(c)

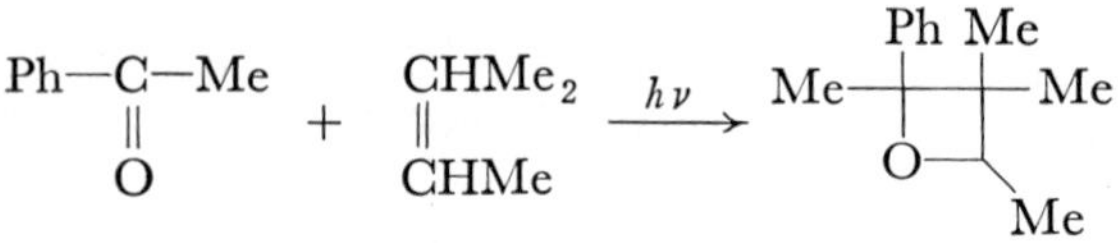

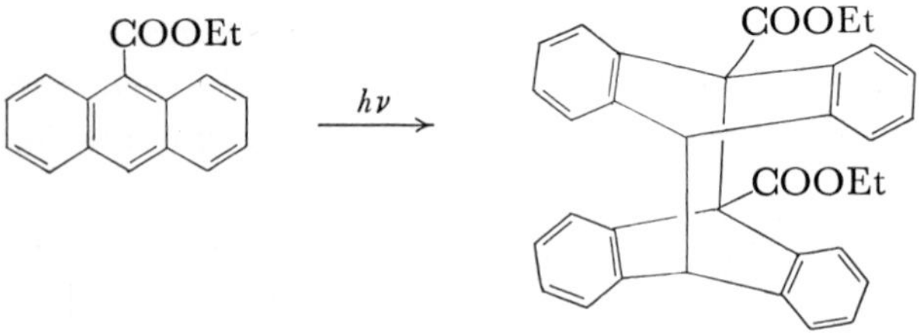

(23) 173(d)

For cyclizations (20) and (22), we cannot as yet say whether it is the carbonyl compound or the olefin which, in the initial step, is converted to a diradical. Note that the cyclization product from acetophenone and 2-methyl-2-butene (reaction 22) is derived from the diradical intermediate CXIX. The alternative product, CXXI (which is not obtained), would be derived from diradical CXX, which is presumably less stable than CXIX; for in the former, the odd electron center on the right is stabilized by two α-methyl groups, whereas in CXX, it is stabilized by only one α-methyl group. In the same way, we may explain why cyclization (23) yields the observed "head-to-head" dimer, rather than the alternative "head-to-tail" dimer, CXXII.

In contrast to the O_2 molecule, the methylene diradical, $\cdot CH_2$,[174] is exceed-

[173] (a) Schonberg and Mustafa, J. Chem. Soc., 1948, 2126. (b) Mustafa, Chem. Revs., 51, 1 (1952). (c) Buchi, Inman, and Lipinsky, J. Am. Chem. Soc., 76, 4327 (1954). (d) Greene, Misrock, and Wolfe, ibid., 77, 3852 (1955).

[174] As in the case of CBr_2 (p. 535), the question may be raised as to whether the methylene molecule has zero or two unpaired electrons. Here, however, complications due to unshared electrons on the halogen atoms are absent, and it seems likely that the two unshared electrons occupy different orbitals about the carbon atom, that is, that these electrons are unpaired.

Me—C· ĊMe₂
|
O—C

Ph
|
CXIX

Ph
|
Me—C· ĊHMe → Me—C——CHMe
| |
O—CMe₂   O—CMe₂

Ph
|
CXX   CXXI

COOEt

COOEt
CXXII

ingly reactive. This species is generally prepared by the photochemical decomposition of ketene $(CH_2=C=O)$[175] or diazomethane (CH_2N_2),[175(a)] or by the thermal decomposition of the latter.[176] By use of the Paneth technique (p. 683), methylene produced in the gas phase may be made to remove mirrors of elemental selenium or tellurium, converting these elements to the polymeric substances $(CH_2Se)_x$ and $(CH_2Te)_x$.[175(a)]

Like the CBr_2 molecule (p. 535), methylene adds readily to $C=C$ double bonds, forming cyclopropane derivatives, and, once again, the additions appear to be stereospecific.

Me   H   Me
  \ /   CH₂ |
   C=C   ———→   Me—△—Me   177(a)
  / \
 H   Me

Me   Me   Me   Me
  \ /   CH₂   \ /
   C=C   ———→   Me—△   177(b)
  / \
 H   H

[hexene ring] ——CH₂——→ [bicyclic]   177(c)

Another, and a more unusual, reaction of the methylene diradical is its attack on C—H bonds, converting them to C—CH₃ groups. Just how such "homologations" occur is not yet clear. Although it has been suggested that CH_2 somehow "adds directly" into the C—H bond in a single step,[177(c)] the two-step process,

$$-\overset{|}{\underset{|}{C}}-H + \cdot CH_2 \rightarrow -\overset{|}{\underset{|}{C}}\cdot + H-\dot{C}H_2 \xrightarrow{fast} -\overset{|}{\underset{|}{C}}-CH_3$$

cannot, in the opinion of this author, be excluded, especially since ethane is generally formed (possibly from dimerization of methyl radicals) as a side product in such reactions.[175(c)]

It is interesting that the selectivity of attack by methylene on C—H bonds varies with the manner in which this diradical is generated. When methylene,

[175] (a) Pearson, Purcell, and Saigh, J. Chem. Soc., **1938**, 409. (b) Burton Davis, Gordon, and Taylor, J. Am. Chem. Soc., **63**, 1956 (1949). (c) Frey and Kistiakowsky, ibid., **79**, 6373 (1957).

[176] Rice and Glasebrook, J. Am. Chem. Soc., **55**, 4329 (1933); **56**, 2381 (1934).

[177] (a) Doering and LaFlamme, J. Am. Chem. Soc., **78**, 5447 (1956). (b) Skell and Woodworth, ibid., **78**, 4496 (1956). (c) Doering, Laughlin, Buttery, and Chaudhari, ibid., **78**, 3224 (1956).

produced from photolysis of ketene, reacts with propane, the ratio of n-butane to isobutane in the resulting product is about 7 to 4, whereas if attack were sta-

$$H_3CCH_2CH_3 \ + \ CH_2 \longrightarrow H_3CCH_2CH_2CH_3 \ + \ H_3CCHCH_3{}^{175(c)}$$

$$\underset{\text{63 percent}}{} \qquad \qquad \underset{\text{37 percent}}{\overset{|}{C}H_3}$$

tistically random, this ratio should be 6 to 2. Under these conditions, then, secondary C—H linkages are attacked somewhat more easily than are primary C—H linkages. More specifically, attack at a secondary hydrogen is about 1.7 times as rapid as attack at a primary hydrogen, a figure which is in agreement with that obtained from similar experiments using different paraffin hydrocarbons.[178(a)] On the other hand, attack by methylene produced photochemically from diazomethane is much less discriminate.[177(c),178(b)] For example, its reaction with n-pentane gives the three possible hexanes in the proportions shown:[177(c)]

$$Me(CH_2)_3Me \xrightarrow{CH_2} \underset{\text{49 percent}}{Me(CH_2)_4Me} + \underset{\text{34 percent}}{Me_2CH(CH_2)_3Me} +$$

$$\underset{\text{17 percent}}{MeCH_2CHMeCH_2Me}$$

This is in very close agreement with the ratio $6:4:2$ that would result from random attack. Such differences in selectivity are seemingly at variance with the elementary principle that the mode of reaction of a given intermediate is independent of the manner in which it is produced. However, we are dealing here with photochemical reactions, and it may well be that the methylene molecules produced from diazomethane have more excess energy than those produced from ketene, and are thus less selective in the sites that they attack.[179]

Aside from molecular oxygen, the diradicals that we have considered are short lived, and evidence for their existence, although convincing, has been indirect. However, a number of diradicals related to triphenylmethyl are known; some of these are stable almost indefinitely and their diradical character may be confirmed by magnetic measurements (p. 673). Treatment of hexachloride CXXIII with zinc, for example, yields diradical CXXIV, solutions of which are

---

[178] (a) Knox and Trotman-Dickenson, *Chem. and Industry*, **1957**, 731. (b) Frey, *J. Am. Chem. Soc.*, **80**, 5005 (1958).

[179] The *imine* diradical, $\cdot$N—H, is formally similar to methylene. The preparation of this species, by passage of an electric discharge through gaseous HN_3 has been reported:

$$HN_3 \rightarrow H—\ddot{N}\cdot + N_2$$

(Rice and Freamo, *J. Am. Chem. Soc.*, **75**, 548 (1953)). This condenses at liquid air temperatures to a blue solid, which decomposes at $-125°$ to ammonium azide, NH_4N_3.

paramagnetic.[180(a)] The quinoid structure, CXXV, for this compound, in which

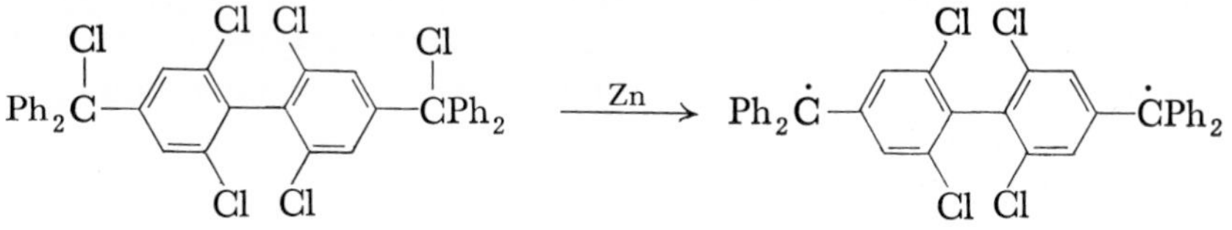

CXXIII CXXIV

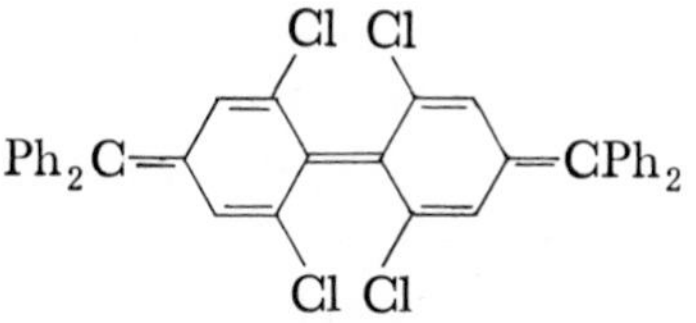

CXXV

all electrons are paired, is not stable, for in such a structure, the two central benzene rings must lie in or near a common plane, a feature prohibited by steric interference between the bulky *ortho*-chlorine atoms. A second stable diradical is hydrocarbon CXXVI;[180(b)] no less than one hundred structures may be drawn for this compound, in which each of the two unpaired electrons may be "placed" on one of ten possible carbon atoms. However, low-energy quinoid structures, in which all electrons are paired, cannot be drawn. It should be noted, however, that the paramagnetic susceptibilities of solutions of CXXIV and

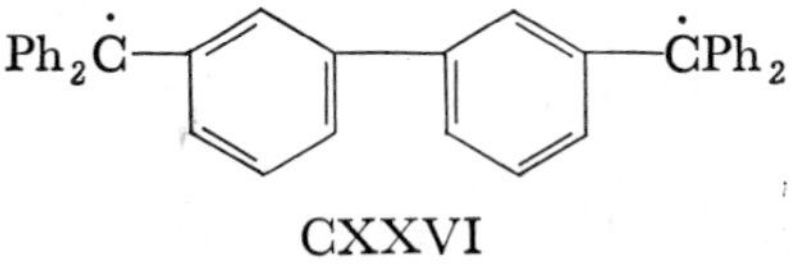

CXXVI

CXXVI are far less than would be observed if all solute were in the diradical form. Some type of association, the exact nature of which is not yet clear, is apparently occurring, the association product presumably being diamagnetic.

Quinoid structures for hydrocarbons CXXVII and CXXIX may be

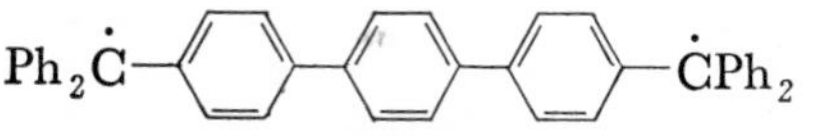

CXXVII 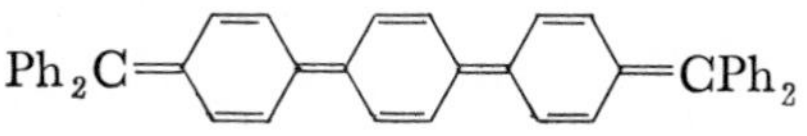 CXXVIII

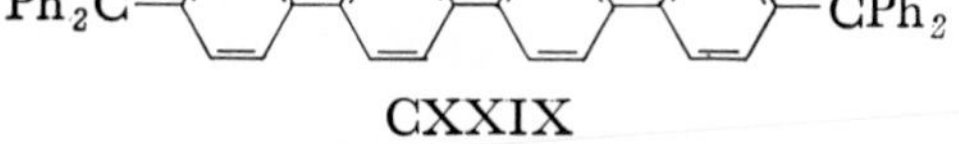

CXXIX

[180] (a) Muller, Neuhoff, and Tietz, *Ber.*, **72**, 2063 (1939); **74**, 807 (1941). (b) Muller and Muller-Rodloff, *Ann.*, **517**, 134 (1935).

drawn; yet, both of these have been found to be paramagnetic, not only in solution, but also as solids.[181] Moreover, solutions of CXXVII and CXXIX in benzene are found to become more strongly paramagnetic as the temperature is raised. Two explanations for this effect come to mind. Association of the diradical may again be occurring, with the degree of association falling as the temperature is raised. Or, it may be that the hydrocarbons exist in two monomeric forms in solution, a paramagnetic diradical form and a diamagnetic quinoidal form (for example, CXXVIII). If this be the case, the increase in the concentration of the diradical with temperature indicates that the diradical is of somewhat higher energy than the quinoidal form, although the difference is probably less than 1 kcal. With hydrocarbon CXXX, the degree of conversion to diradical CXXXI is so small that it cannot be detected magnetochemically,[180(b)] but is easily detectable by the techniques of electron-spin resonance spectroscopy (p. 684).[182] Assuming once again a quinoid-diradical equilibrium, it has been

CXXX   CXXXI

estimated that about 4 percent of this hydrocarbon exists in the diradical form, CXXXI, at room temperature. It is to be emphasized once again that CXXX and CXXXI (or CXXVII and CXXVIII) *cannot* be regarded simply as

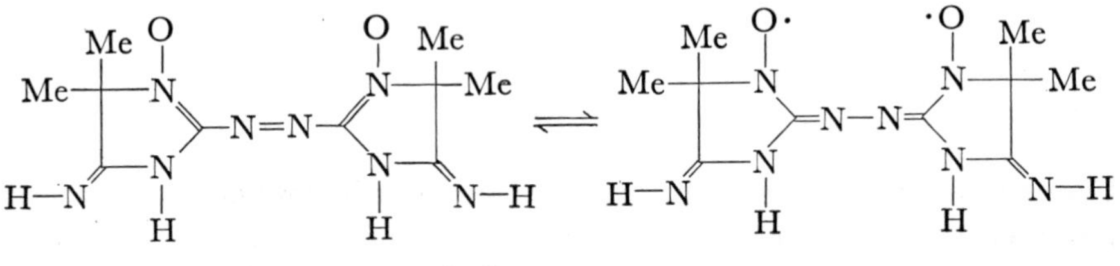

CXXXII   porphryrindine

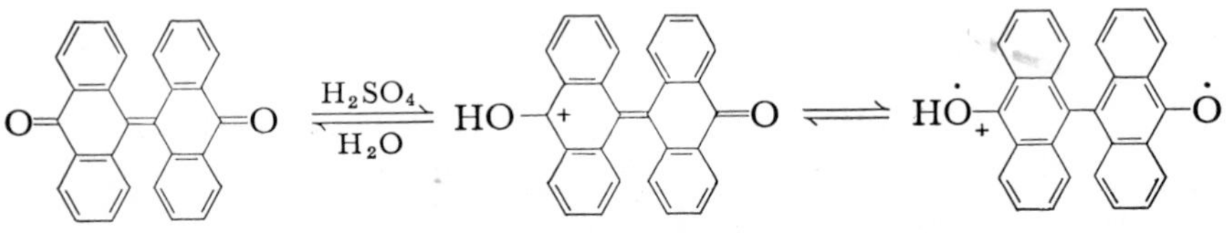

bianthrone
CXXXIII

CXXXIV

[181] Muller and Pfanz, *Ber.*, **74**, 1051, 1075 (1941).
[182] Hutchison, Kowalsky, Pastor, and Wheland, *J. Chem. Phys.*, **20**, 1485 (1952).

canonical forms of a single hydrocarbon; the structures have different numbers of unpaired electrons and resonance between them is forbidden (p. 27).

Two additional species thought to exist, to a significant extent, in diradical forms at room temperature are porphyrindene (CXXXII),[183(a)] and the conjugate acid CXXXIV of bianthrone (CXXXIII).[183(b)]

Rearrangements of Free Radicals

Although it has been recognized for over a century that skeletal rearrangements may occur during heterolytic reactions, rearrangements of free radicals have been known only since 1944. Most homolytic rearrangements observed to date have been 1,2 shifts. In very nearly all of these, the migrator is an aryl, rather than an alkyl or cycloalkyl group.[184] For example, the β,β,β-triphenylethyl radical, CXXXVI, formed by the decomposition of aldehyde CXXXV in the presence of peroxide, rearranges completely to radical CXXXVII; for 1,1,2-triphenylethane (CXXXVIII), rather than the "unrearranged" hydrocarbon, 1,1,1-triphenylethane, is the resulting product:[185]

$$Ph_3CCH_2CHO \xrightarrow{t\text{-}BuO\cdot} Ph_3CCH_2\overset{\cdot}{C}{=}O \xrightarrow{-CO} Ph_2\overset{\cdot}{C}{-}\overset{\cdot}{C}H_2 \xrightarrow{Ph\cdot \text{ shifts}} Ph_2\overset{\cdot}{C}{-}CH_2Ph$$

$$\underset{Ph}{|}$$

| CXXXV | | CXXXVI | CXXXVII |

$$Ph_2\overset{\cdot}{C}{-}CH_2Ph \xrightarrow[\text{(H· transfer)}]{Ph_3CCH_2CHO} \begin{cases} Ph_3CCH_2\overset{\cdot}{C}{=}O \xrightarrow{-CO} \text{etc.} \\ Ph_2\overset{\cdot}{C}H{-}CH_2Ph \quad (\text{no } Ph_3C{-}CH_3) \end{cases}$$

| CXXXVII | CXXXVIII |

Complete rearrangement is likewise observed for the $Ph_3C\overset{\cdot}{C}HMe$ and Ph_2-$C Me\overset{\cdot}{C}H_2$ radicals (derived from $Ph_3CCHMeCHO$ and Ph_2CMeCH_2CHO, respectively).[185] However, rearrangement of the singly phenylated radical, $PhCMe_2\overset{\cdot}{C}H_2$ (whether it be prepared from $PhCMe_2CH_2Cl$ or from $PhCMe_2$-CH_2CHO) is only partial[186(ab)] whereas the nonphenylated radicals CXXXIX, CXL, and CXLI suffer no rearrangement.[186(cd)]

[183] (a) Chu, et al., J. Phys. Chem., **57**, 504 (1953). (b) Hirshon, Gardner, and Fraenkel, J. Am. Chem. Soc., **75**, 4115 (1953).

[184] For possible exceptions see: (a) Kharasch, Liu, and Nudenburg, J. Org. Chem., **19**, 1150 (1954); (b) Friess and Farnham, J. Am. Chem. Soc., **72**, 5518 (1950); (c) Newman and Beal, ibid., **72**, 5163 (1950).

[185] Curtin and Hurwitz, J. Am. Chem. Soc., **74**, 5381 (1952).

[186] (a) Urry and Kharasch, J. Am. Chem. Soc., **66**, 1438 (1944). (b) Winstein and Seubold, ibid., **69**, 2916 (1947). (c) Urry and Nicolaides, ibid., **74**, 5163 (1952). (d) Seubold, ibid., **75**, 2533 (1953).

CXXXIX   CXL   CXLI

The fact that aryl groups, but not alkyl groups, may shift in rearrangements of free radicals suggests that such rearrangements proceed through a bridged activated complex or intermediate such as CXLII, analogous to the phenonium-ion intermediate CXLIII which has been shown to intervene in a number of

CXLII   CXLIII

heterolytic rearrangements (p. 575). However, such an aryl shift generally does not occur unless there is considerable crowding at C_β. Thus, no migration of aryl groups is observed in reactions of radicals of the type $Ar_2CH\dot{C}H_2$, even if one of the aryls is p-anisyl (which might be expected to be a very effective bridging group).[185] It appears then that the formation of bridged radical intermediates such as CXLII is by no means as easy as the formation of a bridged carbonium ion such as CXLIII. This should not be surprising if we note that a rearrangement through CXLII is, in effect, a radical displacement at C_1 of the benzene ring, whereas a rearrangement through CXLIII is an electrophilic displacement at this carbon. As has been pointed out (p. 691), radical displacements on carbon are rare and presumably require considerable activation energies, whereas electrophilic displacements on aromatic carbon comprise one of the most familiar classes of organic reactions.[187]

Nevertheless, for those few cases in which aryl migration is facile, the question arises as to whether the unrearranged radical may exist at all; for it is not inconceivable that formation of the alkyl radical and shift of the aryl group

---

[187] In this regard it may be noted that anchimeric assistance to radical formation by a migrating aryl group (analogous to anchimeric assistance to carbonium ion formation, p. 577) has not yet been observed. Thus, the rate of a transformation of the type

$$\underset{CMe_2—CHMe—N\!=\!N—CHMe—CMe_2}{\overset{\text{Ar}\qquad\qquad\qquad\qquad\qquad\text{Ar}}{|\qquad\qquad\qquad\qquad\qquad|}} \rightarrow 2\underset{CMe_2—\dot{C}HMe}{\overset{\text{Ar}}{|}} + N_2$$

is not increased when a p-methoxy substituent is incorporated into the migrating aryl group, even though such a substitution should significantly increase its "bridging effectiveness" (Overberger and Gainer, *J. Am. Chem. Soc.*, **80**, 4561 (1958)).

within this radical are synchronized (as is sometimes the case in rearrangements proceeding through carbonium ions). Recently it has been shown that radicals of the type $Ph_2CMe-\overset{\cdot}{C}H-CH_2R$ may exist in solution for a significant time interval, even though they are rapidly transformed to radicals of the type $Ph\overset{\cdot}{C}Me-CHPh-CH_2R$. Specifically, it is found that homolytic addition of *n*-BuSH to 3,3-diphenyl-1-butene (CXLIV) yields an adduct in which essentially no phenyl migration has occurred, whereas addition of *n*-butyraldehyde to the same olefin results in an adduct in which phenyl migration is very nearly complete.[188(a)] The addition of the mercaptan obviously proceeds through radical CXLV, and it may be inferred that addition of the aldehyde proceeds through the analogous intermediate CXLVI. Since there is no reason why the rearrange-

$$Ph_2CMe\overset{\cdot}{C}H-CH_2SR \xrightarrow[\text{fast}]{RSH} Ph_2CMeCH_2CH_2SR$$

CXLV   (no rearrangement)

$Ph_2CHMe=CH_2$

CXLIV

$$PhCMe-\overset{\cdot}{C}H-CH_2\underset{\overset{\|}{O}}{C}R \xrightarrow{\text{rearrangement}} Ph\overset{\cdot}{C}Me-CHPhCH_2\underset{\overset{\|}{O}}{C}R$$

CXLVI

$$\xrightarrow[\text{slower}]{RCHO} PhCHMeCHPhCH_2\underset{\overset{\|}{O}}{C}R$$

ment of radical CXLVI should be significantly faster than that of radical CXLV, we may conclude that rearrangement is not observed in the addition of the mercaptan simply because the transfer of H· from RSH is much faster than the phenyl shift. In contrast, the transfer of H· from RCHO to radical CXLVI is considerably slower, allowing time for the intervening phenyl shift. Similarly, it has been found that the extent of phenyl migration in the decomposition (decarbonylation) of $PhCMe_2CH_2CHO$ is decreased by addition of benzyl mercaptan,[188(b)] for again, the mercaptan may transfer a hydrogen atom to the $PhCMe_2\overset{\cdot}{C}H_2$ radical intermediate before the latter undergoes rearrangement.

The migration terminus in a homolytic 1,2 shift need not be a carbon atom. Radicals of the type $Ar_3C-O\cdot$ (which are generally derived from triarylmethyl peroxy derivatives) likewise undergo rearrangement, for example:[189,190]

[188] (a) Weinstock and Lewis, *J. Am. Chem. Soc.*, **79**, 6243 (1957). (b) Winstein, Heck, Lapporte, and Baird, *Experimentia*, **12**, 138 (1956).
[189] Wieland, *Ber.*, **44**, 2553 (1911).
[190] Kharasch, Poshkus, Fono, and Nudenberg, *J. Org. Chem.*, **16**, 1485 (1951). When the rearrangements are carried out in cumene, the rearranged fragment is isolated mainly as a phenoxy (or aryloxy) derivative such as CXLVII, which is presumably formed in the sequence:

$$ArCPh_2-O-O-CMe_3 \rightarrow \left\{ \begin{array}{l} Ar\overset{\cdot}{C}Ph_2O \xrightarrow[PhCHMe_2]{\text{rearrangement}} Ph_2\overset{\cdot}{C}-OAr \\ Me_3C-O\cdot \xrightarrow{} PhCMe_2 \end{array} \right\} \rightarrow \begin{array}{l} Ph_2C-OAr \\ | \\ PhCMe_2 \end{array}$$

(CXLVII)

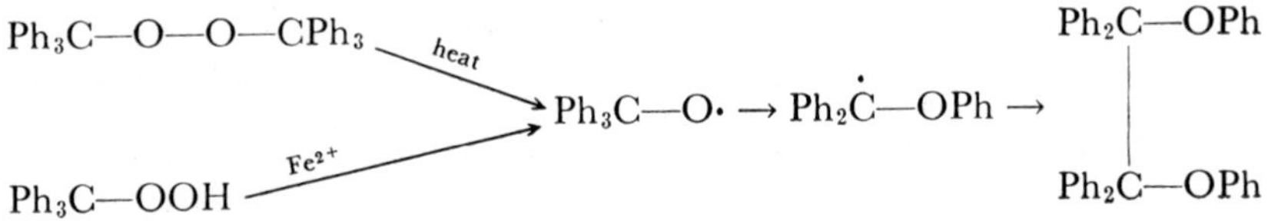

$$Ph_3C-O-O-CPh_3 \xrightarrow{heat}$$
$$Ph_3C-OOH \xrightarrow{Fe^{2+}}$$
$$Ph_3C-O\cdot \rightarrow Ph_2\dot{C}-OPh \rightarrow$$

$$Ph_2C-OPh$$
$$|$$
$$Ph_2C-OPh$$

Such rearrangements are of particular interest when two different aryl groups are bound to the migration origin. By comparing the yields of the possible rearrangement products, we may estimate the relative migratory aptitudes of a number of aryl groups in homolytic rearrangements. (Conformational effects, which sometimes complicate migratory aptitude studies, do not enter the picture here.) Thus, by carrying out decompositions of peroxides of the type $ArCPh_2-O_2-CMe_3$ in cumene (Me_2CHPh),[190] it has been shown that the phenyl and p-tolyl groups have very nearly the same migratory aptitude, but the α-naphthyl and p-biphenylyl groups migrate about six times as readily as phenyl. Further, the decomposition of the nitro-substituted peroxide CXLVIII in benzene yields over three times as much p-nitrophenol (resulting from migration of the p-nitrophenyl group) as phenol (resulting from phenyl migration). This suggests that in-corporation of a p-nitro group increases, by a factor of about 6, the migratory aptitude of the phenyl group in homolytic rearrangements,[191] contrary to what is observed in carbonium-ion rearrangements. It appears then that the migratory

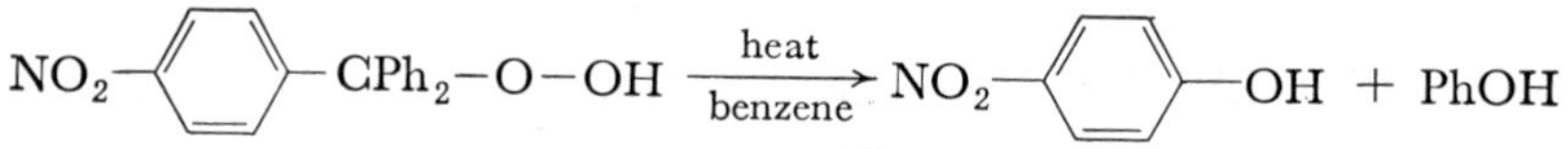

$$NO_2-\!\!\!\bigcirc\!\!\!-CPh_2-O-OH \xrightarrow[benzene]{heat} NO_2-\!\!\!\bigcirc\!\!\!-OH + PhOH$$

CXLVIII   3   1

(+ further products)

aptitude of a substituted aryl group is related to the effectiveness of the substit-uent in stabilizing the bridged transition state (or the bridged intermediate) in the rearrangement. As shown below, the p-nitro group (CXLIX) and the p-phenyl group (CL) (as well as most other *ortho* and *para* substituents) would be expected to stabilize such a bridged radical by aiding in the delocalization of the unpaired electron.[192]

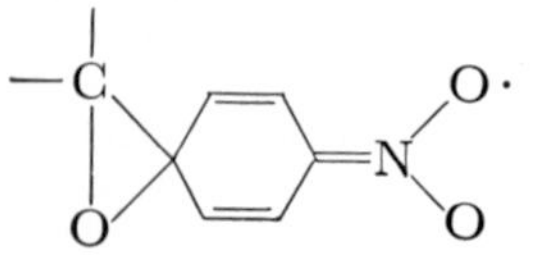

(CXLIX) 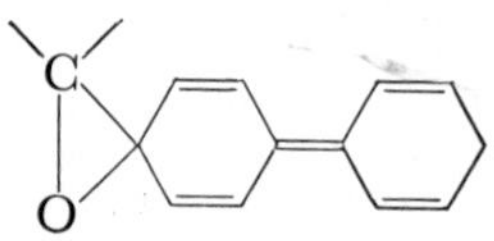   CL

---

[191] Bartlett and Cotman, *J. Am. Chem. Soc.*, **72**, 3095 (1950). This reaction is complicated by formation of rather large amounts of additional products, among them p-nitrobenzophe-none and p-nitrotriphenyl carbinol. No benzophenone was isolated.

[192] The decomposition of optically active PhCHMe—O—O—CMe₃ in the presence of

The 1,2 migration of halogen atoms appears to be involved in the reactions of polyhalomethanes with diazomethane.[193] The net result of such reactions is the insertion of a methylene group between the carbon and halogen atoms in each of the carbon-halogen bonds; for example, with CCl_4:

$$CCl_4 + 4CH_2N_2 \xrightarrow{h\nu} C(CH_2Cl)_4 + 4N_2$$

The mechanism which perhaps comes first to mind for this transformation involves intervention of the methylene diradical:

$$CH_2N_2 \xrightarrow{h\nu} \cdot\ddot{C}H_2 \xrightarrow{CCl_4} \begin{cases} \cdot CH_2Cl\ + \\ \cdot CCl_3 \end{cases} \rightarrow \begin{matrix} CH_2Cl \\ | \\ CCl_3 \end{matrix} \xrightarrow{\cdot\ddot{C}H_2} \begin{cases} \cdot CH_2Cl\ + \\ \cdot CCl_2CH_2Cl \end{cases} \xrightarrow[\text{etc.}]{} \rightarrow C(CH_2Cl)_4$$

Since the intermediate chloro compounds, Cl_3CCH_2Cl, $Cl_2C(CH_2Cl)_2$, and $ClC(CH_2Cl)_3$, cannot be isolated from the reaction mixture, the mechanism above requires that these presumed intermediates react with the methylene diradical more rapidly than does CCl_4 itself. In actuality, however, the first of these tetrachloro compounds, Cl_3CCH_2Cl, is much less reactive toward diazomethane than is CCl_4, and it is very likely that $Cl_2C(CH_2Cl)_2$ and $ClC(CH_2Cl)_3$ are less reactive still. A second serious objection to the mechanism suggested above is that diradicals react without regenerating additional diradicals; hence, the sequence above is inconsistent with the chainlike character observed for the reaction. The sequence shown below, which involves only monoradicals, is in much better accord with the facts.

$$CCl_4 \xrightarrow[-Cl\cdot]{h\nu} \cdot\dot{C}Cl_3 \xrightarrow[-N_2]{CH_2N_2} Cl_3C\dot{C}H_2 \xrightarrow[\text{shift}]{Cl\cdot} Cl_2\dot{C}CH_2Cl \xrightarrow[-N_2\quad\text{shift}]{CH_2N_2\quad Cl\cdot} Cl\dot{C}(CH_2Cl)_2;$$

$$Cl\dot{C}(CH_2Cl)_2 \xrightarrow[-N_2\quad\text{shift}]{CH_2N_2\quad Cl\cdot} \dot{C}(CH_2Cl)_3 \xrightarrow[-N_2]{CH_2N_2} \begin{matrix} \dot{C}H_2 \\ | \\ C(CH_2Cl)_3 \end{matrix} \xrightarrow{CCl_4} \begin{cases} C(CH_2Cl)_4\ + \\ \dot{C}Cl_3 \xrightarrow{\text{etc.}} \end{cases}$$

---

thiophenol yields t-BuOH and PhCHMe—OH, but no methoxy or phenoxy derivative, indicating that no phenyl or methyl shift within the PhCHMeO· radical intermediate has occurred (Kornblum and Teitelbaum, *J. Am. Chem. Soc.*, **74**, 3079 (1952)). Moreover, since conversion of the peroxide to the carbinols results in negligible racemization of the α-phenyl-ethyl group, hydrogen-atom migration may likewise be ruled out, for this would lead to the radical intermediate ·CPhMe—OH, which, in turn, should yield a racemic carbinol. Although the results seem clear cut, it may be argued that these workers insured them by choosing the very active hydrogen donor, thiophenol, as a hydrogen-transfer agent; for even if the radical intermediate were capable of rearranging, it probably would be converted to the carbinol before such rearrangement could occur. It is possible that phenyl migration (but almost certainly not methyl or hydrogen migration) might be observed if chloroform or an aldehyde were substituted for thiophenol in this work.

[193] Urry and Eiszner, *J. Am. Chem. Soc.*, **74**, 5822 (1952).

Note that the formation of the observed product requires no less than three Cl·
shifts. Since no olefins appear to be formed in the reaction, these shifts may be
assumed to be intramolecular. The CCl_4 in this reaction may be replaced by
CCl_3Br, $HCCl_3$, and $Cl_3CCOOMe$.

Further types of radical rearrangements have been observed, but they are
not common. Among the reported transformations that appear to involve such
rearrangements are the following:

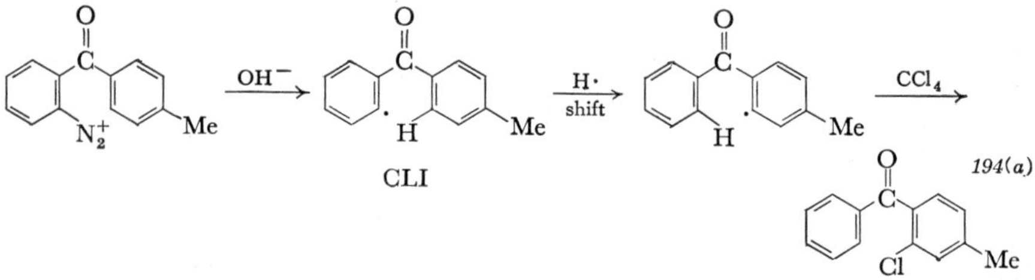

CLI

194(a)

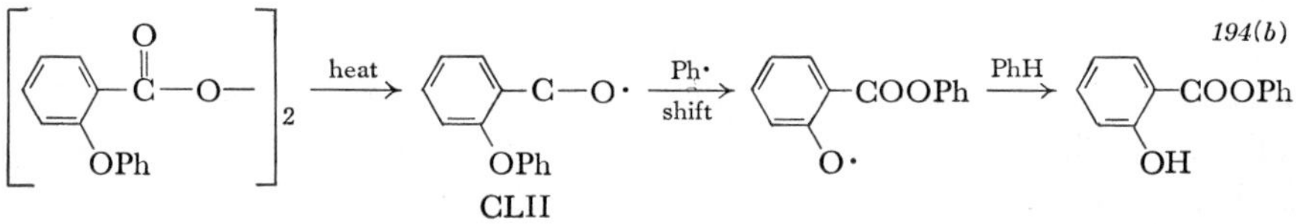

194(b)

CLII

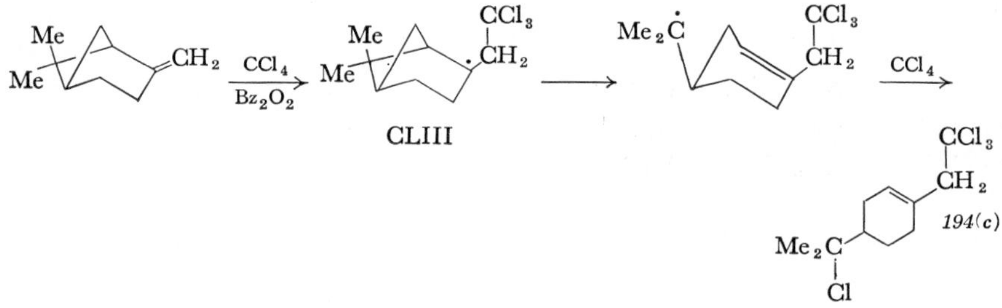

CLIII

194(c)

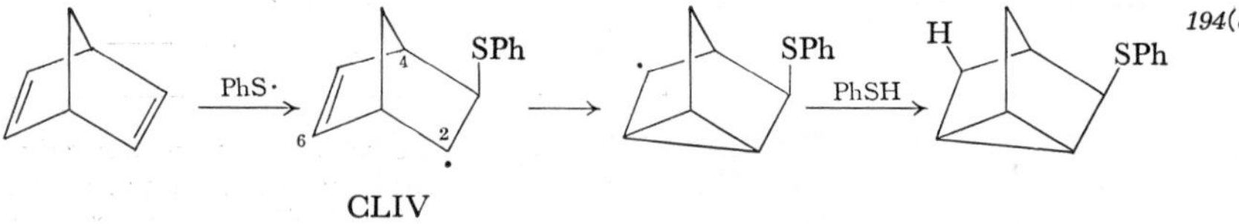

CLIV

194(d)

The rearrangements of radicals CLI and CLII are intramolecular radical displacements,[195] whereas the rearrangement (ring opening) of CLIII is a homo-

[194] (a) Relyea and DeTar, *J. Am. Chem. Soc.*, **76**, 1202 (1954). (b) DeTar and Hlyinsky,
ibid., **77**, 4411 (1955). (c) Oldroyd, Fisher, and Goldblatt, *ibid.*, **72**, 2407 (1950). (d) Cristol,
Brindell, and Reeder, *ibid.*, **80**, 653 (1958).

[195] It is interesting that no clear-cut evidence exists at present for the occurrence of intermolecular analogs of the displacements by which radicals CLI and CLII are presumed to

lytic β-elimination reaction, proceeding in the direction indicated largely because of the relief of steric strain accompanying the opening of the four-membered ring. The rearrangement of radical CLIV is, in essence, an intramolecular addition reaction, resulting from interaction on the "underside of the ring" between the odd electron at C_2 and the π-electron lobe at C_6. This transformation, sometimes called a *homoallylic* rearrangement, is closely analogous to rearrangements observed during heterolytic additions to norbornadiene; for example,

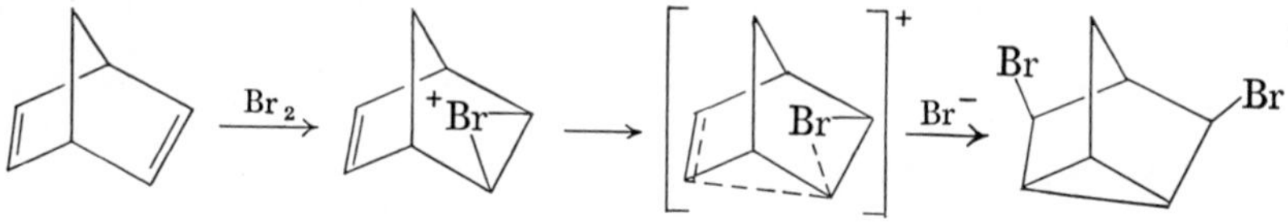

196(a)

and similar also to certain rearrangements observed during solvolyses of norbornenyl derivatives.

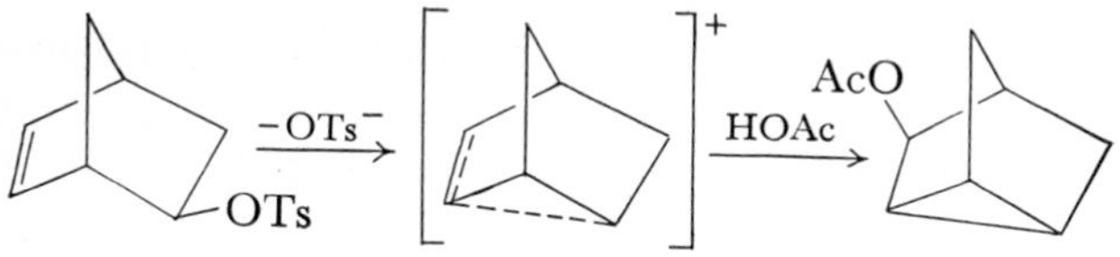

196(b)

EXERCISES FOR CHAPTER 16

1. Consider the following sequence for the homolytic halogenation of a hydrocarbon RH:

$$X_2 \xrightarrow[k_1]{h\nu} 2X\cdot \quad \text{(initiation)}$$

$$\left.\begin{array}{l} X\cdot + RH \xrightarrow{k_2} R\cdot + HX \\ R\cdot + X_2 \xrightarrow{k_3} RX + X\cdot \end{array}\right\} \quad \text{(propagation)}$$

$$2R\cdot \xrightarrow{k_4} R_2 \quad \text{(termination)}$$

Using the steady-state approximation with respect to radical intermediates $X\cdot$ and $R\cdot$, derive an expression for the rate of the reaction, $d(RX)/dt$.

---

rearrange, that is, for displacements of the types,

$$Ar\cdot \;+ H{-}Ar' \to Ar{-}H \;+ \cdot Ar'$$

and

$$\underset{\overset{\|}{O}}{R{-}C}{-}O\cdot + ArOAr' \to \underset{\overset{\|}{O}}{R{-}C}{-}OAr + \cdot OAr'$$

[196] (a) Winstein and Shatavsky, *J. Am. Chem. Soc.*, **78**, 592 (1956). (b) Winstein, Walborsky, and Schreiber, *ibid.*, **72**, 5795 (1950).

2. The mixture of monochlorohexanes obtained from the vapor phase chlorination of 3-methylpentane at 450° has the following composition:

$ClCH_2CH_2CHMe$ $\quad\quad\vert$ $\quad\quad Et$	$CH_3CHCl\text{---}CHMe$ $\quad\quad\quad\quad\vert$ $\quad\quad\quad\quad Et$	Et_2CHCH_2Cl	Et_2CClMe
28 percent	44 percent	14 percent	14 percent

Predict the composition of the mixture of monochlorohexanes obtained in the chlorination of 2-methylpentane under the same conditions.

3. Consider the sequence for decomposition of a peroxide ROOR in a solvent SH:

$$ROOR \xrightarrow{k_1} 2RO\cdot$$
$$RO\cdot + SH \xrightarrow{k_2} ROH + S\cdot$$
$$S\cdot + ROOR \xrightarrow{k_3} SOR + RO\cdot$$
$$2S\cdot \xrightarrow{k_4} S_2$$
$$2RO\cdot \xrightarrow{k_5} \text{nonactive products} \left.\begin{array}{c}\ \\ \ \\ \ \end{array}\right\} \text{(possible termination steps)}$$
$$RO\cdot + S\cdot \xrightarrow{k_6} ROS$$

Assume that the concentration of SH remains constant. Taking into account both the unimolecular (spontaneous) decomposition and the induced decomposition, show that the rate expression may take the following forms, depending upon the mode of chain termination:

(a) rate $= \dfrac{-d(ROOR)}{dt} = k_1(ROOR) + k'(ROOR)^{3/2}$; if termination is by reaction between two S· radicals.

(b) rate $= k_1(ROOR) + k''(ROOR)^{1/2}$; if termination is by reaction between two RO· radicals.

(c) rate $= k'''(ROOR)$; if termination is by a reaction between RO· and S·.

(d) Show that the rate law in (a) is applicable also to the decomposition of a diacyl peroxide via the following path:

$$\left[\begin{array}{c} O \\ \parallel \\ R\text{---}C\text{---}O\text{---} \end{array}\right]_2 \xrightarrow{k_1} 2RCOO\cdot$$
$$RCOO\cdot \xrightarrow{k_2} R\cdot + CO_2$$
$$R\cdot + \left[\begin{array}{c} O \\ \parallel \\ R\text{---}C\text{---}O\text{---} \end{array}\right]_2 \xrightarrow{k_3} \begin{array}{c} O \\ \parallel \\ R\text{---}C\text{---}OR \end{array} + RCOO\cdot$$
$$2R\cdot \xrightarrow{k_4} R_2 \text{ (termination)}$$

4. Predict the major products resulting from each of the following reactions. Justify your guess in each case:

(a) Me_2PH + ⟨hexagon⟩$=CH_2$ $\xrightarrow{Bz_2O_2}$

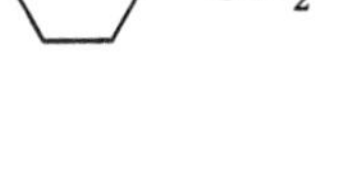

(b) $Me_2CHNO_2 \xrightarrow[O_2]{Ag_2O}$

(c) $\left(MeO-\underset{}{\bigcirc}-\right)_2 C{=}O$ + Na $\xrightarrow{xylene}$

(d) $HO-\bigcirc-NH-\bigcirc-OH + Ag_2O + KOH \longrightarrow$

(e) Isobutane + $Cl_2 \xrightarrow{350°}$

(f) $O_2N-\bigcirc-N_2^+$ + $HFeBr_4$ $\xrightarrow{H_2O}$

(g) cis-Stilbene + $I_2 \xrightarrow[PhH]{h\nu}$

(h) $Ph_3CSPh + O_2 \rightarrow$

(i) $O_2N-\bigcirc-N_2^+Cl^-$ + $CH_2{=}CH{-}CN$ $\xrightarrow[CuI_2^-]{I_3^-}$

(j) $\underset{\overset{|}{Ph_2C{=}CH{-}CPh_2}}{\overset{Cl}{}}$ + Ag metal $\xrightarrow[benzene]{O_2}$

(k) $PhCH_2N{=}NCH_2Ph + Sb \xrightarrow{300°}$

(l) $i\text{-}BuPh + Me_2C\underset{\overset{|}{CN}}{}N{=}N\underset{\overset{|}{CN}}{}CMe_2 + O_2 \xrightarrow{50°}$

(m) $Ac_2O_2 + Ph_2CH_2 \xrightarrow{CCl_4}$

(n) Ph_3CCPh_3 + $O{=}\bigcirc{=}O$ $\xrightarrow{benzene}$

(o) $CoSO_4 + H_2O_2 + CH_3CN \xrightarrow{water}$

(p) $Ph_2Se_2 + (i\text{-}Bu)_2CHOH + HgCl_2 \xrightarrow{160°}$

(q) $CH_2{=}CHMe + PhSO_2Cl \xrightarrow{t\text{-}Bu_2O_2}$

(r) $Ph_2N{-}OH + Ag_2O \xrightarrow{Et_2O}$

(s) $\underset{Ph_2CCl \quad CPh_2Cl}{\bigcirc\bigcirc}$ + Zn $\longrightarrow$

(t)  $+$ CCl_3Br $\xrightarrow{h\nu}$

(u) $Bz_2O_2 + CuBr_2 \xrightarrow{CCl_4}$

(v) $ClCH_2CH_2CH_2Cl + Cl_2 \xrightarrow{350°}$

(w) 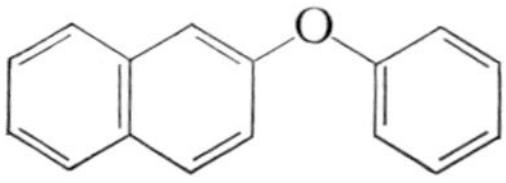 $+$ PhNAc $\underset{\text{NO}}{|}$ $\xrightarrow[\text{PhH}]{\text{heat}}$

(x) 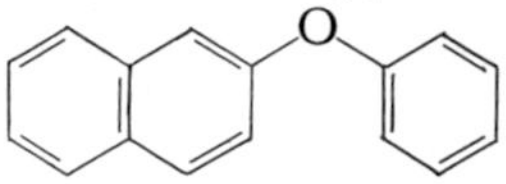 $+$ Bz_2O_2 $\xrightarrow[\text{PhH}]{\text{heat}}$

(y) $PhCMe_2-O-O-\underset{\overset{\|}{O}}{C}-CHMePh \xrightarrow{\text{heat, benzene}}$

(z) 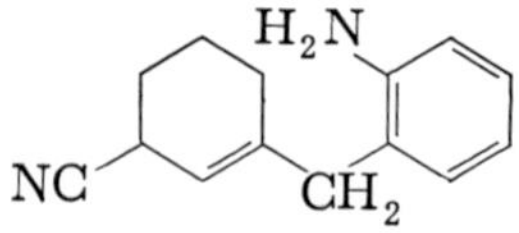 $+$ HNO_2 $\xrightarrow[\text{HCl}]{\text{CuSO}_4}$

5. Predict the major products in each of the following reactions. These are more difficult than those in Exercise 4.

(a) $CF_3I + CH_2{=}CF_2 \xrightarrow{h\nu}$

(b) $CF_2Br-CFClBr + CH_2{=}CH_2 \xrightarrow{Bz_2O_2}$

(c) $CH_3CHO + CH_2{=}CHCH_2OAc \xrightarrow{Ac_2O_2}$

(d) $CH_2N_2 + \text{benzene} \xrightarrow{h\nu}$

(e) 3-Methylcyclohexene + N-bromosuccinimide $\rightarrow$

(f) $Ac_2O_2 + Hg \text{ (metal)} \xrightarrow{\text{heat, benzene}}$.

(g) $\left(PhCMe_2-\overset{\overset{\displaystyle O}{\|}}{C}-O- \right)_2 \xrightarrow[\text{CCl}_4]{50°}$

(h) 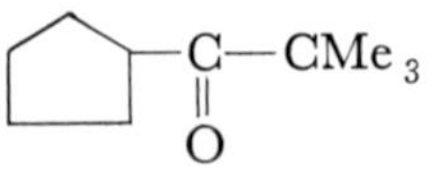 $\xrightarrow[\text{vapor phase}]{h\nu}$

(i) 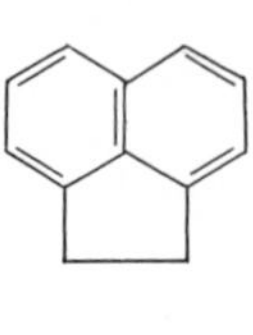 $+$ 2 $\xrightarrow[\text{CCl}_4]{Bz_2O_2}$

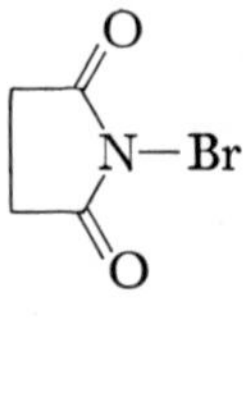

(j) $PhCH_2OOH + HCHO \xrightarrow{dark}$

(k) $Bz_2O_2 + i\text{-PrOH} \xrightarrow{heat}$

(l)
$\xrightarrow{h\nu}$

(m) $F_2 + toluene \xrightarrow[\text{vapor phase}]{\text{diluted with } N_2}$

(n) $HC\equiv CH + 2HSiCl_3 \xrightarrow{Ac_2O_2}$

(o) Cyclopentene $+ N_2O_4 \xrightarrow{benzene}$

(p)
$+ \quad CBr_4 \xrightarrow{h\nu}$

(q) $CCl_3CHO \quad + $
$\xrightarrow{Bz_2O_2}$

(r)
$+ \quad O_2 \longrightarrow$

(s)
$MeO\!-\!\!\langle\ \rangle\!-\!CHO \quad + $
$\xrightarrow{h\nu}$

(t)
$+ \quad PhSH \xrightarrow{t\text{-Bu}_2O_2}$

(u) $FeSO_4 + H_2O_2 + CH_3CN \xrightarrow{t\text{-BuOH}}$

(v) $CH_2N_2 + Ph_2S_2 \xrightarrow{h\nu}$

(w) $CH_3\!-\!\!\underset{\underset{O}{\|}}{C}\!-\!NHBr + MeCH\!=\!CHPh \xrightarrow{h\nu}$

(x) *erythro*-Cl$-\!\!\langle\ \rangle\!-\!CDBr\!-\!CHDPh + $ N-bromosuccinimide $\longrightarrow$

(y) $Me_3CO-\overset{\displaystyle ||}{\underset{\displaystyle O}{C}}-O-O-\overset{\displaystyle ||}{\underset{\displaystyle O}{C}}-OCMe_3 \xrightarrow[\text{heat}]{CCl_4}$

(z) $\left(F_3C-\!\!\left\langle\!\!\bigcirc\!\!\right\rangle\!\!-\right)_2 \overset{\displaystyle |}{\underset{\displaystyle \bigcirc}{C}}-O-O-CMe_3 \xrightarrow[\text{heat}]{\text{benzene}}$

6. Consider the homolytic addition of a halogen, X_2, to a $C=C$ double bond:

$$X_2 \xrightarrow[k_1]{h\nu} 2X\cdot \text{ (initiation)}$$

$$X\cdot + \underset{/}{\overset{\backslash}{}}C=C\underset{\backslash}{\overset{/}{}} \underset{k_{-2}}{\overset{k_2}{\rightleftharpoons}} \overset{X}{\underset{|}{-C}}-\overset{\cdot}{\underset{|}{C}}- \xrightarrow[k_3]{+X_2} \overset{X}{\underset{|}{-C}}-\overset{X}{\underset{|}{C}}- + X\cdot \xrightarrow[\text{etc.}]{k_2} \text{(propagation)}$$

(a) Show that if chain termination involves two haloalkyl radicals, the rate law will be of the form,

$$\text{rate} = k(X_2)^{3/2}I^{1/2}$$

where I is the intensity of the radiation bringing about dissociation of X_2. Show that this is true whether or not the addition step is reversible.

(b) Show that if chain termination involves two $X\cdot$ radicals, the rate law becomes

$$\text{rate} = k\left(\overset{\diagup}{\underset{\diagdown}{}}C=C\overset{\diagdown}{\underset{\diagup}{}}\right)(X_2)^{1/2}I^{1/2}$$

(c) Show that if termination involves a reaction between $X\cdot$ and $\overset{X}{\underset{|}{-C}}-\overset{\cdot}{\underset{|}{C}}-$, the rate law becomes

$$\text{rate} = k\left(\overset{\diagup}{\underset{\diagdown}{}}C=C\overset{\diagdown}{\underset{\diagup}{}}\right)^{1/2}(X_2)I^{1/2}$$

(Assume that the rate of initiation is much less than the rate of propagation—that is, that the kinetic chains are long.)

7. Suggest mechanisms for each of the following transformations:

(a) $Ph_3CCPh_3 + CH_2N_2 \xrightarrow{h\nu} Ph_3CCH_2CPh_3$

(b) [structure] $+$ PhCHO $\xrightarrow{h\nu}$ [structure] BzO   OH

(c) $VOSO_4 + H_2O_2 \xrightarrow{t\text{-BuOH}} Me_2\overset{|}{\underset{|}{C}}-(CH_2)_2-\overset{|}{\underset{|}{C}}Me_2$
    $\qquad\qquad\qquad\qquad\qquad\quad OH \qquad\qquad OH$

(d) + $\xrightarrow{\text{Bz}_2\text{O}_2}$

$$\underset{\substack{50 \\ \text{percent}}}{} + \underset{\substack{25 \\ \text{percent}}}{} + \underset{\substack{25 \\ \text{percent}}}{} + \underset{}{}$$

(e) $CF_3N{=}NCF_3 \xrightarrow{h\nu} N_2 + (F_3C)_2N{-}N(CF_3)_2$

(f) $+ Na \longrightarrow$ $+ CO + NaOEt$

(g) $HN_3 + F_2 \rightarrow F{-}N{=}N{-}F + N_2 + HF$

(h) $2Cl_2 + Et_2O \rightarrow Cl_2CHCHCl{-}OEt + HCl$

(i) $C_6H_6 + Pb(OAc)_4 \xrightarrow{\text{hot HOAc}} PhCH_2OAc + Pb(OAc)_2$

(j) $+ CH_2{=}CH{-}CH{=}CH_2 \xrightarrow{Ag_2O}$

(k) $\overset{*}{C}H_2{=}CH{-}CH_2I + I_2 \xrightarrow{h\nu} CH_2{=}CH{-}CH_2\overset{*}{I}$

(l) $Cl_2 + PhCH{=}CHSO_2Cl \xrightarrow{h\nu} PhCHClCHCl_2 + SO_2$

(m) $EtSH + CO + MeCH{=}CH_2 \xrightarrow{t\text{-Bu}_2O_2} EtS{-}CH_2CHMeCHO$

(n) $CH_3{-}\overset{\overset{\text{OOH}}{|}}{\underset{\underset{\text{OH}}{|}}{C}}{-}CH_2COOEt + Fe^{2+} + CH_2{=}CHCH{=}CH_2 \rightarrow$

$$AcOH + \underset{\underset{\text{EtOOCCH}_2}{|}}{CH_2{-}CH{=}CH{-}\underset{\underset{}{|}}{CH_2}} \quad \overset{\overset{\text{CH}_2\text{COOEt}}{|}}{}$$

(o) $CH_2N_2 + AsCl_3 \xrightarrow{h\nu} Cl_2AsCH_2Cl$

8. Suggest mechanisms for the following conversions (some of these are quite difficult):

(a) $EtCHMe{-}SH + (EtO)_3P \xrightarrow{h\nu} EtCH_2Me + SP(OEt)_3$

(b) $t\text{-BuOCl} \xrightarrow{h\nu} Me_2C{=}O + MeCl$

(c) $Cr^{2+} + NH_2OH + C_6H_6 \rightarrow PhNH_2$

(d) $PhCHO + \text{cyclohexene} \xrightarrow{O_2} trans\text{-cyclohexanediol monoacetate}$

(e)

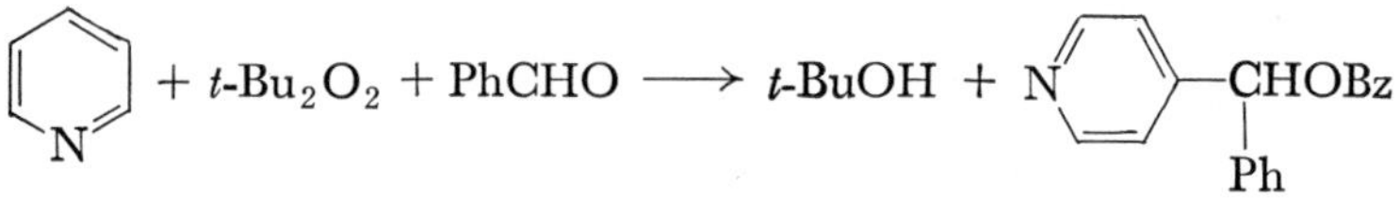

$+ t\text{-Bu}_2O_2 + PhCHO \longrightarrow t\text{-BuOH} + $

(f) $CH_2{=}CMe{-}CH_2Cl \xrightarrow{h\nu} (ClCH_2)_2CMeCH_2CMe{=}CH_2$

(g) $Me_2C(OH)C(OH)Me_2 + Mn(H_2P_2O_7)_2^- \rightarrow Me_2C{=}O + Mn(H_2P_2O_7)_2^{2-}$

(h) $PhN_2^+ + CH_3OH \rightarrow PhH + HCHO + N_2$

(i) $CCl_2{=}CCl_2 + Cl_2 + O_2 \xrightarrow{h\nu} CCl_3COCl$

(j) 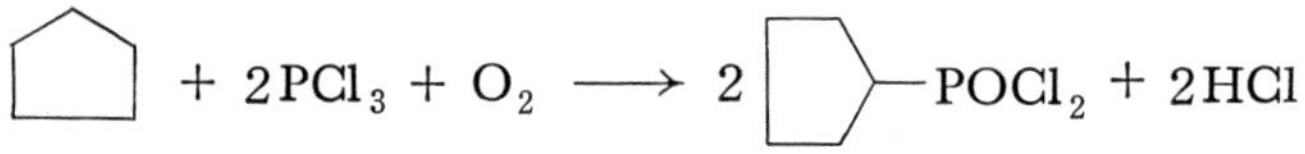 2 $+ 2PCl_3 + O_2 \longrightarrow 2$ $\text{POCl}_2 + 2HCl$

(k) $PhN_2^+ + H_2PO_2^- \rightarrow H_3PO_3 + PhH + N_2$

(l)

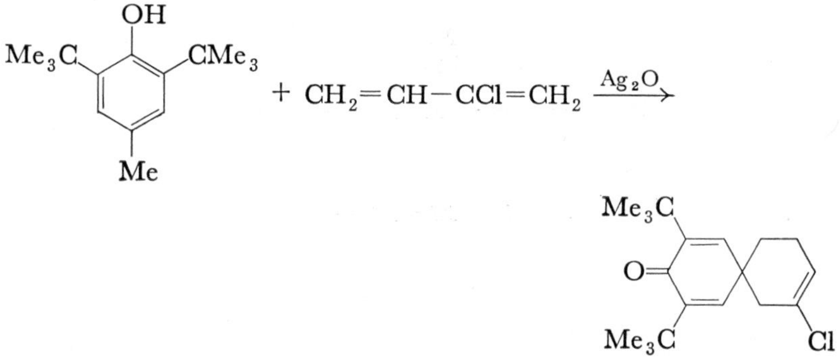

$+ CH_2{=}CH{-}CCl{=}CH_2 \xrightarrow{Ag_2O}$

(m) 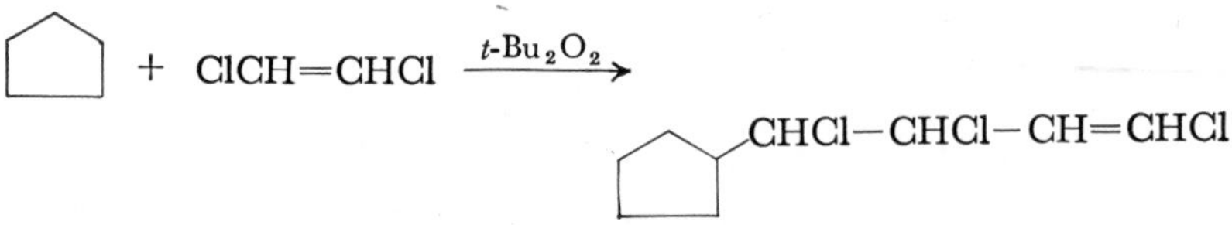 $+ ClCH{=}CHCl \xrightarrow{t\text{-Bu}_2O_2}$

(n) 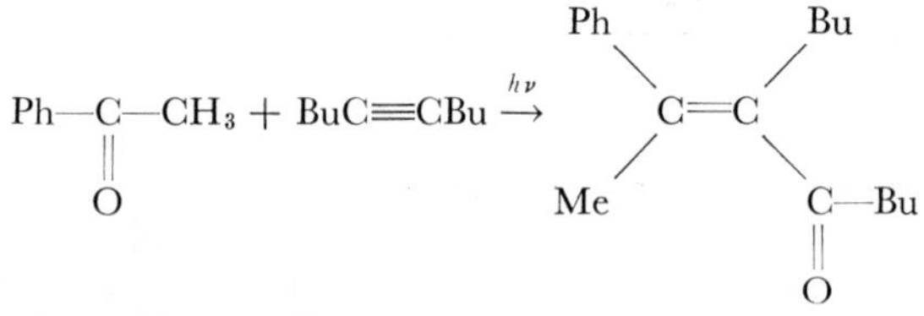 $Ph{-}C{-}CH_3 + BuC{\equiv}CBu \xrightarrow{h\nu}$

9. Explain each of the following:

(a) Mixtures of $SnSO_4$ and H_2O_2 are generally ineffective as free-radical initiators, in contrast to mixtures of $FeSO_4$ and H_2O_2, which are often very effective initiators.

(b) The peroxy ester $PhCH{=}CHCH_2{-}\overset{\overset{\displaystyle O}{\|}}{C}{-}OO{-}CMe_3$ decomposes about 5000 times as rapidly as t-butyl peroxyacetate.

(c) Azonitrile CLV decomposes about 75 times as rapidly as does azonitrile CLVI.

$$\begin{array}{cccc} \text{CN} & \text{CN} & & \text{CN} & \text{CN} \\ | & | & & | & | \\ \text{Me}_3\text{C}-\text{C}-\text{N}{=}\text{N}-\text{C}-\text{CMe}_3 & & \text{EtCHMe}-\text{C}-\text{N}{=}\text{N}-\text{C}-\text{CHMeEt} \\ | & | & & | & | \\ \text{Me} & \text{Me} & & \text{Me} & \text{Me} \\ & \text{CLV} & & & \text{CLVI} \end{array}$$

(d) "Chlorophenylation" of MeCH=CHCOOMe with PhN$_2$Cl and CuSO$_4$ (the Meerwein reaction) yields ester CLVII in which the β-carbon has become phenylated, whereas in the chlorophenylation of PhCH=CH—COOMe, the α-carbon is phenylated.

$$\text{MeCHPh}-\text{CHClCOOMe}$$
$$\text{CLVII}$$

(e) Homolytic addition of HBr to 3-bromocyclohexene gives a *trans* dibromo compound, whereas homolytic addition of HBr to 1-bromocyclohexene gives a *cis* dibromo compound.

(f) Homolytic additions to carbon-carbon triple bonds tend to be slower than additions to double bonds under comparable conditions.

(g) The reaction of thiophenol with methyl acrylate gives a higher yield of simple addition product in the presence of *t*-BuOK than in the presence of *t*-BuOOH.

(h) The "Wurster salt" obtained by oxidation of *p*-phenylene diamine is more stable in moderately acidic solutions than in either strongly basic or strongly acidic solutions, whereas the radical obtained from oxidation of 4,4′-dihydroxydiphenyl-amine is more stable in strongly basic or strongly acid solutions than in neutral.

(i) The organometallic compounds Ph$_3$PbPbPh$_3$ and Ph$_3$GeGePh$_3$ are not measur-ably dissociated into radicals at ordinary temperatures, even though Pb—Pb and Ge—Ge bonds are, in general, much weaker than carbon-carbon bonds.

(j) Alkyl nitrates, which readily yield alkoxy radicals when heated, are nevertheless poor initiators for free-radical chain reactions.

(k) The apparent hydrogen isotope effect in the homolytic bromination of PhCH$_2$D may be made to increase by removing HBr from the reaction mixture as it is formed.

(l) In the fluorination of Cl$_3$CCHCl$_2$, the chlorocarbons Cl$_2$C=CCl$_2$ and C$_2$Cl$_6$ are formed, along with the expected product Cl$_3$CCFCl$_2$.

(m) Molecular oxygen may accelerate free-radical brominations but almost in-variably inhibits free-radical chlorinations.

(n) A mixture of tetralin and cumene undergoes autoxidation much more slowly than does either pure hydrocarbon.

(o) The (small) yields of ethane and ethylene formed in the decomposition of propionyl peroxide in isooctane are not affected by addition of iodine or quinone to the solution.

(p) The ratio of *cis* to *trans* addition products resulting from the addition of N$_2$O$_4$ to cyclohexene is very nearly the same as that resulting from the addition of NO$_2$Cl to this olefin.

(q) The extent of rearrangement in the decarbonylation of PhCMe$_2$CH$_2$CHO is greater when the reaction is carried out in a dilute solution of chlorobenzene than when carried out in the absence of solvent.

(r) Polymerization of styrene in the presence of *n*-butyraldehyde yields polymers of much higher molecular weight than polymerization of styrene in the presence of a corresponding amount of *n*-butyl mercaptan.

(s) The ratio of isomerization to addition in the photochemical reaction of bromine with *cis*-1,2-dichloroethylene is independent of the intensity of incident radiation and is not affected by addition of traces of O_2.

(t) When two methyl radicals in the vapor phase collide, they are much more likely to dimerize than are two H· radicals.

(u) Benzyl iodide undergoes photochemical exchange with radioactive iodine more rapidly in CCl_4 than in CCl_2=$CClCCl$=CCl_2. (Neither solvent is consumed in the reaction.)

(v) The electrolysis of the deuterated acid CD_3CH_2COOH yields at the anode not only $D_3CCH_2CH_2CD_3$, but also CD_2=CH_2. The yield of this olefin increases as the intensity of the current is increased.

Author Index

771

Subject Index

Acetoacetic acid, decarboxylation of, 346, 350
Acetoacetic ester
  acidity of, 365
  alkylations of, 298
  enolization of, 377
Acetone, halogenations of, 162, 175, 372ff, 382
Acetyl peroxide, decomposition of, 717f
Acetylacetone
  acidity of, 365
  cleavage of, 338
Acetylene, molecular orbitals in, 19
Acid anhydrides, conversion to amides, 361 (Ex. 6)
Acid-base catalysis, 110ff, 195 (Ex. 4)
  mechanisms for, 188f
  of mutarotation of sugars, 139, 542
  of semicarbazone formation, 543, 555 (Ex. 4)
  specific vs. general, 110, 189
  of tautomerization, 373, 385
Acidity, 122 (Ex. 1, 3)
  of alicyclic dicarboxylic acids, 242
  Brønsted system of, 93
  of C=C—C=O systems, 117
  of C—H bonds, 365ff
  of diketones, β-keto esters, and aliphatic nitro compounds, 365f
  effect of structure on, 200ff, 244 (Ex. 4, 11), 367, 404 (Ex. 1)
  leveling effect in, 96
  Lewis system of, 115ff, 125 (Ex. 11)
  of phenols, 215
  quantitative evaluation of, 100, 103ff, 122 (Ex. 2)
  and resonance, 215
  of sulfones, 369
Acidity scales
  Hammett (h_0 scale), 103ff. See also H_0 function
  and reaction rates, 190
  in water-ethanol mixtures (Grunwald scale), 107ff, 124 (Ex. 7), 192, 198 (Ex. 12)
  in water-hydrazine mixtures, 107
Acids
  Brønsted, 94
  conjugate, 94
  Lewis, 115
  very weak, 97, 369ff
Acrylonitrile, additions to, 528
Activated complex, definition of, 129, 178
Activation
  Arrhenius energy of, 179
  entropy of, 179, 181ff, 196 (Ex. 8)
  free energy of, 130, 179
  volume of, 716
Activities and activity coefficients, 101
Activity coefficients, degenerate, 101
  evaluation of, 108ff, 124 (Ex. 7)
Acyl azides
  formation of, 623
  rearrangement of, 624

Acyl chlorides
  alcoholysis of, 332
  hydrolysis of, 334
Acyl iodides, exchange with iodine, 705
Acylations, aromatic (Friedel-Crafts reactions), 450
Acylium ions in esterification and hydrolysis, 325
Addition compounds
  acid-base, 118, 231
  stabilities of, 231
Addition reactions
  1,2- vs. 1,4-, 530
  homolytic vs. heterolytic, 732
  nucleophilic vs. electrophilic, 121, 125 (Ex. 11), 527
Additions to C=C double bonds
  of aryl halides, 729
  of CBr$_3$, 535
  cis-additions, 533ff, 743
  to conjugated dienes, 530
  of halogens, 137, 150, 520ff, 553 (Ex. 2), 736ff
    halide catalysis of, 524
    intermediates in, 521
    kinetics of, 524
    stereospecificity, 523
  homolytic, 730ff
  of hydrogen halides, 140, 516ff, 527, 732ff
    kinetics, 517
    orientation in, 518, 733
    rearrangement during, 517
  of hypochlorous acid, HOCl, 525
  of methylene, CH$_2$, 751
  of N$_2$O$_4$, 739
  nucleophilic, 527f
  of polyhalomethanes, 743f
  of thiols, 741
  of water, 514, 553 (Ex. 1)
Additions to C≡C triple bonds, 520
Additions to C=O double bonds, 539ff
  of alcohols, 541
  of hydroxylamine, phenylhydrazine, and semicarbazide, 543, 555 (Ex. 4)
  stereochemistry of, 549
  of water, 540
Adducts, see Addition compounds
Alcohols, configuration of, 552
Aldehydes
  addition to C=C double bonds, 747
  autoxidation of, 708
  hydration of, 540
  rearrangement in acid, 637
Aldol condensation, 389ff, 406 (Ex. 3, 4)
Alkyl aryl ethers, rearrangement of, 648
N-Alkylanilinium salts, rearrangement of, 652
Alkylation, aromatic (Friedel-Crafts reaction), 447
Allophanates, formation from alcohols, 136
Allylic rearrangements, 286
  bimolecular, 290
  in ester hydrolysis, 343

Sommelet-Hauser rearrangement, 641f
Sommelet reaction, 133
Spectra, molecular, 76ff, 90 (Ex. 9–14)
  electronic, 85
  electron-spin resonance, 684
  and hydrogen bonding, 30, 83, 90
    (Ex. 10)
  microwave and radiofrequency, 76
  Raman, 76
  rotational, 78, 92 (Ex. 14)
  use in determining acid strengths, 369
  vibrational, 77, 79ff
Spin, electronic, 7
Steady-state approximation, 170, 694
Steric assistance, 234
  to dissociation of hexaphenylethanes, 676
  to unimolecular eliminations, 475, 477
  to unimolecular nucleophilic substitution,
    279, 586
Steric hindrance, 180, 230ff
  in aromatic substitution, 457
  in bimolecular nucleophilic substitution,
    275
  in ester saponification, 317
  in esterification, 322
  in keto-enol equilibria, 378
Steric strains, 231ff
Stevens rearrangement, 640
Substituent constants
  Hammett's, 221, 226
  for substitution on aromatic rings, 435
  Taft's, 230
Substitution reactions
  classification of, 120ff, 125 (Ex. 11)
  homolytic vs. heterolytic, 121f
  polar vs. free-radical, 121
Substitutions
  electrophilic
    in aromatic systems, 418ff
    orientation in, 429ff
    structure and reactivity in, 428
  nucleophilic, 250ff
    with allylic rearrangement, 286ff
    in aromatic systems, 452ff
    attacking reagents, 258
    borderline cases, 312 (Ex. 12)
    catalyzed by Ag^+ and Hg^{2+}, 274
    competition with elimination, 263,
      473f, 485ff, 507 (Ex. 2)
    effects of solvent, 254
    internal (S_Ni), 294
    internal, with rearrangement (S_Ni'),
      296
    isotope effects in, 285
    kinetics of, 254
    leaving groups, 261
    in nonpolar solvents, 272ff
    quantitative correlation of rates
      (Swain treatment), 299
    steric effects, 274ff
    stereochemistry of, 147f, 263ff, 309
      (Ex. 7)
    structure-reactivity relationships in,
      281ff
Succinimido radical, 701
Sulfonation, aromatic, 445f, 466 (Ex. 4)

Sulfones
  β-chloro, elimination reactions of, 499
  conversion to selenides, 155 (Ex. 8)
Sulfonium ions
  acidity of, 372
  elimination reactions of, 474
Sulfonyl (—S—) group, electron attraction
by, 218, 369
Sulfuric acid, freezing-point lowering studies in, 97ff, 123 (Ex. 4)
Sulfuryl chloride, chlorination with, 702
Swain equation (for correlation of nucleophilic substitution rates), 299
Sydnones, 417

T effect (tautomeric effect), 217
Taft treatment of inductive effects, 227ff
Tautomerism, 366ff
  acid- and base-catalyzed, 373
  mechanisms for, 384
Telomerization, 745
Termination step in free-radical reactions,
  694
Tetrahedral carbon atom, 17, 31 (Ex. 7)
Tetramethyl lead, methyl radicals from,
  683
Tetramethyl-p-phenylenediamine as an
  antioxidant, 709
Tetramethylglucose, mutarotation of, 139,
  542
Tetraphenylhydrazine, radical from, 678
Tetrazoles, formation in Schmidt reaction,
  627
Thiazole-2-carboxylic acid, decarboxylation
  of, 349
Thiols, addition to C=C double bonds, 529,
  741
Thionyl chloride, reaction with alcohols,
  295
Tiglic acid, addition of hydrogen iodide to,
  519
Titanium(III) salts, in the production of
  free radicals, 691
o-Tolylmagnesium bromide, reaction with
  benzil, 636
Transition state, definition of, 129, 178
Transition-state theory, 178ff
Trialkylamine oxides, conversion to ole-
  fins, 501, 504
Triarylmethyl ions, 273, 305
Triarylmethyl peroxides and hydroperox-
  ides, rearrangements of, 757
Triarylmethyl radicals, 672ff
Trifluoroiodomethane, addition reactions
  of, 744
Trifluoromethyl group, electron attraction
  by, 218
Trihalomethanes
  acidity of, 371
  hydrolysis of, 381, 397ff
Trimethylaluminum dimer, 585
Trinitroanisole, reactions of, 454